The Monograph and its Chapters

This is one of five volumes that make up the Monograph on the Planning and Design of Tall Buildings. For reference purposes the broad outline of the material contained in the five volumes is as follows:

PC PLANNING AND ENVIRONMENTAL CRITERIA FOR TALL BUILDINGS

1. Philosophy of Tall Buildings
2. History of Tall Buildings
3. Social Effects of the Environment
4. Sociopolitical Influences
5. Economics
6. Architecture
7. Interference and Environmental Effects
8. Urban Planning
9. External Transportation
10. Parking
11. Operation, Maintenance, and Ownership
12. Energy Conservation
13. Motion Perception and Tolerance
14. Project Management
15. Application of Systems Methodology

SC TALL BUILDING SYSTEMS AND CONCEPTS

1. Structural Systems
2. Mechanical and Service Systems
3. Electrical Systems
4. Vertical and Horizontal Transportation
5. Cladding
6. Partitions, Walls, and Ceilings
7. Foundation Systems
8. Construction Systems

CL TALL BUILDING CRITERIA AND LOADING

1. Gravity Loads and Temperature Effects
2. Earthquake Loading and Response
3. Wind Loading and Wind Effects
4. Fire
5. Accidental Loading
6. Quality Criteria
7. Structural Safety and Probabilistic Methods

SB STRUCTURAL DESIGN OF TALL STEEL BUILDINGS

1. Commentary on Structural Steel Design
2. Elastic Analysis and Design
3. Plastic Analysis and Design
4. Stability
5. Stiffness
6. Fatigue and Fracture
7. Connections
8. Load and Resistance Factor Design (Limit States Design)
9. Mixed Construction

CB STRUCTURAL DESIGN OF TALL CONCRETE AND MASONRY BUILDINGS

1. Characteristics of Concrete and Masonry Tall Buildings
2. Design Criteria and Safety Provisions
3. Concrete Framing Systems for Tall Buildings
4. Optimization of Tall Concrete Buildings
5. Elastic Analysis
6. Nonlinear Behavior and Analysis
7. Model Analysis
8. Stability
9. Stiffness, Deflections, and Cracking
10. Creep, Shrinkage, and Temperature Effects
11. Design of Cast-in-place Concrete
12. Design of Structures with Precast Concrete Elements
13. Design of Masonry Structures

This Monograph is a major focus of the Council on Tall Buildings and Urban Habitat. The objective is to document the state of art relative to the planning and design of tall buildings and to indicate possible future advances and areas of further research. Please inform the Headquarters of any significant omissions or of additions that should be made.

The opinions expressed are those of the committees and do not necessarily reflect those of the publisher, the professional society sponsors, or the U.S. National Science Foundation which partially supported the work that led to this Monograph.

Published by
American Society of Civil Engineers
345 East 47th Street
New York, N.Y. 10017

Council Headquarters
Fritz Engineering Laboratory—13
Lehigh University
Bethlehem, Pennsylvania 18015

Structural Design of Tall Concrete and Masonry Buildings

Library of Congress Catalog card number: 78-60643

Printed in the United States of America

Monograph on

Planning and Design of Tall Buildings

Volume CB

Structural Design of Tall Concrete and Masonry Buildings

Group Coordinators

Raymond C. Reese
Ignacio Martín
Bruno Thürlimann
Georg Wästlund, Emeritus

Group Editors

James G. MacGregor
Inge Lyse

Group Secretary

Ti Huang

Council on Tall Buildings and Urban Habitat

Steering Group

D. Sfintesco*	Chairman	C.T.I.C.M.	Paris
F. R. Khan*	Vice-Chairman	Skidmore, Owings & Merrill	Chicago
L. S. Beedle*	Director	Lehigh University	Bethlehem
G. W. Schulz*	Secretary	Universitat Innsbruck	Innsbruck
L. W. Lu	Research Advisor	Lehigh University	Bethlehem

F. L. Codella*	Tower International	Cleveland
H. J. Cowan*	University of Sydney	Sydney
B. M. Dornblatt	B. M. Dornblatt and Associates, Inc.	New Orleans
P. Dubas	Swiss Federal Institute of Technology	Zürich
G. F. Fox	Howard, Needles, Tammen, & Bergendoff	New York
Y. Friedman	Architect	Paris
B. Frommes*	IFHP	Luxembourg
J. M. Garrelts	Columbia University	New York
M. P. Gaus	National Science Foundation	Washington
J. A. Gilligan	United States Steel Corporation	Pittsburgh
T. R. Higgins	Consulting Engineer	New York
B. G. Johnston	University of Arizona	Tucson
T. C. Kavanagh	Iffland Kavanagh Waterbury	Hastings-on-Hudson
H. R. Lane	H. R. Lane AIA Assoc. Architects	Los Angeles
I. Martin	Capacete-Martin & Assoc.	San Juan
C. Massonnet	Universite de Liege	Liege
W. A. Milek	American Institute of Steel Construction	New York
T. Naka	University of Tokyo	Tokyo
E. O. Pfrang	National Bureau of Standards	Washington
J. Rankine	Rankine & Hill Engineering Consultants	Sydney
R. C. Reese	Consulting Engineer	Toledo
L. E. Robertson	Skilling, Helle, Christensen, Robertson	New York
P. H. Sedway	Sedway/Cooke	San Francisco
R. Thoma	Hentrich, Petschnigg & Partners	Dusseldorf
E. K. Timby	Howard, Needles, Tammen & Bergendoff	New York
A. W. Turchick	American Society of Civil Engineers	New York
B. Thürlimann	Swiss Federal Institute of Technology	Zürich
I. M. Viest	Bethlehem Steel Corporation	Bethlehem
G. Wästlund	Kungliga Tekniska Hogskolan	Stockholm

*Member of Executive Committee

Editorial Committee

L. S. Beedle (Ch.), D. Sfintesco, F. R. Khan, L. W. Lu, G. W. Schulz, R. Kowalczyk, M. Gaus, P. A. Parisi

Group PC: T. C. Kavanagh, Y. Friedman, R. Thoma, R. C. Herrenkohl, W. Henn, C. Norberg-Schulz

Group SC: F. R. Khan, J. Rankine, W. P. Moore, H. D. Eberhart, H. J. Cowan

Group CL: L. E. Robertson, T. Naka, R. J. Mainstone, E. H. Gaylord, L. W. Lu

Group SB: T. R. Higgins, P. Dubas, C. N. Gaylord, M. Watabe, L. W. Lu

Group CB: R. C. Reese, I. Martin, B. Thürlimann, G. Wastlund, J. G. MacGregor, I. Lyse, T. Huang

Chairman, Vice-Chairman and Editors of each committee (identified in each chapter), affiliates representing sponsors, and selected national representatives.

Professional Society Sponsors

International Association for Bridge and Structural Engineering (IABSE)
American Society of Civil Engineers (ASCE)
American Institute of Architects (AIA)
American Institute of Planners (AIP)
International Federation for Housing and Planning (IFHP)
International Union of Architects (UIA)

Foreword

This is the first of five volumes of a comprehensive Monograph on the Planning and Design of Tall Buildings. Taken as a whole the books are a compendium of knowledge not only about tall buildings themselves, but also about their interaction with the urban environment of which they are a part. The volumes cover such aspects as structural systems, the various loading systems, service systems, structural safety, foundations, and structural design methods for both steel and concrete buildings. They include architecture, urban planning, cultural, social, and political aspects, and management and operation aspects.

A "Monograph" is defined as a "treatise on a single topic." Our "single topic" is presented in 52 chapters collected in the following five volumes:

Volume PC: Planning and Environmental Criteria for Tall Buildings
Volume SC: Tall Building Systems and Concepts
Volume CL: Tall Building Criteria and Loading
Volume SB: Structural Design of Tall Steel Buildings
Volume CB: Structural Design of Tall Concrete and Masonry Buildings

Although Volume CB was anticipated to be the fifth in the series, it was the first to be completed, and on that basis was released in advance of the others (which will follow in the sequence in which they are completed). From an historical context even though the first "skyscrapers" were of steel, there is no doubt that the first structures to reach such heights that they created special problems for designers and builders were those built of masonry. As is clear from historical accounts, the third century B.C. Lighthouse of Pharos (variously estimated at from 100 m to 200 m in height), with its floors for equipment and personnel, had a remarkable resemblance to what we now call a tall building. Even at the present time, although the tallest skyscrapers are of steel, the majority of the tall buildings in the world are of concrete—perhaps as many as 65%. This reflects the more frequent use of concrete for taller buildings in most countries of the world except the USA and Japan, where the use of steel predominates.

The Monograph is intended to be of value to those responsible for planning and design practice. It is written for those who plan, design, construct, or operate, and who need the latest information as a basis for judgment decisions. It includes a summary and condensation of research findings for design use, it provides a major reference source to recent literature and to recently developed design concepts, and it identifies needed research.

The Monograph is not intended as a primer. Its function is to communicate to all knowledgeable persons in the various fields of expertise the state of art and most advanced knowledge in those fields. Our message has more to do with setting design policies and general approaches than with detailed applications. It aims to provide adequate information for experienced general practitioners confronted with their first high-rise, as well as opening new vistas to those who have designed them in the past.

Many chapters have embarked imaginatively into future concepts, because the aim is not the status quo. Where more than one point of view was appropriate, those views have been set forth. Since in many instances there is no final answer, there are numerous points of controversy; and such controversy has not been avoided.

What is a tall building? The important criterion is whether or not the design is influenced by some aspect of "tallness." A tall building is *not* defined by its height or number of stories. A suggested definition, then, might be "a building in which 'tallness' strongly influences planning, design and use"; or "a building whose height creates different conditions in the design, construction, and use than those that exist in 'common' buildings of a certain region and period."

As a consequence, there is some variation among chapters on this matter of tallness. Each one has proceeded on the basis that "tall" constitutes whatever creates the "tall building problem" for that particular subject. Topics are not included in the Monograph simply because they pertain to buildings in general. If, on the other hand, a topic is particularly important for a *tall* building, then it has been the objective to treat that topic even if it is also a problem for *all* buildings.

A "building" is a structure that is designed essentially for residential, commercial, or industrial purposes. Other categories include institutional, public assembly, and multiple-use structures. An essential characteristic of a building is that it has floors. Structures designed for entertainment such as towers, monuments, and "space needles" generally are excluded from consideration.

This Monograph has been prepared by the various topical committees of the Council on Tall Buildings and Urban Habitat. The Council is an activity sponsored by engineering, architectural, and planning professionals throughout the world, an organization that was established to study and report on all aspects of the planning, design, construction, and operation of tall buildings. The Monograph effort has been a major focus of the Council since its formation in 1969 by the International Association for Bridge and Structural Engineering (IABSE) and the American Society of Civil Engineers (ASCE). (The Council at that time was known as the Joint Committee on Tall Buildings.) Subsequently the following organizations became full professional society sponsors: American Institute of Architects (AIA), American Institute of Planners (AIP), International Federation for Housing and Planning (IFHP), and International Union of Architects (UIA).

The Council is concerned not only with the building itself but also with the role of tall buildings in the urban environment and their impact thereon. Such a concern also involves a systematic study of the whole problem of providing adequate space for life and work, considering not only technological factors, but social and cultural aspects as well. It is not an advocate for tall buildings per se; but in those situations in which they are viable, it seeks to encourage the use of the latest knowledge in their implementation.

The concept of a Monograph coincided with the concept of the Council (actually of its predecessor, the Joint Committee on Tall Buildings). The decision followed to hold an international conference at Lehigh University in 1972: it would not only bring together specialists from all over the world, but its Proceedings could form a first draft of the Monograph. Those Proceedings were published by ASCE in 1973. Commencing in 1972 a series of "Regional Conferences" provided opportunity for significant new input from every part of the world. Thirty-eight of these conferences were held in thirty different countries from the period 1972 to 1976. An editorial committee (three leaders for each chapter and four or five Coordinators and Editors for each volume) was assembled, and meetings were held at each of the regional conferences. An outline for the Monograph was developed and distributed for criticism. An abstract was prepared for each chapter. Reporters were selected for topics not covered in the "Lehigh Proceedings." Work on the first drafts began. Three successive drafts were prepared as a result of the critique of the committee members and the reworking by the 52 committee editors. On completion of the individual chapters, the leaders for the five volumes (22 Group Coordinators and Group Editors evenly divided between USA and non-USA) reviewed them especially regarding the interaction between chapters.

In addition to the fact that the Monograph has had input from so many people and so many countries, there are two further distinctive features. One is that so much of the material has been prepared by designers themselves. Nearly two-thirds of the 175-member editorial team are affiliated with design firms or with industry. The other feature is that it has been jointly prepared by people from many disciplines, people who "sat down around the table" during the planning phases. They shared reviews in the later writing. The result is a treatment that is much more interdisciplinary than is normally the case. No other such international interdisciplinary effort has been attempted by professionals connected either directly or indirectly with the construction industry.

It was decided at the outset that in case of disagreement final decisions would mainly be in the hands of the committee responsible for a particular chapter. Therefore one finds considerable variation amongst the various chapters. Each one is essentially a committee effort.

Who wrote the Monograph? Although the title page for each chapter shows that it was prepared by such and such a committee, obviously a committee doesn't write anything. After the preliminary organizational work, it was up to the committee editor to develop a first draft, to respond to the criticism, and to develop subsequent drafts. In addition to the editorial committee (175 persons) more than 800 individuals made specific contributions. All told, about 1300 committee members had opportunity to review at least one chapter. They represent 78 countries.

With regard to the units, it will be evident to the reader that complete uniformity in the text was not achieved. The general guideline was to use SI units first, followed by American units in parentheses, and metric when necessary. A conversion table is supplied at the end of the volume. The guide for symbols was Draft ISO/1015 3898 (December 1975). Again, because of the extensive revisions that would have been required, complete uniformity of symbols was not achieved. The list of symbols appears at the end of the volume. Because of the variations, the chapter is identified at the end of the definition.

The spelling was agreed at the outset to be "American" English.

The following format is suggested to those who wish to refer to a chapter, to a volume, or to the Monograph as a whole in their writing:

To refer to a Chapter:

Council on Tall Buildings, Committee 27, 1978
DESIGN OF MASONRY STRUCTURES, Chapter 13, Vol. CB of Monograph on Planning and Design of Tall Buildings, ASCE, New York.

To refer to a Volume:

Council on Tall Buildings, Group CB, 1978
STRUCTURAL DESIGN OF TALL REINFORCED CONCRETE AND MASONRY BUILDINGS, Vol. CB of Monograph on Planning and Design of Tall Buildings, ASCE, New York.

To refer to the Monograph:

Council on Tall Buildings, 1978
PLANNING AND DESIGN OF TALL BUILDINGS, A MONOGRAPH, 5 volumes, ASCE, New York.

This work would not have been possible without the financial support of the National Science Foundation and the American Iron and Steel Institute, who supported the program out of which the Monograph developed. The understanding and support of Dr. Michael Gaus of NSF has been most appreciated.

Acknowledgment is next due the staff at the Fritz Engineering Laboratory with whom it has been my pleasure to be associated. Special mention is due Le-Wu Lu who has been codirector of the project from which this effort has evolved. Ti Huang has given particular attention to Volume CB as "Group Secretary," providing not only a technical review, but maintaining contact with the editorial committee for this volume. Ryszard Kowalczyk assisted in this phase as well. Other staff members involved were: Sarah-Louise Melcher (Administrative Assistant), Ricky Troxell (Draftsman), Richard Sopko (Photographer), Susan Craig (Publications Assistant), and Mary Snyder and Rebecca Villari (Secretaries).

Special acknowledgment is due Jamie Moyer, who since 1975 has served as my associate responsible for all of the processing and production phases of the Monograph effort at Lehigh. She performed outstanding service not only to us on the headquarters staff but to each member of the editorial committee.

We are indebted to Paul Parisi and Richard Torrens (ASCE) for guidance and direction during the publication phases of the work. Janet Davis served notably as Editorial Consultant. Her attention to editorial detail was remarkable.

Next, tribute is due the chairmen and vice-chairmen who provided leadership to committees. To the committee editors fell the major burden of writing, editing, adjusting, and rewriting. Their contributions have been most significant. All of these are identified on the title page of the respective chapters. An additional group under the leadership of T. Y. Lin submitted information pertaining to prestressed concrete for use throughout the volume.

The true "authors" of the Monograph were sometimes the committee editors, but in most cases they were the Contributors and Reporters whose papers formed the essential first drafts—the starting point. These are identified in the acknowledgment page that follows the title page for each chapter.

The coordinating and editing effort on the volume as a whole has been the work of the Group Coordinators (Raymond Reese, Ignacio Martín, Georg Wästlund and Bruno Thürlimann) and the Group Editors (James MacGregor and Inge Lyse). Inge Lyse brought to the volume his years of research experience that, in fact, had their beginning in 1929 at the Fritz Engineering Laboratory (where he served as its director). James MacGregor contributed his editorial skill to all of the chapters—in addition to serving as editor of Chapter CB-8, "Stability." Ignacio Martín lent the volume a practical emphasis that reflects his valuable experience as a designer. Bruno Thürlimann as both academician and designer represented the non-USA group in his evaluation of the chapters. Georg Wästlund played a major role in both the early organization of the concrete group and also the technical phases as the Monograph went through its major first drafts.

Our final tribute is to Raymond C. Reese. He was involved from the very beginning (during what he called his "second retirement"). He must have spent a most substantial portion of this, his "third retirement," not only in leading, but in providing very significant editorial contributions. His efforts have been an inspiration, and the entire Council is indebted to him.

Lehigh University   Lynn S. Beedle
Bethlehem, Pennsylvania   *Editor-in-Chief*
1978

Preface

Volume CB of the Monograph presents topics of particular interest to designers of concrete or masonry tall buildings. It is assumed that the readers will have a working knowledge of the theory and design practices for reinforced and prestressed concrete and masonry, and no attempt is made to reproduce basic design concepts, codes, or handbook material in this volume. Similarly, it should be borne in mind that Volume CB is one volume in an integrated five-volume Monograph and a regular cross-referencing by the reader of the appropriate parts of the other volumes would be appreciated. This is particularly true in the case of Volumes SB and CB, which are complementary in many areas. Thus, for example, mixed steel and concrete construction has been described in Volume SB.

Volume CB is divided into four major divisions, each composed of several chapters. The divisions present information on the selection, analysis and design of tall concrete and masonry buildings.

Division I—Introduction. The first division consists of an introductory Chapter CB-1, and Chapter CB-2, which describes the basic philosophies of working stress design, ultimate strength design, and limit states design as applied to concrete structures. The application of safety theories to reinforced concrete structures is also presented.

Division II—Selection of Concrete Structural Systems. Division II consists of two chapters. Chapter CB-3 reviews concrete framing systems for tall buildings and includes guidance for the selection of appropriate systems. An Appendix to this chapter describes some of the factors involved in the selection of the structural systems for four actual tall concrete buildings.

Chapter CB-4 is a guide to the factors to be considered in optimizing a structural frame. Most of this chapter deals with empirical rather than mathematical optimization. The principles of mathematical optimization of frames are discussed briefly and the reader is also referred to Chapter SB-2.

Division III—Analysis of Tall Concrete Buildings. Six separate chapters present a wide ranging presentation of many aspects of the analysis of such structures.

Chapter CB-5, Elastic Analysis, is a concise survey of the assumptions necessary and procedures available to carry out elastic analyses of tall structures. The text generally assumes that computers will be used in the analysis of tall buildings, and reviews analyses ranging from simple to complex.

Chapter CB-6, Nonlinear Behavior and Analysis, consists of two major parts. The first describes the nonlinear behavior of reinforced concrete cross sections, members, and structures. Discussions of the behavior of shear walls and the response of concrete buildings to earthquakes are included. The second part reviews the assumptions and procedures used in carrying out nonlinear analyses of concrete structures.

Chapter CB-7, Model Analysis, briefly reviews the use of model tests in the analysis of structures and presents an extensive list of references on this subject.

The remaining three chapters in this division each examine particular aspects of the response of concrete construction that must be given special consideration in the design of tall concrete buildings. Chapter CB-8, Stability, reviews the response of concrete columns, frame stability, and the second-order analysis of concrete frames. The final section of this chapter presents recommendations for design oriented second-order frame analyses. Chapter CB-9, Stiffness, Deflections and Cracking, discusses various aspects of these topics, with emphasis on lateral deflections. The reader is also referred to Chapter SB-5 in this regard. The length changes and deflections of columns, walls, and other members due to creep, shrinkage, and temperature cannot be ignored in the design of tall buildings. This topic is discussed extensively in Chapter CB-10.

Division IV—Design of Tall Concrete and Masonry Buildings. The final division of Volume CB consists of Chapters CB-11, CB-12, and CB-13, which present aspects of the proportioning of tall cast-in-place concrete buildings, tall precast concrete buildings, and tall masonry buildings, respectively.

Raymond C. Reese
Ignacio Martin
Bruno Thürlimann
Georg Wästlund

James G. MacGregor
Inge Lyse

Contents

SELECTION OF CONCRETE STRUCTURAL SYSTEMS

CB-3   Concrete Framing Systems for Tall Buildings

CB-4   Optimization of Tall Concrete Buildings

Contents

CB-7 Model Analysis

CB-8 Stability

DESIGN OF TALL CONCRETE AND MASONRY BUILDINGS

CB-11   Design of Cast-in-Place Concrete

CB-12   Design of Structures with Precast Concrete Elements

CB-13 Design of Masonry Structures

Nomenclature

References/Bibliography

Contributors

Building Index

Name Index

Subject Index

Structural Design of Tall Concrete and Masonry Buildings

Chapter CB-1

Characteristics of Concrete and Masonry Tall Buildings

Prepared by Committee 20 (Commentary on Structural Standards) of the Council on Tall Buildings and Urban Habitat as part of the Monograph on the Planning and Design of Tall Buildings

Jean Despeyroux   Chairman
Emory L. Kemp   Vice-Chairman and Editor

AUTHOR ACKNOWLEDGMENT

Special acknowledgment is due those individuals whose contributions and papers formed the substantial first drafts of the various sections of this chapter. First are the state-of-art reporters from the 1972 International Conference whose material was published in the Lehigh Proceedings. These individuals are:

N. A. Amaral
D. M. Anastasescu
C. N. Avram
K. E. Bruinette
H. K. Cheng
E. Cohen
J. Despeyroux
E. L. Kemp
J. Nasser
M. Stiller.

Subsequent to the conference the emphasis of this chapter changed; the first draft of the present version having been prepared by J. Despeyroux with E. L. Kemp in charge of the editing.

CONTRIBUTORS

The following is a complete list of those additional persons who have submitted written material for possible use in the chapter, whether or not that material was used in the final version. The Committee Chairman and Editor were given quite complete latitude. Frequently length limitations precluded the inclusion of much valuable material. The Bibliography contains all contributions. The additional contributors are: J. Brakel, M. Z. Cohn, T. Karman, F. Levi, J. G. MacGregor, A. Paduart, J. Perchat, F. Robles, M. Tomii.

COMMITTEE MEMBERS

N. A. Amaral, D. Anastasescu, C. N. Avram, J. G. Batanero, S. C. Bate, W. B. Bennett, J. G. Bodhe, J. Brakel, T. Brondum-Nielsen, K. E. Bruinette, H. K. Cheng, E. Cohen, M. Z. Cohn, H. J. Cowan, A. M. Da Rocha, J. Despeyroux, J. Fauchart, J. Ferry Borges, L. Finzi, B. C. Gerwick, Jr., E. Giangreco, A. A. Gvozdev, B. Hesketh, R. A. Heydenrych, E. Hognestad, N. Horodniceanu, B. Isaacs, D. Jevtic, T. Karman, E. L. Kemp, F. R. Khan, M. Kokubu, W. Kukulski, M. Laredo, F. Levi, B. Lewicki, P. A. Lorin, C. J. Louw, J. G. MacGregor, A. G. Meseguer, J. Nasser, F. Robles, E. Rosenblueth, H. Ruehle, G. Sebestyen, A. Short, S. Soretz, M. Stiller, E. Thorenfeldt, B. Thurlimann, M. Tichy, J. Trokan, H. Umemura, T. Van Langendonck, A. Winokur, S. Zaczek.

CB-1 Characteristics of Concrete and Masonry Tall Buildings

1.1 INTRODUCTION

In many respects concrete is an ideal building material, combining economy, versatility of form and function, and noteworthy resistance to fire and the ravages of time. The raw materials are available in practically every country, and the manufacturing of cement is relatively simple. It is little wonder that in this century it has become a universal building material. Because of its high dead-load characteristics compared to metal structures, the utilization of concrete in high-rise structures was thought to be limited, on economic grounds, to those of less than 20 stories. This height limit was perceived largely on the basis of skeletal structures. With more appropriate structural forms such as shear walls and "tube" structures, and improved material properties, the maximum height of concrete buildings has soared in recent decades. An impressive array of structural types has been built recently in concrete, and by way of introduction a few examples are shown in this chapter (Figs. 1.1, 1.2, 1.3, and 1.4). A discussion of the selection of concrete structural systems is presented in Chapters CB-3 and CB-4. The design aspects are discussed in Chapters CB-2, CB-11, CB-12, and CB-13.

Design problems common to all types of tall buildings, irrespective of the structural materials utilized, are treated in other volumes of this series. The study of concrete structures is presented and discussed in this volume. The object of this chapter is to draw attention to more specific aspects of tall concrete and masonry buildings as an introduction to the following chapters of this volume. The evaluation of design criteria for tall concrete and masonry buildings is presented in a collection of papers listed in the bibliography of this chapter.

Concrete, prestressed concrete, and masonry are proven building materials widely used in tall buildings. Each has its own unique characteristics which must be recognized in the design process. Those aspects which are specific to concrete and masonry structures can be perceived intuitively, for example, through a comparison with metal structures. Their origin is clearly to be found in the radical differences existing between the respective properties of the different materials. In the following discussion it is important to keep in mind the idea of a comparison of material

3

properties. Because the material properties rigidly condition the determination of safety and the establishment of design criteria, they should be the "primary thread" in considering the problems and benefits involved in concrete or masonry construction.

1.2   CHARACTERISTIC FEATURES OF CONCRETE AND MASONRY

Putting the distinctive characteristics of concrete and masonry in decreasing order of importance with respect to their consequences, one can list them as follows:

1. Intrinsically, both masonry and concrete have a low resistance to tension. Although this resistance is not negligible, its ratio to the resistance to compression remains small, and cracks may appear as a consequence of tension. Design procedures have evolved, therefore, that disregard tensile strength or recognize the low tensile strength, and reinforcement is provided where tensions occur. (See Chapters CB-2 and CB-9.) In prestressed concrete an initial compression is provided to offset the effects of tensile stresses.

2. Concrete and masonry structures are subject to dimensional variations which are time dependent. Creep and shrinkage play a determining role in the behavior of mortars and products and elements of concrete. The swelling associated with rehydration of masonry units should not be disregarded. Creep may have favorable effects in readjusting stress concentrations.

3. The properties of all the materials under consideration vary slowly with time, and they show variability from point to point in the same structure. This

Fig. 1.1 Torres Blanca, Madrid, Spain

variation depends on the method of production and the utilization of the materials. Therefore, quality control is an important part of the construction process. The fact that time must elapse before the concrete gains strength must be recognized in planning the construction process through proper form design, precasting and other available techniques.

4. Dimensional precision associated with actual construction practice varies depending on the level of workmanship and degree of quality control.

Fig. 1.2 One Shell Plaza, Houston, Texas (Courtesy: F. R. Khan; photo by Ezra Stoller—ESTO)

5. In general, concrete structural members have larger cross-sectional areas than steel members. As a result, dead load tends to be more significant in concrete structures. On the other hand, however, their stiffness also tends to be greater. As a result, sway deflections, floor vibration, and local column buckling are less severe problems in concrete structures than in steel structures. (See Chapters CB-8 and CB-9.)

6. The behavior of concrete members under cyclic loading shows a deterioration in stiffness, which is more marked than that shown in metal members. However, by eliminating tensile stresses and associated cracking, prestressing can result in members with excellent fatigue characteristics.

Fig. 1.3 Atrium of Water Tower Place, Chicago, world's tallest reinforced concrete building (full view in Chapter SC-1). Associated Architects-Engineers: Loebl, Schlossman, Dart and Hackl; C. F. Murphy Associates; Architectural Consultant (commercial spaces): Warren Platner and Associates (photo by Greg Hursley, Daniel Bartush Architectural Photography)

7. The resistance to fire of tall concrete buildings is appreciably higher than that of metal buildings, which usually must have fire protection.

8. Concrete structures respond more slowly to temperature changes, with the result that a smaller daily or yearly temperature range needs to be considered in design (see Chapter CB-10).

1.3 CONSEQUENCES REGARDING LOADS AND STRENGTH

The fundamental characteristics of concrete and masonry have important consequences on structures utilizing such materials. The variability of the mechanical properties dominates the selection of the nominal strength of these materials and the selection of properties for use in design. This variability also can affect the response of the structure to the various actions, as well as the distribution of loadings between resisting elements. In particular, it may be responsible for the torsional oscillations liable to appear even in nominally symmetrical structures in the case of a dynamic excitation.

The dimensional variations may have significant consequences as far as weight is concerned, but they especially merit attention when considering the uncertainties which they introduce in assessing the strength and rigidity of members. In this

Fig. 1.4 Mei Foo Sun Chuen apartments, Hong Kong. Shown is stage 1 of this private development, completed in 1969. When all 8 stages are completed the project will have approximately 100 twenty-story buildings, containing 13,000 apartments housing about 80,000 people (Courtesy: Arthur Haddon)

domain, they interact with the variabilities of the mechanical properties. Thus, the problem of tolerances is important and must be considered in both design and construction.

The loads that result from time-dependent variations are important in the kind of structures we are discussing. In particular, internal tensions caused by shrinkage are one of the causes of cracking in concrete and masonry structures. In tall buildings, shrinkage and creep are the cause of additional loadings resulting from the differential shortening of long columns and walls. Creep plays a more specific role since its magnitude is related to the intensity of the load and to the duration of the application of the load. In this sense, it appears as an element of the response of the structure. In addition, it is a factor in the origin of the nonlinear behavior of concrete and masonry elements or structures, and affects their stability. The effects of creep and shrinkage are discussed in Chapter CB-10.

The nonlinear stress-strain relationships for concrete in compression, cracking, and creep are the three principal causes of the nonlinear behavior of concrete structures. A major area of study at the present time (1978) is the analysis of the redistribution of forces and moments caused by these phenomena. This is discussed in Chapter CB-6.

1.4   CONSEQUENCES REGARDING LIMIT STATES

The concept of limit-states design and the establishment of the necessary safety provisions are discussed in Chapter CB-2. The utilization of materials such as concrete and masonry, which are weak in tension, leads to a consideration of limit states such as cracking and deflections, as well as to the ultimate load limit state. It also leads in practice to three types of solutions:

1. To resist loads by compression only (in the case of unreinforced materials).

2. To supply the deficiency of internal tensile strength by the addition of passive or active reinforcement (that is, reinforced concrete or prestressed concrete).

3. To supplement those elements lacking in tensile capacity with elements whose specific function is to resist the effects of tension (that is, mixed construction such as masonry with reinforced concrete, or plain concrete with reinforced concrete; or composite concrete/steel members or mixed concrete/steel structures). A solution of this type is dealt with in Chapter SB-9.

Depending upon the amount of reinforcement and the way the elements are loaded, these elements or structures may show different kinds of behavior ranging from brittle to ductile.

A typical case of ductile behavior is that of flexural members with normal or small percentages of reinforcement. It is characterized by the fact that rupture is preceded by deformations of a large amplitude corresponding to plastic lengthening of the steel. Thus there is a possibility for the member to sustain loads beyond the yielding point and of a favorable redistribution of forces and moments.

In brittle failures, rupture is preceded by small deformations that are of a magnitude belonging to the elastic range. Such failures tend to cause a sudden decrease or loss (or both) of bearing capacity, without any possibility of a favorable redistribution of forces and moments. This is true, for instance, in the case of unreinforced elements, especially if they are eccentrically loaded, or for shear, bond, and compression failures of prestressed and reinforced concrete members. The possibility of a rupture of this type must be avoided, either by providing adequate reinforcement, or by reducing the probability of failure through the use of higher safety factors, or by changing the configuration of the structure to avoid possible brittle failures. Most building codes recognize this problem and provide rules to limit structures to those which will fail in a ductile manner.

It must be noted that cracking has not the same significance in these two cases. In ductile elements, it introduces a nonlinear behavior because of the reduction of rigidity resulting from cracking. However it is not considered as the upper bound of the elastic range, since the zone between the cracking and yielding deformations remains in the elastic range. Because there is generally a large margin between cracking and ultimate loads in ductile elements, cracking may be treated as a serviceability limit state.

In the case of brittle failure, cracking, when liable to occur, may precede the rupture by only a small margin. It may even coincide with it and then lead to a form of instability. This is the reason why, in such elements as unreinforced walls or panels loaded at the same time by horizontal and vertical forces, the integrity of the panel with respect to diagonal tension must be checked as an ultimate limit state.

Intermediate cases between brittle elastic and fully plastic failures are treated in more detail in Division III of this volume, particularly Chapters CB-5, CB-6, and CB-7. For the purposes of this introduction, we shall only recall that ductility is sometimes defined as the ratio of deformation at ultimate to the deformation at yielding (or conventionally, in the case when there is no yielding, to the deformation at some arbitrary load level, such as 60% of ultimate). This ratio provides an estimate of the capacity of the element to suffer deformations beyond the elastic range, while the area of the load-deformation diagram is representative of the energy the member can absorb before it fails. These concepts are useful when the possibility actually exists that the element may be loaded beyond the design values, as is the case for large differential settlements or for earthquakes. Problems associated with concrete structures in seismic regions are discussed more fully in Chapter CB-6.

In the field of repeated or alternating loadings a distinction must be made between loadings within the elastic range (fatigue) and beyond the elastic range (the so-called low-cycle fatigue). In both cases, the peculiarities of the behavior of reinforced concrete may be ascribed again to the lack of tensile strength. By eliminating tensile stresses through prestressing, excellent fatigue resistance can be obtained.

The problem of a decrease in the strength of reinforced concrete elements after a few cycles of loading in the postelastic range has long been controversial. It now seems established that such a reduction may be observed with respect to shear in a number of cases in relation to the destruction of bond properties around the cracks. When such a possibility is expected, for instance in the case of earthquakes, it is reasonable to take into account these deteriorated limit states as design ultimate limit states. In any case, repeated or alternating loadings beyond the elastic range result in a reduction of rigidity which affects the response of the structure. This reduction is favorable in the case of earthquakes, and unfavorable in the case of wind excitation.

1.5 CONDENSED REFERENCES/BIBLIOGRAPHY

The following is a condensed bibliography for this chapter. Not only does it include all articles referred to or cited in the text, but it also contains bibliography for further reading. The full citations will be found at the end of the Volume. What is given here should be sufficient information to lead the reader to the correct article: the author, date, and title. In case of multiple authors, only the first named is listed. In this chapter the listing is according to the categories indicated below.

Current Design Criteria (Selected Bibliography)

The initial work of the committee was directed toward producing a concise set of statements on current design criteria for tall concrete buildings as reflected in worldwide building codes. A collection of papers by committee members appeared in the proceedings of the International Conference on Planning and Design of Tall Buildings, Bethlehem, Pennsylvania, August 1972, Vol. III, together with discussions of the various papers. Subsequently the emphasis of this chapter changed. As a consequence, much of the valuable material on design standards and criteria could not be included. The individual papers are available in those Proceedings as follows:

Amaral 1973, *South American Standards for Reinforced Concrete*
Avram 1973a, *General Review of Standards for Concrete Buildings in East European*
Bruinette 1973, *Structural Standards for Reinforced Concrete in South Africa*
Cheng 1973, *Concrete Design Standards in Asia*
Cohen 1973, *U.S.A. Structural Standards for Reinforced Concrete*

Despeyroux 1973, *Theme Report: Commentary on Structural Standards*
Kemp 1973, *Summary Report: Commentary on Structural Standards*
Nasser 1973, *Concrete Design Standards in Arab Countries*
Stiller 1973a, *Review of Codes of Practice in West European Countries—Concrete Tall Buildings*

General References

Allen 1973, *Strength Factors for Composite Members*
Avram 1973b, *Problems in Analysis*
Brakel 1973, *List of Limit States*
Kármán 1973, *Load Factors*
Levi 1973, *Theme Report: Limit States Design*

MacGregor 1973a, *Load Factor Variables*
MacGregor 1973b, *Design for the Limit State of Instability*
Paduart 1973, *Current Applications of Limit State Philosophy*
Perchat 1973, *Serviceability Factors*
Robles 1973, *Strength Factors: Material and Geometrical Aspects*

Sandi 1973, *Limit States for Dynamic Loads*
Stiller 1973b, *Standardized European Regulations for Construction*
Tomii 1973a, *Japanese Structural Standards for Reinforced Concrete Buildings*
Yokel 1973, *Summary Report: Limit States Design*

Structural Design of Tall Concrete and Masonry Buildings

Chapter CB-2

Design Criteria and Safety Provisions

Prepared by Committee 26 (Limit States Design) of the Council on Tall Buildings and Urban Habitat as part of the Monograph on the Planning and Design of Tall Buildings

Franco Levi   Chairman
Felix Y. Yokel   Vice-Chairman and Editor

AUTHOR ACKNOWLEDGMENT

Special acknowledgment is due those individuals whose contributions and papers formed the substantial first drafts of the various sections of this chapter. First are the state-of-art reporters from the 1972 International Conference whose material was published in the Lehigh Proceedings. These individuals are:

A. Paduart, Section 2.1
J. Brakel, Section 2.2
J. Perchat, Section 2.2
T. Karman, Section 2.3
F. Robles, Section 2.3.

In addition to this, other sections were based on special contributions prepared by:

F. Levi
F. Y. Yokel.

CONTRIBUTORS

The following is a complete list of those who have submitted written material for possible use in the chapter, whether or not that material was used in the final version. The Committee Chairman and Editor were given quite complete latitude. Frequently length limitations precluded the inclusion of much valuable material. The Bibliography contains all contributions. The contributors are: D. E. Allen, N. Amaral, D. M. Anastasescu, C. Avram, J. G. Batanero, J. Brakel, T. Brondum-Nielsen, K. E. Bruinette, H. K. Cheng, J. Cohen, J. Despeyroux, J. Ferry Borges, T. Karman, F. Levi, J. G. MacGregor, G. Nasser, A. Paduart, J. Perchat, A. M. Reese, F. Robles, H. Sandi, M. Stiller, M. Tichy, R. N. Wright, F. Y. Yokel.

COMMITTEE MEMBERS

D. E. Allen, J. G. Batanero, J. Brakel, T. Brondum-Nielsen, J. Ferry Borges, J. Hajek, T. Karman, S. Kokusho, K. Kordina, F. Levi, B. Lewicki, G. Macchi, J. G. MacGregor, A. Paduart, J. Perchat, F. Robles, H. Sandi, J. C. Schotanus, R. G. Sexsmith, M. Tichy, J. A. Torroja, J. Witteveen, R. N. Wright, F. Y. Yokel, K. Zilch.

CB-2

Design Criteria and Safety Provisions

2.1 DESIGN PHILOSOPHY

1 General Concept

Since the 1940s, under the increasing pressure of political and economic conditions, the civil engineer has been confronted by heightened demands for safety, durability, and economy in planning and design. Indeed, in the field of construction, the engineer cannot evade the need for exploiting, as fully as possible, all the means available for the well-being of the community. These considerations may serve to explain and justify the need for a radical revision of safety principles and calculation methods to make up for the former lack of precision in the schematic treatment of the behavior of the material. This is true in all branches of construction technology, including the field of reinforced concrete.

At first sight, it might seem that design safety criteria and calculation methods could advance independently. Yet such an approach is not practical. Actually, any step forward in the philosophy of safety criteria requires the development of tools for analyzing more carefully the performance of structures, and, vice versa, any advance in calculation methods requires a clearcut definition of its field of application before it can be used in practice.

A rational study of the recent developments in the design philosophy of major structures, including tall buildings, must therefore deal with safety principles as well as calculation methods. The aim of this chapter is to first define all the different "limit states" (or states of undesirable behavior) that the verification of structural behavior must refer to, and then to discuss the probabilistic methods which serve as bases for determining the safety margins that must be considered for each limit state.

As a logical introduction to a study of the modern limit states design method we shall make a comparative survey of the principles of safety that have served as bases for the theory of structural behavior during the course of its evolution. The survey is all the more timely in view of the fact that different design philosophies still coexist today in many branches of civil engineering. Our aim is to compare the various approaches and to evaluate the reliability and range of validity of the methods adopted within these approaches. The description of the difficulties inherent in each method will serve to justify the more rational procedure which is treated in detail in the following articles.

2   Evolution of Code Formats

The code formats used or proposed can be classified in three ways:

1. By their philosophical basis, which leads to the definition of two categories: deterministic codes and probabilistic codes.

2. By the methods and accuracy of the calculations involved. Three methods can be distinguished: working stress design (WSD); ultimate strength design (USD); and limit states design (LSD).

3. From an historical viewpoint. The first two methods (WSD and USD) were established on deterministic bases because, when they were proposed, the application of probabilistic concepts to structural engineering had not yet evolved.

The introduction of the probabilistic approach coincided with the adoption of limit states concepts. We must, however, recognize that, in the meantime, the other two methods (working stress design and ultimate strength design), which are still in use, have absorbed a certain amount of probabilistic ideas even though they remain essentially deterministic.

Hereafter the three methods (WSD, USD, LSD) are considered chronologically and examined from the point of view both of the philosophy of safety and of the extension of their range of validity, with particular attention to methods adopted to cope indirectly with aspects of structural behavior that are not explicitly taken into consideration.

Working Stress Design.   This is the classical method developed during the first half of the 19th century and still widely used in many countries.

The basic idea is to impose an upper limit to the stresses acting on all points of the structure in order to assure simultaneously that the materials will remain within the elastic range, and that the design will offer a sufficient margin of safety. This ingenious method is based on the direct application of the theory of elasticity which, during the 19th and the first decades of the 20th centuries, formed the almost exclusive basis of the study of deformable bodies.

For reinforced concrete sections, the method is applied by establishing upper limits for the stresses in the concrete and in the steel reinforcement caused by various load effects (such as bending and shear), under service conditions. Since these limits involve margins on the order of 2 (for steel) or 3 (for concrete) with respect to the strength, the result is that, under average service conditions, the sections behave elastically and that, theoretically, the margin of safety with respect to failure is at least equal to 2. In the calculations the tensile resistance of the concrete is not taken into account, leading to risk of cracking. However, no specific indication is provided on the width of cracks or on the magnitude of the deformations.

Doubts as to the validity of such an elastic approach arise when we attempt an evaluation of the actual margins of safety of the structures. It is well known in fact that reinforced concrete structures are far from satisfying the definition of an elastic and homogeneous body. We therefore conclude that most of the premises on which the working stress design method is based can be criticized rationally, as follows:

1. It is not true that, even under service conditions, the laws of linear elasticity always apply.

2. Elastic calculation also does not give precise indications of the margin between service conditions and failure. This is especially true when several external actions of different origins (such as loads, thermal effects, and settlement of supports) are combined.

3. For a material such as concrete which has a very complex response due to nonlinear behavior, cracks, creep, and shrinkage, it is not possible to consider all the aspects of behavior with which the designer has to deal if we consider only the allowable stresses.

All this explains why the working stress design method requires ample margins of safety, and why it is difficult to extend it to new fields of application (lightweight concrete, for instance), since its use is based mostly on experience.

Let us summarize briefly the methods that are used to improve the partial representation of structural behavior on which the working stress design method is based. In practice, these methods include: (1) Reduction of the stresses in the reinforcement to control the width of cracks and the deformability of structural elements; and (2) the definition of adequate limits for slenderness of beams or slabs (span-depth ratios) to avoid excessive deflections.

At the present time, it is current practice to adopt larger margins of safety for concrete than for steel to account for the greater dispersion of the mechanical properties of concrete. Similarly, the intensities of the external actions (for example, loads, imposed deformations) are often adjusted to cover the risks involved. For example, the live load adopted to design a theater or a stadium is systematically overestimated to account for the great risks of loss of human lives in case of failure, while the intensity of seasonal thermal variations is reduced to account for the adaptability of concrete structures.

It is clear that these purely empirical procedures are very subjective and may give rise to dangerous designs if used by inexperienced designers.

Several other disadvantages of the working stress method cannot be remedied. For example, it is impossible to take full advantage of the compression steel of beams due to the fact that in the elastic range the stresses applied to adjacent steel and concrete are related by the ratio of the moduli. Analogous problems arise in the dimensioning of columns, where the elastic theory severely underestimates the contribution of the reinforcement. Errors of evaluation also occur in shear and torsion.

In general, we can say that the shortcomings of the working stress method in the field of reinforced concrete are the consequence of the introduction of superfluous conditions that are not closely related to the requirements of safety. At the same time, no attention is given to other aspects of behavior that are of substantial importance. For example, it is almost irrelevant to limit the stresses in the compression zone in bending, while, on the contrary, the method does not give a clear representation of the behavior of cracked sections in the presence of shear. Similarly, the substantial influence of the distribution of the reinforcement in the tension zone is not evidenced at all.

With reference to other chapters, it should be noted that the working stress method is still widely applied to steel and masonry structures. Elastic theory is acceptable when no other interpretation of the behavior is available. For instance, the scarcity of knowledge on the actual behavior of brickwork justifies, at least to some extent, the use of procedures that are approximate but cautious.

Ultimate Strength Design. The basic ideas that underlie this more modern method, often referred to as the "load factor approach," are well known. Given the fact that the existence of a predetermined margin between resistance of structural members and materials and local stresses does not furnish any precise indication on the margin of safety available, it seemed wiser to adopt as reference the limit state of failure, and to fix the ratio that must exist between ultimate load and service load.

While the working stress method sought the necessary safety by dealing solely with resistance, ultimate strength design applies the "safety factor" entirely to the intensity of external actions. One might then, on first sight, consider the new method to be just as conventional as the previous one, since the most probable incidence of the collapse of a structure is associated with a simultaneous variation of actions and strengths, that is, an increase of the former and a reduction of the latter. [These statements do not apply to the ultimate strength design used in the United States (ACI-318, 1956), in which the variation of strength is considered by a capacity reduction factor (ϕ).]

A closer analysis, however, shows that the load factor method has several advantages, theoretical as well as practical.

First, it should be noted that, in agreement with reality, ultimate strength design deals with the response of a cross section or of an entire structural member, instead of considering the stress acting locally. Moreover, the method has the merit of making designers worry about the behavior of the structural members throughout the range between service conditions and ultimate limit states, taking into account the effects of inelastic deformations (cracks or plastic deformations) which may, in some cases, appear under normal service conditions, and whose importance will, from then on, increase very rapidly. The effects of imposed deformations of all origins (thermal gradients, shrinkage, creep, settlement of supports) usually are much more marked during the elastic phase of behavior, owing to the high rigidity of the structural elements prior to cracking. These effects tend to disappear in the vicinity of the ultimate limit state. In fact, by thinking in terms of load factors the designer is able to carry out more logical dimensioning.

Ultimate strength design also provides the opportunity of verifying theoretical estimates through tests on models or on prototypes. Thus, even though it maintains a conventional character, the global approach to safety associated with the ultimate limit state corresponds to a fruitful interpretation of reality, since it relates to a well-defined state of reference.

The application of ultimate strength design to statically determinate constructions in ordinary or prestressed reinforced concrete has been carefully studied and is amply treated in Chapters CB-6, 8, 9, 10 and 11. It appears that the evaluation of the load capacity of the sections subjected to normal forces, simple or composite bending, shear, or torsion, can be performed with great precision. More complex is the case of statically indeterminate structures, in which the influence of local and over-all inelastic phenomena must be taken into account. This problem is treated in Chapter CB-6. In Chapter CB-8, the case of structures that are influenced by second-order effects is considered.

In this chapter we intend to consider the probabilistic aspects of the problems both in the statically determinate and indeterminate fields. However, since these developments are the same in connection with limit states design, they will be discussed in later paragraphs.

Within the load factor approach, similarly to what happened for the working stress method, the problem arises of taking into account those aspects of behavior that are not directly considered by the verification procedure. In the present instance it is obvious that, once safety with regard to maximum load capacity is assured, we must be concerned with the performance of the structural elements under service conditions (cracking, deformation, etc.). Again, we tend to apply indirect methods such as introduction of appropriate limits to slenderness, or percentage or spacing of reinforcement, and of regulations on good construction practice. We must however admit that these procedures are rather imprecise. The conclusion is that for ultimate strength design, just as for working stress design, the unilateral character of the calculation is a drawback.

Other objections to this method concern the global nature of the verification procedure and, in many instances, the lack of statistical references. They can be summarized as follows:

1. The margin of safety we adopt is important, just as in the working stress method, since it must account for factors of uncertainty of all origins (regarding external stresses, resistance, calculation hypotheses, and so on). From this point of view, then, the new method still presents the disadvantage of giving to the people in charge of the construction process—designer, manufacturer of the materials, and builder—the feeling of having the interval between service conditions and the ultimate limit state at their full disposal to remedy possible imprecisions, errors of design, or faults of execution.

2. By adopting a global coefficient of safety, practically, we put all the resistant members into identical conditions: in particular, for reinforced concrete, one obtains equal safety for concrete and steel, which is illogical in view of the unequal degrees of dispersion involved in the mechanical properties of the two materials and the highly variable consequences that may result from the failure of the one or of the other.

3. Finally, we may logically advance some doubts about the validity of factors of safety that are fixed without taking into account either the variability of the actions applied to the structure, nor the risks involved in a possible failure. [Items 2 and 3 do not apply to the ultimate strength design procedures in the ACI Building Code (1971). This code was based on an elementary statistical analysis that attempted to account for the variability of concrete, steel, and loads.]

Probabilistic Approaches to Limit States Design. Earlier in this section where a classification of the code formats was proposed, it was pointed out that the limit states theory and the probabilistic methods were developed simultaneously. It is logical then to link together the treatment of these two concepts that actually refer to two separate aspects of the design procedure: the former to the extension of the verifications to all aspects of behavior, and the latter to the philosophy of safety.

The bases of LSD are clearly described in the following Principles of the International Recommendations for Design and Construction of Reinforced

Concrete Structures issued by CEB and FIP (CEB-FIP, 1970). The main ideas put forward by CEB-FIP have also been recommended by the International Organization for Standardization (ISO Norm 2394).

P.12.1. Aim of design.

All structures or structural elements must be designed to sustain safely all loads and deformations liable to occur during construction and in use and should have adequate durability during the life of the structure. The design method aims at guaranteeing adequate safety against the structure, or structural element, being rendered unfit for use. The durability of a structure is as important as its strength.

P.12.2. Definition of limit states.

A structure, or a part of a structure, is rendered unfit for use when it reaches a particular state, called a "limit state," in which it ceases to fulfill the function or to satisfy the conditions for which it was designed. The limit states can be placed in two categories: (a) the ultimate limit states, which are those corresponding to the maximum load-carrying capacity; (b) the serviceability limit states, which are related to the criteria governing normal use or durability.

P.13. Application of the probability theories.

In a structure, a limit state may be reached as the result of a number of random factors affecting the safety factors which combine and originate:

in the uncertainty of the values taken into account by the engineer for the strengths of the materials used, bearing in mind the conditions in the structure and the parameters which affect the particular limit state (prolonged loads, fatigue, etc.);

in the uncertainty of the realization of the assumed geometry of the structure and sections;

in the uncertainty of permanent loads or variable imposed loads, or imposed deformations which it is impossible to foresee accurately for the entire intended life of the structure;

in the departure of the actual loading effects from the calculated values.

The object of the calculations is to keep the probability of a limit state being reached below a value previously established for the type of structure in question.

The application of probability theory to decision making will eventually be founded upon optimization principles. In the field of structures it is necessary to bring into harmony safety criteria and economic requirements, considering also moral, social, and esthetic imperatives that can hardly be put into figures. One method of doing this would be to follow the concept of minimum total cost, defined as the sum of the initial cost of construction, the maintenance cost capitalized over the life of the structure, and the capitalized cost of insurance to cover the risks of losses arising from reaching the specified limit states. At the same time, however, it would be illusory to ascribe a precise quantitative character to such considerations. Practically they are but conceptual aids for a logical treatment of the problem.

CEB-FIP semiprobabilistic approach. For practical considerations, due to the complexity of a full probabilistic treatment of safety, the International Recommendations of CEB-FIP (1970) adopted a simplified procedure, conventionally referred to as the semiprobabilistic approach. This is conceptually very similar to the approach introduced by Soviet specifications in 1955, and then accepted by several Eastern European codes and by the unified code of the Comecon.

The method suggested by CEB-FIP (1970) can be summarized as follows:

P.14. Principles of the determination of safety.

A complete probability analysis requires a knowledge of the statistical nature of the permanent loads (dead loads), the variable imposed loads, and the imposed deformations acting on the structure, and also of the load effect produced by these actions, and of the variability of the mechanical properties of the material and the geometry of the individual sections and the construction as a whole. As a study of this type is very difficult and can in practice involve very complicated calculations, the necessary data not being available, it is convenient to:

1) take into account "characteristic values" both of the strength defining the mechanical properties of the materials and the external loads, each value being determined in advance by fixing the probability that the actual values would be effectively less than or greater than the values selected;

2) cover the other uncertain factors by transforming the characteristic values into design values by multiplying by certain coefficients. The design strengths of the material are obtained by multiplying the characteristic strength by $1/\gamma_m$ where γ_m is greater than or equal to unity. The design loads and load effects are obtained by multiplying the characteristic loads and load effects by appropriate coefficients γ_f, which may be greater than or less than unity. The values adopted for the different coefficients depend on the seriousness of attaining the limit state considered, the behavior of the material and the structure, and the probability of the combinations of loading;

3) verify that the calculated load effects do not exceed those that can be sustained by the structure for the state considered.

The first order-second moment method. This procedure, proposed by Cornell (1969), tries to follow as closely as practical the theoretical treatment of the correlation between safety and probability. With this aim in mind, Cornell outlines the following steps to establish his code format.

1. All uncertainty is treated in a uniform way using the simplest and most familiar measures of dispersion, the means and standard deviations or coefficients of variation. These parameters are used both for measurable uncertainty, such as dispersion of the resistances and of the intensities of climatic actions, and for the uncertainty whose evaluation is up to the judgment of the engineer (inaccuracies of calculation or construction, for example).

2. Structural analysis is based on approximations analogous to those adopted by conventional methods; subsequent inaccuracies are covered by "engineering" coefficients of variation.

3. The designer may adopt "nominal values" of actions (loads) and resistances which practically coincide with the "characteristic values" of the CEB-FIP

Recommendations. These values are significant, as lower and upper limits, in view of methods of control and a definition of the legal responsibility.

4. No accurate assumptions as to the precise form of the frequency distribution are made. However, the method makes use of mathematical models that permit the formulation of a probabilistic evaluation of safety.

In practice these ideas are translated into the following formulations.

Definition of resistance. The expected or mean value of the parameters which characterize resistance $\bar{r}$ (such as ultimate moment capacity, shear capacity, or stiffness) can be expressed by

$$\bar{r} = g(\bar{m}_1, \bar{m}_2 \ldots \bar{f}_1, \bar{f}_2) \tag{2.1}$$

in which the quantities $\bar{m}$, $\bar{f}$ are the expected value of the material properties and member dimensions. The uncertainty in $\bar{r}$ is measured by a coefficient of variation V_R obtained from

$$V_R^2 = V_M^2 + V_F^2 + V_P^2 \tag{2.2}$$

in which V_M = the "material coefficient of variation" representing the uncertainty of the material properties in place; V_F = the "fabrication coefficient of variation" representing the uncertainty connected with the construction; and V_P = a "professional coefficient of variation" representing the uncertainties linked to the assumptions adopted in calculating the cross-sectional response.

It is important to state at this point that the adoption of Eq. 2.2 implies two assumptions; first that the resistance may be written in the form of a product like

$$R = C. M. F. P \tag{2.3}$$

in which C = constant; and M, F, P = factors representing respectively the material properties, the quality of the construction process, and the quality of the design. The second assumption is that, in the evaluation of V_R, one can neglect the terms of higher order (first-order theory). It should also be stated that the term "second moment" which appears in the title of the method refers to the fact that the dispersions are taken into consideration by the coefficients of variation, that is to say, by the quantities related to the second-order moment of the area subtended by the curve representing the frequency distribution.

Definition of loads. Analogously, the best estimate $\bar{S}$ of the force acting on the section is assumed to be a function of the total load, T, and of a factor, E, characterizing the passage from the action to the load effect. Starting from

$$S = CTE \tag{2.4}$$

the coefficient of variation

$$V_S^2 = V_T^2 + V_E^2 \tag{2.5}$$

is obtained, in which V_T = coefficient of variation of the total load (taking into account combinations of loads of different origin); and V_E covers the uncertainties connected with structural analysis and also those depending on the spatial distribution of the loads.

The verification of the section is then considered satisfactory if the condition

$$\bar{r} \geq \theta . \bar{s} \qquad (2.6)$$

is fulfilled. In Eq. 2.6 the safety factor θ is a function of the coefficients of variation V_R and V_S involved, that is

$$\theta = \exp{(\beta\sqrt{V_R^2 + V_S^2})} \qquad (2.7)$$

and β is a measure of the degree of reliability required. One can discern in Eq. 2.7 the theoretical correlation between probability of failure and safety factor (Rjanit-zin, 1959). However, in the Cornell approach the value of the parameter β is not strictly linked to the mathematical formulation of distributions, but is fixed by the code on the basis of a calibration based upon experience and on comparison with current standards.

An alternative presentation consists in starting from the "nominal values" r and s. These values will be defined by means of expressions such as

$$r = \bar{r}(1 - K_R V_R) \qquad (2.8)$$

$$s = \bar{s}(1 + K_S V_S) \qquad (2.9)$$

The condition that must be fulfilled is then

$$r \geq \theta'.s \qquad (2.10)$$

and the new (nominal) factor of safety will be related to the central factor of safety θ by means of

$$\theta' = \frac{1 - K_R V_R}{1 + K_S V_S} \cdot \theta \qquad (2.11)$$

Other probabilistic code formats. In 1955 the USSR regulations (NITU, 1955) on structural design introduced the probabilistic concept and the limit states approach. These procedures are still followed in the present codes of eastern countries and constitute the basis of the international CMEA code (Eastern Common Market). The form of presentation of these documents is, however, slightly different from the one adopted by CEB-FIP Recommendations.

The main aspects of these codes are as follows (SNiPII-V.1-62, 1962; Avram, 1974):

1. The design loads are evaluated by application of load factors to "standard loads" established on a statistical base. Reduction factors for combination of loads are also taken into account.

2. In a similar manner, the design strengths are obtained by combination of "standard strengths" having a statistical character with "homogeneity factors."

3. In practice the design values of loads and strengths correspond to fractiles of an order of magnitude of from 1×10^{-3} to 1.5×10^{-3}.

4. A third category of parameters called "factors of working conditions" is then applied to strengths to cover imperfections of design approach, or special conditions of structural behavior.

5. As in the CEB-FIP method, the calculation is related to all relevant limit states.

In 1956, the American Concrete Institute Building Code first allowed the use of ultimate strength design with arbitrarily established load factors and no factors on strengths. The 1963 ACI Code included both load and resistance factors. These provisions are essentially unchanged in the 1971 ACI Code (ACI, 1971; MacGregor, 1976). The 1963 ACI safety provisions were based on the assumption that if the probability of "understrength" members was roughly 1 in 100, and the probability of an "overload" was roughly 1 in 1000, then the probability of an overload on an understrength member would be roughly 1 in 100 000. It should be noted that the actual probability of failure would be somewhat higher than this, however. Although the original derivation was based on a semiprobabilistic study, subsequent modifications and compromises have somewhat reduced its rationality.

The main aspects of the safety and limit states design provisions of this code are:

1. Design loads are evaluated by applying a series of load factors to loads specified in a number of separate documents.

2. The concrete strength used in design is statistically defined as the 10th percentile strength. The reinforcement strength is taken as the manufacturer's guaranteed minimum mill test strength.

3. A factor ϕ is used to reduce the member strength to give a probability of understrength of roughly 1 in 100. Based on values of concrete and steel strength corresponding to a probability of 1 in 100 of understrength, the strengths of a number of typical sections were computed. The ratio of the strength based on these values to the strength based on nominal material strengths was called ϕ.

4. The ϕ factors for columns include a factor $1/\gamma_{n1} = 1/1.1$ to allow for the increased consequences of a column failure.

5. The ϕ factor for columns failing in a brittle manner (tied columns) includes a second factor $1/\gamma_{n2} = 1/1.1$ to reflect increased consequences of a brittle failure.

6. The ϕ factor for beams is taken higher than that for columns, accounting for the fact that flexural failure is more ductile and is controlled by the steel strength which has smaller variability. To assure that flexural failure will be ductile, the ACI Code limits the allowable reinforcement ratio so that yielding of the steel will cause the rupture.

7. The design is based on the ultimate limit state, but the designer is required to check limit states of deflection either by calculation or by allowable span-to-depth ratios. For reinforcement yield strengths greater than 280 MPa (40 000 psi, 2900 kgf/cm²) the reinforcement must be distributed in such a way as to prevent excessive crack widths.

Other probabilistic codes have been issued in several western countries such as Great Britain, Denmark, the Netherlands, Portugal, and France (for prestressed concrete), which are more or less in agreement with the CEB-FIP proposal. Other interesting regulations of a probabilistic nature have been published in Mexico, in which a probabilistic description of the geometrical data is introduced. In Canada limit states design was first applied to concrete structures through adoption of the 1971 ACI Code, and more recently to steel structures (Allen, 1975). The general design equation adopted is

$$\phi R \geq \text{effect of } \gamma[\alpha_D D + \psi(\alpha_L L + \alpha_q Q + \alpha_T T)] \tag{2.12}$$

in which D, L, Q and T = specified dead, live, wind, or earthquake loads and imposed deformations; the α terms = load factors taking into account variability of the loads, load pattern, and inaccuracy of analysis; ψ = a combination factor; γ = an importance factor which takes into account the consequences of failure as it relates to the use of the structure; R = resistance corresponding to specified material properties and dimensions; and ϕ = a performance factor related to variability of materials properties, dimensions, workmanship, and type of failure.

Comparison between approximate probabilistic code formats. For an exhaustive discussion of the purely theoretical aspect of the probabilistic philosophy of safety, the reader should refer to Chapter CL-7. Here we shall only briefly compare the two main approximate procedures described previously, the semi-probabilistic approach and the first order-second moment code format.

An analysis of these two methods shows that both succeed in solving fully only the simplest difficulties presented by the application of the probability theory to structural safety, and that, in this field, the difference between the two is less substantial than it seems at first. The semiprobabilistic method, which introduces from the start correction coefficients, may give the impression of being less scientific; but actually it is possible to assign a meaning to these coefficients, by referring to the theoretical procedure considering γ_m as a correction intended to reduce the fractile to which correspond the design strengths, and γ_f as the real factor of safety. As to the first order-second moment method, it follows a somewhat reverse pattern. The operation involved at first gives the impression of respecting all the rules of probability theory, but in reality each step of the procedure calls for approximations or assumptions that are just as debatable as those comprised in the definition of the correction coefficients of the other method. This applies especially to the way in which the coefficients of variation of loads and resistances are evaluated.

One advantage of the second-moment method is that it handles combinations of loads and combinations of materials in a more correct and simple way. On the other hand, there is difficulty in applying it to the treatment of nonlinear effects since the safety factor is determined after analysis. To approach these problems of over-all practical importance, one must rely upon a correct analytical representation of reality and must introduce, in each case, rigorously controlled approximations. This is the aim of the so-called Level II methods that will be considered in Section 2.4.

2.2 LIST OF LIMIT STATES FOR REINFORCED CONCRETE STRUCTURES

1 Categories of Limit States

Referring to Clause 12.2 of the CEB-FIP Recommendations quoted earlier we have already stated that the limit states can be subdivided into two categories:

1. The ultimate limit states, which are related to the maximum load and the carrying capacity. Since events associated with the ultimate limit states can endanger lives or cause major economic loss, their probability of occurrence must be very low.

2. The serviceability limit states, which are related to criteria governing normal use or durability, and have a much higher probability of occurrence.

The main categories of ultimate limit states are the following:

1. Loss of equilibrium of a part or the whole of the structure, when considered as a rigid body (overturning, sliding).

2. Rupture of critical sections or parts of the structure.

3. Transformation of the structure into a mechanism.

4. Instability by deformation.

5. Deterioration arising out of fatigue effects.

6. Plastic or creep deformation or cracking, leading to a change of geometry which necessitates replacing the structure.

Ultimate limit states may also be caused by the sensitivity of the structure to the effects of accidental events such as explosive pressure, collision, or fire. It is necessary to consider such effects in the structural concept.

The main categories of the serviceability limit states are:

1. Excessive deformations with respect to normal use of the structure.

2. Premature or excessive cracking.

3. Deterioration and corrosion.

4. Excessive displacement without loss of equilibrium.

5. Excessive vibrations, or other conditions.

These limit states apply to concrete structures in general, and hence also to tall concrete buildings. Most of them also apply to structures made of other materials. In tall buildings, however, some of the limit states are of primary importance, while others are less important or important only in special cases.

Generally, the effect of lateral deformations of tall buildings caused by deformations of the structure and its various parts, as well as that due to deformations of the foundation (the soil or piles) is very significant, particularly with regard to stability and damage to partitions, etc.

2 Ultimate Limit States

Loss of Equilibrium of Part or Whole of the Structure, When Considered as a Rigid Body. A rigid body is in equilibrium when the resultant of the actions is equal, opposite, and colinear to the resultant of the reactions of the subsoil. When the resultant lies within the kern of the section of the contact surface, all stresses in the contact area will be compressive; if not, there are also tensile stresses. If the tensile stresses cannot be taken by the surface, the resultants may still be in equilibrium, but the maximum compressive stress will increase considerably (Fig. 2.1).

For a tall building the actions are mainly dead weight and live load, both vertical, and wind, horizontal. Sometimes inertia forces due to machines or earthquakes are significant. The contact surface is the surface of the foundation soil or the top surface of the foundation or the piles. Sometimes the foundation is integral with the building as, for example, a caisson foundation in which case the whole might be considered as a rigid body.

The foundation soil normally cannot take tensile stresses, although a pile foundation can, to a limited extent. For large forces ground anchors may be effective. The equilibrium is lost when the resultant of the actions cannot be resisted by the reaction forces of the soil or foundation. When this occurs the body overturns. It is important to determine this limit state as accurately as possible, to be able to verify whether the building has sufficient safety against overturning. Theoretically, therefore, all possible combinations of horizontal and vertical loading have to be considered and the soil resistance for every combination determined to see which combination gives the lowest safety. Because this would give a large number of combinations, the combinations of maximum H + maximum $(G + P)$ and maximum H + minimum G are taken as critical in design (Fig. 2.2). When the live load can be all on the lee side of the wind, which is very unlikely in normal cases, the combination of maximum $G + \frac{1}{2} P$ and maximum H may give even greater stresses than maximum H + maximum $(G + P)$.

Here it is assumed that the dead weight G and the full live load P have their resultant in the center of gravity of the section. The stresses resulting from the decisive load combinations generally are only compared with the soil resistance, determined on the basis of subsurface investigations and laboratory tests, or with allowable soil bearing values, prescribed by building codes or derived from soundings, from tables in books, or from experience. The factor of safety that is assumed is generally high with these empirical methods (also because it is often preferred to use only the linear branch of the load-settlement diagram of the soil).

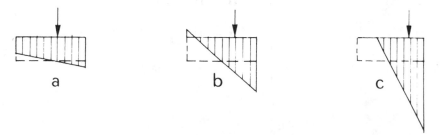

Fig. 2.1 Stress distribution at foundation level

However, not only equilibrium should be checked, but also estimated deformations of the soil should be compared with the allowable settlement of the building.

In compressible soils such as clays, and where dead and live loads act eccentrically, the building may get progressively out of plumb, leading to failure by loss of stability, either by soil stability failure or by instability of parts or all of the building. However, a tall concrete structure, in reality, is not a completely rigid body, particularly when it consists of frames, or frames in combination with shear walls or cores. The structure deforms, and thereby foundation pressures are influenced; the pressures generally increase under the stiffer parts, while the pressures under other parts are reduced. This new equilibrium can differ considerably from that of the original rigid body. Moreover, horizontal drift of the building will cause a displacement of the center of gravity in the same direction, and the overturning moment should be increased accordingly. In tall buildings this may be of importance (see Chapter CB-8).

In addition to vertical loads the foundation must also resist horizontal forces. Generally this is accomplished by friction between the underside of the foundation and the soil; with deep foundations the horizontal soil resistance against vertical foundation elements (from neutral to passive) can also be taken into account. In the case of a pile foundation, the friction between underside of foundation and soil cannot be relied upon, since the loads are transferred to the soil at greater depths, and an open space between the two may occur in the course of time. Horizontal forces can then be preferably resisted by batter (sloped) piles or, under appropriate conditions, by the horizontal soil pressure (from neutral to passive), provided sufficient depth is available. However, it is generally not possible to count on the development of the full passive soil pressure since lateral displacements of several centimeters may be necessary. During this process the piles will also resist a significant portion of the horizontal load, provided that the soil conditions and the pile design can supply this resistance. The piles are then loaded in bending and shear.

Effective resistance to lateral loads can also be provided by sheet-pile walls of steel or concrete or massive concrete walls, formed in the soil (deep walls) in the direction of the force. Also, sloped or horizontal ground anchors may be effective (see Chapter SC-7).

Rupture of Critical Sections of Structure.   These limit states can be related to bending moment, shear, torsion, stability failures, or losses of bond, and are carefully analyzed in any standard text on reinforced concrete and in Chapters CB-6 and CB-8.

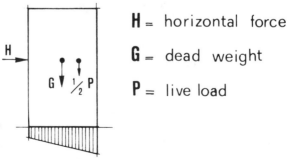

H = horizontal force

G = dead weight

P = live load

Fig. 2.2 Critical load combination

Local rupture of a critical section of a structure may cause an ultimate limit state of collapse for the whole structure, if this rupture results in a chain reaction.

For instance, the rupture of one of the anchor rods of a sheet-pile structure may cause successive overloading and failure of the neighboring anchors. The same applies to the hangers of a suspension building, the columns of a frame building, particularly of a tall one, and the failure of a wall panel in a panel structure. The collapse of a floor panel might also cause a progressive failure, if the underlying floors cannot resist the load effects (dynamic and static) of the broken floor slab, or when the destruction of the floor leads to an instability of the columns. These problems will be dealt with in a subsequent article.

Transformation of Structure or Part of Structure into a Mechanism. Normally, in concrete structures, other limit states such as failure of critical members would occur before a mechanism develops. However, a mechanism is considered in the yield-line analysis of slabs, and local mechanisms could develop in frame structures. In structures designed to withstand earthquake load as ductile frames, this type of failure could occur under earthquake loads.

Failure of a complete frame can often occur before all critical sections have reached their ultimate strength because heavily loaded columns or other parts with high compressive forces, including very high degrees of prestress, and heavily reinforced elements have only limited rotation capacity. For this reason a mechanism should be chosen so that hinges will form only in members with sufficient rotation capacity, generally beams rather than columns, and care should be taken that hinges cannot develop first in the more brittle sections. This is sometimes difficult to accomplish, because when members are strengthened, by reinforcement or by increased dimensions, they are stiffened also and attract greater moments.

Great care should be taken when inelastic analyses are applied to unbraced frames because the deformations may cause instability of the structure long before the anticipated mechanism has fully developed. Strictly speaking, with the formation of every new plastic hinge, the stability of the correspondingly deformed building would have to be recomputed.

Inelastic analyses of concrete structures are discussed in Chapter CB-6.

Instability Induced by Deformations (Second-Order Effects). Failures of this type can occur in slender structures and in slender structural members subjected to heavy compressive load, due to second-order effects caused by deformations. These limit states tend to become critical under combinations of maximum horizontal and vertical load; they may also be caused by creep in presence of sustained loads. Instability of the whole structure of a tall building by deformation, in principle, does not differ from that of any other building, but due to the great height this limit state may control the design and an accurate analysis of the phenomenon is frequently of primary importance.

Other difficulties associated with the nonlinear behavior of the structural response arise in the field of safety principles. This aspect, which concerns also the ultimate analysis of buildings without second-order effects, will be dealt with in Section 2.3 (Guidelines for Design Analysis).

The deformations of the structure that cause second-order effects may have their origin in:

1. Horizontal forces, mainly wind, but also earthquake, blast, etc.

2. Vertical forces, eccentric loading (dead weight or live load, or both), temperature differences between opposite sides, as well as shrinkage and creep differences.

3. Rotation of the foundation caused by eccentric loading, different soil properties, unequal settlement, variable stiffness of the basement, different loading from cores and frames or adjacent buildings, or unequal depth or kind of foundation (directly on the soil or on piles).

4. Initial deviations from the vertical axis, caused by shortcomings during construction, or errors or inaccuracies in surveying.

Some of these deformations are present from the beginning, while others develop or increase during the lifetime of the building due to creep or settlement.

Because the horizontal deflection plays a principal role in the stability of a tall building, it should be calculated as realistically as possible, ideally taking into account all possible influences of cracked and uncracked sections and their distribution over the length of each member, the effects of shrinkage and creep, redistribution of moments and forces, etc. From the dimensions of the sections, the amount and arrangement of the reinforcement and the mechanical properties of the materials, moment-curvature and moment-rotation diagrams can be derived, including the rotation capacity and the "plastic length" of a hinge. For practical applications, however, most diagrams can be simplified to the safe side.

When a structure is composed of elements with different deflection behavior, such as shear walls and frames, the deflection of the composite structure has to be calculated. The same applies to other combinations such as tube and frame or tube-in-tube.

With the ever-increasing height of buildings, the stiffness of the joints of prefabricated elements should be given special attention, because they often are less rigid than monolithic joints. Tests should give adequate information on this point.

For precast members used in a tall building care must be taken to prevent possible progressive failure, that is, the failure of one component in a building which might turn the entire structure or a major portion of it into a mechanism. This can be attained by proper arrangement of the various precast elements or by good joinery between the elements, including post-tensioning the various elements into one unit.

For stability design, a tall building is often viewed schematically as a vertical cantilever, restrained in the basement or foundation, which in turn rests directly on the subsoil or on the intervening piles or other types of foundations (Fig. 2.3). As shown in Fig. 2.3, foundation rotations have a major effect on the stability of the building.

Torsional moments due to wind or earthquake forces may cause torsional displacements of the building which could also lead to instability. The phenomenon of torsional instability may be described as follows. When a structure is subjected to an initial torsion, causing a constant specific rotation θ over the whole height (Fig. 2.4), the point of application of each column load will undergo a horizontal displacement that depends upon the total angle of rotation at the considered height and the distance from the center of rotation. This displacement produces a second-order torsional moment that must be summed over all columns and over the total height. The additional torsional moments will increase the initial torsional displacements, etc., until either static equilibrium or collapse is reached.

The resistance against torsion is highly dependent on the arrangement and shape of the cores or shear walls. Normally the floors have sufficient strength and can be assumed to have infinite stiffness to carry horizontal loads to the shear walls or cores.

Under dynamic loading, if that portion of the wind or seismic energy that is absorbed by the structure is larger than that dissipated by the structural damping,

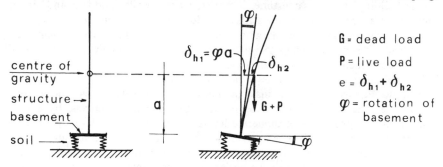

Fig. 2.3 Stability scheme of tall building

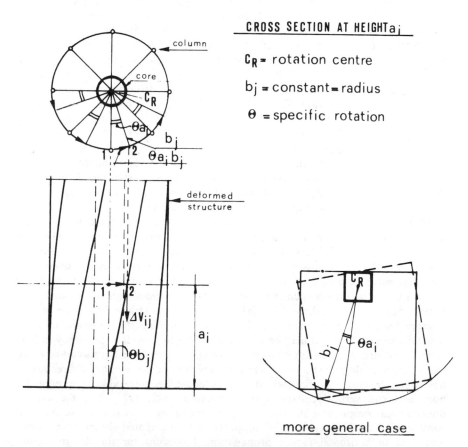

Fig. 2.4 Torsional instability of rotationally symmetrical structure

then the amplitude of the oscillation will continue to increase and will finally lead to destruction. For concrete structures dynamic instability is generally only critical for very tall and slender structures such as towers, chimneys, and masts, or for certain thin-walled unstiffened shell structures, as for instance concrete cooling towers. In the more massive concrete structures with large exposed areas, the mass and the damping capacity are so high that wind energy will not lead to destruction of the whole building. At the same time, however, curtain walls, cladding and similar elements may be subjected to oscillations due to wind or gusts. Thus in most instances when a concrete building has been designed to resist the equivalent static wind loads, it is not necessary to verify aerodynamic stability, except for very tall and slender structures or in special cases.

The stability limit state is discussed in Chapter CB-8.

Fatigue Failures. Failure may be induced by repeated cycles of loading. High-cycle fatigue failures could be induced by temperature effects, by a great number of repeated cycles of moderate levels of live or wind load, or by vibration induced by machinery. There is no evidence that fatigue failures constitute a major problem in concrete structures properly designed against temperature effects; however, care must be taken in the design of the connection of floors to columns and considering the effects of stiffness at the upper floors of tall buildings (see Chapter CB-10). Low-cycle fatigue failures could be caused by extreme wind and earthquake loads and must be given consideration by designers (see Chapter CB-6).

Deformations or Cracking Leading to Change in Geometry. This limit state does not involve collapse from instability by deformation, but only excessive deformation that makes the building unfit for use. There is only a difference of degree between this limit state and that of excessive deformations which affect normal use of the structure. The criteria involved in the decision to replace the structure depend on the use of the building, and on the over-all safety of the deformed structure. These problems are discussed in Chapter CB-10.

In the case of an earthquake or similar effects, various degrees of cracking and permanent plastic deformations may occur. In this case it should always be determined whether the deformed structure is still able to resist normal loading with the required safety margins, and also whether it is able to sustain another earthquake or blast of the magnitude anticipated in the design.

Effects of Accidental Events. Ultimate limit states due to accidental events are implicitly included in the categories considered above. However, to take such events into account from the safety point of view, special approaches are required.

For example, it is impossible to design the structure to resist every conceivable load that might be caused by explosions or collisions, but it is logical to take into account the occurrence of such events in the planning and design of the building in order to limit the area that would be affected by the failure of one or several primary load supporting members. Instead of designing the structure to resist specific abnormal loads, it may be more reasonable to provide redundancy in load support and structural continuity to avoid "progressive collapse." It should be noted that collapse could progress in the vertical as well as in the horizontal direction. It has been observed that flat-slab structures could be vulnerable to progressive horizontal and vertical collapse (ACI Committee 442, 1971). For the vertical direction the weight of potential debris generated by a local collapse must be considered. Lateral movements of supports or unanticipated shears or moments may lead to horizontal failure propagation. Provisions for the design against progressive collapse are given in the British Standard Code of Practice (BSI, 1970).

Another dangerous accidental event, if not the most dangerous, is fire. It is often forgotten that the probability of a fire is greater than that of overloading, and that its consequences are generally more severe.

In determining the effect of a fire the behavior of steel reinforcement is decisive. When the reinforcement reaches high temperatures [400°C to 500°C (1040°F to 1400°F)] it loses almost all its strength. This is particularly dangerous in the case of prestressing steel, and even more critical in the case of unbonded tendons. This loss of strength may be permanent. The main factors involved are the thickness of the concrete cover and, of course, the intensity and duration of the fire (see Chapter CL-4).

Monolithic structures with continuous reinforcement should be preferred in the case of fire, because generally only one side of a structural member will be exposed to the highest temperatures, while at the other side the temperature increase is much smaller and the reinforcement keeps most of its strength. Calculations can be made, under the assumption that the reinforcement at one side has failed, to determine whether the weakened structure still has sufficient safety left. The possibility of progressive collapse, when one member has failed (for instance, a simply supported element) should be considered.

3   Serviceability Limit States

Excessive Deformations with Respect to Normal Use of Structure.   Checking of deformation is necessary where there is a danger that one of the following conditions may occur:

1. Harmful cracking of secondary members such as partitions brought about by excessive deformability of the structures.

2. Excessive deflections due to too great a deformability of the structure.

3. Cracking due to incompatibility of the deformation of the structure under the influence of shrinkage, creep and loads imposed by adjacent or supporting members (for example, horizontal cracks at the corners of slabs built into brickwork).

4. Structural loads being applied to nonload-bearing members, such as windows or partitions, following deflection.

5. Inadmissible vibrations under the effects of machinery, wind, people walking, or moving loads.

To avoid troubles of this nature, all possible consequences of the deformations should be examined and all necessary precautions taken.

Excessive deformations with respect to normal use of a prestressed concrete floor system can usually be avoided in the vertical direction by balancing the major part of the dead or sustained load. This will result in a nearly level floor system that will not deflect up or down by any excessive amount. Such serviceability under the normal conditions may often be more important than the empirical requirements to meet certain stress limitations such as those set up in building codes in what could be a more or less arbitrary manner. A particular case is the concern about tensile stress in prestressed systems. In order to avoid some tensile stresses (which are not really harmful at all), engineers often went to the extreme of providing too much prestress, which will result in excessive camber and shortening of the member, both of which are more harmful to the building than some high local tensile stresses which are really of no significance.

The aforementioned limit states apply to concrete structures in general, and also in most cases to steel or masonry buildings.

Specific serviceability problems for tall buildings are:

1. Deformations caused by a difference in temperature between outside and inside columns (or cores, or shear walls); or between the sunny and shady sides of the building (see Chapter CB-10).

2. Deformations caused by differential creep and shrinkage of columns subjected to high compressive loads and having moderate dimensions, and the more massive cores or shear walls, where the average compressive stresses are generally much lower (see Chapter CB-10).

In both cases, the top floors show the greatest deformations. These phenomena also occur in suspension buildings, but here the lower floors show the greatest deformations.

Different vertical movement may also be caused by a difference in settlement of the shear-wall or core foundations and those of the adjacent frames. Such deformations may cause cracks in the floor slabs or in the columns, or both. Particularly rigid columns with high loading or heavy reinforcement may not be able to supply the required rotations. The deformed floors will frequently load the partitions and thereby may also cause cracks in them.

The serviceability limit states with regard to deformation and cracking of partition walls, and also the functioning of doors and windows, depend to a large degree upon the materials involved and the connection details of these walls. The tolerable slope and deflections of floors and roofs depends upon the use of the building.

Deflections should be calculated under working loads, and combined with realistic creep and shrinkage deformations. The influence of reinforcement, both in the cracked and uncracked state, should be taken into account. For permanent loads the rheological behavior of the concrete should be considered, as well as the influence of the reinforcement on this behavior. The number of factors involved is so large that precise calculations are very difficult. For this reason many regulations give values of "allowable slenderness ratios" (depth/span ratios) which must be observed; these values are related to the principal parameters that influence deformation, such as conditions of restraint, steel stress, percentage of tensile or compressive reinforcement, and ratio between dead and live load.

Special designs may also be necessary in several cases. For example, in a very long building it may be advisable to design the columns near the far ends with hinges to prevent bending moments due to differential shrinkage and creep between the ground floor and the floor above it. Dilatation joints can also reduce cracking in floors with rigid cores applied at the ends of a long building. Excessive deformations may also impair the functioning of elevators.

Deflections are discussed more fully in Chapters CB-9 and CB-10.

Premature or Excessive Cracking.   The limit states for cracking should be the same for normal buildings and for tall buildings, as far as corrosion of the reinforcement is concerned. Cracking may cause an important reduction of stiffness and a considerable increase of the deformation, particularly when torsional stiffness is concerned. The different codes (ACI Code, CEB-FIP Recommendations, etc.) give formulas to evaluate: (1) The distance between cracks; and (2) their width. This problem is also treated to some extent in Chapter CB-9, in which special recommendations for detailing of reinforcement are listed. A minimum percentage of reinforcement is generally required to avoid brittle failure by cracking.

Cracking should be checked under working loads. Premature or excessive cracking should not occur in a normal concrete structure under working loads, except for earthquake or blast. Premature cracking might be caused by shrinkage, temperature, settlement, too early or too heavy loading. It can be avoided by proper curing, well-supported formwork, early prestressing (partial or total) and proper distribution of reinforcement. Excessive cracking in concrete structures in general might be caused by extreme overloading, unequal settlement, or injudicious distribution of the reinforcement, and further by earthquakes, blasts, or explosions.

These statements are generally valid for all types of concrete structures. In tall buildings specifically, excessive cracking may appear in the floors, in the floor-to-column connections, or floor-to-core connections, when there is a considerable difference in deformation between the various vertical elements of the structure, for example, differential creep of heavy stressed columns and the lower stressed core, differences in temperature or shrinkage between the outer and inner elements, or between slender and massive elements. A properly designed concrete hinge at these connections may be able to avoid excessive cracking. The horizontal expansion of a long roof slab by temperature may also cause severe cracking in the walls under it, unless a good thermal insulation is applied.

The horizontal expansion or contraction of a prestressed roof or floor slab may cause cracking in the supporting elements, such as walls and columns. Such cracking may or may not be structurally significant because the cracking itself may relieve the stresses and the ultimate strength of the structure may not be reduced. However, its appearance may be somewhat impaired.

Deterioration and Corrosion.   The limit states for cracking described earlier have been established so that harmful corrosion of the reinforcement caused by exposure of the reinforcement at cracks is avoided if the cracking conditions are fulfilled. However, corrosion of the reinforcement can also be the result of the permeability or insufficient thickness of the concrete cover, so that CO_2 can penetrate and lower the pH, or if other aggressive gases or liquids can penetrate and do their destructive work. Therefore the quality and thickness of the concrete cover should be such that attack of the reinforcement in this way is avoided. In addition, the concrete itself may be attacked by aggressive gases or liquids, as well as by mechanical effects (temperature, frost, etc.). To avoid the harmful effects of these phenomena, a concrete cover of excellent quality should be provided. This is a question of proper mix design, batching, placing, and curing of the concrete; an arrangement of the reinforcement, such that the concrete can be placed correctly, without honeycombing; and taking appropriate measures, so that adequate cover is assured in all locations.

The limit states criteria for corrosion should be the same for tall buildings and for other concrete structures. An exception might be made for the hangers (cables or rods) of suspension buildings, where corrosion or other damage might lead to a catastrophe which could lead to a progressive collapse, even if only two or three adjacent cables were to be attacked and break at the same time or directly one after another. The resulting chain reaction would probably lead to total collapse.

For concrete at the outside of a tall building the great quantities of rain and the air pressures, caused by wind (even upward), might lead to increased corrosion because the water is pressed into the pores and cracks. In other circumstances the rain has a cleansing effect on the walls and washes away the dust and salts which might otherwise promote corrosion. Little is known about this subject.

The separation of cladding elements on the outer walls by failure of the anchorages due to corrosion or fatigue or both, and due to temperature and gust effects, should also be considered. This danger should be carefully monitored, and the design of the anchorages should be in accordance with the risk involved.

Excessive Vibrations and Lateral Sway.   Excessive vibrations may be caused by wind, machines, earthquakes, blasts, etc. Depending on the frequency, their acceleration, velocity, or amplitude may be unpleasant or even irritating to people. Also however, relatively slow sway motions may produce effects that are unpleasant or even unbearable. The average human response to vibrations is shown on the accompanying graph (Fig. 2.5) by Van Koten (undated). This problem is discussed extensively in Chapter SB-5 and in Chapter CL-3.

Floor vibrations are primarily vertical, while earthquake, wind, and blast effects are primarily horizontal, even though vertical components may be significant. The amplitude of vibrations is increased by resonance, but it does not reach an infinite value due to the damping properties of the structure and the material. To judge if resonance may occur, the spectrum of the generating forces should be known, as well as the fundamental frequency of the structure, and some higher harmonics. The fundamental frequency is a function of the stiffness, the height, and the mass of the building. Damping is a question of energy absorption, by the building system (joints, interaction with partitions), by the materials (yielding), by cracks and other irregularities (internal friction), and by the soil.

The stiffness can be influenced by prestressing to prevent cracks at service loads, by loading, again to reduce the cracking, compression reinforcement and, of course, by changing the dimensions of the members. Stiffness and mass are influenced by making use of lightweight concrete. It is possible, with our present knowledge, to have a good estimate of the response of a structure to certain vibrations, by calculation as well as by model tests.

The limit states could be derived from Fig. 2.5 and the information in Chapters CL-3 and SB-5. Vibrations seldom give rise to fatigue, since the stress amplitude is too low (with the exception of earthquake and blast). Equivalent static wind loads are generally chosen high enough to compensate for dynamic effects.

2.3   GUIDELINES FOR DESIGN ANALYSIS

In Section 2.1 the concept of "Limit State Design" was introduced as the logical achievement of the modern developments of the philosophy of safety. The aim here is to discuss the practical applications of the method.

Before getting to the heart of the subject, it is, however, useful to examine briefly the present practice in the field of the philosophy of safety.

In fact, it appears that, up to now, the limit states approach has been applied to only a relatively small range of problems and, at the same time, that the introduction of probabilistic concepts still meets with considerable resistance.

The contradiction between current practice and the modern trend of the safety

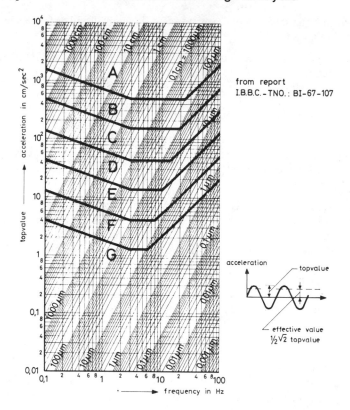

Fig. 2.5 Limits of accelerations for people and buildings (from Van Koten, undated)

Degree or description of perceptibility (1)	Admissibility for people in buildings (2)	Rough judgment for influence on structure (3)	Examples (4)
A Cannot be tolerated	inadmissible	collapse	emergency cases
B Can hardly be tolerated	inadmissible	local damage	sudden stopping of automobile
C Very strongly perceptible	hardly admissible	crack formation	elevator or tramway
D Strongly perceptible	at heavy manual labor	beginning slight crack formation	beginning of seasickness
E Perceptible	for a short time in houses	no influence on normal buildings	
F Hardly perceptible	for a long time in houses	no influence	
G Not perceptible		no influence	

theories must be ascribed, in our view, to several factors, listed as follows in order of decreasing importance:

1. Excessive attachment to tradition, mainly due to inadequate information for designers.

2. Lack of statistical data.

3. Complexity of the probabilistic methods.

4. The still debatable character of the results produced by the probabilistic approach, since many factors such as human error cannot be put into probabilistic terms at the present time.

We must emphasize, nevertheless, that none of these arguments is decisive and the trend to probabilistic design is likely to prevail in the long term.

Yet to avoid misunderstanding, it should be noted that even by means of procedures that seem totally to contradict the more rational method, it is possible to attain acceptable results. Skill and experience may in fact overcome the theoretical shortcomings through the adoption of appropriate procedures. There is, however, evidence that the introduction of any empirical procedure, even if skillfully controlled, is always confusing and that a systematic application of the new concepts of safety is more rational.

1   Practical Application of Semiprobabilistic Limit States Approach

Statically Determinate Linear Problems.
Basic procedure. The CEB-FIP Recommendations give the following directives, which are the practical consequences of the Principles outlined in Section 2.1.

P.21. Characteristic values.
P.21.1. Characteristic strength of materials.
The characteristic strengths of materials are, by definition, those which have an agreed probability of not being attained. To determine the characteristic strength, a statistical distribution is assumed; generally a normal distribution will be taken.
The characteristic strengths, R_k, are then defined by:

$$R_k = R_m - ks$$

where:

R_m is the arithmetic mean of the different test results,
s is the standard deviation,
k is a coefficient depending on the agreed probability of test values less than R_k.
When statistical data are not available, the nominal values given in Standards, Codes of Practice or other regulations relating to a specific form of test and used for classification, may be taken as the characteristic values, provided they offer an equivalent guarantee.
P.21.2. Characteristic loads.
P.21.21. Loads.

For the external loads, the characteristic values,
F_k, are by definition those which have an agreed probability of not being changed (toward more unfavorable values) during the envisaged life of the structure. Where a reduction in load is more dangerous for the stability of the structure, the minimum values should be taken as the more unfavorable.

P.22. Design values.

P.22.1. Design strengths of material.

The design strengths R_d are defined by:

$$R_d = \frac{R_k}{\gamma_m}$$

P.22.2. Design load effects.

Design load effects are given by the following relations:

$$S_d = \gamma_f \,(\text{effects of } F_k)$$

(local increase in the effects of the characteristic loads, assessed using elastic theory), or

$$S_d = \text{effects of } (\gamma_f F_k)$$

(increase in the characteristic loads and assessment of their effects).

It must be emphasized that the two approaches given in CEB Section P.22.2 are equivalent only in the simple case of a linear problem, considered in the present paragraph. The general case of a statically indeterminate structure will be treated in the following. In addition to the load factors quoted, in the case of a combination of loads or imposed deformations, special factors γ_{f2} less than unity are introduced to take into account the reduced probability that all the loads simultaneously reach their extreme values. Then the formula becomes

$$S_d = \gamma_f \text{ effects of } (F_{1k} + \gamma_{f22}F_{2k} + \gamma_{f23}F_{3k} + \ldots) \tag{2.13}$$

In the CEB-FIP Recommendations (Section P.21.1.) the coefficient k introduced in the formulas for computing characteristic values is the coefficient which, for a normal (or Gaussian) distribution, corresponds to the probability that 5% of the data be lower (or, if appropriate, higher) than the characteristic value.

The example that follows shows the application of the procedure.

Suppose we intend to compute the ultimate limit state capacity of a reinforced concrete section having the geometrical reinforcement ratio $A_s/bh = 0.01$. Assume the mean concrete compressive strength $f_{cm} = 29.4$ MPa (4260 psi, 300 kgf/cm²) and the mean steel yield strength $f_{ym} = 430$ MPa (62 500 psi, 4400 kgf/cm²), and let $s_c = 3.5$ MPa (511 psi, 36 kgf/cm²), $s_s = 17.2$ MPa (2480 psi, 175 kgf/cm²) be the corresponding standard deviations.

According to the CEB-FIP Recommendations, the characteristic resistances are to be derived from

$$f_{ck} = f_{cm} - 1.64s_c$$
$$f_{sk} = f_{sm} - 1.64s_s$$
(2.14)

which give

$$f_{ck} = 23.7 \text{ MPa (3420 psi, 241 kgf/cm}^2)$$
$$f_{sk} = 403.4 \text{ MPa (58 400 psi, 4110 kgf/cm}^2)$$
(2.15)

The design values are obtained using the reduction factors $\gamma_c = 1.5$ (for concrete), and $\gamma_s = 1.15$ (for steel), so that

$$f_{cd} = 15.8 \text{ MPa (2270 psi, 160 kgf/cm}^2)$$
$$f_{sd} = 350.8 \text{ MPa (50 700 psi, 3570 kgf/cm}^2)$$
(2.16)

The mechanical reinforcement ratio of the section in terms of design values is then

$$\omega_0 = 0.01 \times \frac{350.8}{15.8} = 0.22$$
(2.17)

and this value must be used to calculate the ultimate resisting moment.

The same procedure will be applied to evaluate the design value of the load effect. Usually the nominal loads given by the codes are taken as characteristic loads. Then if we are dealing with a statically determinate structure it is sufficient to multiply the nominal loads by the γ_f factor (usually taken equal to 1.5) and to apply them to the structure in order to compute the design value of the bending moment.

The safety verification will involve checking that the design (factored) value of the moment is equal to, or smaller than, the ultimate resisting moment.

The procedure for the other limit states is the same. However, for serviceability limit states, γ_m and γ_f are normally equal to 1, which means that the calculation is done directly with characteristic values.

It is interesting to note that the semiprobabilistic limit states method shown overcomes most of the objections that were made against ultimate strength design. First, it is obvious that the new method is concerned with all aspects of behavior relating to service and ultimate conditions. A further shortcoming eliminated is the inconvenience of using a large and ill-defined margin of safety that leaves excessive room for individual initiatives on the part of the designer. The problem of distinguishing between ruptures originating in the concrete and those due to the weakening of the steel is also solved. Finally, it is obvious that the method takes into account the variability of the factors involved and calibrates the safety in accordance with the risks.

Shortcomings of the method. Without going into too much detail it is useful to list the main difficulties that arise when we try to interpret the foregoing method from a practical point of view. In the following we shall consider as an example the ultimate limit states.

Following a suggestion given by Ferry Borges and Castanheta, the application of the coefficient γ_m can be considered as a correction intended to lower the fractile of the strength, for example from 0.05 to 0.005. Then the reduction of the scatter so obtained enables us to adopt the same load factor γ_f regardless of whether failure is due to crushing of concrete or yielding of steel. In that manner the coefficient γ_f appears as the true factor of safety which controls the convolution between the distribution of strengths and loads. However, the first difficulty arises in evaluating the characteristic resistance of the section by substituting the characteristic strengths of the materials in the expression of the resistance of the section itself. This procedure is correct only if the section resistance is a linear function of only one variable (that is to say only at the extremes of the M-N interaction diagram). Further doubts concern the definition of the stress-strain diagrams of the design strength materials on the load-deflection characteristics of the structure, particularly when stability is critical.

Analogous problems appear in connection with shear and torsion, both because of the concurrent effect of behavior of steel and concrete and because of the effects of deformability on the redistribution of internal forces. Similar difficulties arise in the evaluation of the characteristic value of the load effects in the presence of a combination of actions, consideration of variability in time and of the vectorial character of load effects, etc. The second-order method overcomes this problem by applying the law of propagation of errors to the parameters as they occur in the design equations for load and resistance.

Finally, the procedure described does not explicitly account for errors in the calculation model or for differing consequences of failure, except insofar as the latter depends on whether concrete or steel causes the failure. Although the CEB-ISO Safety Recommendations include a parameter γ_n to account for these quantities, this parameter is taken equal to 1.0 in the CEB Recommendations. These effects can be accounted for in the Cornell procedure for evaluating safety provisions and are included in the ACI Code (see Section 2.1 of this chapter).

These remarks are intended to emphasize the approximate character of the semiprobabilistic approach.

Nonlinear Problems (Statically Indeterminate Structures and Second-Order Effects). When the relation between actions (loads) and load effects is nonlinear, as in statically indeterminate structures beyond the elastic limit or in any structure in the presence of second-order effects, the application of the semi-probabilistic method meets with additional difficulties. In fact, for the same problem one may obtain totally different results depending on whether the safety factor is applied to the elastically computed load effects based on the characteristic values of the actions (loads), or whether it is applied to the characteristic values of the actions themselves before the linear or nonlinear analysis is carried out.

It is apparent that both procedures are open to criticism, as they yield markedly different probabilities of reaching the limit state considered. Actually, in the first case, the initial assumption implies an incorrect estimate of the influence of conditions of restraint and deformation; in the second, the assumption is that the evolution of nonlinear phenomena is completely insensitive to the factors of uncertainty related to local behavior, which is the same as overestimating the redistribution of the forces that characterize nonlinear behavior. In fact these arguments show that it is logical to distinguish between the causes of uncertainty that affect over-all structural behavior and those having only local effects.

These considerations are of considerable theoretical importance since it is difficult to admit that starting from an arbitrary idealization of the mechanical properties of the structure one might set up a correct probabilistic analysis. This is precisely what happens when one assumes, on deterministic bases, that in a structure the load effects can be calculated up to the ultimate limit state by applying the theory of linear elasticity, introducing afterwards the probabilistic considerations of safety; or alternatively when one requires that all uncertainties must be taken into account *a priori* by applying to the actions a probabilistic safety factor whose influence is then exerted within a nonlinear or rigid plastic calculation providing, on arbitrary premises, for the formation of plastic hinges.

Another important pragmatic consideration is that the use of an incorrect procedure might dangerously mislead the intuition of the designer. This is what happens when one employs the same coefficient to cover uncertainties with entirely different origins and effects. It is not correct, for instance, to foresee that the actions can exceed by so large a margin their characteristic value as seems to be implied in the adoption of an increase factor $\gamma_f = 1.5$. Actually, as is clearly stated in the CEB-FIP Recommendations, γ_f serves equally to cover errors in the estimate of conditions of restraint, geometrical imperfections, and the appearance of unforeseen local load effects. Similarly, the Recommendations clearly state that the correction coefficient for the resistances must take into account the influence of different phenomena, some of a local character, others of a generalized nature. Should one omit all these distinctions, the representation of structural behavior might be completely distorted.

These difficulties have been considered by the CEB-FIP Recommendations which have proposed the following qualitative solution. It replaces the procedure outlined in Section 2.3 of this chapter for linear problems.

P.22.2. Design loadings.(...)
To allow the values of γ_f to be derived, the following treatment must be adopted. The coefficient γ_f is assumed to be a function of partial coefficients γ_{f1}, γ_{f3}[*] where: γ_{f1} takes account of the possibility of unfavorable deviations of the loads from their characteristic value, and γ_{f3} takes account of the possibility of adverse modifications of the load effects.

Thus:
a) the design external loads may be derived by using coefficients γ_{f1} (and eventually γ_{f2}) applied to the characteristic value F_k

$$F_d = \gamma_{f1} F_k$$

b) the design load effects S_d may be determined by introducing a coefficient γ_{f3} on the load effects resulting from the design external loads F_d.

$$S_d = \gamma_{f3}(\text{effects of } \gamma_{f1} F_k)$$

P.22.1. Design strengths of materials.
The design strengths R_d are defined by:

$$R_d = \frac{R_k}{\gamma_m}$$

[*] Note that γ_{f2} has already been introduced as a load combination factor.

The reduction coefficient γ_m is in principle a function of two coefficients γ_{m1} and γ_{m2} which take account respectively of the reduction in the strength of the materials in the structure as a whole and reductions in the strength due to local effects.

It is worth noting that this procedure, conventionally called "method of graduated coefficients," can be interpreted as a linearization of the relationship between loads and load effects at an intermediate level $\gamma_{f1}F_k$. From this point of view, we can observe that the graduation of the coefficients is practically equivalent to the devices that consist of admitting a "transfer" of the moments (in the calculation of continuous beams, for example), or in adopting a reduced rigidity EI (for the evaluation of second-order effects). As a matter of fact, in these two approaches the nonlinear behavior is also linearized at a level that is beyond the elastic limit but lower than the ultimate limit state.

Exceptional and Accidental Events. In the current terminology an exceptional event can be described in statistical terms but does not belong to the same population as normal events. Typical examples are the distinction between normal wind and tornadoes, frequently occurring earthquakes and catastrophic earthquakes. In the semiprobabilistic code formats exceptional actions are considered only for the verification of ultimate limit states and their characteristic value is multiplied by a factor of safety ranging from 1 to 1.5, before they are combined with characteristic values of permanent and semipermanent loads.

On the other hand, accidental events like explosions and collisions are considered deterministically, since a probabilistic handling of these phenomena is practically impossible or would be excessively expensive. As we have already shown in Section 2.2 in the paragraphs on "Effects of Accidental Events," some codes attempt to guarantee a minimum of safety in this respect by requiring special measures in the conception of the building to confine the damages involved to a restricted zone of the structure.

2.4 FUTURE IMPROVEMENTS AND NEEDED RESEARCH

1 Philosophy of Safety

Chapter CL-7 deals with present trends in the application of probabilistic concepts. Here we shall only list the most important problems in need of a solution and touch upon a few of the proposals already put forward, which may be of merit for practical use in the future.

The schemes that have been examined in the preceding articles correspond to what has been termed the "Level I" approach. Studies based on a more accurate but still approximate use of probabilistic concepts are grouped under what have been termed Level II methods, with the understanding that Level III will correspond to the integral application of probability theory in structural design.

As a matter of fact, Level II will be the basis of the improvement of probabilistic codes in the near future. The following items require more information.

Treatment of Uncertainty. As was seen previously in the simplified methods, the representation of probabilistic distributions of resistances and intensities of actions is often made in a summary form through the adoption of characteristic values or adoption of a second-moment approach. Such procedures can involve serious inaccuracies, particularly in the presence of functions of many variables. Consequently progress in this field will require a more accurate representation of the variables, suitable to be used correctly in all combinations of loads.

The use of more sophisticated theoretical approaches will require an equivalent improvement of the statistical information used in the calculations.

Treatment of Variability in Time of Actions (Stochastic Phenomena). Problems arise when we want to study the combination of several variable forces, such as live loads, wind, and earthquakes. In this case, to evaluate the probability of occurrence of the most adverse values, we surely cannot consider separately the distribution of the intensity of each single action, since the effects produced obviously depend upon the variability of the actions as a function of time.

To overcome such a difficulty, Level II methods usually adopt the following hypotheses:

1. Description of the evolution of the actions referred to an "elementary time interval" within which the phenomenon may be assumed to be stationary and may be defined by the value of a single parameter. In addition, the length of the elementary interval must be chosen so that there is no correlation between the intensities reached during separate intervals.

2. To increase the statistical population available it may be assumed that the variability in time is equivalent to spatial variability, in the sense that one can group together observations carried out on structures that are very far from one another and hence surely are not correlated.

3. Further assumptions concern analytical simplifications admissible in the presence of very low probabilities of occurrence. Practically, the actual distributions of the variable actions are modified to take into account: (a) The number of repetitions of the actions during the life of the structure (estimated by dividing the expected service life of the structure by the elementary interval), and (b) the ratio of the number of repetitions corresponding to the different actions.

This procedure is quite intuitive from the standpoint that the probability of occurrence of the extreme values is, of course, dependent upon the relationship between the length of the elementary intervals and upon the number of effective repetitions.

In this direction the study of the combination of stochastic phenomena can be brought back to the fundamental problem, that is, the definition of the safety factor that must be applied to a mean value estimated by the combination of the distributions of the various actions modified as shown previously.

In this respect the improvements required are related to the need to define simplified rules for the most usual cases, and also to the need of a better interpretation of experimental data on wind and seismic effects.

Vectorial Combination of Load Effects That Depend on More Than One Parameter. A typical case involves actions giving two load effects, such as normal force and bending. The study of safety conditions is done operating in the M-N plane where we plot, at first, the interaction diagram of the resistance. On such a diagram one can show the median interaction diagram and curves corresponding to the various fractiles. The dispersion of these curves will vary so that the curves are closer together in the area corresponding to yielding of the steel, and farther apart in the area corresponding to failure of the concrete.

Comparison with the load effect is done by plotting, first of all, the mean position $\bar{X}$ of the resulting load effect, obtained by geometrical summation of vectors $\bar{X}_1$ and $\bar{X}_2$ corresponding to the mean values of the individual actions. It is then clear that the variability of the position of the end of the resulting vector depends both on the orientation of the component vectors and on the combination of their own variability. The problem is to arrive at a reliable evaluation of the spatial convolution between load effect and resistance. In practice the operation is simplified by the introduction of some hypotheses making it possible to identify a preferential direction along which the convolutive operation is transformed into a plane problem (Ferry Borges and Castanheta, 1971).

Here also a simplified representation, suitable for particular use, is needed. The validity of the approximations involved must be carefully controlled.

Nonlinear Problems.   As was stated previously, this item has been treated up to now only in a qualitative form. A thorough theoretical treatment would be particularly welcome due to the great practical importance of these problems.

2 Design Methods

It was stated at the beginning of this chapter that safety principles and calculation methods must evolve in parallel. As a corollary, the improvement of the probabilistic approach outlined previously will require a corresponding development of the knowledge of structural behavior. That is the aim pursued in the chapters of this Monograph related to the theory of structural behavior.

3 Concluding Remarks

As a conclusion to this survey of desirable developments in the theory of structures, we want to call attention to the need to always respect the requirements of engineering practice when passing from theory to application. This is true for both fields, philosophy of safety and calculation methods, in which the inevitable complexity resulting from widening of theoretical knowledge might hide from sight the concrete character of the aims pursued.

In the interpretation of structural behavior we must avoid situations where abstract calculations, performed mainly with the aid of computers, prevent the engineer from maintaining a clear vision of the essential physical aspects of the problem.

As to the philosophy of safety, where the danger is greater since the engineer cannot be expected to possess adequate knowledge of the sophisticated algorithms of probability theory, one ought to avoid the temptation of founding elaborate calculations on debatable or incomplete basic data. Care must be taken here to enable the engineer to preserve the intuitive control of the procedures he is using. It also must be kept in mind that for some significant aspects of the philosophy of safety no theoretical progress will ever be able to replace the engineer's rational belief. This applies, for instance, to: (1) The lack of statistical knowledge on basic data (resistance of materials or soils, geometrical dimensions, actions); (2) the incidence of variables which do not presently lend themselves to statistical analysis, such as calculation errors and faults of execution; (3) the intervention of a high proportion of phenomena which cannot be treated in a probabilistic form (accidental events); and (4) the complications stemming from the nonlinear relation existing between basic data and the parameters describing limit states, and also from the inapplicability of the principles of superposition.

Let us then, at the end of this chapter, express the wish that, in evaluating the significance of the steps forward that are constantly being made, researchers and engineers always display the greatest caution and an unquestionable objectivity.

2.5 CONDENSED REFERENCES/BIBLIOGRAPHY

The following is a condensed bibliography for this chapter. Not only does it include all articles referred to or cited in the text, but it also contains bibliography for further reading. The full citations will be found at the end of the Volume. What is given here should be sufficient information to lead the reader to the correct article: the author, date, and title. In case of multiple authors, only the first named is listed. The list below is arranged according to the indicated categories.

References

ACI Committee 442 1971, *Response of Buildings to Lateral Forces*
Allen 1975, *Limit States Design—A Probabilistic Study*
Avram 1974, *Design of Concrete Structures—Development of Specifications*
British Standard 1970, *British Standard Code of Practice for Large Panel Structures*
CEB-FIP 1970, *International Recommendations for the Design and Construction of Concrete*

Cornell 1969, *A Probability Based Structural Code*
International Standard Organization (undated), *Guide for the Evaluation of Human Response*
International Standard Organization 1973, *General Principles for the Verification of the Safety*
MacGregor 1976, *Safety and Limit States Design for Reinforced Concrete*
National Research Council 1975, *Limit States Design*

Rjanitzin 1959, *Design of Structures for Strength and Safety*
SNiPII-V.1-62 1962, *Codes and Technical Recommendations for Design of Concrete and Reinforced*
Van Koten (undated), *Limits for Dynamic Movements*

General documentation

General on probabilistic approach

Benjamin 1970, *Probability, Statistics and Decision for Civil Engineers*
Ferry Borges 1971, *Structural Safety*
IABSE 1969, *Symposium on Safety Concepts in Structures*
Kármán 1973, *Load Factors*
Manuzio 1973, *Present Trends in Probabilistic Studies of Structural Safety*

Mathieu 1975, *The CEB Manual of Structural Safety*
Murzewski 1972, *Safety of Tall Buildings and Probabilistic Methods*
Rackwitz 1975, *Principles and Methods for a Practice Probabilistic Approach to Structural Design*
Robles 1973, *Strength Factors: Material and Geometrical Aspects*
Tichy 1972, *Statistical Theory of Concrete Structures with Special References to Ultimate Design*

Codes based on ultimate strength

ACI 318-56 1956, *Building Code Requirements for Reinforced Concrete*
DIN 4224 1968, *Design of Concrete and Reinforced Concrete Structures*
DIN 1045 1972, *Concrete and Reinforced Concrete, Design and Construction*
NB-1 1960, *Design and Construction of Reinforced Concrete Structures*
NITU 3-39 1939, *Codes and Technical Recommendations for Design of Reinforced Concrete*
ONORM B4200 1970, *Reinforced Concrete Structures, Design and Construction*

Codes based on limit state design

ACI 318-71 1971, *Building Code Requirements for Reinforced Concrete*
Avantprojet 1972, *Proposal for Danish Code of Concrete Design*

CP 110 1972, *Code of Practice for the Structural Use of Concrete—Part 1: Design Materials and*
Ministerial Decree 1974, *Technical Norms for Composite Steel-Concrete Structures Utilizing Plain*
Ministry of Public Works 1973, *Instructions for the Projection and Execution in Building*

National Printing House 1970, *Specifications for Reinforced Concrete Structures*
NBN 15 1972, *Concrete Structures, Initial Draft of the 7th Edition*
NEN 3861 1973, *Specifications for Concrete Type A, B, and E*
Office of the Ministry 1971, *Preliminary Rules for the "General Standards for Design of Structures"*
SNiPII-V.1-62 1962, *Codes and Technical Recommendations for Design of Concrete and Reinforced*

Special problems

Allen 1973, *Strength Factors for Composite Members*
Allen 1974, *Limit States Design in Canada*
Amaral 1973, *South American Standards for Reinforced Concrete*
Ang 1969, *Safety Factors and Probability in Structural Design*
Avram 1973a, *General Review of Standards for Concrete Buildings in East European Countries*

Avram 1973b, *Problems in Analysis*
Bertero 1971, *Research Needs in Limit Design of Reinforced Concrete Structures*
Brakel 1972, *Limit States Design*
Brakel 1973, *List of Limit States*
Bruinette 1973, *Structural Standards for Reinforced Concrete in South Africa*

CEB 1967, *International Recommendations for Design and Construction of Large Panel*
Cheng 1973, *Concrete Design Standards in Asia*
Cohen 1973, *U.S.A. Structural Standards for Reinforced Concrete*
Despeyroux 1973, *Theme Report: Commentary on Structural Standards*
Ditlevsen 1973, *Structural Reliability and the Invariance Problem*

Ellingwood 1972, *A Probabilistic Study of Safety Criteria for Design*
Ferry Borges 1974, *The Checking of Non-Linear Structures*
FIP 1970, *Report of the FIP Commission on Durability*
Hasofer 1973, *An Exact and Invariant First Order Reliability Format*
Kemp 1973, *Summary Report: Commentary on Structural Standards*

Levi 1968, *The Problem of Safety in Hyperstatic Structures*
Levi 1970, *Graduated Introduction of Semi-Probabilistic Correction Coefficients*
Levi 1973, *Theme Report: Limit States Design*
Lewicki 1972, *Commentary on Design Safety Margins for Tall Concrete Building*
Lind 1971, *Consistent Partial Safety Factors*

MacGregor 1973a, *Load Factor Variables*
MacGregor 1973b, *Design for the Limit State of Instability*
Mathez 1969, *Report on Permissible Deformations in Buildings*
Nasser 1973, *Concrete Design Standards in Arab Countries*
Paduart 1971, *Limit States Design*

Paloheimo 1970, *A Method to Determine the Dimensions of a Structural Element Corresponding*
Paloheimo 1974, *Structural Design Based on Weighted Fractiles*
Perchat 1973, *Serviceability Factors*
Rosenblueth 1972, *Reliability Basis for Some Mexican Codes*
Sandi 1973, *Limit States for Dynamic Loads*

Stiller 1973a, *Review of Codes of Practice in West European Countries—Concrete Tall Buildings*
Strating 1972, *Load Factor Design*
Tomii 1973a, *Japanese Structural Standards for Reinforced Concrete Buildings*
Veneziano 1974, *Contribution to Second Moment Reliability Theory*
Yokel 1973, *Summary Report: Limit States Design*

**Structural Design of
Tall Concrete and Masonry Buildings**

Chapter CB-3

Concrete Framing Systems
for Tall Buildings

Prepared by Committee 21A (Selection of Structural Systems) of the
Council on Tall Buildings and Urban Habitat as part of the Monograph on the Planning and Design of Tall Buildings

Victor F. Leabu   Chairman
William C. Krell
Bruno Thurlimann   Vice-Chairmen
William E. Paxton   Editor

AUTHOR ACKNOWLEDGMENT

Special acknowledgment is due those individuals whose contributions and papers formed the substantial first drafts of the various sections of this chapter. First are the state-of-art reporters from the 1972 International Conference whose material was published in the Lehigh Proceedings. These individuals are:

J. P. Colaco
B. Thurlimann.

The drafting of the various sections was the work of the Chairman, Vice-Chairmen, and Editor, working as a team. They made use of special contributions prepared by the following individuals:

W. B. Bennett, Section 3.4
F. Levi, Section 3.4
T. Y. Lin, Section 3.4
J. G. MacGregor, Section 3.4, Appendix
R. C. Reese, Section 3.4
B. Sundara Rao, Sections 3.5 and 3.6.

CONTRIBUTORS

The following is a complete list of those who have submitted written material for possible use in the chapter, whether or not that material was used in the final version. The Committee Chairman and Editor were given quite complete latitude. Frequently length limitations precluded inclusion of much valuable material. The Bibliography contains all contributions. The contributors are: W. B. Bennett, J. P. Colaco, W. C. Krell, V. Leabu, F. Levi, T. Y. Lin, J. G. MacGregor, W. E. Paxton, R. C. Reese, B. Sundara Rao, B. Thurlimann.

COMMITTEE MEMBERS

D. M. Anastasescu, K. E. Bruinette, T. Z. Chastain, M. Z. Cohn, A. Coull, R. D. DeCossio, V. J. DeSimone, M. Franco, A. Ghali, E. Giangreco, A. W. Hendry, J. O. Jirsa, E. L. Kemp, G. König, W. C. Krell, V. Leabu, G. F. Leyh, E. Mancini, I. Martin, K. Muto, R. R. Nicolet, A. Paduart, A. Pauw (deceased), W. E. Paxton, D. Pume, R. Rosman, I. Schousboe, B. Stafford-Smith, B. Sundara Rao, B. Thurlimann, M. Tomii, M. Yorulmaz.

CB-3

Concrete Framing Systems for Tall Buildings

3.1 INTRODUCTION

The considerations in the proper selection of the structural system to be used in a given tall building are of concern to all involved parties.

The owner is concerned with obtaining a building that optimizes the best use of spatial volume, maximizes tenant convenience and satisfaction, and minimizes initial construction costs, insurance and energy costs, and future maintenance costs.

The architect is concerned with a structure that will best satisfy the functional and esthetic design needs of the over-all project. The mechanical, electrical, and acoustical consultants, and a host of other specialized technical consultants, have special needs which the structural system must satisfy.

The general contractors who bid and construct the building in any given locale have specialized talents and building techniques, which may be of great concern in the selection of the system.

The structural engineer who will ultimately design the selected structure must have a system that is workable and best utilizes available materials and techniques in an orderly, efficient manner.

The proper selection of the structural system involves all such centers of interest, as well as the interests of the public. The adjoining property owners and tenants are vitally interested in the nuisance factor inherent in the construction of the building. From the installation of foundations to the topping out of the structure, such parties are concerned with noise, traffic, cleanliness, and speed of construction. The design team must, therefore, be vitally concerned with such matters when selecting the scheme. The selection of the structural system should be considered during the initial discussion phases of a project and decided upon early in the design stages. The general steps that are ideally followed in the development of the system are described in the concluding summary of this chapter.

The design team is faced with a great variety of structural systems in concrete that may be used on a tall building. Each of these systems may be used in its entirety or may be mixed with other systems, depending on functional requirements.

49

The selection of structural systems is also discussed in Chapter SC-3. Although many of the principles presented in this chapter apply equally to masonry and precast concrete buildings, the selection of masonry or precast systems is discussed more fully in Chapters CB-12 and CB-13. The special characteristics of prestressed concrete that affect its use in tall buildings are discussed later in this chapter.

3.2　GENERAL DESIGN CONSIDERATIONS

Prior to describing the many optional floor systems available, a few general factors can be mentioned here to guide the design team.

1. In the United States, the cost of formwork is from one-third to one-half the total cost of concrete construction. In countries such as Mexico, Brazil, and Turkey, however, the cost of the formwork is one-third or less of the total cost of concrete construction. In any case, the structural system should minimize this formwork cost by the use of repetition and of prefabricated, large-size forms ("flying" or "gang" forms). Simple details, the use of the structure for finished exposed surfaces, and the use of precast concrete or other cost-reducing techniques, should be considered.

2. The cost of columns and the cost of the foundations (especially where poor soil conditions exist) can be minimized by reducing the weight of the structure. Weight reduction is accomplished by the use of lightweight aggregate and thin or hollow floors. The serviceability requirements for cracking and deflection rather than strength usually limit floor thickness. Thinner floors can result from the use of shrinkage compensating cements (see Chapter CB-9), or prestressing to minimize cracking and deflections. The ideal minimum thickness is often that required for fire protection. The use of lightweight aggregates can achieve given fire ratings with thinner slabs than with normal-weight aggregates. The slab thickness of ribbed slabs can be reduced to a minimum for structural purposes by applying sprayed-on insulation to achieve the required fire protection.

    It is to be noted, however, that thinner slabs must be thoroughly checked to assure tolerable deflections within acceptable limits, and should be reviewed to assure that they can serve as a diaphragm to transfer lateral loads to vertical elements of the building. Some structures rely on the dead load to assist the vertical members in resisting tensile stresses due to wind forces. This may be the case with unreinforced panel structures and with portions of a building surrounding a narrow, shear wall. Here, weight reduction would mean an increase in reinforcement or connections, or would cause other problems that might increase the cost rather than reduce it.

3. The structural scheme should be consistent with the function of the building. For example, short spans and low story heights are generally more economical but are usually acceptable only in residential buildings. Likewise, precast floor units without a topping may be acceptable in buildings where carpet can be used as the finished floor to cover the unevenness between units. In such a case the designer should determine whether the unevenness will lead to carpet damage.

4. Selection of the structural scheme should consider other elements of the construction. In some cases, a small penalty to the structural system will result in substantial savings in other areas. For example, in residential buildings, concrete bearing walls may provide sound isolation, thermal insulation, and the necessary wall surfaces, as well as serve a structural function. In another case, wide, shallow beams rather than narrow, deep beams may provide the necessary mechanical distribution space between ceiling and floor without increasing story heights, and also allow vertical passage of piping through the beams. The savings in building height and mechanical services may more than offset any increase in the cost of structural framing.

Peachtree Hotel, Atlanta, Georgia (Courtesy: John Portman)

5. Local conditions may influence the selection of a structural scheme. Examples are the availability of precast concrete elements, the experience and enthusiasm of local contractors, the capability of local labor, and the cost of labor as compared to the cost of material.

6. Construction methods can influence the cost; for example, the use of slip forms or flying forms, the adaptability of cranes and other material handling equipment to the project, and tolerances required for fitting of the structural frame between members and to other parts of the construction.

7. The speed of erection affects cost, not only as it determines the time when the building will be available for use, but also because of financing charges.

8. The building site itself may influence selection of a suitable framing system, because of foundation conditions and accessibility for construction operations.

9. The most efficient use of material will minimize the cost when all other factors are constant. While true optimization does not consist of merely minimizing material quantities, this certainly will be a general objective in selection of a structural scheme, and a specific objective in the final selection of member sizes and reinforcing steel. (Also see Chapter CB-4 on optimization.)

3.3 FLOOR SYSTEMS

The options available to the design team and described in this chapter apply to the choice of a floor framing system to support gravity load. In a tall building, even more important is the choice of an appropriate framing system to resist lateral forces. Several of the more common possibilities are outlined and discussed later in the chapter.

The construction cost of floors is often more than half the cost of the structural framework, except in extremely tall buildings. Therefore, selection of the floor framing system deserves considerable study to provide the maximum resistance to both lateral forces and gravity loads, and to minimize cost.

The final determination should be made on the basis of selecting a system that simultaneously satisfies these two loading conditions. Often selections involve something of a compromise between the ideal economical system for gravity loads and an ideal economical system for lateral forces. The selected system must also provide means of ingress, egress, and movement within the structure.

1   Floor Systems Commonly Used to Support Gravity Loads

Concrete floors in tall buildings can be divided into the following types based on structural response:

1. Two-way construction, including flat plate, flat slab, waffle slab, and two-way slab structural systems.

2. One-way construction, usually solid slabs or ribbed pan joist slabs supported on beams or bearing walls.

Concrete floor construction can also be categorized by the method of construction used, as follows:

1. All cast-in-place construction.

2. Precast forms (sometimes containing principal reinforcement) combined with cast-in-place concrete.

3. Precast structural members with cast-in-place concrete topping used to develop the composite section and, often, as the finish topping.

4. All precast floor framing members.

These systems serve different functional purposes, which will be described together with the general usages, advantages, and disadvantages of each system. Table 3.1 summarizes much of the following discussion.

Flat Plate. This structural floor system consists of a concrete slab of uniform thickness throughout, which frames into columns, as shown in Fig. 3.1, or onto isolated bearing walls. This sort of system is economical on spans up to about 7 m to 8 m (23 ft to 26 ft) with mild reinforcing, and can be economical on spans to about 11 m (36 ft) in slabs that are post-tensioned.

Advantages. The two-way flat plate is one of the most efficient structural systems for construction economy. Flat plates can be constructed in minimum time with minimum field labor, because the flat plate utilizes the simplest possible formwork and reinforcing steel layout. Flat plates result in minimum story height for required clear headroom, with a consequent savings in other building materials, and provide for most flexibility in layout of columns, partitions, and small openings. Where job requirements permit direct application of the ceiling finish to the flat-plate soffit, elimination of ceiling construction permits additional substantial cost and construction time savings compared to other structural systems. Flat plates have become increasingly economical and widely used as the cost of field labor has increased relative to construction materials. They have been applied with particular advantage to multistory motel, hotel, hospital, dormitory, and apartment buildings.

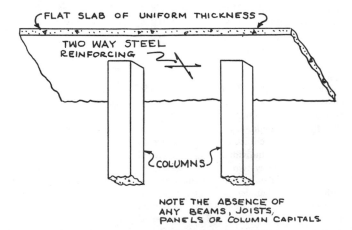

FLAT SLAB OF UNIFORM THICKNESS

TWO WAY STEEL REINFORCING

COLUMNS

NOTE THE ABSENCE OF ANY BEAMS, JOISTS, PANELS OR COLUMN CAPITALS

Fig. 3.1 Flat plate system

Table 3.1 Selection of

Description (1)	Span range, in meters (feet) (2)	Loading, in kilograms per square meter (pounds per square foot) (3)	Type of occupancy (4)	Under floor duct (5)
Flat plate	7.3 to 7.9 max. (24 to 26) up to 10.66 (35) pre-stressed	light to 30.2 (60)	motel, hotel, hospital, dormitory and apart-ments	requires much coordination
Waffle flat plate	up to 15.2 (50)	moderate to 50.4 (100)	monumental, libraries	very difficult
Two-way solid flat slab	up to 9.1 (30)	suitable for heavy loads up to 252 (500)	warehousing, commercial	difficult
Two-way slabs on beams or walls	ratio of $L/W = 1/2$ 4.6 (15)	medium to 50.4 (100)	special appli-cations, housing, light manu-facturing	difficult
One-way slab beam and girder con-struction	13.7 (45) and greater	up to 100.8 (200)	hospitals, hotels, hous-ing, parking, commercial	difficult
One-way slab on beams or walls	0.2 (0.7) max. thickness 7.3 maxi-mum span	up to 100.8 (200)	housing and residential	normally parallel to the span
One-way slab joists and beams	4.6 to 7.6 to 12.2 (15/25 to 40)	up to 50.4 (100)	offices, schools	easily handled
Lift slab	depends on choice of individual system	depends on choice of individual system	apartments	depends on choice of individual system
Precast forms with cast-in-place	depends on choice of individual system	depends on choice of individual system	apartments, housing	depends on choice of individual system
Precast mem-bers with cast-in-place	depends on choice of individual system	depends on choice of individual system	apartments, housing, some office applications	depends on choice of individual system

concrete structural system

Remarks (6)	Formwork (7)	Fire resistance (8)	Interface (9)
minimum story height—can be left exposed	simple, economical	excellent	poor, not flexible
may be left exposed	domes are normally 30 in. square, can be expensive, reduced dead load	excellent	good, domes may be used for holes
usually has capitals and drops, holes near columns are a problem	costly	excellent	poor, not flexible
wall in two directions generally not appropriate	moderate	excellent	poor
depth increases with span	pans are 20 in. or 30 in. wide, 6 in., 8 in., 10 in., 12 in., and 14 in. deep	excellent	good
not flexible, increases floor depth when beams are used	variety of forms available, permanent forms have been used	excellent	good
subject to considerable cracking limited by the number of jacks that can be used	reusable and available on a rental basis may be omitted or substantially reduced	doors require additional methods individual designs require investigation	easily adaptable
depends on local producer's ingenuity	may be none or minimum	individual designs require investigation	
depends on local producer's ingenuity	may be none or minimum	individual designs require investigation	

Such systems may be cantilevered at the exterior of the building to permit the use of exterior balconies, and permit the building columns to be hidden if the esthetic requirements dictate. Such cantilevers require the use of a very light curtain-wall construction to reduce the supported dead load.

This system is particularly suited to the use of lift slab construction, which is discussed later in this chapter.

Disadvantages. The principal limitation of the use of flat-plate construction is imposed by the shear area, which is defined as the summation of the perimeter of a locus located at a distance of one-half of the effective floor depth from the face of the column multiplied by the effective plate depth available. This precludes the use of all but the smallest of sleeves and ducts adjacent to columns. Generally, at least three-span continuity should be available, the edge of slabs should be at least flush with the outer face of the edge columns, and spans should be reasonably equal (at least within 20%). Particular attention should be given to the ability of the column-slab joint to perform under lateral load conditions. In addition, the structural design for concentrated loads is difficult to perform.

The lateral load stiffness of flat-plate buildings is low unless a stiff lateral load transfer system is provided. For this reason, this floor system will frequently not be usable in regions of high wind load or moderate to high seismic loads for buildings higher than 20 stories.

Waffle Flat-Plate Floor Slabs.   Waffle-slab construction, as shown in Fig. 3.2 consists of rows of concrete joists at right angles to each other with solid heads at the columns. The joists are commonly formed by using standard square "dome" forms of sizes to about 0.75 m (30 in.) square and 0.5 m (20 in.) deep. The domes are omitted around the column to form the solid heads. Special deeper forms are available for special uses. Domes can be formed using steel, plastic, or paper forming materials, and many unique and imaginative shapes may be provided. The top slab over the dome forms is usually reinforced with welded wire fabric, and the slab can be of various thicknesses as dictated by structural, electrical, fireproofing, and other considerations.

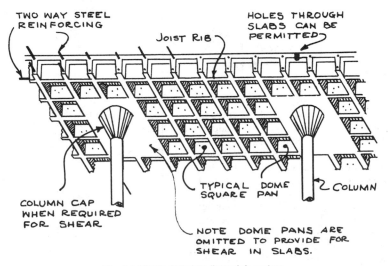

Fig. 3.2 Waffle flat plate floor slab system

As column spacings increase from those mentioned under flat plates, slab thicknesses increase rapidly, and the dead weight of the slab becomes an increasingly more significant factor. Since the concrete in the bottom of the slab in the middle portion of the bay between columns has little structural value, the domed forms displace it and reduce the dead load.

Advantages. Most of the advantages of flat-plate construction also apply to waffle-slab construction. Often the coffered underside of the system makes a desirable ceiling if it is left exposed and painted. The round columns shown on Fig. 3.2 can be square or rectangular, and the column capital can be omitted entirely when peripheral shear permits.

Waffle slabs can be used for spans up to about 15 m (50 ft). The slab above domes may be easily pierced for necessary building functions.

Disadvantages. Again, most of the disadvantages of flat-plate construction also pertain to waffle-slab construction. The area within the shear periphery of columns should not be pierced except by very small sleeves, and full continuity of the floor system should always be provided.

The cost of domed forms is frequently quite high, and considerable reuse is often necessary to make them economical.

Depending on the spans, the over-all depth of waffle flat plate will be greater than that of a flat plate, and to this extent, it would increase floor heights.

Two-Way Solid Flat Slabs. Two-way flat slabs include two-way reinforced slabs with capitals or brackets on columns, drop panels in slabs, or both. The use of both capitals and drop panels, traditional in earlier years, is favored less today because of the higher form costs and the increased total thickness of the structural system. The arrangement is shown in Fig. 3.3.

Advantages. The flat slab is suitable for a heavy duty design, with heavier loads and longer spans than the flat plate. The system requires less concrete and reinforcement and can often utilize smaller columns than the flat plate, since an extra thickness of concrete is provided at the columns where the shears and moments are greatest. Generally, the system is most suitable for square or nearly square panels. Most of the advantages of the flat-plate system pertain to the flat slab with capitals or drop panels, or both.

Disadvantages. Generally, the same disadvantages enumerated under the section on flat plates apply to the two-way solid flat slab, with the added disadvantage that the cost of the forming of drop panels and column capitals is substantially more than that of forming the flat plate. The area within and adjacent

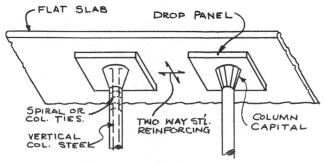

Fig. 3.3 Two-way solid flat slab system

to the shear periphery of the column should still be avoided in the installation of sleeves or ducts unless rigorous calculations are performed. The edge of the slab should be at least flush with the edge of the column, and quite frequently a column bracket may be required at the exterior slab column intersection.

Two-Way Slab on Beams or Walls. This system consists of a flat slab designed to span in two directions to either concrete beams or walls; the beams, in turn, span to columns or to bearing walls. Fig. 3.4 shows the general arrangement of such a system. The limiting ratio of length to width of the two-way slab is approximately 2. Beyond this ratio the slab essentially acts as a one-way slab spanning in the short direction.

Advantages. The primary advantage of the system is the saving in reinforcing steel as a consequence of being able to take advantage of two-way action in the design of the slabs, presuming the length-span ratio to be as nearly square as practical. If the column-beam layout lends itself to the layout of partitions, heavier partitions may be placed on beams without penalty to the slabs.

The two-way design permits the use of shallower slabs and beams than does a one-way slab and beam design.

Disadvantages. The disadvantages of the two-way system generally considerably outweigh the advantages. The presence of the beams in both directions does not permit the passage of larger ductwork except below the beams, with a consequent increase in floor-to-floor height as compared to a flat-plate or flat-slab design. Formwork is substantially more complicated than formwork for a flat plate. This increase in form cost will usually outweigh the cost advantages associated with the savings in reinforcing steel and concrete permitted by the two-way design.

The use of bearing walls to support the two-way slab in a tall building is not often possible due to the functional layout of such buildings. Designers of a tall, wall-bearing building generally provide bearing walls in one direction only, with shear walls provided in the other direction for the purpose of resisting lateral forces. Nonbearing lightweight partitions are provided at locations where such shear walls are not required.

One-Way Slab, Beam, and Girder Construction. Fig. 3.5 indicates a relatively thin slab, possibly from 75 mm to 150 mm (3 in. to 6 in.) in thickness, spanning to concrete beams spaced several meters apart, supported in turn by

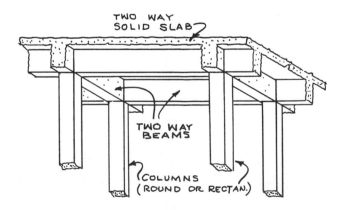

Fig. 3.4 Two-way slabs on beams

girders at right angles to the beams, to carry loads into the columns. Obviously, arranging the beams to straddle the midspan of the girder and frame directly into columns reduces the bending moment in the girder. Placing beams and girders on column grid lines also provides vertical frames to resist lateral forces. Spans of 14 m (46 ft) and greater may be attained with a beam-slab arrangement, with girder depths ranging up to any desired economical depth.

Advantages. This system generally affords the opportunity to span longer distances than two-way systems, by designing deeper beams and girders. Since girders are generally deeper than beams, mechanical systems may run parallel to the girders above their soffits, and the girders may be sleeved to permit duct headers to pass through them within reasonable limitations. Vertical sleeves and ducts may occur adjacent to columns on either side of the girders by offsetting beams. Long and narrow rectangular bays are possible. The use of flying-form systems is possible at an increased cost by sloping the vertical faces of beams and girders.

Disadvantages. The increased depth of a slab, beam, and girder system increases the height of a tall building substantially, with consequent cost increases from a multitude of other trades. Forming is expensive compared to the forming cost of a flat plate. The economical design of long heavily loaded girders can induce substantial bending moments in exterior columns, thereby increasing column sizes and reinforcing quantities far beyond those required using other systems.

One-Way Concrete Slabs Supported on Beams or Bearing Walls. Fig. 3.6 indicates a modification of the slab, beam, and girder system that eliminates secondary beams. The use of a solid slab with a maximum thickness of about 200 mm (8 in.), with a maximum span of about 7 m to 8 m (approximately 24 ft) with continuity and supported by monolithic beams or by bearing walls of masonry or concrete is common, and can be efficient and economical.

Advantages. If no secondary beams are present, and if girders and bearing walls run perpendicular to the long direction of the building, a flying-form system may be used quite economically. If beams or bearing walls are sleeved, mechanical systems may be placed immediately under the slabs, thereby obtaining the advantages of flat-plate construction in relation to minimal floor-to-floor heights of

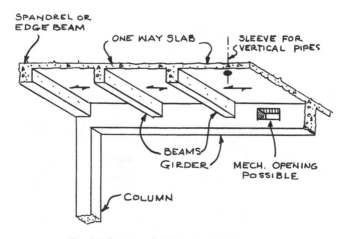

Fig. 3.5 One-way slab, beam, and girder system

construction. Slab soffits may be left exposed in many types of buildings by use of a one-way slab system. Placement of reinforcing steel is relatively simple and, where slabs are post-tensioned, large areas may be tensioned in one operation. Placement of openings is generally not a critical concern.

Disadvantages.   Generally thicker slabs and more reinforcing are required with a one-way slab design. Columns cannot easily be offset, except from grid lines running perpendicular to the beam lines. There is a lack of stiffness in the direction perpendicular to beams or bearing walls that must be accounted for in the structural design.

One-Way Pan Joists and Beams.   Fig. 3.7 indicates the general nature of this system, which consists of a series of uniformly spaced beams or joists 0.5 m to 0.75 m (20 in. to 30 in.) apart formed with removable "pans" whose frequent reuse minimizes their cost. Forms vary in depth from 150 mm to 500 mm (6 in. to 20 in.) in 50-mm (2-in.) increments, and are suitable for spans from 4.6 m (15 ft) to 11 m or

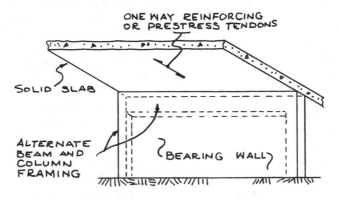

Fig. 3.6 One-way concrete slab, supported on beams or bearing walls

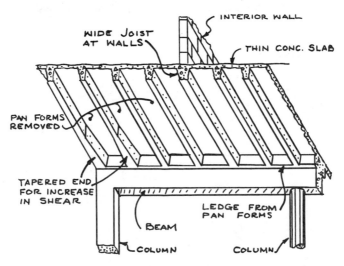

Fig. 3.7 One-way pan joist and beam system

12 m (36 ft to 40 ft) or more. A ceiling is ordinarily required with pan-joist construction, and is applied after the forms have been removed.

A joist system may also be constructed using clay tile or concrete masonry fillers instead of removable pans. These fillers remain in place after forms have been stripped, and permit the application of a ceiling system directly to the slab soffit. The fillers have been used to assist the joist in computations for shear capacity.

The advantages of a deeper system with a consequent reduction in steel requirements, coupled with the reduction of concrete volume in the tensile area where its dead load contributes little strength, combine to create a structural system that lends itself quite well to long spans and rectangular bays. If the supporting beams have relatively short spans, they may have their soffits flush with the soffits of the joist system, thereby maintaining a uniform thickness throughout the system, which simplifies forming and reduces costs. The slab over the pans may be as thin as 64 mm (2-1/2 in.), presuming load-carrying capacity and fire codes are satisfied, and is normally reinforced with a wire mesh.

Advantages.   On spans of 5 m (16 ft) or more, joists are more economical than solid slabs or slabs on beams. However, the cost advantage of pan joists as compared to slab and beam framing is presently questionable, due to the high cost of pan rentals.

Joists are extremely adaptable to architectural layout and mechanical requirements. By laying out pans and ribs in a required manner, large openings may be provided in slabs. Wider, stronger ribs may be provided where required to support the reactions from headers, and heavy partitions may be carried with relative ease and economy.

By the use of wide, shallow beams, a relatively thin structural floor slab may be attained, thereby providing minimal floor-to-floor distances and facilitating mechanical distribution systems, as well as permitting a relatively simple forming system. The thin slab over pans is easy to core for electrical distribution systems, and the system is generally quite adaptable to future alteration work.

Disadvantages.   The rental cost of forms where they can, indeed, be rented, is presently (1977) quite high, although, as with all building costs in the present construction market, the cost relation to other systems can change extremely rapidly. The finished appearance of the lower surface of pan construction is usually quite rough unless extremely vigorous specifications are enforced on the project. Quite often fire codes require a minimum thickness of slab of 115 mm (4-1/2 in.) or more. The long-term deflection of double joists under partitions must be carefully checked as it can be a serious problem. Curing of thin slabs is critical since they may be subject to severe crazing.

Prestressed Concrete Systems.   Prestressed concrete has been used in tall buildings in the form of precast, prestressed floor, roof, and structural frame elements, or of cast-in-place post-tensioned concrete floors, with bonded or unbonded tendons (see Figs. 3.8 to 3.11). Specialized applications of prestressed concrete, such as transfer girders, cantilevers, trusses, shear walls, and foundations, are gaining in use.

Large prestressed concrete beams at the top of high-rise buildings may be economically used with suspended systems or cantilevered systems (Figs. 3.12 and 3.13).

Advantages.   The advantages to be gained from prestressed concrete systems are:

Fig. 3.8 High-rise student apartment building (Courtesy: Prestressed Concrete Institute)

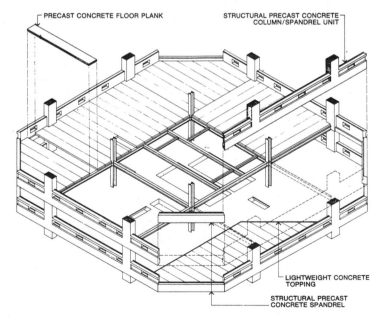

PRECAST CONCRETE FLOOR PLANK

STRUCTURAL PRECAST CONCRETE
COLUMN/SPANDREL UNIT

LIGHTWEIGHT CONCRETE
TOPPING

STRUCTURAL PRECAST
CONCRETE SPANDREL

Fig. 3.9 Typical structural precast components

Fig. 3.10 Precast "ladder" components (Courtesy: Prestressed Concrete Institute)

Fig. 3.11 Nine-story medical center (Courtesy: Prestressed Concrete Institute)

1. Efficiency of cross section through optimum use of the properties of steel in tension and concrete in compression.

2. Balancing stresses and deflections under dead and live loads, controlling service-load cracking and thus enhancing durability. Increase in service-load stiffness due to lack of flexural cracks.

3. Economy of materials, reduction in weights, increase in spans, and decrease in structural depths.

4. Earlier or automatic decentering for cast-in-place concrete.

5. Suitability for production methods.

Fig. 3.12 High-rise office building—Gulf Life Building (Courtesy: Prestressed Concrete Institute)

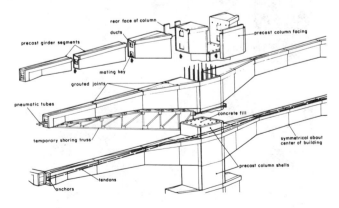

Fig. 3.13 Segmental precast post-tensioned assembly

Vertical Supports. Prestressing is used for vertical supports both in tension (hangers) and in compression (columns). Prestressing can play an essential role in hangers, reducing deflections of the hangers and the floors; in this case prestressing may be introduced in stages.

Prestressing of columns generally is used to improve the handling characteristics of long precast columns. It can be used to increase the bending and buckling capacity of columns. It does not increase their axial compressive capacity.

Fire Effects. Another matter to be considered is the behavior of buildings comprising prestressed elements in the presence of exceptional conditions, such as fire or seismic effects. The greater sensitivity of prestressing steels to high temperatures is taken into account in the design. Design procedures have been developed that permit the relatively rapid design of prestressed concrete for any required fire resistance (FIP, 1975).

Disadvantages. The designer must be concerned with the effects of shortening due to post-tensioning when the members are restrained by heavy columns or walls. To minimize or eliminate such effects it is necessary to limit the degree of deformation, to reduce the rigidity in the restraining elements, or to provide slip joints that allow movement between the various interdependent parts. Obviously, a reduction in these effects may be obtained by decreasing the intensity of prestressing, but this may limit the beneficial effects of prestressing.

Time-Dependent Effects. It is known that prestressing, no matter how it is achieved, creates time-dependent deformations. Such long-time deformations give rise to deflections which may be either positive or negative. Creep deflections must be properly considered in the design stage.

Upward wind pressures in tornadoes have been reported that will exceed the dead-load weights of most structures. A wind of this nature could induce the upward forces of prestress to combine with the wind to cause potential damage to the building.

Connections. The details of connecting prestressed elements deserve a great deal of attention. Well thought-out and engineered connections will benefit the entire project. Usually the best answers are the simplest solutions. Frequently connections are made by bonding units with cast-in-place concrete, by welding, with prestressing forces applied to combine units, and even by simple gravity. Regardless of the degree of technology that is available, the connection should be simple, typical without many variations, and also be capable of being produced with speed and economy (PCI, 1973).

Shortening Effects. Shortening due to prestressing may not be serious in vertical or shear walls, since the ensuing axial deformation may have little effect upon the behavior of adjacent elements.

Sometimes designers overlook the shortening effects of the prestressing of floors and let the secondary stresses be relieved by the formation of small cracks at the top and bottom of columns. This should only be done after a careful analysis of related effects, however.

There is a great variety of possible solutions to minimize the effects of prestressing. One relatively simple method consists in delaying the casting of the concrete around the reinforcement that connects the columns to the horizontal structural elements, adopting provisional hinges which only transfer compression stresses from the elements to the columns. Notice that in a multistory building it is sufficient to apply this device to the upper and lower ends of the columns located on one side of the ground floor. These provisional hinges must be fixed as late as possible. It is obvious this may require an accurate study of over-all stability throughout the provisional stage.

An efficient method for the elimination of shortening effects due to prestressing consists in providing sliding joints which either can be temporary during the construction phase only, or can be permanently effective. These sliding connections (graphitized metal plates, Teflon strips, etc.) are located at the joints where the floor is supported by the vertical elements (wind bracing columns and cores). If desired, such connections can be fixed at a later stage by encasing in concrete or by use of local post-tensioning tendons. Often such a device is applied only adjacent to stairs and elevator cores, because the transverse rigidity of shear walls and columns may not be sufficient to give rise to severe problems. In a building having two stiffening cores, Leonhardt has used the device of resting one of the cores on steel rollers. In this manner the floors could act monolithically with the cores. After a few months, the moving core was fixed by closing the connection.

In framed buildings made of prestressed, prefabricated long-span beams resting on brackets protruding from the columns, the movement of the beams with respect to the columns, achieved by means of appropriate connections with the supports, may permit completion of the floors with an in-place prestressed concrete topping.

Summary. In conclusion, the designer of a prestressed building must concern himself with more than just the design of the structural elements. He must visualize the erection sequence, design the connections, and pay special attention to the deformation effect of prestressing. With this in mind, the use of prestressing in high-rise buildings is most advantageous under the following conditions: (1) In very large buildings where the number of expansion joints can be reduced by the use of a moderate degree of prestressing; (2) in industrialized building systems where connection design is reduced to certain standardized solutions; (3) in high-rise buildings where the secondary effects of horizontal shortening are limited essentially to the ground floor, since the upper floors will tend to shorten together as a unit; and (4) in sophisticated structures (such as great cantilevers or large spans) that may justify the choice of complex construction methods.

A detailed example covering many aspects of the design of a precast prestressed apartment building has been published by the Prestressed Concrete Institute (PCI, 1975).

2 Other Concrete Systems

Most of the systems described thus far in this chapter have been composed of cast-in-place concrete elements supported on cast-in-place columns or on bearing walls.

Such systems may be either conventionally reinforced with mild steel reinforcing bars generally of 276 MPa or 414 MPa (40 ksi or 60 ksi, 28 120 kgf/cm² or 42 180 kgf/cm²) yield steel with sizes ranging from #3 to #11, or may be post-tensioned using grouted or nongrouted tendons with ultimate strength of 1862 MPa (270 ksi, 190 000 kgf/cm²). Larger-sized reinforcing bars and higher-yield steels may be coming into increasing use.

Conventionally reinforced concrete systems imply thicker slabs and beams, greater structural dead loads, shorter spans, and larger quantities of reinforcing materials than prestressed, post-tensioned systems.

Prestressed systems, on the other hand, permit longer spans, thinner, lighter structures, and less material, but require specialized equipment and materials with more exacting field labor for placing and stressing. The unit cost of material and hardware is currently quite expensive. The shop detailing of reinforcing is more demanding.

In either case, the choice of the reinforcing system is an important factor in the final selection of the structural system for a tall building.

Several specialized methods of forming cast-in-place floor systems in their final position are available to the design team, besides the conventional shoring and forming procedures. These include "flying forms," which have been mentioned already, precast concrete units that serve as forms and remain in place as a composite part of the structure, and lift slab construction. Precast construction is described briefly in a later portion of this chapter, and is more fully discussed in other chapters.

3 Lift Slab Construction

Lift slab construction is a procedure wherein concrete slabs are cast on top of one another, then lifted into place on columns by means of hydraulic jacks, and firmly anchored in final position by mechanical devices to columns which are usually structural steel, wide flange sections.

Lift slab construction has been widely used since 1950. The system requires the use of a flat-plate structural system, and post-tensioned reinforcing quite often adds some economy.

Advantages. By casting slabs at the ground level, all forming except an edge form is eliminated. Field placing of reinforcement is greatly expedited, since reinforcing may be placed on previously cast slabs without a delay for field curing and form stripping and rebuilding. All labor and concrete casting may be done under cover in extreme conditions of temperature and weather. Lift slab construction has an optimum economy for tall buildings up to about nine stories in height. However, heights of 15 stories are also economical, particularly if several slabs can be lifted together. The number of slabs lifted together is determined by the jack capacity and the stability of the columns during the lifting stage. At least two slabs must be lifted together in the 15-story range to make lift slab construction economically feasible.

Disadvantages. In tall buildings in which column splices are required, structural steel shapes are mandatory. Currently, the maximum number of columns at which lifting jacks can be used at one time is 28, limited by the capacity of controls for present lifting equipment. On buildings with a larger number of columns, cast-in-place strips can be used to tie the structure together. On exterior columns at least 150 mm (6 in.) of slab must project beyond the exterior face of the column to accommodate the lifting collars which are cast in the slabs. Generally, in order to justify the consideration of lift slab construction, each column should support an average area of at least 28 m^2 (300 sq ft). Recesses or depressions in floors should be avoided where possible, and changes in slab thicknesses are not economical.

Since the use of lift slab construction requires a flat-plate structural system, all the previously outlined advantages and disadvantages of flat-plate floors are pertinent to the discussion of lift slabs. In addition, the control of deflections may become a serious problem, since camber of forms is not readily possible.

Frequently the rental costs and availability of the lifting equipment rule out this system of construction.

4 Precast Forms Combined with Cast-In-Place Concrete

Several systems are presently available in which precast, often prestressed, concrete elements are supported on minimal shoring. These elements are reinforced to serve as forms during concrete casting operations, and, by virtue of composite action with the cast-in-place concrete, become structural elements of the system.

Several such systems consist of a thin precast concrete slab with shear connectors to the cast-in-place concrete. This system can be supported on beams or bearing walls.

Another system that is not uncommon consists of prestressed concrete joists, spaced at a usual distance of 1.2 m (4 ft) clear, which support plywood forms. The joists can span to bearing walls or to concrete beams which may utilize a prestressed concrete soffit as a side form support. This system is shown in Fig. 3.14. Joist spans to 13.7 m (45 ft) and beam spans to 19.5 m (64 ft) can be economically accomplished by use of this system.

A unique system, developed in such countries as India by the Structural Engineering Research Centre (George and Mani, 1974), consists of preformed domes (also known as funicular shells) which are widely used for floors and roofs of both residential and institutional buildings. These shells have a surface which develops a state of membrane compression without tension when subjected to vertical loads. They are used to make a floor or roof in different ways.

One scheme consists of a number of such doubly curved shells placed over shuttering or forming strips to provide a grid, and the rib-gaps formed in between the shells are provided with required reinforcement. Over this, concrete is laid, giving a flat surface to provide the desired floor finish. A second type of floor using these shells consists of precast slabs with the shells supported on them. The slabs are

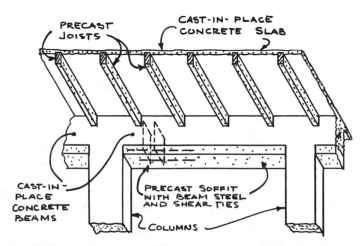

Fig. 3.14 Precast joists and beam soffits in composite action with cast-in-place concrete

kept in position and shored at the center. The shells are then inserted between the slabs, and in-place concrete is laid in the troughs above the slabs to the level of the crown of the shell (Fig. 3.15). Over this concrete, a level surface is made with filler material and floor finish is laid. A third type of flooring, similar to the first, consists of using the required number of shells arranged on the ground to serve as a mold, with space between them forming the ribs. The reinforcement for the ribs, fabricated according to the design, is placed in position and concrete is laid to a level 25 mm (1 in.) above the crown of the shells forming the mold. The shells and in-place concrete make an integrated panel. The panel after curing can be hoisted and placed in position as a unit (Fig. 3.16).

Advantages. The use of precast structural forming systems provides the advantage of reduced field labor for forming and for placement of reinforcing materials. Precast elements generally have a better appearance than cast-in-place concrete and better quality control procedures.

Since many of the various systems are prestressed, longer spans and shallower structural elements are usually associated with the use of such systems.

Disadvantages. Composite precast systems are less adaptable to other trades. The use of field-attached anchorage devices is not usually possible due to the presence of prestressing strands, and preplaced attachments may be difficult to

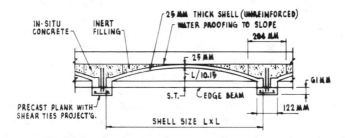

Fig. 3.15 Details of roof with funicular shells and reinforced concrete plank

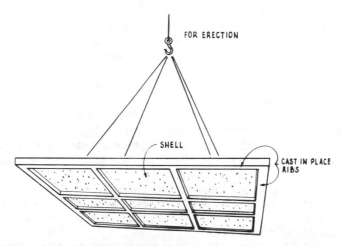

Fig. 3.16 Intergrid panel showing funicular shells supported on grid rib

provide due to manufacturing techniques and the high degree of technology required.

For units of great length, such as beam soffits, shipping and erection difficulties may increase the cost. Such products are often not available in many places or, when available, may be in short supply.

5   Precast Structural Members with Cast-In-Place Topping

These systems include precast cored slabs, double and single tee units, and other precast shapes, with or without prestressing. On them a thin (usually 50-mm, 2-in., minimum) topping is cast, to level the floor and often to act in the development of the floor system as a diaphragm to resolve lateral loads. The topping must be coordinated with the camber of the units.

Such systems may include precast beams and columns, or may be limited to precast slabs, with beams and columns being cast in place. Often in residential high-rise buildings and hotels, bearing walls cf masonry or concrete may be used instead of a structural beam and column frame.

In housing structures and in parking structures that are a part of a larger tall building, the cast-in-place topping may often be omitted, and weld plates or grout keys between adjacent units may serve as the connections instead of the topping. This presupposes that such details, especially in parking structures, are not in any way subject to corrosive elements, such as salt or other chlorides, or the freeze-thaw cycle common in colder countries. Such use of precast systems implies a high degree of dimensional tolerance control.

In precast concrete a system of framing has been developed that is finding considerable success in the United States. It is based on two fundamental concepts.

The first is that the connections in precast concrete are usually complex, making them difficult to fabricate, time-consuming to complete in erection, and generally a major part of the expense of the basic precast concrete system. In addition, camber must be considered in all areas.

The second is that concrete is normally a heavy construction material with a considerable amount of dead-weight or self-weight.

By utilizing the dead load of the structure as a vertical force, much like prestressing a concrete beam, a joint constructed of simple precast elements can be analyzed as a normal frame similarly to a conventional reinforced concrete frame.

The columns are supplied with a pipe that serves to pin each successive tier of construction. The girders and beam soffits are precast with ties extended above their roughened top surface. When the precast elements are in place, a topping of cast-in-place concrete is used to tie all the elements together and to develop composite soffits character with the precast girder and beam.

This type of construction has the advantages of a framed structure and can be used for commercial and office use. Because it is flexible in bay width and span it could also be used for residential occupancy.

Another form of gravity-resisting structure involves use of precast wall and slab units or complete box elements, with each containing a room or space that can be occupied. The very mass of this type of construction can be used to resist the overturning due to lateral loading.

The methods of developing lateral resistances of tall buildings utilizing entirely precast systems often become quite complex, and much attention must be devoted to the design of economical connection details.

The design team considering the use of precast elements in a given area must carefully evaluate the availability of such products, the expertise of available manufacturers, and the degree of acceptance on the part of local constructors.

The subject of precast structural systems is covered more fully in Chapter CB-12.

3.4 LATERAL LOAD RESISTING SYSTEMS

From a structural engineering standpoint, one of the major distinguishing characteristics of a tall building is the need to resist large lateral forces due to wind or earthquake. The lateral load resisting system must do this, and at the same time must prevent excessive deflections or accelerations and must help to provide stability. However, the lateral load resisting elements must not be too large, and must conform with the architectural, structural, and mechanical schemes, or vice versa. A lateral system is generally considered to be efficient if the provision of the lateral load resistance does not increase floor and column sizes beyond those required for gravity loads.

Because of the inherent mass of a concrete building, it has a greater capacity for resistance of vibrations and energy absorption than buildings of structural steel and other materials.

The design methods used for analysis were for many years fairly simple. Many tall buildings have been constructed which have been analyzed using the simple portal or the cantilever method. While these methods can be applied to steel buildings which have relatively stiff beams compared to columns, they tend to underestimate the moments in the lower-floor columns of concrete buildings. In the lower stories of concrete buildings the columns are usually considerably stiffer than the beams, because of the size required for axial loads, the cracking of the beams, and the use of high-strength concrete in columns. As a result, it is not unusual not to find a point of contraflexure in the first-floor columns of tall concrete buildings, and this violates a basic assumption of the portal and cantilever methods. While these problems should be recognized, many competent engineers do use the portal or cantilever methods, giving due consideration for their limitations.

The use of computers has greatly increased the ease of analyzing a tall building, but it is important that the user know the basis of the program and that he actually develops a "feel" for the structural action of the structure he is designing. The infinitely rigid connection that is assumed between floors and columns, for example, is one area that the designer should respect and consider when he actually details the construction drawings for the building.

The floors of a tall building must have sufficient rigidity and strength to act as a diaphragm for the transfer of horizontal forces to distribute them to the vertical elements. Reinforced concrete floors generally do possess this necessary rigidity and this should seldom pose any problem.

Part of the input to the final selection of a total framing scheme must be a consideration of the designer's ability to analyze and proportion the structure within the assigned design budget.

Although there are as many concepts of structural systems to resist lateral load as there are designers, it is possible to classify these systems into categories. Each

Table 3.2 Systems to provid

Type (1)	Engineering Analysis (2)	Architectural Layout (3)	Use (4)	Construction Complexity Shop fabrication (5)	Supervision (6)	Labor Quality (7)	Quantity (8)
Moment frame	complex, special for earthquake	open, flexible	versatile— offices	high	good supervision and inspection required	high	high
Tube	varies from simple to complex	limited	offices	high	same as above	high	high
Framed tube	highly complex	limited	offices	high	same as above	high	high
Shear wall	elementary	limited, but has variety	housing, apartments	simple	low	low	low
Shear wall and frame	complex— requires design aids or computer	opens to most advantages of frame	versatile, offices and housing	high	good supervision and inspection required	high	high
Staggered truss (staggered wall)	complex but well documented	limited	housing, apartments	very high	high quality required	very high	high
Gravity system	simple, usually proprietary	limited	limited by precaster repetition	prefabricated	high	high	low
Diagonal (braced frame)	simple	interior may be free	exterior may be restricted	can be high	good supervision required	high for diagonal elements and details	varies
Braced from other structures	can be complex or simple	no problem	limited in size by capacity of restraint	only in details	high, sophisticated	may be low except for details	usually low
Composite (steel and concrete)[b] Bridged system[b]							

[a]Mechanical and electrical, elevators, etc.
[b]These are highly specialized and must be studied for specific applications and effectiveness.

lateral resistance for tall concrete buildings

Material		Story height, in meters (feet)	Total height	Remarks	
Reinforcing steel (9)	Formwork (10)	(11)	(12)	General (13)	Interface[a] (14)
complex, requires shop fabrication	complex, often special engineering	depends on allowable column size	limited only by drift and sway	very flexible in use	excellent
complex, requires a good fabricator	often slip formed	unlimited	limited only by practicality	limited by basic geometry selected	no major problems
very complex	complicated	normal limits	limited only by practicality	limited by basic geometry selected	no major problems
simple	usually jump formed— simple— may be slip formed	usually 3.7 to 4.6 (12 to 15)	usually limited to 20–30 stories	walls must be continuous for economy	may severely limit mechanical ducts and shafts
complex, requires shop fabrication	complex, requires special engineering	depends on column size— shear wall efficiency contributes	limited by practicality	moderately flexible in use	good
complex	complex	3.7 to 4.3 (12 to 14), or truss depth	limited by test data	must have engineering involvement from the beginning	must frame specifically for these facilities
shop fabrication	engineered reusable	usually 3.7 to 4.6 (12 to 15)	presently to about 30 stories	should work very close to engineer of manufacturer	must be handled specially
very complex	on diagonal itself—other is basic	not critical 45° for maximum efficiency of braces	practicality of bracing	variety of systems, single or multiple diagonals, K bracing (vertical or horizontal), lattice, knee, etc.	
not difficult	not dependent on any bracing	floor heights of supporting structure	requires height and capacity of supporting structure	only suitable with certain conditions	usually limited to small appendages such as elevator shafts, etc.

category tends to be most efficient for a certain height range or a certain type of occupancy. The following concepts are suggested as general fields rather than as specific systems (see Table 3.2).

1   Shear Walls

The shear wall is a thin slender beam cantilevered vertically to resist lateral forces. It can also take the form of a rectangular or box-shaped core which can be used at stairs, elevators, and other shafts. Frequently a vertical row of doors or windows occurs in a shear wall, dividing it into two walls coupled by the beams at each floor. This is referred to as a "coupled shear wall."

If the bearing wall must serve as wind bracing, or as a shear wall, prestressing may be beneficial in the absorption of bending in high-rise buildings.

The shear wall is often used in hotels and apartments, only to disappear at the base of the building where it could be utilized the most. Many architects and owners desire the base level to be free of walls and open and, as a result, much of the advantage of the shear wall is lost. In seismic regions the shear walls should extend to the foundation if at all possible.

Shear walls, like the flanges of a steel beam, are much more effective on the exterior walls, but are often used in the core to interface with the architectural features.

Cast-in-Place Slab and Wall System.   This is a good example of a structural framing system that combines the floor system and lateral system to resist the gravity and lateral loads for low and high-rise buildings.

The use of cast-in-place concrete walls as bearing walls to support gravity loads, and at the same time as shear walls to resist lateral loads, is not necessarily economical and is limited to medium-rise buildings of up to 20 to 25 stories.

This system also has limited flexibility. It is adaptable to hotels and apartment structures, but not to office or multipurpose buildings.

Shear Walls and Diagonals.   Place Victoria in Montréal is a 47-story office building rising 190 m (624 ft) from lobby to penthouse. This structure utilizes shear walls that cross the building from corner to corner. In addition to these shear walls are concrete trusses, diagonal X shape in elevation, which have been designed to resist earthquake forces.

Shear Walls with Frame.   The combination of frames consisting of floor systems and columns interacting with shear walls to resist lateral loads has been the subject of much discussion. Today, we accept this interaction and many structures have been built using these two elements in a mixed system. Shear wall-frame structures can be used in office buildings up to about 40 stories and in apartment buildings up to about 60 stories.

Generally, the solution has been to solve for the convergence of the deflected position of the two elements by proportioning the load between them until they both assume the same deflected position. Shortcuts have been developed and charts or computer programs are available which speed up this process and make it practical for routine engineering design (see Chapter CB-5).

2 Moment-Resisting Frames

Moment-resisting frames consist of linear, horizontal members (beams) in plane with and connected to linear, vertical members (columns) with monolithic rigid joints. A moment-resisting frame is identified by the prominence of its flexibility due to the flexure of the individual beams and columns and the rotation at their joints. A moment-resisting frame may be internal, that is, in planes within the building, or external in the plane of the exterior walls or facade. The strength and stiffness of the frame is proportional to the column and beam size and inversely proportional to the story height and column spacing. In general, an increase in beam stiffness has a greater effect on the frame stiffness than an increase in column stiffness (see Chapters CB-4 and CB-9).

Internally located frames have serious disadvantages that severely limit their usefulness in tall buildings. The floor space requirements of most buildings limit the number of interior columns available for frames. Also, the floor beams are generally of long span and limited in depth.

Externally located frames do not necessarily have these disadvantages. It is often possible and even desirable to provide closely spaced columns and deep spandrel beams, thus achieving an efficient frame. Many fine designs have been done with the columns and beams serving as exposed architectural finish, with only the addition of glass required to complete the enclosure of the building. When the exterior columns are closely spaced, say from 1.2 m to 3 m (4 ft to 10 ft) on center, it is possible to develop the entire perimeter of the structure as a lateral load resistant system. This system has been called the "boxed frame" or "framed tube," which will be discussed later.

Medium-rise to high-rise apartment buildings in areas not subject to seismic or hurricane loads sometimes develop frame action by utilizing a portion of the flat-slab floor as a shallow beam continuous with the columns. An example of this system is the 46-story, 149-m (490-ft) high Excelsior apartment building in New York City. Flat-plate floors and columns provide the wind load resisting system. It is interesting to note that the normal 165-mm (6-1/2-in.) flat-plate slab had to be increased to 215 mm (8-1/2 in.) in the lower stories in order to resist lateral loads.

Generally speaking, moment-resisting frames are efficient for office buildings up to about 15 stories, and for hotels or apartments up to about 20 stories.

Tapered Frames.   Engineers have recognized the efficiency of diagonal bracing and architects have favored the open framework.

Frames have been considered in which the building frame slopes in from the base to a narrower width at the top. This has the practical effect of increasing the stiffness of the total structure where such stiffness is required, and theoretically it offers a potential reduction in the amount of material required for the total building. It does reduce the lateral area for wind.

Frame Action.   The floor system of a framed building must carry all the gravity loads and also act as a flexural element in resisting the lateral induced moments from the columns.

High shears are produced in the floor system and may reverse themselves, depending on the direction of the lateral load. These shears are over the length of the floor members and, in addition, there are large concentrations of flexural stress at the ends of the panel. These shears must also be accounted for in the design of the columns.

Floor elements that resist high lateral stresses can have tension stresses top and bottom throughout their length, and consideration of reinforcement details is important.

Staggered Wall Beams. This system was developed to compete with the staggered steel truss that was promoted by the steel industry in the United States. The basic concept uses walls that are a full story height, and span the full width of the space to columns located on the exterior walls. These walls are staggered on alternate floors (see Fig. 3.17) and provide areas that are twice as wide as the span length of the supported floor system.

The floors act as a continuous diaphragm to distribute lateral loads, and in the design are assumed to be infinitely stiff. If each transverse frame were to be considered separately, it would be required to undergo an irregular distribution as shown in Fig. 3.18(a). However, the rigid diaphragm of the floor system forces the horizontal deflections to be equally distributed, and the actual deformation of the structure is a uniform curve as shown in Fig. 3.18(b).

The restraint against lateral (shear) deformation of the columns that is furnished by the wall beams in alternate frames results in a structure with considerably more stiffness than the conventional framed structure.

Lateral loads in a direction along the longitudinal axis of the building can be accommodated by a normal frame analysis. Taller buildings may require spandrel beams to provide the necessary resistance. Normally there are enough columns available to act in resisting the forces and, with less area exposed to wind forces, this direction of resistance will not be critical.

The staggered wall-beam system lends itself particularly to high-rise residential uses up to about 40 stories. It offers an alternate type of reinforced concrete construction for hospitals, apartments, motels, and dormitories. A variety of bay widths is possible, as indicated in Fig. 3.19. This flexibility makes possible a variety of apartment layouts (Fintel, 1968).

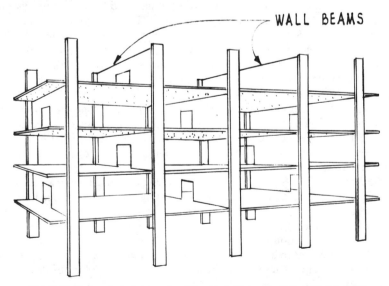

WALL BEAMS

Fig. 3.17 Concept of staggered wall-beam multistory building (Fintel, 1968)

3 Tube Concept

The tube concept has been employed on a number of tall office towers as an efficient framing system for tall slender buildings. It describes a structural system in which the perimeter of the building, consisting of the vertical supports interconnected by beams or bracing members, acts as a giant vertical, internally stiffened tube, resisting the horizontal forces from wind or earthquake, and providing lateral support to all vertical supporting members against buckling.

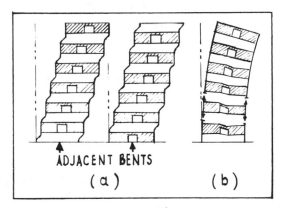

(a) STIFF BEAM-FLEXIBLE
COLUMN DEFORMATION
OF ADJACENT BENTS ARE
ALLOWED TO DEFLECT
INDEPENDENT.

(b) ACTUAL DEFORMATION
OF ALL BENTS TIED
TOGETHER BY FLOOR
SLABS.

Fig. 3.18 Under lateral loads, wall-beam structure behaves differently from stiff beam, flexible column design (Fintel, 1968)

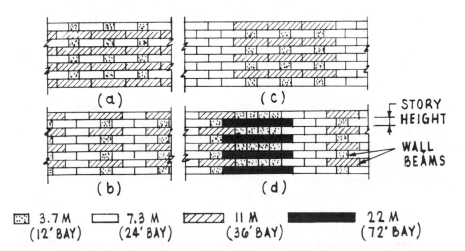

Fig. 3.19 Variety of bay widths possible in wall-beam buildings (Fintel, 1968)

Deflections of the tube in a very tall building consist of the "chord" drift caused by the shortening and lengthening of the column elements of the tube, and the "web" drift created by shear and bending deformations of the individual tube members. Both of these values may vary considerably, depending on the properties of the tube. In order to force all columns of the "flanges," or windward and leeward sides of a tube, to participate in resisting overturning moments by direct forces in the columns, the sides of the tube must be sufficiently stiff to reduce what is known as "shear lag." This stiffening can be accomplished in various ways:

1. By diagonal bracing members across each side.

2. By a system of spandrel beams forming with the columns a rigid frame (therefore the name "framed tube"), such as was used in the Standard Oil Building in Chicago.

The tube concept has numerous significant advantages over other framing systems, not only for reasons of economy and efficiency, but also for structural reasons, such as:

1. Because the wind-resisting system is located on the perimeter of a building, maximum advantage is taken of the total width of the building to resist overturning moments.

2. Since the wind-resisting system is concentrated on the perimeter, it is generally possible to design the interior framing for gravity loads only. As a result, there is a greater freedom in locating columns and beams within the core, and their size is considerably less. Consequently, the core framing may be arranged to best suit the many nonstructural requirements within the core, which in turn leads to a significant gain in rentable space.

3. The tube system leads to an identical framing for all floors, because the floor members are not subjected to the varying internal forces due to lateral loads.

4. The tube concept also leads to a great number of identical framing units in the tube itself, which can be produced with standard forms allowing a very speedy erection. Frequently this advantage more than outweighs the fact that more elements must be constructed due to the closer spacing of columns.

5. In a framed tube with close column spacing and deep spandrels, the tube has an enormous load distribution capacity, which leads to a nearly uniform column loading, permitting many columns in each tube wall to be identical.

From a practical point of view there is another significant advantage: once the basic perimeter spandrel conditions have been resolved with the architects, the final analysis and design of the tube can proceed unaffected by the lengthy process of resolving detail layout and service requirements in the core area.

There are, however, some important factors inherent in all tube concepts, which must be carefully studied and considered by the structural engineer to arrive at an economical, efficient structure. These include:

1. The tube concept in itself does not guarantee stiffness in the frame adequate to satisfy deflection and vibration limitations. Fortunately, in most instances there is sufficient space available along the perimeter to use deep girders and wide, closely spaced columns.

2. The corners of the tube must get the utmost design attention to assure an efficient flow of shear forces around the corners into the "flanges" of the tube. Kinks in the tube at the corners should preferably occur at midspan of the spandrel beams and not at columns, although this can hardly ever be avoided in re-entrant corners.

3. Since computer programs used to analyze framed tubes generally consider columns and beams only as linear elements, the computer results do not represent the complete picture of the internal forces acting at the intersections. It is therefore necessary to superimpose a local system of forces onto the main internal force pattern obtained from the computer for the design of members and to determine the deformations.

4. Unless the columns are inside the building facade, serious problems may arise with respect to the effects of temperature differences in the columns of the building.

5. The floor diaphragm becomes a vital element, and is required not only to carry wind forces to the side walls of the tube, but also to provide lateral support to all columns.

6. Dead-load stresses are normally much smaller in the perimeter tube columns than in the core columns. It is therefore necessary to compensate for the differential elastic shortening between these two sets of columns. (Vertical shortening is discussed later in this chapter and in Chapter CB-10.)

Several variations of the basic tube concept have been developed. A brief description of each system follows.

Framed Tube.   The first framed tube structure for a tall building was used for the 43-story DeWitt Chestnut apartment building in Chicago. Because the apartment building has a small floor plan width, and does not have a large service core to provide for a stiff shear wall, the entire lateral stability of this building was achieved by spacing the exterior columns at 1.7-m (5.5-ft) centers. Interior columns were provided wherever needed to support the 200-mm (8-in.) thick flat-plate concrete slab.

Tube-In-Tube System.   Faced with the challenge of developing an optimum economical solution for the 52-story One Shell Plaza building in Houston, Texas the designer combined the framed-tube concept with the shear wall-frame interaction concept. He devised a structural system consisting of an exterior tube system with very closely spaced columns [1.8-m (6-ft) centers] together with a shear-wall core enclosing the central service areas, as shown in Fig. 3.20. This tube-in-tube system made it possible to design the 52-story One Shell Plaza building at the unit price of the traditional shear-wall structure for only 35 stories. The resulting building, now finished, stands 217 m (715 ft) above ground level and is presently the world's tallest reinforced, all lightweight concrete building.

Column Diagonal Truss Tube.   The exterior columns of a building can be spaced reasonably far apart and yet be made to work together as a tube by connecting them with diagonal members intersecting at the center line of these columns and spandrels (Fig. 3.21). For extremely tall buildings, the diagonals should be approximately at a 45° angle, resulting in large, widely-spaced crosses.

This use of diagonal members to connect the far spaced columns makes the diagonal members themselves act also as columns, and therefore they do not normally develop any tension stresses, even under the influence of full wind load. Because of the dual function of these diagonals, acting as inclined columns as well as taking the major portion of wind shear, this structural system is generally very efficient for tall buildings.

The column diagonal truss tube system, however, can only be used for truly tall buildings where special solution of the curtain-wall system can be economically

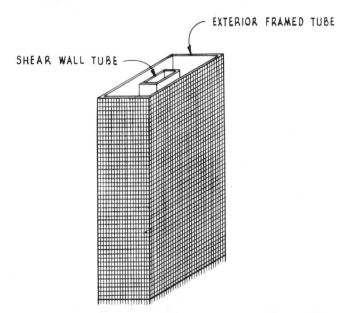

Fig. 3.20 Schematic sketch of tube-in-tube system (Khan, 1972)

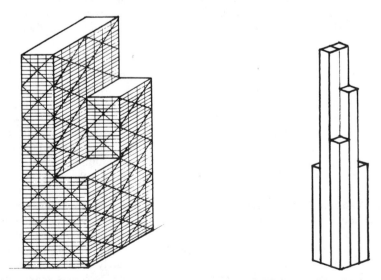

Fig. 3.21 Column diagonal truss tube (Khan, 1972)   Fig. 3.22 Multiple or bundled tube (Khan, 1972)

justified. The congestion of column, spandrel beam, and diagonal reinforcement must be carefully considered during the design.

Bundled Tube System. As larger and taller buildings are needed in the future, it is possible that the framed tube, as well as the column diagonal truss tube, may be used by bundling module tubes to create larger tube envelopes. In a tall building with extremely large floor areas, the exterior column system may comprise only a small percentage of the total number of columns. Therefore, in such a building, to use an exterior tube system would be to lose the advantage of possible participation of the interior columns. This can be overcome by arranging all columns of such a building into modular tubes, as schematically shown in Fig. 3.22. This has the further advantage of greatly reducing the amount of shear-lag in the tubes, making the "flange" column more effective.

For large buildings of extreme height in the future, it is conceivable that megamodules of column diagonal truss tubes, as schematically shown in Fig. 3.21, may be effectively used to optimize the total structural system. Perhaps a somewhat less economical but architecturally more efficient bundled tube system can be made up of framed tubes arranged in modules similar to those shown in Fig. 3.22.

An interesting side benefit of this system allows termination of each module at different levels without any loss of structural integrity.

Combined Tube Systems. In tube-in-tube structures, the central shear-wall core can drastically reduce the flexibility in planning and utilization of the area. For instance, when elevators are discontinued at different height levels, the free space cannot be retrieved in an efficient way because the shear walls cannot suddenly be eliminated. In tall steel structures the most important advantage, of course, is that the structure can be built at a relatively fast speed, generally one floor every three days, whereas in concrete construction even one floor every seven days is an optimistic projection. In steel buildings, the central cores are much more flexible than in concrete buildings, and any free area due to discontinuing the elevators can be immediately utilized as a fully rentable area by adjusting the partition walls as necessary. Why not combine the advantages and eliminate the disadvantages in a composite system? This is what led to the combined tube system, consisting of structural steel columns, beams, and floor construction, whereas the exterior closely-spaced columns and spandrels, together with the curtain wall, are formed of reinforced concrete.

4 Special Systems for Lateral Bracing

Bridged Structures. Extensive lateral and overturning resistance may be developed by using two or more slender concrete shaped buildings linked together by one or more levels of bridges or other types of large-span framing systems. This concept may be a composite of concrete and steel, in which the towers are made from concrete and the connecting bridges or framework may consist of steel, precast prestressed or cast-in-place concrete. Examples of this type of construction are the Earth Science Building at MIT in Cambridge, Massachusetts, or the 52-story bank office building in Singapore.

The Singapore structure employs two slipformed tower service cores with connecting steel and concrete bridges between the towers. The trusses and girders act as independent elements spanning 35 m (115 ft) between the semicircular cores.

The main bridge trusses and girders located at the 4th, 20th, and 35th floors support the floors between these levels. The floors are constructed of reinforced concrete with intermediate columns at 6.1-m (20-ft) centers.

Other examples of this type of construction have used suspension cables between concrete towers and are similar to suspension bridges. These cables support intermediate floors, with the gravity loads primarily carried by the cables and the lateral loads resisted by the concrete towers.

Box System. The box system, using precast units of floor slabs and wall units tied together by wet or dry joints similar to the cast-in-place slab and wall system, is another variation of a floor and wall system used to resist lateral loads of wind and earthquake in combination with floor system for gravity loads.

Other modifications of the precast concrete box may consist of the floor slab and wall unit cast as an L-shaped unit and erected to form a series of stacked boxes. A floor slab and two wall units cast as a single U-shaped unit and erected by stacking is another variation of the precast box. The ultimate box system consists of precasting a six-faced box and erecting the units by stacking one box on top of another to form a high-rise structure resisting lateral loads by using the walls of the boxes as shear walls.

Examples of this type of construction are the 22-story Hilton Palacio Del Rio hotel at San Antonio, Texas; the Habitat in Montréal; and apartment structures of 6 to 11 floors constructed in many cities in western and eastern Europe.

The box system using precast units has the advantages of yard casting and reduced field labor. Economically the system still is more expensive, especially in the United States, than other framing systems used to resist lateral loads.

Long distance transportation and erection limit the size, length and weight of precast units and may be a deterrent to their frequent use. Most projects using this type of construction must be located within a given radius of operation to be economical and practical from the standpoint of transportation. The use of lightweight structural concrete to reduce the dead load will reduce the cost of transportation. Lightweight concrete is generally used with the precast concrete box system.

Many combinations of materials are possible. Since concrete is an ideal material to use with compression loading, it is often one of the basic components in this combined type of construction.

Buildings Braced from Other Structures. It is possible to construct a simple building unit that is not required to develop a lateral resistance to loads.

This principle is limited in its application and is only discussed to indicate the innumerable possibilities that can be developed when considering a structural system for a building.

There are numerous examples of smaller ancillary structures that are secured to a major building structure to obtain its resistance to lateral forces. Elevator towers have been connected to the building they serve at each floor level. This connection transfers the lateral load to the main structure.

Structural systems have been developed that supply a basic skeleton frame to resist the lateral load. Into this a subsystem of building is attached so that the final structure is a series of simple units supported by a master framework.

5 Special Considerations

Torsion.   Torsion is the twisting of a structure around its vertical axis. Torsion will occur when the resultant of the lateral loads does not pass through the centroid of rigidity of the various vertical load resisting elements.

The resisting moments of the bents of a frame, shear wall, diagonal restraint, or other lateral load resisting element will be proportional to its distance from the center of the load, and also to the relative stiffness.

It is strongly recommended that tall buildings have symmetrical lateral load resistance. This is especially important in buildings using curtain walls, where the perimeter walls have little resistance. A design using a core wall as the only resistance to lateral loads may result in a building too weak in polar moment of inertia to resist even accidentally induced torsion.

Earthquake.   In many areas of the world, design of structures to resist the forces induced in them by earthquakes is of serious concern. Earthquakes may indeed be the primary external force to consider in the design of the gravity system and the lateral systems.

Most accepted building codes define the forces that must be considered in design according to the particular geographic area in which the building is to be located.

Generally, these codes specify the lateral forces which the frame must resist based on a combination of factors, including the seismic history of the area in which the structure is to be located, the type of lateral bracing system in the structure, and the dead and live loads in the structure. Such codes also indicate criteria for design and anchorage of nonstructural components of the building, such as parapets, curtain walls, partitions, and many other items of concern. Generally, structures designed to resist earthquake forces have foundations tied together by grade beams or other acceptable means.

Of great concern in earthquake-resistant design is the ductility of the structure —that is, its ability to resist lateral forces with consequent movement without serious structural damage to the frame. The need for ductility, the need to reduce nonstructural damage and to reduce torsional moments and deflections, must all be considered in selecting structural systems in a seismic region. The ductility of concrete structures is discussed in Chapter CB-6.

Concerning seismic design, theoretically, within the noncracked stage, prestressed members have lower critical damping than reinforced concrete, but they possess similar critical damping after cracking. In the elastic range, prestressed concrete offers reliable response, while in the plastic range it offers high energy absorption. The versatility of prestressed concrete permits the designer to fulfill all the requirements of correct seismic design. Furthermore, the use of partial prestressing with the combination of prestressed and nonprestressed reinforcement permits one to take fullest advantage of prestressing under normal service conditions, while keeping in store sufficient additional strength accompanied by great capability for energy absorption in case of catastrophic overloads.

Many excellent technical books have been published which fully treat the subject of earthquake-resistant design, and much research is being done to improve design and construction methods. (See also Chapter CL-2.)

Vertical Shortening.   Another subject of concern in the design of high-rise concrete structures is that of vertical shortening in columns and bearing walls. Due to the elastic nature of concrete and its basic characteristics of initial shrinkage during the curing process and creep, the high-rise structure will shorten during construction and for some period thereafter.

Differential shortening of columns due to their different loading patterns may cause a redistribution of forces in various columns. Many computer programs recognize this fact and provide for it.

The cumulative effect of a slight amount of shrinkage per floor may have a serious effect on the work of subsequent building trades, such as curtain walls and vertical transportation. It is, therefore, important that the designer recognize the presence and effect of vertical shortening, and provide for it in his design. This problem is discussed extensively in Chapter CB-10.

3.5   SELECTION OF SYSTEM

This chapter has only briefly covered the myriad systems available to the design team to be considered for use in the tall building. Many tall buildings may efficiently utilize a few or many of the systems, depending on the requirements of the individual area of the building. Often, hybrid systems may be utilized which combine attributes of a combination of systems to satisfy specific requirements.

The multitude of systems available presents an opportunity for an experienced design team to provide a structure that will serve its optimum function in the over-all project.

It must be, however, emphasized that the design and construction of tall concrete buildings imply careful and complete field inspection by the designing engineer or his chosen representatives. This vital phase of the structural engineer's activity should never be overlooked or minimized.

The selection of the structural system requires adequate knowledge of systems available, in consideration of both gravity and lateral systems. Some general guidance regarding the technical considerations in the selection is included here.

No exact methodology is used at present to select an appropriate system. Value engineering appears to be one scientific approach to an optimum choice. The optimizing of reinforced concrete structures is discussed in Chapter CB-4.

The information required to make a selection should include consideration of a variety of items, including:

1. The materials of construction should be available and within the economic reach of the budget.

2. All major parties, owner, designer, and the potential constructor, should be familiar with or aware of the structural system. Before embarking on unusual building techniques, union reaction must be considered.

3. The structural system must be consistent with the architecture and use of the structure and the functions and economics of the entire project.

4. The system should be integrated or compatible with the mechanical and electrical requirements of the structure.

In order to satisfy these basic items the designer must consider all of them at once to select the best system. Since this is humanly impossible, the designer must search out the items that are fixed and by themselves limit the choice of design. For example, the designer may not be qualified or experienced enough to design certain systems, the owner may also own a structural steel fabricating firm, or the architect may not wish to have any walls in the structure. This type of input may be all the criteria necessary to establish the one system that should be selected.

Once these initial items are programmed, the designer can proceed to evaluate the physical limits of the structure. The floor systems should be reviewed to select those that are most appropriate (see Table 3.1), and at the same time, the lateral resisting systems must be analyzed (Table 3.2). Only those deemed suitable should be retained for further consideration.

The confirmation of these two concepts should follow naturally. The optimum gravity load resisting floor system may not be compatible with the best lateral load

Place Victoria, Montréal, Canada (Courtesy: W. C. Tall Co.; photo by Arnott Rogers Batten, Ltd.)

resisting system. The designer must probe and analyze to the best of his ability, and when he has analyzed the benefits and disadvantages of these combinations he can make his final selection.

The selection of a gravity and lateral system can be a very personal thing. Most designers have strong feelings for a particular type of system and then proceed to establish the proper proof to clearly indicate that they are correct. The concrete frame is a sympathetic structure. Often the selection is not clear cut: economies can change even between the selection and the execution of a design. In many cases, the ingenuity of the contractor or the enthusiasm of one of the major parties of the construction group can overcome past opinions and build a structure successful in all ways, and yet the system may not be the most theoretically appropriate for the specific building system selected.

It is proposed then that the selection of a specific system for lateral bracing in a tall building is not an exact science. The reader would do well to review Table 3.2, which attempts to categorize the lateral load systems to certain definable requirements. The structural designer will generally proceed through such a logic automatically to arrive at his decision. For example, he probably will not consider a shear-wall system for a building such as an office, which will require large open spaces and must be flexible for changes of tenant, as well as changes in the operations of the individual tenant.

It must be emphasized that two different designers may make two different choices, and both may be excellent. The choice should be made early to allow reaction from other parties to the total structure.

It is important to recognize that once a structural system has been selected by any form of responsible analysis, and the project is started into working drawings, it is seldom changed. Even when a definite cost saving can be shown for the construction budget of a project, the cost of starting the project on a new direction may be more than the construction saving.

Human nature resists change, and the inertia of a project under way can be a substantial force. It has been noted that when the keen edge of engineers and architects actively producing construction documents is dulled it can affect morale. This in itself is not important to the structure, but often with a loss of thrust, errors and general lethargy will plague the new second choice. This makes it doubly important for the original selection to be made following a sound and logical procedure.

Consideration of the design method to be used offers more variety in the design of the lateral system.

A generalized procedure for selection may be in order. While exact items vary, a logical procedure is outlined in what follows.

1 Preliminary Steps in Selection of System

1. Obtain all necessary data reliably, so that intelligent decisions can be made from the start. Such data include soil borings, surveys, building codes, anticipated loadings, available materials and technology, unit costs of materials and labor, and any other such required information. Such data also include the general outlined requirements of the project. The requirements are often best discussed by the entire design team, including the architect, mechanical and electrical engineers, and special consultants, such

as those with expertise in elevators, acoustics, landscaping, and finance, in conjunction with the structural engineer.

2. It is usually advantageous for a team of very experienced designers to spend some time in roughing out the structural system for a tall building. At this time, the contributions of a preselected contractor, if the contract is to be negotiated, are extremely valuable. Generally, a small team of such people can make more rapid progress than a single engineer. During this initial period the relative economies of the various schemes in the particular locality should be carefully evaluated.

3. Preliminary selection at this stage should be regarded as tentative and not firmly resolved, until over-all group discussions among all members of the project team indicate that the needs of all interested parties to the project appear to be satisfied.

4. In-depth discussions of the pros and cons of the tentative system should be made during this period to avoid costly starts and detailed design time in the wrong direction.

5. With the preliminary structural system verified functionally, and economically, and properly interfaced with the other components of the tall building, the system or systems should be blocked out with soft pencils on grid paper to discover problem areas, such as bottlenecks. Roughly calculate determining dimensions on the sketches, do preliminary calculations to determine column sizes, slab thicknesses and so on. Do not develop the details of all the items, since the structural designer will detail the finer points as the problems develop and the preliminary design matures.

6. Distribute copies of these sketches to all interested parties and strive for tentative approval. The design team can work together, each knowing what the other is doing. Continue to revise the sketches as necessary, with dates and changes plainly indicated, and redistribute the sketches as material is duplicated or altered. At this point, do not hesitate to completely change the system if a considerably better solution becomes apparent.

7. Eventually, with the preliminary sketches as a guide, final framing plans can be developed and completely dimensioned, with every likelihood that the interferences and tight features have already been resolved. During this whole procedure, frequent over-all reviews are made to see that all of the different parties are properly provided for, and that the principles of simplicity, ease of construction, and optimization of the system are being reasonably well upheld.

8. Very often, past experience, common sense, and a knowledge of market conditions will enable the team of preliminary designers to arrive at a single solution. Sometimes such a single choice is not immediately apparent. It may be found desirable to make rough blockout sketches for two or even three alternative schemes of framing, carrying these sketches to a point at which reasonably reliable estimates of cost can be identified, and permitting a decision to be based on such an economic analysis.

9. Early decisions will involve the location of expansion joints (if any), shear walls, stiff cores, tube-in-tube, and exactly how lateral stiffness is to be provided.

10. If all of these steps are carefully executed by intelligent, knowledgeable designers, practically all of the problems associated with the design of tall buildings will have been solved on the preliminary sketches, and the

Renaissance Center, Detroit, Michigan (Courtesy: John Portman and Associates; photo by Win Brunner)

finished structural framing plans and supporting calculations need be made only once in the proper sequence.

In fact, if speed is essential and the construction is to be started before the entire design is completed, foundation plans can be prepared and contracts may even be let, based upon a reasonably complete picture of what the superstructure will eventually look like.

While experience in system selection can best be obtained by serving on such groups, the necessary prerequisites include experience in the "bread and butter" work of designing structures, and equally importantly, a broad general knowledge of the state of the art.

This knowledge must include a knowledge of history, of what has been done in the past and how it has worked. Reading about successful solutions past and present, observation of successful structures, study of technical periodicals, reading the biographies, accomplishments, and methods of successful designers, even the study of unsuccessful solutions, and the reasons, are all part of the development of a critical viewpoint and a creative mind.

Experience and knowledge, combined with an open mind, are the tools which a designer must apply to solving the problem of selecting an optimum structural system for any building.

3.6 APPENDIX—EXAMPLES OF SELECTION OF STRUCTURAL SYSTEMS

This appendix will review the selection of the structural systems used in four multistory buildings recently designed or built, or both, in Sydney, Australia. The considerations affecting the choice of system will be explained, and the development of each selected system will be followed through schematic proposals and detailed coordinated design to the final construction stage. Particular points of interest on each building will be highlighted, including, where possible, a few construction details to show how these were affected by the structural selection.

The structural systems vary from cast-in-place concrete floors with cast-in-place or slipformed cores and columns, through precast concrete slabs on an in-place concrete frame with a slipformed core, to a structural steel frame with metal deck integral with concrete slabs. In each case, the system was chosen as being the most economical related to prime cost, taking into account the effect of construction time upon final cost.

1 Description of Buildings

Lanray Building (Sydney Hilton).   The 44-story Lanray Building is shown in Fig. 3.23. It has three levels for car parking, three levels of arcades, loading and storage areas, and two levels of hotel function rooms, including a large column-free ballroom. These all occupy the complete site area.

Over this on a T-shaped plan (Fig. 3.24) are nine office floors, which are topped by a rectangular 24-story hotel accommodation block (Fig. 3.25). A two-level plant room area is utilized to transfer the loads from the accommodation block to the office structure below.

The A.M.P. Centre.   Fig. 3.26 shows the 50-story A.M.P. Centre, which is 195 m

(654 ft) high, and consists of three below-ground floors and the ground floor, which cover the whole site area, plus a rectangular tower. The tower section contains 46 floors (Fig. 3.27) with plant rooms at the basement, 20th, and 44th floors, and lift motor rooms at the 11th, 19th, 23rd, and 45th floors. There is parking for 275 cars in the lower floors, together with shopping arcades and other amenities.

Hyde Park Square.   This 48-story building, which is 179 m (588 ft) high, is part of a complete block development shown in Fig. 3.28. It consists of two car parks, a

Fig. 3.23 Lanray Building (Sydney Hilton)

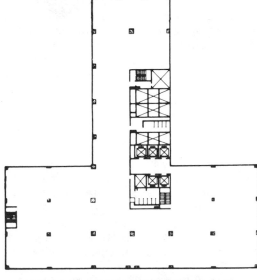

Fig. 3.24 Lanray Building—typical office floor plan

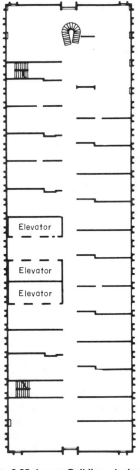

Fig. 3.25 Lanray Building—typical hotel floor plan

shopping arcade, plaza level with landscaping, 34 floors of office space (Fig. 3.29), and six floors of plant room.

The M.L.C. Centre.   Fig. 3.31 shows the 68-story M.L.C. Centre, 246 m (808 ft) high, which is part of a redevelopment scheme including parking, shopping, theatres, and an open plaza. A typical floor plan is shown in Fig. 3.30.

Fig. 3.26 A.M.P. Centre, Sydney, Australia

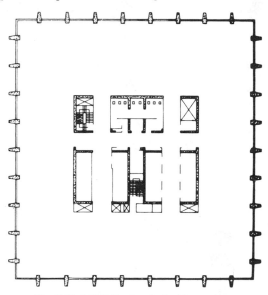

Fig. 3.27 A.M.P. Centre—typical floor plan

Fig. 3.28 Hyde Park Square

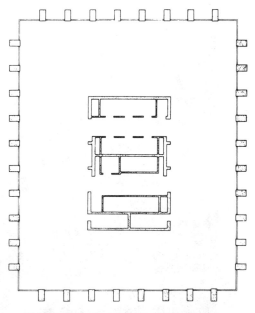

Fig. 3.29 Hyde Park Square—typical floor plan

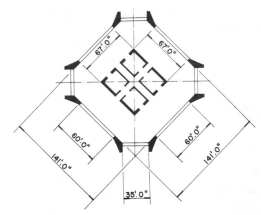

Fig. 3.30 M.L.C. Centre—typical tower floor plan

Fig. 3.31 M.L.C. Centre (Courtesy: N. Abdallah, Civil and Civic Pty., Ltd.)

The Lanray Building, the A.M.P. Centre, and Hyde Park Square were designed by Rankine and Hill Consulting Engineers, Sydney, Australia; the M.L.C. Centre by Civil and Civic Pty. Ltd., Sydney, Australia. This appendix is based on papers by Wells (1974) and Abdallah (1973).

2 Lanray Building

Design. With the Lanray project the multiplicity of usage dictated to a large extent the system or systems to be used. Considerable time was spent endeavoring to find a common system, without success, and the final result was a combination resulting in the need to transfer loads from one system to another.

The accommodation block resolved itself fairly easily. Room dividing walls are continuous vertically as far as the underside of level 44, the plant room. The material cost of load-bearing brickwork would have been marginally less than that of the lightweight concrete blade walls used, but time savings by slipforming these walls outweighed the material cost. Lightweight concrete was used here to reduce dead load on the transfer beam system at level 20. The 3.7-m (12-ft) spacing of the vertical walls made a 127-mm (5-in.) thick continuous in-place lightweight concrete slab the most economical floor system. As the walls were proceeding three levels ahead of the floors, continuity and bearing of the slab was obtained from blockouts in the walls.

Precast facade panels connected to the walls and slabs give stability against wind loads in the long direction, as do the blade walls in the transverse direction. Thus it becomes a stiff box sitting on its foundations at the 20th level.

The flat soffit of the slab provides an ideal surface for the sprayed-on ceiling finish. Air-conditioning distribution is through a central corridor duct and a bulkhead in the entrance lobby to each room.

Although the accommodation area is rectangular, the building spreads to a T-shape at the 20th level.

Whereas a column grid of 9.4 m by 7.3 m (31 ft × 24 ft) is not ideal for pure economy of materials, the ramifications of parking and hotel functions, and access, made it the most acceptable. However, even with this spacing, two columns had to be stopped off on transfer beams at lower levels.

In the choice of floor systems, consideration was given to: (1) Beam and slab; (2) waffle slab; (3) one-way ribbed system; (4) flat slab—both dense-weight and lightweight concrete; (5) steel beams and metal deck topped with concrete; (6) steel beam and cast-in-place concrete slabs; and (7) steel beam and precast concrete planks.

Limitations imposed were the maximum floor-to-floor height available [2.74 m (9 ft) in basements, 3.5 m (11-1/2 ft.) in offices] and the need for flexibility for service layouts, especially related to the hotel function area.

Costing of these schemes showed that a lightweight flat slab, 240 mm (9-1/2 in.) thick with 63-mm (2-1/2-in.) drop panels, in conjunction with reinforced concrete columns and a slipformed concrete core which carried the wind load, was the most economical. This took into account a longer construction period than would have been required for steel beams and metal deck.

The ballroom area, because of the large spans, and parts of levels 4, 5, 6, and 7, where the location of columns on level 4 caused problems with trucks unloading, were designed with 300-mm (12-in.) thick prestressed lightweight slabs spanning 14 m (46 ft). Although it was not desirable to mix construction in such a way, clearance limitations dictated the necessity.

Construction. Because of its multiple use, Lanray appeared ideal for a staged construction sequence. The lower car park floors and arcade levels were to be operated on a commercial basis, so that early occupancy of these floors was important to producing revenue. The car park and arcades opened approximately 2 yr and 1 yr, respectively, before the offices and hotel accommodation levels were completed.

The most critical area affecting the construction schedule was the 20th level, where 3-m (10-ft) deep transfer beams were required to carry the accommodation floors. It was an advantage to get to this area as quickly as possible, to construct these beams and commence construction of the accommodation walls and slabs before all the lower floors had been poured.

The method devised to permit this was to slipform the office portion core and columns under the rectangular accommodation block up to the 18th level, and to erect steel beams and to lay metal deck as a working platform. Using this platform, the level-20 beams were formed up using angle trusses to support the dead weight of the wet concrete and formwork, which was bolted to the trusses. This eliminated the problems of propping, and allowed the 18th-level beams to be designed for their true load and not a much heavier construction load. Reinforcement additional to the steel trusses was added to the beams to carry the dead and live load of the accommodation tower. The slipformed columns were braced to prevent buckling. Following this, construction proceeded on the accommodation walls and slabs above level 20, with the walls and columns being slipformed, and the slab construction following up to three floors behind. While the slipforming was proceeding, the lower office floors were being poured using a completely separate work force. By the time the 17th floor had been poured, thus completing the office section structurally, 10 levels of the hotel section had been constructed.

On the lower floors outside the tower areas, the need to mix types and materials of construction caused many delays. The building rhythm was broken as a result of using reinforced concrete, composite steel and concrete, and prestressed concrete slabs in close proximity. Because of the elastic shortening of the prestressed areas, shrinkage gaps were allowed, but this prevented the builder from following up with finishes in these areas.

The construction system for the Lanray Building has not shown the time saving anticipated, but this has been mainly due to major industrial unrest. Problems also occurred due to construction commencing before documentation was completed.

3   A.M.P. Centre

Design. Whereas the Lanray Building had a definite envelope by the time the consultants became involved, this was not so with the A.M.P. Centre and Hyde Park Square. The shapes of these evolved from evaluating the pros and cons of a large number of solutions from all consultants.

It is interesting to note that the final layouts for the typical floor are similar in geometry, A.M.P. being approximately 39.6 m by 40.9 m (130 ft by 134 ft), and Hyde Park Square 33.5 m by 41.2 m (110 ft by 135 ft). Both have a central core and a net to gross efficiency of approximately 80%. The actual structural system differs considerably in material used, A.M.P. being all concrete and Hyde Park composite steel and concrete (see Figs. 3.27 and 3.29).

For A.M.P., the structural consultant was asked to provide an ideal floor plan and structure for a typical floor of the tower. Altogether 40 schemes were considered. These included various plans and core positions with alternative structural floor systems, and covered: (1) Steel beams with cast in-place concrete floors; (2) steel beams with metal deck topped with concrete; (3) cast-in-place concrete beams and slabs; (4) cast-in-place concrete beams with precast prestressed slabs; (5) cast-in-place concrete beams with precast prestressed T beams; (6) cast-in-place concrete flat slab; (7) cast-in-place concrete ribbed floors; and (8) cast-in-place concrete waffle slab.

Of all these schemes, four were selected for further study:

1. Scheme 22F: A rectangular plan with offset core, using a structural steel frame with braced or rigid frames at each end, and welded facade frames for stiffness on the long axis. An alternative in reinforced concrete was considered (see Fig. 3.32).

2. Scheme 34: A square plan with central core using a reinforced concrete frame and one-way cast-in-place ribbed floors (see Fig. 3.33).

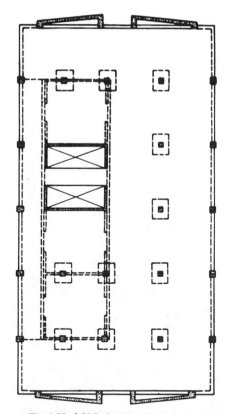

Fig. 3.32 A.M.P. Centre—Scheme 22/F

3. Scheme 36: An offset core with cast-in-place flat slab. This scheme was also considered using steel beams with metal decking (see Fig. 3.34).

4. Scheme 40: A rectangular plan with offset core and cast-in-place flat slab (see Fig. 3.35).

Scheme 40 was particularly favored by the real estate consultant because he considered it to be the best prospect for renting. It was decided to pursue development of this proposal, with the object of preparing preliminary drawings to obtain cost estimates. The lack of symmetry in the floor plan posed some major engineering problems, such as racking of the building under wind load and differential deflections between the cast-in-place core and external columns.

Considerable investigation was done into methods of establishing actual wind loadings, and the loadings obtained from these methods were compared. In the end the work of Davenport and Vickery was used to establish a wind loading.

Concern was felt about the effect on the occupants of lateral acceleration at the top of the building as it swayed under wind loading, and some studies were made. This concern was greatly reduced when a concrete frame was decided on.

Calculation showed that the effects of creep and elastic shortening due to progressive construction loading and strength development of the concrete would give, at the 22nd floor, a differential deflection of approximately 20 mm (3/4 in.) between the core and the adjacent corner columns. The raking beams at the intermediate and top plant rooms were designed to compensate for this difference. In addition, the lateral deflections due to this differential shortening were studied.

At this stage in the design, the building plans and documentation were submitted

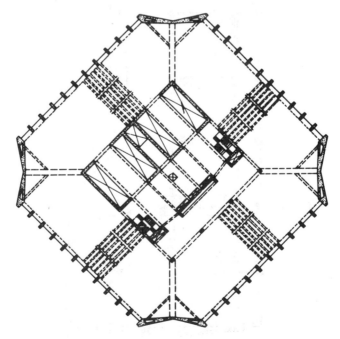

Fig. 3.33 A.M.P. Centre—Scheme 34

to the Planning Service Council of the Building Owners and Managers Association International in Chicago, for a critical review. This review dealt with the management and servicing aspect of a commercial building including all facets of engineering services, such as air conditioning, lighting, lift services, plumbing, and general layout. Two main points emphasized in their review were that window space rents offices, and therefore the core should be in the centre of the building, and that the space from window to core should not be more than about 11 m (36 ft) for ideal office subdivision.

As a result of this review, major alterations were made to the building as proposed at that time. The floor plan was changed from that shown in Fig. 3.35 to the plan shown in Fig. 3.27. The changes also involved the general design approach to all building services.

The final design consists of a slipformed reinforced concrete core that provides 90% of the lateral strength required to resist wind loading. The strength of the core concrete varies from 38 MPa (5500 psi) to 20.7 MPa (3000 psi), and the core was designed to be in normal-weight concrete up to the 12th floor, and above that in lightweight. At the 24th floor, about one-third of the lower core area is added to the rentable area, and the walls are replaced as a vertical load-bearing element by three columns. The walls commence 600 mm (24 in.) thick, and decrease in 75-mm (3-in.) increments to 300 mm (12 in.).

The floor system consists of cast-in-place beams continuous with the columns at

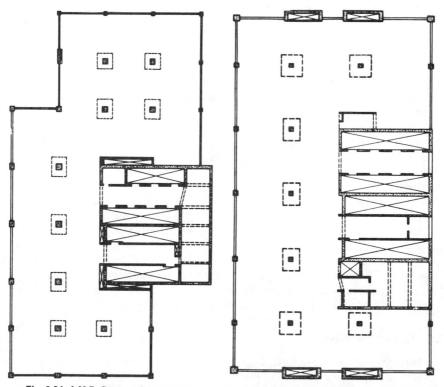

Fig. 3.34 A.M.P. Centre—Scheme 36   Fig. 3.35 A.M.P. Centre—Scheme 40

the outer ends and simply supported on the core walls. The beams are haunched at the outer ends to increase their stiffness.

The floor deck system is of precast lightweight planks 100 mm (4 in.) thick, which have a recess formed in the top side to take an electrical services duct. A 64-mm (2-1/2-in.) layer of lightweight concrete is placed over the planks as an integrating membrane.

The design team's approach was to keep options on alternatives open as long as possible, without impeding progress. So for some time, consideration was given to the use of a steel deck floor and a steel frame. Final costing confirmed the original decision that construction in reinforced concrete was more economical than structural steel for this project, even after accounting for the shorter construction period of a steel frame.

The columns are of concrete with a maximum strength of 45 MPa (6500 psi) and hard grade 38-mm (1-1/2-in.) square bar reinforcement, which was specially rolled by The Broken Hill Proprietary Company Limited. End bearing splices were made with mechanical connectors which were developed in association with the reinforcement supplier and the building consultant. The over-all size of the columns is about 1.90 m by 0.6 m (6-1/4 ft by 2 ft), which is maintained for the full height of the building.

Construction.   As there is a reasonably large plaza area to be built adjacent to the A.M.P. Centre, to reduce construction time for the whole project it was necessary to get to the typical floors of the tower and thus to the routine operation, and to follow up with the plaza areas using a separate labor force.

Since the construction of the core was not on the critical path for the building, and since the reinforcement in the coupling beams which spanned passageways in the core was complex, the builder elected to stageform the walls rather than to place them continuously.

To construct a floor, the steel formwork for the beams was first erected, the beam reinforcement placed, the precast floor planks put in position on the beam forms, and the beams concreted.

The columns are clad with precast exposed aggregate concrete, which is utilized as formwork during construction. These precast concrete column liners are made off-site in two halves, each L-shaped. They were put together on site to form a U. The track that guides the window cleaning unit runs down the center of the outside column face and covers the joint. Stout polyethylene sheeting was glued over the units to protect them during construction. Some staining of the surface occurred under the polyethylene due to mildew caused by the very humid weather conditions at the time. After assembly the column liners were hoisted into position and set on top of the previous cover, using small hard rubber blocks for levelling purposes, and a soft round rubber seal on the inside to prevent concrete filling the joint between the units. The success of this operation was due to close cooperation between the builder and consultants, in order to develop reinforcement arrangements and fixing details which could avoid, as far as possible, on-site problems.

4 Hyde Park Square

Design.   When conceptual design on Hyde Park Square commenced, rising costs and industrial unrest made speed of construction an important factor.

From the experience gained from A.M.P., designed 2 yr earlier by the same firm, a central core was adopted from the start, and the emphasis on speedy construction led to the development of a composite steel and concrete frame with the steel acting as a basic support medium over a height of approximately six floors. That is, the steel columns were designed to carry the floor and construction loads of up to six floors before the additional column reinforcing and concrete were constructed to take the final loads of the building. This allows for speed of erection combined with positive steel construction. Expensive large-size structural steel columns are eliminated, and advantage is taken of the economical steel beam and decking floor system.

The lateral wind forces are resisted by the interaction of the core and the perimeter frame. This varies from the perimeter frames carrying 100% of the lateral forces at the top, to the core carrying 95% at the bottom, in accordance with the relative stiffnesses of the components. Lateral drift was not a problem. The evolution of the final scheme utilizing a reinforced concrete core was due to the relative sophistication of the slipforming technique in Australia. It proved quicker to use the slipform process to keep ahead of the floor cycle than to use vertical steel members in the core. Therefore by using slipform, the core was not on the critical path, and earlier completion of the elevator motor rooms became possible.

Because of the selected geometry of the building and experience gained on A.M.P., only a few systems were considered, and these were mainly variations of the internal framing of the steel beams. The spacing of the perimeter columns was fixed by architectural considerations and this finally gave rise to the beam layout which, after full investigation, proved to be the most economical.

The adoption of rectangular hollow steel sections for the perimeter columns carrying the construction loads had the added advantage that they also were used as vertical risers for the air conditioning of the perimeter zone.

To simplify the construction procedure, the steel beams were supported on projecting steel brackets which were incorporated in the slipping process by the use of static formwork panels. The perimeter is tied to the core only by the structural steel beams. This flexible jointing of the floor to the core overcomes any problems of differential settlement due to creep and elastic shortening between the core and the columns.

The floor system consists of a 114-mm (4-1/2-in.) dense weight concrete slab acting integrally with galvanized steel decking spanning 2.8 m (9 ft) between secondary beams. These were supported by 10.7-m (35-ft) long beams spanning from core to perimeter. These beams were composite with the deck. The underside of the steel decking and the steel beams were sprayed to achieve the required fire rating. The factors related to floor-to-floor heights and air-conditioning requirements led to the choice of the system as adopted. The system also gives minimum construction time, minimum dead load on columns and core, and allows a clear span from perimeter to core despite a floor-to-floor height of only 3.7 m (12 ft).

The plant room floors consist of a 203-mm (8-in.) slab spanning between primary beams made up of universal beams plated on the bottom, and acting compositely with the slab. This system was adopted to provide a relatively stiff floor for acoustic and vibration requirements.

Construction.   In this building emphasis was given to the ability to have work carried out simultaneously at different levels. The tower section is isolated from the podium levels, which are supported by a nib on the perimeter beams of the tower.

The core shape was rationalized with the cooperation of all consultants to give a shape suitable for slipforming, thus making it outside the critical path. The outside walls commence at 690 mm (27 in.) thick and reduce in 76-mm (3-in.) steps to 300 mm (12 in.) minimum. The inside walls have constant thickness from 150 mm (6 in.) to 250 mm (10 in.). Above the 27th level, the core reduces in size to give more rentable space. The core construction proceeds independently of the floor system and perimeter columns. The floor slabs are not connected to the core, both to minimize cost and also to allow the core to proceed at a faster rate without the provision of blockouts and starter bars.

In order to get quickly to the first typical floor (level 7), unencased structural steel columns were used. These were designed to take the full loading from the building. The floor beams and temporary bracing were used to stabilize these columns until the lower floors were poured.

As soon as the frame was braced, the 300-mm (12-in.) square tubular perimeter columns, designed to carry the slab weight plus 25 psf construction load, were erected up to six floors ahead of the final concrete columns. The figure of six floors was obtained because of optimization of the column section size, which was related to air conditioning and also to the bracing requirements. The main beams and girders were then supported on the tubular columns. A 140-mm (5-1/2-in.) steel channel section trims the perimeter between main beams to enable the floor slab to be poured prior to the final encasing of the erection columns and pouring of the concrete perimeter beams (see Fig. 3.36).

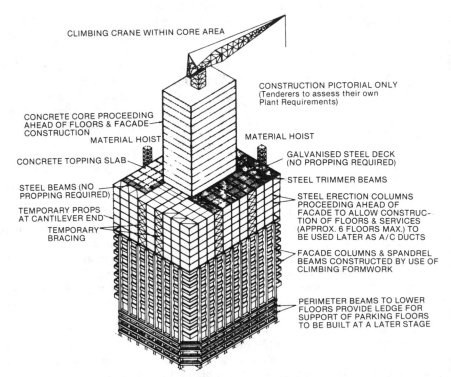

CLIMBING CRANE WITHIN CORE AREA

CONSTRUCTION PICTORIAL ONLY
(Tenderers to assess their own
Plant Requirements)

CONCRETE CORE PROCEEDING
AHEAD OF FLOORS & FACADE
CONSTRUCTION
MATERIAL HOIST   MATERIAL HOIST

CONCRETE TOPPING SLAB   GALVANISED STEEL DECK
                                (NO PROPPING REQUIRED)

STEEL BEAMS (NO   STEEL TRIMMER BEAMS
PROPPING REQUIRED)
                                STEEL ERECTION COLUMNS
TEMPORARY PROPS   PROCEEDING AHEAD OF
AT CANTILEVER END   FACADE TO ALLOW CONSTRUC-
                                TION OF FLOORS & SERVICES
TEMPORARY   (APPROX. 6 FLOORS MAX.) TO
BRACING   BE USED LATER AS A/C DUCTS

                                FACADE COLUMNS & SPANDREL
                                BEAMS CONSTRUCTED BY USE OF
                                CLIMBING FORMWORK

                                PERIMETER BEAMS TO LOWER
                                FLOORS PROVIDE LEDGE FOR
                                SUPPORT OF PARKING FLOORS
                                TO BE BUILT AT A LATER STAGE

Fig. 3.36 Hyde Park Square—construction staging

The support brackets for the steel beams were cast into the core and have a three-dimensional tolerance allowance. As construction proceeded with the typical floors, the nontypical lower floors and perimeter were also being constructed.

A critical path analysis for the construction was made to assure the minimum floor construction cycle.

Apart from industrial problems, the system has operated as planned. One example of the industrial problems was that after the structural steel was erected up to the 10th floor, the unions refused to work on site if the steel beams had studs prewelded before erection. This resulted in the remainder of the steel being erected without studs and the studs being welded on site. Fortunately, this did not slow down the project because the operation was not on the critical path.

5 M.L.C. Centre

Design. The M.L.C. Centre is being constructed on two acres of land in the center of Sydney. A severe site restraint is the presence of two underground railway tunnels which cross it diagonally at about 2.4 m (8 ft) below foundation level.

Commercial considerations and the presence of one major unacquired property have resolved the planning into a tall tower building on one part of the site, and on the remainder a development complex of parking, shopping, a cinema, a theater, a tavern, and other amenities culminating in a courtlike open plaza.

In the last 20 years, lateral resisting systems for high-rise buildings have received a great deal of attention. In the optimum solutions, the amount of sway and the increase in cost over what is needed to sustain vertical loads are kept within acceptable limits. The reinforced concrete tower will rise some 246 m (808 ft) from its base and will comprise 68 levels. For a tower of this height, the tube-in-tube concept was selected.

As shown in Fig. 3.30, the services core is formed by connecting eight channel-shaped sections by 1.3-m (4 ft-3 in.) deep beams to form a square box. This core is reasonably large and is favorably disposed to offer a major contribution in resisting lateral loads. Thus, the core serves as the inner tube. Eight columns, symmetrically arranged around the perimeter of the tower and joined by 1.8-m (6-ft) deep spandrel beams, form the rigid outer tube of the building.

The classical framed outer tube has closely spaced columns 1.2 m to 3.6 m (4 ft to 12 ft) center to center. Despite its efficiency, the closeness of the columns in such an outer tube is a major drawback in the plaza, shopping, and parking areas, and has drawn strong objections from clients and architects. In an effort to overcome these objections, transfer girders varying in depth from 1 to 2 stories have been introduced to allow a reduction in the number of columns at these lower levels. However, in terms of construction time and visual considerations such transfer girders have been found to produce more problems than they have solved.

In the M.L.C. Centre tower, apart from the restrictions on location of columns imposed by the underground railway tunnels, other architectural restraints are such that the possible choice of small spans between perimeter columns was promptly rejected by the client. The problem then became one of evolving an outer tube with large spans but possessing the structural efficiency inherent in the classical tube.

In essence, the three major parameters controlling the behavior of a rigid frame were investigated. They are:

1. The column shortening effect, which is controlled by the cross-sectional area of the columns.

2. The flexural stiffness of the columns.

3. The flexural stiffness of the beams, which is important with respect to both sway deflections of the frames parallel to the wind and the shear lag between the columns forming the flanges of the tube.

Figs. 3.37 to 3.39 show the effect of these three parameters on the deflection of the building. The major effect of the beam stiffness can be seen.

A four-column tube was quickly rejected by inspection. An eight-column tube linked by deep girders was then considered. Having established a floor-to-floor height of 3.45 m (11 ft 4 in.) and a necessary window opening height of 1.63 m (5 ft 4 in.) clear, 1.8-m (6-ft) deep spandrel beams were possible. The requirement for deeply recessed windows for sun protection in the form of a hood suggested the use of deep I-section spandrel beams. The disposition of the columns as shown in Fig. 3.30 was conceived for the following reasons:

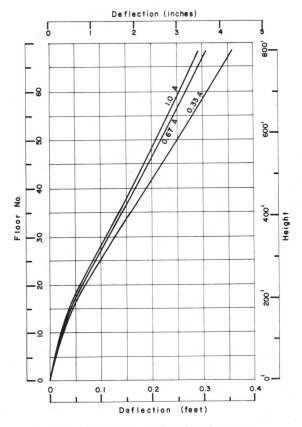

Fig. 3.37 Change of deflection with column area

1. Replacing a multitude of closely spaced columns with a small number of necessarily large columns produced vertical members which have themselves the characteristics of walls rather than of columns. These columns, when associated with deep, stiff connecting beams, comprise a frame akin to the desired classical tube.

2. A wall acquires extra stiffness if some return on the ends is provided. Such returns were provided gently and in harmony with the 45° splays at the four corners of the building. Then, as the principal axes of the building are set at 45° to the axes of the streets, each pair of columns provides a positive and logical entrance to the building—indeed, the appearance of the building is greatly enhanced by the sense of direction contributed by this arrangement of the columns. The selection of large columns with deep spandrel beams spanning 18 m (60 ft) and 10.7 m (35 ft) clearly provides a remarkably stiff outer tube which, interacting with the core, undergoes a deflection of only 89 mm (3-1/2 in.) under the effect of the design wind load. The sharing of the static wind moment resistance is about 50% by the core and the remainder by the outer tube.

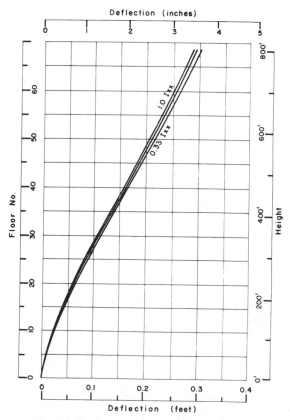

Fig. 3.38 **Change of deflection with column inertia**

In isolation, the cost of the structure for the M.L.C. Centre is a little higher than for a structure with columns extending to the foundations. Because of the disruptions introduced by the plaza and underground levels, however, a number of transfer girders would have been required if closely spaced columns had been used. Studies suggested that the costs of these transfer girders in lost time alone more than offset the extra cost of using widely spaced columns.

The services core will be called upon to carry some 670 MN (150 000 kips) of dead and live load, while the eight perimeter columns will have an aggregate total load of 890 MN (200 000 kips).

The effect of lateral load due to wind was derived from extensive tests carried out in the boundary layer wind tunnel in the Department of Civil Engineering at the University of Sydney. The structure was modelled in such a way as to take into account its mass, length, stiffness, period of vibration, and damping.

The results obtained for a wind of 166 km/hr (103 mph) in the most critical direction were:

    Maximum wind force on the building: 12 000 kN (2700 kips)

    Maximum base moment due to wind: 1870 MN.m (1.38×10^6 kip-ft)

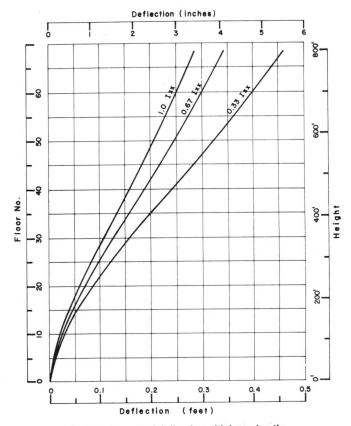

Fig. 3.39 Change of deflection with beam inertia

Due to the symmetry of the outer tube it was felt from the outset that mathematical modelling need be carried out in two dimensions only. However, since this frame was a novel concept for a project of such magnitude, some reservations were expressed regarding the validity of this comparatively simple mathematical modelling. To dispel any doubt a physical model was built and tested in the University of Sydney at the Department of Architectural Science. The correlation between the computer and the test results exceeded all expectations and fell well within the 15% compatibility range expected in that type of work.

Due to the large sizes of members and the long spans of the beams, inelastic strains in the structure were given serious consideration.

The first step taken in this area was to commission the Cement and Concrete Association to carry out a three-month investigation during which trial mixes were designed and the properties studied. The aim was to obtain the following characteristics:

1. Low specific shrinkage.

2. Low specific creep.

3. High modulus of elasticity.

4. Low heat of hydration.

The problem of thermal movement was studied on the basis of daily, weekly, and monthly variation of temperature in Sydney using the records of the weather bureau and the techniques outlined in Chapter CB-10. Total and differential strains due to shrinkage and creep were fully analyzed using data by the Portland Cement Association and Comité Européen du Béton.

Of great interest and concern is the problem of thermal cracking. Due to the heat of hydration, concrete sets at a higher temperature than ambient and it is possible, after a drop in temperature, for a member to be at a temperature up to 40°C (70°F) higher than ambient. If at that time the concrete has not developed sufficient strength, large cracks can develop. In this building it was established that thermal cracking could be a problem, and it was decided that the spandrel beams should be poured with each end resting on a slip joint which allows it to move. After three days the connecting columns were poured.

6 Conclusions

Conclusions coming out of the design and construction of these four projects are:

1. Each project must be fully considered on its own merits for all functions and must be related to the total project, not just the structure.

2. Consideration must be given to construction methods in an endeavor to overcome or bypass complicated areas, that is, to get to repetitive areas quickly and treat the slow areas independently. The design must take account of this.

3. Projects should be fully documented before construction commences, especially in the case of expedited building systems.

4. Close coordination must be maintained with the building consultant during the design and documentation phase.

5. Before commencing on unusual building techniques, union reaction must be considered.

6. In general, the effect of mixing various forms of construction in close proximity slows down construction, and is thus expensive in time, if not also in materials.

7. For two apparently similar projects over-all consideration can show that differing structural systems are the most economical for each project.

3.7 CONDENSED REFERENCES/BIBLIOGRAPHY

The following is a condensed bibliography for this chapter. Not only does it include all articles referred to or cited in the text, but it also contains bibliography for further reading. The full citations will be found at the end of the Volume. What is given here should be sufficient information to lead the reader to the correct article: the author, date, and title. In case of multiple authors, only the first named is listed.

Abdallah 1973, *The M.L.C. Centre*
Agaskar 1972, *Automated Design of Tier Buildings*
Chadha 1970, *Wind-Excited Oscillations of Cantilever Structures*
Colaco 1971, *Preliminary Design of High Rise Buildings with Shear Walls*
Colaco 1973, *Concrete Floor Systems*

Coull 1971, *Strength of Sections and Connections—Ultimate Strength Design*
Crisfield 1971, *Equivalent Plate Approach for the Analysis of Cellular Structures*
Dickson 1970, *Analysis of Cellular Buildings for Lateral Loads*
Elstner 1970, *Tests of Elastic Models of Flat Plate and Flat Slab Floor System*
Emilian-Davidovici 1969, *Slab Floors, Comparative Study of Various Methods of Calculation*

Faulkes 1975, *The Design of Flat Plate Buildings Subjected to Lateral Loads*
Fintel 1968, *Staggered Wall Beams of Multistory Buildings*
FIP 1975, *FIP/CEB Recommendations for the Design of Reinforced and Prestressed Concrete*
Fling 1973, *Theme Report: Elastic Analysis—Strength of Members and Connections*
Fransson 1973, *Unsymmetrical Multi-Storey Buildings*
George 1974, extract from *Prefabrication Techniques in India*

Goschy 1975, *Structural Systems*
Guy 1970, *Design for Movement in Buildings*
Khan 1964, *Interaction of Shear Walls with Frames in Concrete Structures Under Lateral Loads*
Khan 1972, *The Future of Highrise Structures*
Kirk 1970, *Natural Frequencies of Stiffened Rectangular Plates*
Kostem 1970, *The Stresses in Folded Plate Roof Traverses*

Kostem 1972, *Thermal Stresses and Deformations in Pneumatic Cushion Roofs*
Kostem 1973a, *Optimization of Folded Plate Roofs*
Kostem 1973b, *Optimum Shaped Pneumatic Roofs*
Kulicki 1973a, *Nonlinear Analysis of Concrete Flexural Members*
Kulicki 1973b, *Further Studies on the Nonlinear Finite Element Analysis of Beams*

Kulicki 1973c, *User's Manual for Program BEAM*
Kulicki 1973d, *Applications of the Finite Element Method to Inelastic Beam-Column Problems*
Liauw 1972, *Modern Development in Structural Design Concepts for Tall Buildings*
Mihailescu 1975, *Tall Buildings with Peripheric Shear Walls*
PCI 1971, *PCI Design Handbook*

PCI 1973, *PCI Manual on Design of Connections for Precast Prestressed Concrete*
PCI 1975, *Design Considerations for a Precast Prestressed Apartment Building*
Pretzer 1972, *Unusual Application of Prestressed Waffle Slabs and Composite Beams*
Reese 1973, *A Method to Determine the Sensitivity of Mathematical Models in Deterministic*
Reiss 1972, *Calculation of Continuous Orthotropic Ribbed Floors Without Torsional Rigidity*

Richter 1971, *Three-Dimensional Finite Element Dynamic Analysis of a Multistory Office Building*
Schrefler 1971, *Calculation of General Type Reinforcing Systems for Tall Buildings*
Stevenson 1970, *Reliability Analysis of Frame Structures*
Thürlimann 1971, *Tall Buildings, Yes or No—Technology, Curse or Blessing*
Wegmuller 1972, *Elastic-Plastic Analysis of Plates*
Wells 1974, *Structural Systems of Three Sydney High-Rise Buildings*

**Structural Design of
Tall Concrete and Masonry Buildings**

Chapter CB-4

Optimization of
Tall Concrete Buildings

Prepared by Committee 21B (Optimization) of the Council on Tall
Buildings and Urban Habitat as part of the Monograph on the
Planning and Design of Tall Buildings

Vincent J. DeSimone   Chairman and Editor
George Kostro   Vice-Chairman

AUTHOR ACKNOWLEDGMENT

Special acknowledgment is due those individuals whose contributions formed the substantial first draft of the various sections of this chapter. These include:

V. J. DeSimone, Sections 4.1, 4.2, 4.3, 4.4, 4.5
T. Jumikis, Section 4.6
G. Kostro, Section 4.7.

In addition, special credit should be given to R. C. Reese, who suggested the inclusion of this chapter, and J. G. MacGregor, who organized the material into a continuous chapter.

CONTRIBUTORS

The following is a complete list of those who have submitted written material for possible use in the chapter, whether or not that material was used in the final version. The Committee Chairman and Editor was given quite complete latitude. Frequently length limitations precluded the inclusion of much valuable material. The Bibliography contains all contributions. The contributors are: K. E. Bruinette, M. Z. Cohn, V. J. DeSimone, T. Jumikis, G. Kostro, J. G. MacGregor, R. C. Reese.

COMMITTEE MEMBERS

K. E. Bruinette, V. J. DeSimone, J. Ferry Borges, G. Kostro, F. Levi, G. Sebestyen.

CB-4

Optimization of Tall Concrete Buildings

4.1 INTRODUCTION

1 Need for Optimization

Tall buildings are an integral part of the economic and physical fabric of modern urban environments. There are two fundamental differences between designing tall buildings and designing buildings of a lesser scale. These are:

1. The environmental technology of a tall building is more complex.

2. The consequences of a designer's decisions are more critical and more costly.

Tall concrete and steel buildings represent enormous private and public investments. Most importantly, tall buildings are large consumers of resources in the form of manpower and construction materials (Forwood, 1975). As a result of this large consumption, increased interest is developing in optimization and optimization techniques leading to reduced consumption of resources. Interest in optimization is more urgent because of the magnified waste, and expenditure of finances and time, resulting from the sheer size of the tall concrete building.

2 Optimization—A Multifaceted Problem

Newmark and Rosenblueth (1971) have defined optimization as follows:

> The aim of any purposeful activity is optimization of the outcome. When the result can be graded by a scalar quantity called utility and which is a monotonically increasing function of desirability, optimization is synonymous with the maximization of this quantity. Accordingly, the purpose of engineering design is to maximize the utility to be derived from the system produced.

Within the frame of this definition the way to maximize the utility of a building is to maximize its marketability or, in other words, its response to its function.

In broad terms, meaningful optimization should include all relevant factors, such as structural efficiency, erection costs of both the structure and finish, quality of space and comfort, mechanical and electrical requirements, and the effect on rental revenue where applicable (Iyengar, 1973). Add to this such things as initial land cost, maximum utilization of real estate, interest on borrowed money, maintenance, and depreciation, and one can see that the task of optimizing a tall building is extremely complex, and at times the input appears unmanageable.

A further complexity in optimization is to determine which quality or merit function yields the greatest results for the building when optimized. For example, an architect may want optimum planning flexibility; an engineer may desire optimum structure, thus less material; and an environmentalist may want optimum energy use, and thus minimum waste. One can see from a number of examples such as this that the optimum future flexibility may conflict with investment return and other qualities desired to be optimized. As a result of the myriad qualities that can be optimized, a method using weighted values or priorities must be attached to the systems which make up the modern tall building in order to develop rationally a well-balanced and usable approach to optimization. It is common experience that, considering all of the most desirable results, the goal of maximum building area and quality for minimum cost is most acceptable as an optimization criterion. As a result, an optimized building should be one in which the over-all cost of the adequately functioning building is a minimum, with cost being measured not only as money for construction, but all soft costs including interest and the cost of money.

Fig. 4.1 shows diagrammatically the distribution of costs of the various types of expenditure shown as a proportion of the total development cost, not as a

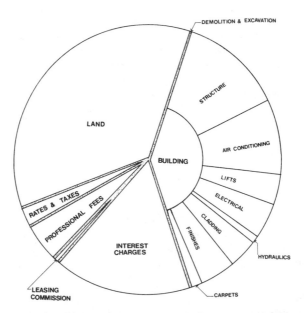

Fig. 4.1 Cost distribution of tall office building development

proportion of the construction costs alone (Jumikis, 1973). Clearly, interest charges represent a significant proportion of total expenditure. Even for moderately tall office buildings, the interest charges on development funds employed will exceed the total cost of the structure. This suggests that reductions in the over-all construction time may be more important in minimizing the cost of a building than minimizing the cost of any one system in the building.

Successful optimization of buildings involves the integration of their systems, including construction systems, so that the optimized total building becomes the goal rather than the optimization of any particular individual system or discipline (McMillan, 1975). Before attempting to optimize a tall concrete building, it is necessary to categorize the different systems which make up the total building. It is necessary, as in any problem, to state those systems or disciplines which, when integrated properly, result in the optimized building.

3 General Parameters to Optimize

The parameters to be optimized in a modern concrete high-rise building may be broadly classed as function, quality, and esthetics as related to cost (McMillan, 1975).

Function is concerned with assuring both that the space provided should serve its planned purpose effectively, thus satisfying the needs of the user; and that the building structure, mechanical services, elevators, and performance to exterior environment all work well. Function has a direct bearing on cost.

Quality relates to the standards chosen for the building, such as finishes, lighting levels, and internal environmental comfort, and this also has a direct bearing on cost.

Esthetics refers to those subjective qualities of beauty and form which result in visual and emotional satisfaction. Esthetics also has secondary benefits, such as the relationship of a building to the community and the acceptance of the building by the community. This acceptance results in greater marketability and thus higher revenues.

4 Building Systems

In most instances the first step to optimizing a building is to establish the major systems. While it has previously been stated that an optimized building does not necessarily result from individual optimized systems, the optimization of major systems must be the first step prior to adjusting these systems into the whole building. The design process for an entity as unique and complex as a tall concrete building involves the relationship between specialists who form a team for a particular project. This multidisciplinary approach embraces the skills of the owner, architect, structural engineer, and mechanical engineer. This subject is treated further in Chapter PC-14.

5 Levels of Optimization

The first level of optimization deals with the initial selection of a system for each specialist who considers the integration of his system with those of his team members. The second level of optimization deals with a more detailed study of systems, and includes the preliminary sizing of members or systems, and in some instances even subsystems optimization. The final level of optimization involves a final design and systems optimization in which the interdependence between systems specialists may require compromise of their optimized systems towards the desired optimization of the whole building (Iyengar, 1973). During this entire process of the three levels of activities described, the key to success depends primarily on the ability of the various members of the team to communicate. These specialists must constantly adjust their parameters for the success of the entire building.

6 Role of Owner-Developer

Current practice in the design and initiation of a tall concrete building starts with the owner. The owner, recognizing the need for a specific type of building (commercial, residential, or cultural) establishes within his organization the resources required, capital expense, rate of depreciation, and expected return on investment. Essentially the future owner establishes the market feasibility and financial feasibility of the contemplated project. The owner's market study defines for him the optimum amount of space required for his needs. His financial feasibility studies determine the amount of earnings required to result in an optimum yield on his investment, which implies optimum building cost, since yield and cost are related.

7 Role of Design Team

Following the initial feasibility study, the professional team is posed with a package of optimum financial statements by the owner-developer. These statements include the size and location of the land, the area that can be marketed, the general cost of construction to make the project feasible, the type of building required, and when the building should be ready for occupancy.

After the owner has arrived at these conditions, the next step in optimization requires the assembling of building specialists. The architect in most instances becomes the over-all coordinator of the individual optimizing efforts of each specialist. Each specialist will initially determine the optimum system for which he is responsible. Continuous information is exchanged, with adjustments made in the process to allow for interferences. This stage of preliminary optimization of specialized systems relies to a large extent on the intuition of the individual specialist, his grasp of his specialty, and the manner in which his system interacts with the other systems. Eventually the design experience is advanced to final design and final coordination with necessary compromises towards the optimization of the building.

There is no doubt that the present design procedures followed by most building specialists are optimizing procedures whether they have been labeled so or not. Recent articles and commentaries clearly establish that each specialist enlists either his experience or experience coupled with computers to develop the optimizing technique. It is worth noting that a large amount of design today is computer assisted. This cuts down on the amount of laborious calculations, adjustments, and time.

It should also be noted that structural and mechanical construction comprise approximately 70% of the total cost of construction (ignoring land costs and interest), and efforts to design complex buildings in excess of 30 stories without the use of computers yield approximate results which tend to be on the conservative side, and thus fractionally more costly.

The goal of this chapter is to discuss the state-of-the-art techniques available for optimizing major systems and subsystems, with practical computer and non-computer programs toward the goal of maximum building optimization.

The following list is an attempt to represent the systems comprising a total building with the subsystems that belong to each of the building specialists or major systems.

Optimal Goals of Team Specialists

1. Owner:
   a. Market feasibility.
   b. Financial feasibility.

2. Architect:
   a. Spatial requirements of envelope and building services.
   b. Energy consumed by service system.
   c. Quality of internal environment.
   d. Cost of producing this internal environment.

3. Mechanical engineer:
   a. Hydraulics.
   b. Electrical.
   c. Elevators or lifts.
   d. Air conditioning.

4. Structural engineer:
   a. Gravity load system.
   b. Lateral load system.
   c. Foundations.

5. Construction engineer:
   a. Labor.
   b. Time.

4.2 OPTIMIZATION FOR MARKET AND FINANCIAL FEASIBILITY

The optimization process includes and begins with the owner of the building. Whether the use of a building is intended to be public, corporate, or speculative, certain goals are common to all. The first activity of the owner is to make a determination of the type of building desired by the market. Concurrently with this study, he determines the amount of space desired, the quality of the space, the prevailing construction cost, the availability of money and what he must pay for it, and thus his net return.

Although building designers are not directly involved in the owner's optimization procedures, it is necessary to describe the process so that the designer can understand the impact of his involvement on the feasibility of the building.

1 General Investment Philosophy

A theory of investment behavior (Jorgensen, 1972) is based on the concept that a business entity chooses a production plan "so as to maximize the present value of the productive enterprise" (Linzey, 1973). Essentially the "net present value" (NPV) can be expressed in a simplified equation, in which each term is a function of the interest rate, as

$$\text{NPV} = \underset{t=0}{\overset{t = \text{construction completion}}{\sum}} \frac{\text{construction cost}}{\text{construction time}} + \underset{\text{start of productive life of building}}{\overset{\text{finish of productive life of building}}{\sum}} (\text{rentals} - \text{expenditures}) \times (1 - \text{tax rate}) \quad (4.1)$$

For the purposes of this chapter, the first half of Eq. 4.1 is that portion of the present net value which can be directly controlled by the structural engineering and construction engineering members of the team. Other members of the team must carefully study the second term since operating costs are an important parameter in the NPV equation.

It should be noted that many analyses have been performed on a systems approach to planning and design for the optimization process involving the owner (Linzey, 1973; Swanson, 1975; Russell and Reinschmidt, 1973).

2 Obligation of Designers to Owner

In reference to Eq. 4.1, it is the designer's duty to be aware of his ability to affect construction cost and construction time. Minimum cost and time optimize the owner's investment and create an economically viable project. Excellent examples of computer techniques are available (Linzey, 1973; Swanson, 1975). They take into account land values, rates and taxes, plot ratios, incorporated community goals, tradeoffs, communication, designing for the future, effects of obsolescence, adverse building conditions, and demolition. The most important factor to note is that under actual field conditions it is the owner who has evaluated the NPV, and the second half of Eq. 4.1. The owner then comes to the designers with the information that he requires a building of certain qualities to be constructed within a specified budget in a specific construction time. It is the designer's responsibility to respond factually as to whether or not this can be done, relying on his judgment and past experience with similar problems.

4.3 OPTIMIZATION OF ARCHITECTURAL SYSTEMS

As the leader of the design team of an optimized building, the architect's primary responsibility is to coordinate the other building consultants with his over-all design objectives.

1 Architect's Optimization Goals

The design objectives of the architect are: (1) To develop a facade treatment; (2) to develop a floor plan and land-use plan; (3) to develop a building module; and

(4) to determine the optimum building height consistent with the owner's financial goals.

Studies show that those urban areas in which there is a requirement for tall concrete buildings always have zoning regulations that set the allowable statutes (McArthur, 1973). "Given today's economic conditions and continually escalatory land cost, . . . buildings will be built to their maximum allowable floor area" (Russell and Reinschmidt, 1973).

2   Optimal Design of Shape and Height of Building

The following building requirements influence the plan, size, shape, and height of buildings:

1. Type of internal space required (office, residential, commercial), including the need for air conditioning and subdivisions.

2. Influence of land value on height. If land is expensive, height is essential for economic reasons.

3. Ratio of facade area to plan area.

4. Effect of facade area on heat load, and consequently on air conditioning.

5. Increasing structural cost with height.

6. Cost of mechanical room floors.

Studies have been performed by a number of design teams that show comparisons between buildings of various heights and their optimized floor plans (McMillan, 1975). Using the parameters of unrestricted land and zoning, the results of these studies show that the least expensive building is square in plan (minimum facade), and has as few stories as possible to meet the owner's area requirements.

A typical result of this optimizing process is given in Table 4.1, in which comparisons are made between:

1. Twenty typical floors of 1000 m^2 (10 800 ft^2) in a square building.

2. Twenty typical floors of 1000 m^2 (10 800 ft^2) in a slender rectangular building.

3. Sixteen typical floors of 1250 m^2 (13 500 ft^2) with an offset core.

4. A four-story square building of 25 000 m^2 (269 000 ft^2).

The study of these four schemes of was based upon the use of the same type of facade and material standards. A comparison of the four types shows that the square low-rise building results in the optimum cost. Naturally, the land cost itself may well offset any advantage of this shape and generally preclude it from being economically viable in large urban centers.

In urban areas which use tall buildings to solve their problems, the cost of land is such that the general rule is to build the maximum building area possible according to local zoning (McArthur, 1973).

The interdependence of cost and floor area or building height is shown in a different manner in Figs. 4.2 and 4.3. It can be seen in Fig. 4.2 that, for a given

Table 4.1 Alternative buildings to provide 20 000 m² of rentable accommodation—comparison of influence of plan form and height

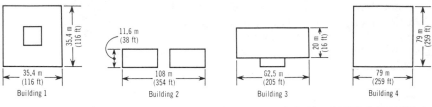

Building specification and costs (1)	Building 1 (2)	Building 2 (3)	Building 3 (4)	Building 4 (5)
Number of typical rentable floors	20	20	16	4
Rentable area per floor, in square meters[a]	1 000	1 000	1 250	5 000
Gross area per floor, in square meters[a]	1 250	1 250	1 560	6 250
Façade length, in meters[a]	141.5	239.2	185	316
Floor-to-floor height, in meters[a]	3.85	3.85	4.1	4
Façade area, in square meters[a]	12 500	19 300	9 400 +3 900 core	5 050
Plant room area, in square meters[a]	1 floor — 1 250	1 floor — 1 250	1 floor — 1 560	1 000
Roof area, in square meters[a]	1 250	1 250	1 560	6 250
Comparative costs:[b] Structural penalty	R 60 000	R 60 000	R 200 000	R 0
Façade cost @ Rand 80 per square meter	1 000 000	1 544 000	830 000	404 000
Air-conditioning penalty due to façade and roof heat load	223 000	400 000	166 000	106 500
Plant room penalty	50 000	50 000	62 000	40 000
Roof penalty	50 000	50 000	63 000	250 000
Elevator penalty	260 000	260 000	290 000	0
Total cost penalty	1 643 000	2 364 000	1 611 000	800 500
Cost penalty per square meter of rentable area	82.15	118.20	80.55	40.02

[a] 1 m = 3.28 ft; 1 m² = 10.75 ft²
[b] Costs are expressed in South African currency (R = Rand)

volume, the cost of all systems decreases with an increase in typical floor area and a corresponding reduction in height. Fig. 4.3, in which typical floor area = 700 m^2 (7500 ft^2), shows the significant cost increase as building height increases.

3 Optimal Design of Facade and Building Module

The facade design and development of the basic building module is a multi-disciplinary activity involving many subsystems. Many influences affect the design, including:

1. Need for effective enclosure of the space to keep out weather and to regulate climate and internal environment. Insulation and glazing are important factors.

2. Importance of facade treatment to architectural expression.

3. Number of windows necessary.

4. The fact that, if possible, the facade should include vertical structural elements, or vertical elements should extend beyond the building envelope area in order to provide a smooth interior face for subdividing partitioned space.

5. Inclusion of window-cleaning facilities.

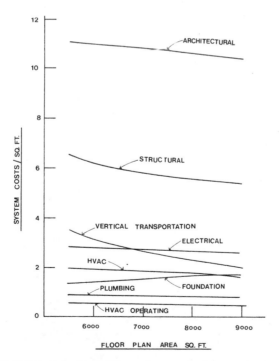

Fig. 4.2 Variation of system costs for buildings of approximately equal volume but different configuration

A computer study optimizing all of the factors listed resulted in an optimum facade of the building and its interior reflecting a module of 1.5 m (5 ft) (McMillan, 1975). Lighting strips and room sizes all fit this module well. In addition to internal partitioning, it was found that alternating solid and glazed panels of 1.5 m (5 ft) gave the most satisfactory results with respect to optimum energy consumption while maintaining the interior open feeling so important if people are not to feel trapped.

4   Examples of Present Practice

None of the basic logic of what has been discussed is new, and it must be noted that these system and subsystem analyses have been and continue to be performed by hand calculation and based upon experience. Generally speaking, the longhand or the noncomputer-assisted approaches did recognize optimum conditions, and, within general parameters, recognized and addressed themselves to the over-all solution. The following is an example of a realistic optimization exercise, presently performed by the architect, which could be improved with the benefit of computers.

The first step consists of an owner commissioning an architect for a high-rise building in an urban area. Realistically, zoning is strict, in that there is a limitation on maximum floor area allowed, with some bonuses of which the developer can take

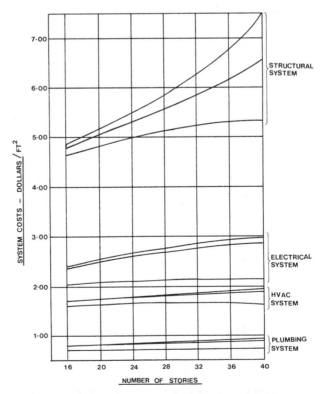

Fig. 4.3 Assumed variation of subsystem costs with height

advantage if he does not build on the entire site. The architect's first actions are to advise the owner of the maximum floor-to-area ratio he is allowed to build in this zone, and also to inform him of any bonuses he may acquire as a result of zoning. Working with the property line setback requirements and allowable floor area ratios, he then advises the owner of the maximum floor space allowed in the building and the minimum without bonuses. The owner, having previously determined his NPV (see Section 4.2 of this chapter), is then in a position to decide what is optimum for him to build in terms of total floor area and total building area.

There are occasions when this exercise results in the conclusion that there is no feasible way to make a profit. If so, the building process is terminated. It could be considered that not to build at this site might be the optimum condition for this particular developer.

If it has been found that the building is practical, the architect must then determine his optimum facade and interior layout module. This operation is carried out in an iterative process in trying to find the least common denominator that fits into optimum room sizes, facade systems available on the market, maximum net rentable space, ceiling modules available, lighting modules, and ultimately the air and heat supply systems.

As stated, the approach is iterative. The architect will balance his priorities one against the other until the module is decided upon. Fabricators of facades will have standard sizes which must be considered; studies will have been performed by the mechanical engineer comparing the cost of heating and air conditioning based upon the energy loss or gains for facades, including varying percentages of windows. Calculations should show at this time what the optimum facade treatment will be.

5　Computer Studies and Techniques for Optimizing

There exists today a thrust to use and develop computer programs that will take the guesswork out of the iterative process, and for computer-analyzed solutions (Russell and Reinschmidt, 1973). The results of such studies using the Concept Generation approach to optimization are shown in Figs. 4.2 and 4.3. Many programs have been developed that attempt to solve the optimization of systems and subsystems. The most ambitious undertaking would be to develop a program in which all the parameters previously discussed could be stated, and the computer would then make all the comparisons.

An important part of the systems optimization approach is the construction and testing of models. It is possible to manipulate a working computer model of a building, whereas it is very difficult to manipulate a working design. In model analysis, one can emphasize by analogy systematic trends in common between systems which have the same form of model. For example, recognizing that pedestrian circulation has the same behavior pattern as the flow of compressible fluids enables predictions to be made on the circulation behavior based upon fluid mechanics models and theories.

To be useful, a computer model must be capable of manipulation by the user, and must accurately reflect the response of the project to corresponding design decisions. Computer models for various aspects of building design and planning have been developed. A few examples are:

    1. PRELAN—Program for preliminary economical analysis based upon model computer analysis.

2. LIFTDES—A program that allocates lifts or elevators within a multistory building.

3. TOPAZ—A program that allocates user activities within a building.

4. BUILDER—An integrated program that includes versions of those already listed as subprograms, assesses and evaluates the interaction between subsystems, and optimizes the over-all merit at the building level.

In conclusion, it is apparent that the optimization of architectural systems, while adequately achieved with present longhand iterative methods, can probably be improved with the use of digital type models. They can be manipulated so that new relationships of use, area, and comfort may be discovered, which can further enhance the utility and economic viability of a given building.

4.4 OPTIMIZATION OF MECHANICAL SYSTEMS

The solution to the mechanical systems in tall buildings resulted more than anything else in the ability to utilize tall buildings (Baum, 1973). For centuries, residential buildings were not built over five stories. This stagnation in building heights was destined to continue until solutions could be found to the following problems:

1. The occupants of buildings would not willingly transport themselves with their own power to building levels above the fourth or fifth story.

2. Occupants would not willingly carry buckets of water from a well to an upper story, nor carry away the waste.

3. Occupants would not carry fuel for their stoves up to any great height.

4. Occupants needed to raise their level of lighting in a safe manner. Oil lamps were not a solution because of the fire danger.

The advent of the high-rise building had to await the solutions to these problems. These solutions took the form of elevators for vertical transportation; municipal water systems when they became fact and pumps were developed to lift water to desired heights; development of heating systems using either steam or hot water; and finally, development of a series of municipal sewers to carry away the waste. Other advances in high-rise structures were redundant without comparable solutions for mechanical systems. The development of air conditioning was made necessary because all rooms could not face out on the open perimeter of the building.

1 Major Mechanical Systems to Optimize

The major mechanical systems employed in a tall building fall into the following four categories: (1) Hydraulic systems; (2) electrical systems; (3) heating and air-conditioning systems; and (4) elevators. The characteristics and design of these systems are discussed extensively in Volume SC.

Hydraulic Systems. The optimization of hydraulic systems is generally based upon superimposing a series of smaller building systems one upon another to create an over-all system for the tall building.

Electrical Systems. Electrical services consist of two subsystems: (1) Power distribution; and (2) emergency generator.

Air-Conditioning Systems. Air-conditioning systems include the following four subsystems: (1) Low-pressure reheat system; (2) high-pressure double-duct system; (3) single-duct high-velocity variable volume system; and (4) high-pressure induction unit system.

Each of the subsystems listed can be optimized with present manual and computer programs. With each mechanical service, there is a limit to which the service can be designed (Baum, 1973). As an example, air-handling equipment and air-conditioning systems are limited in size to their maximum weights for erection, and their maximum size for transportation. When the requirements of a system exceed the size available, it becomes necessary to duplicate or even triplicate the service required. The interface requirements of mechanical equipment and its attendant space requirements with architectural and structural systems are those which bear the most benefits when optimized.

In a tall building an important consideration with respect to air conditioning is duct and shaft size. Duct-shaft space is a cost against the building; it represents a cost penalty and an intrusion into the net rentable space. Optimizing should balance duct-space requirements against revenue production. Baum (1973) presents an example of this optimizing technique for three separate schemes.

The air-conditioning and heating requirements are a function of the amount of heat gain or loss through the skin of the building. Analysis will determine the amount of glazing required and its effect on energy expenditure for the building envelope. Russell and Reinschmidt (1973) have examples of optimizing techniques employed to optimize elevators, unit costs of heating, ventilating, and air conditioning, and plumbing and electrical systems, as a variable with story height and building stories. Baum (1973) has many examples of optimization of cooling tower and chilling plant locations with respect to first costs, and total mechanical room requirements.

Elevators. As building heights have increased, the area taken by the service core (which includes the elevators) becomes more significant as a factor in building design. Optimization studies show that elevator questions are particularly well adapted to the concepts of computer analysis. The number of elevators, number of banks, speed of elevators, the cost for this speed, the total area of the core saved as a result of increased lift speed, all must be considered. Typical solutions to the optimization of these factors are given by Norman (1973).

Conclusion. It should be noted that this review of the state of the art with respect to optimizing the four major mechanical systems was limited. Yet it would appear that since most of the mechanical quantities are objective in nature, programs dealing with every facet of mechanical systems should abound. Much of the material published on the optimization of mechanical systems has been part of over-all computer modeling examples in which the mechanical system cost was minimized.

4.5 OPTIMIZATION OF STRUCTURAL SYSTEMS

As was previously stated in this chapter, optimization is an attempt to derive maximum effect for minimum effort, the most economical system for the most acceptable results. Optimization of structures may be achieved when minimum material is used to serve the function of the building, when minimum effort is used to construct the building, when minimum time is used to construct the building, or some combination of these three. Because nations differ with respect to geographic location, labor forces and access to material, cost once again becomes the criterion that defines optimization. Whereas labor-saving devices may be important in one location, minimum material usage may be most critical in another.

Because the structure represents 25% to 50% of the construction cost of a reinforced concrete building, part of the key to the optimization of a building is the optimization of the cost of the structure. Iyengar (1973) states that optimization procedures for structures have always been a part of structural design. In the past, however, techniques of application of such procedures have largely been based upon judgment, experience, and member optimization. As the need for larger, taller multipurpose buildings has grown, so has the need for a variety of systems to cope with the demands in economical terms.

As shown in Fig. 4.3, the structural part of the base building cost appears to increase more rapidly with height than other costs. Consequently there is an increased demand for optimized structural systems.

1   Loads on Tall Buildings

A tall concrete building must transfer gravity loads to the ground, and also resist lateral loads due to wind or seismic forces. Until recently, the tradition of building design treated tall buildings as a series of one-story buildings, one set upon the other with all members sized for gravity loads only. Then, as though an afterthought, an equivalent lateral load was superimposed. This approach resulted in a gravity supporting structure, which was quite efficient for vertical loads, now being used for horizontal forces for which it was neither analyzed nor sized.

Gravity systems consist of bending (flexural) members which span between the vertical (sometimes diagonal) elements that carry the loads from the bending members and any incidental eccentricities to the ground (see Chapter CL-1). Optimization techniques for the gravity system can be defined relatively easily since it is usually a state of stress that determines the amount of material, labor, and finally construction time required in this system.

Unlike gravity systems, isolated lateral support systems are usually designed for stiffness. The condition of stress is frequently unimportant, and the major criterion becomes one of limiting the over-all lateral deflection or drift (see Chapters CB-9 and SB-5). Lateral support systems are either frames that resist lateral forces through flexure and shear deformation, trusses that resist forces through direct compression or tension, or shear walls that resist through bending deformations. The tubular concept acts as a three-dimensional frame (see Chapter CB-3).

It can be seen from this description that a tall concrete building may be considered to be one in which the original gravity load structure has reached a height where its over-all drift due to lateral loads exceeds the allowable drift.

Various criteria are available for this drift, such as $H/500$ for wind or $H/300$ for seismic loads (see Chapters CB-9 and SB-5).

Once the drift of a gravity system is excessive and the added stresses exceed the stresses allowed for the combined loads, then an augmented system consisting of additional bracing material is required. This added material may take the form of additionally stiffening the existing frames with the introduction of added material, shear walls, or diagonal bracing. An ultimate goal of systems optimization would be the elimination of this cost premium altogether by holding lateral stresses to an amount less than the difference between the allowable stresses for gravity loads and lateral loads and that for gravity loads alone (Iyengar, 1973). In reality, a certain premium for wind is to be expected.

2   Structural Systems

In the course of performing optimization studies different structural systems are applicable for the heights shown in Table 4.2 (Khan and Iyengar, 1973).

Table 4.2 is a rough guide; the input from the architect and contractor may affect the system chosen. As an example, the fact that elevators and their attendant shafts need to be enclosed results in sufficient shear-wall material to take lateral forces in all but the highest wind or seismic zones. In this area, judgment and experience are all-important factors. The selection of structural systems is discussed extensively in Chapter CB-3 and is reviewed briefly in the following paragraphs.

Use of Type I Structures (Total Frame).   Type I or totally frame buildings are usually associated with office, apartment, and cultural use. The spans are usually between 5.5 m (18 ft) and 9 m (30 ft), with some spans higher. If a flat slab is the frame system, bents consisting of slabs and columns can be utilized to resist lateral loads provided ductility is not important. A second system that is used extensively consists of spandrel beams at the perimeter of the structure acting as the lateral frame bents. Finally, two-way pan slabs can be used, leaving the slabs solid between columns to produce moment bents.

Use of Type II Structures (Shear Wall).   Type II structures, which derive all their lateral stiffness and strength from shear walls, are feasible up to a maximum of 40 stories. Because this system does not utilize the floor to develop lateral resistance, a gravity load support system can be utilized essentially independently. The general approach is to optimize the gravity system separately from the shear-wall system.

Table 4.2 Structural systems and building heights

Type of structure (1)	Description of structure (2)	Height to which structural system is applicable (3)
I	Total frame building	up to 20 stories
II	Shear-wall building	up to 35 stories
III	Frame and shear-wall building	up to 50 stories
IV	Framed tube	up to 55 stories
V	Tube in tube	up to 65 stories
VI	Modular tube	up to 75 stories

Use of Type III Structures (Frame Shear-Wall Systems). Type III (frame and shear-wall) systems are most applicable in office buildings, where the shear wall can be provided in the service core of the building, and perimeter frames provide the frame action.

Use of Type IV Structures (Framed Tube). Framed-tube structures, if properly proportioned, can develop high efficiencies and eliminate walls around the core. Effective cantilever action can be developed if the perimeter columns can be spaced from 1.8 m (6 ft) to 3 m (10 ft) connected with a spandrel.

Use of Type V and VI Structures (Tube in Tube and Modular Tube). Type V structures are used when the framed-tube structure is insufficently stiff because of height, and the additional stiffening is achieved by combining the tube with a shear core wall. Modular tubes, Type VI, are bundled Type IV or V systems for even greater stiffness.

It should be noted that more than 90% of all tall concrete buildings fall within the 0 to 55-story range of height. Other chapters in this volume describe the various systems in much greater detail. It is our intention to review them in relation to optimization. Note that in those systems which rely on the core and perimeter frames, or both, for lateral support, the gravity system forming the mass of the interior space can be optimized separately.

3　Optimizing the Gravity System

The structural engineer, using experience and judgment, will determine the best system to fulfill the architectural, mechanical, and economic requirements. Systems of flat slabs, beams and slabs, two-way pans, or one-way joists can be evaluated based upon known economic criteria for the geographic location. The engineer's choice of proportions is limited, since codes limit the dimensions of the minimum material, and local wages set the cost of production. The possibilities of eliminating beam forms, architectural ceilings, or excessive spans are considered during the preliminary stage of this operation, as they interact with the mechanical and architectural requirements.

The final design of the initially chosen system consists of accurate analysis and final material proportioning. Three objectives of merit in optimizing the cost of gravity structures are:

1. To provide continuity wherever possible in order to reduce positive bending moments and their attendant downward deflections.

2. To utilize techniques such as prestressing which reduce the dead load and thus the material required to resist gravity.

3. To utilize the finished structure as the final architectural finish at ceilings where possible. This approach has often given optimum results with apartments and hotels.

Many papers have been written on the computer optimization of structural systems. One of the best known (McDermott et al., 1972) primarily has application to the selection of gravity load systems, but the procedure would also be applicable to braced and unbraced frames.

4   Optimizing Shear Walls

In optimizing shear-wall systems it may be assumed that they act like vertical flexural elements. As a result, a basic criterion for the development of shear-wall stiffness is to place as much material away from the center of gravity of the wall as possible. Fig. 4.4 presents a comparison of four shear walls and the effect on their stiffness as the wall material is moved from the web to the flange. It should be noted that shear effects may be critical if the wall becomes too thin. Barring shear failures, the ductility of shear walls increases as more of the reinforcement is placed in the flanges.

Frequently, in 40-story buildings or where lateral loads are high, the designer can further reduce material and increase stiffness by the coupling of shear walls. Fig. 4.5 indicates typical ways in which shear walls may be coupled. Because shear at the connecting link of coupled walls is high, the engineer must be cautious in the design of this beam (see Chapter CB-6). Comparing two shear walls in series with two walls of similar proportion which are coupled indicates that the coupled walls can be several times more stiff than the walls in series (see Chapters CB-6 and CB-9 or Popoff, 1973).

Frequently rectangular buildings are stiffened by placing the shear walls on the outside faces of the ends of the building to keep the interior clear of walls. Fig. 4.6 shows an end wall with typical window openings, which frequently are architecturally required (floor slab thicknesses successively taken as 150 mm, 175 mm, 200 mm, and 230 mm). Analysis shows that if the relative stiffness of the solid wall were taken as unity, the stiffnesses of the punched walls would be: (a) = 0.91; (b) = 0.76; (c) = 0.68; (d) = 0.58. The potential for stiffening shear walls and increasing their ductility by prestressing vertically must also be considered when developing maximum stiffness per cost.

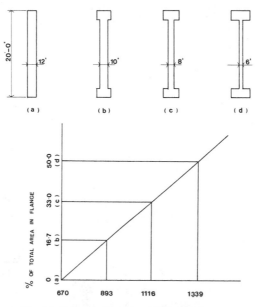

Fig. 4.4 Moment of inertia of flanged sections

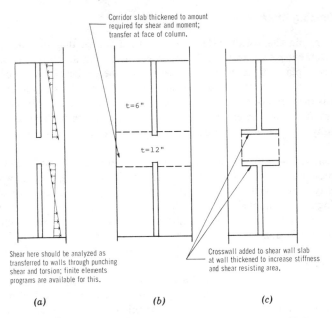

Corridor slab thickened to amount
required for shear and moment;
transfer at face of column.

t=6"

t=12"

Shear here should be analyzed as
transferred to walls through punching
shear and torsion; finite elements
programs are available for this.

Crosswall added to shear wall slab
at wall thickened to increase stiffness
and shear resisting area.

(a)   *(b)*   *(c)*

Fig. 4.5 Methods available to couple shear walls and analyze effect

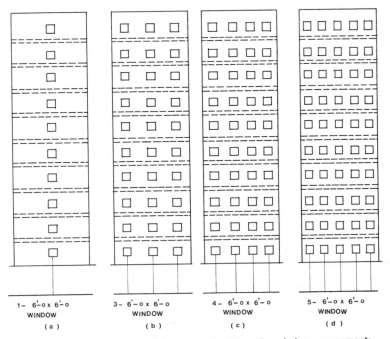

1– 6'–0 x 6'–0
WINDOW
(a)

3– 6'–0 x 6'–0
WINDOW
(b)

4– 6'–0 x 6'–0
WINDOW
(c)

5– 6'–0 x 6'–0
WINDOW
(d)

Fig. 4.6 Comparison of stiffness of end walls with varying window arrangements

5 Optimizing Type I (Frame) Structures

In the analysis of framed structures, note that if drift is the criterion for design, only the addition of material will stiffen the structure. Where to put this material to derive maximum stiffness is a question for optimizing. Fig. 4.7 shows a typical flat plate column frame. By varying the concrete thickness in 25-mm (1-in.) increments, keeping the column sizes the same, it can be seen from Table 4.3 that the stiffness of the frame increases at a greater rate than the added material.

In frames with typical column spacings and story heights the lateral stiffness is much more sensitive to the beam moment of inertia than to either the moment of inertia of the columns or their cross-sectional area, as shown in Figs. 4.8, 4.9, and 4.10 (Gero, 1973). Figs. 4.9 and 4.10 consider the frame shown in Fig. 4.8. A comparison of Figs. 4.9 and 4.10 shows that for frames with relatively stiff beams, the lateral deflections are more sensitive to variations in column area than column inertia. This is shown in the Appendix to Chapter CB-3. Iyengar (1973) has presented a procedure for selecting the optimum beam and column size at a joint to obtain the optimum frame stiffness.

Table 4.3 Frame stiffness related to increase in slab thickness

Thickness of slab, t, in millimeters (inches) (1)	Relative frame stiffness (2)	Increase in stiffness, as a percentage (3)
150 (6)	1.0	0
180 (7)	1.33	33
200 (8)	1.71	71
230 (9)	2.14	114

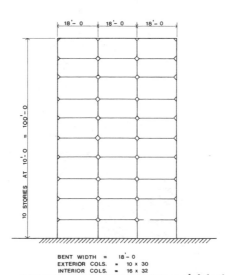

BENT   WIDTH   =   18'- 0
EXTERIOR COLS.   =   10 x 30
INTERIOR COLS.   =   16 x 32
FLOOR SLAB THICKNESSES SUCCESSIVELY TAKEN AS 6", 7", 8" & 9"

Fig. 4.7 Typical flat plate structure

6 Optimizing Type III (Frame-Shear Wall) Structures

Type III structures usually consist of perimeter spandrel beams and columns linked to shear walls which generally form the core. The link is important in that it has been found that the interaction between the frames and the walls is such that the

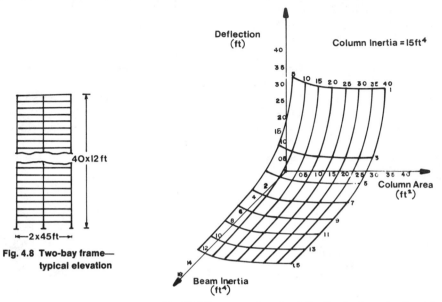

Fig. 4.8 Two-bay frame—typical elevation

Fig. 4.9 Influence surface for deflection for beam inertia and column area with constant column inertia

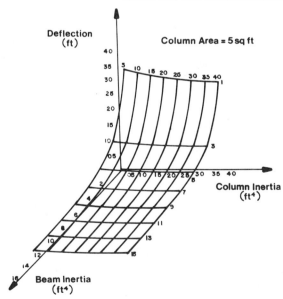

Fig. 4.10 Influence surface for deflection for beam inertia and column inertia with constant column area

frame tends to reduce lateral deflection of the shear walls at the top, while the wall supports the frame laterally at the base. A typical pattern for this deflection has a point of inflection near the top of the building (Derecho, 1973). More important, however, the deflections of the coupled structure are less than for the wall or frame. For this type of structure, member sizing for preliminary evaluation can be achieved without the aid of a computer, but when exact results are required in the final design to develop optimum results, computers are essential.

The preliminary stage can start with the perimeter columns being sized for gravity loads only, and the spandrels connecting these columns having the same stiffness. Next, determine the size of the core wall that would be required to resist one-half the lateral load on the building, keeping drift for this reduced load within the allowable limit. The third preliminary step is to compare the summation of the moments of inertia of the walls to the summation of the column moments of inertia for this same floor. If the value falls between 800 and 1200, then the structure is close to the optimum frame proportions (Khan and Iyengar, 1973). Figs. 4.12 to 4.14 show a set of influence surfaces for the shear wall-frame building shown in Fig. 4.11. In this type of building the moments of inertia of the beams and the wall have the greatest effect on building stiffness as shown in Fig. 4.14, while the areas and moments of inertia of the columns have little effect, as shown in Figs. 4.12 and 4.13 (Gero, 1973).

7   Optimizing Type IV (Framed Tube) Structures

Although framed tubes are as important as other tall building systems, for a complete discussion of their optimization the reader is referred to Khan and Amin

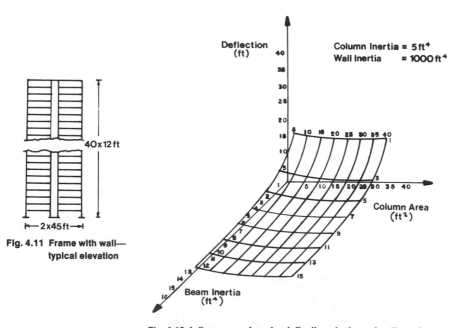

Fig. 4.11 Frame with wall—
typical elevation

Fig. 4.12 Influence surface for deflections for beam inertia and
column area

(1973). In this paper a method of preliminary design of tubular buildings is discussed, with reference to the final design techniques applicable. The influence surfaces in Figs. 4.16 and 4.17 (considering the frame shown in Fig. 4.15) show that in addition to the beam stiffness, the influence of the column areas and moments of

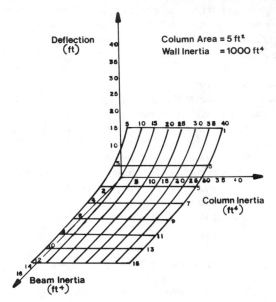

Fig. 4.13 Influence surface for deflection for beam inertia and column inertia

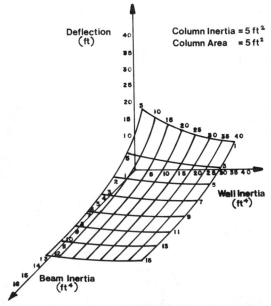

Fig. 4.14 Influence surface for deflection for beam inertia and wall inertia

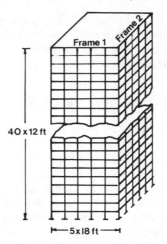

Fig. 4.15 Isometric of tube structure

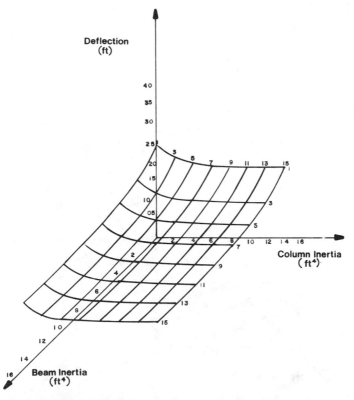

Fig. 4.16 Influence surface for deflection for beam inertia and column inertia

inertia are important in stiffening the building, unlike other systems. This is due to the shear lag effect in which the columns parallel to the axis of bending act as a "flange" for the tube. Final design of Type IV structures can be performed on a generalized computer program such as STRESS or STRUDL.

8   Optimizing Type V and VI Structures (Tube in Tube and Modular Tube)

For even taller buildings, where the framed tube may not develop the necessary stiffness, additional stiffness can be achieved by interaction with the core walls. The preliminary design approach is similar to that for Type III structures, in that the first step is to size the core for roughly 50% of the lateral loads, with perimeter columns and beams spaced and sized as in the examples shown for Type IV structures. The structural tube is then proportioned to resist the remaining loads.

Once again, the final computations require the assistance of a computer program. It is worth noting in conclusion that if closely spaced columns cannot be allowed architecturally, the tubular concept is inefficient with widely spaced columns. The designer's recourse is to utilize the frame-shear wall concept (*Engineering News Record*, 1974), stiffening the frame further and thickening the core.

Foundations as subgrade structures should also be subjected to the optimizing concept, yet little work has been done in this area. An example of least foundation cost can be achieved by viewing the foundations as structures whose imposed loads

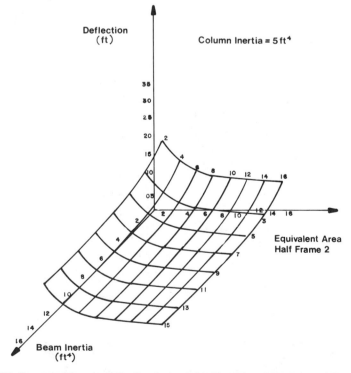

Fig. 4.17 Influence surface for deflection for beam inertia and equivalent area of Frame 2

due to lateral forces can be manipulated by manipulating the stiffnesses of the structure above. One Biscayne Tower, a 40-story building in Miami (*Engineering News Record*, 1974) is an example of the redistribution of lateral loads which made it possible to substitute a mat foundation for a more costly pile foundation.

4.6 OPTIMIZATION OF THE CONSTRUCTION PROCESS

1 Optimization of Labor and Time to Complete a Building

Various studies have shown that labor can account for as much as 50% of the total cost of construction. Labor or effort can be minimized in two ways. The first is when factory or prefabrication techniques create finished building products with fewer man hours involved; and the second follows the development of concrete construction systems in which forms are used in such a manner as to gain many reuses with little additional field labor. The scope of optimizing field procedures for minimum effort is extensive. This section will review those techniques which exist, and is not intended to overlap or supersede Chapter SC-8. The following labor-saving devices have merit.

Prefabricated Reinforcement.   Prefabricated steel mat or mesh can reduce the labor of individually placing reinforcing bars in the field. While the total cross-sectional area of reinforcing is higher with mats, the significant savings in labor frequently offset the extra cost of the material.

Prefabricated Forms.   Prefabricated concrete forms fall into two categories, those for columns and those for flat work (slabs). Prefabricated column forms are usually made of plywood, or externally braced steel, and are hinged at one side to place and strip. The concept of closely spaced columns on the perimeter of a building has also led to the concept of the ganged form. Ganged column forms consist of a battery of column forms tied together with the form for the connecting spandrel. Up to eight columns have been erected at one time.

Today, as a result of systematic design and layout by the designers of a building, columns are arranged to line up in plan in an orderly fashion. This lining up of columns has led to the development of the flying form, a prefabricated floor form that can be lifted by crane from floor to floor without dismantling. Flying forms currently have areas up to 75 m² (800 ft²). This technique of placing and stripping large floor form segments has resulted in form costs half those of hand-built forms.

Prefabricated Concrete Members.   Prefabricated concrete members were developed as a result of the traditional difference in wages and productivity between field and factory workers. Precasters generally find floor members most attractive to fabricate and erect. These members take the form of precast prestressed slabs and ribbed members with flanges for long spans, such as single T's and double T's.

Prefabricated Structures.   Because of the successful results achieved in the precast flat-member industry, an attempt has been made to develop systems buildings in which the total structure is prefabricated. Precast structural systems have taken two approaches, those consisting of columns, beams, and slabs, or load-bearing walls with slabs.

Prefabricated Composite Structures.   Because of the weight of the components of precast systems, composite systems were developed to create thin precast members which could be transported easily to the field, with cast-in-place concrete added to give continuity. These systems generally evolved into two types. The first type used thin 40-mm to 50-mm (1 ½-in. to 2-in.) slabs which were precast and often prestressed. These slabs have shear elements protruding from them. The placing of concrete in contact with the surface and the ensuing bond renders the total slab effective in carrying load. A variation on this for longer spans is to prefabricate joists or beam soffits which also act compositely when concrete is cast in place.

Prefabricated Building Systems. The ultimate goal of precast systems designers has been the ideal concrete box, which would be prefinished and erected in the field with minimum effort. Independent studies have shown that this approach can be successful if weight is minimized, and if 80% to 90% of the labor is done in the plant.

2 Optimizing Construction Time

The second area of possible optimization in construction engineering deals with the cost of time required to complete construction. Presently the interest rate in many countries is in excess of 10%.

A simple calculation shows that for a $24-million building estimated as taking 36 months to complete, the interest rate for the developer could average $4000 per day. The saving of 6 months' construction time could represent a saving of $720 000, or 3% of the total cost. If the structure represents one-third of the entire cost, then this saving amounts to 10% of the cost of the frame, a cost saving nearly impossible to achieve by the reduction of material as discussed previously. The method of construction is the only technique that can optimize the time of construction.

The reduction of material has little to do with reducing construction time. A technique that is presently employed to save time is to design a structure or building to take into account a specific method of rapid construction. Some major techniques that have been valuable in reducing construction time are: (1) Slipforming, which literally extrudes all walls and columns; and (2) lift slab construction, which allows the floor slabs for a building to be constructed on the ground and then lifted into place. The use of slipforming was responsible for constructing a 25-story building in 28 days (DeSimone and Camellerie, 1965).

Fig. 4.18 represents a simplified bar chart derived from the critical-path network of the construction of a high-rise office building. The principal critical construction activities are shown in bold lines. The principal noncritical activities are shown in light lines.

It can easily be arranged to demolish existing buildings and bulk excavate over the site concurrently with the design and documentation of the redevelopment. Although income from existing buildings ceases, this procedure is frequently the most economic when land values are high.

On the average, the completion of elevator services requires on the order of 6 months from the time the lift motor room is finished ready for the elevator contractor to begin work. It does not seem that this time requirement is much different even for very tall buildings. In the present situation completion of elevator services generally governs office building completion for a relatively constant time period, irrespective of building height. This implies that the construction of the structure is a critical path activity for a greater proportion of the total construction period as the building height increases.

For apartment buildings, completion of finishes generally governs building completion. Early completion of finishing trades is principally a builder's organizational task, a task growing in magnitude as the range of standard details grows. Even for apartment buildings the structure must rise rapidly in the early stages in order to provide a sufficient number of floors to the finishing trades for their efficient progress.

Fig. 4.18 shows that the construction of the structure is a critical path activity for the greater part of the total construction time. The speed at which the structure is built will, therefore, most affect the amount to which interest charges upon the development accumulate. For tall office buildings the portion of building time over which construction of the structure is the critical path activity is dominant.

From these facts it may be concluded that structural consultants of tall buildings will minimize the total cost of these buildings if the design and detailing of the structural components lead to minimum construction time. Least cost structures will rarely optimize construction time, and therefore will rarely lead to minimum total cost building developments.

3 Design for Construction Speed

At one time the primary concerns of structural engineers were safety and performance, and sometimes they tried to design structures to minimize building complications and have fast construction times. The design approach was intuitive. Now, however, the economic importance of fast construction of tall buildings is

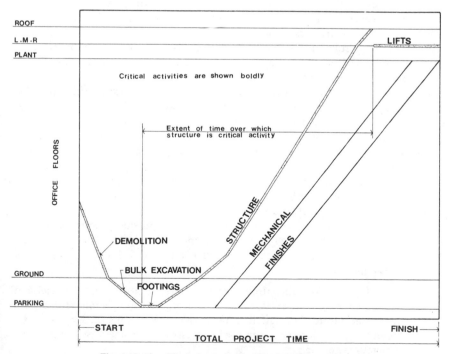

Fig. 4.18 Simplified chart of tall office building construction

such that a design strategy must be evolved and followed. The essential elements of a strategy to design for construction speed are listed in the following paragraphs.

Recognition. It is essential in the case of tall buildings to understand the needs, the total economics, and the interrelationships before a method of design attack can be formulated. Before beginning the design of a tall building, it is useful to clarify items on the following check list:

1. The aims and needs of the project.

2. The restraints imposed by statutory authorities.

3. The restraints of the particular site location.

4. The broad distribution of costs on the total development expenditure chart.

5. The work load and consequently time needs of the major building process activities.

6. The apparent sequential major building activities.

Once these items are clarified a picture of the particular peculiarities of the project should emerge, permitting valid principles of design approach to be formulated (see also Chapter PC-14).

Cooperation. If time performance is to be improved it is essential that cooperation of the client and the members of the design team is obtained right from the outset. The aims must be clearly understood, and the formulation of a design strategy must have the participation of and input from all members of the team.

In the process of clarifying the aims and needs of the project it will progressively emerge what specialist skills must be added to the team. In the formulation of a design strategy it will also emerge which of the design team members should take an active leadership role in the pursuit of methods leading to improvement of construction time performance. For tall buildings the role should most naturally fall to the consulting structural engineer.

Attack. Construction time can be shortened by only two means. Either the time allocation for some of the critical construction path activities is shortened, or arrangements are made to permit a critical activity to commence at an earlier date. The effect of the latter is to remove the particular activity from the critical path.

It is sometimes possible to shorten some critical path activities by assigning a larger labor team and working longer hours than the construction industry is accustomed to provide. This approach is becoming less successful because of: (1) Increasing reluctance of the various authorities to permit extension of working hours; and (2) the incitement to labor unrest which it causes.

The best way to shorten construction time is to pursue a design approach permitting those activities which take longest and normally fall upon the critical construction path to be commenced at an earlier date. The following examples will illustrate this approach.

1. The early letting of subcontracts for the fabrication of structural steel and precast concrete components, often well before a building contract is let, will remove the fabrication activities from the critical construction path. Although this procedure has been used successfully in some areas, contractual problems may ensue.

2. Requirement of small-sized columns in tall buildings, consistent with the use of most economical materials, has often led to structural designs calling for exceedingly heavily reinforced concrete columns in the lower stories. To fit the reinforcement within the small-sized columns, bundled bars which are butt-spliced using special purpose sleeves are often needed. The design of column reinforcement cages to the maximum bar length procurable, resting upon the footing reinforcement mat as distinct from the normal practice of using column starter bars, permits prefabrication of the cages and saves many hours of labor at points of time when its expenditure is a critical path activity.

3. The early completion of structure for plant rooms and elevator motor rooms permits early commencement of trades that are of long duration. It is almost always possible to design the structure in such a way that progress in the vital areas is advanced at the expense of retarding progress in the noncritical areas. A cost premium on the structural components may be involved. If this is the case, the cost-benefit study must show beyond reasonable doubt that the potential for total development cost savings substantially outweigh the structural cost penalty before the approach is adopted.

Analysis and Review. Effective tools are required to assess the effectiveness of the proposed method of attack upon construction time. Construction network programming must be understood and used from the very inception of design activity. The initial brief networks used for comparison purposes must be progressively expanded as the details of design approach are developed. Cost planning of the project must also be instituted at the inception of design.

With the aid of these two methods of control a number of design approach proposals may be analyzed and compared, selecting one leading to least total expenditure for further development.

As the design is developed a process of review must be instituted to assure that the design restraints are met.

Detail. It is important to pay a great deal of attention to detail. If a short construction period is to be achieved, it is necessary to assure that site construction activities are simple. Complications lead to mistakes. Mistakes require time to correct. They also dislodge the set program of activity, placing considerable additional burdens upon the construction management team.

Communication. Success demands good communication between the client, members of the design team, and the builder. Effective means of transmitting concepts to the builder's management team must be evolved. When an expedited construction program is instituted it is necessary to transmit the principles of expedition to the builder effectively. The proposed construction network and bar chart must be prepared for the builder. These should be augmented by a short description of the steps in the construction program upon which the principles of design for construction speed are based.

It is necessary to obtain the participation, input, and confidence of the builder's management team. To do so the engineer must be willing and available to discuss the proposed construction principles, material handling methods, and construction details with the builder. The suggestions of the builder must not be discarded, but analyzed and the effects upon the construction program jointly assessed. The builder should ultimately decide upon and be confident that the construction methods finally chosen suit the abilities of his team and his construction equipment. Only then is success possible.

Follow-Up. The construction of buildings is a complicated matter, subject to innumerable delays even at the best of times. With growing industrial unrest the burden on construction management is mounting continuously.

Mistakes occur. Material supplies are interrupted. Labor shortages are experienced. In these circumstances some dislodgement of the construction program of a tall building is certain to occur. It is necessary to update the construction network and minimize the effects of the interruptions. The follow-up of the design for construction speed must extend throughout the construction period to completion.

4.7 TECHNIQUES FOR OPTIMIZATION

The earlier sections of this chapter have reviewed many of the factors that influence the choice of an optimum structure. Based on these, a number of intuitive procedures have been presented to carry out this choice of structure. In this section two additional optimization techniques are presented, the first approximate and the second based on mathematical optimizing.

1 Building Cost Diagrams

The diagram presented in Fig. 4.19 represents one of several types of Building Cost Diagrams. The one shown is preferred to others only because it is concise, easy to evaluate visually, and similar in its layout to other types of diagrams with which the designer might be familiar, such as a prevailing wind diagram.

The diagram presented in Fig. 4.19 consists of a series of concentric circles which represent in some scale, starting from their common center, the increasing cost of different building items ascribed to various radial lines. The connecting points on these lines represent costs of corresponding building elements pertaining to a given variant of the examined project. The total cost is then shown in some scale by the area of the diagram, and is numerically evaluated by the sum of cost items written down in the summation ring for corresponding solution variants. By examining various solutions one will see immediately how a modification of one building component influences the cost of others.

As an example, a glass-clad building will require a smaller volume of spandrel beam than a building with exterior brick walls. However, the first cost and operational cost of the necessary air-conditioning installation should be much higher in the first case than in the second. On the other hand, if the building during its life can produce much higher rental income as a result of the distinction of the glass wall, an optimal solution may still result from the first combination.

It can be shown then that by assuming various solution variants and estimating the corresponding costs of all their elements, and by visualizing the numerical results in the cost diagram, one arrives at such a trial and error solution to the optimum. Since the cost diagram represents only a summation of costs, a requirement for its proper use is to have a table of all components available for combination on a given project, and secondly, computation sheets on which the corresponding estimates are performed. The following systems and subsystems are a partial and simplified listing of items to be considered in such cost estimates in tall concrete buildings.

1. Cost of land.

2. Cost of foundations. Spread footings. Piling: steel piles, reinforced concrete piles, prestressed concrete piles, timber piles, reinforced concrete mat, post-tensioned concrete mat.

3. Cost of superstructure. Core shear walls: reinforced, post-tensioned. Frames: reinforced, post-tensioned, precast and prestressed. Simple columns: precast, reinforced, prestressed, post-tensioned. Precast beams: prestressed, reinforced. Continuous beams: precast, reinforced, prestressed,

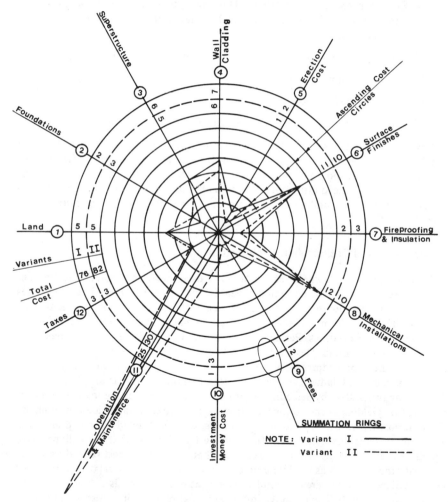

Fig. 4.19 Building cost diagram

post-tensioned. One-way slabs and Two-way slabs: reinforced, precast, post-tensioned. Flat slab: reinforced, post-tensioned. Waffle slab: reinforced, post-tensioned. Bearing walls: poured in place, reinforced or post-tensioned, precast, reinforced or post-tensioned.

4. Cost of cladding elements. Glass walls: prefabricated metal/plastic. Brick walls: prefabricated or built on site. Precast concrete walls: reinforced plant or site constructed, or prestressed.

5. Erection cost. Cost of formwork, ganged forms, flying forms, pumped concrete, bucket-placed concrete, hand-placed concrete, slipforms, lift slab.

6. Cost of surface finishes. Floors, walls, exteriors, toilets, special rooms.

7. Cost of fireproofing and heat insulation.

8. Cost of mechanical installations. Heating systems, air-conditioning systems, steam, water. Elevators. Electrical installation. Telephone. Television. Intercoms. Sanitary.

9. Cost of fees. Architectural, engineering, municipal, insurance, etc.

10. Cost of investment money.

11. Taxes for the life of the building.

12. Cost of operation and maintenance during the building's life.

In conclusion, by taking all parameters into account and with the use of the Building Cost Diagram, one can arrive at a subjective optimal solution, after a series of trial estimates. It should be pointed out that such trial estimates are not difficult to make. An experienced estimator should be able to complete the job in about two weeks, because the number of variants is limited when local conditions are considered.

2 Mathematical Optimization Techniques

Since the mid-1960s, some investigators have used linear programming techniques to optimize the design of continuous beams and simple frames. These analyses generally involve minimizing the reinforcement volume or some similar cost function. The basic formulation can be based on elastic analysis or on variations of inelastic design procedures. Perhaps the most promising of the latter are based on Cohn's Optimum Limit Design method (Cohn, 1965, 1972), Grierson's modifications of these procedures (Cohn and Grierson, 1968; Ishikawa and Grierson, 1972; Grierson and Gladwell, 1971), or similar methods (Munro et al., 1972).

These analyses start by selecting as unknowns the ratios of the load or moment causing first yielding at each critical section to the desired ultimate load or moment. These ratios, the so-called yield safety indices, are constrained so that hinges will not form at loads less than a specified service load, and so that the collapse load equals or exceeds the desired limit load (see Chapter CB-6). A cost related function, or merit function, such as total volume of reinforcement, can be related to the yield safety indices since the area of reinforcement at each section is a function of the yield moment eventually chosen. Using linear programming, it is possible to choose a set of yield safety indices to minimize the volume of reinforcement in the structure.

Any algebraical optimization process consists in finding the maximum or minimum, that is, the optimum value of the merit function, coefficients of which are tied together by a system of simultaneous equations containing equality and inequality of expressions. Theoretically, if one takes as the merit function the summation of costs of all elements contributing to the cost of the building, and then writes a system of equations that will describe these partial costs in function of all requirements imposed on that building (including loading, deflection, geometry, building code, structural, mechanical, electrical, architectural, legal, environmental, and fiscal criteria), then by solving the resulting system of scores of simultaneous equations and by determining algebraically the minimum value of the merit function, one should find the optimum costwise combination of all components considered. Unfortunately, not only are there few computers capable of solving such huge systems of equations, but we do not yet know how to write them. The procedures described in this section are a step toward this goal, however.

4.8 CONCLUSION

In the previous sections we have seen that the optimized solution of each system is vital as a first step toward optimizing the total building. Sections 4.2 through 4.6 refer to certain approaches based on experience or computer programs, which can be used to include other major systems in the optimization process. Close scrutiny of the reference material and the given examples reveals that while the programming and technique are explained, the simulated optimizing models are general and result in narrowly defined results.

It was stated earlier herein that an optimum building solution does not exist in itself but is the function of economic, legal, and labor-market conditions of the country where a given project is located, and depends as well on the technical capabilities of its builder. Therefore, what one may call optimum in one place will not be optimum in another.

For example, if in a particular country the building code requirements for flat slabs are based upon mathematical results of a theoretical analysis, and tend to penalize the design of concrete flat slabs, the optimum solution of a floor slab could hardly be of the flat-slab type. On the other hand, if the building code rules are based on test results and tend to favor the flat-slab floor, as is the case in the United States, the flat slab may well be the optimum solution.

Similarly, if the contractor has access to heavy cranes, slipforming equipment, or concrete pumps, the relative merits of precast elements, slipformed walls, or prefabricated large forms can be examined in the search for an optimum solution. If, however, the construction site is far away from a precast plant, or has a limited availability of crane equipment, any discussion of the optimal advantages of prefabrication is purely academic.

In a country where labor is cheap but reinforcing steel and cement are expensive, there is no point in advocating criteria for optimization which were developed in societies where materials are readily available, but labor is expensive.

In summation, at present (1978) tall concrete buildings can be optimized for their major systems, and the potential exists for simplified total building optimization. However, purely mathematical algorithms and their application must await further development.

4.9 CONDENSED REFERENCES/BIBLIOGRAPHY

The following is a condensed bibliography for this chapter. Not only does it include all articles referred to or cited in the text, but it also contains bibliography for further reading. The full citations will be found at the end of the Volume. What is given here should be sufficient information to lead the reader to the correct article: the author, date, and title. In case of multiple authors, only the first named is listed.

ACI Committee 318 1971, *Building Code Requirements for Reinforced Concrete*
ACI 1974, *American Concrete Institute Building Code Requirements*
Avram 1975, *A Mathematical Model to Choose the Optimum Construction Solution*
Baum 1973, *Mutual Influences Between Building Concept and Mechanical Systems in Tall*
Bruinette 1975, *Optimizing Slabs, Beams, Column Slab Strips, Comparative Slab Panels*

Cohn 1965, *Optimum Limit Design for Reinforced-Concrete Continuous Beams*
Cohn 1968, *Optimal Design of Reinforced Concrete Beams and Frames*
Cohn 1972, *Optimal Limit Design for Concrete Structures*
Cohn 1974, *Optimal Design of Reinforced Concrete Structures*
Derecho 1973, *Frames and Frame-Shearwall Systems*

DeSimone 1965, *Novel Structural Frame Combined With Slip Form*
Engineering News-Record 1974, *One Biscayne Tower, Miami's Tallest*
Forwood 1975, *A Systems Approach to the Design of Tall Buildings*
Gero 1973, *The Behavior of Building Structures Under Lateral Loads*
Grierson 1971, *Collapse Load Analysis Using Linear Programming*

Ishikawa 1972, *Iterative Optimal Limit Design of Reinforced Concrete Frames*
Iyengar 1973, *Preliminary Design and Optimization of Steel Building Systems*
Jorgensen 1972, *Investment Behavior in U.S. Manufacturing*
Jumikis 1973, *The Role of Structural Consultants in the Design of Tall Buildings*
Khan 1973a, *Analysis and Design of Framed Tube Structures for Tall Concrete Buildings*

Khan 1973, *Optimization Approach for Concrete High-Rise Structures*
Linzey 1973, *A Systems Approach to Building Planning and Design*
McArthur 1973, *Architecture of Tall Buildings*
McDermott 1972, *Computer Program for Selecting Structural Systems*
McMillan 1975, *Optimum Design of High-Rise Buildings—A Multi-Disciplinary Engineering*

Munro 1972, *Optimal Design of Reinforced Concrete Frames*
Newmark 1971, *Fundamentals of Earthquake Engineering*
Norman 1973, *Service Systems*
Popoff 1973, *What Do We Need to Know About Behavior of Structural Concrete Shear Wall*
Russell 1973, *A Coordinated Building Design System*

Swanson 1975, *The Economics of High Rise Office Buildings*
Thakkar 1973, *Possible Optimization of Structural Layout in Design of Tall Buildings*

Structural Design of
Tall Concrete and Masonry Buildings

Chapter CB-5

Elastic Analysis

Prepared by Committee 21C (Elastic Analysis) of the Council on Tall Buildings and Urban Habitat as part of the Monograph on the Planning and Design of Tall Buildings

Joseph P. Colaco   Committee Chairman
Alex Coull   Vice-Chairman
Bryan Stafford-Smith   Editor

AUTHOR ACKNOWLEDGMENT

Special acknowledgment is due Bryan Stafford-Smith and Alex Coull whose state-of-art reports from the 1972 International Conference, held at Lehigh University, formed the substantial first draft of this chapter.

CONTRIBUTORS

The following is a complete list of those who have submitted written material for possible use in the chapter, whether or not that material was used in the final version. The Committee Chairman and Editor were given quite complete latitude. Frequently length limitations precluded the inclusion of much valuable material. The Bibliography contains all contributions. The contributors are: D. M. Anastasescu, C. Avram, J. P. Colaco, A. Coull, A. Danay, N. Deschapelles, R. S. Fling, M. Gellert, J. Glück, B. Goschy, I. Kalev, G. Karrholm, M. Krauss, T. Y. Lin, I. A. MacLeod, E. Mancini, I. Martin, O. Mirsu, H. Petersson, W. Savassi, B. Stafford-Smith, B. Thurlimann.

COMMITTEE MEMBERS

D. M. Anastasescu, J. P. Colaco, A. Coull, H. K. Cheng, A. Danay, B. Deschapelles, M. Gellert, P. Gergely, K. H. Gerstle, J. Glück, B. Goschy, E. Grasser, J. Harvancik, A. C. Heidebrecht, G. Karrholm, S. Lichardus, I. A. MacLeod, E. Mancini, R. Rosman, W. Savassi, J. Schwaighofer, B. Stafford-Smith, M. Tomii.

CB-5

Elastic Analysis

5.1 INTRODUCTION

The tall concrete building structure differs from its steel counterpart mainly in the probability of its including diaphragm elements such as walls or cores. The high horizontal in-plane stiffness of these elements causes them to be an important and often dominant factor in the behavior of the structure. Apart from their inherently high in-plane stiffness, diaphragm elements often differ from frame members in requiring a separate analysis of the stresses within the element; further, when such elements are connected together or to a frame, horizontal interactive stiffnesses can be developed to a far higher degree than usually occur in conventional frame structures. Consequently a range of analytical techniques is necessary for tall concrete structures additional to those normally needed for frame analysis. The determination of the loads in the elements of tall concrete building structures is at present almost invariably carried out by elastic methods of analysis, regardless of their eventual method of design. Although ultimate load methods of analysis may eventually become available, their development for tall concrete building structures is, as yet, in its infancy.

It is proposed to discuss initially the assumptions commonly adopted for tall building structural analysis. Tall building structures are then classified into some simple categories and it is explained how, for certain categories, their analysis may be simplified and reduced. The next section considers the two-dimensional analysis of plane frames, walls, and various planar combinations of walls and frames. Structures requiring a three-dimensional analysis are then considered; these include some of the recent structural forms that have been developed for extremely tall buildings. The influence of the foundations and the use of elastic models for analysis are also discussed. The chapter concludes with a list of references which have been selected primarily for their practical utility, but also for their accessibility, and occasionally for their "historical" significance. Inevitably, with the vast international effort that has recently taken place and is continuing in this field, the reporters' knowledge of references must be incomplete. They therefore ask the understanding of those researchers whose work might unjustly have not been mentioned.

Many of the methods are relatively new and have been published only in research papers. The majority of the methods require electronic computation, and some need special programming also. A prerequisite for the appreciation and application of the techniques is an understanding of matrix methods of structural analysis, and especially of the stiffness approach. Two other comprehensive sources of information on the analysis of tall concrete buildings are recommended as associated reading (Coull and Stafford-Smith, 1967; ACI Committee 442, 1971).

This chapter explains the methods of elastic analysis which are appropriate to, or have been especially developed for, the horizontal resistance of high-rise concrete building structures. Outlines of the theoretical approaches and their limitations are given.

The basic assumptions which are often adopted for the methods of analysis and the idealizations for certain categories of tall building structures are covered first.

Methods of analysis for separate frames and walls are followed by consideration of their various two-dimensional combinations, such as connected walls and walls with frames.

General methods of analysis for three-dimensional combinations of walls, cores, and frames are also described, together with particular methods for specific structural forms such as framed-tube and hull-core structures.

5.2 ASSUMPTIONS FOR ANALYSIS

The analysis of tall building structures subjected to lateral forces is possible only on the basis of making simplifying assumptions. The most usual of these are that:

1. Concrete behaves linearly elastically and therefore the structure is amenable to a linear method of analysis involving superposition of actions and displacements. This assumption is probably reasonable for reinforced concrete under short-term horizontal loads due to wind, since the structure is subjected to a compressive prestress due to its own weight, and is especially valid for prestressed concrete within the working load range. Generally, seismic analyses assume elastic action also. In making this assumption, however, designers implicitly take account of the ductility of the structure that permits a reduction in the equivalent lateral loads.

2. The cladding and other nonstructural components do not influence the behavior of the building. This assumption can be grossly untrue; however, since it is extremely difficult to quantify, and its effect is generally conservative, the assumption is usually adopted.

3. Due to the in-plane rigidity of the floor slab, the vertical elements at any floor level undergo the same components of translational displacement and rotation in the horizontal plane. This is reasonable for structures of normal length to width proportions; however, the assumption should be used only with discretion for long narrow structures where in-plane bending of the floor slabs may have to be considered (Goldberg, 1967). The assumption may be unreasonable also in cases where architectural considerations

require the building cross section to be locally reduced in width. The localized loss of in-plane stiffness due to the reduction in slab width may require special consideration.

4. Following from Assumption 3, certain types of structure can be considered by the two-dimensional analysis of typical or equivalent bents.

5. For cast-in-place concrete structures, joints between members are assumed to be rigid. In precast structures, or, for example, where slabs are connected to preformed cores, this assumption may be inappropriate.

6. The cross-sectional area and stiffness can be based on the gross concrete section. This assumption is adequate at service loads, but will lead to an underestimate of deflections at the onset of yielding. Section 8.7 of Chapter CB-8 recommends stiffness for use at this stage.

7. The shear deformation of slender flexural members (for example, columns and shear walls whose ratio of story-height to width is greater than about 3) and the torsional stiffnesses of slender beams, columns, and plane walls, are insignificant.

8. The out-of-plane action of slabs and the out-of-plane action of walls or frame bents can usually be disregarded.

9. The axial deformation of the vertical elements may often be disregarded. However, the influence of these deformations increases with the vertical slenderness of the building and with the bending stiffness of any beams or slabs which connect rigidly between the vertical elements.

10. A concrete structure is elastically stable. The possibility of instability due to the interaction of horizontal deflections with vertical loading, the so-called $P\text{-}\Delta$ effect, has been the subject of considerable research in recent years and is referred to in more detail in Chapter CB-8.

These are typical assumptions used to simplify the structural analysis of tall buildings. However, the set of assumptions adopted in any particular case must be decided on the basis of the design concept, the structural form, and the structural proportions of the building.

5.3 CLASSIFICATION OF PROBLEMS

An important first step in the analysis of a tall building is the selection of an appropriate idealized structure to include all the significant working elements and their dominant modes of behavior. Although it is possible to formulate the full three-dimensional analysis of almost any tall building structure, the size of the problem is often larger than can be handled by available computers. It is often necessary therefore to reduce the size of the problem and, for this purpose, it is useful to assess in which of the following categories the structure lies:

1. Symmetrical over-all plan with parallel and identical assemblies of walls, columns, etc. [as in Fig. 5.1(a)] subjected to a symmetrical load system. Since all plane assemblies will deflect identically, the analysis of one only is sufficient.

2. Symmetrical over-all plan including nonidentical plane assemblies [as in Fig. 5.1(b)] subjected to symmetrical loading. This form of structure can also be analyzed as a plane system by assembling the frames in "series" with axially rigid pinned-end links connecting them at each floor. The links simulate the effect of the floor slabs in constraining the assemblies to deform identically, and thus cause the same redistribution of load. If any assemblies are oblique to the axis of symmetry, only the appropriate components of stiffness must be used. The analysis can be performed using one of the techniques described later.

3. Symmetrical plan as in Category 1 or 2 [Fig. 5.1(b)] subjected to eccentric loading. The load can be replaced by a concentric transverse load and a torsional couple whose effects can be analyzed separately and superposed. The effect of the concentric transverse load can be analyzed as described in Category 1 or 2. The torsional couple can be considered as an equivalent pair of concentrated forces at each floor level applied to a convenient pair of symmetrically located frames. The remaining frames can be assembled in the same planes, and a plane analysis conducted as in Category 2, provided that appropriate transformations are made on the frame stiffnesses and resulting displacements (Coull and Stafford-Smith, 1973).

4. Nonsymmetrical plan, as in Fig. 5.1(c). In this case, the structure will undergo both bending and torsional displacements, and a three-dimensional analysis is required in order to determine the load distribution between the various elements.

The general classification of tall building structures corresponding to their arrangement in this chapter is summarized in Fig. 5.2.

5.4 TWO-DIMENSIONAL PROBLEMS

Plane structural systems amenable to a two-dimensional analysis are considered in this section. The basic elements are examined first, and then their combination into coupled assemblies of walls and frames.

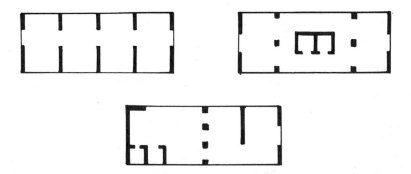

Fig. 5.1 Plans: (a) Symmetrical repetitive structure; (b) symmetrical nonrepetitive structure; (c) asymmetrical structure

1 Structural Elements

Framed Structures. The matrix form of the stiffness and flexibility methods of analysis allows a concise and systematic approach to the solution of rigidly-jointed frames by digital computation. The methods, now well established and documented (Gere and Weaver, 1965; Rubenstein, 1966), provide the basis for the analysis of frames and, as discussed later, other structural systems. Standard programs are now available commercially which demand little more of the engineer than the specification of the structural geometry, stiffness, and loading (STRUDL II, User's Manual, 1971).

Various approximate methods are available for hand calculation; these are described in Chapter SB-2.

Plane Wall. The simplest form of bracing is the plane cantilevered shear wall. If the wall has a height to width ratio greater than about 5, ordinary beam theory gives an acceptable estimate of the stresses and deflections due to horizontal loads. However, if the ratio is lower, or if large variations in width occur, or if the wall contains openings for windows, corridors, or doorways, the assumption for beams that plane sections remain plane is no longer valid; a more sophisticated approach is then required for accurate assessments of the stresses and deflections, particularly near structural discontinuities. The following two techniques are the most powerful for the solution of practical problems.

Grid or lattice analogy. The continuous plane structure is replaced by an equivalent framework, Fig. 5.3(a), which is solved by standard matrix procedures using any of the widely available computer framework programs. The distributions

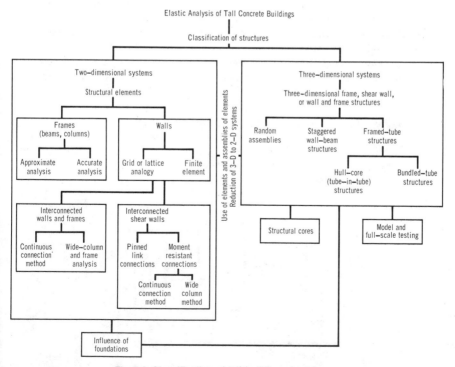

Fig. 5.2 Classification of tall building structures

of direct and shear stresses in the wall are then deduced from the corresponding axial and shear forces in the framework. Different analogous systems have been proposed, using either rigidly jointed or pin-jointed frameworks (McCormick, 1963). Several methods have been applied successfully to the analysis of shear walls. This earlier method has now been almost entirely displaced by the finite-element method.

Finite-element method. The continuous plane structure is replaced by an equivalent structure consisting of plane connected elements, Fig. 5.3(b). The elements can be of any shape, although rectangular or triangular elements are the most convenient for shear walls. Simplified assumptions are made for the mode of deformation or stress distribution in each element, from which the stiffness matrix corresponding to the nodes is established. Then, combining these element stiffnesses to form a total stiffness matrix for the wall, a solution for the nodal displacements and forces is achieved by a procedure similar to that for a frame analysis. The stresses and displacements within the elements follow. The method is now well established and documented (Zienkiewicz, 1971). Simple rectangular elements have been found to give satisfactory results for many plane wall problems, provided the subdivisions are not coarse (MacLeod, 1967).

Of the two methods, the finite-element technique gives more accurate results for the same computational effort. The use of triangular, or a mixture of triangular and rectangular elements, allows greater flexibility in considering irregularly shaped walls and, by reducing the size of the elements locally, a more detailed investigation of critical regions can be made. The grid and lattice analogies have been found useful, however, for analyses in situations where a frame program was available but not a finite-element program. In the design office, the use of either of these techniques for analyzing a shear wall is rarely justified because of the time and expense involved. However, they are particularly valuable for the detailed analysis of localized stresses and displacements in complex situations; for example, in the neighborhood of structural discontinuities, where considerable stress redistributions occur. For the over-all analysis of shear-wall structures, the techniques described in succeeding articles are more economic and usually accurate enough for practical purposes.

2   Shear Walls Connected by Beams or Floor Slabs

The stability of a shear-wall structure is often provided by several walls connected together by beams or floor slabs.

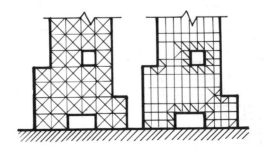

Fig. 5.3 (a) Lattice or grid analogy; (b) finite-element analogy

If the bending stiffness of the connecting members or their wall connections is low and they behave effectively as pinned-end links, as in Fig. 5.4(a), the total wind moment at any level will be shared between the walls in proportion to their flexural rigidities, provided that they bear a constant ratio to each other throughout their height. If the walls are geometrically dissimilar, as in Fig. 5.4(b), such an assumption, although used often in practice, might lead to gross errors, and it is necessary to perform a more accurate analysis. If a computer is available with a standard framework program, the analysis can be performed by specifying the walls as cantilevered columns and the connections as pinned-end links with arbitrarily high sectional areas. A simple method of solving the problem on a small computer (Khan, 1967) first considers the entire horizontal load applied to the stiffest wall, with the others constrained to follow the resulting deflected shape. The corresponding shear forces in the other walls, necessary to produce this mode of deformation, are computed and applied in reverse to the stiffest wall, thus producing a second approximation to the deflected shape. An iterative procedure follows, in which further trial deflections are derived until equilibrium is achieved. A practical manual method of solution (Glück, 1969) consists of two parts: in the first (basic solution), the load distribution is determined on the assumption of a common deflection line, continuous throughout the height of the structure; in the second, a correction (complementary solution) is applied, taking into account that the deflections are equalized only at floor levels.

The problem is complicated if, as more usually, in-plane walls are joined by moment-resistant connecting members. When the walls deflect, shears and moments are induced in the connecting beams or slabs, which consequently induce axial forces in the walls, Fig. 5.5(a). The resulting structure is much stiffer and more efficient than the pin-connected system. The effect of the finite width of a wall subjected to horizontal forces is to impose a significant vertical displacement as well as a rotation on the end of each connecting beam; this causes a much greater effective stiffness of the connecting member than in a column-supported structure. Planning requirements for multistory apartment blocks frequently evolve parallel sets of perforated shear walls, with a regular series of openings allowing corridor access along the building or window openings on the end walls. Many papers have dealt with the analysis of such structures, based on an idealization of the system as a frame using two distinct approaches to solution (Beck, 1959, 1962; Rosman, 1960, 1964; Albiges and Goulet, 1960; Nauman and Walter, 1961; Arcan, 1964).

The first approach (Beck, 1959; Arcan, 1964) which is most appropriate to

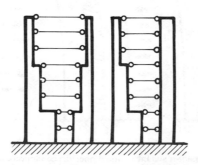

Fig. 5.4 Walls with pin-ended links: (a) Similar walls; (b) dissimilar walls

systems where the walls are of uniform section throughout the height and are connected by regularly spaced uniform beams [although a limited number of discontinuities can be incorporated (Coull, 1974a; Rosman, 1967)] uses an analogous structure in which the discrete system of connecting beams is replaced by an equivalent continuous medium of the same stiffness, Fig. 5.5(b). By assuming a fixed point of contraflexure in the connecting system, conditions of compatibility and equilibrium yield a governing differential equation of the second order, so that a closed mathematical solution to the problem is achieved. The simplicity of the technique has made possible the production of simple design curves (Coull and Choudhury, 1967; Coull and Chantaksinopas, 1974) and tables (Rosman, 1966), which enable a rapid and accurate analysis of the structure for standard load cases and different base conditions, such as elastic foundations and column or portal frame supports. By using computer techniques to solve numerically the governing differential equations, the range of applicability can be extended to multibay systems and nonuniform walls, using the transfer matrix (Tso and Chan, 1973) techniques.

The second approach adopts an equivalent "wide-column" frame structure, in which the walls and beams are represented by line members of corresponding stiffness along their centroidal axes, the influence of the finite width of the wall being incorporated by stiff arms connecting the ends of the beams to the centroidal axes of the walls (MacLeod, 1967), as in Fig. 5.5(c). By formulating the stiffness matrix for displacements of the column nodes of the wide-column frame, a solution may be derived using standard matrix procedures. Alternatively, and more conveniently for those with in-house computers, a subroutine can be written to modify a standard framework program, thereby achieving the same result (Kratky and Puri, 1971). A further alternative method (Schwaighofer and Microys, 1969) is to use a framework analysis program that incorporates a variable member stiffness subroutine. If high stiffness values, within recommended limits, are assigned to simulate the "rigid" ends at the wide-column beam, an accurate analysis is possible. A special general rigid-ended element that can be added to existing frame programs to cater for shear-wall problems has been developed (MacLeod, 1973). This may be used also to take account of the effect of column supports to the wall and a transfer girder at first-floor level (MacLeod and Green, 1973). If the structure is symmetrical, the wide-column beam may be replaced by an analogous uniform element of the

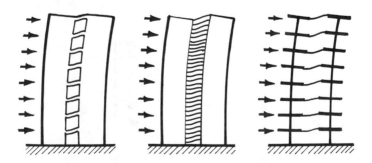

Fig. 5.5 (a) Walls with moment-resistant connections; (b) continuous medium analogy; (c) wide-column frame analogy

same rotational end-stiffness, allowing it to be treated by a standard program without the need for a variable member stiffness subroutine (Stafford-Smith, 1970). If the connecting beams are relatively deep compared to the widths of the walls, it may be necessary to incorporate a rigid column element to simulate the beam end rotations. A general comparison between discrete and continuum methods is given in Section 5.5. The physical behavior of reinforced concrete coupled walls is discussed in Section 6.4 of Chapter CB-6.

If pairs of rectangular walls are connected solely by flat floor slabs, an analysis can be performed with the slabs replaced by beams of equivalent stiffness (Qadeer and Stafford-Smith, 1969, 1974).

It has been demonstrated that under certain circumstances heavy horizontal interactive forces can occur at the top of a pair of unequal coupled shear walls, and should be considered in the design process as high axial forces in the topmost connecting beams.

3 Interconnected Walls and Frames

When walls are used to brace a framed structure, it may be acceptable to disregard the lateral stiffness of the frame and assume the horizontal load carried entirely by the walls. However, if the frame portion is capable of making a significant contribution to the lateral stiffness, it is necessary to assess the distribution of the horizontal forces between the wall and frame elements. If allowed to deform independently while subjected to similar horizontal load conditions, the cantilevered wall adopts a flexural configuration and the frame adopts a shear configuration, Fig. 5.6(a). When the two systems are constrained to deflect together by the stiff floor slabs, a redistribution of load occurs throughout their height, with heavy interactions near the top and bottom, Fig. 5.6(b).

Two methods of analysis, based on either a continuous or a discrete approach, are again available for this problem.

The continuous connection approach assumes the frame portion of the structure is replaced by an equivalent shear cantilever (Heidebrecht and Stafford-Smith, 1973a) with equivalent stiffness properties. If the flexural (wall) cantilever and shear (frame) cantilever are assumed to be linked continuously throughout their height, a single fourth-order governing differential equation may be derived, of the same

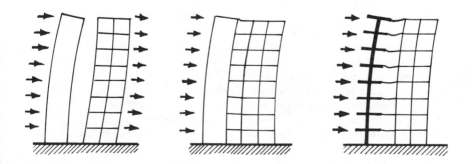

Fig. 5.6 (a) Configurations of separate wall and frame; (b) wall and frame constrained to same configuration; (c) equivalent wide-column system

form as that obtained for coupled shear walls. The closed solutions which result again allow the derivation of simple design curves.

Discrete, equivalent frame methods of analysis similar to those employed for interconnected shear walls are also appropriate in such cases. If the members connecting the wall to the frame act only as axial links without any significant bending restraint the analysis can be performed with the wall replaced by an equivalent column, connected to the frame by pinned-end links, and using a standard framework program. If the wall is joined to the frame by bending-resistant connections, the wide-column analogy may be used, Fig. 5.6(c), and a solution obtained by a standard framework program.

Although particular methods, suitable for desk calculator and small computer, were developed earlier for the solution of this problem, they tended to be lengthy in preparation and use compared to the more recent possibility of using standard framework programs (Clough et al., 1964). However, one of these methods was used to develop a very useful set of preliminary design curves (Khan and Sbarounis, 1964).

A more approximate method which assumes that the shear on the frames is constant with height is described by MacLeod (1970). The method involves only simple calculations and can be used to identify the important parameters of the problem. It is applicable to most practical situations, but tends to become rather inaccurate when the frame stiffness exceeds the wall stiffness. The charts given by Khan and Sbarounis (1964) also cover a fairly comprehensive range of situations.

As occurs in the case of unequal coupled walls, it has been shown (Heidebrecht and Stafford-Smith, 1973a) that heavy concentrated horizontal interactive forces exist at the topmost level of wall-frame structures. Their senses and magnitudes may be such that the net horizontal force at the top of the wall or frame may be in the reverse direction to, and considerably greater than, the externally applied load at that level. These forces are additional to the normal interactions that occur as a result of the different modes of deformation of walls and frames mentioned earlier.

5.5 THREE-DIMENSIONAL PROBLEMS

If a tall building has an asymmetrical structural plan and is subjected to horizontal loading, torsional as well as bending displacements will occur, and hence a full three-dimensional analysis is required. The previously described methods for planar or analogous planar systems are not appropriate, while intuitive or approximate methods, often based on the mistaken concept of a shear center, can be grossly misleading. Particular cases involving twist which do not necessarily require a full three-dimensional analysis are symmetrical framed-tube and hull-core structures, for which simpler methods have been devised, and elementary core-supported structures involving warping. Methods for these are described later.

Both discrete and continuum methods of analysis may be used for three-dimensional structures, although the former are of greater practical importance.

A comprehensive review of the literature up to 1972 was given by Stamato (1972).

1 Frame, Shear-Wall, or Wall and Frame Structures

The large increase in the number of degrees of freedom inherent in the three-dimensional analysis of a tall building often causes a direct stiffness approach to be either extremely lengthy or beyond the capacity of the available computers. It is essential, therefore, to recognize and take account of only those factors which significantly affect the behavior of the structure. For example, it has been shown that it is usually unnecessary to consider the individual torsional stiffness of slender beams, columns, and plane walls, or the transverse bending stiffness of slender walls; and, in relatively squat buildings, it may be reasonable to disregard also the axial deformations of the columns and walls.

If there is doubt about the validity of any particular assumption, it will generally be possible to apply the displacement results of a primary analysis to the neglected stiffnesses and determine as a secondary effect the approximate magnitude of the neglected actions. This will usually give an adequate indication of the errors incurred by the assumption.

Although special concise methods of solution for three-dimensional frameworks have been developed (Clough and King, 1964; Weaver and Nelson, 1966) they have been largely superseded by more comprehensive commercial programs (STRUDL II, 1971), which have accompanied the development of larger computers. These are now generally available and are relatively simple to use. However, it is important that the assumptions made and limitations inherent in the programs should be understood by the engineer.

For three-dimensional structures including shear walls and frames, one approach analogous to the substructure method (Winokur and Gluck, 1968a) considers the structure subdivided into its major bracing panels, or bents (Fig. 5.7) for which the separate in-plane stiffness matrices are determined. Equations are formulated for the contributions of the panels to the equilibrium of the floors with respect to translations along a pair of arbitrary orthogonal horizontal axes, and rotations about an arbitrary vertical axis. Their solution gives values for the translations and rotation of each floor, and hence the in-plane displacements of each panel, from which the panel actions are determined.

If a tall building has slender proportions and stiff horizontal members, vertical deformations of the walls and columns become important. A method which also uses bracing panel substructures has been developed to account for these vertical deformations (Stamato and Stafford-Smith, 1969).

An approximate manual method (Rutenberg and Heidebrecht, 1975), for the analysis of structures consisting of an asymmetric assembly of walls and frames which are uniform with height, is based on decoupling the coupled torsion-bending equations of equilibrium. The deformations and stress resultants in the wall and frame assemblies are obtained by combining the respective coefficients which have been tabulated from the solved decoupled equations. Stresses in the members are obtained from simple force distribution formulas.

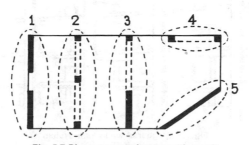

Fig. 5.7 Plan: separate bents or "frames"

A method for the manual solution of a three-dimensional structure with dissimilar shear walls (Glück, 1970b) adopts a two-part approach similar to that described for two-dimensional shear wall structures in Article 2 of Section 5.4 (Glück, 1969).

More recent methods (Weaver et al., 1971) have been developed which reduce the restrictions on structural geometry inherent in the early analyses, and which can include the warping of thin-walled elements, setbacks, and more general layouts of frames, walls, and cores.

Methods have recently been developed to allow the three-dimensional behavior of shear-wall buildings to be tackled using only plane-frame elements (MacLeod, 1973). The method takes account of walls at right angles to the loading, and can be used to predict the redistribution of vertical load that occurs in these buildings.

Although most methods of analysis have adopted the displacement approach, the force method of analysis (Majid and Croxton, 1970) can also be used to solve three-dimensional rectangular assemblies of skeletal frames, together with a grillage of shear walls and floor slabs, including in-plane deformations of the latter.

In applying the continuous medium technique to the analysis of three-dimensional structures, the main problems lie in the integration of the linear simultaneous equations that arise. Standard computer programs are not yet available for this purpose, since the methods have been developed only recently. Several methods have been presented for the analysis of general three-dimensional interconnected thin-walled assemblies, the only significant differences lying in the method of formulation and the redundant action considered. Two recent papers (Danay et al., 1974; Biswas and Tso, 1974) use the translational and rotational displacements of each cross section, together with axial displacement functions for the walls, as the unknowns. An alternative possibility (Rosman, 1971) is to consider each wall unit as an individual plane rectangular element, and to introduce the vertical shear flows at wall junctions as the redundants. Continuous solutions to three-dimensional wall-frame systems are possible if each frame is replaced by an equivalent shear cantilever (Stamato and Mancini, 1973).

Mixed continuum-discrete procedures are also possible. The stiffness matrix of each assembly can be obtained by inversion of the flexibility matrix which is determined from the continuous medium technique (Coull and Irwin, 1970). After determining the component stiffness matrices, the complete structure is solved by discrete techniques. The method relates particularly to buildings incorporating parallel systems of connected walls, frames, and core elements.

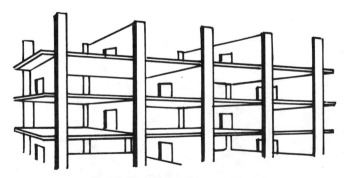

Fig. 5.8 Staggered wall-beam system

All continuum methods tend to be restricted to buildings whose geometrical and stiffness properties are sensibly uniform throughout the height.

A recently-developed structural form suitable for tall buildings is the staggered wall-beam system. The structure consists of a series of parallel bents, each consisting of columns with story-height walls spanning between them in alternate stories. Each wall acts in conjunction with, and supports, the slab above and below (Fig. 5.8). Since the story level of the walls is staggered in adjacent bents, which gives rise to heavy interactions between bents through the floor slabs, the analysis must consider the total three-dimensional behavior of the structure (ACI Committee 442, 1971).

The analysis of orthogonal space structures with two planes of symmetry composed of frames and shear walls, in which a two-stage iterative solution is employed, is described by Avram et al. (1970).

2   Framed-Tube, Hull-Core, and Bundled-Tube Structures

This article considers the analysis of three particular types of framed structures evolved by Khan for very tall buildings.

Framed-Tube Structures.   A framed tube is essentially a perforated box with its exterior walls comprising closely spaced columns and rigidly connecting spandrel beams around the perimeter at each floor level, Fig. 5.9(a). The outer "tube" is designed to resist the lateral forces.

In an approximate analysis, it may be assumed that only the side frames parallel to the wind forces carry the lateral loading so that a plane frame analysis can be used. However, in a more accurate consideration the frames normal to the wind direction tend to deform as flanges in response to the side frames as webs, and they can play a significant part in resisting wind loads. In this case, the normal frames are subjected mainly to axial forces, while the side frames are subjected to shearing actions. The primary flange action of the normal frames is complicated by the flexibility of the spandrel beams allowing a shear lag, which increases the stresses in the corner columns and reduces those in the inner columns of the normal frame. The major interactions between the two types of frame are the vertical shear forces at the corner. Recognizing this effect, a more accurate assessment of the structural

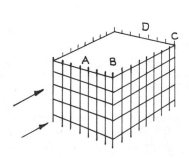

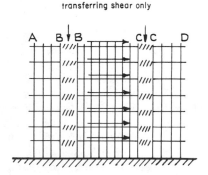

Fig. 5.9 (a) Framed tube; (b) analogous plane structure

behavior can be achieved, using a plane frame matrix analysis in which the frames parallel and normal to the external horizontal forces are connected in such a way that only vertical forces are transmitted between them. This may be achieved in one of two ways. In the first method (Coull and Subedi, 1971) the frames are connected in series by fictitious linking members whose stiffnesses are appropriately chosen to allow only vertical forces to be transmitted. In the second method (Rutenberg, 1972), the force transmission is achieved by the introduction of fictitious beams of very short length with moment and horizontal thrust releases, Fig.5.9(b). The latter is at present more convenient for use with standard frame programs. If the framed tube is symmetrical in both coordinate directions, conditions of symmetry require only a quarter of the structure to be analyzed (Coull and Subedi, 1971). However, when this is done in a general stiffness frame analysis which automatically includes axial shortening effects, the boundary conditions on the plane of symmetry must account for this shortening. A third method (Ast and Schwaighofer, 1974) based on a plane frame approach is claimed to be efficient for large symmetric tube structures. It involves determining the interaction forces at a limited number of points on the junctions of the peripheral frames, and superimposing their effect on that of the horizontal external loading acting on the frames parallel to the external loading.

A method of analysis convenient for design purposes has been developed from repeated analyses of framed tubes with various bending and shearing stiffness ratios of columns to beams. The results have been used to construct influence curves that can be used in conjunction with a reduction modelling technique to give the axial forces in the columns and shear forces in the beams for a wide range of structural parameters (Khan and Amin, 1973).

If a symmetrical framed-tube structure is subjected to bending and twisting forces, the two actions may be considered separately. In the case of pure torsion, the stiff floors assure that the cross-sectional shape of the structure is maintained at each level, so that the applied torque is resisted primarily by the in-plane shearing resistance of each plane frame around the periphery. The main interactive forces between the adjacent panels are again the vertical shear forces at the corners. Since the plan rotation of each frame relative to the center of the building is the same, the shearing deformation in the plane of each frame is equal to the product of the rotation and the distance from the center. Knowing the in-plane shear stiffness of each frame, and using over-all conditions of compatibility and equilibrium, the horizontal forces on each frame, and the vertical interaction forces at the corners, can be established.

Commercially available computer programs can be used for an accurate analysis of a complete three-dimensional framed structure. If a standard space-frame program is used, it will not generally have the capacity to include directly the high in-plane stiffness of the floor slab which maintains the cross-sectional shape of the building. Consequently, relative structural deformations normal to the planes of the frame panels at floor level positions, which cannot occur in practice, may be predicted. Cognizance of the influence of the floor system may be achieved by assigning high axial stiffnesses to the spandrel beams, and introducing fictitious diagonal ties of high axial stiffness at each floor level, to prevent lozenging of the cross section. However, with over-all bending as the dominant mode of action, this is not normally likely to be a substantial problem.

Hull-Core Structures. The hull-core or tube-in-tube structure consists of an outer framed tube (or hull) linked by the floor slabs to a central core which incorporates the services, elevator shafts, and stairwells, Fig. 5.10(a). The system has been used for very tall buildings in both steel and concrete. Lateral loads are resisted by both the hull and the core, their mode of interaction depending on the design of the floor system.

If the floors are effectively pin-jointed to both outer tube and core, horizontal forces only will be transmitted under the action of wind forces. If torsional effects are insignificant, a hull-core structure may then be treated as a plane wall-frame problem, as discussed earlier, with a system of pin-jointed links simulating the in-plane action of the floor slabs. The outer framed tube may be replaced by a pair of equivalent plane frames, Fig. 5.10(b), using the side frames only in the approximate case. For a more accurate solution, the equivalent plane frames should include both side and normal frames, as described under "Framed-Tube Structures" and shown in Fig. 5.9(b).

If torsional deformations occur, the high in-plane stiffness of the floor slab constrains the horizontal deflection and rotation of the hull and core to be the same at each floor level. Consequently, the applied horizontal forces and twisting moments are distributed between the two elements to satisfy this condition. Writing the equilibrium and compatibility equations at each level produces a set of simultaneous equations which are solved to give the lateral deflection and rotation at each level.

An approximate solution for a hull-core structure in bending uses the continuous connection concept for an inner perforated core and a shear cantilever concept for the peripheral frames (Rosman, 1969b). Based on the plane frame representation, an approximate solution has also been developed for the torsion of hull-core structures (Rutenberg, 1974).

Disregarding any slab interaction moments, which would vary throughout the height of the building, allows a uniform slab design to be achieved. However, if the floor system is capable of transmitting bending moments, the interaction between the inner core and outer tube is much more complex, and the coupling effects between the two should be considered. This involves the assessment of the effectiveness of the floor slab in linking the core to the outer hull, but as yet no simple method has been devised to incorporate this.

Bundled-Tube Structures. A relatively recent innovation, devised particularly for very tall buildings, is the bundled-tube or modular-tube system named because

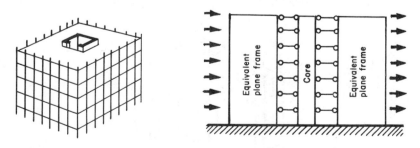

Fig. 5.10 (a) Hull-core structure; (b) analogous plane structure

of its resemblance to a bundle of framed tubes (Fig. 5.11). The external and internal frames parallel to the external horizontal forces act as the webs, and the normal frames as flanges, so that the entire system behaves as a multicell perforated box girder. The individual tube modules may be discontinued at different heights as required to reduce floor areas in the upper levels. Both interior and exterior webs contribute to working the normal frame panels and thus reduce considerably the shear lag that occurs in the standard framed-tube structure. Similar assumptions to those for framed-tube structures may be used to give approximate analyses, but it is no longer possible to reduce the system to an equivalent plane frame. Consequently, it is necessary to carry out a three-dimensional analysis to obtain an accurate solution.

3 Core-Supported Structures

In some buildings the elevators and other services are grouped in a vertical core which may serve alone in supporting the structure, as in a suspended building, or which may act in conjunction with other walls or columns. If twisting is insignificant, the core can be analyzed as a shear wall by one of the methods described earlier. However, if from structural asymmetry or eccentric loading the building is subjected to a torque, the core may be expected to play a useful part in resisting the twist. The commonly used E, H, or U-shaped open-section arrangement of the core walls, and the low thickness to width and width to height ratios of the walls, cause the core to behave as a thin-walled beam; that is, the core tends to warp, as well as bend, as shown in Fig. 5.12(a). Since the base of the core is invariably restrained by a stiff foundation, the walls have induced in them axial and shear warping stresses which, although usually disregarded, can be of such magnitude as to merit consideration in the design.

The torsional stiffness of the core and the magnitude of the warping stresses will be modified by the bending action of beams or slabs which span across the opening and partially close the section of the core, Fig. 5.12(b) (Khan and Stafford-Smith, 1975). Analytical approaches to this problem (Michael, 1969; Rosman, 1969a; Glück, 1970; Laredo, 1969) have coupled the warping-torsion theory with the continuous medium techniques. More recent methods adopting this approach allow convenient graphical solutions and the possibility of varying the core thickness with height (Heidebrecht and Stafford-Smith, 1973b).

Alternative more versatile methods of analysis (Heidebrecht and Swift, 1971) have been developed using the stiffness matrix method, in which the core is taken as

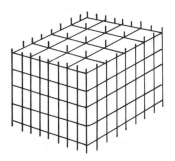

Fig. 5.11 Bundled tube

a line member and the warping deformation of the core section is taken as an additional degree of freedom at each floor level. It is then possible to analyze a structure incorporating several cores and to include also the bending interaction of slabs or beams connecting the cores (Stafford-Smith and Taranath, 1972).

4   Random Systems of Walls or Columns, or Both

All the structures considered so far have plan forms allowing the possibility of subdivision into a few simpler assemblies, thus easing their analysis. Extreme cases can arise, however, in which the walls and columns are arranged randomly in plan with a system of interconnecting slabs or beams for which it is difficult to devise a convenient analogous structure. Such structures have to be analyzed as a unit and are probably best approached by a three-dimensional stiffness analysis. As usual, it is assumed that the floor slabs are rigid in plane while free to bend transversely.

The total stiffness matrix is assembled from the stiffness submatrices, one for each floor level. These relate to the rigid-body translations and rotation of the floor slab, and the vertical displacement and rotations about two horizontal axes of each column or wall at that floor level. To each submatrix must be added the stiffness matrix for the interconnecting beam or floor system so as to represent the contribution to the interactions between the various walls and columns at that floor level. The stiffness matrix for a floor slab in bending must be obtained from preliminary analyses by the finite-element or finite-difference method, whereas that for a beam system can be assembled directly by hand. The solution then follows standard procedures taking advantage, where possible, of the identical floor stiffnesses (Choudhury, 1974).

A continuum method has been devised (Petersson, 1974a) to enable solutions to be obtained for combinations of shear walls, boxes, and thin-walled beam elements. A series routine for solving the differential equations of the total system may be performed by an economic computer program.

5   Comparison of Discrete and Continuum Methods of Analysis

Certain structural forms of tall building are amenable to analysis by two alternative methods, a discrete approach and a continuum approach. The existence of the two alternative approaches has been stressed throughout Sections 5.4 and 5.5, and it is of value to consider briefly the differences between the two.

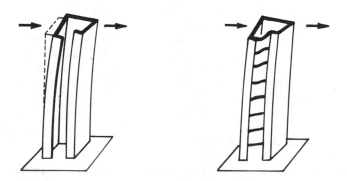

Fig. 5.12 (a) Core subjected to bending and twisting; (b) warping of core restrained by lintels

In the discrete method, the structural model consists entirely of a number of finite line or plane elements connected at a discrete set of nodes. The load-deflection relationships for each element are expressed in terms of the nodal forces and displacements, and the satisfaction of the over-all equations of equilibrium and compatibility at the nodes leads to a set of algebraic simultaneous equations for solution. The analysis normally employs the matrix displacement formulation, and a digital computer is a prerequisite for solving the large number of equations.

In the continuum method, the properties of the horizontal connecting beams or slabs are distributed uniformly up the height of the building as an equivalent continuous connection or continuum. The behavior of a pair of vertical elements, coupled in this way, can be represented by a differential equation in terms of one of the redundant structural actions. A general closed solution is possible, which can be presented graphically for future use. For a number of vertical elements, a differential equation arises for each connecting medium, and the problem reduces to the integration of a set of simultaneous linear differential equations. A numerical method, requiring the use of a computer, is necessary for more than two equations.

The main differences between the two methods can be summarized as follows.

The discrete method usually requires a computer for solution. It is much more versatile in allowing any variation of layout and properties of the structural members, in the type of foundation or supporting structure, and in the pattern of applied loading. The results of displacements and actions are given for each individual member. The discrete method can be used to account for nonlinear behavior by iterative solutions involving successive variations of the elastic modulus. The method is generally useful for producing an "exact" analysis of a particular structure. Its versatility is particularly useful for unsymmetric three-dimensional structures, especially when irregularities occur in the vertical direction.

The continuum method usually allows a rapid hand or graphical solution. In more complex cases demanding the use of a computer, only a relatively small storage is required. The distributed representation of the structure requires that for a dependable solution the structure is uniform with height, although approximate solutions for structures with limited nonuniformity can be used for trial designs. In certain cases a restricted number of variations can be accounted for by combining the continuum approach with the transfer matrix method to allow a hand solution. The continuum method restricts the application of loading to relatively simple patterns. The resulting actions in the members are obtained by accumulating the distributed actions over story heights. The method is much less suitable for examining the effects of nonlinearity. The continuum approach has led to the development of characteristic parameters for certain types of structures, for example, coupled walls. These parameters can serve as useful indicators to the general behavior of a structure and to the influence of varying the member properties. The method increases in accuracy as the number of stories increases, with no additional computational effort. Its main application is in the analysis of two-dimensional systems.

5.6 INFLUENCE OF FOUNDATION

When the vertical load-supporting elements in a building are carried on separate footings in a deformable subgrade, their relative rotation or displacement under load can significantly affect the actions in the superstructure. Little information exists about the analysis of soil-structure interaction problems, but, if an estimate can be made of the "elastic" parameters of the subgrade, it is possible to make an approximate assessment of its influence by including it in a total elastic analysis of the structure. A very approximate but simple way of including the foundation effects is to consider the base of each column or wall to be restrained by springs which have the same translational and rotational stiffnesses as estimated for the column or wall bases on the subgrade. If the computer program does not have the facility for including spring supports, fictitious additional members with appropriate stiffnesses can be incorporated at foundation level to give the desired flexibilities.

In preliminary analyses of structures founded on a single very stiff raft or pad, the base can be assumed to be rigid. However, in structures with extremely stiff walls or columns, a slight bending or twisting of the raft can allow relative displacements between the wall or column bases which may reduce an assumed rigid base to one closely representing a pinned condition. It is advisable, therefore, to attempt to include the base in a complete analysis of the structure to assess the effects of its deformation. A raft can be reasonably represented by an analogous gridwork of line members with similar over-all bending and torsional stiffnesses. This should be supported at the nodes on spring elements to represent the interaction with the foundation and the analysis then undertaken for the complete analogous structure.

Soil-structure interaction problems are discussed by Chamecki (1969).

5.7 USE OF ELASTIC MODELS

Some structures are so complex that it is difficult to be certain that the mathematical model used for the analysis will represent accurately the behavior of the real structure. In such cases, it may be necessary to build to some convenient scale a model of the structure which may be employed either in a qualitative or a quantitative aspect. In the former case, the model—or even a representative section may suffice—can be used to deduce the dominant mode of structural behavior, and from this a suitable mathematical model may be devised. In the latter case, the model is used to give directly the deformations and stresses of the prototype. It should be noted, however, that stress results derived from models can occasionally be grossly misleading, especially when measured near discontinuities; they should therefore be subject to close scrutiny before using in design. Such a scrutiny might include equilibrium checks and comparisons with stresses derived from approximate calculations. Since model manufacture and testing is expensive and time-consuming, the designer should be reasonably certain of the final structural form before a structural model test is commissioned.

The manufacture and testing of the model is greatly simplified if only an elastic analysis is contemplated. Theoretically, any elastic material will suffice, but Perspex (Plexiglas) has been most commonly used because of its cost, low elastic modulus, and ease of fabrication, although it is prone to creep. Asbestos cement, which has a Poisson's ratio approximately equal to that of concrete, is also a useful model material for elastic structures, although the elastic modulus is appreciably higher than that of Perspex. If only the dominant mode of behavior of a simple structure is required, such commonplace materials as cardboard, foamed plastics, or rubber may be adequate.

The general use of models is considered specifically in Chapter CB-7.

The value of information from full-scale tests, especially from actual tall building structures, cannot be too highly emphasized. The need for more research of this nature is underlined by the notable lack of convincing experimental verification for many of the theories outlined in this chapter.

5.8 OTHER PROBLEMS

Lateral drift of tall buildings may be a problem due to discomfort of the occupants or damage to nonstructural elements. This problem is discussed in Chapter CB-9 and Chapter SB-5. The drift computed by standard frame analyses will include any drift due to differential shortening of the various columns and walls. If such drift occurs under gravity loads alone, the possibility of increased drift due to creep should be considered (see Chapter CB-10). The interaction of gravity loads and lateral deflections gives rise to P-Δ moments and second-order effects (see Chapter CB-8).

In the case of drift under seismic loading calculated using the equivalent lateral force procedure, the actual drift of the structure will be considerably higher than the computed drift, approaching the computed drift times the ductility of the structure. This is important when designing expansion joints between adjacent portions of a building.

The elastic analysis of tall buildings for differential column shortening due to temperature or shrinkage and creep is discussed in Chapter CB-10.

5.9 CONDENSED REFERENCES/BIBLIOGRAPHY

The following is a condensed bibliography for this chapter. Not only does it include all articles referred to or cited in the text, but it also contains bibliography for further reading. The full citations will be found at the end of the Volume. What is given here should be sufficient information to lead the reader to the correct article: the author, date, and title. In case of multiple authors, only the first named is listed:

ACI Committee 442 1971, *Response of Buildings to Lateral Forces*
Albiges 1960, *Bracing of Buildings*
Anastesescu 1975, *Considerations of the Analysis of Reinforced Concrete Multistory*
Arcan 1964, *Calculations & Methods for Shear Walls with Openings*
Ast 1974, *Economical Analysis of Large Framed-Tube Structures*

Avram 1970, *Research Regarding the Analysis and Behavior of Tall Building Frames and Shear*
Avram 1973, *Research Regarding the Interaction of Shear Walls and Frames*
Beck 1959, *Calculation of Frames with Slender Members*
Beck 1962, *Contribution to the Analysis of Coupled Shear Walls*
Biswas 1974, *Three-Dimensional Analysis of Shear Wall Buildings Subject to Lateral Load*

Braga Da Cruz 1974, *Comparative Study of Shear Walls with Openings*
Chan 1974, *Stiffening of Shear Walls*
Chamecki 1969, *Calculation of Progressive Settlements of Foundations in Interaction*
Cholewicki 1972, *Distribution of Wind Forces on Shear Walls in a Skeletal Tall Building*
Choudhury 1974, *Elastic Analysis of Spatial Systems of Interconnected Shear Walls and Frames*

Clough 1964, *Analysis of Three-Dimensional Building Frames*
Clough 1964, *Structural Analysis of Multistory Buildings*
Cortes 1973, *Structural Analysis and Design of Las Americas*
Coull 1967, *Tall Buildings*
Coull 1967, *Analysis of Coupled Shear Walls*

Coull 1970, *Analysis of Load Distribution in Multi-Storey Shear Wall Structures*
Coull 1971, *Strength of Sections and Connections—Ultimate Strength Design*
Coull 1971, *Framed-Tube Structures for High-Rise Buildings*
Coull 1973, *Torsion Analysis of Symmetric Building Structures*
Coull 1974a, *Pierced Shear Walls of Stepwise Variable Thickness*

Coull 1974b, *Stiffening of Coupled Shear Walls Against Foundation Movement*
Coull 1974, *Design Curves for Coupled Shear Walls on Flexible Bases*
Coull 1974, *Coupled Shear Walls with General Support Conditions*
Da Costa 1974, *Calculation of High Buildings for Loads During Construction*
Danay 1974, *The Axial Strain Effects on Load Distribution in Non-Symmetric Tier Buildings*

Darwin 1976, *Analysis of RC Shear Panels Under Cyclic Loading*
Deschapelles 1973, *Methods of Analysis*
Estrada 1973, *Use of Computer for Structural Analysis in Bogota*
Finzi 1972, *Elastic Analysis and Design of Steel Frames*
Fling 1973, *Theme Report, Planning and Design of Tall Buildings*

Gere 1965, *Analysis of Framed Structures*
Glück 1969, *Lateral Load Analysis of Multi-Storey Structures Comprising Shear Walls*
Glück 1970a, *Lateral Load Analysis of Asymmetric Multistory Structures*
Glück 1970b, *Lateral Load Analysis of Irregular Shear Wall Multi-Storey Structures*
Glück 1972, *Computer Method for Analysis of Multistory Structures*

Glück 1973, *Elastic Analysis of Tall Concrete Buildings*
Glück 1973, *Stress Analysis of Group of Interconnected Thin-Walled Cantilevers*
Goldberg 1967, *Analysis of Multi-Story Buildings Considering Shear Wall and Floor Deformations*
Goschy 1974, *Torsional Stiffness of "Tube-in-Tube" Systems*
Heidebrecht 1971, *Analysis of Asymmetrical Coupled Shear Walls*

Heidebrecht 1973a, *Approximate Analysis of Tall Wall-Frame Structures*
Heidebrecht 1973b, *Approximate Analysis of Open Section Shear Walls Subject to Torsional*
Hongladaromp 1972, *Approximate Analysis of Tall Buildings Frames*
Hongladaromp 1974, *An Approximate Analysis of Shear Wall-Frame Buildings*
Hongladaromp 1974, *Analysis of Asymmetric*

Jurica 1973, *Statical Analysis and Behavior of TV-Tall Building*
Kärrholm 1973, *Stresses in Walls Due to Vertical Loads*
Khan 1964, *Interaction of Shear Walls with Frames*
Khan 1967, *On Some Special Problems of Analysis and Design of Shear Wall Structures*
Khan 1973, *Analysis & Design of Framed Tube Structures for Tall Concrete Buildings*

Khan 1975, *Restraining Action of Bracing in Thin-Walled Open Section Beams*
Kratky 1971, Discussion, Stafford-Smith, 1970
Krishnaswamy 1974, *Analysis of Coupled Shear Walls Subjected to Concentrated Loads at Floor*
Laredo 1969, *General Theory for the Behavior of Large Structures*
Lewicki 1972, *Structural Design of Tall Concrete Buildings*

MacLeod 1967, *Lateral Stiffness of Shear Walls with Openings*
MacLeod, 1970, *Shear Wall-Frame Interaction*
MacLeod 1973, *Analysis of Shear Wall Buildings by the Frame Method*
MacLeod 1973, *Frame Idealization for Shear Wall Support Systems*
Majid 1970, *Wind Analysis of Complete Building Structures by Influence Coefficients*

Mancini 1974, *Continuous Analysis of Tall Building Structures Subject to Lateral Loads*
Mancini 1975, *Three-Dimensional Association of General Panels*
Marinov 1975, *The Torsional Behavior*
Martin 1973, *Reinforced Concrete Columns*
Mazzolani 1971, *Static of Framed Space Systems with Walls Variously Shaped*

Mazzolani 1975, *Wall-Floor Interaction in Multi-Storey Buildings Under Torsional Loads*
McCormick 1963, *Plane Stress Analysis*
Michael 1969, *Torsional Coupling of Core Walls*
Narayanswami 1972, *Static and Dynamic Analysis of Shear Walls by Finite Element*
Nauman 1961, *Calculation of Horizontally*

Onn 1974, *Computer Analysis of Frame Shear-Wall Interaction*
Petersson 1974a, *Analysis of Load Bearing Walls in Multi-Storey Buildings*
Qadeer 1969, *The Bending Stiffness of Slabs*
Qadeer 1974, *Action in Slabs Connecting Shear Walls*
Ramadrishnan 1976, *Comparison of Three-Dimensional Analysis of Concrete Shear Wall*

Ramesh 1973, *Tall Buildings with Shear-Wall Systems*
Rosman 1960, *Contribution to the Statical Calculation*
Rosman 1964, *Approximate Analysis of Shear Walls Subject to Lateral Loads*
Rosman 1966, *Tables for the Internal Forces of Pierced Shear Walls*
Rosman 1967, *Pierced Shear Walls with Stepped Variations in Cross Sections*

Rosman 1969a, *Torsion of Perforated Concrete Shafts*
Rosman 1969b, *Investigation of High Buildings with a Central Core and Multi-Story Frames*
Rosman 1971, *Statics of Non-Symmetric Shear Wall Structures*
Rubenstein 1966, *Matrix Computer Analysis of Structures*
Rutenberg 1972, Discussion of Coull 1971

Rutenberg 1974, *Analysis of Tube Structures Using Plane Frame Programs*
Rutenberg 1975, *Asymmetric Wall-Frame Structures*
Savassi 1975, *Finite Element Method Analysis of Tall Buildings*
Scordelis 1972, *Finite Element Analysis of Reinforced Concrete Structures*
Schwaighofer 1969, *Analysis of Shear Walls Using Standard Computer Programs*

Schwaighofer 1972, *Models of Shear Wall Structures*
Seetharamulu 1974, *Analysis of Tall Building Structures by Transfer Matrix Method*
Sethurathnam 1974, *Interaction of Frame and Shear Wall with Openings*
Smolira 1975, *Analysis of Tall Buildings by the Force Displacement Method*
Stafford-Smith 1970, *Modified Beam Method for Analysis*

Stafford-Smith 1972, *Analysis of Tall Core-Supported Structures to Torsion*
Stafford-Smith 1973, *Elastic Analysis of Tall Concrete Buildings*
Stamato 1969, *Approximate Method for the Three-Dimensional Analysis of Tall Buildings*
Stamato 1972, *Three-Dimensional Analysis*
Stamato 1973, *Three-Dimensional Interaction of Walls and Frames*

STRUDL II 1971, *User's Manual*
Thürlimann 1972, *Elastic Analysis, Strength of Sections*
Thürlimann 1973, *Summary Report, Planning and Design of Tall Buildings*
Tomii 1971, *Part 2.1 Shear Walls*
Tso 1973, *Static Analysis of Stepped Coupled Walls by Transfer Matrix Method*

Weaver 1966, *Three-Dimensional Analysis*
Weaver 1971, *Tier Buildings with Shear Cores, Bracing, and Setbacks*
Winokur 1968a, *Lateral Loads in Asymmetric Multi-Storey Buildings*
Zienkiewicz 1971, *The Finite Element Method*
Zienkiewicz 1971, *Three-Dimensional Analysis of Buildings Composed of Floor and Wall*

Structural Design of
Tall Concrete and Masonry Buildings

Chapter CB-6

Nonlinear Behavior and Analysis

Prepared by Committee 22 (Nonlinear Analysis and Limit Design) of the Council on Tall Buildings and Urban Habitat as part of the Monograph on the Planning and Design of Tall Buildings

Giorgio Macchi	Chairman
Herbert A. Sawyer, Jr.	Vice-Chairman
Hans Gesund	Editor

AUTHOR ACKNOWLEDGMENT

Special acknowledgment is due those individuals whose contributions and papers formed the substantial first drafts of the various sections of this chapter. First are the state-of-art reporters from the 1972 International Conference whose material was published in the Lehigh Proceedings. These individuals are:

Kurt H. Gerstle, Section 6.2
Vitelmo V. Bertero, Section 6.3
Giorgio Macchi, Section 6.5
Herbert A. Sawyer, Sections 6.5 and 6.7
Sven Sahlin, Section 6.6
Jean C. Maldague, Section 6.7
A. L. L. Baker, Section 6.8.

In addition to this, other sections were based on special contributions prepared by:

Hans Gesund, Sections 6.2 and 6.6
Thomas Paulay, Section 6.4
M. Z. Cohn, Section 6.9.

CONTRIBUTORS

The following is a complete list of those who have submitted written material for possible use in the chapter, whether or not that material was used in the final version. The Committee Chairman and Editor were given quite complete latitude. Frequently length limitations precluded the inclusion of much valuable material. The Bibliography contains all contributions. The contributors are: H. Aoyama, A. L. L. Baker, V. V. Bertero, M. Z. Cohn, R. W. Furlong, K. H. Gerstle, H. Gesund, J. Gluck, E. Grasser, N. Jackson, C. N. Kostem, J. M. Kulicki, G. Macchi, J. C. Maldague, A. Negoita, T. Paulay, I. G. Pop, S. Sahlin, H. A. Sawyer, Jr., C. E. Vandevelde, M. Yamada.

COMMITTEE MEMBERS

T. Arakawa, A. L. L. Baker, V. V. Bertero, H. Bomhard, F. L. Carneiro, M. Z. Cohn, W. G. Corley, D. Dumitrescu, J. Eibl, J. Ferry Borges, R. W. Furlong, K. H. Gerstle, H. Gesund, J. Gluck, E. Grasser, A. A. Gvozdev, N. Jackson, C. N. Kostem, R. Kowalczyk, J. M. Kulicki, R. Lenschow, F. K. Ligtenberg, G. Macchi, J. C. Maldague, R. P. Pama, T. Paulay, S. Sahlin, H. A. Sawyer, Jr., B. Thurlimann, M. Tichy, C. E. Vandevelde, P. C. Varghese, M. Yamada.

CB-6

Nonlinear Behavior and Analysis

6.1. SCOPE OF CHAPTER

The inelastic and nonlinear behavior of reinforced concrete structures significantly affects their response to loads, especially for severe overloads. This nonlinearity is recognized at various levels in the design process. The traditional elastic design procedures count on certain types of inelastic behavior for redistribution of force and stress concentrations from overloads, and they often limit reinforcement ratios or increase transverse steel to assure a certain capacity for this behavior. Nonlinear design procedures, on the other hand, explicitly take the actual section response into account, and hence lead to a more realistic estimate of the moments and forces in a structure.

This chapter consists of two major parts. Part 1, consisting of Sections 6.2, 6.3, and 6.4, describes the inelastic response of reinforced concrete members and structures, and is primarily a review of the results of tests of such elements. This material is provided as necessary background, not only for the methods of nonlinear analysis and design presented in Part 2 of this chapter, but also for a proper understanding of the shortcomings of elastic analyses (Chapter CB-5) and a proper assessment of the problems in member design (Chapter CB-11).

Part 2, consisting of Sections 6.5 to 6.9, presents the basic philosophy of nonlinear analysis of concrete structures in Sections 6.5 and 6.6 and in portions of Section 6.7. Several specific nonlinear design procedures are summarized in Sections 6.7 to 6.9.

Part 1—Inelastic Response of Reinforced Concrete Members and Structures

6.2 FLEXURAL CHARACTERISTICS OF REINFORCED CONCRETE MEMBERS

The behavior of structural elements can be described in terms of the following characteristics: (1) Strength; (2) stiffness; and (3) ductility. The first item will not be discussed here. A knowledge of stiffness, or resistance to deformation, is necessary

171

to describe the structural deformations at all load stages, as well as for dynamic and stability analyses. Ductility is necessary to allow the plastic deformations presupposed by limit analysis. This chapter is intended to give an overview of the current state of knowledge regarding stiffness and ductility of structural components.

The behavior of a structure depends above all on the component material characteristics; these will be discussed in Article 6.2.1, which follows. By use of the principles of structural mechanics, the behavior of linear members can be deduced from the material properties. For flexural members, the moment-curvature relation provides a useful method of describing this behavior. In Article 6.2.2, moment-curvature relations for beams and columns are discussed, and appropriate simplifications are suggested. Approaches to the determination of moment-rotation relations, and of the rotation capacity of members, which is a useful criterion of ductility, are discussed in Article 6.2.3. Secondary effects, such as those due to shear, torsion, and variable repeated loadings, are also touched upon in this article. Engineering conclusions regarding the behavior of beams and columns are summarized in Article 6.2.4.

In recent construction practice, walls and slabs are often relied on to contribute to the structural action. As contrasted with the primarily uniaxial stresses prevailing in linear members, these plane components are subject to biaxial stress states, and any analysis becomes accordingly more involved. Available data for walls and similar elements are presented: walls and panels are treated in Article 6.2.5 and again more completely in Section 6.4. Connection design is mentioned in Article 6.2.6.

The derivation of the flexural stiffness characteristics of columns from the material properties is discussed in Article 6.2.7, and torsion-flexure interaction is considered in Article 6.2.8.

In each article, the state of current knowledge is presented with reference to published studies, and conclusions are drawn with regard to its adequacy for design of tall buildings.

1   Material Characteristics

The properties of steel and plain concrete are discussed herein. Of the two, the steel properties are relatively straightforward; those of concrete are much more involved and depend on many parameters. The behavior of concrete under uniaxial stresses will be covered first, followed by a summary of available knowledge of the concrete response to multiaxial stresses.

Steel. Fig. 6.1 shows the tensile stress-strain curve of a typical mild steel reinforcing bar; we will, in general, designate this function $\sigma = f_1(\epsilon)$. The assumption of bilinear, elastic-perfectly plastic behavior is adequate for many purposes. The newer type, higher-strength steel has in general a shorter yield plateau and more pronounced strain hardening, which should be considered in cases where high strains occur prior to failure of the structure. This strain hardening can be represented with sufficient accuracy by a trilinear stress-strain curve.

When reinforcing steel is likely to be subjected to alternating plasticity, such as might occur during earthquake shocks, the Bauschinger effect must be considered. Fig. 6.2 (Singh et al., 1965) shows the premature deviation from linearity that occurs when a steel is first yielded in tension, then in compression.

Mild steel has in general sufficient ductility so that rupture need not be considered unless welding introduces stress concentrations, nor need its creep be considered under usual conditions.

Concrete.

Uniaxial stress states. The slight amount of tensile strength of concrete can be disregarded in flexural strength (but not in shear and bond) calculations, and this article will consider only the compressive properties of concrete.

Short-time behavior. Fig. 6.3 shows a typical compressive concrete stress-strain curve obtained from a short-time cylinder or cube test; we will, in general, designate this function $\sigma = f_2(\epsilon)$. This behavior can be idealized in a number of ways (Hognestad et al., 1955); the rectangular stress block according to the American Concrete Institute (ACI, 1971) is adequate for determination of ultimate strength of beams. The parabolic-straight line approximation, according to Comité Européen du Béton (CEB, 1963), is a more versatile idealization that can serve to compute complete deformation histories of member sections. Ductility of concrete decreases in general with increasing strength, as indicated in Fig. 6.3.

There is evidence (Shideler, 1957) that lightweight concretes fail with less deformability than gravel concrete, and a conservative procedure would be to assume a more nearly elastic stress-strain curve to failure, as shown in Fig. 6.4.

Of particular importance is the ultimate strain ϵ_u of concrete in compression. Evidence suggests two primary variables affecting the ultimate strain:

1. The strain gradient (Shah et al., 1965; Clark et al., 1967). In a beam section, the transverse strain gradient across a section depends on the location of the

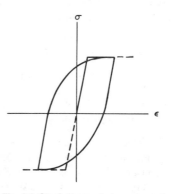

Fig. 6.2 Steel stress-strain curve under load reversal (Singh et al., 1965)

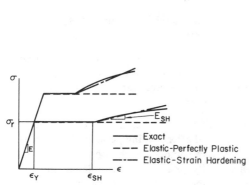

Fig. 6.1 Steel stress-strain curves

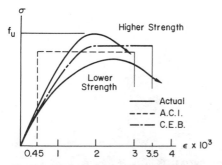

Fig. 6.3 Compressive concrete stress-strain curves (Hognestad et al., 1955)

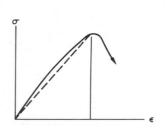

Fig. 6.4 Compressive lightweight concrete σ-ϵ curve (Shideler, 1957)

neutral axis at failure (thus, on the shape of beam, reinforcing index, and presence of axial load), and the longitudinal gradient depends on the rate of change of moment (thus the shear in the beam). While crushing of concrete in an axial cylinder test can occur at a strain of about 0.003, there is considerable evidence that this value can increase to values up to 0.006 or more in the presence of strain gradients.

2. Degree of confinement of concrete (Roy and Sozen, 1965; Sargin, 1971; Rüsch and Stockl, 1963). Multiaxial compression of the concrete, as would occur in an interior beam-column joint in a building frame or due to the presence of ties or stirrups in a beam, increases the ultimate compression strain considerably. Values of crushing strain above 0.010 have been measured in such cases. As has been pointed out (Rüsch, 1960), it follows that the concrete stress-strain curve is not a unique property of the material, but is very much influenced by its environment.

In any case, it appears that the code values for ϵ_u of 0.003 or 0.0035 as stipulated in the ACI or CEB provisions are safe lower bounds that can be vastly exceeded under appropriate conditions.

Effect of sustained loading.   The behavior of concrete is greatly influenced by the rate of loading, and by the creep occurring under long-time loads. Fig. 6.5 (Rüsch et al., 1968), for instance, shows the effect of sustained loads of various levels on the increase of strains. The following conclusions can be drawn from available test results from axially loaded specimens:

1. Creep strain rates diminish with time under stress levels up to $0.80 f_u$ for new concrete, and up to $0.60 f_u$ for old concrete.

2. Under loads in excess of $0.80 f_u$, explosive failure can result after relatively short load durations. Because of the continuing gain in concrete strength, there is a critical period during which such failures can occur (Rüsch, 1960); thereafter the safety will increase with time.

3. Creep strains can increase vastly with time. Values of up to six times the instantaneous values have been recorded after loading periods of 1 yr (Rüsch et al., 1968). It is not clear whether, and under which conditions, eventual stabilization sets in. When instability may be a problem, the creep deformations tend to reduce structural safety and must be considered (Manuel and MacGregor, 1967; Ghosh and Cohn, 1970).

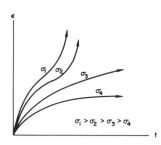

Fig. 6.5 Creep curves

For prestressed concrete members, the effect of sustained loading is modified by creep and shrinkage strains. Such loading produces stresses that may be computed on a lower modulus of elasticity. At ultimate load the effect of creep strain may or may not be significant, and will depend upon the over-all conditions of the particular structure.

Effect of repeated loading.   Some results of concrete tests under various load histories (Sinha et al., 1964; Karsan and Jirsa, 1969) indicate that the stress-strain curve obtained from monotonically increasing strains can define the crushing conditions for concrete under fluctuating loads. Karsan and Jirsa (1969) also present limiting criteria for incremental deformations of the plain concrete under cyclic compressive loadings.

Multiaxial stress states.   The behavior of concrete under multiaxial stress states must be known for a rational analysis of the deformations of walls, slabs, connections, and in confined portion of beams. Only sparse test results are available at this time (Chinn and Zimmerman, 1965; Kupfer et al., 1969), from which the following preliminary conclusions can be drawn:

1. Triaxial compression increases the concrete ductility greatly.

2. Concrete strength is also increased by multiaxial compression.

No evidence regarding the validity of any stress-strain laws beyond the elastic range for multiaxial stress states (such as the flow rule of ideal plasticity) appears available.

2   Moment-Curvature Relations

The behavior of flexural cross sections is conveniently represented by the moment-curvature relation $M = f_3(\Phi)$. The stresses must satisfy equilibrium of forces and moments, and the strains are customarily assumed to vary linearly across the section (plane-section assumption). The stresses and strains are related by the appropriate stress-strain relations discussed in the preceding article, which are generally represented by the expressions $\sigma_s = f_1(\epsilon)$ for steel, and $\sigma_c = f_2(\epsilon)$ for concrete.

For a once-symmetrical cross section of width $b(y)$ subjected to planar bending moment M and axial force N, shown in Fig. 6.6(a), the procedure leads to the

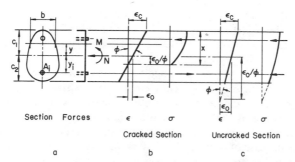

Fig. 6.6 Forces and deformations in member section

equilibrium equations in terms of the curvature Φ and the axial extension ϵ_o, shown in Fig. 6.6(b). These are

$$\Sigma F = 0: \quad \int_{y=\epsilon_o/\Phi}^{c_1} f_2(\epsilon_o + \Phi y)b\,dy + \sum_i f_1(\epsilon_o + \Phi y_i)A_i = N \tag{6.1}$$

$$\Sigma M = 0: \quad \int_{y=\epsilon_o/\Phi}^{c_1} f_2(\epsilon_o + \Phi y)b \cdot y\,dy + \sum_i f_1(\epsilon_o + \Phi y_i)y_i A_i = M \tag{6.2}$$

in which the variable y is measured from the line of action of the axial force N.

The analysis of an uncracked section in which the tensile concrete stress is below the cracking value is of importance insofar as it can furnish an upper bound to the stiffness of the reinforced concrete section. In practice it can usually be disregarded for two reasons:

1. Once the cracking moment has been exceeded, the crack exists for all subsequent loadings.

2. The deformation of beam sections subject to low moments (such as in the vicinity of inflection points) does not heavily influence the over-all structural behavior.

The case of predominant axial force N can lead to the strains and stresses shown in Fig. 6.6(c); for such cases, the lower limit c_2 should be substituted in the first term of Eqs. 6.1 and 6.2.

Fig. 6.6 also shows that the curvature can be defined as $\Phi = \epsilon_c/x$, in which ϵ_c = extreme compressive fiber strain, and x = distance from the neutral axis to the extreme compression fiber. The ultimate curvature is attained when the maximum compressive concrete strain reaches its ultimate value ϵ_u, that is

$$\Phi_Q = \frac{\epsilon_u}{x} \tag{6.3}$$

For nonsymmetrical sections, or those subject to biaxial bending, similar considerations involving two moment and one force equilibrium equations lead to equations analogous to Eqs. 6.1 and 6.2, which, however, because of complicated boundary conditions, are usually solved by iterative or inverse computer techniques (Aas-Jakobsen, 1964; Eloseily, 1967).

Before a solution can be effected for a particular cross section, the appropriate stress-strain relations $f_1(\epsilon)$ and $f_2(\epsilon)$ must be introduced in Eqs. 6.1 and 6.2, whereby due regard should be taken of the various parameters influencing these functions, as discussed in the preceding article.

Under increasing load, two critical conditions can occur: either the steel yields by attaining its yield strength f_y, or the concrete crushes by attaining its ultimate strain ϵ_u. The first case, which occurs in sections with low reinforcing index and predominant bending, is the case of tension failure, or *underreinforced* case; the latter, which arises in sections with high reinforcing index or predominant axial compression, is the case of compression failure, or *overreinforced* case.

The distinction between the two cases is all-important in describing the ultimate behavior of the member, as shown in the case of pure bending in Fig. 6.7. In underreinforced sections, yielding of the steel leads to high steel strains, a propagation of the tensile cracks toward the compression zone, and gradual increase of the compression strain in the concrete until the ultimate strain ϵ_u is reached at an essentially constant or only slightly increasing moment M_u at an ultimate curvature Φ_u. The behavior is thus of a ductile nature, allowing large curvatures. On the other hand, once the compressive concrete of overreinforced sections crushes, the internal lever arm is reduced and the moment resistance of the section decreases rapidly without allowing the steel to reach its yield stress. The behavior is brittle, and will not allow large rotations to take place prior to failure.

Therefore, an underreinforced design is essential for all sections of a structure in which plastification is relied upon to attain the ultimate strength of the structure.

It must, of course, be remembered that yielding of the steel of an underreinforced section causes severe tensile cracking, which may lead to unserviceability of the member. Safety against this condition must be considered along with strength criteria. The width and distribution of tensile concrete cracks is a function of the steel ratio, bar size, concrete cover, and bar surface characteristics (RILEM, 1958; Rehm, 1961; Jorgensen, 1962).

In underreinforced sections, the exact shape of the concrete stress-strain curve is not very important; only the ultimate strain ϵ_u, which determines the ultimate curvature Φ_u, matters. The over-all behavior is controlled mainly by the steel stress-strain curve; if, for instance, the strain hardening of the steel is considered (Jorgensen, 1962; Eiklid et al., 1969), the dashed lines of Fig. 6.7 result. The strain-hardening effect becomes obvious only in highly underreinforced sections that allow high steel strains prior to crushing of the concrete.

The effect of axial compression on the section deformations is shown in Fig. 6.8 (Pfrang et al., 1964; Breen and Ferguson, 1964). With increasing axial force, the ultimate curvature is reduced, until, at the balanced stage, brittle failure takes place. Under such conditions, it appears advisable to design structures always in such a fashion that any plastification takes place in the beams rather than in the columns.

The shape of the curves of Figs. 6.7 and 6.8 suggests an elastic idealization for overreinforced sections, and a bilinear or trilinear representation for under-reinforced sections (Cohn, 1965b; Macchi, 1969). The results of such simplifications will be studied in the next article.

The deformation of members under bending with and without axial load has been studied extensively, and is well documented by test results (Bachmann and Thurlimann, 1969; Mayer, 1967; Breen, 1965). The behavior of such members under

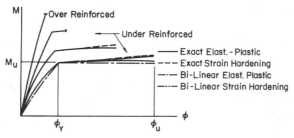

Fig. 6.7 Moment-curvature relations

sustained loading can be taken into account by substituting the appropriate stress-strain-time relation of concrete to be discussed later. A large number of studies (Ghosh and Cohn, 1970) of the time-dependent curvatures shows that, at least for limited loading times, the creep deformations can be predicted with fair accuracy.

On the other hand, the influence of shear and torsion on the deformability of members has been subject only to limited investigation (Bachmann, 1971; Collins and Lambert, 1971). It appears that, at present, members which are required to deform plastically should be designed so as to be safe against excessive diagonal cracking due to shear stresses.

The effects of variable load history have also been studied (Bertero and McClure, 1964; Gerstle and Tulin, 1971). When no or only slight cracking occurs, then the curvatures can at all load stages be predicted by appropriate extension of Eqs. 6.1 and 6.2; the appropriate material functions for loading and unloading must, of course, be known. If cracking is severe, then the curvatures seem to be highly dependent on crack and bond deterioration.

3 Deformations of Members and Rotations of Plastic Hinges

If the curvatures are continuously distributed along the member, all deformations can be obtained by integration of curvatures. The continuity of curvatures in reinforced concrete members depends on the bond characteristics between steel and concrete (Mayer, 1967; Broms, 1965). In the extreme case of perfect bond, the tensile concrete cracks will be infinitesimally narrow and closely spaced, and thus continuity of curvatures can be assumed.

On the other hand, in the case of zero bond, large, widely spaced cracks will occur, discrete rotations will take place at these cracked sections, and in between only slight curvatures arise. Integration of theoretical curvatures in this case leads to unrealistic results.

Actually, the situation is in between these two extremes. Fig. 6.9 shows a possible crack pattern and distribution of curvatures. If the reinforcing bar surface is deformed so as to prevent excessive slippage between steel and concrete, the cracks

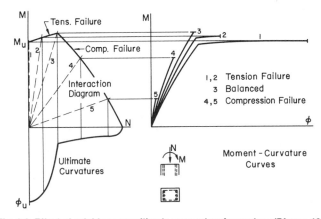

Fig. 6.8 Effect of axial force on ultimate moment and curvature (Pfrang, 1964)

will be sufficiently distributed to allow an average curvature to be associated with the moment that lies between the extreme cases of the uncracked and the cracked case. Tests under working loads, prior to yielding of the steel, have shown reasonable agreement between actual deformations and those predicted on this basis (Mayer, 1967). When no cracking at all arises, as in columns under slight eccentricities, excellent agreement between theory and experiment can be obtained (Breen and Ferguson, 1964); short-time and creep deformations can be predicted with good correlation (Ghosh and Cohn, 1970).

As the moments are increased in underreinforced beams, and the steel yields, the increased crack widths must lead to bond deterioration, and the integration of curvatures leads to less and less satisfactory results. We will consider this situation in terms of the behavior in the vicinity of the moment peak shown in Fig. 6.10(a). If an idealized elastic-perfectly plastic moment-curvature relation is assumed, as suggested in Fig. 6.7, the moment cannot exceed the value M_u, and no spread of plasticity can occur. The curvature can attain an undetermined value, but since it is of zero length, no unique rotation can be associated with it. This type of behavior can be represented by a localized plastic hinge able to undergo an indeterminate amount of rotation (Ernst, 1958).

The above reasoning can be visualized in terms of a single crack, which, however, requires bond deterioration and yielding of the reinforcing over a finite length to allow it to open up. However, then the assumption of plane sections, and therefore the very existence of a curvature in this region, become unrealistic, and it follows that a curvature approach will not serve to determine the ultimate rotation capacity of the hinge.

This anomaly suggests that strain hardening must be considered to allow spread of the plastic zone and integration of curvatures (Smith and Sidebottom, 1965) to determine the rotations. This case is shown in Fig. 6.10(b), where the curvatures associated with the moments by the strain-hardening diagram of Fig. 6.7 are shown; the total area under the curvatures exceeding Φ_y represents the total rotation over the plastic length, and the shaded area represents the plastic rotations in excess of those due to elastic behavior. The shaded area at the instant when the maximum curvature reaches its ultimate value Φ_u is equal to the ultimate inelastic rotation of the member. It can be deduced that the ultimate rotation increases with decreasing strain-hardening stiffness and with decreasing gradient of moments.

If the plastified portion of the member is reasonably short, it is convenient to think in terms of concentrated hinge rotations θ of a discrete hinge; these can be plotted in terms of a moment-rotation diagram, as shown in Fig. 6.11. The

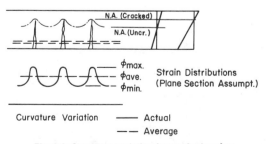

N.A. (Cracked)

N.A. (Uncr.)

ϕmax.
ϕave.
ϕmin.

Strain Distributions
(Plane Section Assumpt.)

Curvature Variation ——— Actual
— — Average

Fig. 6.9 Curvature variation in cracked region

strain-hardening M-θ curve can be linearized, so as to show a constant rotational strain-hardening hinge stiffness. This would correspond to the assumption of a strain-hardening hinge represented by a linear-rotational spring, analogous to the concept of a perfectly plastic hinge. For the case of concentrated loads on continuous beams, some tests (Eiklid et al., 1969) have shown that this assumption can lead to reasonable results.

Here again, the crucial question is how to determine the ultimate rotation of hinging regions. Some studies (Nawy et al., 1968; Corley, 1966) have shown that in beams, ultimate strains between 0.006 and 0.010 furnish reasonable results. On the other hand, it has been shown that in pure bending, crushing of compression concrete, even in the unconfined outer shell, does not necessarily lead to loss of flexural capacity. An attempt has been made (Thomas and Sozen, 1965) to explain this puzzling behavior in terms of nonlinear strain distributions in the cracked region.

It is apparent that a wholly satisfactory rational explanation of the rotational behavior of hinging regions is lacking. To circumvent the questionable points, a widely used approach to the prediction of rotation capacities has been to assume a plastic hinge length l, over which the ultimate curvature $\Phi_u = \epsilon_u/x$ acts (Corley, 1966; Mattock, 1965). The appropriate value of ϵ_u then depends on the gradient of moment, the degree of confinement, and other factors as mentioned previously. One can now either assume a constant plastic hinge length l [a length equal to the effective depth d has been suggested (Corley, 1966)] and vary the ultimate compression strain, or one can assume more conventional values of ϵ_u, as specified in codes, and vary the plastic hinge length to suit test results. Baker and Amarakone (1964) established general rules for determination of rotation capacities.

The methods of predicting rotation capacities cited have been verified by tests of beams under concentrated loads. The rotation capacity of hinges occurring under distributed loads and in the vicinity of connections needs further study.

Shear deformations appear to play a definite role in the rotations occurring in cracked portions of beams. This matter has been treated (Dilger, 1967) on basis of tests (Leonhardt and Walther, 1962) for the case in which the longitudinal reinforcement remains elastic. These shear deformations do not play a major role in building frames at working loads, but they do affect the rotation capacity of plastified zones. Inclined cracks due to the presence of shear cause spreading of the

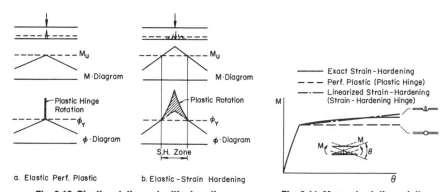

a. Elastic Perf. Plastic   b. Elastic-Strain Hardening

Fig. 6.10 Plastic rotations at critical section   **Fig. 6.11 Moment-rotation relations**

plastic zone and thus tend to increase the rotation capacity (Bachmann, 1971). Tests have led to the conclusion (Bachmann and Thurlimann, 1966) that shear can be transmitted across a plastic zone up to the point of yielding of stirrups.

It thus appears that shear may have a beneficial effect on the rotation capacity of plastic zones if care is taken to design these regions to prevent premature shear failure.

Torsional effects in tall building frames (such as in spandrel beams or in columns of a twisting building) are likely to be of the "compatibility torsion" type (Collins and Lambert, 1971), in which torsion is not necessary to maintain static equilibrium. Some recent tests (Lampert, 1971) of such cases have shown that a truss analogy can serve to predict the behavior of members subject to torsion, bending, and shear. Upon cracking, such analyses show that the torsional stiffness decreases faster than the flexural stiffness, so that under further load increase, flexural behavior predominates, and torsion can be disregarded in ultimate load analyses. Thus, torsional reinforcing should be provided for the main purpose of minimizing torsional cracking (Lampert, 1971). If this is done, the presence of torsion does not appear to inhibit the rotation capacity of members.

In structures subject to cyclic overloads, such as might occur due to earthquake shocks, some studies (Gerstle and Tulin, 1971) have shown that strain hardening plays a major role in determining the continuing or incremental deformations. In such cases, the bond between steel and concrete may deteriorate rapidly, thereby increasing the danger of shear-type failures (Singh et al., 1969).

4 Conclusions Regarding Stiffness and Deformability of Structural Members

It appears useful to summarize the preceding discussion of the behavior of structural members as follows:

1. The stiffness of members prior to yielding of steel can be determined by rational means. Only the range subsequent to tensile cracking of concrete is important.

2. The distinction between overreinforced and underreinforced sections is crucial in determining the ductility of members.

3. The moment-rotation behavior can be linearized. For overreinforced sections, it can be idealized by perfectly elastic behavior. For underreinforced sections, it can be represented by bilinear or trilinear relations.

4. For underreinforced members, the assumption of perfectly-plastic or strain-hardening hinges of limited rotation capacity can be made. Approximate methods are available to predict the rotation capacity of these hinges.

5. Creep effects are important for the determination of the deflections of beams, and the strength of slender columns. They can be included in the analysis by rational means.

6. Shear and torsion need not inhibit the rotation capacity if reinforcing is provided to prevent failure in these secondary modes.

5   Behavior of Walls

The increasing use of reinforced concrete shear walls, panels, and cores to provide lateral resistance requires knowledge of the behavior of such elements. It is necessary at the outset to distinguish between walls acting as deep beams, vertically as shear walls in low buildings or horizontally as transfer girders; tall shear walls acting essentially as slender beams; and shear panels used as infills in frames, etc. Relatively little of use to the analyst is available in this respect. A comprehensive summary of the state of the art regarding deep beams (Leonhardt, 1965) contains some useful information.

A rigorous stress and deformation analysis of walls involves biaxial stress states, and is thus more involved than that of linear members. A considerable body of work is available regarding the elastic behavior, but usually the emphasis has been on strength rather than on deformations, and the effect of cracking has been largely disregarded.

The principal conclusion of the analytical studies of the elastic behavior of single-span and multiple-span deep beams of interest to the designer is the following: deep beams whose ratio of span to depth is greater than 2 may be analyzed by beam theory. This approximation appears valid for shear walls of tall buildings, since such elements usually fall within this range of proportions. Section 6.4 deals extensively with slender shear walls.

A large amount of testing of deep reinforced concrete beams (Leonhardt and Walther, 1966; Koor, 1957) has been aimed at answering questions regarding proper arrangement of reinforcing to prevent shear failure and local cracking at corners. The specimens tested were in general so supported as to allow arch action to occur upon inclined cracking; it is questionable to what extent any conclusions might apply to shear walls where such arch action is unlikely to occur. In such beams shear deformations play a considerable role, and it appears that the use of truss analogies (Dilger, 1967) can be used to calculate their stiffness. Since most of the experimental efforts were directed at strength determination, few load-deflection curves are available. Some studies, however, do include this information (DePaiva and Siess, 1965) and it appears that, similar to ordinary beams, a clearcut distinction can be made between walls failing in shear, those failing in brittle flexure by crushing of concrete, and those failing in a ductile manner by yielding of steel.

The latter type of failure, which is necessary to allow redistribution of forces in the structure, is entirely similar to that of underreinforced beams, and can be represented reasonably well by bilinear moment-rotation curves (DePaiva and Siess, 1965; Paulay, 1970a). However, no clearcut criteria for the design of such ductile shear walls have so far been proposed.

Of greater applicability is a study of the response of wall panels (Paulay, 1970a) under monotonic and earthquake-type loadings. Here again, the emphasis is on strength, but numerous curves describing the deformations enable correlation with analysis (Cervenka and Gerstle, 1972). Studies describing the behavior of single-story walls with and without cutouts are also available (Benjamin and Williams, 1958).

Considerable experimental research on behavior of shear walls is currently being carried on in Japan. These studies indicate the effectiveness of suitably designed walls consisting of concrete frames infilled with block in resisting lateral forces (Tomii, 1971). (If poorly designed, such walls can be undesirable in seismic areas.) Other tests seek to establish reinforcing criteria to assure ductile behavior of concrete shear walls (Hirosawa, 1971).

It should be noted that the tests and analyses cited have considered only panels subjected to transverse forces without axial loads. Shear walls in tall buildings will be subjected to high axial forces due to gravity loads in the lower sections subject to maximum shear and bending. This interaction, which will tend to increase compressive stresses and thus diminish ductility, appears not to have been studied.

The effects of wall openings on the over-all response of panel elements has been studied in the elastic range (Rosman, 1964). Their effect within the postcracking range is unknown, but it should be of great importance to know how far irregularities can be accommodated within a beam-type analysis.

A rational approach to the determination of the gradual deterioration of walls must be based on the behavior of reinforced planar elements under biaxial stress states. A useful, if fragmentary, study of this behavior is available (Peter, 1964), and indicates that the action is that of an anisotropic medium in which principal stress and strain trajectories do not coincide. After cracking, the dowel action of the steel also plays a role, as has been borne out by analyses (Cervenka and Gerstle, 1972) of the results obtained by Peter (1964).

Recently, finite-element analyses have been used to study the postcracking behavior of beams (Ngo and Scordelis, 1967; Nilsen, 1968) and wall elements (Cervenka and Gerstle, 1972). These studies show clearly that this method, which is based on a numerical continuum mechanics approach capable of including realistic material behavior and boundary conditions, is capable of predicting the response of wall elements at all load stages to failure. Some results (Cervenka and Gerstle, 1972; Clark and MacGregor, 1968) also verify the earlier conclusion that underreinforced sections with sufficient shear reinforcement show considerable ductility, and that moment-rotation relations can be represented by bilinear behavior. If this is so, it follows that the ductile response of walls can be analyzed by means of the appropriate insertion of plastic or strain-hardening hinges, analogous to the procedure suggested for ordinary beams.

The detailed response of closed thin-walled cores as shear-resistant elements has not been studied. The action of such components is related to that of shells or folded plates, and possibly shear lag effects may play a role here.

It is likely that precast panel or box construction will gain in importance. For such structures, the strength and deformability of cast-in-place joints between precast elements must be known, because it seems likely that these will be the soft spots of the structure. While information on the strength of such joints is in part available (Pume, 1967, 1970; Paulay et al., 1974), the deformation behavior appears unknown.

A problem related to that of walls under in-plane loadings is that of the stiffness and ultimate deformations of horizontal diaphragms of cast-in-place or precast concrete, since this behavior will affect the distribution of lateral forces to the vertical shear elements. Only a few contributions relating to this matter are known (Khan and Sbarounis, 1964; Goldberg, 1966), and these appear to attack the problem only in its elastic range.

6 Behavior of Connections

Tall structures are particularly vulnerable to lateral loads; under such loadings, the critical sections will usually be in or adjacent to beam-column connections, and recently considerable attention has been directed toward an understanding of the action within such connections. This is a problem involving multiaxial stress states of great analytical difficulty. In addition, the behavior of joints for precast concrete members is of particular significance to the ultimate strength of concrete frames.

Tests of connection behavior are available (Yamashiro and Siess, 1962; Ernst, 1957). All test results emphasize the need for confinement of concrete by means of ties or hoops to increase the ductility of the connection concrete. This need is particularly emphasized when the connection is subject to reversal of loads, as in the case of earthquake shocks (Hanson and Connor, 1967). In general, the trend is to design connections subject to such action sufficiently strong so that any plastic action will occur in the members adjacent to the connections. Thus, the detailing of reinforcing in the connection area becomes of paramount importance (ACI, 1971). If connection strength can be assured, then it will be possible to analyze the structure as rigid-jointed, with plastic zones in adjacent members. This problem is also discussed in Chapter CB-11.

7   Stiffness of Reinforced Concrete Columns in Biaxial Bending

A basic problem in the analysis of tall structures is the interaction between bending and axial load in the columns. This problem becomes particularly acute when the materials involved have nonlinear stress-strain relationships, and when biaxial bending stiffnesses of the columns must be considered in order to carry out a three-dimensional frame analysis at very high loads, as in the step-by-step method of limit analysis. Since the moments acting in each direction at each end of the column may be different, one cannot predict the shape into which the column will be bent, but must, as part of the analysis, determine the shape in each principal direction in order to take into account the effect of interaction between axial load and transverse deformation of the column axis. The shape may be anything from a simple bowing to an S, and may be different in each direction. The effects of cracking, creep, and shrinkage further complicate the matter when the columns are made of reinforced concrete.

Procedure. A procedure has been developed (Shah and Gesund, 1972; Gesund and Vandevelde, 1973; Gesund, 1973) that makes it possible to obtain the complete axial load-biaxial moment-biaxial curvature relationship of cracked reinforced concrete cross sections directly, and to integrate such relationships numerically over the length of the column. Iteration is then used to obtain the correct shape of the column axis, taking into account interaction between the axial load and lateral deflection, for any combination of applied end loads and moments. The biaxial end rotations and moments can then be used to find the terms of the member rigidity matrix which, when inverted, gives the stiffness matrix.

Assumptions. The following assumptions will be made: (1) The stress-strain relationship of the materials can be expressed either as a continuous function or in tabular form; (2) the materials must be elastic though nonlinear—that is, the unloading curve must be congruent with the loading curve; (3) sections plane before bending remain plane after bending; (4) the effect of shearing stresses on the axial stress-strain behavior of the materials can be ignored; and (5) the cross sections will have two mutually perpendicular axes of symmetry.

Cross-Section Analysis. The first step in the procedure must be the analysis of reinforced concrete column cross sections subjected to axial load combined with biaxial bending moments. The following steps outline a program to analyze such a section completely:

1. A set of rectangular coordinate axes and a rectangular grid are imposed on the section, and the coordinates of each bar and of the center of each grid rectangle are determined. A grid that divides each side of the column into 10 equal spaces is probably sufficiently accurate (see Fig. 6.12).

2. The location of a neutral axis (axis of zero strain), whose equation is $y = ax + b$, is assumed. The axis may lie within or outside the cross section.

3. The perpendicular distances of the centers of all grid rectangles and of all bars from the assumed neutral axis are calculated.

4. A value is chosen for the total compression strain, including shrinkage and creep, at the center of the grid rectangle furthest from the neutral axis.

5. The curvatures about the x and y directions, ϕ_x and ϕ_y, associated with the given strain and location of the neutral axis, are calculated by dividing the value of compression strain, chosen in step 4, by the distances from the neutral axis in the y and x directions, respectively, of the center of the grid rectangle in which the strain is applied. The values of ϕ_x and ϕ_y are stored.

6. Strains in all bars are calculated proportional to the chosen compressive strain and their relative distances from the neutral axis. If the neutral axis lies inside the cross section, some bars will probably be in tension.

7. Strains at the centers of all grid rectangles are calculated similarly. The shrinkage strain of the concrete, ϵ_{cs}, is subtracted from them. If a column shortening term is to be included in the stiffness matrix, total vertical strain is also calculated at the center of the column.

8. Using the material stress-strain relationships previously established, stresses are found in all bars and grid rectangles. Zero stress will be allocated to grid

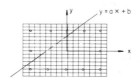

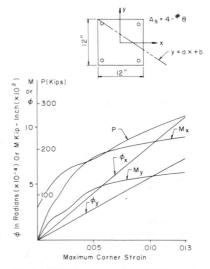

Fig. 6.12 Column cross section for biaxial bending

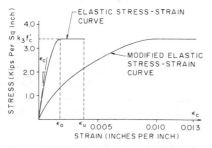

Fig. 6.13 Elastic and modified elastic stress-strain curves for concrete

Fig. 6.14 Total cross-sectional response for single location of neutral axis

rectangles with tensile stress greater than the concrete may be assumed to be able to resist.

9. The force in each grid rectangle and each bar is found by multiplying stress by area.

10. Summing forces gives P, the axial load the cross section will be resisting under the given conditions. Summing moments of forces about the axes of symmetry, one obtains the vector bending moments, M_x and M_y, that the cross section is resisting.

11. A new value may now be chosen for the compression strain and the procedure repeated from step 4. After as many compression strains as desired have been used, a new location of the neutral axis is chosen, and the procedure is repeated from step 2. This, also, may be done as often as desired.

12. The results of the calculations are arranged in a table of $\{P\} \equiv \{M_x\} \equiv \{M_y\} \equiv \{\phi_x\} \equiv \{\phi_y\}$.

Fig. 6.14 shows an example of cross section results obtained, using the concrete long-term (modified elastic) stress-strain curve of Fig. 6.13, a steel yield stress of 345 MPa (50 kips/in.²), and a shrinkage strain of 0.0008.

Column Analysis. When columns are part of a frame, the shape into which they will be bent cannot be predetermined. For this reason the relations between axial loads, biaxial end moments, and biaxial end rotations must be found by iteration, taking into account the interaction between lateral deformations and axial loads and the nonlinear moment-curvature relationships. The following steps are involved:

1. The column is divided into short segments for use with finite-difference equations or numerical integration. Since the column may be bent into an S shape, it would be advisable to use only about 20 segments per column.

2. An initial deflected shape is assumed for the column. For the first loading increment on a structure the deflections along the entire length of the column may be assumed to be zero in both the x and the y directions. For later loading stages the deflected shape obtained from the immediately preceding loading stage should be used.

3. Using the applied end moments and the interaction between axial load and biaxial lateral displacement of each segment, one can readily calculate the biaxial moments in each segment.

4. Using the previously obtained $\{P\} \equiv \{M_x\} \equiv \{M_y\} \equiv \{\phi_x\} \equiv \phi_y\}$ tables (note that a different table may, if necessary, be used for each cross section present in the column), the corresponding biaxial curvatures can be obtained. Depending on the density of the tables and the accuracy desired, interpolation may be necessary between available data. This will be discussed later.

5. Numerical integration of the segment curvatures, or substitution into the finite-difference form of the differential equations of the elastic curves, give new displacements of the segments in the two directions. These can be

compared with those used in step 3 above. If the difference, anywhere, is greater than some acceptably small value, the new displacements are substituted for the old ones and steps 3 to 5 are repeated.

6. When desired convergence has been obtained, the biaxial end rotations are readily calculated from the displacement. Total column shortening can also be calculated by numerical integration. An excessive number of cycles, or an increase in rate of lateral displacement, indicate probable instability of the column under the given system of loads, and should cause termination of the program with printing of an appropriate message.

As an example of the foregoing method, a column with the cross section shown in Fig. 6.15(a) was analyzed. It was 4.6 m (15 ft) long, reinforced with #8 bars having a yield strength of 345 MPa (50 kips/in.²), and made of concrete with the stress-strain curve shown in Fig. 6.13 and ϵ_{cs} = 0.0008. Some results, for an applied axial end load of 890 kN (200 kips), and for equal applied moments at the two ends, are shown in Fig. 6.15(b). The interaction effect, that is, the effect of moment in one direction on the end rotation in the other direction, is clearly shown.

Column Stiffness Matrix.   To obtain the column stiffness matrix, one now proceeds as follows (Shah and Gesund, 1972):

1. Given a column, A-B, with a known axial load-biaxial moment-biaxial curvature relationship (expressed in tabular or some other form) for each segment of length, and with known end loadings, P, MAX, MAY, MBX, and MBY.

2. For these end loadings, biaxial end rotations θAX, θAY, θBX, and θBY, may be calculated by the procedure outlined previously.

3. Changing the end loadings to P, (MAX + $DMAX$), MAY, MBX, and MBY, in which $DMAX$ is a small increase in MAX, one can obtain changes in end rotations, $D\theta AXAX$, $D\theta AXAY$, $D\theta AXBX$, $D\theta AXBY$. Dividing each of these changes in end rotation by $DMAX$ gives the first column of the column flexibility matrix. Next, increasing end moment MAY by $DMAY$, a small increase in MAY, while holding all other loadings at their original values, one can obtain changes in end rotation $D\theta AYAX$, $D\theta AYAY$, $D\theta AYBX$, and $D\theta AYBY$. When divided by $DMAY$, these become the second column of the flexibility matrix. The other two columns are obtained similarly, operating on the moments at B. The column shortening term can be obtained by varying the axial load independently of the moments.

4. Inversion of the flexibility matrix then gives the stiffness matrix.

Interpolation Problem.   It is obvious that use of tables requires either that the values of the data sets (rows) be sufficiently close together so that a search with any entry number or numbers will locate a unique data point within an acceptable margin of error, or else that some interpolation routine be available. For the stress-strain data table, which contains only two columns, ordinary linear interpolation is relatively simple and will normally give excellent results. The $\{P\} \equiv \{M_x\} \equiv \{M_y\} \equiv \{\phi_x\} \equiv \{\phi_y\}$ table for column cross sections, on the other hand, contains five columns, making both the choice of the correct data set, as well as possible interpolation, a major problem. A completely rational interpolation algorithm would require use of a system of merit functions to assign appropriate weights to the various parameters involved, and would therefore be quite difficult to implement.

As an approximation, a planar interpolation algorithm was devised, using two data sets with approximately (within ±5%) the entry P, with one having both M_x and M_y slightly larger than the entry values, while the other has both moments slightly smaller than the entry values. This was used for the work reported herein. It appeared to work satisfactorily most of the time, although it does not consider the influence of data sets with one moment larger and one smaller than the entry values, and occasional lack of convergence of the iteration process could be traced to difficulties with the interpolation routine. Other interpolation algorithms tried out did not give noticeably "better," or very different, results. Obviously, the density of the data and the evenness of their distribution will greatly influence the effectiveness of any interpolation routine.

An additional weakness of the tabular method is the fact that the table must be single-valued with respect to ϕ, that is, there must be only one curvature or combination of curvatures for any given end loading combination. This eliminates use of a descending branch in the moment-curvature relationship. As a means of overcoming the drawbacks of the tabular method, some thought has been given to using a statistical routine to obtain a polynomial expression that would be a "best fit" to the tabular data. No suitable algorithm has yet been found in the literature, but there is a possibility that one could be formulated.

Summary and Conclusions on Stiffness of Columns. A procedure has been outlined that makes it possible, with some computational effort, to obtain the complete bending stiffness matrix of a reinforced concrete column, subjected to axial load and biaxial bending, at all load levels. This is most useful in the three-dimensional step-by-step analysis of a tall building frame, in which the deflected shape of the column cannot be predicted.

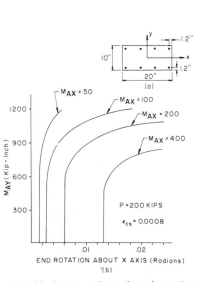

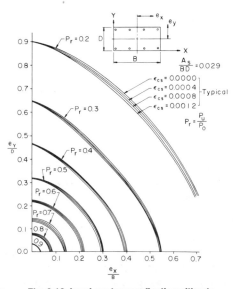

Fig. 6.15 Maximum end rotation about X axis for various end moments (shrinkage strain = 0.0008)

Fig. 6.16 Load contours reflecting ultimate column cross section capacity

It is evident from Figs. 6.14 and 6.15 that moment in one direction will have an appreciable effect on stiffness in the other direction. This probably should not be disregarded. Fig. 6.16 is presented to show the great effect of biaxial bending on ultimate strength when no length effects are present.

Programs based on this procedure have been integrated into over-all structural analysis programs as subroutines, and are most useful in that environment.

8 Torsion/Flexure Interaction

A complete analysis of nonlinear behavior requires a thorough understanding of the effects of the interaction of the different forces at a section upon the individual force-deformation characteristics.

One aspect of this interaction is that of torsion on the flexural moment-curvature relationship and vice versa; comparatively few experimental results in this connection are available. Some recent work (Estanero, 1972; Jackson and Estanero, 1971) included tests on more than 80 rectangular reinforced concrete beams, with varying aspect ratio and percentages of longitudinal and transverse reinforcement, under the combined action of flexure and torsion. Torsional and flexural rotations were measured throughout each test, as the bending and twisting moments were increased, simultaneously up to failure.

The results of the investigation on reinforced members in flexure and torsion show that the pseudoplastic rotation vectors are everywhere normal to the interaction curves relating the bending and twisting moments at failure. This is in accordance with the flow rule of ideal plasticity, namely the plastic potential flow law or normality criterion.

An analysis of the nonlinear behavior of structures, in which some regions undergo plastic deformations before the limit state of collapse is reached, is only possible when the associated plastic flow law is known.

Where the only significant deformations are those associated with simple flexure, the corresponding pseudoplastic deformation vector will effectively coincide with the (resultant) moment vector. However, where other deformations are significant, for example where biaxial bending or bending and twisting occur, this will not necessarily be the case, and the plastic flow law is required.

For prestressed concrete members under combined torsion and flexure, a certain amount of moment will generally improve the service load torsional resistance. This is due to the fact that under some moment, generally the dead-load moment, the stress across the section of a prestressed member would be essentially uniform, giving it greater torsional strength. This has also been proved by tests.

6.3 ULTIMATE STRENGTH UNDER REPETITIVE LOAD

The nonlinear analysis of a reinforced concrete frame may be regarded as a tool to evaluate the dynamic response of such a structure to earthquake motions. Hence it has to be a dynamic analysis, ultimately. However, an extension of static analysis to dynamic analysis is a relatively simple matter. One can concentrate on static nonlinear analysis without losing generality. On the other hand, the analysis has to deal with gradually varying load. A nonlinear analysis to get a solution for one point is not usable. It will inevitably involve a step-by-step method. Furthermore, the analysis has to consider the reversal of loading.

Repeated loading is the essential part of the analysis, and the path that the structure follows during the reversal is significant. "What happens to the structure when the load is reversed?" is more or less the question that should be asked. The main objective of this section, therefore, is to present the general problem, that is, the behavior of reinforced concrete structures under generalized excitations, to review previous work and its significance, and to indicate what remains to be done.

1 Design Problem

It is generally accepted that the logical approach to the design of a structure is the so-called limit-state approach, or comprehensive design (Sawyer, 1964; Bate, 1968). To design a structure, one must be able to predict its mechanical behavior at each significant level of the critical combination of all actions to which the structure may be subjected during its service life. Because it is usually impractical to consider real behavior under the actual generalized critical actions to which the structure may be subjected during its useful life, it is common to base structural design on idealized conceptions of mechanical behavior under simplified actions. In trying to assess the reliability of any proposed method of design one should recognize, first, that it is not possible to separate prediction of the mechanical behavior of a structure from the actual actions that will be exerted on it during its service life; and second, that in general real behavior can be determined only by carefully planned experimental and analytical studies.

The sources, treatment, and effects of the different types of actions that may be exerted on structures are summarized in Table 6.1 (Bertero, 1971). Most of the experimental evidence available regarding real mechanical behavior has been obtained under the assumption that the actions controlling the design of the structure are only external forces, which can be treated as quasi-statically applied loads.

Furthermore, it has been assumed that these forces increase monotonically and proportionally from zero up to the values necessary to induce what has been termed the "instantaneous collapse." In practice, of course, no building ever enjoys this type of action. It may be subjected not only to force, but to imposed deformations and to the effects of changes in the environment to which it is exposed. All these

Table 6.1 Sources, treatment, and effects of actions on structures

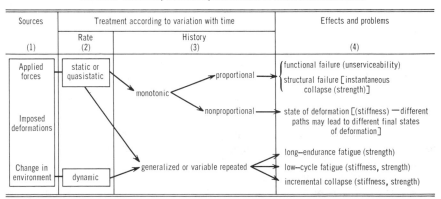

actions are, strictly speaking, dynamic rather than static in nature. Most often the sequence of actions to which a structure may be subjected consists of unpredictable fluctuations in the magnitude, direction, or position of each of the individual actions, and the only things that may be estimated with accuracy are the extreme values between which each of these actions will oscillate. These types of actions have been classified in Table 6.1 as generalized or variable-repeated actions.

The two patterns in which variable-repeated actions have been idealized—when the phenomena of incremental collapse and low-cycle fatigue have been treated separately—appear to produce similar undesirable effects on a structure, that is, increase in deformation (Bertero, 1966). Therefore, in investigating the importance of real generalized actions, the effects of alternating excitations cannot be isolated from the effects of excitation patterns leading to incremental deformation (Bertero, 1971). In this section attention will be focused on the effects of earthquake ground motion on structural concrete buildings, because this excitation is perhaps the most typical kind of generalized (dynamic, variable-repeated) action that occurs in practice.

To recognize the significance and pinpoint the limitations of results obtained in previous studies, and to plan rational future programs, it is convenient to discuss first the real seismic-design problems of buildings. In the case of earthquake excitations, it is usually necessary to predict the force-displacement relationship for each story with accuracy. The possibility of low-cycle fatigue as well as incremental collapse, as shown in Fig. 6.17, must be considered. The lateral displacement of any story, Δ_{H_i}, can be expressed as a function of excitations acting on the structure and the dynamic characteristics of the whole soil-structure system. In case of earthquake, the main excitations are due to: (1) Gravity forces, $G(t)$, with the associated effects due to creep of concrete; and (2) the three components of the ground

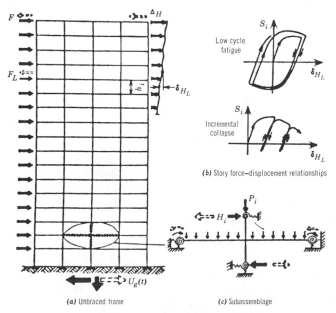

(a) Unbraced frame   (c) Subassemblage

Fig. 6.17 Problems in framed structures

displacement, $U_g(t)$. The dynamic characteristics of the whole system, which changes continuously as the structure is deformed into the inelastic range, might be represented symbolically by the instantaneous fundamental period $T(t)$ and damping coefficient $\xi(t)$. Then

$$\Delta_{H_i}(t) = f[G(t), U_g(t), T(t), \xi(t)] \tag{6.4}$$

Analysis of the parameters involved in Eq. 6.4 clearly indicates the difficulties that arise when one tries to predict response to earthquake ground motions. The first difficulty is that, strictly speaking, these parameters are functions of time, although the gravity forces usually remain practically constant for the duration of an earthquake. Therefore we are dealing with a dynamic problem in which it is necessary to consider the following two important effects of the time variation of the actions and of the response: (1) The effect of the inertia forces developed at the masses; and (2) the rate of change in intensity of the actions with time (rate of loading or straining). This rate might be high enough to affect considerably the so-called static-mechanical characteristics of the materials on which the dynamic characteristics of the structure, $T(t)$ and $\xi(t)$, are usually predicted.

Because the inertia forces depend not only on $U_g(t)$ but also are influenced by the behavior of the structure $[\Delta_{H_i}(t), T(t), \xi(t)]$, it is clear that this interaction between the structural response and the forces themselves causes serious difficulties not only in the theoretical prediction of the response, but also in the programming of any rational experimental investigation. As will be discussed later, the only efficient way to overcome these difficulties is through close integration of analytical and experimental studies of the same problem.

Another source of difficulty is that $\Delta_{H_i}(t)$ depends on the response of the whole soil-building system rather than on the structural system alone. The soil-building interaction affects the so-called free-field ground motion $U_g(t)$, which is the one usually measured. Furthermore, the response of the building depends on the couple interaction between the structural and the nonstructural elements.

To predict response it is necessary to have information regarding the dynamic characteristics, $T(t)$ and $\xi(t)$. More specifically, it is necessary to know the actual excitation-deformation relationship or restoring force characteristic, which includes stiffness, strength, energy absorption and energy dissipation capacities (which usually are loosely defined as ductility), and the different sources of damping. The interaction difficulties mentioned previously clearly indicate the need for experimental studies of real buildings under actual earthquake conditions. This discussion starts with a brief review of what has been done to date in this field. It then covers the different approximate experimental approaches that have been used. A more comprehensive review is offered by Bertero (1972).

2 Studies of Behavior of Actual Structures

Under Real Dynamic Excitations. Several buildings and their surroundings have been thoroughly instrumented and have been under observation for several years (Osaka et al., 1969; Kitagawa, 1972). Some significant results have been obtained regarding the behavior $[T(t), \xi(t),$ etc.] of these structures under what can be called service actions. However, no information has been obtained yet regarding their behavior in the inelastic range.

Under Simulated Dynamic Excitations. Using underground explosion tests, the effect of possible real earthquake ground motions has been studied, but again most of the data obtained have been in the elastic range. Shaking tables have also been used to simulate ground motion. Although the research potential of these tables is excellent, they can test only full-scale structural elements and assemblies or small-to-medium-scale models of complex structural systems. These models are usually inadequate for detailed investigation of the actual dynamic characteristics and failure mechanism of the prototype. Furthermore, reproduction of the actual ground motion (three components of displacement) is not easy. Most shaking tables reproduce only one component at a time. An extensive study of simulator facilities carried out at Berkeley (Penzien et al., 1967) proved that it will be feasible to construct a shaking table that can simultaneously undergo the three translational components of ground motion. However, the test structure can still be no larger than a 30-m × 30-m (100-ft × 100-ft) three-story reinforced concrete building.

From these considerations, it is clear that testing actual complex structures under extreme dynamic excitations, real or simulated, does not appear feasible. Subjecting actual structures or large-scale models to equivalent pseudostatic forces that induce effects similar to those of real dynamic excitations seems to be the most logical approach.

Tests to Failure Under Equivalent Pseudostatic Forces Associated with Small Amplitude Free and Forced Vibration Tests

Actual structures. In the pseudostatic tests up to failure, time effects are apparently eliminated. That is, inertia forces are replaced by equivalent pseudostatic loads, and by applying these loads slowly enough effects of the rate of straining and $\xi(t)$ become negligible.

It is essential that the limitations of this method are recognized from the start. In real situations, the inertia force at each concentrated mass varies with time, depending on the interaction of the real dynamic excitation and the dynamic characteristic of the building. Therefore, simulating the actual inertia forces by simple static forces is a difficult problem. The only solution is to simulate what can be considered the critical combination of inertia forces that could develop at a certain time. Rational selection of this critical combination requires integrated analytical and experimental studies (Bertero, 1972).

For earthquakes it is not easy to predict the actual critical distribution of inertia forces at different times, so tests are usually carried out using a distribution of static forces recommended by codes. The magnitude of these static forces is considered varied according to arbitrarily selected sequences, which usually are not the most critical ones. Furthermore, the effects of the vertical component of the ground motion are usually disregarded in the tests.

Japanese researchers have already tested several actual structures up to failure using repeated reversal pseudostatic lateral forces on buildings up to seven stories (Penzien et al., 1967; Funahashi et al., 1969; Aoyama et al., 1970). Some of these tests have been described in Chapter CB-9. Important data about how $T(t)$ and $\xi(t)$ vary with increased damage in the structure have been obtained by small amplitude free vibration and forced vibration tests. The curves of Fig. 6.18 show the behavior of one frame of the Hachinohe Technical College Building (Aoyama et al., 1970).

Because there are few opportunities to do field tests of actual buildings up to failure, and because of the difficulty of instrumenting and loading buildings in the field (which usually leads to tests on a simple isolated frame of a building), the next approach for determining the actual behavior of buildings is to carry out laboratory tests on large-scale models of actual buildings.

Laboratory tests of full-size buildings.   Since 1967, Japanese researchers have been carrying out static and dynamic tests on full-size apartment buildings up to five stories built of cast-in-place reinforced concrete, precast reinforced concrete, and precast concrete with a prestressed construction system. New and complex frame-walled structural systems have been tested. The results have been published in a series of reports (Koizumi et al., 1970; Ohsaki et al., 1970; Shinagawa and Hirosawa, 1971; Nakano et al., 1971). These studies have clarified the actual seismic behavior of these complex structural systems, particularly the interaction of their different elements. These results would have been almost impossible to predict analytically or by means of separate tests of their individual structural components. In complex structures like these it is difficult to estimate the interaction of different elements accurately. Only tests of this nature can give an idea of actual behavior. There are no clearly defined girders and columns, and it is not easy to estimate how much of the slabs and walls contributes to the strength and stiffness of idealized girders, columns, and shear walls. From results obtained in later tests and related analytical studies, it has become evident that it will be possible to build 15-story housing structures of either cast-in-place reinforced concrete or precast-prestressed concrete that will endure extreme earthquakes (Koizumi et al., 1970).

Regarding the effects of repeated reversal loadings, the most significant conclusions obtained from these full-size structural tests can be summarized as follows:

1. There is a degradation in initial stiffness and in the energy-dissipation capacity when the structure is subjected to a new reversal loading cycle after the deformation has been increased in the previous cycle.

2. The fundamental period for walled structures at working load level varied from 0.1 sec to 0.15 sec. In the inelastic range, this period became larger and

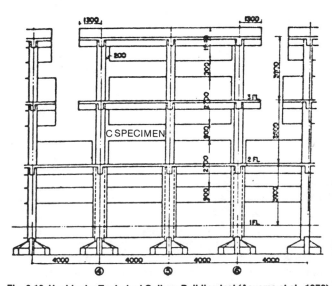

Fig. 6.18 Hachinohe Technical College Building test (Aoyama et al., 1970)

larger as the structures were subjected in larger numbers of loading cycles with increasing peak deformations. After the cycle in which the maximum static lateral forces were applied, the period varied from 0.17 sec to 0.47 sec.

3. The damping coefficient, which in the elastic region ranged from 1.4% to 2.2% under small amplitude vibration, increased to values ranging from 4.7% to 8.7% after the loading cycle in which the maximum static external force was applied.

4. When the specimens tested had walls whose strength and rigidity were not uniformly distributed, the weaker walls cracked under very small lateral forces and failed severely in shear. In these cases, the load capacities were smaller than those estimated and their strengths decreased rapidly with the increase in number of cycles of reversal loading. By improving the distribution of rigidity and strength of the walls and the detailing of the reinforcement, considerable increase in strength has been achieved, and the over-all behavior has not been significantly affected by application of repetitive alternating forces. They also had sufficient ductility and energy-dissipation capacities to withstand the effects of the generalized forces that could develop in extreme earthquakes.

Regarding the validity of these results, it is important to recognize that the distribution and sequence of the applied forces that were used might not represent the critical patterns that can be induced in extreme earthquakes. The hysteresis loop for fixed peak deformation depends on the previous history of loading. This is shown in Figs. 6.19(a) and 6.19(b). If the fixed peak deformations have not been exceeded before, [Fig. 6.19(a)], the peak resistance, initial stiffness and energy dissipation are larger than in the case where the fixed peak deformations have been exceeded in a previous cycle [Fig. 6.19(b)]. From these observations, it appears that the application of repeated reversal loading cycles in which the peak values of the load or deformation, or both, are increased gradually (which is the usual method) might not be a conservative way of testing. The structure may show considerably

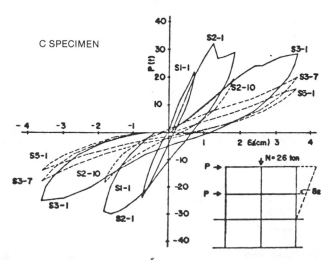

Fig. 6.18 (continued)

less energy dissipation capacity, and even less maximum strength, if it is loaded near or up to its ultimate resistance (deformation) during the first cycle.

3   Studies of Behavior of Structural Elements and Subassemblages

It would be ideal to test a real building under the actual loading conditions to which it may be subjected during its service life, but such tests are not usually feasible due to economic considerations. Logically, the next best approach is to try to predict the response of the complete building or its structural system from results obtained in studies carried out on its structural elements. This has been the approach of most investigators. Because members interact with one another in a complex way, it is difficult to predict behavior of the whole structure from the behavior of individual members. It is believed that, to predict the response of a building under generalized actions accurately, it is necessary to have information regarding behavior of certain basic subassemblages of elements. The type of basic assemblage to be studied depends on the structural system used. Even if discussion is restricted to reinforced concrete buildings, there are several structural systems that can be and have been used. However, for the purpose of this review only two systems will be considered: (1) Ductile moment-resisting space frames; and (2) shear walls.

Elements of Ductile Moment-Resisting Frame.   For this type of structural system it is necessary to know the behavior of subassemblages such as those indicated in Figs. 6.17 and 6.20. Detailed reasons for selecting these subassemblages can be found in Bertero (1968, 1971) and Bertero et al. (1969). To facilitate interpretation of results obtained in the studies of the behavior of these sub-assemblages, and to recognize the importance of their interaction, it is convenient first to review the behavior of their elements. Results obtained in experimental studies (Bertero and Bresler, 1969; Umemura and Aoyama, 1969; Aoyama, 1967) indicate that under variable-repeated actions, the real problem in reinforced concrete structures properly designed in accordance with current requirements appears to be degradation of stiffness and energy dissipation rather than strength. The question arises: "What is the reason for this observed degradation?" It must be a direct consequence of localized inelastic deformation that occurs at certain overstressed regions along the members of the structure. These regions, shown in Fig. 6.21 for just one floor, will be denoted from now on as "critical regions."

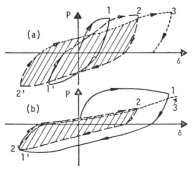

Fig. 6.19 Effect of loading history on energy dissipation

In reviewing the behavior of reinforced concrete regions, it is convenient to classify them according to their controlling state of stress as follows: (1) Critical regions in which inelastic behavior is controlled by bending (flexural critical regions); (2) critical regions whose inelastic behavior is controlled by high shear existing at the region, rather than bending; and (3) critical regions whose inelastic behavior is controlled by high axial and shear forces, rather than bending.

Flexural critical regions.　　Many researchers have experimentally investigated the behavior of these critical regions under variable repeated loadings [see Section 6.2 and Bertero et al., (1969); Bertero and Bresler (1969); Umemura and Aoyama (1969); Aoyama (1967); Ruiz and Winter (1969); Brown and Jirsa (1970); Park et al. (1972); and Park (1972)]. From an analysis and evaluation of the results obtained in these studies, the following observations can be made:

1. Concrete regions, properly designed and adequately reinforced according to present knowledge of their behavior under generalized (repeated reversal) bending moments, can develop ductility factors and offer energy absorption and energy dissipation capacities exceeding the values that might be required at these regions in case of a major earthquake. This is clearly shown by the results presented in Fig. 6.22.

2. The behavior of the critical regions of the double reinforced-concrete

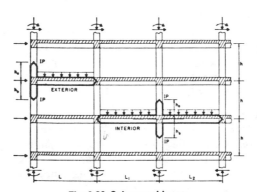

Fig. 6.20 Subassemblages

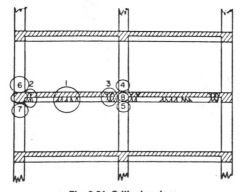

Fig. 6.21 Critical regions

members tested has been affected by repeated reversal of moments, when compared with the behavior expected under monotonically increasing moments, as follows: (a) The instantaneous stiffness is reduced after each reversal of moment in which the value of the peak moment or the deformation (or both) is increased beyond its previous value; (b) the maximum and ultimate strengths are increased if the peak of the moment or deformation (or both) of each successive reversal loading cycle is increased gradually; (c) larger curvature and deflection ductility factors are obtained when the peak values of the moment reversals are increased gradually; and (d) the energy absorption and energy dissipation capacities under reversal moments are higher than those expected under monotonically increasing moment. Due to the degradation of the instantaneous stiffness and the effect of strain hardening of the steel, prediction of these capacities cannot be based on a linear elastic-perfectly plastic model.

3. The behavior under reversal moments as the deformations imposed on the critical regions increase beyond the first yielding is controlled by the mechanical characteristics of the steel. This is a consequence of bond deterioration that occurs between main cracks as the reversals of moment increase in number and in magnitude of peak value. Predicting such behavior will require knowledge of the variation of the stress-strain relationship of the steel reinforcement under a strain history similar to that to which it is subjected in the critical region of the member. The Bauschinger effect is a controlling factor in the observed degradation of the stiffness. A method for predicting this degradation has been presented by Bertero and Bresler (1969). The influence of load history on the deterioration of bond has been studied experimentally at the University of California at Berkeley (Bresler and Bertero, 1966) and at Rice University (Ismail and Jirsa, 1972a).

4. Final failure usually has been due to buckling of the main reinforcement. The main factors controlling this buckling are: (a) Concrete cover; (b) the spacing, size, and detailing of hoops; and (c) strain history of the steel bar. Application of results obtained in the test of small-size elements to larger members should be made with caution, especially if some of these parameters are not simulated properly.

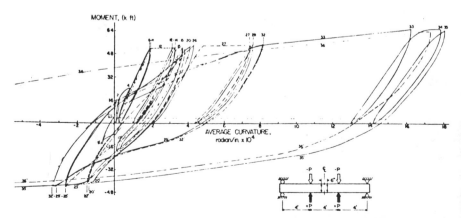

Fig. 6.22 Moment-curvature relationship, Beam 4 (Bertero et al., 1969)

5. The degradations in stiffness and in energy absorption and energy dissipation capacities with repeated reversal loading cycles of increased magnitude of deformation are not so severe as those observed in the case of frames and buildings.

6. There is no clear correlation among the strain, curvature, and deflection ductility factors, except after very severe cycles of reversals. This is shown in Fig. 6.23.

7. Most of the data have been obtained from tests carried out on beams with rectangular sections. Research is needed on specimens composed of beam integral with slabs in which the beam is loaded through the slab (Bertero, 1971), and on beams with different top and bottom steel areas.

Flexural critical regions with high shears. As has been pointed out in Section 6.2, the shear deformation appears to play a definite role in the rotations occurring in cracked portions of beams, and has given reference to some work done under monotonic increasing loads. In the case of generalized actions, the effect of high shear is considerably more important. Information is scarce on the behavior of this type of critical section subjected to variable repeated loadings (Brown and Jirsa, 1970; Krawinkler et al., 1972; Kano et al., 1969; Paulay, 1971a). It should be recognized that to predict the load-deformation relationship of members having this

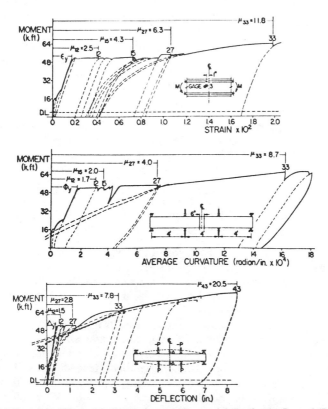

Fig. 6.23 Variation of ductility factors for strain, curvature and deflection for Beam 4 (Bertero et al., 1969)

type of critical region, it is necessary to obtain not only its moment-average curvature relationship (M versus ϕ) but also its shear force-shear angle distortion relationship (S versus γ). Evaluation of the available test results indicates:

1. Reduction in the shear span or increase in the shear forces at the critical region reduced the number of cycles to failure.

2. As soon as the average shear stress at the critical region reaches values larger than about $250\sqrt{f'_c}$ N/m² ($3\sqrt{f'_c}$ psi), the degradations in stiffness with reversal of load and in energy absorption and energy dissipation capacities with increase in the number of cycles become considerably larger than those for flexural critical regions with very low shear stresses. Also, degradation in strength occurs as the number of similar loading cycles increases. Failure is initiated by shear. Mechanisms of failure have been suggested by Brown and Jirsa (1970) and Krawinkler et al. (1972).

3. The ability of critical regions to maintain load and energy dissipation capacity (hysteresis loop stability) is significantly improved by reducing hoop spacing. For cases where shear stresses reach values on the order of $415\sqrt{f'_c}$ N/m² ($5\sqrt{f'_c}$ psi) or larger, and where web reinforcement has been designed according to present code recommendations, the degradations in strength, stiffness, and in energy absorption and energy dissipation, increased considerably with an increase in the number of cycles and the magnitude of deformations. To improve these mechanical characteristics it is necessary to design web reinforcement, neglecting any contribution of the concrete in resisting shear stress, and considering the actual bending capacity of regions. That is, this capacity should be based on actual strength of reinforcing steel, including strain hardening, and not just on minimum specified yielding strength.

4. To avoid excessive damage, and therefore degradation, when a region can be subjected to severe repeated loading reversal, the shear force that could develop at the critical sections should be limited in magnitude to a value considerably lower than that recommended by the ACI Building Code, which is $830\sqrt{f'_c}$ N/m² ($10\sqrt{f'_c}$ psi). The larger degradations observed in this type of critical region cannot be predicted by considerations of bond deterioration and Bauschinger effect alone, as in the case of pure flexure. Several significant additional factors have already been suggested by Bertero and Bresler (1969); Brown and Jirsa (1970); and Krawinkler et al. (1972).

It should be noted that if the behavior of this type of critical region is described by a measured load-displacement relationship, rather than by its moment-curvature relationship, the previously mentioned degradations are considerably larger, because the contribution of shear deformations is not detected just by measuring flexural rotation at the critical region.

The behavior of shear walls is discussed extensively in Section 6.4.

Flexural critical regions with high axial and shear forces.   It is well known that the presence of axial forces not only changes the moment capacity of reinforced-concrete sections, but also considerably affects ductility. This has been shown clearly in Fig. 6.8 of Section 6.2. However, it should be noted that in case of real critical regions with sufficiently large cross sections of well confined concrete, brittle failure at the balanced stage indicated in Fig. 6.8 does not really occur. New moment-axial force and axial force-average ultimate curvature interaction curves should be drawn for the confined concrete core of the section. The relative position of the new interaction curves with respect to the original ones will depend not only on the relative size of the confined core with respect to that of the whole cross section, but also on the spacing and detailing of hoops or spiral and strain-hardening characteristics of the reinforcements.

Japanese investigators have carried out numerous experimental and analytical studies on flexural members subjected to significant axial and shear forces (Aoyama et al., 1970; Umemura et al., 1970; Kokusho and Oguro, 1970; Yamada and Furui, 1968; Hisada et al., 1972; Wakabayashi et al., 1971; Kokusho and Hayashi, 1971).

Test results show that as the axial stress is increased, the reduction in strength and in deformational energy absorption and energy dissipation capacities increases with the number of cycles of repeated reversal loadings. However, for columns with shear span ratios larger than 2, by increasing the amount of web reinforcement, especially by decreasing the spacing of hoops, the reduction is limited, and it is possible to have very ductile column behavior even under high P/P_y ratios and large numbers of repeated alternating bending moment cycles. This is clearly shown in the results given in Fig. 6.24, which were obtained in a specimen having a shear span ratio of 2.14 (Hisada et al., 1972).

Very short columns, in which shear forces predominate, become brittle. Studies carried out by Yamada (Yamada and Furui, 1968) on very short columns (shear span ratio = 1.2) subjected to constant high axial forces and repeated alternating transverse loads, show that when the web reinforcement ratio $p_w < 0.44\%$, the columns show an explosive brittle failure immediately after diagonal cracking. On

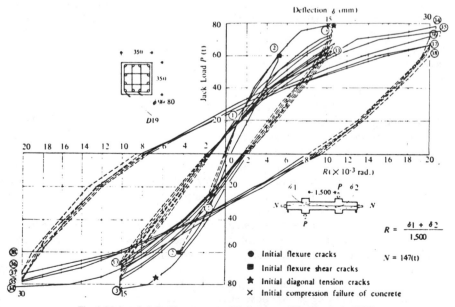

Fig. 6.24 Load-deflection curves of tied column (Hisada et al., 1972)

the other hand, columns with $p_w \geq 0.88\%$ show ductility after diagonal cracking. Yamada concludes that web reinforcement ratios necessary to prevent a shear explosion failure and to give sufficient ductility under the effects of severe ground motion are shown by tests to be larger than 1%. This requires very closely spaced hoops.

In summary, although extensive test data are available, different results have not yet been compared and interpreted to deduce general rules that will permit proper design of these members against extreme generalized excitations. Furthermore, all the available data have been obtained under excitations that produce only a constant compressive axial force, and shear and bending in only one main plane of the element. Since columns are usually subjected to biaxial shear and bending, there is an urgent need for experimental and analytical studies of the inelastic behavior of columns under the combined effects of axial force and biaxial shear and bending. Furthermore, due to overturning moments and the vertical component of acceleration that can be developed during extreme earthquakes, the sustained compressive axial load acting in the column due to gravity forces can be not only increased but also decreased to values that can crack the concrete throughout the column section, especially when the effects of creep and shrinkage are great. Therefore, it is of paramount importance to study columns on which the axial force is varied from compression to tension, while the columns are subjected to reversals of moment and shear.

Beam-Column Subassemblages. Experimental studies carried out on simple beams and columns, particularly on their critical regions, failed to show the accentuated degradation in stiffness and energy capacities that has been observed in most tests carried out on frames and on actual structures. This discrepancy has been explained by analyzing tests on beam-column subassemblages. Most of the available experimental evidence to date has been provided by the tests conducted by: (1) The Portland Cement Association (PCA) (Hanson, 1971; Hanson and Conner, 1967; Corley and Hanson, 1969); (2) University of Canterbury (Megget and Park, 1971; Smith, 1972; Reaton, 1972; Patton, 1972); (3) Japanese investigators (Umemura and Ikeda, 1963, 1964; Koreishi, 1970; Inomata, 1969; Higashi and Ohwada, 1969); and (4) Townsend (1972).

The curves of Fig. 6.25 show the performance of one unit of a series of six specimens tested at the University of Canterbury (Megget and Park, 1971; Smith, 1972). Each specimen consisted of a column with a beam framing into one side at midheight, representing full-size assemblies of a reinforced-concrete external-beam-column joint of a frame of a two-story building. In all six specimens, failure occurred in the joint regions rather than in the adjoining members due to the large joint shears. The results shown in Fig. 6.25 correspond to the unit whose performance was superior. It is interesting to note the considerable degradation in initial stiffness at the reversal of the loading.

Higashi and Ohwada (1969) have tested large numbers of specimens representing, in about 1/3 scale, interior beam-column connection subassemblages of actual reinforced concrete frames. The results of these tests are discussed and illustrated in Chapter CB-9.

From analysis of the results available on behavior of beam-column subassemblages the following general observations can be made:

    1. In the case of exterior beam-column subassemblage, the degradation in stiffness observed with reversal of loading is considerably larger than that

obtained for critical regions under pure flexure or bending and low shear forces. An explanation of this larger degradation has been offered by Bertero and Bresler (1969); Reaton (1972); and Townsend (1972). The major factors contributing to this degradation appear to be the increased deterioration of anchorage of bars due to diagonal cracking in the joint, the crushing of the concrete around the curved portion of the anchorage of the beam-reinforcing bars, and the grinding abrasion of the concrete along the diagonal cracking, which increases with the number of cycles. The behavior of anchored bars under low-cycle overloads producing inelastic strains has been studied recently at Rice University (Ismail and Jirsa, 1972b).

2. The behavior of interior beam-column subassemblage is sensitive to the detailing at the panel zone of the beam main reinforcement.

3. The most effective way of avoiding reduction in strength with an increase in the number of cycles is to confine the concrete in the panel zone with beams framing into the four faces of this zone.

4. The mechanism of stiffness degradation and even that of failure at the panel zone can be explained qualitatively, so that proper detailing can prevent premature failure.

Shear Walls.   In view of its high resistance to lateral forces, the reinforced concrete shear wall is regarded as useful for buildings designed to withstand wind and earthquake excitations. Different types of shear walls have been used in building construction. Some have already been tested against the effects of repeated

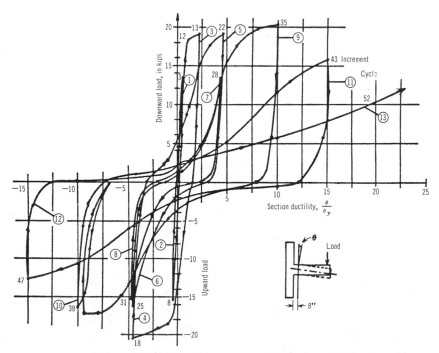

Fig. 6.25 Load-section ductility relationship of beam-column subassemblage (Smith, 1972)

forces such as might develop during an extreme earthquake (Hirosawa, 1969; Matsushita et al., 1971; Tomii, 1973b; Umemura, 1970; Muto, 1969). Tomii (1973b) gives a detailed discussion of the state of the art on shear walls. From results available, methods and equations have been suggested to obtain load-deflection curves for the seismic design of shear walls (Tomii, 1973b; Umemura, 1970). The behavior of tall shear walls is discussed in Section 6.4 of this chapter. Short walls loaded primarily in shear are discussed in Chapter CB-11.

4   Effects of Rate of Loading

For many years it has been recognized that the behavior of materials under dynamic conditions is vastly different from their behavior under static conditions, especially in three respects (Faupel, 1964; Norris et al., 1959; Air Force Design Manual, 1962; Newmark and Rosenblueth, 1971; Griswell, 1970). First, the normal static stress-strain relationship is altered, permitting different deformational energy absorption and energy dissipation capacities. In general, the mechanical characteristics of materials tend to improve with increasing rate of load application. Second, the dynamic loading may alter the mode of failure. In general, it enhances brittle failure; therefore the interaction of and influence on cracking tendency of such conditions as severe restraint, residual stresses, discontinuous flaws, thickness of materials and joints, and transfer of stresses from one material to another in composite materials must be studied. Third, dynamic loading can cause failure by fatigue, being the low-cycle fatigue of special interest in this discussion.

Despite these differences, at present (1978) most civil engineering structure designs are based on results obtained in quasistatic tests. Therefore, it is not surprising that questions continually arise concerning the effects of the actual strain rate induced as a consequence of the dynamic excitations to which the structure is

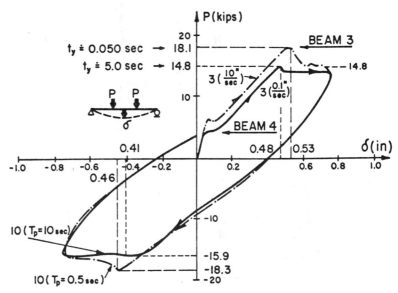

Fig. 6.26 Effect of loading rate (Bertero et al., 1972)

subjected. Because the mechanical characteristics of materials, especially strength, tend to improve with increased rate of strain, it seems conservative to use pseudostatic test results to predict the behavior of structures under actual dynamic excitations.

Most research on the effect of strain rate on reinforced concrete elements has been carried out on flexural members (Inomata, 1969; Norris et al., 1959; Air Force Design Manual, 1962; Newmark and Rosenblueth, 1971; Griswell, 1970; Bertero et al., 1972; Shiga et al., 1970; Takeda et al., 1970; Gulkan and Sozen, 1971). In this case, the main effect has been an increase in the yield moment as it could be expected according to the known behavior of each of the component materials under high straining rates. A series of tests has been carried out recently (Bertero et al., 1972) to study the effects of repeated reversal loadings at different rates on uncracked and repaired reinforced concrete members. Some results are given in Fig. 6.26. The results show that: (1) The only significant effect of high rates of strain is the increase of the first yield moment; (2) when the deformation is increased beyond that required for first yielding, the effects of rate of loading gradually decrease; and (3) after a cycle of loading in which the member is subjected to deformation beyond its first yielding, the hysteresis loops are affected very little by the straining rate.

Significance of Results Available and Conclusions. The question that designers would like to see answered concerns the significance of the available test results to the design of structures against real dynamic excitations. It should be noted, in answering this question, that it is the response of the whole structural system, rather than the frequency content of the excitation, that determines the dynamic effect felt by its critical regions and their component materials. For example, in case of earthquake, the ground motion might have very high frequencies, but the rate of straining at the critical regions of the structure will

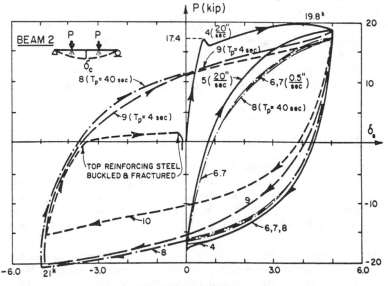

Fig. 6.26 (continued)

depend on the dynamic characteristics of the structural system, especially on its fundamental period of vibration. Therefore in evaluating for seismic design the possible effect of the rate of straining, it is necessary to consider the range in which the instantaneous fundamental period of actual structures can vary. In the case of very rigid structures with very short periods, 0.1 sec for example, the rate of straining at the critical regions can be as high as 2.5 mm/mm/sec (2.5 in./in./sec) or even more. On the other hand, in the case of very tall, slender structures in which the fundamental period can be as long as 10 sec, it is clear that the rate of straining will be very low, perhaps only 0.025 mm/mm/sec (0.025 in./in./sec).

Therefore, it is clear that significant effects from the rate of straining during earthquake may occur only in rigid structures. Even in this case, due to the fact that the rate of straining will be only about 2.5 mm/mm/sec (2.5 in./in./sec), the only significant effect will be an increase in the first yield-moment resistance at the critical regions, which might amount to about 25%. Since this is the only apparent beneficial effect, most investigators and engineers agree that it may be conservative to use just the pseudostatic test results as a basis for design. While this will certainly be true in cases of members subjected to practically pure flexure, it might not be true in cases where shear and axial forces are important. A 25% increase in moment capacity might result in a 25% increase in the shear forces acting at the critical regions. Then the question is whether the rate of strain that has induced a 25% increase in moment capacity also produces an increase in the shear resistance of these critical regions. Because reliable information about the effect of the rate of strain on the shear resistance of critical regions is lacking, it would be desirable to design the web reinforcement of these critical regions with consideration for the possible increase in moment capacity according to the maximum rate of strain probable.

Results are already available from a series of tests on models of structural elements and simple frame structures. In general, they confirm that the only important effect of the rate of strain that could be induced in extreme earthquakes is a possible increase in moment capacity (Shiga et al., 1970; Takeda et al., 1970; Gulkan and Sozen, 1971). In evaluating the results of tests on models, it should be kept in mind that the smaller the model, the higher the frequency range for the model test. In small models, the rate of strain could have a significant influence on such material characteristics as strength, modulus of elasticity, and internal damping.

5   Proposed Models for Nonlinear Analysis

Guided by some of the experimental results reviewed here, several investigators have suggested models for the load-deformation relationships of reinforced concrete incorporating the observed changes in stiffness with cyclic loading (Bertero and Bresler, 1969; Brown and Jirsa, 1970; Park et al., 1972; Higashi and Ohwada, 1969; Park, 1972; Takeda et al., 1970; Gulkan and Sozen, 1971; Clough and Johnston, 1966; Aoyama, 1971). Several different models are discussed in Chapter CB-9. Although these models have been proposed for nonlinear dynamic analysis of seismic response, they are based on static force-deformation relationships. While some of the proposed models (Bertero and Bresler, 1969; Brown and Jirsa, 1970; Park et al., 1972) have been derived theoretically from the static stress-strain relationships of the materials under cyclic straining, taking into account the main factors that contribute to stiffness degradation, other models can be constructed only by following a series of rules established from direct analysis of results obtained in static tests (Takeda et al., 1970; Gulkan and Sozen, 1971; Clough and Johnston, 1966). One of the most significant contributions in this area is the work of Takeda et al. (1970). Those investigators have checked their static force-displacement model against a series of static tests and have used it to predict responses against those measured in a series of tests carried out on a shaking table. The agreement was excellent, except that measured maximum accelerations exceeded the calculated values. The main reason for this discrepancy was that, as the tests were carried out on models, the strain rate was very high and therefore affected the models' static resistance. A third group of investigators has suggested that the experimental hysteresis loops can be expressed as polynomials in terms of two or three test parameters (Townsend, 1972; Shiga et al., 1970).

All the proposed models are for frame structural elements and are based on the assumption that failure is controlled by ductile flexural behavior. No model has been suggested for frame elements in which failure is controlled by shear, or for the case of shear-wall elements and subassemblages. These are areas in which further research is needed.

Efficient computer programs for nonlinear dynamic analysis of tall buildings have been developed (Powell, 1972). However, all these programs are based on simple idealized moment-curvature or rotation hysteresis loops. One program has been used in analysis of the seismic damages of an actual reinforced concrete structure (Bertero et al., 1974; Chopra et al., 1976).

6 Suggestions for Research

At present, no realistic models can be formulated for the prediction of the nonlinear behavior of tall reinforced concrete buildings subjected to severe generalized excitations. However, modern testing techniques and facilities have permitted investigators to improve their understanding of this subject appreciably. It is now possible to understand the different mechanisms of failure that can develop and to design structures that will withstand these excitations. From the review and discussion presented here, it is clear that much remains to be learned regarding the actual behavior of tall concrete buildings under this type of excitation. Research is needed in the following areas:

1. Thorough instrumentation of a large number of actual tall buildings and surroundings, to obtain reliable data regarding the history of actual excitations, the dynamic characteristic of the structures, and their response.

2. Dynamic and static testing of real structures or of large-scale models under realistic sequences of excitation. This is needed to study the interaction of different structural components, as well as their interaction with non-structural elements. The variation of T and ξ with increasing damage should be studied. The sequence of excitation should be determined through integrated (iterative) experimental and analytical studies.

3. According to the range in which the sequence of actual excitations on structures can vary, it is necessary to establish well-defined loading conditions to test conservatively real structures and large-scale models and their elements and subassemblages.

4. Behavior of flexural critical regions should be studied in order to establish a better criterion for delaying buckling of the main reinforcement.

5. Testing of flexural critical regions with high shear (uniaxial and biaxial), and with combined high shear (biaxial) and axial forces. Standard ways of testing should be established to facilitate comparison and interpretation of results. Emphasis should be placed on the evaluation of degradation in strength, stiffness, and energy dissipation with the number of cycles, and in finding ways of detailing the reinforcements to avoid brittle shear type of failure.

6. Experimental studies on realistic beam-column assemblies, including the contribution of floor slabs and walls, should be initiated. The effective widths of these elements should be determined from the point of view of stiffness as well as strength. Emphasis should be given to the mechanism of failure at the joint panel zone.

7. Studies are needed on the behavior of different types of shear walls with various boundary frames to improve their ductility and energy dissipation capacity, and to formulate mathematical models for their hysteretical behavior.

8. The effect of the rate of straining, especially in the case of combined states of stress, needs to be determined.

9. Investigations should be made of repair methods on structural components that have been damaged during high-intensity excitations. The strength, stiffness, and energy dissipation capacity of these repaired components should be compared with that of the original elements.

10. Studies are needed to develop hysteretical models that are both simple enough to be incorporated into practical computer programs and close enough to reality to depict the essential features of the observed degradation effects.

6.4 RESPONSE AND DESIGN OF SHEAR WALLS

In many tall buildings shear walls will provide most, if not all, of the required strength for lateral loading resulting from gravity, wind, and earthquake effects. Their incorporation into an over-all plan, dictated by various functional requirements, will usually determine their geometry (Christiansen, 1972; König, 1972; Kozak, 1972). For this reason it is not possible to specify a unified treatment for the nonlinear analysis or the evaluation of the limit of ultimate strength for shear-wall structures. However, the fundamental behavior of typical shear-wall structures has been identified in numerous studies (Symposium on Tall Buildings with Particular Reference to Shear Wall Structures, 1967; Winokur and Gluck, 1968) in which the techniques of elastic analysis have been used, or suitably modified, to evaluate internal load disposition, stresses, and deformations. Unfortunately, at present only limited experimental evidence is available from which the range of validity of such analyses, as applied to reinforced concrete shear walls, could be gaged. Many problems arising from cracking and the nonlinear flexural response of reinforced concrete structural members, including walls, have been discussed in Section 6.2.

Normally, for wind loading, the governing design criterion or limit state will be deflection. When drift limitations in tall buildings are satisfied, it is usually found that it is not difficult to provide for the strength requirements using appropriate load factors specified by codes (ACI, 1971).

In addition to the limit states for strength and deflection, the requirement for ductility arises, particularly for shear walls used for seismic resistance. Only in exceptional cases will it be possible to resist earthquake-generated inertia forces within the elastic range of behavior. In case of very large earthquakes it is generally accepted that energy dissipation, involving considerable excursions into the postelastic range, will have to be relied upon. This nonlinear response of shear walls is further complicated by the fact that dynamic response to random vibratory motions is involved. The effects of variable repeated and reversed loading, rate of loading, and strength and stiffness degradations of reinforced concrete structures, have been discussed and illustrated with experimental observations in Section 6.3.

The main purpose of this section is to review the strength criteria for shear walls when large intensity reversed cyclic loading is involved, and when a demand for large ductilities in the shear-wall structure and its components may exist. The source of ductility—energy dissipation—is briefly discussed, with the intention of drawing designers' attention to desirable and possible energy dissipating mechanisms, and pointing out the modes of potentially brittle failures under seismic load conditions. Strength and ductility have also previously been considered in Article 6.2.5.

Shear walls, when carefully designed and detailed, hold the promise of giving the greatest degree of protection against nonstructural damage in moderate earthquakes, while assuring survival in case of catastrophic seismic disturbances, on account of their ductility. This was clearly demonstrated, for example, by the Banco de America building, which responded successfully to intense shaking during the Managua earthquake in 1972. The performance of this and several other shear-wall buildings during recent earthquakes was critically examined by Fintel (1974a).

1   Potential Failure Modes and Geometry

A single cantilever shear wall, such as the one shown in Fig. 6.27, can be expected to behave in the same way as a reinforced concrete beam. The narrow cross section suggests that problems of lateral instability may arise. However, floor slabs of multistory buildings, when effectively connected to the wall, acting as stiffeners, provide adequate lateral strength.

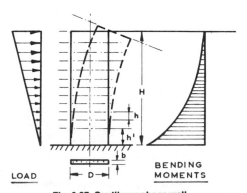

Fig. 6.27 Cantilever shear wall

Such shear walls, as large cantilevers, will be subjected to bending moments and shear forces originating from lateral loads, and to axial compression induced by gravity. Accordingly the flexural strength of the critical section, normally at the base of the structure, can be evaluated from first principles of flexure-axial load interaction. The vertical reinforcement in the web portion of such a wall may be considerable, and its contribution to flexural strength must be taken into account. As essential prerequisites, adequate foundations and sufficient connection to all floors, to transmit horizontal loads, must be assured.

Flexural Strength of Tall Shear Walls. In shear walls with moderate height, particularly in areas not affected by earthquakes, the flexural steel demand may not be large. Consequently the vertical reinforcement is often uniformly distributed over the whole section. Such an arrangement does not efficiently utilize the reinforcement when developing the ultimate moment. Moreover, the ultimate curvature, and hence, the curvature ductility, may be seriously reduced (Cardenas and Magura, 1973). Fig. 6.28 shows, by means of an example wall section (Cardenas and Magura, 1973), that the ductility properties improve when the bulk of the flexural reinforcement is placed near the edges of the wall section. This will also enable a considerable portion of the flexural compression to be resisted by reinforcement when the wall is subjected to alternating reversed loading causing yielding.

Where a shear wall also carries considerable gravity load in addition to large lateral force, it may be necessary to improve the ductility properties of the critical region, normally at foundation level, by providing confinement to the concrete in the compression zones. Wall ties can be arranged in the same way as in tied columns. Closely spaced transverse ties are required around vertical flexural bars, which may be subjected to alternating yielding and hence Bauschinger effect, to assure that local buckling of individual bars does not occur. Tie spacing for such situations should be considerably less than the distance recommended by codes for columns receiving static gravity loads (Bresler and Gilbert, 1961).

For vertically post-tensioned shear walls the flexural strength can be computed by the usual beam theory as applied to prestressed concrete beams.

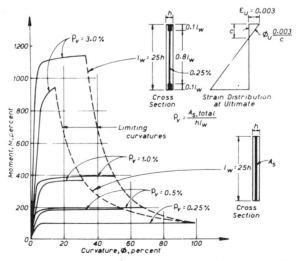

Fig. 6.28 Effect on ultimate curvature of amount and distribution of vertical reinforcement (Cardenas and Magura, 1973)

Shear Strength of Tall Shear Walls.   The shear strength of shear walls with a height to depth ratio >3 can be assessed in the same way as that of beams. Due allowance can be made for the contribution of the axial compression (ACI, 1971) in boosting the share of the shear resisting mechanisms, other than web reinforcement (Fenwick and Paulay, 1968). (This share is usually referred to as the contribution of the concrete.) However, the adverse effect of vertical accelerations, induced by earthquakes, should be considered. At the base of the wall, where yielding of the flexural reinforcement in both faces of the section can occur, the contribution of the concrete towards shear strength should be disregarded where the axial compression on the gross cross section is less that 12% of the cylinder crushing strength of the concrete. This relatively small compression may be offset by vertical accelerations inducing tension. Moreover, cyclic reversed loading, causing diagonal cracking in two directions, is known to diminish the shear strength of the concrete rapidly. This implies that in most cases horizontal stirrups must be provided to resist the whole of the shear force generated near the base of the wall by the lateral forces. This shear reinforcement must extend at least over the possible length of the plastic hinge, where yielding of the flexural bars will also affect the width of diagonal cracks. The length for full shear reinforcement should not be taken less than the over-all depth (D in Fig. 6.27) of the shear wall section. Tests show that the existing requirements of the American Concrete Institute (ACI, 1971) predict conservatively the shear strength of shear walls under monotonic load conditions (Cardenas et al., 1973).

Where it is essential that the lateral and gravity strength of a tall shear wall be maintained in a ductile manner, as is the case in seismic areas, every attempt must be made to suppress a shear failure. This is only possible if the shear force, associated with the maximum possible flexure strength of the critical section, and taking into account the increased yield strength of the flexural reinforcement due to strain hardening, is provided for in such a way that the shear (web) reinforcement will not yield. The shear strength of tall shear walls may also be controlled by combined moment and shear failure at the base of the wall. This is true for both prestressed and reinforced walls.

Construction Joints Across Shear Walls.   Earthquake damage in shear walls of high-rise buildings (Jennings, 1971) has often been observed at construction joints, along which sliding movements occurred. For monotonic loading the failure along a construction joint may be quite ductile. However, after load reversal very large slips and a reduction of shear resistance result (Paulay et al., 1974). The failure mechanism dissipates diminishing energy under cyclic loading when the reinforcement crossing the joint yields. Fig. 6.29 shows the shear stress-shear slip relationship for a construction joint specimen subjected to a few cycles of reversed static loading. It should be noted that after yielding slips in excess of 2.5 mm (0.1 in.) in each direction have been recorded. These involve damage almost beyond repair. It is evident that this mechanism is unsuitable in earthquake-resistant structures. For this reason a failure along construction joints should be suppressed, just as diagonal tension failure due to shear is to be prevented by all means, in order to allow a ductile flexural energy dissipating mechanism to develop when required.

The dominant mode of shear transfer across a horizontal construction joint is by aggregate interlock action, also called shear friction. Dowel action of the reinforcement, crossing a horizontal construction joint (once believed to be the major component of shear resistance) is relatively insignificant, because the full strength of dowel action can be mobilized only after a significant slip along the joint has occurred. By that time the shear friction resistance is greatly diminished.

Fig. 6.30 shows the shear stress-slip relationship for construction joint specimens subjected to monotonic loading. In Fig. 6.30, f'_c = concrete cylinder strength in pounds per square inch; f_y = yield strength of reinforcement crossing the joint; and ρ_v = reinforcing content. The top curves show the shear stress transferred by shear friction only, using different surface preparations. The bottom curve gives the contribution of the dowel action of the vertical bars only in terms of average shear stress. It is seen that up to a slip of 0.01 in. the contribution of the dowel action is negligible (Paulay et al., 1971) and that dowel strength becomes significant at a very large sliding movement of 0.1 in. or more.

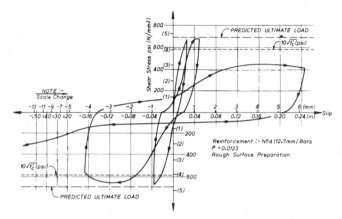

Fig. 6.29 Shear stress-slip relationship observed at construction joint transferring cyclic reversed shear forces (Paulay et al., 1971)

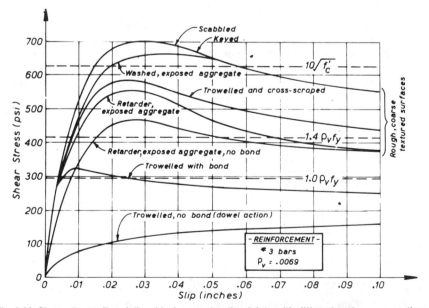

Fig. 6.30 Shear stress-slip relationship for construction joints with different surface preparations (Paulay et al., 1971)

To assure efficient shear transfer, the potential crack along a construction joint must be prevented from opening so that the contact between the rough surfaces at either side of the crack is not lost. Thus the prime function of the vertical reinforcement, passing across a construction joint, is to supply the necessary clamping force and to enable friction forces to be transferred.

It does not seem to matter how the surface of the old concrete at a construction joint is prepared. As long as it is rough and clean and the freshly placed concrete, placed upon it, is well bonded to it, a shear force corresponding with a friction factor of unity can be repeatedly transferred with insignificant slip (Paulay et al., 1971). The basic strength of a construction joint can be assessed as

$$v_{uf} = \frac{A_{vf}f_y + N}{A_g} = \rho_v f_y + \frac{N}{A_g} \tag{6.5}$$

in which v_{uf} = average ultimate shear stress transferable across a well prepared rough construction joint; A_{vf} = total vertical steel to be utilized for the required clamping force; A_g = gross area of a rectangular shear wall section; N = axial force on the section taken as positive when producing compression; f_y = yield strength of the reinforcement used; and ρ_v = reinforcing steel ratio.

It is normal practice to provide a nominal minimum amount of vertical reinforcement equal to $\rho_v = 0.0015$ to 0.0025, and this steel will provide a considerable clamping force across construction joints. However, in the lower parts of shear walls, carrying large lateral forces, this steel content may have to be considerably increased in accordance with Eq. 6.5 if a sliding shear failure is to be suppressed. It is important that the required vertical reinforcement be provided at close spacing because the clamping force, supplied by each bar, is effective only in the bars' immediate vicinity. Reinforcement provided for flexure and situated near the edges should not be included in the evaluation of clamping force to be developed across the core of the section.

Tests have clearly shown (Paulay et al., 1971) that when the reinforcement across the construction joint commences to yield, the control over crack width is lost and a sliding shear failure is imminent. This point coincides with the top of the upper curves shown in Fig. 6.30. Sliding movement dislodges aggregate particles and drastically reduces the effective surface roughness so that the shear strength of the joint, particularly for reversed loading, is greatly diminished. For this reason mechanisms relying on shear friction for energy dissipation, sometimes advocated in precast panel construction for shear walls, are unsuitable for earthquake-resistant structures.

For vertically post-tensioned shear walls, the presence of vertical prestress will help to eliminate cracking along construction joints.

Squat Shear Walls. In shear walls with a height to depth ratio <2 it may be more difficult to assure ductile flexural failure mechanisms. Fortunately, such structures seldom occur in tall buildings. For this reason their strength and behavior will not be discussed here. Their performance is sometimes compared with that of deep beams. Such comparisons must be evaluated with great care because the introduction of load, generating shear stresses, is generally very different in these two types of structures (Paulay, 1970b).

Even though the shear forces acting in squat walls may be considerable, by careful proportioning of the flexural and shear reinforcement, and in particular with thoughtful detailing, it is possible to enforce also upon these structures a ductile failure mode (Paulay, 1970b). For these walls, the use of vertical post-tensioning will greatly increase shear strength. Such post-tensioning should be continued to near the bottom of the foundation to be fully effective (Lin, 1965). The limit to the lateral load capacity of low-rise shear walls is often set by the inability of the foundations to provide stability against overturning moments.

Moment Axial Load Interaction for Shear-Wall Sections. There is no reason to expect that tall shear walls with flanged cross sections would behave differently. In symmetrical sections usually the internal "steel couple" can carry the external moment, and the contribution of the concrete is governed by the magnitude of the gravity load. When significant gravity compression is present the whole area of flanges may be subjected to compression when the tension steel is at yield. In such cases it may be necessary to provide secondary, confining reinforcement in the compression flanges.

Flanges may boost the moment of resistance of shear walls so that shear stresses in the webs, causing diagonal tension cracks or possible slip along construction joints, may become critical. Appropriate horizontal and vertical shear reinforcement must be provided so that at no stage of the loading should yield be expected in such reinforcement.

The moment capacity of unsymmetrical wall sections, in the presence of axial load, needs to be assessed for each possible direction of the loading. As the over-all sectional dimensions of tall shear walls remain usually sensibly constant over the height of the building, it is sometimes expedient to derive the complete moment-axial force $(M_u - P_u)$ interaction for such sections. This allows ready selection of the appropriate steel content at any level. Fig. 6.31 shows such a chart for a channel-shaped shear-wall section with a sectional aspect ratio of 3, in which the vertical reinforcement is uniformly distributed (Paulay, 1972). Positive moments are considered to cause tension, and negative moments will induce compression, in the web portion of the wall section. The radiating straight lines indicate the position of the neutral axis, C, measured from the compression edge, as a fraction of the depth, D, of the section. This shows the extent of compression area at the development of full strength. In this region special transverse reinforcement for confinement of the concrete and for stability of compression bars, subjected to Bauschinger effect, may be required.

2   Shear Walls with Openings

Windows, doors, and service ducts require that certain shear walls be provided with openings. It is important that at the early stages of planning suitable decisions are made with respect to the positioning of openings so that a rational structure results. One may define a rational shear-wall structure as one whose essential behavior can be assessed by bare inspection.

Irregular shear-wall structures usually defy solutions by routine techniques of structural analysis, and in such cases model investigations or finite-element studies may assist in the evaluation of the internal forces. This may be sufficient when only wind loading is to be resisted. However, only special experimental studies can disclose the important aspects of ultimate strength, energy absorption, and ductility demand in irregular shear walls which have to survive severe seismic disturbances.

It is imperative that the openings to be provided should interfere as little as possible with the moment and shear carrying capacity of the structure. A good example of an irregular shear wall is shown in Fig. 6.32(a). The flexural resistance of the cantilever structure is drastically reduced at the critical section near the base. The staggered arrangement of openings seriously reduces the contact area between the two walls where shearing forces should be transmitted. The legs of the wall illustrated in Fig. 6.32(b) could lead to an undesirable situation in which the wall tilts excessively in a direction opposite to the sway displacement of the sloping legs. Observations after earthquakes indicate that such structures invite disaster (Sozen, 1968).

3 Coupled Shear Walls

Many shear walls contain one or more rows of openings. Common examples are "shear cores" of tall buildings that accommodate elevator shafts, stairwells, and service ducts. Access doors necessarily pierce the walls of such cores. Therefore the

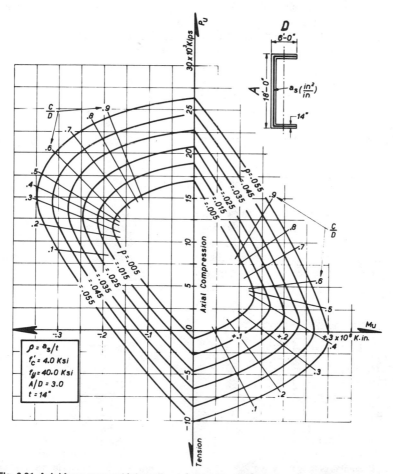

Fig. 6.31 Axial force-moment interaction relationship of channel-shaped shear wall section

walls are interconnected only by beams, often short and relatively deep, left between openings. It is customary to refer to such walls as being coupled. An idealized coupled shear-wall structure and its deformations caused by lateral loading are shown in Fig. 6.33.

Assessment of Behavior and Effectiveness of Coupling. Because of the great difference in the stiffnesses of the walls and coupling beams, and the significance of certain deformations, normally neglected in ordinary first-order frame analyses, manual techniques of structural analysis when applied to coupled shear walls will rarely provide sufficient accuracy. Apart from flexural deformations of the various components, the axial deformations of the walls and the shear deformations of the coupling beams must be considered. Standard computer programs, which include the appropriate terms for these deformations, can be used to assess the linear elastic response of these structures.

In a mathematical model, much better suited for coupled shear-wall structures, the discrete beams are replaced by an equivalent continuous set of connecting laminae. This idealization enables the shear force across the coupling system to be expressed as a continuous function of the height, provided that no discontinuities in structural properties or the external load pattern occur. The Beck-Rosman laminar analysis (Beck, 1962; Rosman, 1964) utilizes this. It has been extended and slightly modified so as to deal with a number of load and boundary conditions (see also Chapter CB-5). The technique is efficient and is well suited for sensitivity analyses if a designer happens to have the opportunity to select structural dimensions.

The overturning moment, M_o, generated at any level by the external lateral load, is resisted by three intenal actions. With reference to Fig. 6.34 these will be: (1) A moment induced in wall 1, M_1; (2) a moment induced in wall 2, M_2; and (3) equal and opposite axial forces, T, generated in both walls. The corresponding equilibrium statement

$$M_o = M_1 + M_2 + lT \tag{6.6}$$

shows the interaction between these three components of the internal moment of resistance. The axial force induced in the walls at any level results from the summation of the shear forces in the coupling system above that level. It is evident that efficient shear transfer between the two coupled shear walls will generate large axial forces, and hence the lT component of the internal moment of resistance, defined by Eq. 6.6, is large. This is desirable because a full utilization of a large

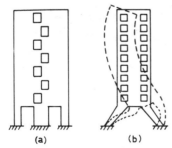

Fig. 6.32 Examples of irregular shear walls for seismic areas

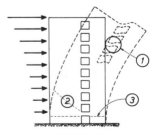

Fig. 6.33 Distortions in laterally loaded coupled shear wall

internal lever arm, l, normally determined from functional requirements for a building, will result in minimum internal forces and consequently a minimum in vertical wall reinforcement. Moreover, an efficient coupling system provides the greatest stiffness and hence assures minimum lateral deflection and interstory drift.

Surprisingly, above a certain minimum stiffness of the coupling beams, the efficiency of shear transfer is not significantly affected by the stiffness of the coupling system. Fig. 6.35 illustrates this phenomenon. Here the shear core of a 20-story building is examined. The two channel-shaped walls are interconnected by 1.8-m (6-ft) long rectangular coupling beams. It is seen that the mode of internal moment of resistance is hardly affected when beams in excess of 0.6-m to 0.75-m (24-in. to 30-in.) depths are used, effective shear transfer being assured in all cases. The outermost curve gives the total external overturning moment, M_o, at any level.

The pattern of the internal actions in coupled shear walls may be significantly affected by cracking (Paulay, 1969a). In particular the stiffness of deep coupling beams, shown as 1 in Fig. 6.33, is drastically reduced when, as a result of cyclic reversed loading, diagonal cracking in two directions sets in (Paulay, 1971c). For this reason, in an elastic analysis allowance should be made for the loss of stiffness, at least in an approximate way, if meaningful results for high intensity loading are to be obtained.

Elastoplastic Behavior of Coupled Shear Walls. The strength of a coupled shear-wall structure under lateral load is developed when a satisfactory admissible collapse mechanism is formed. This involves two plastic hinges in the coupling beams and one plastic hinge in each of the walls. The sequence of hinge formation during the nonlinear response of the structure to monotonic loading will depend upon the relative stiffnesses and strengths of the components. In earthquake-resistant structures the spreading of yielding will be of great importance. Therefore the designer must aim at establishing an intelligent hierarchy in the formation of collapse mechanism. In fact, collapse is not expected. Instead the coupled shear-wall structure and its components must possess adequate ductility so that significant excursions beyond the yield level of loading can be made, several times in each direction if necessary, without significant loss of ultimate strength and capacity for energy dissipation. These desirable properties can be achieved if the coupling system is made to yield first. When the coupling beams have yielded over say 90% of

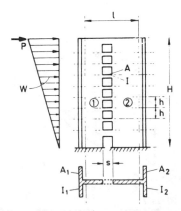

Fig. 6.34 Typical coupled shear wall subjected to lateral loading

the height of the structure, the walls can be made to sustain the large load just below yield level. This will assure that at the development of the near full strength of the structure no permanent damage in the walls will occur, and hence no misalinement of the building results. The coupling beams, subjected at this stage to extensive yielding, lend themselves to repair. Moreover, they are normally not part of the gravity load carrying system, and therefore even serious damage will not jeopardize the stability of the building after a disturbance.

When very large seismic excitations are encountered, further lateral deflections will occur, and these will cause plastic hinges to develop also in the walls, normally at their base. The elastic laminar analysis can be conveniently extended to deal also with this situation (Winokur and Gluck, 1968) including partial or full plastification of the laminae (Gluck, 1973). At this stage large ductility demands may be imposed upon the coupling system (Paulay, 1970a).

Fig. 6.36 shows the results of an elastoplastic analysis (Paulay, 1971b) for the structure illustrated in Fig. 6.35. Six different stages during monotonic loading, well into the plastic range, are shown. Stage 1 represents full elastic response corresponding with a code-specified lateral load, W, of the type shown in Fig. 6.35. At Stage 2 the laminar shear intensity, q, causes the first lamina to yield. By Stage 3 all laminae in the upper 90% of the height of the building have developed their full strength, q_u. Only a small increase in load is required to cause plastic hinges in the tension wall (Stage 4) and the compression wall (Stage 5) to develop. With this the theoretical full strength of the structure, $W_u = 5030$ kN (1130 kips), is developed. Further entirely plastic deformations are assumed to increase so that the deflection at the 20th floor increases to over 0.5 m (20 in.). A series of curves indicates the laminar ductility factors, in terms of the total rotation of the laminae at their boundaries, for these six stages of the loading. The wall moments, M_{1u}, M_{2u}, the axial force T_u developed at Stages 5 and 6, and the vertical steel content in each wall, ρ, are shown in the insert of Fig. 6.36.

It is evident that in earthquake-resistant coupled shear-wall structures the ductility of the coupling beams must be assured, unless the structure is designed for

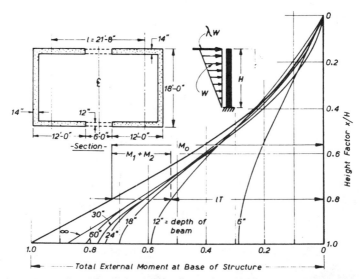

Fig. 6.35 Mode of internal moment of resistance in coupled shear wall structure

much higher lateral forces, consistent with an elastic dynamic response. If the coupling system can be ductile enough and also efficient in shear transfer, so that the IT component of the internal moment resistance remains large as shown in Fig. 6.35, a great proportion of the total energy to be dissipated will allocate itself to the coupling beams. With such dispersion of energy dissipation over the whole structure, a greater degree of protection of the wall bases will ensue.

Strength and Ductility of Coupling Beams. Because coupling beams, to be efficient, are usually short and relatively deep, they can develop a large flexural strength with relatively small flexural steel content. This is associated with large shear forces, which in turn may dominate the behavior of these beams. Fig. 6.37(a) shows failure by brittle diagonal tension following the Alaska earthquake of 1964 (Berg and Stratta, 1964). Fig. 6.37(b) shows brittle diagonal tension in a test beam (Paulay, 1971a); Fig. 6.37(c) shows sliding shear (Paulay, 1971a); and Fig. 6.37(d) shows ductile diagonal tension (Paulay and Binney, 1974). Observations after earthquakes, for example in Alaska (1964) and Managua (1972), have repeatedly shown that coupling beams containing insufficient web reinforcement fail by diagonal tension [see Fig. 6.37(a)]. Such failures are brittle and they follow a high rate of stiffness and strength degradation under reversed cyclic loading [see Fig. 6.37(b)]. If a ductile failure mechanism is essential, as in seismic areas, this mode of failure must be suppressed.

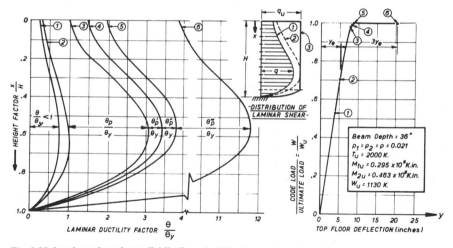

Fig. 6.36 Laminar shear force distribution, ductility demand, and top floor deflections for 20-story coupled shear wall structure with coupling beams of uniform strength

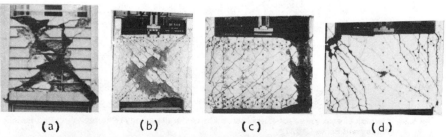

Fig. 6.37 Failure modes in deep coupling beams: (a) Brittle diagonal tension, Alaska, 1964 (Berg and Stratta, 1964); (b) brittle diagonal tension in test beam (Paulay, 1971a); (c) sliding shear (Paulay, 1971a); (d) ductile diagonal tension (Paulay and Binney, 1974)

It was found that the critical diagonal tension crack, along which a separation of a beam into two parts can occur, forms along a diagonal from one corner to another, not necessarily at an angle of 45° (Paulay, 1971c). Under cyclic loading the contribution of the shear resisting mechanisms, other than stirrups, quickly diminishes. For this reason in coupling beams the whole of the shear force, developed when the flexural tension steel yields at the face of the coupled walls, must be resisted by stirrups. Again, due attention must be paid to strain hardening of the flexural bars, to assure that as they develop maximum yield strength the stirrup reinforcement operates in the elastic range.

The disposition of internal forces in coupling beams, with a span to depth ratio <1.5 and conventional top and bottom flexural bars, is different from that encountered in normal reinforced concrete beams (Paulay, 1971c). Interaction between flexure and shear does exist and the development of flexural strength, based on the location of the internal concrete compression resultant at limit strain of the extreme fiber, is somewhat inhibited (Paulay, 1971c). The customary assumption that plane sections remain plane does not hold. The flexural reinforcement at the top and the bottom of a coupling beam may be in tension over the entire clear span. Ductility in such beams under cyclic reversed loading can be expected to be available only if the average shear stress at the development of flexural yielding is low, that is, on the order of $v_u < 5\sqrt{f_c'}$ psi.

When the ultimate shear stress to be developed in coupling beams is higher —when it approaches the maximum value recommended, for example, by the current ACI Code (ACI, 1971)—a sliding shear failure adjacent to the face of the walls will occur after a few load reversals at ultimate. A typical example of a test beam that failed in this manner is shown in Fig. 6.37(c). Only limited amount of ductility is available in such beams, even though considerable dowel forces can be transmitted by the flexural reinforcement. This is mainly due to kinking in these bars after large transverse sliding movement occurs. Hysteresis curves for shear-displacement relationships in such beams clearly show (Paulay, 1971a) large loss of stiffness at very low loads. Hence such beams must be considered unsuitable when large ductilities are expected to be developed in coupled shear walls.

To overcome the limitations of conventionally reinforced coupling beams, the principal reinforcement can be placed along the diagonals of the beams. Fig. 6.38

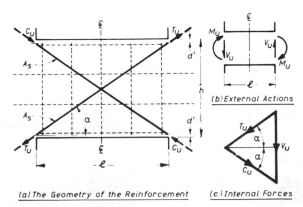

(a) The Geometry of the Reinforcement   (c) Internal Forces

(b) External Actions

Fig. 6.38 Interplay of external actions and internal forces in diagonally reinforced coupling beams (Paulay and Binney, 1974)

shows the model for such a beam, and from it the disposition of external and internal forces and the mode of moment and shear resistance is self-explanatory. It should be noted that this reinforcement replaces entirely the horizontal flexural bars and vertical stirrups of conventionally reinforced coupling beams. At first loading the diagonal steel, consisting of a number of bars in a cage, can resist all the diagonal tension, while in the other direction the diagonal compression is resisted by reinforcement and the concrete surrounding it. The strength of the beam is limited by the yield strength of the diagonal tension bars. As yielding can develop over the entire length of these bars, extending across the beams, large yield displacement can occur. Upon load reversal the bars previously in tension must first yield in compression before the wide cracks in the concrete can close, and this will enable compression to be transferred also by the concrete. In spite of Bauschinger effect, at this stage the diagonal compression reinforcement will carry the bulk of the diagonal compression force. For this reason it may be said that in such beams, after reversed cyclic loading causing yielding, all forces are essentially carried by the diagonal sets of reinforcing bars. Using steel that has a long yield plateau, very large ductilities can be achieved. Test beams have shown stable hysteretic characteristics (Paulay and Binney, 1974).

A typical arrangement of such reinforcement for an example coupling beam is shown in Fig. 6.39. If the compression yield capacity of diagonal reinforcement is to be sustained, and this indeed is a prerequisite for fully utilizing the desirable qualities of such beams, the buckling of individual bars, after possible spalling of the cover concrete, must be prevented. Closely spaced individual ties or rectangular spirally wound continuous binding will assure this. Allowing for the lower buckling strength of such bars, because of Bauschinger effect due to alternating plasticity, a maximum ties spacing of four times the diameter of the principal diagonal bars is suggested. This secondary reinforcement also serves the purpose of confining the concrete within the cage, formed by at least four diagonal bars. This concrete contributes towards the flexural rigidity, and assists in preventing the buckling of this strut as a whole at right angles to the plane of the beam.

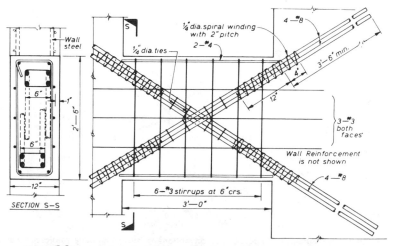

Fig. 6.39 Suggested steel arrangement in diagonally reinforced coupling beams

Additional nominal basketing reinforcement, consisting of stirrups and intermediate horizontal bars, as shown in Fig. 6.39, need be provided only for crack control and to prevent the dislocation of large concrete particles after disastrous seismic shocks. Fig. 6.37(d) shows a test beam so reinforced, after 13 cycles of loading in each direction. The cracks in this beam are very large, but at this stage of the test it still sustained 94% of its theoretical ultimate shear capacity at an end rotation of 0.061 rad (3.5°).

The diagonal reinforcement must be well anchored in the two adjacent shear walls which are to be coupled. Large tensile forces must be transmitted to the walls by a bundle of diagonal bars, and for this reason the anchorage length to be provided should be larger (say by 50%) than that specified by codes for individual bars.

Conventionally and diagonally reinforced coupling beams were subjected to the same kind of cyclic reversed loading, and this enabled a comparison to be made with respect to ductility. The ductilities imposed in each load cycle, inevitably causing some loss of strength, were compared together with the load sustained. Fig. 6.40 presents the results in terms of cumulative ductilities, and shows the superior performance of diagonally reinforced coupling beams.

Strength of Coupled Walls.   Once the load received by one of the coupled shear walls is evaluated—load on one hand from external loading and on the other from internal shear transfer across the coupling system at full strength—the wall can be treated as a cantilever. At the critical section, above foundation level, the reinforcement can then be determined, for example with the aid of an interaction relationship, such as is shown in Fig. 6.31. Shear reinforcement, confining steel, and other details must be provided as outlined in Article 6.4.1. Particular attention must be paid to shear strength in the presence of possible net tension in the wall, and to construction joints. These areas are indicated at 2 and 3 in Fig. 6.33.

Evidence of Ductility in Coupled Shear Walls.   The behavior of cantilever shear walls and that of coupling beams were briefly discussed in the previous sections. It was pointed out that with careful arrangement and detailing of reinforcement large ductilities can be achieved.

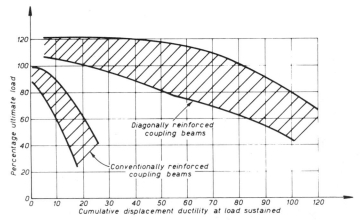

Fig. 6.40 Cumulative ductilities imposed on conventionally and diagonally reinforced coupling beams (Paulay and Binney, 1974)

Some convincing evidence is now available to show that the ductilities experimentally obtained for individual shear-wall test components can be relied upon in a
complete coupled shear-wall structure. This evidence strongly indicates that coupled
shear walls may be designed so as to possess all the features so desirable when large
lateral forces, such as occur during severe seismic disturbances, are to be resisted.
Therefore the highlights of two tests, carried out in 1973 at the University of
Canterbury, Christchurch, New Zealand, are briefly reported here.

Two one-quarter full-size 7-story reinforced concrete coupled shear walls were
tested under simulated earthquake loading. The simulation consisted of three lateral
static point loads, representing a triangularly distributed load similar to that shown
in Fig. 6.27 and applied at the 3rd, 5th, and 7th floors, in each direction several
times. Some of the load was limited to produce stresses within the elastic range, but
generally large yielding was imposed upon the structure in a cyclic fashion. To
qualify as a ductile structure, design practice in New Zealand calls for the ability of
the structure to deflect under lateral load, say at roof level, four times as much as
the deflection that would occur at the onset of yielding or at the attainment of the
specified ultimate lateral load. This deflection must then be sustained at least four
times in each direction, with a strength loss not exceeding 20% of theoretical
ultimate. Consequently the test specimens were subjected to this or more severe
lateral displacements.

Wall A, shown in Fig. 6.41, contained short and relatively deep coupling beams
reinforced in a conventional manner. The wall and beam reinforcement was
proportioned so that the coupling system was expected to yield before the full
strength of the two walls was approached. The gravity load, corresponding with

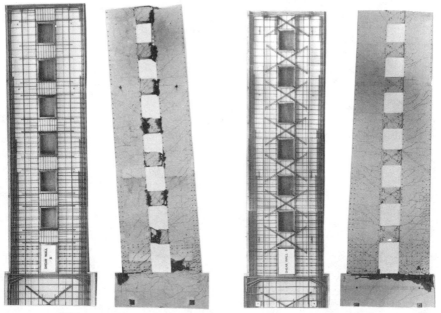

SHEAR WALL A

SHEAR WALL B

Fig. 6.41 Reinforcement in and crack pattern of quarter-scale shear wall models subjected to
reversed cyclic loading (Courtesy: T. Paulay)

typical tributary floor areas in a 7-story building, was replaced by vertical prestressing in the walls, using a single central ungrouted cable. Shear reinforcement and anchorages were provided throughout the structure so that flexure dominated the behavior in accordance with the principles discussed in the previous sections. After several cycles of high intensity reversed loading it became evident that sliding shear failure in the coupling beams was going to occur. Fig. 6.41 shows the damaged Wall A after the completion of the test. The large sliding movements along one or both faces of the coupling beams and the development of well-defined plastic hinges at the wall bases are evident. The load-displacement (roof level deflection) history of the structure may be seen in Fig. 6.42. It is also seen that the structure would meet the over-all ductility requirements as defined previously. The model structure, as shown in Fig. 6.41, maintained 80% of its theoretical ultimate load capacity, P_u^*, at a 7th-floor deflection equal to one-half of a story height. This is evidence of very large ductility indeed. The hysteresis curves in Fig. 6.42(a) show, however, the effect of progressive damage upon diminishing stiffness at low loads and the loss of energy dissipating capacity.

Wall B was identical in every respect to the previous specimen, except for the

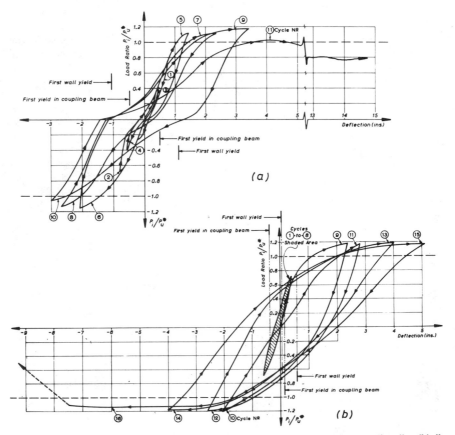

Fig. 6.42 Load-displacement relationship for shear wall model with (a) conventionally, (b) diagonally reinforced coupling beams

couplings. These were diagonally reinforced and were expected to behave as outlined in the preceding article on strength and ductility of coupling beams. The reinforcement and the damaged wall are shown in Fig. 6.41. The stable hysteresis loops shown in Fig. 6.42(b) demonstrate the remarkable ductility and the excellent energy dissipation capacity of this specimen. The load attained several times in both models, P_i, exceeded the theoretical ultimate strength, P_u^*, because of strain-hardening effects in the mild steel used. Fig. 6.42(b) shows the characteristics of a steel member subjected to reversed cyclic loading, and it convincingly demonstrates that a suitably designed and detailed coupled shear wall can be ductile enough to sustain, without strength loss, the largest displacements expected in a very large seismic disturbance.

Design Principles for Ductile Coupled Shear Walls. To assure a satisfactory performance, when coupled shear walls are subjected to severe lateral loading such as results from seismic shocks, it is necessary to be able to assess, at least approximately, their behavior in both the elastic and plastic range of loading. Desirable behavior can be expected only if the structure is made capable of following a preferred sequence of yielding. From the point of view of damage control and possible repair, it is desirable that the wall components be the last ones to suffer in the process of imposing incremental ultimate conditions.

Considerations of the strength of conventionally reinforced coupling beams indicate that full protection against diagonal tension failure, which is an unsuitable energy dissipating mechanism during cyclic loading, is required. Therefore, the flexural steel content in both faces of such beams must be moderate to avoid early failure by sliding shear. Deep coupling beams subjected to large shear forces cannot be expected to be ductile enough to sustain plastic deformations associated with an over-all ductility of 4 for the structure as a whole. When conventionally reinforced coupling beams are used, the ductility demand on the structure must be limited. Satisfactory performance of these beams will be assured for wind loads.

When diagonal reinforcement is used in coupling beams and adequate ties are provided to enable the compression struts to sustain yield load without buckling, very ductile performance can be expected.

The walls that are being coupled can be proportioned in accordance with the principles of reinforced concrete sections at limit states of strains. If necessary, axial load-moment interaction relationships, taking into account lack of symmetry, can be used. Particular care in detailing the potential plastic hinge zones is a prerequisite to assure that premature shear failure, as a consequence of alternating reversed flexural yielding, does not occur, and that adequate stability for yielding compression bars and confinement of compressed concrete is available. This will assure that large ductilities at the base of coupled shear walls will also be available when required during extreme seismic conditions.

The principles outlined in this section are equally valid and readily applicable when more than two walls are coupled by rows of beams between them.

4 Conclusions

1. The behavior of tall cantilever shear walls can be predicted from first principles of reinforced concrete behavior. When seismic forces are to be resisted ductile response becomes a prerequisite.

2. Shear, anchorage, and instability failure mechanisms must be suppressed to assure that shear walls can develop their intended lateral load capacity.

3. Ductile flexural response with large yielding can generally be assured in shear walls because a large proportion of the overturning moment is usually resisted by reinforcement only. When gravity compression loads become large, precautions may have to be taken to boost the deformability of compression zones by appropriate confinement.

4. Shear stresses may dominate the behavior of squat shear walls or wall elements. The behavior of such walls has been extensively studied and reported in Chapter CB-11. With proper arrangement of reinforcement, which can relieve the concrete in carrying shear stresses, even low-rise shear walls can be made ductile (Beekhuis, 1971).

5. Shear walls, which are sometimes provided with boundary frames, should be considered as one integral unit. Boundary frames act as flanges. They may accommodate the bulk of the vertical flexural reinforcement, and they provide stability against possible lateral buckling. The separate treatment of boundary frames and infill panels in monolithic reinforced concrete construction is not in accord with the natural behavior of such structures.

6. Tall cantilever shear walls can provide excellent resistance against lateral load and can greatly reduce deflection. However, for seismic conditions they offer only a single line of defense. Should a large excitation require yielding this is likely to cause permanent deformation near the base, and it may lead to early misalinement in the building.

7. When openings are to be provided in a shear wall this should be done in such a way that a regular structure results in which flexure and shear can be rationally evaluated and effectively resisted.

8. Regular arrangements of openings may enable coupled shear walls to be formed. In seismic areas it is essential that the coupling beams rather than the walls form the weaker elements. With suitable detailing, coupled shear walls hold great promise of giving a large degree of protection by being both efficient in load resistance and sufficiently ductile. Energy dissipation, when required, can be well dispersed over the entire structure and thus, as opposed to single cantilever walls, several lines of defense may be mobilized when extreme displacements are imposed upon a building.

9. Horizontal construction joints may present potential weaknesses in all types of shear walls. By utilizing clamping forces, provided by gravity and reinforcement, in accordance with the concepts of shear friction, this mode of failure can be eliminated. It is essential, however, that the maximum possible shear force that may be induced is evaluated from the most probable maximum flexural strength potential of the structure.

10. In many buildings shear walls may interact with each other and with rigid jointed space frames. Problems related to the elastic response of such structures have been studied (ACI Committee 442, 1971; Khan and Sbarounis, 1964; Portland Cement Association, 1965). However, only limited information is available with respect to the nonlinear response of

such complex structural systems (Adams and MacGregor, 1970) and it is hoped that research in progress will contribute soon to the understanding of the issues involved.

11. The limit states of cellular, thin-walled shear-wall cores, particularly for high-intensity cyclic reversed loading, still require further study.

12. When shear-wall structures with some static indeterminacy are available, it is desirable that an advantageous sequence in the propagation of yielding be established, so that damage in repairable and less critical areas will occur first and the principal gravity load carrying units receive the greatest degree of protection. Therefore the designer must establish an intelligent hierachy in the most probable strength levels that he intends to provide for each shear-wall component. These are the properties that are recognized during seismic excitations.

13. The potential plastic hinge length at the base of a shear wall may be extensive. When detailing the reinforcement, the designer should assure that no lapped splices of the possibly large-size vertical bars occur in this area. Often it will be impossible to carry all the vertical wall steel continuously up from the foundations. In such cases welded connections or mechanical splices will be required to eliminate the necessity of having to transfer large bond forces to the concrete that is likely to become severely damaged in the plastic zone.

14. In many situations vertical prestressing of cantilever or coupled shear walls could offer advantages in crack control, construction joint behavior, and increased stiffness. The nonlinear response of prestressed concrete shear walls, however, has not yet been sufficiently documented.

15. In the process of concentrating on the characteristics of the nonlinear response of shear-wall structures, the designer must not overlook the limits set by the foundations. Many shear-wall structures in seismic areas will never approach yielding because the overturning capacity at foundation level will limit the magnitude of the lateral forces that can be generated. The seismic response of shear walls with rocking foundations, involving superstructure-soil interaction, is an exciting challenge for further research.

Part 2—Inelastic Analyses of Reinforced Concrete Structures

6.5 INTRODUCTION TO INELASTIC ANALYSIS

1 General Principles

Design as Related to Actual Behavior of Structures. It has long been well known that for reinforced concrete structures knowledge of the stresses under service loads does not give a satisfactory idea of the degree of safety.

It is equally well known that in statically indeterminate structures the local reduction of stiffness due to cracking and the plastic behavior of the concrete can result in considerable redistribution of moments with respect to the elastic distribution. For a long time engineers took partial account of these facts in structural design using their own judgment; only recently new knowledge of these phenomena has permitted taking them systematically into account (FIP, 1955; Symposium on the Strength of Concrete Structures, 1956; ACI, 1970).

Efforts naturally have been concentrated on research on the real safety of structures against collapse, and the first attempts were made by application of the theory of perfectly elastic-plastic bodies similar to the contemporary applications to steel structures: a sufficient number of plastic hinges (supposed to be able to develop an infinite rotation) was considered at the critical sections so that collapse could occur by the formation of a mechanism.

This first approach, despite its great simplicity, had to be abandoned for more complicated analyses, mainly for the two following reasons, which characterize the difference between steel and reinforced concrete structures:

1. Many reinforced concrete members have a rather limited ductility, and premature local rupture can well occur before the formation of a mechanism; this fact has been experimentally proved on continuous beams, but more severe results can be expected in frames with highly compressed columns (Macchi, 1955, 1964a). See Fig. 6.43.

2. Control of cracking under service loads is necessary, in order to avoid a possible unserviceability due to excessive crack width.

Limit States and Nonlinear Analysis.   The limit-states method of design takes into consideration all the unfavorable structural events that can occur in a building; but for its practical application it is not sufficient to define the limits of unfitness (collapse, cracking, excessive deflection, etc.). Efficient methods of analysis are needed for a sufficiently accurate determination of the actions (external forces or other actions) giving rise to the specific undesired limit-effect.

Three elements are essential for an effective use of the method (the knowledge of which should really be of a probabilistic nature):

1. Definition of the limit, that is of the kind of unfitness and the degree of safety required against it (for example, width or type of the cracking that is not permissible, maximum amount of the deflection or other deformations, degree of safety against collapse).

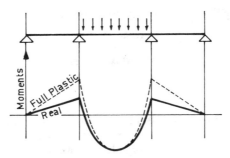

Fig. 6.43 Local failure

2. The connection between the limit and the internal forces associated with it (theory of cracking, theory of rupture in bending), if it concerns a local failure.

3. Computation of the external forces or other actions giving rise in the single cross sections to the previously described internal forces (structural analysis).

In the usual practical design, this last step is generally the first, and the procedure is inverted. For statically indeterminate structures, the determination of the internal forces as a function of the given external forces is usually performed by means of the elastic theory of structures.

Most of the limit states, on the other hand, concern phases of structural behavior in which the structural elements have systematically lost their integrity (cracked phase), or even concern their ultimate strength, considerably beyond the limits of elastic behavior (ultimate limit state).

For those states the elastic theory is not a satisfactory idealization, and a consistent structural analysis can only be based on the nonlinear deformation laws, which better follow the real behavior of the elements in the cracked phase and near the ultimate state. The assumptions have to be the same as those used in the second part of the design (connection between the limit and the internal forces—for example, the determination of the ultimate bending moment of a simple section); otherwise, considerable errors can sometimes be made in determination of the external forces giving rise to the undesired limit state.

A structural analysis which substantially fulfills these requirements (eventually with some minor simplifying assumptions) is hereafter called a "nonlinear analysis."

Nonlinear Analysis for Reinforced Concrete.   The analysis of single sections at the limit states is mainly based on the following simplifying assumptions (limited to the case of bending and axial load). For the serviceability limit states:

1. Plane sections remain plane.

2. Concrete and steel still behave elastically for short-term loadings.

3. When the tension is higher than the tensile strength of concrete, the members are systematically cracked.

4. The width of each crack is a function of the loss of bond on the two sides of the crack.

For the ultimate limit state:

1. Plane sections remain plane.

2. Concrete has a parabolic (or parabola-rectangle) stress-strain curve in compression with a limited ultimate strain $\epsilon_\omega = 0.003$ or $\epsilon_\omega = 0.0035$.

3. Steel is perfectly elastic-plastic or has an elastic strain-hardening behavior.

Using these assumptions for all the sections of lightly or normally reinforced nominally straight members, in order to be consistent in the structural analysis, moment-rotation diagrams similar to the idealized one of Fig. 6.44 are obtained which are satisfactorialy close to the test results (Baker and Amarakone, 1964; Maldague, 1965; Macchi, 1964).

In these diagrams, three phases can be easily recognized:

Phase I: The straight line OC represents the member as an uncracked elastic body; the curvature is given by M/EI.

Phase II: At point C the strength of concrete in tension is reached and cracks appear. The slope of CY is reduced by cracking, but both steel and concrete are still in a linear elastic range.

Phase III: At point Y the steel yields and the phase YR is then characterized by the resulting large rotations; the final point R indicates rupture, which is the limit of rotational resistance.

Fig. 6.45, on the other hand, represents the diagram for an idealized highly reinforced member which fails before the yield point of steel is reached. The inelasticity just before failure is due in this case to the plasticity of concrete.

Diagrams similar to Fig. 6.46 are obtained for columns when the axial load is relatively high; in this case the cracking point C is higher. Rupture can also occur without cracking, for small eccentricities, when the entire section is compressed (N_2).

A behavior similar to that of columns results for prestressed concrete members (Fig. 6.47), except that prestressed members usually exhibit negative rotation at zero moment, with zero rotation at an imposed moment approximately one quarter of the ultimate.

All these diagrams are characterized by the points CYR and therefore by their nonlinearity. Section 6.2 contains more detailed information on moment-deformational relationships.

An analysis based on such real nonlinear flexural characteristics is then preferably called a "nonlinear analysis," distinguishing it in this way from a linear analysis. The term "plastic analysis," which is sometimes used, can lead to some confusion with the theory of perfectly elastic-plastic or rigid-plastic members.

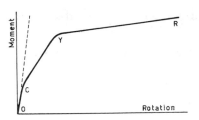

Fig. 6.44 Low reinforcement

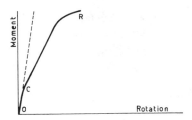

Fig. 6.45 High reinforcement

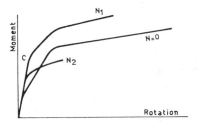

Fig. 6.46 Bending and axial load

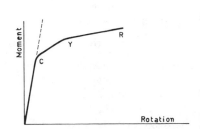

Fig. 6.47 Prestressed beams

Plasticity is only one of several causes of the inelastic rotations of phases CY and YR in Fig. 6.44. The term "inelastic analysis" has also been used for nonlinear analysis, with the aim of clarifying its difference from theoretical plasticity.

It is well known that consideration of the second-order effects in structures (that is, the effect of deformations on the mode of action of external forces) also leads to a nonlinearity between loads and deflections, and between loads and internal forces, even if the basic assumption is that of linear elasticity. The second-order effects are such a complex problem that it is wise to treat it in a separate chapter (Chapter CB-8). In practice, when a first-order theory is not considered sufficient, due to the amount of lateral sway, a unique "nonlinear analysis" may have to be carried out, considering simultaneously both of the sources of nonlinearity: that is, the one due to the real flexural characteristics of the members, and the one due to the second-order effect. Superposition of the results of separate analysis for these sources of nonlinearity is in error on the unsafe side.

Advantages of Nonlinear Methods.　　There is no doubt that the nonlinear analysis of a complex structure requires considerable work in computation. Is it worthwhile to do it? This seems a reasonable question, and an interesting discussion on the subject can be found in the proceedings of the International Symposium on Flexural Mechanics of Reinforced Concrete (ASCE-ACI, 1964).

It appears that no substantial progress in the development of structures can be achieved without a sufficiently realistic idealization of their behavior.

Today, an accurate analysis can lead to a more homogeneous safety of various structures and members, compared to the results of the method of permissible stresses. Tomorrow, awareness of the accomplishment of a good description of the structural behavior could lead to a reasonable reduction of the safety factors; the consequences would be particularly appreciated for high-rise construction, the cost of which is very sensitive to the weight of the structure.

Still thinking of high-rise buildings, in any extrapolation to higher constructions, some phenomena that were previously disregarded can become essential. In this field the experience of lower buildings can scarcely help. Only an accurate analysis close to reality can adequately account for the possible behavior of an unusual structure. The same can be said of the analysis for exceptional actions, as for instance seismic action.

Some economical advantages can also be obtained within the limits of ordinary structures and of the existing safety provisions:

1. Due to the greater freedom in design, the moments in the various critical sections can be chosen within a reasonable range, so that beams of constant section can be used, and congestion of reinforcement can be reduced in the sections of maximum negative moment. These details result in better and more economical structures.

2. A second advantage is obtained when the structure is proportioned for various loading schemes. In the ordinary design, each critical section has to be proportioned for its worst condition (and the structure for the envelope of the maximum moments). Some of these maxima can be considerably reduced through a redistribution of moments, provided the validity of this assumption is checked by a nonlinear analysis; for example, see Fig. 6.48 for a case in which the live load is 75% of the total load.

Limits of Validity and Usefulness of Linear Elastic Analysis. In some cases design for the specific limit state requires the structural analysis of elements which are not yet cracked and are far from their ultimate state. This is the case for some serviceability limit states, such as the deflection of large-span floors under service loads, the lateral drift of tall buildings, and the effects of short-term temperature variations.

The linear elastic theory may provide in such cases a satisfactory correlation between loads and internal forces, local stresses, and consequent deformations (although a nonelastic analysis may yet be needed for the effects of shrinkage, creep and local stress concentrations).

In other cases, for a limit state even at the ultimate of the structure, an insufficient knowledge of the ultimate strength or deformability of some very stiff and brittle structural elements (for instance, unreinforced concrete walls) justifies a temporary consideration of a somewhat preceding state, which is better known as the ultimate state. In this case also, for temporary lack of better knowledge, the elastic theory is generally applied within the limit-states method: see, for instance, the CEB Recommendations for precast and panel construction (CEB-CIB-UEAtc, 1969). Sometimes this elastic analysis needs complex and specific methods (Chapters CB-5 and CB-11).

The preceding paragraphs also imply the condemnation of the systematic use in a structural design of elastic structural analysis with the ultimate design of single sections (ultimate strength design). This combination is indeed not consistent, and is not always on the safe side, as has been proved both theoretically and by tests (Macchi, 1964a). The elastic distribution of the moments is only one of the infinite number of statically admissible distributions, and therefore it is also subject to the possibility of premature local failures of brittle members, which are not predicted by the analysis.

The procedure is nevertheless used in many countries. If associated with valid practical rules preventing brittleness (rules concerning the percentages of reinforcement in all members and the maximum axial load in the columns), it can be reasonably admitted as a temporary practical procedure for the following reasons:

1. The inaccuracy in determining the real moment distribution is usually compensated for by the additional safety introduced by proportioning the structure for the envelope of the maximum moments obtained for various loading schemes.

2. The distribution of the reinforcement is likely to provide satisfactory behavior under service loads as the state of cracking is considered.

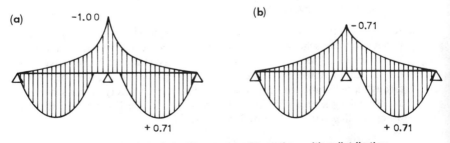

Fig. 6.48 (a) Envelope of elastic moments; (b) envelope with redistribution

2 Availability of Nonlinear Methods of Analysis

Can the methods of nonlinear analysis and design be considered available for practical use in a design office? Can their use be extended to the design of tall buildings?

The answer is substantially positive despite the lack of knowledge that still exists on the behavior of some structural elements, and despite computational complexity. As far as computational complexity is concerned, the acceptable degree of complexity is necessarily related to the size and economic importance of the building, so no general conclusion can be expected. A description of the types of available computer programs is given in Section 6.6.

In the following paragraphs the principal elements needed for the practical adoption of the new method of design are considered. These elements are:

1. A clear definition of the requirements of the safety philosophy.

2. Knowledge of the strength of the single sections (structural members and their connections); knowledge of the cracking conditions.

3. Knowledge of the laws of deformation of the various structural elements.

4. Procedures (analytical, numerical, or graphical) adequate for the imposition of equilibrium and compatibility.

5. Procedures for a preliminary design.

It will also be emphasized that nonlinear analysis is not a self-sufficient method of design, but only a part of it.

Requirements of Safety Philosophy. The methods of analysis can be strongly influenced by safety requirements, which first must be clearly defined.

The assumption of a monotonic increase of the live load for the analysis of the ultimate state is usually considered reasonable and acceptable. If cycles of loading and unloading or reversal of loading have to be considered in the ultimate phase (which could be required for seismic actions), this assumption has to be abandoned, and only an incremental analysis can be used.

It is also important to know whether the ultimate state is reached by increase of the external forces (or actions), or by increase of the local internal forces (for instance, the bending moment). In the first case the structural analysis has to be carried out up to the ultimate strength of the structure as a whole, whereas in the second case it has to be stopped at a preceding stage, in which a possible local defect can lead to failure of one critical section.

This latter criterion today seems accepted (Levi, 1970), and requires the knowledge of the moment distribution at a stage somewhat preceding over-all failure for increase of the external forces (the factor of safety is partially applied to the external forces and partially to the local bending moment; Fig. 6.49).

Some of the methods listed in succeeding articles of this section fulfill this requirement; others do not.

When loads and other actions of a different nature are to be simultaneously considered, probabilistic considerations lead to a reduction of the single load factors of safety. This effect simplifies determination of the worst condition, and reduces the number of computations.

Because of the large variability in the stiffness of concrete and reinforced concrete, the stiffness assumed for a structural analysis should be:

1. A mean value for actions from imposed loads, which would lead to the most probable values of service deflections. For first-order force evaluation only the correct relative stiffnesses are important.

2. Below the mean (for instance, the characteristic value) for second-order effects in buildings and their members.

The serviceability conditions (maximum cracking, maximum deflections, etc.) may be satisfied with general rules, or a structural analysis involving phase II may be used. The latter analysis involves a redistribution of moments under the service load, and a trilinear idealization of the moment-curvature diagram is then necessary.

Strength of Structural Members and Connections. An essential part of the analysis at the ultimate state is that of the strength of the individual sections under given values of bending moment, axial load, shear, etc. Our knowledge of these strengths is satisfactory except for very large elements and some connections both of ordinary and precast construction. For precast concrete members the connections are particularly important, because they often control the ultimate strength and the moment redistribution of concrete frames. The conditons of cracking are also satisfactorily known for ordinary linear members, for the purpose of practical design.

Laws of Deformation of Structural Members. The imposition of the compatibility conditions requires a knowledge of the deformation laws of the various members under single or combined internal forces (bending moment, shear, axial load, or torsion).

The effect of bending is most prominent. Therefore in practice the flexural characteristics are needed: moment-rotation diagrams in phase II and in phase III, and the ultimate rotation of the elements (see Figs. 6.44 to 6.47).

The slope in phase II (C-Y) is known satisfactorily. The cracking point C is subject to some uncertainties, particularly when axial load is present, but they are of little practical consequence in the inelastic analysis when second-order effects are small. In phase III (Y-R) the most important data are the ultimate rotations of the members.

The fact that these rotations cannot usually be obtained by integration of a moment-curvature relationship, because of local concentrations, both in the sections of maximum moment and in the beam-column connections, causes some difficulties (Kulicki and Kostem, 1974; Baker and Amarakone, 1964; Macchi, 1964b, 1966;

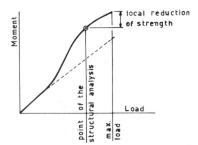

Fig. 6.49 Effect of local reduction of strength

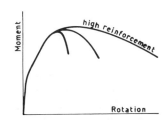

Fig. 6.50 Effect of transverse reinforcement on falling branch of moment-rotation curves

Yamashiro and Siess, 1962). But practical safe rules based on tests are availabe for such determination, and their accuracy is good for brittle members, for which the ultimate rotation is an essential element of the analysis.

In general the available knowledge is sufficient for a structural analysis giving the essential behavior of framed structures in phases II and III.

It should also be remembered that, for experimental moment-rotation diagrams the attainment of the maximum moment is followed by a post-rupture "falling branch" in which the structure can still withstand decreasing moments and develop higher strain [Fig. 6.50 (Roy and Sozen, 1964)]. This phase is sometimes useful in statically indeterminate structures (Gvozdev and Krylov, 1964), but is usually disregarded in the analysis, because its characteristics are not sufficiently guaranteed. It is nevertheless useful for designers to know that with an increased transverse reinforcement the falling branch can be considerably raised, thus increasing the ductility of the member.

Methods of Nonlinear Analysis.   Nonlinear analytical, numerical, or graphical methods lead to knowledge of the internal forces and deformations of a given structure under given external forces or other actions. They can be applied to structures being designed or to structures already designed, in order to check the fulfillment of the limit-states requirements.

These methods simply impose the conditions of equilibrium and of compatibility of deformation, using the nonlinear flexural characteristics of the members or their trilinear or bilinear idealizations.

Every existing method of elastic analysis of statically indeterminate structures can be extended to the nonlinear case; nevertheless, these extensions are often very difficult. For this reason, specific methods, having differing accuracies, have been developed, such as the incremental analysis and the imposed rotations methods.

Incremental analysis.   This analysis is like a simulated test; it follows step by step the evolution of the nonlinear phenomena as a function of the increase of parameters defining the external system of loading.

The available methods are nonlinear extensions of computer iteration methods already used for elastic statically indeterminate structures (Ferry Borges et al., 1964). The procedure is complex because the stiffness matrix of each part of a member has to be calculated for each value of the external load as a function of the real moment distribution. This is determined by a current iteration procedure at each step of loading.

The procedure is slow, and its capacity at present is limited to structures with a rather small number of members. It is nevertheless of great utility as a "precise" reference for every other simplified procedure, and as the only way for studying various loading histories.

Section 6.6 contains a more complete exposition of this method.

Imposed rotations method.   This method can be applied using conventional calculation tools to structures of a low degree of indeterminacy, and it has a great capacity if a computer is used (Macchi, 1959, 1966; Sawyer, 1955; Johnson and Sawyer, 1958).

The following simplifying assumptions are used: (1) Trilinear or bilinear moment-rotation diagrams; (2) concentration of the inelastic rotations at the critical sections; and (3) analysis is carried out directly at the limit-state condition without following the complete evolution of the nonlinear phenomena.

These assumptions allow a considerable reduction of work, although they are usually sufficiently close in representing the real behavior of the structures.

The basic idea, which considerably simplifies analysis, is nevertheless that of considering inelastic rotations as rotations artificially imposed in critical sections of a still elastic structure. Imposed rotations cause an equilibrated system of internal forces (in practice a set of moment redistributions). By superposition of the latter and the elastic moments due to loads, the real distribution of moments is obtained.

The advantage consists in dividing the analysis into these two parts, each of which can be calculated with ordinary elastic analysis. The analysis can be done at every stage of loading, in particular in that phase preceding the ultimate which is required by the safety philosophy (see "Requirements of Safety Philosophy" earlier in this article). If a trilinear idealization is used, the redistribution at service load due to cracking can be taken into account.

The basic idea is that of taking advantage of the great simplicity of full plastic analysis (plastic hinges theory), checking however that the critical sections are able to develop the rotations required for the attainment of the chosen moment diagram. Section 6.7 presents a more complete explanation of this design method.

Limit Design and Plastic Analysis.   The term "limit design" is frequently used to indicate a well-defined method of nonlinear design based on the assumption of plasticity without strain hardening and with regard for rotational limitations (Baker, 1966, 1967a; Cohn, 1964, 1965a, and 1971). In these methods serviceability is checked by means of an approximate elastic analysis. Sections 6.8 and 6.9 contain a fuller exposition of these methods.

Preliminary Design.   Analytical procedures of different accuracy (and therefore of different complexity) have been outlined, not only because they can find their field of application according to the importance of the structure, but also because analysis can only be applied to an already designed structure, and the designer therefore needs some elementary tools for his preliminary work.

Plastic analysis can be a useful tool for the first design concept; if accompanied by some restrictions on the percentage of reinforcement of the beams, and the maximum amount of axial load in the columns, as well as by some rules concerning crack control, it can well lead to a design that has good probabilities of being satisfactory when tested by a subsequent nonlinear analysis. For prestressed concrete frames, the existence of secondary moment at the ultimate is of particular concern, since it may seriously affect the behavior of the frame.

A further useful way of detecting brittle members, and of enabling the designer to modify in the most convenient way the first trial design, is the graphical method of the "compatibility path" (Macchi, 1969, 1970a). It is presented as a preliminary procedure for the "imposed rotations" method.

Simplified Method.   A simplified plastic design methodology, based on limit-design concepts for reinforced concrete, has been described by Furlong (1970) for use in proportioning beams and columns in braced frames. It does not require an elastic analysis of a complete nor of a partial frame, but simply uses limit values for coefficients of maximum moments in simple beams. The limit values are derived such that service loads cannot create tensile steel stresses greater than 80% of the yield strength of the reinforcement.

The method employs a rather strict limit on the amount of "balanced" tension reinforcement, in order to assure enough ductility so that beam mechanisms will always form prior to a spalling failure on the compression face of a beam. It permits a more efficient use of structural materials than that which results from the use of design coefficients presently permitted in Section 8.4.2 of the ACI Building Code (ACI Committee 318, 1971).

3 Nonsimultaneous Ultimate Resistances and Nonlinear Design

Nonsimultaneous Ultimate Moments. Nonlinear analysis and design provide a more realistic and safer evaluation of ultimate resistance than does current linear design practice. Most present codes allow calculation of the ultimate resistance of a structure by the assumption of simultaneous ultimate resistances of a sufficient number of critical sections and statics. Since in general the assumed ultimate sectional resistances are not realized simultaneously, this evaluation is merely an upper bound which may greatly exceed the true ultimate.

Use in design of even a nonlinear elastic-perfectly-plastic moment-rotation diagram provides unjustified support for this error. Actually, a section's difficulty in attaining its ultimate resistance before serious loss of resistance at other sections largely depends on the ratio of M_e, the moment at which inelastic rotations become important, to M_u, the ultimate moment. The difficulty increases as this ratio decreases. This ratio is generally significantly smaller than the value of unity implied by perfect plasticity. Fig. 6.51 shows the values of this ratio calculated from the classic beam test results of Mattock (1965) and Corley (1966) using a bilinear moment-curvature model. (These ratios would be larger using a bilinear moment-rotation model.)

Nonsimultaneous Ultimate Shears. Nonsimultaneous ultimate resistances are at least as important for shear as for moment. Yamada (1973) has presented

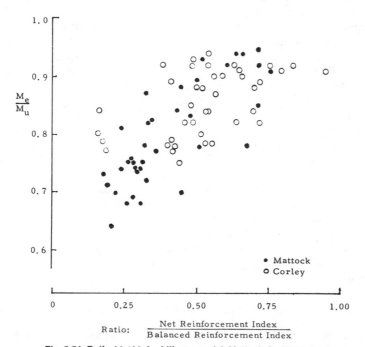

Fig. 6.51 Ratio M_e/M_u for bilinear model, Mattock-Corley tests

evidence of this importance for tall buildings with shear walls. For a particular story of such a building with a combination of short and long columns and a shear wall, subjected to increasing shear, he found that:

1. The short columns would explosively lose their shear resistance at the instant when the shear-wall resistance is as low as 20% of its ultimate and the long column resistance as low as 10% of its ultimate.

2. At the instant of ultimate shear-wall resistance the short columns will have lost their resistance, and the long columns may have developed but 50% of their resistance.

3. The ultimate resistance of the long columns would not be realized until after loss of short column resistance, and until as much as 50% loss in shear-wall resistance.

This example, and the tests cited in Article 6.3.3 in a paragraph headed "Flexural Critical Regions with High Axial and Shear Forces," show that a designer should not uncritically assume plastic deformability in either columns or shear walls. Rather, a designer should emphasize ductility in the design of shear resisting members, and then at least check ultimate strength by a nonlinear analysis.

Admittedly, a great difficulty of such nonlinear analysis is the determination of force-deformational relationships for shear walls, for which the parameters affecting such relationships are so numerous and so influential, and about which so little is known. Section 6.4 is an excellent summary of the state of the art for shear walls.

Nonsimultaneous Ultimate Resistance and Codes. The assumption that ultimate (inelastic) strengths for a redundant structure will be attained simultaneously if they are provided to match an elastic distribution of moments is of course self-contradictory and unconservative. However, there is an increasing trend in the standard building codes, including CEB, ACI, and DIN, to allow additional arbitrary changes in provided ultimate moment with respect to the elastic distribution. These provisions, in effect, allow most of the available benefits of nonlinear design without requiring nonlinear analysis. Therefore, they artificially discourage the use of authentic nonlinear analysis and design.

Unfortunately, nonlinear design benefits must be earned by the labor of nonlinear analyses. Since ultimate strengths are not attained simultaneously even for elastic distributions of moment, arbitrary changes of design moments in one direction from an elastic moment will tend to facilitate simultaneous attainment, and in the opposite direction, of course, tend to further prevent simultaneous attainment. Without a nonlinear analysis to provide guidance, these deviations increase variance in structural strength and thus reduce the reliability of design, and strict maintenance of structural safety then requires a commensurate increase in load factor, avoidable by a limit analysis.

It is hoped that these inequitable and progress-impeding developments in codes will be corrected so that nonlinear analyses and designs may be used on their own merits and judged fairly.

4   Economics of Structural Strength and Nonlinear Design

Nonlinear design is indispensable in approaching a rational answer to the central question of all building design: how strong should the building be? An equivalent statement of this question is: for what values of load factors should the building be designed?

The equation that determines the optimum strength is conceptually simple, but evaluation of its terms requires the full use of nonlinear analysis, and, of course, the best quantitative, statistical predictions of all the loadings or actions to which the building will be subjected.

An understrength building will have high probability of failure, and if its strength is increased the probabilities for all types of failure will generally decrease, with a corresponding decrease in the monetary losses associated with failures. At optimum building strength the cost of a small increase in building strength will be equal to the corresponding decrease in expected losses from failures. Clearly, for conservative design all failures from all possible loads or actions must be included in this equation. Also all levels of failure must be included, ranging from the extremes of high-probability, low-loss minor cracking to low-probability, high-loss sudden collapse with loss of life (Sawyer, 1964).

On the other hand, in all history, man's intuitive solutions to this equation have usually in effect ignored the very rare, very high-loss failures from catastrophes, and often entirely ignored failures from some types of loads. Therefore, man has quite consistently underbuilt for strength.

This gap remains even now, as demonstrated by dissatisfaction at every catastrophe with the behavior of most of the modern buildings involved, and by the current slow, continuing trend of increasing design strength, especially apparent now for seismic and extreme-wind loads. The current impulse for this slow closing of the gap is mostly from the impacts of sporadically occurring catastrophes. However, a more rational solution based on the new but still rudimentary contributions of engineering science to better valuation of the equation's quantities holds great promise.

"Strength" here has a broad meaning, including such qualities as ductility, durability, and thermal stability. Obviously, added strength may be ineffectual unless it has the proper qualities and is added to the proper points in the structure.

Clearly nonlinear methods of analysis and design are necessities for improved evaluations of the basic equation, not only in quantitatively correlating load types and levels to failure types and levels, but in determination of the proper qualities and points for added strength.

The influences tending to perpetuate the strength gap also discourage the designer from the extra effort and expense of using nonlinear methods to attain these goals. To laymen in times of tranquillity the designer's job seems minimal and almost automatic, and design costs should be correspondingly low. But after the catastrophe laymen will blame the professional, and with some reason. If the profession believes that the cost of extra nonlinear design effort is less than the resulting reduction in expected failure losses, its duty, despite public pressure to the contrary, is clear.

6.6 METHODS OF INCREMENTAL NONLINEAR ANALYSIS

In this section step-by-step analysis in the nonlinear range of concrete structures is described.

Nonlinearity due to geometric changes and material nonlinearity are both included, although instability phenomena are discussed in greater depth in Chapter CB-8.

In a step-by-step analysis, the load is increased in steps, making possible the analysis of the behavior of the structure in detail up to failure. In the following the deformation or stiffness method is first described for a linear elastic structure, and then the necessary expansions for treatment of nonlinear behavior of the structure are added. Force methods are mentioned.

1 Linear Elastic Structures

In Fig. 6.52 a simple frame which is three times kinematically indeterminate is shown. With reference to Fig. 6.53, the unknown displacements δ_1, δ_2, and δ_3 can easily be transformed into deformations of the finite elements AC and CD by the transformation matrix $\mathbf{B}$, which is dependent only upon the geometry of the structure. This can easily be understood, since the displacements δ_2 and δ_3 and the rotation δ_1 of point C completely determine the elongations and rotations of the beams AC and CE. Once the deformations of the elements AC and CE are known, the corresponding forces and moments N are calculated with help of the stiffness matrix $\mathbf{D}$, which then for slender beams contains stiffness functions (such as Berry functions or Livesley functions). The associated external forces F are obtained by multiplying the just calculated element forces N with the aid of the transposed matrix $\mathbf{B^t}$. The stiffness matrix of the whole system is then $\mathbf{S} = \mathbf{B^tDB}$. The unknown displacements δ are now calculated from

$$F = S\delta \qquad (6.7)$$

by elimination or by any other suitable method.

In computer calculation the matrix multiplication does not need to be performed to establish $\mathbf{S}$. The information stored in the matrix $\mathbf{B}$ is instead stored in a compact table which then is used to place the member stiffnesses in $\mathbf{D}$ in the right places in the over-all stiffness matrix $\mathbf{S}$.

A complication in this procedure is that the stiffness matrix $\mathbf{D}$ contains the unknown axial forces in the stiffness functions which take the lateral deflections of the columns AC and CE into account, giving second-order effects. The calculation for nonlinear material behavior is even more complicated since the modulus of elasticity of the material in the beams may change with increasing axial load or

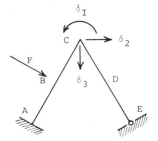

Fig. 6.52 Simple structure with rotations and displacements

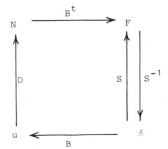

Fig. 6.53 Transformation scheme

bending moment, or a reinforced concrete column may crack or yield in steel or concrete. At some loading level the stiffness matrix may become nonlinear, and therefore the described procedure must be refined.

2   Elastoplastic Structures

In general, the relation between curvature and moment will be nonlinear, as discussed in Sections 6.2 and 6.5.

In a high-rise building, the analysis of the structure can easily become a problem of great complexity if full interaction of all members is assumed and the members exhibit nonlinear behavior. The theoretical aspects of the analysis as well as the practical applications with the aid of computers will be considered to some extent in what follows. In the nonlinear case the constitutive matrix $\mathbf{D}$ depends upon the deformations u and the forces N reached. Therefore, for a given load, the value of the stiffness matrix

$$\mathbf{S} = \mathbf{B}^{t}\mathbf{D}(\mathbf{u})\mathbf{B} \tag{6.8}$$

is calculated by methods for nonlinear numerical analysis, for example iteration, which can be done in several ways. Some of them are listed in the following paragraphs.

Variable Stiffness.   The stiffness matrix $\mathbf{D}_{n-1}$ is given some initial values, for example those corresponding to near zero forces and moments in the members (elements) of the structure. The deformations are now calculated according to the linear elastic stiffness procedure shown in Fig. 6.53, that is

$$u_n = \mathbf{B}(\mathbf{B}^{t}\mathbf{D}_{n-1}\mathbf{B})^{-1}F = \mathbf{B}\mathbf{S}^{-1}F \tag{6.9}$$

in which F = applied external loads. A calculation of the corresponding forces with help of $\mathbf{D}_{n-1}$ gives

$$N_n = \mathbf{D}_{n-1}\mathbf{B}(\mathbf{B}^{t}\mathbf{D}_{n-1}\mathbf{B})^{-1}F \tag{6.10}$$

A new matrix $\mathbf{D}_n = \mathbf{D}_c(u_n)$ is established and the procedure is repeated until no further significant changes in u occur. One disadvantage of this method is that the stiffness matrix $\mathbf{S}$ has to be reestablished for each iteration round and the elimination procedure must be repeated. On the other hand, the iteration may require fewer rounds than do the methods that follow. The variable stiffness method can also be performed in the incremental way, as shown in Fig. 6.54, where one step corresponds to F. The iterations could also be omitted.

Initial Stress.   To avoid the recalculation of the member stiffness matrix $\mathbf{D}$ for each iteration, fictitious member forces N_0 (initial stresses) can be introduced to take the difference between the linearly calculated forces and the correct forces corresponding to the deformations u_n calculated in the nth round. To balance these initial forces, fictitious external loads are introduced. The procedure then goes on as follows.

Calculate the deformations u_n with the aid of the member stiffness $\mathbf{D}_0$, which is to remain unchanged during the whole iteration procedure. See Fig. 6.55, which will be much more complicated in the multidimensional cases since the iteration follows the ever-changing direction of the gradient. This gives

$$u_n = \mathbf{B}(\mathbf{B^t D_0 B})^{-1}(F - F_{0n-1}) \qquad (6.11)$$

in which the starting value of F_{0n-1} is zero in the first round.

The corresponding linear elastic forces N_n are

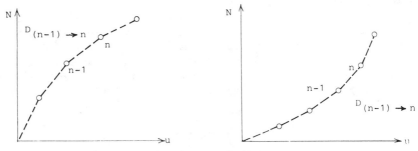

Fig. 6.54 Variable stiffness method in incremental form

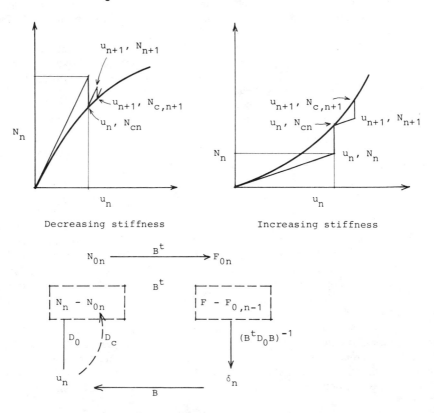

Decreasing stiffness   Increasing stiffness

Transformations

Fig. 6.55 Initial stress method

$$N_n = \mathbf{D}_0 u_n \tag{6.12}$$

which obviously is incorrect, since $\mathbf{D}_0$ is valid only for one specific value of u, namely u_0. The correct forces N_c corresponding to the present value of u_n are now calculated with aid of the correct constitutive matrix

$$N_{cn} = \mathbf{D}_c(u_n)u_n \tag{6.13}$$

and put equal to the value N_n minus the required initial forces

$$N_{cn} = \mathbf{D}_c(u_n)u_n = N_n - N_{0n} \tag{6.14}$$

The member forces $N_n - N_{0n}$ give

$$F - F_{0n} = \mathbf{B}^t(N_n - N_{0n}) \tag{6.15}$$

and the procedure is repeated from Eq. 6.11 on until no significant changes occur in u_n.

Initial Strain.   The outset of the procedure is as before, Eq. 6.11 with $F_{0-1} = 0$ in the first step.

Next, the member forces N_n are calculated according to Eq. 6.12 (see Fig. 6.56). The constitutive law is now assumed to be

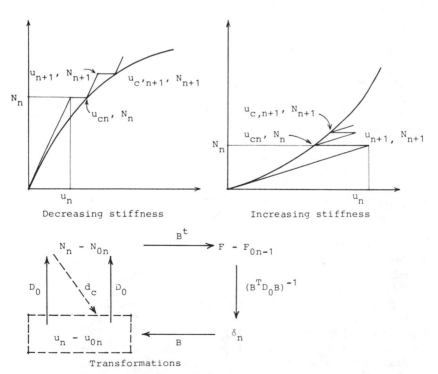

Fig. 6.56 Initial strain method

$$u_c = \mathbf{d}_c N_n \qquad (6.16)$$

Thus the correct deformations u_c belonging to the calculated (but probably incorrect) forces N_n are found from Eq. 6.16, and by introduction of initial deformations (strains) the correct deformations can be simulated in the linear elastic calculation

$$u_c = u_n - u_{0n} = \mathbf{d}_c N_n \qquad (6.17)$$

But to remain in the linear elastic calculation scheme, initial forces N_{0n} corresponding to u_{0n} must be introduced, that is

$$N_{0n} = \mathbf{D}_0 u_{0n} \qquad (6.18)$$

and to balance these forces the external loads must be adjusted accordingly

$$F - F_{0n} = \mathbf{B}^t(N_n - N_{0n}) \qquad (6.19)$$

Then

$$u_{n+1} = \mathbf{B}(\mathbf{B}^t\mathbf{D}_0\mathbf{B})^{-1}(F - F_{0n}) \qquad (6.20)$$

and so on, until no significant changes occur in u.

For numerical reasons the procedure is better suited for calculations in incremental form

$$\Delta u_n = -\mathbf{B}(\mathbf{B}^t\mathbf{D}_0\mathbf{B})^{-1}\Delta F_{0n} \qquad (6.21)$$

The same holds also for the initial stress procedure.

The constitutive law Eq. 6.16 enables us also to take time effects into account, which is an important feature of this method. Besides, it might be impossible to write the constitutive law in the form of Eq. 6.13.

As can be seen from Figs. 6.55 and 6.56, both methods tend to break down under adverse circumstances—the initial stress method in locking situations and the initial strain method in softening situations. Especially when portions of the structure exhibit falling branches (strain-softening materials), sophisticated methods must be employed to guarantee stable and rapid convergence.

For a detailed discussion of these phenomena the reader is referred to descriptions in the literature (CEB, 1966; Oden, 1967; Zienkiewicz, 1971; Oden, 1971a, 1971b; Bergan and Soreide, 1973).

When passing the summit of the force-deflection diagram the structure becomes unstable. The breakdown can be of local or over-all type. Further discussions are to be found in Chapter CB-8.

Step-by-Step Load Increment.   The processes just described can all be thought of as one load-increment in a step-by-step procedure following the behavior of a structure for increasing loads up to failure (Shah and Gesund, 1972; Gesund, 1973). The origin in the described method is now the final result from the previous step, so that some initial stresses (forces) and strains (deformations) must be introduced at the beginning of each step. This is normally a simple matter of bookkeeping in a computer. Thus

$$u_n = u_{s,n} - u_{s,n-1}$$

and (6.22)

$$N_n = N_{s,n} - N_{s,n-1}$$

in Eqs. 6.8 to 6.10, in which $u_{s,n}$ means deformations in the nth step, etc.

Requirements for Member Stiffness Expression. To take advantage of existing computer programs in the analysis procedures described, knowledge of the constitutive law is required in the form of

$$N = \mathbf{D}u \tag{6.23}$$

or

$$u = \mathbf{d}N \tag{6.24}$$

Eq. 6.23 is suitable for the initial stress procedure, and Eq. 6.24 for the initial strain procedure. Eq. 6.23 implies detailed knowledge of the stiffness matrix, which for a beam is

$$
\begin{vmatrix} M_1 \\ M_2 \\ N_1 \\ N_2 \\ T_1 \\ T_2 \end{vmatrix}
=
\begin{vmatrix}
D_{11} & D_{12} & D_{13} & D_{14} & D_{15} & D_{16} \\
 & D_{22} & D_{23} & D_{24} & D_{25} & D_{26} \\
 & & D_{33} & D_{34} & D_{35} & D_{36} \\
 & & & D_{44} & D_{45} & D_{46} \\
\text{Sym.} & & & & D_{55} & D_{56} \\
 & & & & & D_{66}
\end{vmatrix}
\begin{vmatrix} u_1 \\ u_2 \\ u_3 \\ u_4 \\ u_5 \\ u_6 \end{vmatrix}
\tag{6.25}
$$

in which $\mathbf{D}_{11}$ is of the form $(3EJ/L)\,g_{11}$, $\mathbf{D}_{33}$ of the form $(EA/L)\,g_{33}$ and so on, and g = a correction factor for nonlinearity; E, I, and g are functions of u or N.

The stiffness matrix (Eq. 6.25) has not yet been explicitly given in general in an easily handled form. In the general nonlinear case stiffness and displacement matrices cannot be treated separately, since the so-called stiffness matrix also contains displacements as arguments in its elements. Wilson (1960) gives the flexibility matrix for a bent member under axial load, but does not treat the effect of shear or concentrated rotations near cracks and moment maxima.

Tests by Cranston (1970) indicate that shear force has only marginal influence on rotational capacity of yielding segments of beams provided they are designed according to BCP (British Code of Practice). In general, however, a general expression for the effect of shear on the different stiffness parameters seems to be lacking.

Goldberg and Richard (1963) give a stiffness matrix for flexural members based on an assumption of the Ramberg-Osgood type. Ågårdh (1968) establishes the flexibility matrix by systematic integration and combinations of polynomials representing stress-strain curves of rather general character. The fitting to experimentally found stiffnesses is, however, still to be done.

Generally, to obtain the stiffness matrix $\mathbf{D}$ or the flexibility matrix $\mathbf{d}$ it seems necessary to resort to a numerical integration of the type carried out by Ferry Borges et al. (1963), Cranston and Chatterji (1970), Pfrang and Siess (1964), and Pfrang (1966).

In Section 6.2 a survey of possible methods and assumptions is given.

Many tests and the work carried out, for example by Baker (Flexural Mechanics of Reinforced Concrete, 1964), show that under normal practical conditions an assumption of a bilinear moment-rotation diagram is reasonable for underreinforced members, provided some limitations on shear, steel spacing rotation, etc., are observed. Also, for overreinforced members and compressed members, such assumptions can be made if they are carefully executed. However, for large deformations when members may exhibit falling branches (strain-softening materials), more general stiffness functions are needed.

Mixed Methods. Sometimes a simultaneous use of force and displacement variables proves to be the best. For example, the calculation of a beam gives a system equation with forces, moments, and displacements as unknowns (Wiberg, 1971c). Various conditions can be handled by prescribing values of moments and displacement. In such a case the moments are obtained directly from the solution of the system equation. In the general nonlinear case this technique has not yet been explored.

Force Method (Flexibility Method). In some cases it would be easier to work with the force method as described by

$$\mathbf{H^t d\, H}\, R + \mathbf{H^t d\, C}\, F + \mathbf{H^t} u_0 = r = 0 \qquad (6.26)$$

in which r represents the gap openings in a statically determinate auxiliary structure, and R stands for structurally indeterminate forces at the gaps of a structure that is cut to become structurally determinate. From the diagram in Fig. 6.57 it is seen that the matrix product $\mathbf{H}R$ is the contribution from the statically indeterminate forces to the member forces N, where the contribution from the external loads is $\mathbf{C}F$. The member forces N are then transformed by the flexibility matrix $\mathbf{D}$ into member deformations $u - u_0$, in which $u_0 =$ initial strains. The gaps at the cuts of the structure are then

$$r = \mathbf{H^t d}\, N + \mathbf{H^t} u_0 = 0 \qquad (6.27)$$

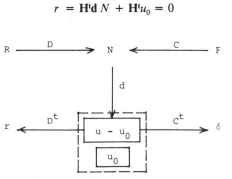

Fig. 6.57 Force method—transformation diagram

In the plastic range of one or more elastic plastic members, the appropriate R's can be set to given values and the corresponding r's calculated as hinge rotations, but in the general nonlinear case the R's vary up to failure. Again, certain assumptions regarding the moment-rotation relationship must be made, as explained for beams in Iyengar and Narayanaswamy (1967).

Certain problems in an automatized process of establishing the correct number of redundant forces and putting them at the critical sections seem to favor the stiffness method. Conditioning difficulties, however, sometimes motivate the use of the force method (Wiberg, 1971c) or the mixed method.

3   Geometric Nonlinearity

When the displacements are large enough to affect the matrix $\mathbf{B}$, the aforementioned equations must be adjusted to read $\bar{\mathbf{B}}$ (Zienkiewicz, 1971). If $\bar{\mathbf{B}}$ is linearly dependent on the displacements during the iteration step

$$\bar{\mathbf{B}} = \mathbf{B}_0 + \mathbf{B}_L(\delta) \tag{6.28}$$

the stiffness matrix then becomes

$$\mathbf{S} = (\mathbf{B}_0{}^t + \mathbf{B}_L{}^t)[\mathbf{D}(\delta)](\mathbf{B}_0 + \mathbf{B}_L) \tag{6.29}$$

which renders the iteration more complicated, but still possible (Zienkiewicz and Irons, 1970; Bergan and Soreide, 1963).

4   Effects of Amount of Reinforcement

Reinforced structures differ from steel structures in that it is possible to change the amount of reinforcement during the design process in order to strengthen heavily stressed sections and weaken less stressed sections of the structure. This means that complete structural design should include a procedure for redesigning sections of the structure as needed. The optimum seeking procedure has been treated, for example, by Templeman (1971), in which a method of seeking the optimum geometry is described. Others have published methods for optimizing the reinforcement in a reinforced structure, but a complete optimization taking into account the nonlinear behavior of a concrete structure seems to be lacking.

5   Shear Walls and their Coupling

Principally, the shear walls can be included in the calculation schemes exemplified for column-beam assemblies. A typical feature of concrete multistory structures is the lateral resistance produced by coupled shear walls, elevator shafts with door openings, etc. This is extensively discussed in Section 6.4. These shear walls are also often asymmetric and thin walled and have considerable warping, which must be taken into account when the stresses in the actual members are computed. The problem has been treated by Glück and others (Glück, 1970, 1973a; Wynhoven and Adams, 1970; Biswas and Tso, 1970; Fransson, 1973). The yielding of the members has been considered by Wynhoven and Adams (1970). This needs further research, especially since cracking of laterally loaded cores drastically reduces their stiffness and thus the stabilizing stiffness against buckling of the whole building. The torsional stability and force distribution of a single-core building are strongly dependent upon the integrity of the core, yet the cracking and nonlinear effects seem to have received little attention to date.

6 Nonbearing Building Members

In many cases only the main structure of a building is taken into account when it comes to the calculation of the load-bearing capacity. However, many filler walls of different materials contribute to the stiffness of the building (Fiorato et al., 1970) but are ignored in many calculation procedures. This is a field for further research.

7 Computer Capacity

Consider a building layout with say 50 columns, whose deformation field requires some 300 variables for its description (3 deflections and 3 rotations at the column end). Assume also that the building has 20 stories, and therefore 6000 unknowns calling for a **D** matrix of the size 6000 × 6000. Problems of this size can easily be beyond the capacity of a computer. There are certain things, however, that can be done to bring the problem down to realistic proportions. First, the stiffness matrix of the problem is, with suitable numbering of the unknowns, banded and can thus be handled with considerable saving in storage and manipulating effort (Argyris and Kelsey, 1963; Spillers, 1963). Furthermore, the structure can be cut into sub-assemblies (Argyris and Kelsey, 1963). Advantage can be taken of the fact that the floor slabs are very stiff in their own plane and therefore force all horizontal column displacements and torsional rotations to be common at each floor level. The deflections at one plane only affect the forces three or at most four to ten stories away (Stamato and Smith, 1969). By suitable approximations the stiffness matrix becomes strongly banded.

If the members are subassembled into a number of "shear walls" consisting of different types of members that can be considered to lie in one plane, and all nonrelevant displacements are eliminated, then the "shear walls" can be regarded as superelements in the total system, which then has a reasonable number of unknowns (Khan and Sbarounis, 1964; MacLeod, 1967; Larsson, 1967; Tezcon, 1967; Rosman,

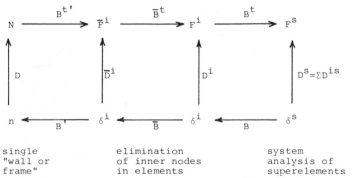

Fig. 6.58 Subassembling technique—transformation diagrams

1968; Stamato and Smith, 1969; Jenkins, 1969; Hoeland, 1969; Wiberg, 1970, 1971a, 1971b). (See Fig. 6.58.)

The effort to solve the system equation is then proportional to the number of stories and to the square of the half band-width of the matrix, if the elimination is done according to Crout (Cholesky). This is a much more reasonable task than treating the whole structure in one step. Most concrete structures should therefore be within reach of a computer of moderate size.

It should be noted that in certain cases the stiffness of a superelement can be obtained experimentally.

8 Available Computer Programs for Nonlinear Analysis

The information presented here was collected by a subcommittee of ACI 428 (Limit Design), consisting of H. Gesund, chairman, H. A. Sawyer, and M. Z. Cohn. A questionnaire was developed and sent to individuals or organizations known or believed to have programs of the type on which information was sought. It is hoped that this publication will stimulate additional interest in the subject and produce further requests for questionnaires and more returns of those already sent out.

Background of Limit Analysis or Design. Discussion of the fundamentals of limit analysis or design can be found in Section 6.5.

In general, any structural analysis or design method can be examined from the point of view of three requirements: (1) Are the equations of statics satisfied? (2) Are the equations of compatibility, that is, geometric continuity, satisfied? (3) Is there a check to assure that the structure will behave satisfactorily in all respects under service-load conditions? The plastic design process customarily used for steel structures directly employs only statics, with a separate check made later for service-load deflections. Adequate rotation capacity, providing geometric compatibility, is assured by restrictions on types of sections and members that can be used, and by comprehensive bracing requirements. The procedure is further simplified by the assumption of rigid-plastic behavior of the materials, members, and structure, which is reasonably valid for structural steel as used in buildings.

The properties of reinforced concrete are such that most of these simplifications can be applied only in a restricted number of situations. A full limit analysis or design of a reinforced concrete structure must include consideration of all three of the requirements stated. Since reinforced concrete is a relatively brittle material (compared to structural steel), the problem of compatibility must be dealt with carefully. Numerous methods have been used to calculate the deformational response of reinforced concrete members to various types of loadings present in an actual structure, and to thus either provide a compatibility check or include the actual continuous deformations of the members in the structural analysis. All involve some assumptions, and thus may provide different levels of accuracy, possibly requiring the use of different safety factors to prevent premature failures in the actual structure. Deflections and cracking under service conditions must also be checked, often separately.

The deformational responses of a member to loads of various magnitudes, characters, and possibly durations, can be expressed in terms of member stiffness or flexibility. This makes it possible to combine the responses of all the members to obtain the total structure response. At the same time, however, the deformations of the structure are likely to engender additional loads in both the structure as a whole and the individual members. These loads must either be included in the analysis, or their effects must be taken into account through some simplifying assumptions or allowances, or else all deformations likely to cause such additional loads must be prevented by external means. Additional features, such as member or structure optimization and consideration of creep and shrinkage effects, may be incorporated into the design or analysis process.

Design Questionnaire. The questionnaire was designed to elicit information on the capabilities of each program; on how the real material properties, the consequent nonlinear member deformations, the structural nonlinearities, and the compatibility problem are treated; on availability of the program and applicable documentation; on hardware and software requirements; on problem size and cost parameters and limitations; and on serviceability check and design capabilities. It was also planned to make the task of responding as quick and simple as possible.

Results Obtained. Most of the frame analysis programs reported were written for plane frames, with only four able to handle space frames. Three of the latter use the step-by-step historical analysis procedure, while one uses iteration at a given load. The majority of the plane frame programs also use the step-by-step method, and a few programs use or make available both schemes.

The effects of nonlinearity of material behavior are considered in many programs, as are the nonlinear geometrical load-deformation effects, but only two programs incorporate shear or torsion effects on member behavior. Six of the programs were reported to use the actual material stress-strain responses, but at the same time only two of them were reported as being able to take into account shrinkage and creep effects in the concrete. Member stability is quite generally considered, as are biaxial bending effects in the space frame programs, though load/torsional deformation interaction is included in only one. Several structural types other than frames are also being analyzed inelastically.

The stiffness matrix method of analysis is generally favored for calculations within each load step, and the loads can be applied both at joints and along the members. Linear programming does not seem to be popular at this time. Stability and serviceability checks are frequently, but not always, included. However only one, two-dimensional, program is suited for dynamic analysis, and only one, a different one, has a design capability. Program capacities, running times, and computer costs vary widely.

9 Fields for Further Research

Load Reversal. Load reversal has been treated very little in literature dealing with computer programs, and therefore further investigation into this field should be valuable. Calculation of this type can only be performed with a step-by-step method.

Shear Deformations. Shear deformations could be included in the computer programs mentioned, but the material and sectional properties are still not well known (Dilger, 1967).

Creep, Shrinkage, and Temperature Effects. The creep phenomenon has stirred increased interest because the materials have been increasingly stressed, and consequently the creep phenomenon often cannot be ignored.

Shrinkage effects have a great influence, especially in precast buildings where many joints are sensitive to tension. A complete computer program should include shrinkage effects. Further research work should be done on creep effects on statically indeterminate systems since much of the research work done up to this time deals with statically determinate axially loaded columns. Temperature effects must also be considered in tall buildings (Khan and Fintel, 1966).

Cyclic Loading. The behavior of reinforced concrete frames under cyclic load has been studied using small concrete models by Sabnis and White (1969). This type of behavior for a concrete structure should also be included in a more complete calculation method for tall building structures of concrete. Again, only a step-by-step method is able to truly reflect the behavior of a structure under cyclic loading. See also Section 6.3 of this chapter.

Alternative Load-Bearing, Partially Damaged Structures. Many building codes require that a building should withstand, with a lower safety factor, the actual loadings even though a smaller portion of the load-bearing system is lost due to an unexpected overload such as a gas explosion or a striking object. This type of loading can in principle be handled by initial stress procedure, removing forces in the members considered, but is not explored in the literature. The phenomenon is akin to the problem of redesign which has been treated to some extent; see, for example, Wiberg (1971b).

Imperfections. A complete step-by-step analysis should also include the possible geometrical and structural imperfections of the load-bearing structure. Such research work has been started, for example by Sahlin (1971a). Strength and load dispersions are not dealt with in this connection.

Falling Branch. Some of these calculation methods seem to break down if the constitutive law for the members has a falling branch of their force-deformation curve (see Fig. 6.59). Some work has been done on this problem (Cranston, 1965; Oden, 1971) but still more is needed. When some members of the structure exhibit falling branches on the load-deformation curve the problem can become one of instability. Even such a simple case as an axially loaded 130-mm × 130-mm × 650-mm (5-in. × 5-in. × 25-in.) prism with ties exhibits such behavior (Roy and Sozen, Flexural Mechanics of Reinforced Concrete, 1964). One portion of the specimen even has a steeper falling branch than the rest of the specimen, which clearly indicates the necessity to break down the members in sufficiently small pieces to be described by one unique load-deformation curve. The subassembling technique can then be used to build up load-deformation curves for larger assemblies, such as columns and beams.

Materials Having No Tensile Strength. A member of a material having no tensile strength (cracked concrete) can show a peculiar force-deformation law for certain loading conditions (Hellers, 1967; Sahlin, 1971b), and no general nonlinear method of analysis for statically indeterminate structures seems to be available for this type of member behavior.

6.7 IMPOSED ROTATIONS METHOD

1 Moment-Curvature and Moment Rotation Laws

From the results of many tests, it can be assumed that the basic moment-curvature law of structural elements in reinforced concrete subject to bending can be reasonably idealized as having a trilinear shape similar to $OCYR$ as shown in Fig. 6.60.

The curvature in the cracked zones can be decomposed into an elastic curvature and an additional curvature due to cracking, thus facilitating computation of the strains. The intersection of segments I and II at point C determines a cracking moment M_c which does not correspond to a precise physical phenomenon, since the transition from the uncracked state to the fully cracked state follows curve $C\text{-}Y$.

By integration of the moment-curvature laws along the elements of the structure the moment rotation relations are derived.

For the elastic phase, the problem is then solved. When cracked zones exist, however, their length is determined only if the element is statically determinate. In statically indeterminate systems the lengths of these zones are functions of the unknowns, which leads to a series of nonlinear equations for the computation of these unknowns.

In the inelastic phase, the length over which the materials are plastified is not known so that, actually, the computation of the plastic rotations is practically impossible. However, experience shows that the plastified length is relatively small and that the structure behaves as if the plastic rotations were concentrated in discrete hinges.

A problem arises when prestressed concrete members contain unbonded tendons. Since these tendons are free to slide along their entire length, the hinge formation and rotation at a joint are affected by the over-all behavior of the tendons, which depends on the bending of every section of the beam as well as the location of each tendon at each section. The analysis can become rather complicated.

Experience also shows that the plastic rotation is a function of the moment M which acts in this section, and that it is independent from the variation of the moment in the zones which are not plastified.

The concentration of rotations in beams tested with a point load is clearly shown in Fig. 6.61, where the experimental rotations of various sections are plotted for different loading levels. The beam has essentially constant slope at the ends, with a rapid change in slope near the load.

The idea of using moment-rotation relationships stems from the difficulty of defining phase III of the behavior by use of the moment-curvature relations.

2   Imposed Rotations Method

Hypotheses. The basic hypotheses introduced are the following (Macchi, 1970b):

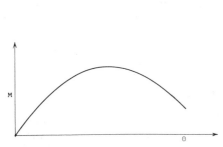

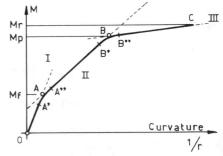

Fig. 6.59 Strain-softening materials with falling branch of moment-rotation relationship

Fig. 6.60 Moment-curvature diagram for reinforced concrete beam

1. The effects of the inelastic deformations can be added to the elastic effect due to the external loads. In particular, it has been shown that the virtual work equations can be subdivided into two sets of equations: (i) Elastic equations which represent the effect of the loads; and (ii) equations which give the effect of an inelastic unit rotation that acts in a critical section. These two sets of equations are elastic, and therefore it is possible to solve them directly by usual methods.

2. The experimental moment-rotation relationship is trilinear.

3. Inelastic rotations are considered as concentrated at the critical sections.

This method allows one to analyze a given structure, after a preliminary design. It is based on the hypothesis of the uniqueness of the limit states considered, which corresponds to the adoption of the convention of monotonic increase of the loads for each loading scheme. It permits taking into account the shrinkage and creep of the concrete, thermal variations, and the settlements of the supports. It assumes, in its present state, that the effects of sidesway and of the eventual second-order effects do not appreciably modify the collapse conditions of the structure.

The manual application of the method is, in practice, limited to structures having a limited degree of redundancy. Application to complex frames is possible using the procedure of Articles 6.7.4 and 6.7.5.

Practical Construction of Moment-Rotation Diagrams. The following describes the Moment-Inelastic Rotation diagrams to be used in the calculations (see Fig. 6.62).

A diagram must be drawn for each critical section in which the inelastic rotation $\bar{\alpha}$ of the adjacent zone is assumed to be concentrated. The moment measured on the ordinate is the moment in the critical section. For critical sections subject to both axial load and bending, a family of diagrams can be drawn taking the value of the axial load as a parameter.

1st segment. Point C corresponds to the cracking of the critical section. In simple bending

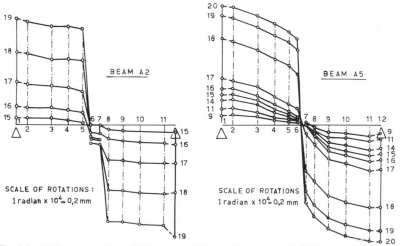

Fig. 6.61 Distribution of measured rotations (slopes) along beam length at various load stages

$$M_c = \frac{f_r I_1}{d_e} \qquad (6.30)$$

in which f_r = modulus of rupture of concrete; d_e = distance from the centroidal axis of gross section to the extreme fiber in tension; and I_1 = moment of inertia of the uncracked gross section. If axial load is present, it has to be taken into account in determining M_c.

2nd segment (cracked phase). In bending, the second segment is fairly straight because of the essentially constant depth of the neutral axis. The ordinate of Y is the moment M_y for which the elastic limit of steel is reached; M_y is calculated by the usual reinforced concrete theory.

The Y abscissa (inelastic rotation $\bar\alpha_y$ due to cracking) may be approximately calculated through integration of the curvature over that part of the beam where M_c has been exceeded, that is

$$\frac{1}{r} = \frac{M - M_c}{E_s I_2} - \frac{M - M_c}{E_c I_1} \qquad (6.31)$$

in which E_c = modulus of elasticity of concrete; and E_s = modulus of elasticity of steel.

For rectangular sections in bending

$$I_2 = A_s z(d - x) \qquad (6.32)$$

in which A_s = area of tension reinforcement; z = lever arm; d = distance from extreme compression fiber to centroid of tension reinforcement; and x = distance from extreme compression fiber to neutral axis. The effect of concrete in tension between the cracks is emprirically taken into account by this idealization.

The approximate determination of the cracked lengths may be carried out starting from points of contraflexure determined under the hypothesis of complete redistribution.

3rd segment. For beams in which the elastic limit of the steel is exceeded, a third segment, with a slight slope, extends to the rupture point R.

The ultimate moment M_2 is known. The additional concentrated inelastic rotation θ can actually be deduced only from experimental diagrams such as that of

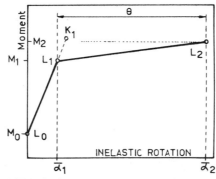

Fig. 6.62 Inelastic portion of moment curvature diagram

Fig. 6.63, which collects the results obtained in six laboratories during research sponsored by CEB.

The rotations are plotted as functions both of the position of the neutral axis, and (for beams) of the mechanical index of reinforcement $\psi = (A_s f_y)/(bd f_c)$.

Fig. 6.63 gives two curves, of which one corresponds to an upper limit and the other to a lower limit of the experimental rotations.

The great dispersion of limit-rotations in the cases of low reinforcement index (left in Fig. 6.63) has limited consequences, because of the generally adequate ductility of such members.

Steps of Analysis.   Performing the analysis requires the following steps:

1. Determination of the critical sections. The critical sections are sections of maximum moment in each zone subject to a moment of the same sign. There are as many critical sections as zones in which inelastic rotations of different sign are supposed to exist; this number is generally different from the number of hinges necessary to make the structure determinate. Their exact locations would require a knowledge of the results of the calculation, but an approximate location based on the temporary hypothesis of complete redistribution is usually sufficient.

2. Calculation of the ultimate moments in the critical sections. This is performed following the limit-states approach, that is by applying the partial safety coefficients γ_m to the strength of steel and concrete.

3. Calculation of the elastic effect of the loads. The elastic moment diagrams corresponding to a unit load are drawn for each possible loading scheme. Any method of elastic analysis may be used.

4. Calculation of the effects of the unit rotations. An imaginary cut is effected in each critical section, and the elastic moment diagrams due to a

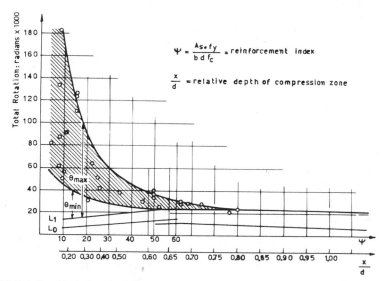

Fig. 6.63 Relationship between total rotational capacity of cross section and neutral axis depth ratio, x/d

corresponding unit rotation imposed in the section are drawn. Any method of elastic analysis may be used.

5. Construction of moment-rotation diagrams. The procedure previously described in Article 6.7.2 may be used.

6. Analysis at the ultimate limit state and the serviceability limit states is carried out as described in the following paragraphs.

Analysis at the Ultimate Limit State. The elastic diagram of the moments due to dead load is drawn, having applied γ_s as partial safety factor for loads. Use a method of verification consisting then of checking that the factor η applied to live loads, which leads the structure to the ultimate limit state, is at least equal to γ_s.

This verification can be done, for each live-load scheme, according to the following steps:

1. One first supposes that $\eta = \gamma_s$ (the real safety is exactly the safety required).

2. According to this hypothesis an elastic diagram of the total moments is obtained by superimposing on the dead-load diagram (with the γ_s factor) the diagram of live load amplified by $\eta = \gamma_s$ (see Fig. 6.64).

At this stage of the calculation, two possibilities may occur: (1) The elastic diagram obtained is statically inadmissible, the ultimate moment being exceeded in one of the critical sections; one then proceeds as further indicated in Ⓐ; or (2) the elastic diagram obtained is statically admissible; the calculation is then continued as in Ⓑ.

Ⓐ *Case when the total elastic diagram is statically inadmissible.* The limit moment is, for instance, exceeded in the critical section E (Fig. 6.65).

A moments redistribution is effected by superimposing on the elastic moments a combination (indicated as 3 in Fig. 6.65) of the moment diagrams due to the unit rotations, in such a way as to make the resulting diagram statically admissible.

However, the resulting diagram will be the correct diagram only if the total deformation compatibility is verified; the elastic diagrams 1 and 2 being compatible, one must check that redistribution diagram 3 is actually the one due to the inelastic rotations that occur in the critical sections D, B, E subject to the moments of $(1+2+3)$.

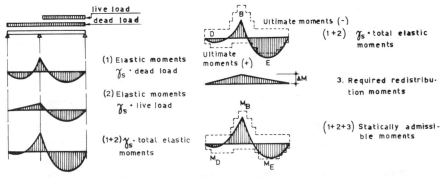

Fig. 6.64 Elastic moment diagrams   **Fig. 6.65 Elastic and redistribution moments**

The values $\bar{\alpha}_D$, $\bar{\alpha}_B$, $\bar{\alpha}_E$ of the inelastic rotations which correspond to the moments M_D, M_B, M_E, must therefore be read on the moment-rotation diagram (step 5 of the analysis previously described) of the critical sections D, B, E.

The ordinate $\overline{\Delta M}$ which characterizes the redistribution diagram (more generally the ordinates at the supports) will be given by an equation of the type

$$\overline{\Delta M} = E_c I_1 (k_D \bar{\alpha}_D + k_B \bar{\alpha}_B + k_E \bar{\alpha}_E) \tag{6.33}$$

in which the coefficients k_D, k_B, k_E are the values obtained during step 4 of the analysis previously described.

If $\overline{\Delta M}$ is greater than the ΔM value assumed in diagram 3, this means that it will be possible to obtain a statically admissible and compatible configuration with the ultimate moment in E, under a live load higher than the one assumed, that is with $\eta > \gamma_s$.

This check is generally sufficient if there is in Ⓑ an adequate margin to assure the condition of equilibrium. The method described in Ⓒ will make it possible to control doubtful cases.

If $\overline{\Delta M}$ is smaller than ΔM, or opposite in sign, the compatibility of the deformations cannot possibly be reached. The structure will have to be modified, expecially section E, which is in this case generally brittle.

Ⓑ *Case when the total elastic diagram is statically admissible.* The ultimate moment is not exceeded at any section. However, the elastic configuration is not generally compatible.

This fact may be controlled by calculating $\overline{\Delta M}$, which is generally different from zero. The sign of this redistribution moment indicates the critical section which is overstressed because of the effect of the inelastic deformations.

The ultimate moment is thus assumed to be reached in this section and one proceeds as in Ⓐ.

Ⓒ *Determination of the ultimate limit state.* In current practice, the inequality $\eta \geq \gamma_s$, which has been verified, is usually sufficient.

The real amplification factor η of the live loads which leads to the ultimate limit state may eventually be found by trials as the smallest value of η for which $\overline{\Delta M} = \Delta M$.

Analysis at the Cracking and Deformation Limit States.

Cracking limit state. The opening of the cracks is a function of the stresses in the steel, which must first be calculated.

The structure is considered subject to the characteristic load without any increment.

For the most unfavorable configurations of the live loads, the elastic diagrams of the moments are drawn and one proceeds as follows:

1. Extension of the second segment of the inelastic moment-rotation diagrams up to the K value (Fig. 6.62), which corresponds to the characteristic stength of the steel (Y corresponds to the design strength).

2. Reading on the diagrams the inelastic rotations $\bar{\alpha}$ which result from the elastic distribution of moments.

3. Computation of the redistribution diagram (step 4), as per Figs. 6.64 and 6.65, and corrections of the moments (by trials) in order to obtain $\overline{\Delta M} = \Delta M$.

4. Verification of the fact that in no section is the characteristic strength of the steel exceeded.

Deformation limit state. The deflections under the characteristic loads can be calculated from the equation of the curvatures in phase II. The calculation must start from the real configurations of the moments previously determined.

3   Design of Concrete Frames for Two Failure Stages

A procedure similar to the one just described (which follows the safety criteria of the CEB Code) has been developed in parallel by Sawyer (1960, 1964b) for application in connection with the ACI Code. It takes advantage of the separation of the effects of inelastic rotations in the same way, so that it can well be considered an "imposed rotation" method.

The linearization of the moment-curvature law is obtained by means of "plasticity factors" k_p, the meaning of which is clearly shown in Fig. 6.66.

With the same notation used in Article 6.7.1, the total curvature for a given moment in stage III will be

$$\frac{1}{r} = \frac{1}{E_c I_1}[M + k_{1p}(M - M_f) + k_{2p}(M - M_p)] \qquad (6.34)$$

Eq. 6.34 permits the calculation of rotations with the same moment-area principles used for purely elastic curvatures: in addition to the total moment-area, the total area above M_f expanded by the factor k_{1p}, and the total area above M_p expanded by the factor k_{2p} have to be included.

For the analysis of the effects of inelastic rotations in frames, the moment distribution method has been extended (Johnson and Sawyer, 1958). The fixed-end moments caused by inelastic angles are distributed, and the resulting moments added to the elastic moments for the loading.

For the analysis of the effects of inelastic rotations in single-span variable section beams, frames, or closed rings, the elastic center or column analogy method has been extended (Sawyer, 1955); the displacements of the cut-back statically determinate structure from inelastic angles, as well as elastic deformations, are used in an iterative calculation of the required restorative forces.

Though this linearization procedure can be used for analysis based on any multilinear idealization, Sawyer (1964b) recommends a bilinear moment-curvature idealization for practical use, Fig. 6.67.

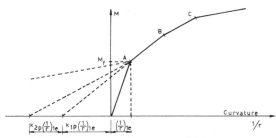

Fig. 6.66 Moment curvature diagram

The first line is a practical approximation of lines OC and CY of Fig. 6.60. Point C is ignored because of the variability and even disappearance of point C, resulting from shrinkage stresses, prior loadings, and cracking. The second line reaches the ultimate moment M_r, which Sawyer recommends as being the ultimate moment of the ACI Code with a curvature corresponding to a concrete compressive strain of 0.0038. This approximation is substantially different from the elastoplastic idealization, in which the second line is horizontal.

The proposed constant ratio, $M_p/M_r = 0.85$, is a further simplification. This assumption is justified by the fact that the results are rather insensitive to variation in this ratio (unless second-order effects are important). However, for calculated ultimate rotations to conform to observed actual inelastic rotations at regions of highly localized maximum moments (for example, at a concentrated load or column support), Sawyer found it necessary to increase the theoretical inelastic length (the length over which the moment exceeds M_p) by d, without otherwise changing the shape of the inelastic moment area.

With this bilinear idealization, one "plasticity factor" k_p is sufficient for analysis or design in which second-order effects are unimportant. This design may be executed for the following two failure stages, using appropriate load factors for each stage: (1) Wide-cracking failure stage at M_p (serviceability); and (2) crushing-spalling failure stage at M_r (ultimate strength). As shown by Fig. 6.68, k_p is a function of the net reinforcement index $(q - q')$ and steel yield stress (f_y) for pure bending. For combined bending and axial load, see Sawyer (1964b).

The better precision of this method, compared with ultimate strength design of the ACI Code based on the elastic distribution, seems to justify a 10% reduction of the Code load factor for the ultimate stage.

For building analysis or design for which second-order effects are significant, including those for almost all unbraced frames, an elastic, single-line approximation of the curve of Fig. 6.60 is unsatisfactory and usually nonconservative. Both the trilinear and bilinear methods which have been described require only an approximate evaluation of E_1I_1 to provide the deflections basic to a realistic second-order analysis or design.

4 Mathematical Programming Methods for Complex Frames

The methods presented in the preceding Articles, as long as they are used with a manual trial-and-error procedure, are limited to structures having a low degree of indeterminacy. For complex frames they can be used only as approximate tools, in

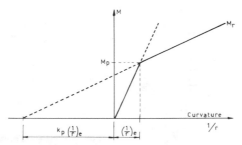

Fig. 6.67 Bilinear moment-curvature diagram

the cases and within the limits in which the procedure of analyzing the individual beams separately is permissible.

When the problem is complex, the analysis of the actual moment distribution in the nonlinear field can be systematically performed by means of recent algorithms used in Operations Research, and therefore with the powerful help of computers. DeDonato and Maier (1970) in this way generalized the imposed rotations method.

The superposition of the effect of inelastic rotations and of the elastic moment distribution is still the basis of the analysis; furthermore, the assumptions of concentrated rotations and of a reversible moment-rotation law (holonomy) are retained.

The linearization of inelastic rotations is also the same as in Fig. 6.62. Its analytical description is nevertheless done by means of yield functions ϕ and plastic multipliers λ, in a way which plays an essential role in the proposed procedure.

With reference to Fig. 6.69, the moment-inelastic rotations law for a single critical section can be represented by the set of relations

$$\bar{\alpha} = \lambda_1 + \lambda_2$$

$$\phi_1 = M - K_1 - H_1\lambda_1$$

$$\phi_2 = M - K_2 - H_2\lambda_2$$

$$\phi_1\lambda_1 = 0 \qquad \phi_2\lambda_2 = 0$$

in which K_1 and K_2 (moments at cracking and at yield), as well as H_1 and H_2 ($1/H_1$ and $1/H_2$ are the relative deviations of the straight lines in the diagram), are given constants of the section. When $\phi_1 = 0$, the points above K_1 are represented; when $\phi_2 = 0$, the points above K_2 are represented.

The bending moments in the structure (vector $\mathbf{M}$) are expressed as the sum of the elastic moments due to loading (vector $\mathbf{M^E}$) and the redistribution moments $\mathbf{Z}\bar{\alpha}$ ($\bar{\alpha}$ are the actual inelastic rotations, and $\mathbf{Z}$ is the matrix of the influence coefficients), giving for all critical sections the effects of imposed unit rotations

$$\mathbf{M} = \mathbf{M^E} + \mathbf{Z}\bar{\alpha} \tag{6.35}$$

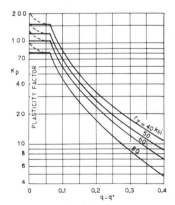

Fig. 6.68 Plasticity factor

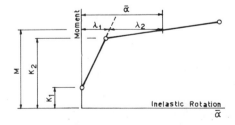

Fig. 6.69 Inelastic portion of moment rotation diagram

For the equations associated with the above set of relations, the determination of the actual moment distribution under the given loads has been shown to be a linear complementarity problem with a unique solution. This problem is then transformed into a quadratic programming problem, for which efficient algorithms are available.

The advantage of this approach, as compared with the precise incremental methods of analysis described in Section 6.6, should be found in the amount of work and in the capacity.

A first advantage is due to the fact that the determination of the compatible configuration is only done for the loadings corresponding to the limit states of the structure (ultimate state and service state).

A second advantage is due to the preliminary independent calculation of the elastic moments M^E and of the matrix Z, which can be done with existing subroutines; the quadratic programming solution can also be obtained by existing subroutines.

This approach is promising and the first applications seem to show a relatively wide capacity.

5 Example Analysis of Multistory Frame

The procedure described in the preceding Article (Mathematical Programming Methods) has been applied to the reinforced concrete frame of Fig. 6.70, taking into account both the nonlinear flexural characteristics and second-order geometric

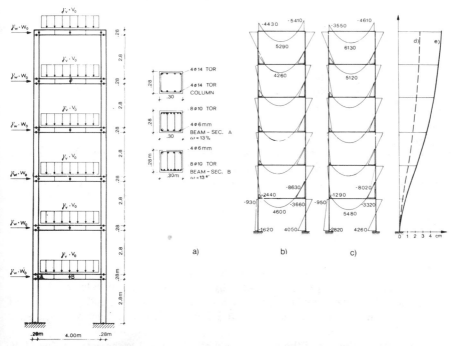

Fig. 6.70 Moment diagrams for reinforced concrete frame: (a) Frame, loading and section properties; (b) first-order elastic moments; (c) second-order inelastic moments; (d) first-order elastic deflections; (e) second-order inelastic deflections

effects. Second-order effects are taken into account by simply changing the computation of vector $\mathbf{M^E}$ and matrix $\mathbf{Z}$, which still can be performed by means of standard elastic procedures (Maier et al., 1972a).

The frame in Fig. 6.70 was solved by this method (Corradi et al., 1972). Constitutive laws for beams and columns were assumed as indicated in Macchi (1970a), where the preliminary design for the same frame is shown. Fig. 6.70 shows some of the results obtained for the load condition characterized by a vertical uniform load $\gamma_v V_o = 5000$ kg/m (3350 lbs/ft) on the beams, and a concentrated wind load $\gamma_w W_o = 500$ kg (1100 lbs) at each floor.

Linear elastic first-order moment distribution and lateral displacements are given by Fig. 6.70(b) and (d), respectively, while the corresponding inelastic second-order quantities are shown in Fig. 6.70 (c) and (e).

6   Approximate Method for Preliminary Design

For a first dimensioning or for calculations preceding more exact computations, and to identify the initial section of rupture (especially in the case of the brittle sections), the following method (Fig. 6.71) has been proposed (Macchi, 1969, 1970a):

1. Transformation of the span considered into a mechanism with hinges located at the critical sections.

2. Computation of the ratios k between the rotations of the various hinges ($\alpha_B = k\alpha_E$).

3. Superposition of the $M_E/k\alpha_E$ and M_B/α_B diagrams for the critical sections on the opposite sides of the abscissa's axis.

In these diagrams, any vertical line (compatibility path) realizes the condition of deformation compatibility and cuts on the M/α diagrams pairs of points which represent possible configurations. The line nearest to the origin which passes through a rupture point (R_B) defines the rupture configuration. Points X and R_B give the moments in the two critical sections at the rupture limit state; this makes possible the computation of the corresponding load.

A simple graphical construction makes possible the application of the method to the case for which several linear elements belonging to a structural frame converge in a joint. In these cases, the rotation α_J of the joints must be taken into account (Fig. 6.72); in the case of the figure, the compatibility condition of deformability is

$$\alpha_B + \alpha_J = \frac{\alpha_E}{2} \tag{6.36}$$

if the absolute value of the rotations is considered.

The rotation of the joints is affected by the deformation of columns 2 and 3, which is itself a function of the axial load N. At the left of Fig. 6.72, the family of moment-rotation curves of columns 2 and 3, which have as a parameter the axial load N, is therefore shown.

Adding the ordinates of the two curves that correspond to the actual value of N, the moment-rotation M_B/α_J curve of the joint is obtained underneath (the limit rotation is that of the most brittle column).

The compatibility path at the ultimate limit state is drawn with a dotted line: $R_B HX$ on one side, $R_B QST$ on the other, the rupture happening in section B. As a matter of fact

$$\alpha_B + \alpha_J = \overline{QR_B} = \overline{OH} = \frac{\alpha_E}{2} \qquad (6.37)$$

if the $R_B H$ line is obtained by translating horizontally the M_B/α_B curve until it passes through R_B.

The statically determinate limit moment $M = q_u(l^2/8)$ is read directly on the figure as the sum of the ordinates of X and R_B.

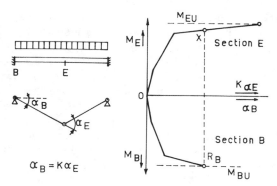

Fig. 6.71 Load moment diagram for two sections of fixed end beam

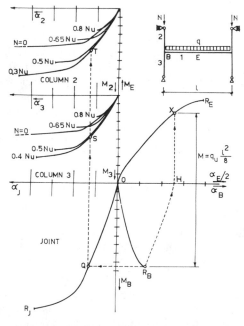

Fig. 6.72 Analysis of frame subassemblage

6.8 PLASTIC DESIGN, ELASTIC-PLASTIC (BAKER) METHOD

The rigid-plastic theory of structural steel frames is well known (Baker, 1949). This theory, however, cannot be applied without modification to reinforced concrete frames, since the rotation of plastic hinges, which accompanies any redistribution of bending moments that occurs as failure is approached, is limited by lack of ductility. However, if the sections of a reinforced concrete frame have been dimensioned to resist bending moments and stress—obtained from preliminary approximate calculations—it is not difficult to design more precisely the reinforcement to resist the load with a bending-moment distribution at the ultimate limit state, which is optimal in terms of cost and simplicity of construction. It is also easy to calculate the angles of discontinuity or rotations taken up by plastic hinges, so as to limit them at that state and to verify the correctness of their assumed positions or, alternatively, to determine the positions at which plastic hinges will develop, given a particular arrangement of reinforcement.

When the designer is satisfied that the arrangement of steel is optimal and the rotations of plastic hinges at the ultimate limit state have the correct sign and are not excessive, he has established, in terms of the idealized moment-rotation characteristics assumed, that the ultimate moments of resistance which he has assumed at critical sections are compatible with the deformations of the frame members and the angles of discontinuity at critical sections, alternatively referred to as rotations of plastic hinges. In addition, for most designs that satisfy ultimate limit state requirements, such serviceability requirements as limited crack width and deflection are also satisfied. If there is any doubt, say, in water-retaining structures, it is not difficult to adjust the ultimate limit state calculations to check the stresses, strains, and crack widths for working-load conditions. The diagram $OL_0L_1L_2$ may be used for greater precision (see Fig. 6.73; also Macchi, 1956).

The merits of basing calculations on simple, idealized assumptions can be studied by examining a large number of tests of strengths and deformations of beams, columns, and frames loaded to failure, and comparing them with calculated values. Those recorded by Baker and Amarakone (1964) show that a simple bilinear moment-rotation diagram OL_1AL_2 (Fig. 6.73), based on well-established yield and ultimate limits of strength and strain of test specimens, provides a sound basis of design. Also, because of the nature of concrete and the usual uncertainty in regard to loads, there is little point in more precision.

1 Basic Assumptions

Calculations are based on the following assumptions:

1. The distribution of strain across frame member sections is linear.

2. The distribution of compressive stress across concrete sections is determined by the characteristics of Fig. 6.74. In the case of columns, a reduction should be made in the value of σ_b in accordance with CEB International Design Recommendations.

3. The following parameter values define limits (see Fig. 6.73): L_0 = cracking limit; L_1 = yield limit (steel 0.001 offset strain, concrete 0.002 direct strain); and L_2 = ultimate limit (steel 0.01 direct strain, concrete 0.0035 direct strain). This applies to material test or member section (see Figs. 6.73 and 6.74).

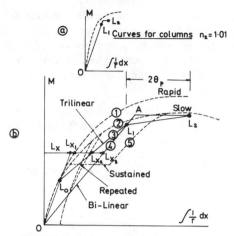

Fig. 6.73 Typical moment-rotation diagrams

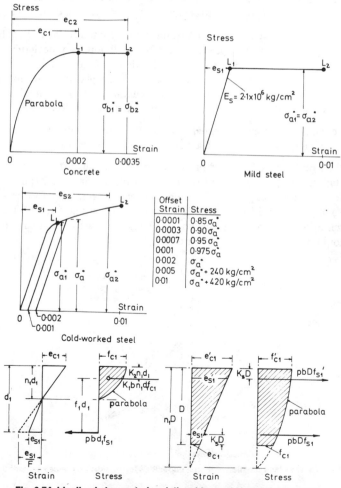

Offset Strain	Stress
0.0001	$0.85\sigma_a^*$
0.0003	$0.90\sigma_a^*$
0.0007	$0.95\sigma_a^*$
0.001	$0.975\sigma_a^*$
0.002	σ_a^*
0.005	$\sigma_a^* + 240\ kg/cm^2$
0.01	$\sigma_a^* + 420\ kg/cm^2$

Fig. 6.74 Idealized stress-strain relationships and stress distributions

4. The permissible values of the inelastic rotation (or angle of inelastic discontinuity) θ may be determined from the following influential parameters: (1) Increase of concrete strain above 0.002, allowing for binding; position of neutral axis; and (2) longitudinal distribution of inelastic curvature. The curves in Fig. 6.75 give permissible values of θ which have been verified experimentally.

5. The value of EI is constant over the length of a member between plastic hinges and from zero bending moment to the moment at L_1. In the idealized moment-rotation diagram

$$\int \frac{1}{r} ds = \int \frac{M}{EI} ds = \frac{1}{EI} \int M ds \text{ if } EI \text{ is constant. Therefore}$$

$$EI = Mr = \frac{M n_1 d}{e_{c1}}$$

(see Fig. 6.76), in which r = radius of curvature; d = effective depth of section; $n_1 d$ = depth of neutral axis; and e_{c1} = strain of concrete at L_1.

6. Normally, a frame or a part of a frame which is n times statically determinate is designed to develop n plastic hinges before failing as a mechanism, so that, at that stage of loading, it is statically determinate. For convenience, the ultimate limit state is assumed to develop when n plastic hinges have formed. Other critical sections are designed to remain at L_1, but a small increase of load would produce an $n + 1$ hinge, and the structure would fail.

7. The value of θ is concentrated at critical sections, even when M is constant over a length of a member (Carneiro, 1962 and Fig. 6.76).

8. When different systems of plastic hinges requiring different reinforcement details develop for different distributions of load, a "final frame" (Munro, 1965) must be designed with all critical sections reinforced to be at least as strong as required for the most critical case of loading. (To check rigorously such a "final frame," the system of plastic hinges for each case of loading should be found for the "final frame.")

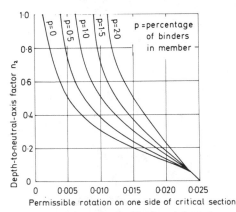

Fig. 6.75 Idealized plastic-rotational capacities for reinforced concrete members

2 Procedure of Design

Design proceeds by a process of trial and adjustment. A continuous structure is made statically determinate by inserting imaginary hinges at sufficient critical sections. The positions selected are those where plastic hinges would probably occur in a continuous elastic system of fairly uniform section. Reinforcement of adequate area is then assumed to act at the hinges at ultimate strength in order to provide an optimum distribution of bending resistance at the ultimate limit state of the frame in opposition to the bending moments, calculated for the statically determinate system. When the frame is continuous, as ultimate load is approached, plastic hinges will develop at the selected sections between L_1 and L_2 (Fig. 6.73), if the sign of their calculated rotation is correct. The value of the rotation also must be within L_1 and L_2, that is, not be excessive.

For illustration, consider the simple case of a continuous beam in Fig. 6.77. The system becomes statically determinate when hinges are assumed, and occur at the supports 2 and 3. The bending moments of the statically determinate system are shown at (c).

The rotations of the hinges at (2) and (3) are

$$= (\alpha_1 - \beta_1) + (\alpha_3 - \beta_3) \tag{6.38}$$

in which α_1, α_2, etc. = end slope at 1, 2, etc., in relation to any joint or hinge of an adjacent member due to external load (see Fig. 6.77); and β_1, β_2, etc. = end slope at

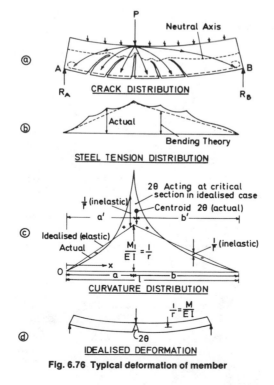

Fig. 6.76 Typical deformation of member

1, 2, etc., in relation to any joint or hinge of an adjacent member due to internal restraints X (see Fig 6.77).

If $M_{12} = M_{23} = M_{34} = M$ and the distribution is parabolic

$$\alpha_1 = \alpha_3 = \frac{1}{3}\frac{Ml}{EI} \tag{6.39}$$

and at hinge (2)

$$\beta_1 = \frac{\bar{X}_2 l}{3EI} \text{ if } \bar{X}_2 = \bar{X}_3 = \frac{M}{2} \quad \beta_3 = \frac{\bar{X}_2 l}{2EI}$$

$$(\alpha_1 - \beta_1) + (\alpha_3 - \beta_3) = \frac{2}{3}\frac{Ml}{EI} - \frac{\bar{X}_2}{EI}\left(\frac{1}{3} + \frac{1}{2}\right) = \frac{Ml}{4EI} = 2\theta_2 \tag{6.40}$$

in which $\bar{X}_1$, $\bar{X}_2$, etc. are equal and opposite internal restraint moments acting at plastic hinges on the adjacent members. The rotation at the section is between L_1 and L_2 (see Figs. 6.77 and 6.78).

The rotation is positive, therefore the hinge "opens" and is correctly positioned. By reference to Fig. 6.75, it can be verified that θ_2 is not excessive or the steel binding, if necessary, may be adjusted, so that the rotation is not excessive. Alternatively the values of $\bar{X}_2 = \bar{X}_3$ assumed $= M/2$ may be increased towards the "elastic" value. When $\theta = 0$, full continuity exists and the values of $\bar{X}_2 = \bar{X}_3 = X_2 = X_3$, values obtained by elastic theory.

3 Building Frames

The design of building frames at the ultimate limit state, by methods in which the restraint of columns to bending of the beams is rigorously considered, is a complex

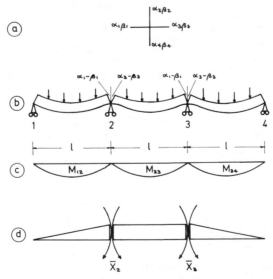

Fig. 6.77 Continuous beam

procedure. However, the experienced designer who can make, as a start, an approximate assessment of the required dimensions of frame members, will have little difficulty in obtaining, by a visual trial and adjustment procedure, a design which, by that same process, is verified in a rational manner to be based on compatibility of bending distribution and deformation. Moreover, at the same time, he can, with experience, produce optimal designs in regard to the distribution of bending moments and hence of reinforcement. He can also check that the frame will not fail by instability. The procedure can be carried out in terms of simple arithmetic with the aid of computation charts from which sections can be selected to satisfy strength and stiffness requirements (Baker, 1970). The computer can be used to help examine the influence of different distributions of load (Munro, 1965) or instability on the progressive formation of plastic hinges (Nahhas and Yu, 1971; Baker, 1967).

The trial and adjustment procedure is carried out story by story, starting from the top. The positions of plastic hinges are first chosen in each story to suit the loading and so that each story can be isolated.

Determination of the sway of an isolated story (which is equal to ψh, in which ψ = story sway angle and h = story height) is basic to the check of stability. After selection of the n plastic hinges for the story (which is n-degrees statically indeterminate), ψ can be found from the equation for the rotation of an imaginary hinge of any beam-column joint of the story which does not have a plastic hinge, as

$$(\alpha_3 - \beta_3) + (\alpha_4 - \beta_4) - \psi = 0 \qquad (6.41)$$

The rotations of all hinges can then be found from the end slopes of adjacent members, using the appropriate expressions indicated in Fig. 6.78, which are obtained directly by integration or Mohr's rule; typical values are given in Fig. 6.79.

The derivation of rotations from end slopes enables a designer to visualize the adjustments he needs to make. He can check his work as he proceeds and produce optimal relative stiffness of members and distribution of bending moments, particularly in the beams where it is generally economic to transfer support moments, as given by "elastic" assumptions, to midspan. It is easy to derive simple rules for calculating directly bending moments in continuous beams which apply

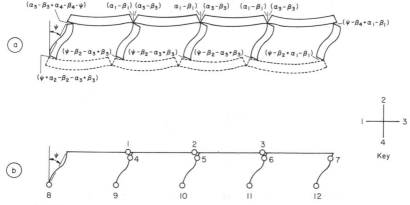

Fig. 6.78 Resultant end slopes of members in terms of α and β on building frame

within the common limits of span, relative stiffness, and live-load and dead-load ratios (Report of Research Committee, ICE, 1964).

The calculation of rotations can also be worked out in terms of the classical Müller-Breslau equations (Report of Research Committee, ICE, 1964; Baker, 1956). The X terms are known in the statically determinate state and are equal to the L_2 values of M for the selected plastic hinge sections and referred to as $\bar{X}$. At the sections, there is an unknown angle of discontinuity θ. In a system n times statically indeterminate, there are n equations and n unknowns, but only one unknown θ in each equation, which is a great simplification. A typical equation then is $\sigma_{ok} + \Sigma \bar{X}_i \alpha_{ik} = -\theta_k$. The use of matrices to express and solve such equations is a help (Munro et al., 1972). When a single frame is considered, but acted upon by several different distributions of load, the procedure described by Munro (1965) may be used. This procedure gives a rigorous check when the design of a frame (Baker, 1956) has been derived from several hypothetical differently reinforced frames satisfying each case of loading, by making each critical section at least as strong as in the hypothetical frames. Computer methods for determining optimum design of continuous beams are given by Rozvany and Cohn (1970).

4 Instability

When there is a possibility of frame instability developing as the ultimate limit state is approached, trial values of the total sway $\delta = \psi h$ may be made and the additional moments due to eccentricity of vertical load treated as additional wind moments. The design is then carried out as follows:

1. Referring to Baker (1972), it is assumed at first that the positions of plastic hinges remain the same when $P(\psi h + \delta)$ bending moments are applied. The value of δ can be calculated from an expression of the form (Baker, 1967a)

$$\delta = \frac{\psi h}{\dfrac{1}{KP} - 1} \qquad (6.42)$$

in which P = reference column load; ψ = sway angle excluding $P(\psi h + \delta)$ moments; δ = total sway due to $P(\psi h + \delta)$ moments; and K = term including stiffness parameters, axial load values, and bending moment distributions.

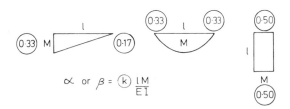

Fig. 6.79 Typical end slopes of members in terms of MI/EI

2. To obtain the additional restraint moments at hinge sections, the additional $P(\psi h + \delta)$ bending moments are distributed for trial in the same way as moments due to wind.

To be quite rigorous, θ values should be rechecked for additional bending due to $P(\psi h + \delta)$ moments, and restraints provided by additional steel to resist these moments. However, since a general increase in stiffness has reduced these moments to a small value relative to the total, it is unlikely that there will be any serious difference in the distribution of hinges and of the bending moments already assumed.

The additional values of θ due to $P(\psi h + \delta)$ moments could readily be calculated from the end slopes due to the bending moments. Fig. 6.80 shows typical $(\psi h + \delta)$ diagrams.

Usually only a normal amount of binding is required to permit the maximum values of θ.

Characteristics of the $\lambda/P(\psi h + \delta)$ **Diagram.** In frames in which the $P(\psi h + \delta)$ bending moments have significant value, the limit state at which the structure becomes statically determinate may be meta-stable, but such a frame would have resisted the calculated value of ultimate load, in a stable condition at a lower value of sway.

The $\lambda/(\psi h + \delta)$ curve for a frame will vary according to the disposition and sequence of formation of plastic hinges, which are influenced by the relative stiffness of members in resisting sway (Nahhas and Yu, 1972). It is important to calculate $P(\psi h + \delta)$ bending moments and to make adjustments of stiffness, when necessary, to assure that sway cannot produce large increases of stress due to the eccentricity of column loads. It is evident that frames could be unstable through failing to give members small increases in depth or width. Deviations of EI values of reinforced concrete members are high and, when safety factor values allow for this, compatibility may be considered established, if required θ values are within about 10%.

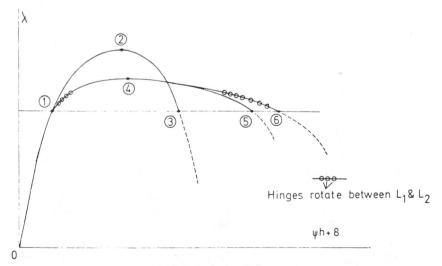

Fig. 6.80 Typical $(\psi h + \delta)$ **diagrams**

6.9 PLASTIC DESIGN, EQUILIBRIUM METHOD

The equilibrium methods constitute a class of design methods based on an idealized elastoplastic moment-curvature diagram for reinforced concrete sections and on the assumption of possible mechanism collapse of the structure (Cohn, 1962b, 1962a, 1965a). The principles of plastic analysis are therefore applicable if due consideration is given to the compatibility requirements (Cohn, 1964, 1966b; Grierson, 1968; Parameswar, 1968).

A basic feature of these methods is that design plastic moments may be derived as percentages of the corresponding elastic envelope moments. This not only enables the designer to operate with concepts familiar to him, but also provides that specified serviceability criteria be satisfied implicitly (Cohn, 1968; Cohn and Grierson, 1970; Cohn et al., 1970).

Optimum limit designs may be obtained by using appropriate objective functions that minimize the cost or material consumption. With reasonable assumptions the flexural steel volume may be expressed as a linear function of the unknowns and the solutions are found by using linear programming techniques (Grierson, 1968; Cohn and Grierson, 1968). Interesting optimal solutions by this approach are available (Cohn and Grierson, 1968, 1970; Cohn et al., 1969) but probably do not constitute a feasible code proposal at this time. It is for this reason that only the full redistribution design (FRD) and limited redistribution design (LRD) approaches are presented. The main concepts and derivations of optimal design techniques as well as FRD and LRD approaches have been presented in a number of studies (Cohn, 1962a, 1965b; Cohn and Grierson, 1970; Cohn et al., 1970). It is felt that these methods have a definite value for the structural designer. However, he may be more interested in a summary of the results and practical guidelines rather than in the complete theory on which they are based.

The object of this section is to give a concise presentation of the basic principles, an elaboration of procedures, and examples of application of the equilibrium methods for limit design to braced frames. While the section summarizes results of research work, it emphasizes only those practical approaches that structural engineers can use with a minimum of theoretical elaboration. A more complete justification of these methods may be found in the references. Detailed examples of analysis, design, and optimization methods, as well as research progress data, are found in Cohn (1972, 1973).

1 Basic Principles

The objective of any limit design method is to produce design solutions satisfying the following requirements (Cohn, 1962b, 1966a):

1. Limit equilibrium. The structure should resist any arrangements of the loads up to the specified ultimate load (W_u).

2. Compatibility. The ultimate load should be resisted by the structure while accommodating acceptable inelastic rotations, consistent with the deformational capacity of reinforced concrete.

3. Serviceability. The behavior of the structure under service loads should be satisfactory in regard to the magnitude of deflections, crack widths, maximum stresses, and the safety against yield of critical sections.

4. Economy. The total cost or material consumption (main steel reinforcement) should be minimized. Other relevant criteria may be substituted for this condition.

The essence of the equilibrium methods consists of adopting appropriate limit equilibrium, serviceability, and economy criteria in generating the design solutions, and leaving the compatibility condition for a separate check (Cohn, 1962, 1965a, 1967, 1968). If all criteria are satisfied, optimal (OLD) solutions are obtained (Grierson, 1968; Cohn, 1968; Cohn and Grierson, 1968).

However, feasible designs may be acceptable in engineering practice while not optimal from a mathematical viewpoint. Such solutions satisfy only some limit equilibrium and serviceability criteria and are representative of limit design techniques that produce solutions with either condition (1) or (3) governing. The corresponding methods are referred to as full redistribution design (FRD, or OLD 1) or limited redistribution design (LRD or OLD 2), respectively (Cohn, 1965a, 1966b, 1967; Cohn et al., 1969, 1970).

Only the latter techniques will be described here, as the optimal solutions provide only relatively small savings compared with LRD and FRD methods, at the expense of mathematical calculations that are too elaborate for current engineering practice (Grierson, 1968; Cohn and Grierson, 1968; Kozvany and Cohn, 1970).

A basic feature of the equilibrium methods is the definition of the unknown design plastic moments M_{pj} for each critical section j as a percentage (x_j) of the factored elastic moment envelope at corresponding sections $\overline{M}_j$, that is

$$M_{pj} = x_j \overline{M}_j \doteq x_j \lambda_0 M_j \qquad (6.43)$$

The scale factor x_j is called the yield safety parameter and, for proportional loading conditions, it is equal to the ratio of the first yield load W_{1j} to the ultimate load W_u (Cohn, 1965a, 1967), that is

$$x_j = \frac{W_{1j}}{W_u} = \frac{\lambda_{1j}}{\lambda_0} \qquad (6.44)$$

in which λ_0 = specified over-all load factor of the structure, i.e., the ratio of the ultimate load W_u to the total service load W

$$\lambda_0 = \frac{W_u}{W} \qquad (6.45)$$

and λ_{1j} is the yield load factor for section j

$$\lambda_{1j} = \frac{W_{1j}}{W} \qquad (6.46)$$

Eq. 6.43 shows that derivation of x_j values for all critical sections of a structure solves the design problem. Eq. 6.44 shows the fundamental nature of the yield safety parameter as a concept synthesizing the basic criteria of the method: limit equilibrium at the specified load factor (λ_0), and serviceability assured by adequate yield load factors (λ_{1j}).

The following basic aspects are noted for the equilibrium methods:

1. Elastoplastic material behavior is assumed.

2. Design plastic moments are defined by Eq. 6.43.

3. Convenient limit equilibrium, serviceability, and possible optimum criteria are adopted.

4. Solutions are found by using the principles of the plastic structural analysis.

5. Solutions are checked for compatibility and serviceability, and adjusted as required.

2 Explanation of Methods

In addition to the idealizations and criteria mentioned previously, the following assumptions are accepted:

1. Any loading arrangements in the structure may take place.

2. Load factors recommended in the ACI Code 318-71 are accepted, even though the methods remain valid for other code provisions, and it is further assumed that all loads increase proportionally between the first yield of a section and the collapse of the structure.

3. The required design plastic moments are the ultimate moment values recommended by the ACI Code 318-71 or an equivalent ultimate strength design theory.

4. Shear and axial forces, bond effects, and instability phenomena are not critical.

Failure Criteria. The plastic collapse occurs at the specified ultimate load $\lambda_0 W$ for at least one, but preferably for as many mechanisms as possible. For structures failing as beam mechanisms only, it can be postulated that all possible collapse modes occur at the prescribed ultimate load.

If m is the number of independent mechanisms of the structure, n its degree of statical indeterminacy, and s the number of its critical sections, the relation $s = m + n$ holds. In order to determine the plastic moments for s critical sections of the structure by Eq. 6.43, s values of x_j are required. For each possible mechanism one limit equilibrium equation of the form $U_i \geq E_i$ can be written, to express the condition that the energy U_i dissipated in the plastic hinge rotations is at least equal to the external work E_i of the specified ultimate load.

Two approaches are possible, depending on whether the condition $U_i = E_i$ is satisfied for a number of mechanisms equal to or less than m:

1. Full redistribution design (FRD or OLD 1) which corresponds to maximum efficiency at collapse, when m mechanisms can take place at the prescribed ultimate load.

2. Limited redistribution design (LRD or OLD 2), which corresponds to a design for which less than m mechanisms take place at the specified ultimate load, with all other modes of collapse occurring at loads larger than $\lambda_0 W$.

Serviceability Criteria. The service behavior is governed by the magnitude of adopted x_j values, better service conditions being associated with higher x_j (Cohn, 1965a, 1966b). Evidently, the best behavior corresponds to an elastic design, for which $x_j = \lambda_{1j}/\lambda_0 = 1$, that is, the yield safety of all sections equals the ultimate safety of the structure.

If a minimum yield load factor λ_j is prescribed in order to assure acceptable stresses, cracking and deflections, then the working conditions can be controlled by satisfying the conditions $\lambda_{1j} \geq \lambda_1/\lambda_0$. From a practical viewpoint, this implies that a serviceable design will be obtained if plastic moments M_{pj} assigned to critical sections are within the limits

$$\lambda_1 M_j \leq M_{pj} \leq \lambda_0 M_j \qquad (6.47)$$

Pending further studies adoption of a value of $\lambda_1 = 1.2$ is suggested (Cohn and Grierson, 1970; Cohn et al., 1969, 1970).

Since s equations are required to determine uniquely all unknown x_j values and because $s = m + n$, it follows that if m limit equilibrium conditions are satisfied to yield a full redistribution design, at most n additional serviceability conditions may be imposed. In a limited redistribution design, with at least one mechanism forming at the specified ultimate load, at most $s - 1$ serviceability conditions can be added. A variety of such conditions may be considered:

1. Equal x_j values for $n + 1$ sections (n conditions leading to an FRD solution).

2. Equal x_j values for all sections ($s - 1$ conditions resulting in LRD solutions).

3. Equal (and assigned) x_j values for support sections, span sections, and column sections (LRD).

4. Equal plastic moments at sections, that is, $x_j M_j = x_k M_k$ (LRD).

By solving the system of equations and inequalities provided by the adopted limit and serviceability criteria, values of x_j for all critical sections of the structure can be found. These constitute the solution of the design problem.

Compatibility Analysis. The compatibility of the adopted design solution should be checked, by assuring that under the worst loading arrangement the inelastic rotation of a section θ_j does not exceed its rotation capacity θ_{pj}

$$\theta_j \leq \theta_{pj} \qquad (6.48)$$

Inelastic rotations θ_j may be calculated by the available methods for plastic analysis of structures and rotation capacities may be derived from test results.

A general and rigorous estimate of θ_j is rather complex. Reliable experimental data on θ_{pj} are still to be obtained. In view of these circumstances the following considerations are suggested for the compatibility check in limit design:

1. Theory and tests (Cohn, 1964; Parameswar, 1968; Cohn, 1968; Cohn and Petcu, 1963; Cohn and Petcu, 1960; Petcu and Cohn, 1961) indicate that under usual conditions beam and column sections can accommodate inelastic rotations because of deviations from the elastic moment distribution of 15% to 25%.

2. For the first intermediate supports of continuous beams the compatibility is satisfied if the following relation holds (Cohn, 1962a, 1962b)

$$x_j \geq [1 + 3\alpha\beta(\phi_u/\phi_y - 1)]^{-1} \qquad (6.49)$$

in which α = fractional length over which inelasticity develops; β = shape factor of the inelastic curvature area; and ϕ_u, ϕ_y = curvatures corresponding to M_u and M_y, respectively.

3. For intermediate supports of continuous beams the following approximate, simplified relation is proposed

$$x_j \geq [1 + \alpha\beta\gamma(\phi_u/\phi_y - 1)]^{-1} \qquad (6.50)$$

in which γ = constant depending on the loading distribution and the degree of end restraint of adjoining spans ($\gamma = 3$ for free ends and $\gamma = 2$ for fixed ends).

In design practice, compatibility checks are necessary only when $x_j < 0.85$. In this case Eq. 6.48 or 6.49 may be used with $\alpha\beta = 1/30 \dots 1/40$ or $\alpha\beta\gamma = 1/12 \dots 1/15$.

3 Procedure

Determine the over-all load factor ($\lambda_0 = W_u/W$) consistent with the data of the problem, and the minimum admissible scale factors, minimum $x_j = \lambda_1/\lambda_0 \simeq 1.2/\lambda_0$.

Determine the elastic moment envelope for the specified ultimate load, $\bar{M}_j = \lambda_0 M_j$.

Write limit equilibrium equations for all possible mechanisms with x_j as unknowns, assuming initially that collapse modes occur precisely at the specified ultimate load.

Make all x_j values equal for each limit equilibrium equation in turn, and thus determine the balanced yield safety parameters $\bar{x}_j$.

For larger economy, attempt a full redistribution design (FRD or OLD 1) by selecting x_j values to satisfy identically m limit equilibrium equations which have the highest $\bar{x}_j$.

For better serviceability (high yield safety) attempt limited redistribution designs (LRD or OLD 2) which satisfy identically less than m equilibrium equations, while for the remaining ones the inequality $U_i > E_i$ holds: (1) Select x_j = maximum $\bar{x}_i$ for all critical sections; or (2) select $x_j = 1$ or 0.9 for span sections and derive x_j values from statics for the remaining sections.

Determine the design plastic moments diagram by scaling down the factored elastic moment envelope through the x_j values.

For the design moments already obtained, determine the required flexural steel. Determine the web reinforcement for the elastic shears calculated for the ultimate load.

Check the rotation compatibility by calculating θ_j, as for an elastoplastic structure, by assuming an ultimate concrete strain of 0.004 in estimating θ_{pj}.

Assure deflection and cracking control by satisfying specific code requirements.

6.10 CONCLUSION

In this chapter it has been shown that for reinforced concrete structures, in addition to the geometric nonlinearities caused by second-order effects (buckling), nonlinearities in the stress-strain relationships of both concrete and steel cause important deviations from linearity in all the force-deformation relationships of a structure, including those for behavior of any cross section, of any member or subassembly, and of the entire structure. Since the geometric and material sources of nonlinearity interact, their total effect cannot be obtained by adding their separate effects. Instead, in all analyses both must be considered. Yet the actual recognition, definition, and use of material nonlinearity in design and analysis is relatively undeveloped for those aspects of design related to member and over-all structural behavior, including buckling.

Therefore, this chapter has primarily presented important available evidence useful for any definition of the many aspects of reinforced concrete material nonlinearities, without hiding the gaps in knowledge. In addition, the recommendations of many engineers aimed at improvement of design by a systematic application of this knowledge have been summarized.

6.11 CONDENSED REFERENCES/BIBLIOGRAPHY

The following is a condensed bibliography for this chapter. Not only does it include all articles referred to or cited in the text, but it also contains bibliography for further reading. The full citations will be found at the end of the Volume. What is given here should be sufficient information to lead the reader to the correct article: the author, date, and title. In case of multiple authors, only the first named is listed.

Aas-Jakobsen 1964, *Biaxial Eccentricities in Ultimate Strength Design*
ACI-ASCE Committee on Limit Design 1968, *Progress Report on Code Clauses for "Limit Design"*
ACI 1970, *Limit Design of Reinforced Concrete Structures*
ACI Committee 318 1971, *Building Code Requirements for Reinforced Concrete*
Adams 1970, *Plastic Design of Coupled Frame-Shear Wall Structures*

Agardh 1968, *Analysis of Non-Linear Beams*
Air Force Design Manual 1962, *Principles and Practices for Design of Hardened Structures*
Andrew 1956, *Symposium on the Strength of Concrete Structures*
Aoyama 1964, *Moment-Curvature Characteristics of Reinforced Concrete Members Subjected*
Aoyama 1967, *Restoring Force Characteristics Under Reversal of Loading of Reinforced Concrete*

Aoyama 1970, *A Study of Damage to the Hachinohe Technical College Due to the 1968 Tokachi-Ok*
Aoyama 1971, *Restoring Force Characteristics and Earthquake Response of Concrete Building*
Aoyama 1973, *Repeated and Cyclic Loadings*
Argyris 1963, *Modern Fuselage Analysis and the Elastic Aircraft*
Argyris 1976, *Limit Load Analysis of Thick Walled Concrete Structures*

ASCE-ACI 1964, *Flexural Mechanics of Reinforced Concrete*
Bachmann 1966, *Shear Design of Beams*
Bachmann 1969, *Experiments on the Plastic Behavior of Two-Span Continuous Reinforced Concrete*
Bachmann 1971, *Influence of Shear and Bond on Rotational Capacity of Reinforced Concrete Beams*
Bäcklund 1972, *Limit Analysis of Reinforced Concrete Slabs by Finite Element*

Baker 1949, *The Design of Steel Frames*
Baker 1953, *Further Research in Reinforced Concrete and Its Application to Ultimate Load Design*

Baker 1956, *The Ultimate-Load Theory Applied to the Design of Reinforced and Prestressed*
Baker 1964, *Inelastic Hyperstatic Frames Analysis*

Baker 1966, *Simplified Bi-Linear Limit Design*
Baker 1967a, *The Inelastic Space Frame*
Baker 1967b, *Frame Instability*
Baker 1970, *Limit-State Design of Reinforced Concrete*
Baker 1972, *Fully Plastic Analysis and Design*

Baker 1973, *Fully Plastic Analysis and Design*
Bate 1968, *Why Limit State Design?*
Beck 1962, *Contribution to the Analysis of Coupled Shear Walls*
Beekhuis 1971, *An Experimental Study of Squat Shear Walls*
Benedetti 1974, *Non-Linear Analysis of Space Trusses*

Benjamin 1958, *Behavior of One-Story Reinforced Concrete Shear Walls*
Berg 1964, *Anchorage and the Alaska Earthquake of March 27, 1964*
Bergan 1973, *A Comparative Study of Different Numerical Solution Techniques as Applied*
Bertero 1964, *Behavior of Reinforced Concrete Frames Subjected to Repeated Reversible Loads*
Bertero 1966, *Effects of Variable Repeated Loading on Structures, a Review*

Bertero 1968, *Inelastic Behavior of Beam-to-Column Subassemblages Under Repeated Loading*
Bertero 1969, *Seismic Behavior of Reinforced Concrete Framed Structures*
Bertero 1969, *Stiffness Degradation of Reinforced Concrete Members Subjected to Cyclic Flexural*
Bertero 1971, *Research Needs in Limit Design of Reinforced Concrete Structures*
Bertero 1972, *Experimental Studies Concerning Reinforced Prestressed and Partially Prestressed*

Bertero 1972, *Rate of Loading Effects on Uncracked and Repaired Reinforced Concrete*
Bertero 1973, *Effects of Generalized Excitations on the Non-Linear Behavior of Reinforced*
Bertero 1974, *Nonlinear Seismic Response Evaluation—Charaima Building*
Biswas 1970, *Discussion of Lateral-Load Analysis of Asymmetric Multistory Structures*
Breen 1964, *The Restrained Long Concrete Column*

Breen 1965, *Studies of Frames with Long Columns*
Bresler 1961, *Tie Requirements in Reinforced Concrete Columns*
Bresler 1966, *Reinforced Concrete Prism Under Repeated Loads*
Broms 1965, *Crack Width and Crack Spacing in Reinforced Concrete Members*
Brown 1970, *Reinforced Concrete Beams Under Load Reversals*

Cardenas 1973, *Design Provisions for Shear Walls*
Cardenas 1973, *Strength of High-Rise Shear Walls—Rectangular Cross Sections*
Carneiro 1962, *Report of Bending Experiments on Three Series of Reinforced Concrete Beams*
Castellani 1966, *Model Analysis of "Shear Type" Buildings Response to Earthquake*
CEB 1963, *Recommendation for an International Code of Practice for Reinforced Concrete*

CEB 1964, *Methods of Analysis for Redundant Structures*
CEB 1966, *News Bulletin No. 53*
CEB-CIB-UEAtc 1969, *International Unified Recommendations for Analysing and Testing*
Cervenka 1972, *Inelastic Finite-Element Analysis of Reinforced Concrete Panels*
Chinn 1965, *Behavior of Plain Concrete Under Various Triaxial Compression Loading Conditions*

Chitnuyanondh 1976, *Shear Failure Due to Web Crashing in Prestressed Concrete Beams*
Chopra 1976, *Response of the Olive View Hospital Main Building During the San Fernando*
Clark 1967, *Effect of Strain Gradient on the Stress-Strain Curve of Mortar and Concrete*
Clark 1968, *Analysis of Reinforced Concrete Shear Wall-Frame Structures*
Clough 1966, *Effect of Stiffness Degradation on Earthquake Ductility Requirements*

Cohn 1960, *On the Influence of Steel Percentage on the Plastic Adaptability of Redundant*
Cohn 1962a, Discussion to the ICE Research Committee Report: *Ultimate Load Design of Concrete*
Cohn 1962b, *Limit Design of Reinforced Concrete Structures for Maximum Yield Safety*
Cohn 1963, *Moment Redistribution and Rotation Capacity of Plastic Hinges in Redundant*
Cohn 1964, *Rotation Compatibility in the Limit Design of Reinforced Concrete Beams*

Cohn 1965a, *Optimum Limit Design for Reinforced-Concrete Continuous Beams*
Cohn 1965b, *Rotation Compatibility in the Limit Design of Reinforced Concrete Continuous Beams*
Cohn 1966a, *Design of Plastic Frames for Maximum Yield Safety*
Cohn 1966b, *On the Optimum Limit Design Method*
Cohn 1967, *Limit Design Solutions for Concrete Structures*

Cohn 1968, *Limit Design of Reinforced Concrete Frames*
Cohn 1968, *Optimal Design of Reinforced Concrete Beams and Frames*
Cohn 1969, *Safety Serviceability and Efficiency of Limit Design for Reinforced Concrete Beams*
Cohn 1970, *Application of Limit Design to Reinforced Concrete Building Structures*
Cohn 1970, *Further Results on the Equilibrium Method of Limit Design*

Cohn 1971, *Optimal Limit Design for Concrete Structures*
Cohn 1972a, *Analysis and Design of Inelastic Structures*
Cohn 1972b, *Equilibrium Methods of Limit Design*
Cohn 1973, *Inelasticity and Non-Linearity in Structural Concrete*
Collins 1971, *Redistribution of Moment of Cracking*

Corley 1966, *Rotational Capacity of Reinforced Concrete Beams*
Corley 1969, *Design of Beam-Column Frames*
Corradi 1972, *Developments in the Imposed Rotations Method for the Inelastic Analysis of ⁻*
Coull 1967a, *Symposium on Tall Buildings with Particular Reference to Shear Wall Structures*
Coull 1967b, *Tall Buildings*

Cranston 1965, *A Computer Method for Inelastic Analysis of Plane Frames*
Cranston 1970, *The Influence of Shear on the Rotation Capacity of Reinforced Concrete Beams*
Cranston 1970, *Computer Analyses of Reinforced Concrete Portal Frames with Fixed Feet*
De Donato 1970, *Mathematical Programming Methods for the Inelastic Analysis of Reinforced*
De Donato 1973, *A Modified Gradient Method for Finite Element Elastoplastic Analysis by Quadrati*

De Donato 1973, *Bounds on Total Dynamic Deflections of Elastoplastic Structures Allowing for*
De Paiva 1965, *Strength and Behavior of Deep Beams in Shear*
Dilger 1967, *Initial and Subsequent Deflections due to Shear*
Eiklid 1969, *Strain-Hardening Effects in Reinforced Concrete*
Eloseily 1967, *Ultimate Strength of Rectangular Reinforced Concrete Sections*

Ernst 1957, *Plastic Hinging at the Intersections of Beams and Columns*
Ernst 1958, *Moment and Shear Redistribution in Two-Span Continuous Concrete Beams*
Estanero 1972, *Moment-Rotation Characteristics of Reinforced Concrete Beams Under Combined*
Faupel 1964, *Engineering Design*
Fenwick 1968, *Mechanisms of Shear Resistance of Concrete Beams*

Ferry Borges 1963, *Non-Linear Analysis of Reinforced Concrete Beams*
Ferry Borges 1964, *Analytical Results Concerning the Non-Linear Behavior of Reinforced Concrete*
Fiorato 1970, *An Investigation of the Interaction of Reinforced Concrete Frames with Masonry Filler*
FIP 1955, *Second Congress*
Fransson 1973, *Unsymmetrical Multi-Storey Buildings*

Funahashi 1969, *Vibration Tests and Test to Failure of a Seven Storied Building Survived a Severe*
Furlong 1970, *Design of Concrete Frames by Assigned Limit Moments*
Gerstle 1971, *Incremental Deformations of Reinforced Concrete Beams*
Gerstle 1973, *Flexural Characteristics of Reinforced Concrete Members*
Gesund 1973, *Computer Analysis of Reinforced Concrete Frames, Inelasticity and Non-Linearity*

Gesund 1973, *Stiffness of Reinforced Concrete Columns in Biaxial Bending*
Ghosh 1970, *Creep of Concrete Columns*
Glück 1970, *Lateral-Load Analysis of Asymmetric Multistory Structures*
Glück 1972, *Non-Linear Analysis of an Elastic Supported and Lateral Restrained Cantilever*
Glück 1973a, *Elasto-Plastic Analysis of Coupled Shear Walls*

Glück 1973b, *An Overall Ductility Factor for Coupled Shear Walls*
Goldberg 1963, *Analysis of Non-Linear Structures*
Grasser 1973, *Serviceability*
Grierson 1968, *Optimal Design of Reinforced Concrete Frames*
Griswell 1970, *Strength and Behavior of Reinforced Concrete Slab-Column Connections*

Gulkan 1971, *Response and Energy-Dissipation of Reinforced Concrete Frames Subjected to Strong*
Gvozdev 1964, *Studies on Redundant Prestressed Concrete Structures*
Hanson 1967, *Seismic Resistance of Reinforced Concrete Beam-Column Joints*
Hanson 1971, *Seismic Resistance of Concrete Frames with Grade 60 Reinforcement*
Hellers 1967, *Eccentrically Compressed Columns Without Tensile Strength Subjected to Uniformly*

Higashi 1969, *Failing Behavior of Reinforced Concrete Beam-Column Connection Subjected to*
Hirosawa 1969, *Ultimate Strength of Reinforced Concrete Walled Frames with Axial Force Subjected*

Hirosawa 1971, *Other Problems Concerning Shear Walls*
Hisada 1972, *Earthquake Design Considerations in Reinforced Concrete Columns*
Hoeland 1969, *On the Analysis of Shear Walls Acting as Frames*

Hognestad 1955, *Concrete Stress Distribution in Ultimate Strength Design*
ICE 1964, *Ultimate Load Design of Concrete Structures*
Inomata 1969, *Comparative Study on Behaviour of Prestressed and Reinforced Concrete Beams*
Ismail 1972a, *Bond Deterioration in Reinforced Concrete Subjected to Low Cycle Loads*
Ismail 1972b, *Behavior of Anchored Bars Under Low Cycle Overloads Producing Inelastic Strains*

Iyengar 1967, *Incremental Load Analysis of Continuous Beams with Non Linear Behavior*
Jackson 1971, *Plastic Flow Law for Reinforced Concrete Beams Under Combined Flexure and*
Jackson 1973, *Torsion/Flexure Interaction*
Jenkins 1969, *Matrix and Digital Computer Methods in Structural Analysis*
Jennings 1971, *Engineering Features of the San Fernando Earthquake, February 9, 1971*

Johnson 1958, *Elastic-Plastic Analysis of Continuous Beams and Frames*
Jorgensen 1962, *Influence of Reinforcement Stress-Strain Curves on a Concrete Member of*
Kano 1969, *Shear Strength of Reinforced Concrete Beams Under Many Cyclic Alternate Loadings*
Karsan 1969, *Behavior of Concrete Under Compressive Loadings*
Kazinezy 1933–34, *The Design of Not Fully Restrained Steel "I" Floorbeams Considering Plastic*

Khan 1964, *Interaction of Shear Walls and Frames*
Khan 1966, *Effect of Column Exposure in Tall Structures—Analysis for Length Changes of Exposed*
Kitagawa 1972, *A Study of the Soil-Building Interaction System by Simultaneous Observation of*
Koizumi 1970, *Lateral Load Tests on Multi-Storied Full-Size Building of Reinforced Concrete*
Kokusho 1970, *Shear Strength and Load Deflection Characteristics of Reinforced Concrete*

Kokusho 1971, *Strength Reduction of Reinforced Concrete Members Due to Alternately Cyclic*
Koor 1957, *Stresses in Centrally Loaded Deep Beams*
Koreishi 1970, *Test of Reinforced Concrete Beam-Column Connection*
Kostem 1975, *Inelastic Analysis of Beam-Columns*
Kostem 1976, *Load Carrying Capacity of Ribbed Prestressed Concrete Roof Panels*

Krawinkler 1972, *Cyclic Behavior of Three Reinforced Concrete Flexural Members with High Shear*
Kulicki 1972, *The Inelastic Analysis of Reinforced and Prestressed Concrete Beams*
Kulicki 1973a, *Nonlinear Analysis of Concrete Flexural Members*
Kulicki 1973b, *Further Studies on the Nonlinear Finite Element Analysis of Beams*
Kulicki 1973c, *User's Manual for Program BEAM*

Kulicki 1973d, *Applications of the Finite Element Method to Inelastic Beam Column Problems*
Kulicki 1974a, *The Effects of Discretization on the Inelastic Analysis of Prestressed Concrete Beams*
Kulicki 1974b, *Inelastic Analysis of Reinforced Concrete Beam-Columns*
Kulicki 1975a, *Analytical Modeling of Material Nonlinearities*
Kulicki 1975b, *Inelastic Response of Prestressed Concrete Beams*

Kupfer 1969, *Behavior of Concrete Under Biaxial Stresses*
Lampert 1971, *Postcracking Stiffness of Reinforced Concrete Beams in Torsion and Bending*
Larsson 1967, *Analysis of Wind Bracing Wall Panels in Tall Buildings*
Leonhardt 1962, *Shear Test of Single-Span Reinforced Concrete Beams*
Leonhardt 1965, *European Committee for Concrete, News Bulletin, No. 65*

Leonhardt 1966, *Wall-Like Beams*
Levi 1970, *The Gradual Introduction of Semi-Probabilistic Correction Coefficients*
Lin 1965, *Design of Prestressed Concrete Buildings for Earthquake Resistance*
Macchi 1954, *Strength and Deformation of Concrete Joints*
Macchi 1955, *Experimental Investigation on Continuous Prestressed Concrete Beams in the Plastic*

Macchi 1956, *Redistribution of Moment in Inelastic Field and Rupture in Pre-Stressed Concrete*
Macchi 1959, *A Proposed Method of Analysis Based on the Theory of Imposed Rotations*
Macchi 1961, *Redundant Structures*
Macchi 1964a, *Elastic Distribution of Moments on Continuous Beams*
Macchi 1964b, *A Proposed Method for Calculating the Deformations in Redundant Concrete*

Macchi 1966, *The Method of Imposed Rotations*
Macchi 1969b, *Limit-States Design of Statically Indeterminate Structures Composed of Linear*
Macchi 1970a, *Preliminary Design of Concrete Frames According to the Limit-States Method*

Macchi 1970b, *The Method of Imposed Rotations*
Macchi 1973, *Theme Report: Non-Linear Analysis and Limit Design*

MacLeod 1967, *Lateral Stiffness of Shear Wall with Opening*
Maier 1972a, *Inelastic Analysis of Reinforced Concrete Frames by Quadratic Programming Allowing*
Maier 1972b, *Inelastic Analysis of Reinforced Concrete Frames by Quadratic Programming*
Maldague 1965, *Studies on the Deformation of Concrete Beams*
Maldague 1973, *Imposed Rotations Method*

Manuel 1967, *Analysis of Restrained Reinforced Concrete Columns Under Sustained Load*
Marcal 1972, *Finite Element Analysis with Material Non-Linearities*
Matsushita 1971, *Strength and Behavior of Autoclaved Lightweight Concrete Panel Wall with Joint*
Mattock 1965, *Rotational Capacity of Hinging Regions in Reinforced Concrete Beams*
Mayer 1967, *Determination of Deflection of Reinforced Concrete Members*

Megget 1971, *Reinforced Concrete Exterior Beam-Column Joints Under Seismic Loading*
Migliacci 1972, *Geometric Second Order Effect on Tall R.C. Chimneys*
Mufti 1972, *A Study of Non-Linear Behavior of Structural Concrete Elements*
Munro 1965, *The Elastic and Limit Analysis of Planar Skeletal Structures*
Munro 1972, *Optimal Design of Reinforced Concrete Frames*

Muto 1969, *Newly-Devised Reinforced Concrete Shear Walls for High-Rise Building Structures*
Nahhas 1971, *The Elastic Plastic Design of Reinforced Concrete Sway Frames Against Instability*
Nahhas 1972, *The Elastic-Plastic Design of Reinforced Concrete Sway Frames Against Instability*
Nakano 1971, *Structural Behavior of Multi-Storied Pre-Cast Reinforced Concrete Construction*
Nawy 1968, *Rectangular Spiral Binders Effect on Plastic Hinge Rotation*

Negoita 1973, *Seismic Analysis of Expanded Clay Lightweight Concrete Frames*
Newmark 1971, *Fundamentals of Earthquake Engineering*
Ngo 1967, *Finite Element Analysis of Reinforced Concrete Beams*
Nilsen 1968, *Nonlinear Analysis of Reinforced Concrete*
Norris 1959, *Structural Design for Dynamic Loads*

Oden 1967, *Numerical Formulation of Problems in Nonlinear Elasticity*
Oden 1971a, *Finite Elements of Nonlinear Continua*
Oden 1971b, *Finite Element Approximations in Nonlinear Elasticity*
Ohsaki 1970, *Experimental Study on Five-Story Full Size Apartment House of Reinforced Concrete*
Osaka 1969, *Earthquake Measurements In and Around a Reinforced Concrete Building*

Parameswar 1968, *Compatibility Problems in Limit Design*
Park 1972, *Theorization of Structural Behavior with a View to Defining Resistant and Ultimate*
Park 1972, *Reinforced Concrete Members with Cyclic Loading*
Patton 1972, *Behavior Under Seismic Loading of Reinforced Concrete Beam-Column Joints with*
Paulay 1969a, *The Coupling of Reinforced Concrete Shear Walls*

Paulay 1970a, *An Elasto-Plastic Analysis of Coupled Shear Walls*
Paulay 1970b, *The Shear Strength of Shear Walls*
Paulay 1971a, *Simulated Seismic Loading of Spandrel Beams*
Paulay 1971b, *An Approach to the Design of Coupled Shear Walls*
Paulay 1971c, *Coupling Beams of Reinforced Concrete Shear Walls*

Paulay 1972, *Some Aspects of Shear Wall Design*
Paulay 1974, *Diagonally Reinforced Coupling Beams of Shear Walls*
Paulay 1974, *Horizontal Construction Joints in Cast in Place Reinforced Concrete*
PCA 1965, *Design of Combined Frames and Shear Walls*
Penzien 1967, *Feasibility Study of Large Scale Earthquake Simulator Facility*

Petcu 1961, *On the Moment Redistribution in Redundant Highly Reinforced Concrete Beams*
Peter 1964, *Reinforcement of Shells and In-Plane Loaded Slabs*
Pfrang 1964, *Predicting Structural Behaviour Analytically*
Pfrang 1964, *Load-Moment-Curvature Characteristics of Reinforced Concrete Cross Sections*
Pfrang 1966, *Behaviour of Reinforced Concrete Columns with Sidesway*

Powell 1972, *Notes on Inelastic Dynamic Analysis of Tall Buildings*
Pume 1967b, *Shear Strength of Vertical Splices*
Pume 1970, *Stress Distribution and Ultimate Strength of Joints*
Rangan 1973, *Limit Design of Slabs Under Uniformly Distributed Loads Using Lower Bound*

Reaton 1972, *The Behavior of Reinforced Concrete Beam-Column Joints Under Cyclic Loading*

Rehm 1961, *Concerning the Fundamentals of Bond Between Steel and Concrete*
RILEM 1958, *Symposium on Bond and Crack Formation in Reinforced Concrete*
Rosman 1964, *Approximate Analysis of Shear Walls Subject to Lateral Loads*
Rosman 1968, *Statics and Dynamics of Shear Wall Systems in Tall Buildings*
Roy 1964, *Ductility of Concrete*

Rozvany 1970, *A Lower Bound Approach to the Optimal Design of Concrete Frames and Slabs*
Ruiz 1969, *Reinforced Concrete Beams Under Repeated Loads*
Rüsch 1960, *Researches Toward a General Flexural Theory for Structural Concrete*
Rüsch 1963, *The Effect of Stirrups and Compression Reinforcement*
Rüsch 1968, *Strength and Deformation of Plain Nonreinforced Concrete Under Sustained Load*

Sabnis 1969, *Behaviour of Reinforced Concrete Frames Under Cyclic Loads Using Small Scale*
Sahlin 1971a, *Imperfections in Structures Constructed with Prefabricated Concrete Elements*
Sahlin 1971b, *Structural Masonry*
Sahlin 1973, *Methods of Step-by-Step Non-Linear Analysis*
Sargin 1971, *Stress-Strain Relationships for Concrete and the Analysis of Structural Concrete*

Sawyer 1955, *Elastic-Plastic Design of Single-Span Beams and Frames*
Sawyer 1960, *A Proposed Method of Limit Design*
Sawyer 1964a, *Status and Potentialities of Nonlinear Design of Concrete Frames*
Sawyer 1964b, *Design of Concrete Frames for Two Failure Stages*
Sawyer 1973, *Summary Report: Non-Linear Analysis and Limit Design*

Scanlon 1972, *An Analysis to Determine the Effects of Cracking in Reinforced Concrete Slabs*
Scordelis 1972, *Finite Element Analysis of Reinforced Concrete Structures*
Shah 1965, *Microcracking and Inelastic Behavior of Concrete*
Shah 1972, *The Analysis of Nonlinear Three Dimensional Frames*
Shideler 1957, *Lightweight Aggregate for Structural Use*

Shiga 1970, *The Dynamic Properties of Reinforced Concrete Frames*
Shinagawa 1971, *Lateral Load Test on Five-Storied Full-Size Building of Precast Reinforced*
Singh 1965, *The Behavior of Reinforcing Steel Under Reversed Loading*
Singh 1969, *Shear Strength of Concrete Beams Under Cyclic Loading*
Sinha 1964a, *Response of Singly Reinforced Beams to Cyclic Loading*

Sinha 1964b, *Stress-Strain Relations for Concrete Under Cyclic Loading*
Smith 1965, *Inelastic Behavior of Load-Carrying Members*
Smith 1972, *Exterior Reinforced Concrete Joints with Low Axial Load Under Seismic Loading*
Spillers 1963, *Application of Topology in Structural Analysis*
Stamato 1969, *An Approximate Method for the Three Dimensional Analysis of Tall Buildings*

Sugano 1970, *Static Test of Concrete Shear Walls Reinforced with Wire Fabric*
Takeda 1970, *Reinforced Concrete Response to Simulated Earthquake*
Templeman 1971, *A Steepest Gradient Method for Optimum Structural Design*
Tezcon 1967, *Analysis and Design of Shear Wall Structures*
Thomas 1965, *A Study of the Inelastic Rotation Mechanism of Reinforced Concrete Connections*

Tichy 1975, *Plastic Analysis of Concrete Frames*
Tomii 1971, *Shear Walls*
Tomii 1973b, *Shear Walls*
Townsend 1972, *The Inelastic Behaviour of Reinforced Concrete Beam-Column Connections*
Umemura 1963, *Study on Improvement of Structural Ability of Reinforced Concrete Construction*

Umemura 1964, *Study on Improvement of Structural Ability of Reinforced Concrete Construction*
Umemura 1969, *Evaluation of Inelastic Seismic Deflection of Reinforced Concrete Frames Based*
Umemura 1970, *Earthquake Resistant Design of Structures*
Umemura 1970, *Experimental Studies on Reinforced Concrete Members and Composite Steel*
Wakabayashi 1971, *An Experimental Study on Shear Failure of Reinforced Concrete Columns*

Wiberg 1971a, *Approximate Methods of Analysis for Tall Buildings*
Wiberg 1971b, *Discussion of Efficient Reanalysis (Kavlie and Powell)*
Wiberg 1971c, *System Analysis in Structural Mechanics*
Will 1972, *Application of Finite Element Method to Analysis of Reinforced Concrete Beam-Column*
Wilson 1960, *Matrix Analysis of Non-Linear Structures*

Winokur 1968, *Ultimate Strength Analysis of Coupled Shear Walls*
Wynhoven 1970, Discussion of *Lateral-Load Analysis of Asymmetric Multistory Structures*
Yamada 1967, *Study on the Elasto-Plastic Flexural Behavior of Reinforced Concrete Members*
Yamada 1968, *Elasto-Plastic Bending Deflections of Reinforced Concrete Columns and Beams*
Yamada 1968, *Shear Resistance and Explosive Cleavage Failure of ReinforcedConcrete*

Yamada 1973, *Fundamental New Aseismic Design of Reinforced Concrete Buildings*
Yamada 1973, *Shear Explosion of Reinforced Concrete Short Columns for the Basis to*
Yamada 1973, *Ultimate Deformation of Reinforced Concrete*
Yamada 1974a, *Shear Strength, Deformation and Explosion of Reinforced Concrete Short*
Yamada 1974b, *Behavior of Reinforced Concrete Beam-Columns Under Cyclic Loading*

Yamada 1974, *Simplified Calculation Method for Flexural and Shear Strength and Deformation*
Yamashiro 1962, *Moment-Rotation Characteristics of Reinforced Concrete Members Subject to*
Zavelani 1971, *Optimal Shake-Down Design of Reinforced Concrete Beams*
Zienkiewicz 1970, *Matrix Iteration and Acceleration Process in Finite Element Problems of*
Zienkiewicz 1971, *The Finite Element Method in Engineering Science*

Zienkiewicz 1971, *Three Dimensional Analysis of Buildings Composed of Floor and Wall Panels*
Zingone 1968, *Limit Analysis of a Beam in Bending Immersed in an Elastoplastic Medium*
Zingone 1972a, *The Limit State of Indefinite Plates on Elastoplastic Continuum*
Zingone 1972b, *Probable Collapse Mechanisms in Indefinite Plates on an Elastoplastic*

Structural Design of Tall Concrete and Masonry Buildings

Chapter CB-7

Model Analysis

Prepared by Committee A38 (Model Analysis) of the Council on Tall Buildings and Urban Habitat as part of the Monograph on the Planning and Design of Tall Buildings

Henry J. Cowan   Chairman and Editor
Paul Zia   Vice-Chairman

AUTHOR ACKNOWLEDGMENT

The subject of this chapter was not included in the 1972 International Conference. The first draft of the entire chapter was the work of H. J. Cowan.

CONTRIBUTORS

The following is a complete list of those who have submitted written material for possible use in this chapter, whether or not that material was used in the final version. The Committee Chairman and Editor was given quite complete latitude. Frequently length limitations precluded the inclusion of much valuable material. The Bibliography contains all contributions. The contributors are: F. D. Beresford, A. Coull, H. J. Cowan, A. R. Flint, E. Fumagalli, J. E. Gibson, O. C. Guedelhoefer, O. Halasz, A. W. Hendry, M. Holmes, W. M. Hopkins, F. R. Khan, S. Lichardus, I. A. MacLeod, I. Martin, R. K. Muller, G. Oberti, M. Paparoni, M. J. Priestley, A. Ravara, R. C. Reese, R. E. Rowe, L. C. Schmidt, J. Schwaighofer, G. S. Somerville, S. R. Sparkes, B. Stafford-Smith, P. Zia.

COMMITTEE MEMBERS

J. Balas, A. Castoldi, H. J. Cowan, E. Fumagalli, J. Granell, O. C. Guedelhoefer, H. Hossdorf, R. K. Muller, G. Oberti, M. Paparoni, A. Ravara, M. Rocha, J. Schwaighofer, G. Somerville, P. Zia.

CB-7

Model Analysis

7.1 HISTORICAL REVIEW

Theoretical and experimental analyses are essentially complementary forms of structural design. Advances in theory tend to reduce reliance on experimental solutions, and vice versa.

The idea of using a model as an aid to structural design is not, of course, new. Models have been made for this purpose at least as far back as the Renaissance. We know of models for the dome of Florence Cathedral, for St. Peter's in Rome, and for many other churches. However, it is unlikely that any model was used quantitatively until well into the 20th century. Although there are reports of model tests as far back as the 16th century, it seems that these are based on a misunderstanding of what the words imply in modern terminology, and that the models were in fact used purely for visual purposes, to assist the architect in understanding the structure.

In the late 18th century the elastic theory made rapid progress. It was used more and more for structural design in the next few decades, and empirical rules gave way to structural calculations. The growing sophistication of structural theory was largely responsible for the increasing complexity of engineered structures in the 20th century. This encouraged the search for a mechanized form of structural design as calculations became more laborious.

The apparatus devised by Beggs (Charlton, 1966) at Princeton University in 1922 was the first successful method of model analysis. This and other early examples may be regarded as mechanical analogs of the elastic theory, rather than scale models of a part of a building. Their significance lay in the fact that they gave the same answer as the mathematical solution; it was incidental that the model dimensions were proportional to those of the structure.

In other fields of engineering the theory of dimensional analysis was well established in the early 20th century. Scale models were regularly used for hydraulic works, and in the 1920s wind tunnels were commonly employed to test models of airplanes and airplane parts.

The techniques of structural model analysis were greatly improved during the same period; but the significant development of the early 1930s was the invention

287

of the Moment-Distribution Method by Cross, which made the design of linear rigid frames simpler by calculation. On the other hand, the 1930s also produced imaginative concrete structures of complex shape, particularly in southern Europe. Both Nervi (1955) and Torroja (1958) used small-scale models to aid their designs, and the techniques devised by Oberti (Fumagalli, 1973; Zelman et al., 1970; Nervi, 1955) for Nervi's long-span single-story designs are the forerunners of those used today for the model analysis of tall buildings.

During the Second World War aircraft design made great progress, and the structural design of airplanes with the aid of scale models, instrumented with the new miniature electric resistance strain gages, was carried to a high degree of perfection. In the late 1940s the method was applied to architectural structures, and rapid design solutions were obtained for problems hitherto soluble only by exceedingly lengthy calculations (Preece and Davis, 1964; Cowan et al., 1968; Hossdorf, 1971; Müller, 1971; Fumagalli, 1973).

The Second World War had produced another powerful design tool which took a little longer to be adapted to structural design. In the 1950s digital computer programmed solutions for structural design problems became available, and the scope of computer-based design solutions is steadily increasing. If the picture had altered rapidly in favor of model design, it now shifted again the other way.

The analysis of the frame for the Chevron Hotel Stage II in Sydney, Australia, is an interesting example of this trend (Cowan et al., 1968, pp. 167-173). In this instance the deflection was particularly important, since the 40-story building for Stage II was to be connected at right angles to the 14-story Stage I building. It was proposed to analyze this frame both by computer and by model analysis; at the time (1959) the model analysis proved quicker and cheaper. At the time of writing (1975) the reverse has been true for several years for this type of structure.

7.2 OBJECTIVES AND PRINCIPAL METHODS EMPLOYED

Model analysis serves basically three purposes: (1) To produce numerical answers for structural design problems for which solutions are not obtainable by mathematical means; (2) to confirm experimentally that the assumptions made in the mathematical analysis are correct; and (3) to serve as a physical demonstration of structural behavior.

Because of the lack of mathematical solutions, model analysis has been used extensively for dams, and for shell and cable structures of complex form. However, since the advent of the digital computer, and particularly since the development of the finite element method, the scope of model analysis in this area has been greatly reduced. The mathematical evaluation of the static behavior of tall buildings presents no difficulties, but there are dynamic problems arising from the response of tall buildings to earthquakes for which model analysis has been particularly helpful.

The second and third purposes are largely complementary. It is necessary to make certain simplifying assumptions in regard to the behavior of building frames, particularly about the stiffness of the joints, and the model either confirms the assumptions made, or else points to the need for different, and perhaps more complex, assumptions.

It should be borne in mind that tall buildings are very expensive. Their cost generally runs into millions of dollars, so that the cost of making and testing a model is a relatively small item in the total cost. The model helps not merely the structural designer, but also the architect and his client to understand the behavior of the structure, and it thus promotes an informed discussion on structural decisions which need to be made.

Four principal techniques have been used for the model analysis of tall buildings. The first is to model the elastic behavior of the entire structure under static loads. This is by far the most common method (Cowan et al., 1968; Fumagalli, 1973; ACI, 1970; Cement and Concrete Association of Australia, 1972). Since the model must have a manageable size, a reduction in size in a ratio between 1:100 and 1:30 is appropriate. Most models have been made of a plastic material (see Section 7.5).

A model made of a dissimilar material can be tested only within the elastic range, and it therefore gives information only on the elastic behavior of the structure. For reinforced concrete structures, in particular, it is sometimes desirable to make a model that can be tested to destruction. It is then necessary to model not only the dimensions of the structure and the loads acting on it, but also the physical characteristics of the structural materials. Thus the steel reinforcement must be modeled by steel wires with similar properties, which often means that they must be especially made. The concrete must also be modeled with microconcrete, in which the aggregate is suitably scaled down in size and in density. Evidently there is a limit to the reduction in scale which can be achieved, if the materials are to be suitably modeled, and tests reported for tall buildings lie within the range of 1:15 and 1:3 (Preece and Davis, 1964; Fumagalli, 1973; ACI, 1972; Canadian Chapter of ACI, 1972). With this scale reduction a complete tall building cannot be modeled economically, so that the ultimate-strength model tests reported have been confined, with the exception of the model for the Pirelli Building (Section 7.7, No. 27), to a portion of a tall building only.

A static load test is adequate for strain analysis due to gravity loads and also, in most cases, due to wind loads. In regions subject to earthquakes, however, the dynamic response of the structure may be required (Duarte, 1975; Pereira, 1965; Priestley, 1969; Ravara, 1976; Burggrabe, 1972). Dynamic model analysis of tall buildings is complicated by the need to include the dynamic characteristics in the dimensional analysis of the structure (Sections 7.4 and 7.7). So far all dynamic model tests of tall buildings have been confined to the elastic range.

The fourth type of model used for tall buildings employs photoelasticity to measure stress concentrations in re-entrant corners, to gage the effect of openings or sudden changes of cross section, particularly in shear walls. It is thus, by definition, a method for a part of the structure, rather than the whole structure.

7.3 SCOPE OF THIS CHAPTER

This chapter deals only with structural model analysis. The testing of aero-dynamic models for tall buildings is discussed in Chapter CL-3.

This chapter deals only with problems of structural model analysis peculiar to tall buildings. Some tests have been reported on structural members which happen to be in tall buildings, but whose design is not affected by the tallness of the building. These have been excluded. Model tests on a number of structures for the roofs of single-cell buildings of some height (for example, cathedrals and assembly halls) have also been excluded because the problems examined did not arise from the tallness of the building.

A great deal of reinforced concrete research has been undertaken, notably in the

United States, using specimens reduced in size, partly to facilitate testing and partly to save money (ACI, 1972; Canadian Chapter of ACI, 1972; ACI Committee 444, 1972). Although some of these tests are being utilized for the design of tall buildings, they are not specifically concerned with the design of tall buildings.

In preparing this chapter, exhaustive inquiries were made in an endeavor to produce a comprehensive list of model tests on tall buildings, knowing that the field is a small one. This inquiry has yielded information on 44 model tests for tall buildings, and these are described in Section 7.7. Although this chapter forms part of Volume CB, the inquiry extended to model tests of steel structures.

Some books have been written on model analysis (Preece and Davis, 1964; Cowan et al., 1968; Hossdorf, 1971; Müller, 1971; Fumagalli, 1973), and several conferences have been held to discuss recent developments (ACI, 1970; CCAA, 1972; ACI, 1972; Canadian Chapter of ACI, 1972; ACI Committee 444, 1972). This chapter does not endeavor to reproduce the information already published on the principles of model analysis, since these are applicable to both tall buildings and other structures; however, the most important aspects are summarized in Sections 7.4, 7.5, and 7.6.

7.4 DIMENSIONAL THEORY

The basic concepts of the dimensional theory of structures were enunciated by Galileo Galilei (Carneiro, 1965). He demonstrated the "weakness of giants" by showing that the bending moment due to weight varied as the fourth power of the geometric scale factor, whereas the resistance moment varied only as the third power.

The modern dimensional theory is based on the principle of homogeneity. This was formalized in 1914 by E. Buckingham (1914) as the Pi-theorem. A functional relationship F_1 exists between r parameters of a physical system

$$F_1 (x_1, x_2, x_3 \ldots x_r) = 0 \qquad (7.1)$$

in which $x_1, x_2, x_3, \ldots x_r$ are the parameters and F_1 is a dimensionally homogeneous function, known or unknown.

The Pi-theorem states that the equivalent relation is given by

$$F_2 (\pi_1, \pi_2, \pi_3, \ldots \pi_{r-n}) = 0 \qquad (7.2)$$

in which F_2 is another dimensionally homogeneous function, known or unknown, n is the number of basic dimensions of the r parameters, and the π-terms are independent dimensionless products. The dimensionless π-terms must be satisfied for both the model and its structural prototype if the model is to represent the prototype accurately.

For an elastic model subject to static loads only three π-terms are required. The basic properties to be considered are:

1. The span and other general dimensions of the model, L.

2. The thickness of the sheet from which it is made, or the cross-sectional dimensions of the bars from which it is built up, t.

3. The loads to which it is subjected, W.

4. The modulus of elasticity of the material from which it is made, E.

5. The shear modulus of elasticity of the material from which it is made, G.

These five quantities can be reduced to the basic dimensions of length, l, and force, P, as follows: the span L is proportional to l; the thickness t is proportional to l; the loads W are proportional to P; the modulus of elasticity E is proportional to P/l^2; and the shear modulus of elasticity G is proportional to P/l^2.

There are thus five primary quantities r reducible to two basic dimensions n, so that $r - n = 3$ π-terms are required. The π-terms may be taken as L/t, E/G, and W/EL^2, and these ratios must be the same for the model and its prototype.

The first of these ratios implies that the model must be accurately scaled, that is if the length is reduced by 1:30, the thickness must also be reduced by 1:30.

The second ratio states that Poisson's ratio must be the same for the model and its prototype. This condition cannot normally be satisfied unless the model and its prototype are made from the same material. However, unless the structure is subjected both to high flexural stresses and to high shear or torsional stresses, the error is not serious.

The third ratio gives the loads to which the model should be subjected. For example, if the model is reduced in the ratio 1:30, and the model material has a direct modulus of elasticity 1/10 of that of the prototype, the loads should be reduced in the ratio $30^2 \times 10 = 9000$. In practice it is customary to take the loads as high as possible without taking the model beyond its elastic range, so as to obtain the highest possible strain and deflection measurements, and the "overload" is allowed for in interpreting the results of the model test. The reduction which can be made in the size of the model depends mainly on the accuracy required for the strain and deflection measurements. The smaller the model, the less accurate are the measurements of strain and deflection.

When a model is to be tested beyond its elastic range to give additional information on the ultimate load of the structure it is necessary to employ model materials which have stress-strain characteristics of the materials used in the prototype. This cannot normally be satisfied without using materials which are identical or very similar.

Most of the ultimate-strength tests have been concerned with reinforced concrete structures. The reinforcing bars are by the scale reduction reduced to the size of very thin bars or wires. Steel wire normally has stress-strain characteristics different from those of reinforcing bars, and it is usually necessary to manufacture small-size bars or wires with appropriate characteristics (Fumagalli, 1973; ACI Committee 444, 1972). The concrete is modeled with a microconcrete which is designed to have characteristics as similar as possible to those of the concrete used in the prototype. As the scale is reduced, the problems of producing a satisfactory microconcrete increase (Fumagalli, 1973; ACI Committee 444, 1972; Burggrabe, 1972).

Dynamic model tests for tall buildings have so far been carried out only in the elastic range. The condition of dynamic equilibrium requires a balance between the inertia and the damping forces which represent the reaction of the system to movement. It is not possible to reproduce simultaneously both forces in the model, and there are therefore two similitude conditions, which are satisfied separately. These are known as the Cauchy number (or Mach number) and the Froude number.

Cauchy's condition assumes that gravitational forces can be neglected, so that the similitude law derived from the relation (inertia force/elastic force) is the constant for the model and its prototype. On the contrary, Froude's criterion neglects relation (inertia force/gravitational force) and the same constant for the model and its prototype. These ratios are derived in a paper by Pereira (1965).

7.5 MODEL MATERIAL AND TYPE

When a model is to be tested to its ultimate strength, the choice of the model materials is restricted by the requirement that they must have the same stress-strain characteristics as those of the prototype. There is a limited range of small-size reinforcing bars and wires with these characteristics, and these may determine the exact scale ratio to be adopted. A large reduction in scale is not possible, and most ultimate-strength tests on tall buildings have therefore been confined to a part of the structure. In recent years a great deal of research has been done on the design of suitable microconcrete mixes (Fumagalli, 1973; ACI Committee 444, 1972; Burggrabe, 1972). Deformed reinforcing bars of small size have been especially made for use in ultimate-strength models, and a list of available sizes may be obtained from the Concrete Reinforcing Steel Institute, 180 North Lasalle Street, Chicago, Ill. 60601, USA.

Elastic models have been made from aluminum and from sheet steel. However, the majority have utilized one of the synthetic plastics. There are two types: thermosetting materials, or casting resins, and thermoplastic materials, which are produced as sheets or rods and can be formed by heat or pressure (or vacuum) or a combination of both. Complicated shapes are more easily produced by casting resins. However, many tall buildings consist of a combination of plates and linear members, such as beams and columns, and these are best modeled with thermoplastics. The material most commonly employed for elastic models of tall buildings is methyl methacrylate, produced under the trade names Perspex and Plexiglas. Scale reductions of up to 1:100 have been used, although a smaller reduction is desirable for accuracy.

The cost and speed of making an elastic model are largely dependent on the choice of a suitable scale ratio. If the concrete slabs of the structural prototype have one or a few predominant thicknesses, it is desirable to select sheets from the available manufactured range so that the amount of machining can be kept to a minimum. The exact choice of the scale ratio thus depends largely on practical considerations.

The forming of microconcrete models and of models made from casting resins is precisely the same as in the prototype, that is, the materials are cast at room temperature. Most casting resins shrink more than concrete, and the contraction must be allowed for in the design of the model (Balint and Shaw, 1965).

Perspex and Plexiglas can be cut and machined to the required shape. Curved members are generally formed by a combination of heat and pressure (or vacuum), and this requires special equipment. The existing equipment of the plastics industry can often be utilized. The component parts can be welded at room temperature, using commercially available glues. Most thermoplastics have a rate of creep much higher than that of concrete, and the model must be loaded and unloaded in accordance with a controlled time scale.

Photoelastic models are normally made in the same way from thermosetting resins or thermoplastic materials. There is a wide variety of plastics with photoelastic properties (Hendry, 1966; Kuske, 1970).

7.6 TESTING OF MODELS

The greater the reduction in size the smaller is the model load. Thus if a model is to be tested to ultimate strength, and the scale ratio is L, the load is reduced according to dimensional theory (Section 7.4) by L^2. For a scale ratio of 1:10, the model load is $1/100$ of that of the prototype.

In elastic models the scale reduction is usually greater, and in addition the elastic modulus of plastics is lower than that of concrete. For a scale ratio of 30 and a modular ratio of 10, the model load is $1/9000$ of that of the prototype.

Although the loads carried by tall buildings are high, the model loads can therefore be reproduced in a laboratory. A laboratory that tests models only occasionally may find it convenient to use weights which can, if necessary, be amplified by a lever. Individual point loads can be combined into a single load by a whiffle-tree loading system. Laboratories conducting frequent model tests may find it more convenient to apply the load by means of a specially constructed device which applies a pressure or a vacuum.

Deflections are important in tall buildings. In addition, the correctness of the assumptions made in the analysis can often be verified satisfactorily merely by measuring deflections. Deflections are easily and accurately measured with dial gages.

Strains are now generally measured with electric resistance strain gages. The results can be centrally recorded, by print-out or on computer tape or both, and the data can be processed directly by computer.

7.7 COMPREHENSIVE LIST OF TESTS

The following geographically arranged record is the result of a survey of model tests of tall buildings compiled for this chapter. The results have been abridged, as it was considered more informative to have brief details of all known tests. Further information can be obtained from the references quoted, or from the testing laboratories cited. In a few cases the data are briefer than intended because no further information was available; some are not illustrated for the same reason.

Australia
Division of Building Research, C.S.I.R.O., Melbourne
  1. Half-scale model of a part of 20-story reinforced concrete panel flats for the Victorian Housing Commission, Melbourne (communication from F.D. Beresford).
Miller, Milston and Ferris, Consulting Engineers, Sydney
  2. Elastic model of the Qantas Centre, a 198-m (650-ft) high reinforced concrete structure in Sydney. Made from Perspex to a scale of 1:80 (Miller, 1972).

University of Melbourne

   3. Elastic model of Nauru House, a 47-story reinforced concrete building in Melbourne. Made from Perspex to a scale of 1:96 (Schmidt, undated).

University of New South Wales

   4. Elastic model of Australia Square Tower, a 51-story reinforced concrete building in Sydney. Made from casting resin to a scale of 1:30 (Cowan et al., 1968; Balint and Shaw, 1965; Gero and Cowan, 1970). A photograph of this model appears on the cover of ACI, 1970.

University of Sydney

   5. Elastic model of the 40-story steel frame for the Chevron Hotel Stage II, made from Perspex to a scale of 1:100 (Cowan et al., 1968; Cowan, 1961a; Cowan, 1961b).

   6. Elastic model of the Centrepoint Tower, a 200-m (660-ft) steel tower atop a 15-story reinforced concrete building in Sydney. Made from steel to a scale of 1:100 (Gero, 1969; Gero et al., 1970; Gero and Cowan, 1972).

   7. Elastic model of the MLC Tower, a 64-level reinforced concrete building in Sydney. Made from Plexiglas to a scale of 1:95 (Gero, 1973). Figs. 7.1(a) and (b) show this model.

Canada

Division of Building Research, National Research Council, Ottawa

   8. An unspecified number of microconcrete models of 7-story flat-slab and shear-wall structures built for research purposes to a scale of approximately 1:10 (Zelman et al., 1970).

University of Toronto

   9. Several photoelastic models of reinforced concrete shear walls for buildings of about 25 stories, made to a scale of 1:120 from Araldite, resin, and Perspex, respectively (Schwaighofer, 1972).

Fig. 7.1(a) Model of MLC Tower, Sydney (No. 7) under construction (Courtesy: University of Sydney)

Fig. 7.1(b) Wind loading test of model (Courtesy: University of Sydney)

Cuba

Sáenz, Cancio, Martín, Consulting Engineers

    10. Model of a 39-story reinforced concrete apartment building made of wood, to a scale of 1:100. Tested statically for wind loading.

Czechoslovakia

Institute for Building and Architecture, Slovak Academy of Science

    11. Model of standardized design for 9-story concrete panel structures, fabricated from acrylic sheets. The tests included static loading due to wind producing simultaneous bending and torsion, and a study of progressive collapse. The tests were carried out according to a strict time-schedule of cyclic loading and unloading to eliminate errors due to creep of the acrylic sheet under load, and the results from 1300 measuring points were recorded with an automatic data logger (Fig. 7.2).

German Federal Republic

Institut für Modellstatik, University of Stuttgart

    12. Photoelastic model for a reinforced concrete shear wall in the Bayer Hochhaus, Leverkusen, made from Araldite resin to a scale of 1:50 (Müller, 1961). Fig. 7.3 shows isochromatic fringes on this model.

Great Britain

City University, London

    13. Perspex and microconcrete models for the National Westminster Bank Building, London. This will be approximately 200 m (600 ft) high and the tallest office block in Europe. The consultants required detailed information about the stresses in the core of the structure (Perspex model to a scale of 1:72) and information about the stress in the core and the mode of collapse of the lobes (microconcrete model to a scale of 1:30) (communication from J. E. Gibson). The model is shown in Fig. 7.4.

Imperial College of Science and Technology, London

    14. Elastic model for the reinforced concrete services tower of the 25-story steel-framed Cooperative Insurance Society Building, Manchester, made from Perspex to a scale of 1:60 (Sparkes and Chapman, 1961).

Fig. 7.2 Model of standardized design for 9-story concrete panel structure, tested in Bratislava (No. 11) (Courtesy: Institute for Building and Architecture, Slovak Academy of Science)

15. Elastic model for the reinforced concrete services core of the 118-m (387-ft) Commercial Union Building, London, made from Perspex to a scale of 1:96; the building has a high-yield steel structure suspended from the core (Williams and Rutter, 1967). Fig. 7.5 shows the model.

16. Photoelastic model of a shear wall tested in connection with the collapse of the Ronan Point block of flats, a 24-story structure built from load-bearing precast concrete panels (confidential report by A.R. Flint).

Fig. 7.3 Isochromatic fringes on photoelastic model of Bayer Hochhaus, Leverkusen (No. 12) (Courtesy: Institut für Modellstatik, University of Stuttgart)

Fig. 7.4 Perspex model of core of National Westminster Bank offices, London (No. 13) (Courtesy: J. E. Gibson)

Fig. 7.5 Model of services tower of Commercial Union Building, London (No. 15) (from Williams and Rutter, 1967)

University of Aston, Birmingham

17. Three-dimensional elastic model of the reinforced concrete shear-wall structure of a 33-story block of flats in Birmingham. Made from Perspex to a scale of 1:48 (Holmes et al., 1969).

University of Edinburgh

18. Elastic model of a 14-story load-bearing brick structure. Made from Perspex to a scale of 1:48 (Soane and Hendry, 1968). Fig. 7.6 shows testing of the model.

University of Strathclyde, Glasgow

19. Elastic model of a 25-story concrete panel building in Glasgow. Made from Perspex to a scale of 1:48 (Coull, 1966).

Hungary

Technical University of Budapest

20. Photoelastic model of shear walls for a 24-story reinforced concrete building for the Medical University in Budapest, made from VP 1257 resin to a scale of 1:165 (Visontai, undated).

21. Elastic model of a 20-story reinforced concrete building. Made from Plexiglas to a scale of 1:70, and tested for wind loading and for asymmetrical vertical loading due to a water tank (communication from O. Halasz). Fig. 7.7 shows the model.

22. Idealized model to study the strength and stability of a 15-story reinforced concrete block of flats before the floors are built. Made from Plexiglas, 1 m (3.3 ft) high. Tested for vertical loading and wind loading (communication from O. Halasz). Fig. 7.8 shows the model.

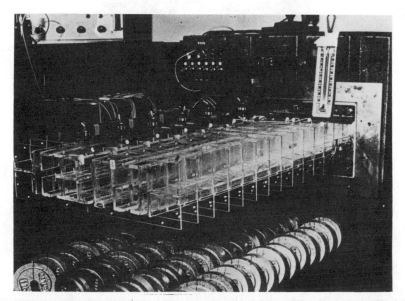

Fig. 7.6 Wind loading test on model of 14-story brick structure (No. 18) (from Soane and Hendry, 1968)

Italy

Istituto Sperimentali Modelli e Strutture, Bergamo

23. Elastic model of the 44-story reinforced concrete Parque Central Buildings, Caracas, Venezuela, tested both statically and dynamically. Made from epoxy resin filled with powdered silica, to a scale of 1:40 (Fumagalli, 1973). Fig. 7.9 shows the model being tested.

24. Elastic model of the 43-story reinforced concrete Victoria Place Tower, Montréal, Canada. Made of celluloid to a scale of 1:52.8 (Fumagalli, 1973). Fig. 7.10 shows the model.

Fig. 7.7 Model of structure of 20-story reinforced concrete building, loaded by asymmetrical water tank (No. 21) (Courtesy: O. Halasz)

Fig. 7.8 Model of 15-story block of flats prior to construction of floors under wind load (No. 22) (Courtesy: O. Halasz)

25. Elastic model of the 18-story reinforced concrete Torre-Sperlinga Building, Palermo, Italy, tested both statically and dynamically. Made from polystyrene to a scale of 1:50 (Fumagalli, 1973). Fig. 7.11 shows a dynamic test of the model.

Fig. 7.9 Dynamic test on model of Parque Central Buildings, Caracas, in ISMES Laboratory (No. 23) (from Fumagalli, 1973)

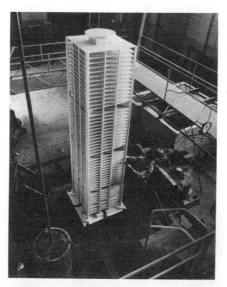

Fig. 7.10 Model of Victoria Place Tower, Montréal, made in ISMES Laboratory (No. 24) (from Fumagalli, 1973)

26. Microconcrete model of the 35-story reinforced concrete Pirelli Building, Milan, to a scale of 1:15 (Fumagalli, 1973). The model is shown in Fig. 7.12.
27. Reinforced microconcrete model of a floor of the Pirelli Building, Milan, to a scale of 1:5 (Fumagalli, 1973). Fig. 7.13 shows the model.
28. Reinforced microconcrete model of a floor of the Torre Velasca Tower in Milan, to a scale of 1:5 (communication from E. Fumagalli). Fig. 7.14 shows the model.
29. Reinforced microconcrete model of a floor of the Galfa skyscraper to a scale of 1:5 (communication from E. Fumagalli). The model is shown in Fig. 7.15.

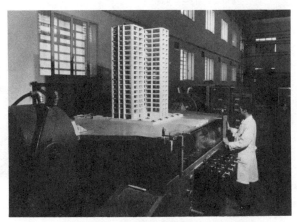

Fig. 7.11 Dynamic test of model of Torre-Sperlings Building, Palermo (No. 25) (from Fumagalli, 1973)

Fig. 7.12 Microconcrete model to scale of 1:15 of Pirelli Building, Milan (No. 26) (from Fumagalli, 1973)

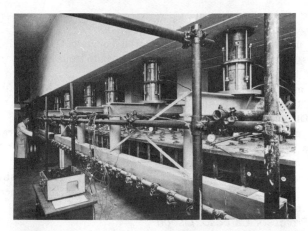

Fig. 7.13 Microconcrete model to scale of 1:5 of floor of Pirelli Building (No. 27) (from Fumagalli, 1973)

Fig. 7.14 Microconcrete model of floor of Torre Velasca Tower, Milan (No. 28) (Courtesy: E. Fumagalli)

Fig. 7.15 Microconcrete model of floor of Galfa skyscraper, Milan (No. 29) (Courtesy: E. Fumagalli)

Portugal

Laboratório Nacional de Engenharia Civil, Lisbon

30. Elastic model of the 22-story reinforced concrete Petunia II Building in Caracas, tested statically and dynamically. Made from Perspex and steel to a scale of 1:30 (Priestley, 1969). See Fig. 7.16.

31. Elastic model of the 25-level reinforced concrete Sol-Mar Building in the Azores, tested statically and dynamically. Made from Perspex to a scale of 1:100 (Duarte, 1975). Fig. 7.17.

32. Elastic model of the 60-story reinforced concrete Parque Central Towers in Caracas, Venezuela, tested both statically and dynamically. Made from Perspex to a scale of 1:80 (Ravara et al., 1976). Fig. 7.18.

33. Two microconcrete models of parts of the 44-story Parque Central Building, Caracas, to a scale of 1:15, subjected to repetitive and incremental loading (communication from M. Paparoni).

Institute of Professor Cardoso, Lisbon

34. Elastic model of the 60-story reinforced concrete Parque Central Towers in Caracas. Made of Perspex to a scale of 1:125 (communication from M. Paparoni).

Puerto Rico

Martinez and Costa and Associates, Consulting Engineers

35. Elastic models of two and three column frames from 23-story reinforced concrete apartment building, Condominio Atlántico, San Juan. Made from

Fig. 7.16 Dynamic test of Petunia II Building, Caracas, tested at LNEC Laboratory (No. 30) (from Priestley, 1969)

Fig. 7.17 Dynamic test of model of Sol-Mar Building, Azores (No. 31) (from Duarte, 1975)

13-mm (½-in.) Plexiglas at a scale of 1:48. Flanges added to beams to simulate T-beam action. Results used to determine stiffness of structure for dynamic analyses (communication from Martinez and Costa). Fig. 7.19 shows the models being tested.

Fig. 7.18 Model of Parque Central Towers, Caracas, made at LNEC Laboratory (No. 32) (from Ravara et al., 1976)

Fig. 7.19 Test on model of two-column bent for Condominio Atlantico, San Juan (No. 35) (Courtesy: Martinez and Costa and Associates; photo by Francisco E. Vando)

Romania

Institut des Constructions, Bucharest

   36. Photoelastic model of the shear walls of a 17-story hospital in Bucharest, and moiré-fringe model of the floors of the same building. Made from Plexiglas (Mazilu et al., 1972).

United States of America

Wiss, Janney, Elstner and Associates, Consulting Engineers, Chicago

   37. Elastic model of three floors of the 20-story Mercy Hospital, Chicago, which has interior floors isolated from the external columns. Made from plastic to a scale of 1:25 (communicated by O. C. Guedelhofer). Fig. 7.20.

   38. Elastic model of the 30-story Carl Sandburg Apartments, Chicago, a reinforced concrete flat-plate structure. Built from Plexiglas to a scale of 1:48 (communicated by O. C. Guedelhofer). See Fig. 7.21.

   39. Photoelastic models of the multistory steel-frame structure of the CB-1 Building, Paris. Cast from photoelastic resin to a scale of 1:47.1 (communicated by O. C. Guedelhofer).

   40. Photoelastic models for the same building, made from Perspex to a scale of 1:31.5, and tested with brittle lacquers (communicated by O. C. Guedelhofer).

   41. Microconcrete model of a panel of the same building to a scale of 1:4 (communicated by O. C. Guedelhofer).

   42. Elastic model to investigate load transfer between the sloping main external columns and a large horizontal tie beam at grade for the First National Bank in Chicago, a 256-m (840-ft) tapering reinforced concrete frame. Made from Plexiglas to a scale of 1:8 (communicated by O. C. Guedelhofer). Fig. 7.22 shows the model.

Venezuela

Paparoni y Holoma, Consulting Engineers, Caracas

   43. Two half-size reinforced concrete models of critical sections of the 44-story Parque Central Buildings in Caracas, tested on the building site under alternate loadings (communicated by M. Paparoni).

Fig. 7.20 Test on model of three floors of Mercy Hospital, Chicago, isolated from external columns (No. 37) (Courtesy: O. C. Guedelhofer)

44. Two elastic models of parts of the 60-story reinforced concrete Parque Central Towers in Caracas, tested statically and dynamically. Made from Perspex to a scale of 1:75 and 1:50, respectively (communicated by M. Paparoni). Fig. 7.23 shows the model.

Fig. 7.21 Model of Carl Sandburg Apartments, Chicago (No. 38) (Courtesy: O. C. Guedelhofer)

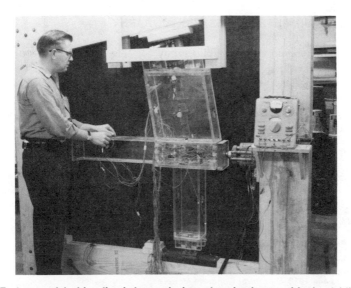

Fig. 7.22 Test on model of junction between sloping external column and horizontal tie in First National City Bank, Chicago (No. 42) (Courtesy: O. C. Guedelhofer)

Fig. 7.23 Partial model for Parque Central Towers, Caracas, made by Prof. Cardoso, Lisbon, for Paparoni y Holoma (No. 44) (Courtesy: M. Paparoni)

7.8   CONDENSED REFERENCES/BIBLIOGRAPHY

The following is a condensed bibliography for this chapter. Not only does it include all articles referred to or cited in the text, but it also contains bibliography for further reading. The full citations will be found at the end of the Volume. What is given here should be sufficient information to lead the reader to the correct article: the author, date, and title. In case of multiple authors, only the first named is listed. In this chapter the listing is according to the indicated categories.

Textbooks on Direct Model Analysis

Cowan 1968, *Models in Architecture*
Fumagalli 1973, *Statical and Geomechanical Models*
Hossdorf 1971, *Model Analysis*
Müller 1971, *Handbook of Model Analysis*
Preece 1964, *Models for Structural Concrete*
Schuring 1977, *Scale Models in Engineering—Fundamentals and Applications*

Conference Proceedings on Direct Model Analysis

ACI 1970, *Models for Concrete Structures*
ACI 1972, *Models of Concrete Structures*
ACI Committee 444 1972, *Structural Concrete Models*

Canadian Chapter ACI 1972, *Models in Structural Engineering*
Cement and Concrete Assoc. of Australia 1972, *Structural Models*

Some Textbooks in Related Fields

Charlton 1966, *Model Analysis of Plane Structures*
Dally 1965, *Experimental Stress Analysis*
Durelli 1970, *Moiré Analysis of Strain*
Hendry 1966, *Photoelastic Analysis*
Holister 1967, *Experimental Stress Analysis*

Kuske 1970, *Photoelasticity in the Design of Buildings*
Theocaris 1969, *Moiré Fringes in Strain Analysis*

Papers Referring Specifically to Model Analysis of Tall Buildings

Aroni 1957, *Full-Scale Tests of Precast Multistory Flat Construction*
Baker 1972, *Manufacture and Testing of Model Brickwork Wind Panels*
Balint 1965, *Structural Model of the Australia Square Tower*
Coull 1966, *Tests on a Model Shear Wall Structure*
Coull 1972, *Model Investigations of Shear Wall Structures*

Cowan 1961a, *The Use of Structural Models in Architecture*
Cowan 1961b, *Some Applications of the Use of Direct Model Analysis*
Duarte 1975, *Seismic Study of Sol-Mar Building*
Fox 1955, *Concrete Apartment House 39 Stories High*
Gero 1969, *Preliminary Report on the Model Investigation of the Centrepoint Tower*

Gero 1970, *Structural Concrete Models in Australia*
Gero 1972, *Feasibility Structural Model Analysis: The "Centrepoint" Tower, Sydney*
Gero 1973, *Structural Model Testing of M.L.C. Centre Tower Building*
Holmes 1969, *Experimental Stresses and Deflections of a Model Shear Wall Structure*
Janney 1970, *The Use of Models in Structural Engineering*

Mazilu 1972, *The Use of Photoelasticity for Dimensioning the Structure of a Tall Building*
Melbourne 1972, *Modelling of Structures to Measure Wind Effects*
Miller 1972, *Model Analysis of the Qantas Centre*
Müller 1961, *Photoelastic Investigation of a Shear Wall Under Wind Load for the W1 Skyscraper*
Oberti 1963, *Experimental Research with Structural Models at ISMES*

Oberti 1972, *Model Analysis as an Extension of Theoretical Structural Studies*
Pereira 1965, *Dimensional Theory for Dynamic Models*
Priestley 1969, *Dynamic Model Study of a 22-Storey Reinforced Concrete Building*
Ravara 1976, *Seismic Study of Parque Central Office Towers*
Schafer 1973, *A Study of Concrete Panel Construction*

Schmidt undated, *Construction and Testing of an Elastic Model of Nauru House*
Schwaighofer 1972, *Models of Shear Wall Structures*
Soane 1968, *The Behaviour of Essex University Tower Block Under Wind Loading*
Sparkes 1961, *Model Methods, With Particular Reference to Three Recent Applications*
Vickery 1972, *On the Aeroelastic Modelling of Structures in Wind*

Visontai undated, *Photoelastic Investigation of a Shear Wall for a 24-Storey Building*
Williams 1967, *The Design of Two Buildings with Suspended Structures*
Zelman 1970, *Practical Problems and Costs of Fabricating Multi-Storey Models*

Bibliographies on Structural Model Analysis

Ady 1970, *Models for Concrete Structures, Bibliography*
Funnell 1972, *A Selective Bibliography on Structural Models*

Additional References

Buckingham 1914, *On Physically Similar Systems*
Burggrabe 1972, *Microconcrete for Structural Model Investigations*
Carneiro 1965, *Galileo, Founder of the Science of the Strength of Materials*

Castoldi 1973, *New Techniques of Model Investigation of the Seismic Behaviour*
Cowan 1972, *What Can We Do With Structural Models?*

Lauletta 1970, *Earthquake Simulation by A Shake Table*
Nervi 1955, *Building the Right Way*
Oberti 1973, *New Trends in Model Research on Large Structures*
Torroja 1958, *The Structures of Eduardo Torroja*

Structural Design of
Tall Concrete and Masonry Buildings

Chapter CB-8

Stability

Prepared by Committee 23 (Stability) of the Council on Tall Buildings and Urban Habitat as part of the Monograph on the Planning and Design of Tall Buildings

Andreas Aas-Jakobsen Chairman
Boris Bresler   Vice-Chairman
James G. MacGregor   Editor

AUTHOR ACKNOWLEDGMENT

Special acknowledgment is due those individuals whose contributions and papers formed the substantial first drafts of the various sections of this chapter. First are the state-of-art reporters from the 1972 International Conference whose material was published in the Lehigh Proceedings. These individuals are:

H. Beck (deceased), Sections 8.1, 8.2, and 8.4
B. Bresler, Section 8.5
E. A. Chistiakov, Section 8.3
A. A. Gvozdev, Section 8.3
K. Kordina, Sections 8.3, 8.4, and 8.7
M. Lorentsen, Section 8.5
J. G. MacGregor, Sections 8.3, 8.4, 8.5, 8.6, and 8.7
A. Popoff, Jr., Section 8.5
K. Zilch, Sections 8.1, 8.2, and 8.4.

In addition to this, other sections were based on special contributions prepared by:

K. Aas-Jakobsen, Sections 8.1, 8.2, 8.3, 8.4, and 8.6
D. Dicke, Sections 8.5 and 8.6
S. E. Hage, Section 8.6
G. König, Sections 8.4, 8.5, 8.6, and 8.7.

CONTRIBUTORS

The following is a complete list of those who have submitted written material for possible use in the chapter, whether or not that material was used in the final version. The Committee Chairman and Editor were given quite complete latitude. Frequently length limitations precluded the inclusion of much valuable material. The Bibliography contains all contributions. The contributors are: A. Aas-Jakobsen, K. Aas-Jakobsen, G. Ambos, H. Beck, B. Bresler, H. J. Bubenheim, W. F. Chen, E. Chistiakov, D. Dicke, R. W. Furlong, M. Gellert, J. Glück, A. Gvozdev, M. Heunisch, N. Jackson, G. König, K. Kordina, M. Lorentsen, J. G. MacGregor, A. Pauw (deceased), A. Popoff, Jr., K. Zilch.

COMMITTEE MEMBERS

A. Aas-Jakobsen, K. Aas-Jakobsen, T. Arakawa, J. E. Breen, B. Bresler, K. E. Bruinette, V. M. Cano, W. F. Chen, E. A. Chistiakov, D. Dicke, R. W. Furlong, M. Gellert, J. Glück, B. Goschy, L. Grencik, A. A. Gvozdev, A. S. Hall, N. Jackson, A. Juntilla, A. P. Kabaila, Y. Kanoh, G. König, K. Kordina, R. Lenschow, B. Lewicki, M. Lorentsen, J. G. MacGregor, R. J. Mainstone, A. Pauw, A. Popoff, Jr., B. Rubanenko, H. Umemura, A. C. VanRiel, G. Winter, F. Y. Yokel, K. Zilch.

CB-8

Stability

8.1 INTRODUCTION

The goal of structural analysis is to assure serviceability of a building under normal conditions and safety against collapse under abnormal conditions. "Failure" of some elements or the entire structure is defined by prescribed limits on forces or deformations. Often it is sufficient to determine the internal forces in the undeformed system (first-order theory) and to verify that the limits of failure are not exceeded. The modern trend towards use of high-strength concrete and reinforcing steels and the more effective utilization of the material strength result in greater slenderness of the members, in which case large deformation increments may be caused by a small increment of loading. In such cases the internal forces have to be calculated with due regard to the effects of deformations on the equilibrium of these slender members (second-order theory). This is the basis for "problems of stability," which were first introduced by Leonhard Euler (1744). For reinforced concrete structures classical methods for investigating stability cannot be used without modification because of the nonlinear behavior of this material. The necessity of sufficient safety on the one hand, and the requirement of an economic design on the other, demand methods of calculation which account for the special behavior of this material.

The possible kinds of failure due to instability depend on the behavior of material, and therefore one must distinguish between an ideal material following Hooke's Law and a real nonlinear material with limited strength. In the case of a classical axially loaded column of ideal elastic material with the load-deflection curve shown in Fig. 8.1, the member remains straight when the loads are less than some critical value P_E. When the load reaches the critical value P_E, equilibrium can be satisfied in many different deformed positions; the equilibrium is unstable and there is no unique relationship between load and deformation. This case is called a buckling problem. In a real material this is only possible if the buckling load P_E is below the strength of the column, based on material failure.

In the case of an eccentrically loaded column, if the material is ideally elastic, then the load-deformation curve is as shown in Fig. 8.2(a), and every level of load

311

has its corresponding definite deflection Δ. There is no neutral or unstable equilibrium. This case is called a second-order stress problem or an instability problem leading to infinite deflection at some critical load P_{cr}. For the eccentrically loaded column of real material, the load-deformation curves are as shown in Figs. 8.2(b) and (c). The load-deformation curve in Fig. 8.2(b) is similar to the one in Fig. 8.2(a), except that in this case the load P is limited by P_u corresponding to the strength of the column. For every load intensity there is a unique value of the deformation Δ, and the problem is again a second-order stress problem. The final failure is referred to as a material failure (see also Fig. 8.9). The load-deformation curve in Fig. 8.2(c) shows quite a different behavior as it peaks at P_{cr}. This is called

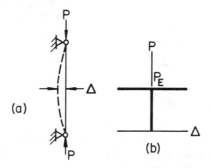

(a)

(b)

Fig. 8.1 Axially loaded column: (a) Buckling mode of column; (b) load deflection curve for "buckling problem"

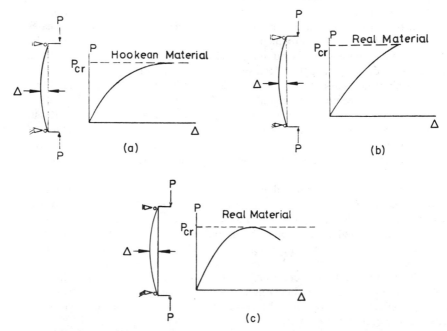

Fig. 8.2 Load deflection curves for eccentrically loaded columns: (a) Hookean material, instability problem; (b) real material (nonlinear elastic, limited strength)—instability problem and material failure; (c) real material (nonlinear elastic, limited strength)—stability failure

a stability problem (see also Fig. 8.9). Henceforth to simplify the discussion all problems dealing with the effects of deformation on equilibrium will be referred to as stability problems. The load causing failure for any reason will be called the load capacity. Since the material characteristics and imperfections of a structure affect the stability, a brief review of these will be given in the next articles.

1 List of Stability Limit States

Chapter CB-2 reviews the limit states to be considered in the design of tall concrete buildings. Those dealing with stability are presented here and will be elaborated on in the rest of this chapter.

The ultimate limit state of instability (buckling) has been described in detail in Section P42.21 of the CEB-FIP Recommendations (CEB, 1970):

> In order to check the buckling conditions of a member, or the overall stability of a complete structure, it is generally necessary to consider, for the different combinations of load, the equilibrium states and the distribution of internal forces, by using *second order* theory (that is, by taking into account the deformation of the structure).
>
> It is then necessary to consider the strength and deformation characteristics of the materials, corresponding as closely as possible to the conditions of the problem under examination, and to consider other factors, such as plastic deformation, creep, cracking and possible shrinkage, which may affect the behaviour of the structure.
>
> The main influences to be considered are:
> – the mechanical properties of the concrete and the reinforcement;
> – the percentage and distribution of the steel;
> – the geometry of the transverse cross-section;
> – the slenderness of the member and eccentricities of the loads;
> – the duration and type of loading;
> – uncertainties over support conditions and positions and directions of loads;
> – the way loads and other actions combine.

Instability of the whole structure of a tall building by deformation does not differ in principle from that of a normal building, but due to the great height an exact evaluation of the deformation, particularly of the horizontal deflection, is of primary importance.

The deformations of the structure that cause second-order effects may have their origin in:

1. Horizontal forces; mainly wind, but also earthquake, blast, etc.

2. Vertical forces; eccentric loading (dead weight or live load, or both); temperature differences between opposite sides, as well as shrinkage and creep differences.

3. Rotation of the foundation caused by eccentric loading, different soil properties, unequal settlement, variable stiffness of the basement, different loading from cores and frames, adjacent buildings, unequal depth or kind of foundation (directly on the soil or on piles, for example).

4. Initial deviations from the vertical axis, caused by construction errors or inaccuracies in surveying, etc.

Some of these deformations are present from the beginning; others develop or increase during the lifetime of the building due to creep, shrinkage, or settlement.

Because the horizontal deflection (from the normal vertical position) plays a principal role in the stability of a tall building, it should be calculated with the greatest accuracy, and as realistically as possible. Ideally, one should take into account all possible influences of uncracked and cracked sections, their distribution over the length of each member, the effects of shrinkage and creep, and redistribution of moments and forces. For practical applications, however, most of these influences can be conservatively estimated.

When a structure is composed of elements with a different deflection behavior, for example shear walls and frames, the deflection of the composite structure has to be calculated. The same applies to other combinations, such as tube and frame buildings, tube-in-tube buildings, etc. The possibility of torsional instability should also be considered.

With the ever-increasing height of buildings, the stiffness of the joints of prefabricated elements should be given special attention, because they are often less rigid than monolithic joints. The possibility that damage or failure of one element may lead to a progressive failure of the entire structure should also be considered. This topic is discussed more fully in Chapters CB-1 and CB-12.

2 Scope of this Chapter

This chapter consists of seven sections dealing with various aspects of the stability of concrete structures. Where possible, various approaches to the problem are considered, and no attempt is made to endorse any particular code of practice.

Section 8.2 reviews those properties of concrete and reinforcement and reinforced concrete cross sections that are important in the study of the stability of concrete members and buildings.

Section 8.3 discusses the stability of individual members and lists the factors affecting it. Most of this section deals with reinforced concrete columns. Various design procedures for individual columns are reviewed in Section 8.4. Prestressed columns are discussed briefly in this section.

In Section 8.5 the elastic and inelastic stability of reinforced concrete frames is considered. In addition to an extensive discussion of planar frames, the stability of three-dimensional frames and precast frames is discussed briefly.

Section 8.6 discusses the concept of second-order analyses of frames and presents several procedures for carrying them out. Finally, Section 8.7 presents practical procedures for considering stability in the design of tall concrete buildings.

8.2 SIGNIFICANT PROPERTIES OF MATERIALS AND CROSS SECTIONS

Deflections in reinforced concrete structures are calculated on the basis of the deformation behavior of concrete and steel.

1 Concrete

The properties of concrete having a strong influence on the deflection of reinforced concrete structures, and therefore on the capacity based on the second-order theory, are:

1. Very small tensile strength. The consequent cracking causes considerable decrease of stiffness.

2. Nonlinear stress-strain relation. The stress-strain curve of concrete resulting from a short-time loading has a convex shape, which depends on many different factors (Rüsch and Stockel, 1967; Sargin, 1971; Kent and Park, 1971). This is discussed more fully in Section 6.2 of Chapter CB-6.

3. Time-dependent strains. The time-dependent strains of concrete can be separated into stress-dependent creep strains and stress-independent shrinkage strains. With time the deformation of concrete in compression is increased by creep and shrinkage, and the stresses are transferred from concrete to steel reinforcement. Thus the influence of creep and shrinkage must be considered in an evaluation of second-order effects. Different approaches may be used in evaluating these effects, some of which are discussed in Section 8.4 of this chapter and in Chapter CB-10.

The Comité Européen du Béton (1970) has suggested that a good approximation to the stress-strain curve for concrete is the parabola-rectangular diagram given in Fig. 8.3. The maximum stress in the diagram is a function of the characteristic strength f_{ck}, which is 1.64 standard deviations below the mean concrete strength. Curve 1 in Fig. 8.3 shows the stress-strain curve for the characteristic concrete strength (specified strength, f_{ck}). Curve 2 represents the yielding state, f_{ck}/γ_c; and Curve 3 the ultimate limit state, $(f_{ck}/\gamma_c)/\gamma_n$. For the design of cross sections the maximum ordinate of the stress-strain curve corresponds to a stress of $0.85 f_{ck}/\gamma_c$ in which $\gamma_c = 1.5$.

2 Reinforcement

In analyses of structures, idealized stress-strain relationships for reinforcement are generally used. The bilinear elastoplastic stress-strain curve shown in Fig. 8.4 is normally used for as-rolled reinforcement with the strength at the yielding state equal to the specified minimum yield. For cold-worked reinforcement a bilinear or an elastic-curved diagram (CEB, 1970) can be used with the yield equal to that of

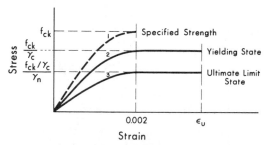

Fig. 8.3 Affine stress-strain curves for concrete

the stress at a 0.002 offset. In the CEB Recommendations (1970) the design strength of the ultimate limit state is taken as f_y/γ_s. Also in those Recommendations, the stress-strain curve for design is derived by dividing the ordinates measured along lines parallel to the initial tangent by γ_s. In this way the initial tangent modulus of the steel remains unchanged.

Strain hardening of the reinforcement is generally disregarded. The effect of strain hardening is to increase the ultimate capacity and to reduce the curvature at failure (Cohn and Ghosh, 1972).

3 Reinforced Concrete

Because assumptions have to be made to simplify the calculations of the internal forces and deformations of reinforced concrete structures, the results should be called "realistic" but not "real." Important simplifications are:

1. The tension stresses in concrete are usually disregarded.

2. A distinction is made between the stress-strain behavior under short-time and long-time loading, although these are interconnected.

3. Normally for short-time loading the stress-strain relation is assumed to be nonlinear elastic. The loading history of a fiber of concrete is disregarded, and the effects of hysteresis for the section are normally not considered.

4. For the strength of the concrete a "design strength" is used.

5. Bernoulli's hypothesis of a plane cross section remaining plane under load is considered valid for cracked reinforced concrete sections.

Based on these assumptions and stress-strain curves such as those described in Articles 8.2.1 and 8.2.2, it is possible to calculate relationships between normal force, moment, and curvature for any given reinforced concrete section (Pfrang et al., 1964; Cranston, 1966; Beck, 1969; Cohn and Ghosh, 1972). The procedure for computing a load-moment-curvature diagram is given in the following paragraphs.

The cross section of a column subjected to uniaxial bending and compression is

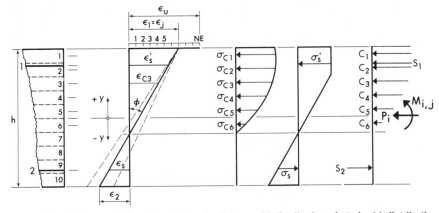

Fig. 8.4 Iterative computation of curvature: (a) Column; (b) distribution of strain; (c) distribution of stress in concrete and steel; (d) fiber forces and force resultants.

divided into a number of concrete and steel fibers perpendicular to the axis of symmetry and parallel to the neutral axis. The ultimate compression strain ϵ_u is also divided into NE segments of strain. These segments are selected as strain increments at the compressed edge of the cross section, as shown in Fig. 8.4. By assuming an arbitrary strain distribution over the depth of the cross section for any value of extreme fiber strain, ϵ_j, the concrete fiber forces C and the steel layer forces S may be computed for the basic stress-strain relationships. Eqs. 8.1 and 8.2 give the forces P and M associated with the assumed strain distributions as

$$\Sigma C + \Sigma S = P \tag{8.1}$$

$$\Sigma(Cy_c) + \Sigma(Sy_s) = M \tag{8.2}$$

By varying the strain distribution for a given value ϵ_j at the compressed edge by a trial and error procedure as shown in Fig. 8.4, the sum of the internal forces P is made equal to the desired external force P_i. By repeating this procedure for all given values of $P_i(i = 1,2, \ldots NP)$ and all given values of $\epsilon_j(j = 1,2, \ldots NE)$ a family of load-moment-curvature relationships results.

Table 8.1 gives values of moment and curvature for three typical rectangular column sections and three typical circular column sections. These values are based

Table 8.1 Moment-curvature for cross sections

ω (1)	Rectangular section[a] $1000\,M/(P_ch)$						Circular section[a] $1000\,M/(P_ch)$					
	P/P_c $=0$ (2)	P/P_c $=0.1$ (3)	P/P_c $=0.3$ (4)	P/P_c $=0.5$ (5)	P/P_c $=0.7$ (6)	P/P_c $=0.9$ (7)	P/P_c $=0$ (8)	P/P_c $=0.1$ (9)	P/P_c $=0.3$ (10)	P/P_c $=0.5$ (11)	P/P_c $=0.7$ (12)	P/P_c $=0.9$ (13)
(a) $Kh = 0.001$												
0.1	27	51	77	77	66	52	22	46	72	72	61	47
0.3	88	84	106	112	105	96	52	68	90	96	89	80
0.5	104	116	135	144	141	134	78	89	108	117	115	108
(b) $Kh = 0.003$												
0.1	80	104	141	159	151		64	88	125	143	137	99
0.3	199	213	236	251	257	302	151	165	188	203	209	195
0.5	305	314	331	344	351	446	225	234	251	264	271	272
(c) $Kh = 0.005$												
0.1	83	120	170	189			75	108	155	168		
0.3	239	274	334	336			200	223	262	268	251	
0.5	395	430	492	488			313	334	369	372	352	327
(d) $Kh = 0.007$												
0.1	83	122	183				79	113	163			
0.3	242	278	343				214	242	279			
0.5	399	435	503				342	365	394			

[a]With $d'/h = 0.1$, $\epsilon_y = 0.002$, $P_c = f'_c A_c$, $\omega = f_y A_s/P_c$, $\phi h = \epsilon_1 - \epsilon_2$, total reinforcement $2A_s$.

on the CEB design stress-strain curves described in Articles 8.2.1 and 8.2.2. A family of load-moment-curvature diagrams from CEB 1972 is given in Fig. 8.5.

In structural analyses the shape of the load-moment-curvature diagrams can be approximated by two or three straight lines. Often, the use of only one straight line (elastic behavior) results in a satisfactory effective bending stiffness EI. The value of EI can be taken as the slope of a radial line in a graph such as Fig. 8.5 using the relationship $EI = M/\phi$. The value of M and ϕ used to compute EI should correspond to the loading stage for which the analysis is to be carried out.

8.3 BEHAVIOR OF SLENDER COMPRESSION MEMBERS

Modern building codes demand that all members of structures shall be designed for maximum and most unfavorable effects of the design loads as determined by an elastic analysis of the structure. Increased loads by means of safety factors and reduced strength values of the materials provide an adequate over-all safety. The design of columns in this way is complicated by two main problems: (1) The instability of the whole structure, which brings additional effects on the internal action due to deflections of the structure; and (2) the potential instability and deflection of each column as an individual member as well.

This section has four principal parts. In the first, some analytical techniques for predicting the load deflection behavior of slender columns are presented. This is followed by a discussion of the major variables affecting the strength and behavior

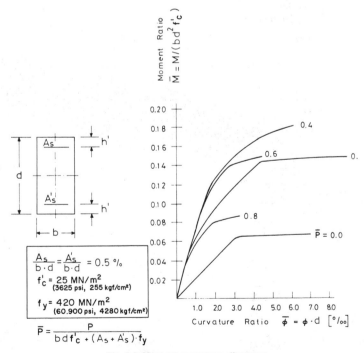

Fig. 8.5 Moment-curvature diagrams

of individual hinged-ended reinforced concrete columns under short-time loads. Article 8.3.3 starts with a discussion of analyses of the effect of sustained loads on columns, and ends with a description of the behavior of columns under sustained loads. Finally, Article 8.3.4 examines the effect of end restraints and frame action on the strength of an individual column. The design of isolated columns will be considered in Section 8.4.

1   Analysis of Load Deflection Behavior of Slender Columns

While theoretical investigations on the stability of steel columns with regard to plasticity had been conducted by Engesser in 1889, and with regard to the geometrical imperfections by Kármán in 1910, there were not any comparable calculations for reinforced concrete columns until Baumann's work (1934). As a result, reinforced concrete columns were designed using buckling factors or long column reduction factors determined experimentally. The strength of concrete, the area of steel reinforcement, the yield strength of steel, and the location of reinforcement were not taken into account. In some cases this design method was unconservative (Kordina, 1959), and therefore better approaches to calculating the capacity became necessary.

The nonlinear moment curvature response of reinforced concrete cross sections results in a system of coupled differential equations not amenable to any direct analytical solution. As a result, other analytical procedures have been used to calculate the load-deflection behavior of slender columns. The more important of these techniques are reviewed below, starting with the most accurate procedures.

Column Deflections by Numerical Integration.   The numerical integration of the curvature from the moments in the deformed system by means of load-moment-curvature diagrams is the most basic calculation procedure used to estimate the deflected shape of columns (Pfrang and Siess, 1964; Breen, 1964). The column is divided into a number of segments and a moment-curvature diagram is developed for each segment for each load level to be considered in the analysis. The deflections of the column are computed by numerical integration using curvatures from the moment-curvature diagrams. This step is repeated using curvatures at each node point corresponding to the moment $M = P(e + \Delta)$, in which e and Δ are the initial eccentricity and the deflection at that node point from the previous cycle. The solution is iterated until convergence is obtained.

Because this procedure requires a fairly complex iterative computation, especially if time effects are considered, simplified calculations have been used. In many cases simplified calculations are rendered possible by assumptions about the behavior of the material or about the shape of the elastic curve.

Deflection Calculations Based on Assumed Elastic Curves.   The numerical integration to estimate the deflected shape can be avoided by assuming the shape of the elastic curve. The maximum deflection at midheight of the elastic curve shown in Fig. 8.6 can be expressed as

$$\Delta_{max} = \frac{\phi l^2}{C} \tag{8.3}$$

in which ϕ = curvature and $C = 8$ if the deflected shape is assumed to be a circular arc corresponding to the initial eccentricities, which are large with respect to the deflections. The value of $C = 9.6$ if the deflected shape is assumed to be a parabola with vertex at midheight, and $C = 9.87$ if the deflected shape is assumed to be a sine wave corresponding to the buckling mode of an axially loaded elastic column.

The Model Column Method developed by Aas-Jakobsen (CEB, 1972) is an example of such a procedure. It will be presented in some detail in the next few paragraphs as an example of a practical method of computing the strength of an isolated slender column.

Model Column Method   A general loading case of the cantilever column is an axial load P, a moment M_t and a horizontal load H at the column top, and a distributed load W (Fig. 8.7), giving a total moment at the column base equal to

$$M = M_0 + P\Delta \qquad (8.4)$$

The deflection Δ of the column top is

$$\Delta = \Sigma\phi z \qquad (8.5)$$

in which ϕ = total curvature along the column, and z = distance from the $\Sigma\phi$-center of gravity to the column top. The curvature for given values of P and $\Sigma M = M_{0x} + P\Delta_x$ is given by moment curvature tables, as explained in Article 8.2.3. The curvature ϕ at the column base is of significant importance in the calculation of Δ, and a good approximation for most practical cases is obtained by taking C in Eq. 8.3 equal to 10 so that

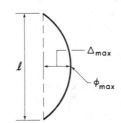

Fig. 8.6 Typical elastic curve

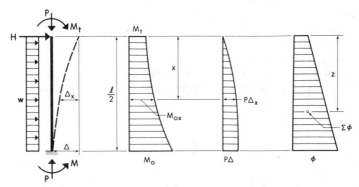

Fig. 8.7 Basic cantilever column: (a) Loading system; (b) first-order moments; (c) second-order moments; (d) total curvature

$$\Delta = \frac{\phi l^2}{10} \tag{8.3a}$$

From the basic moment equation Eq. 8.4 the applied load moment capacity at the column base is obtained as

$$M_0 = M - P\Delta = M - \frac{P\phi l^2}{10} \tag{8.6}$$

The relationship between M and ϕ for a given axial load P is given by the moment-curvature diagram plotted with the solid line in Fig. 8.8. This curve is determined in accordance with the procedures given in Article 8.2.3 and will resemble the curves in Fig. 8.5 or in Table 8.1. The $P\Delta$ moment is given by the dashed line in Fig. 8.8. This is a straight line because Eq. 8.3a assumes that Δ is a linear function of ϕ. The moment capacity available to resist external loads is given by the distance M_0 between the two curves. The computation of the moment capacity is well suited for computer application. Table 8.2 presents a series of moment capacities for two types of cross sections based on this procedure.

A somewhat improved second-order moment can be obtained assuming that the curvature is proportional to the moments. The improvement coefficient β_a of the second-order moment, for the case of constant first-order moment (M_0 = const and $W = H = 0$) then becomes

$$\beta_a = \frac{(M_0/8) + (M_a/10)}{M/10} = 1 + \frac{0.25 M_a}{M}$$

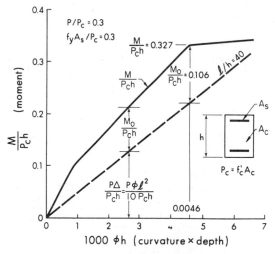

Maximum Moment Capacity :

$$\frac{M_0}{P_c h} = 0.327 - 0.3 \times 0.0046 \times 40^2/10 = 0.106$$

Fig. 8.8 Moment capacity, M_0, of slender column using model column method

The improved moment capacity M_0^{impr} for a constant first-order moment is

$$M_0^{impr} = M_0 \left(1 - \frac{0.25M_a}{M}\right) \qquad (8.7a)$$

The horizontal load H with $W = M_t = 0$ has

$$M_0^{impr} = M_0 \left(1 + \frac{0.17M_a}{M}\right) \qquad (8.7b)$$

The distributed load W with $H = M_t = 0$ has

$$M_0^{impr} = M_0 \left(1 + \frac{0.38M_a}{M}\right) \qquad (8.7c)$$

Table 8.2 External moment capacity $M_0/(P_c h)$

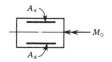   

ω (1)	Rectangular section[a] 1000 $M/(P_c h)$					Circular section[a] 1000 $M/(P_c h)$				
	P/P_c = 0.1 (2)	P/P_c = 0.3 (3)	P/P_c = 0.5 (4)	P/P_c = 0.7 (5)	P/P_c = 0.9 (6)	P/P_c = 0.1 (7)	P/P_c = 0.3 (8)	P/P_c = 0.5 (9)	P/P_c = 0.7 (10)	P/P_c = 0.9 (11)
					(a) $l/H = 0$					
0.1	122	184	196	163	110	101	137	142	123	85
0.3	280	344	352	303	250	212	233	232	209	178
0.5	438	504	511	452	394	314	327	323	300	269
					(b) $l/H = 10$					
0.1	115	163	167	131	79	92	114	112	90	51
0.3	271	322	323	267	211	202	211	201	171	136
0.5	429	482	481	415	351	305	305	290	260	222
					(c) $l/H = 20$					
0.1	102	120	101	72	23	71	66	53	28	
0.3	255	273	236	182	133	176	150	112	79	47
0.5	410	433	391	312	250	278	240	196	143	104
					(d) $l/H = 30$					
0.1	82	60	41	3		47	30	7		
0.3	233	202	128	70	24	141	72	32	2	
0.5	387	358	269	177	109	240	154	70	29	

[a] In which $P_c = f_c A_c$, $\omega = f_y A_s/P_c$, $d'/h = 0.1$, and $\epsilon_y = 0.002$

A top moment M_t with $H = 3M_t/l$ and $W = 0$ has

$$M_0^{impr} = M_t \qquad\qquad (8.7d)$$

Two-Flange Column Solutions. Several authors have idealized the column cross section with the steel and concrete areas concentrated in two flanges. Thus, for example, Warner and Thurlimann (1963) used this model and assumed bilinear stress-strain relationships for concrete and steel and a sinusoidal elastic curve in a study of creep buckling.

2 Behavior of Slender Reinforced Concrete Columns

Influence of Slenderness and End-Eccentricity. It is known that the load-bearing behavior of compression members is affected by their deflections, which in turn are a function of their slenderness ratio. These deflections are determined by means of the second-order theory. Although its application is fairly simple when an elastic and homogeneous material is concerned, it becomes more difficult with reinforced concrete. The difficulties arise mainly from the nonlinearity of the stress-strain diagram of concrete, and the abrupt changes of bending stiffness due to crack formation or yielding of the reinforcing bars. Time-dependent deflections such as creep and shrinkage also require special consideration.

The load-bearing behavior is determined by the bending and axial compression capacity shown by the P-M interaction diagram in Fig. 8.9(c). The figure shows the bearing behavior of three columns of different slenderness: the line labeled "short column" corresponds to a column of very small slenderness. In this case the effect of the deflections of the column on the load-bearing capacity may be disregarded, and collapse occurs when the ultimate load-bearing capacity is attained (material failure).

Line A corresponds to a column of medium slenderness ($l_c/h < 25$) where the deflections reduce the load-bearing capacity, but where collapse is still defined by

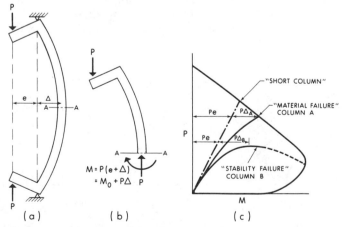

Fig. 8.9 Behavior of slender column: (a) Deflected shape; (b) internal forces at midheight; (c) load-moment interaction diagram

attaining the ultimate strength of material at a point on the ultimate load interaction diagram. The external moment $P(e + \Delta_A)$ is equal to the acceptable internal ultimate moment (see Fig. 8.9). Dimensioning of such a column may be referred to the standard cross-sectional dimensioning procedure, taking into consideration both the additional moment $P \cdot \Delta_A$ and the applied load moment $P \cdot e$.

Line B in Fig. 8.9(c) shows, on the other hand, the load-bearing behavior of a very slender column. Such a compression member fails because, with the increasing deflections of the column, the external moment increases more rapidly than the internal resisting moment. A stability failure results. Material failure is not the primary cause of failure since the collapse point is within the limit-line of the ultimate bearing capacity. As a result, the additional moment $P\Delta_B$ cannot be used for dimensioning with respect to the ultimate load-bearing capacity.

Systematic computation leads to a number of ultimate load-bearing limit-lines [Fig. 8.10(a)], the extreme of which corresponds to the ultimate load-bearing capacity according to the standard dimensioning procedure ($l_c/h = 0$). The other lines represent the capacities of slender compression members ($l_c/h > 0$), each related to the external forces determined according to the first-order theory (MacGregor et al., 1970).

Influence of the Ratio of End Eccentricities.   Figs. 8.9 and 8.10(a) show the load-bearing behavior of slender columns with hinged supports and with equal and unidirectional end-eccentricities (the so-called "standard case of instability"). Here the deflection of the column will always increase the bending moment (single curvature). In practice, however, the end-eccentricities will usually be unequal, often acting in opposite directions. Figs. 8.10(b) and 8.10(c) trace back to papers from Broms and Viest (1961), Pfrang and Siess (1964), Schwarz and Kasparek (1967), and Mehmel et al. (1964), and demonstrate the effects of unequal end-eccentricities on the load-bearing behavior (columns with double curvature).

MacGregor et al. (1970) have summarized these effects as follows:

> A hinged column will be weakened if at any section the sum of the moments due to the end eccentricities or imperfections and the column deflections exceeds the maximum moment in the undeflected column. In a column subjected to symmetrical single curvature the column deflections will always increase the column moments. Thus, in [Fig. 8.10(a)] the

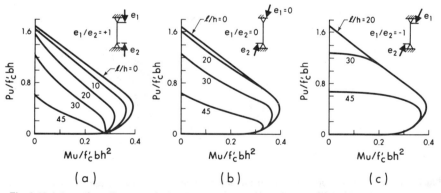

Fig. 8.10 **Interaction diagram of slender columns: (a) Equal end eccentricities; (b) one end eccentricity; (c) equal and opposite end eccentricities**

interaction diagrams for all l_c/h values greater than zero fall inside the interaction diagram for the cross section ($l_c/h = 0$).

In the case of double curvature, however, this will not always be true, since the maximum applied moment occurs at one or both ends of the column while the maximum deflection moments occur between the column ends. This is illustrated by the interaction diagrams for $l_c/h = 30$ in [Fig. 8.10(c)]: This column is weakened by the column deflections for small eccentricities where the sum of the deflection moments and the applied moments lead to maximum moments greater than the applied moments. For larger eccentricities, however, the maximum moments will always occur at the ends of the column and as a result there is no weakening due to length.

Effect of Cross-Sectional Properties.   Other important factors influencing the capacity of a slender column are the concrete quality, steel quality, and percentage of reinforcement, as shown in Fig. 8.11. These graphs are again based upon the standard case of instability.

Broms and Viest (1961) showed that an increase in the proportion of the load carried by the reinforcement led to a more stable column. Thus, columns with high concrete strengths f_c' or low reinforcement percentages ρ, or both, tended to be most

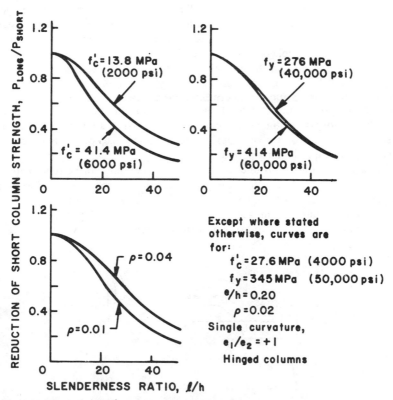

Fig. 8.11 Effect of variables on strength of slender hinged reinforced concrete columns

strongly affected by length. In other words, as the ρ/f_c' ratio is increased, the column tends to be more stable.

The influence of the different factors on the moment capacity of slender columns is given by the moment capacity tables (Table 8.2), in which the most important nondimensional parameters are slenderness l/h, mechanical reinforcement ratio $\omega = f_y A_s / P_c$ and axial load relation P/P_c. Of less importance are the reinforcement cover d'/h and the steel quality.

3   Effect of Sustained Loads

A distinguishing feature of slender concrete columns is the fact that sustained loading causes creep deformations in concrete, and in certain cases inelastic deformations of the reinforcement and cracks in concrete. As a result, the deflections are increased, and consequently the column bending moments are also increased. The creep of concrete under constant moderate stress has a diminishing character. Therefore, under a sufficiently small load for a given element, the increase in deflections, gradually slowing, may in time stop completely.

Thus, there are three distinct load histories of interest to the engineer as shown in Fig. 8.12. First, the column may be subjected to a relatively quickly applied load to failure ("short-time"). Second, the column may fail during the period the sustained load is on the column. The lowest load at which this will occur is called the "critical sustained load." Higher sustained loads will result in failure after a shorter period of sustained load. A column loaded with a sustained load less than its critical sustained load can sustain this load indefinitely. Subsequently this column can be loaded to failure by a rapidly applied load. The resulting failure load will lie between the short-time failure load and the critical sustained load. This loading history will be referred to as a "long-short-time loading history" (see Fig. 8.12).

Methods of Calculating Effects of Sustained Loads.   Different analyses have been used to predict the effects of sustained loads on the strength of columns subjected to a long-short-time loading. In considering such a loading it is customary to assume that creep occurs only during the sustained load period and not during the subsequent rapid loading period.

Dischinger solution.   If one assumes that the column can be represented as a linear viscoelastic element with creep proportional to stress, it is possible to show that the influence of creep can be replaced with an additional permanent deflection of the column. Thus, Dischinger (1937) showed that the creep component which would remain after sudden unloading of the column is given by

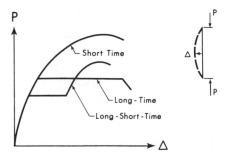

Fig. 8.12 Types of load histories

$$\Delta_k(t) = e\left[\exp\left(\frac{\phi(t)}{P_{cr}/P_s - 1}\right) - 1\right]$$ (8.8)

The final short-term ultimate load capacity of a column which has been subjected to a sustained load for a period t can therefore be computed as the ultimate capacity of a rapidly loaded column with an initial eccentricity

$$e + \Delta_k(t) = e\left[\exp\left(\frac{\phi(t)}{P_{cr}/P_s - 1}\right)\right]$$ (8.9)

A linear viscoelastic analysis obviously ignores many effects of practical importance and gives a highly idealized account of the actual behavior of reinforced concrete members. In particular, the effects of axial load, inelastic action, and cracking on the critical load are ignored. If these effects can be evaluated by some more comprehensive analysis, however, a slightly modified Dischinger procedure can provide a convenient method of expressing time effects for design purposes.

Effective modulus solution. The second general method of analyzing the effects of creep is the effective modulus method, in which the modulus of elasticity is replaced with a reduced modulus. Thus

$$E_R = \frac{E}{1 + \alpha\phi\beta}$$ (8.10)

in which ϕ = creep coefficient for plain concrete; α = function allowing for the restraint of the creep due to the reinforcement; and β = function of the level of compressive stress present. Alternatively, the stress-strain relationship could be redefined increasing all the concrete strains to

$$\epsilon_c = \epsilon(1 + \alpha\phi\beta)$$ (8.11)

Thus, a slender column can be analyzed as outlined in Article 8.3.1 using moment-curvature diagrams based on the modified stress-strain law or the modified E.

This method is theoretically unsound for stress histories involving decreases in stress, because it disregards the stress history and assumes the strain at any time to be dependent on the stress at that time only (Neville, 1970). Generally this is not a serious drawback in the case of columns since the stresses tend to increase during the loading period. In addition, it tends to be inaccurate if the concrete ages significantly during the sustained load period, although this can be overcome (Bazant, 1972) by modifying the term α in Eqs. 8.10 and 8.11. This method is widely used in design analysis because of its simplicity.

Step-by-step analyses of creep effects. Another commonly used group of solutions to creep problems involves the use of iterative numerical solutions of the problem considering the stepwise development of creep in a series of time increments. One such procedure, the rate-of-creep method, is based on the assumption that the creep strains occurring during the time interval $\Delta t = t_2 - t_1$ under the stress σ_c is equal to the creep increase between t_1 and t_2 in a constant-stress creep curve for concrete loaded to the stress σ_c at time $t = 0$ (Neville, 1970). Thus the creep strains in a given time interval are assumed to be independent of the age at loading. For increasing stress the rate of creep procedure is no more accurate than an iterative application of the effective modulus procedure. The two methods tend to bracket the true solution with the rate of creep procedure giving an upper bound of the values of column capacities. If enough time increments are taken the rate-of-creep solution approaches the Dischinger solution.

Alternatively, the method of superposition (Neville, 1970) can be used in the iterative solution. Each stress increment produces a resulting deformation component continuing for an infinite time. The effects of all the stress changes are summed. Thus, creep-time curves are required for the various ages at loading at which an increment is applied. A stress decrement is considered as an increment with a negative sign. Although this procedure is generally considerably more accurate than the rate-of-creep method it is more difficult to apply and requires much more data on the creep properties. Hence the superposition method is not usually used.

Behavior and Strength of Columns Failing Under Sustained Load. The deformations of a reinforced concrete column subjected to a sustained load have four clearly defined stages, as shown in Fig. 8.13.

After application of the load, a decrease in the rate of deformation is always observed for a certain period of time (the first stage). This period may last for several years depending on the magnitude of the load and the characteristics of the compressed element. For example, Tal' and Chistiakov (1952) reported that although the duration of the decreasing rate of deformation of a particular reinforced concrete column was greater than five years, the column failed two years later. Another column from the same series of tests has been under load for 18 years, but its deflection still continues to increase, and, possibly, in time it will fail without an increase in load.

Experiments (Tal' and Chistiakov, 1952) show that such a period may be followed by one with a constant rate of deformation (the second stage). The initiation and duration of this stage depend on the level of the load: the greater the load, the shorter the second stage, and in a number of cases this stage is reduced to a point of inflection on the "deformation-time" curve.

Within the limits of the third stage the rate of change of deflection again becomes variable, but unlike the first stage the rate of deformation increases. The development of such a stage indicates that, sooner or later, the compressed element will fail under the sustained load. One must, however, distinguish this increased rate of deformation from temporary variations caused by changes in the microclimate of

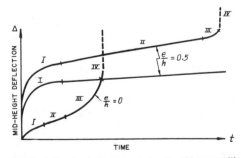

Fig. 8.13 Variation in deflection of slender columns with time

the surrounding environment. In the last (fourth) stage sharp increases in the rates of deformation are observed, which forcefully lead the element to failure.

The duration of the resistance of the element to the action of a constant load depends on the relation of its magnitude, P_s, to the load capacity of such an element under the action of a short-time load, P_{sh}.

In Fig. 8.14 the results are shown of experiments under sustained loads causing failure of elements with slenderness ratios $l/h = 30$ (Tal' and Chistiakov, 1952; Tal' et al., 1969). Simultaneously with the application of the long-time load to the test specimens, control specimens were subjected to a short-time load.

It is apparent that a sufficiently close relationship between the relative level of the long-time load and the period of time to failure of the element can be established, which may be approximated by a linear relationship on a logarithmic time scale. Thus for $l/h = 30$ and $e_0 = 0$

$$\frac{P_s}{P_{sh}} = 0.87 - 0.08 \log t \qquad (8.12)$$

in which $t =$ duration in days of the column's sustained loading.

Eccentrically compressed reinforced concrete elements under the same relative level of long-time load may sustain it for a longer time. In axially compressed elements the development of deformations in time with the identical values P_s/P_{sh} occurs more rapidly than in eccentrically compressed elements, which is mainly related to the greater effect of deflection on the change of bending moment in axially compressed elements.

The reduction in the load-bearing capacity of elements in time depends greatly on their slenderness. With a decrease in slenderness the influence of the long-time loading on the load-bearing capacity decreases, as shown in Fig. 8.15. However, even with a very small slenderness, the long-time strength of elements is always lower than that under short-time loading.

Reduction of the load capacity of elements failing during the sustained loading is due to two causes: (1) The increase in deflection in connection with the development of inelastic deformations; and (2) the reduction in the strength of concrete in time when subjected to high stresses as a consequence of gradual destructive processes in the concrete.

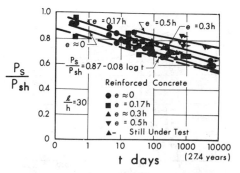

Fig. 8.14 Relationship between time to failure of tested slender elements ($l/h = 30$) and relative level of long-time loading

The investigations of Yashin (1970) and Rüsch et al. (1968) have shown that in elements under long-term loading the compressive strength of concrete can be 0.75 to 0.8 of short-time strength. Investigations of relatively short reinforced concrete columns under axial and eccentric compression confirm this. According to the data from these experiments, failure in the test specimens did not occur in the course of several years with loads less than 0.85 of the short-time failure loads.

Both of the above-mentioned causes simultaneously affect the reduction in the carrying capacity in time. The first is most important for elements of great slenderness, where the initial stress in the concrete is not large, while the second plays a basic role for short elements, although deflections are considerably increased even in these elements.

The amount of reinforcement also influences the load-bearing capacity to some extent. With an increase in reinforcement in the compressed zone the development of deformations in the eccentrically compressed elements is reduced, and consequently the reduction in carrying capacity due to sustained loads is also reduced. With large eccentricities cracking occurs and the actual percentage of reinforcement in the compression zone increases as the depth of the compression zone is reduced.

The tensile reinforcement also has a positive effect. It prevents the free propagation of cracks, and in this manner decreases the general deformation. Moreover, the composite action of the reinforcement with the concrete under tension between cracks further increases the stiffness of the element, in which case the average strain of the reinforcement may be considerably less than the strain of the reinforcing steel at the crack.

Several experimental studies have considered the effect of the age of the concrete at the time of loading on the long-time capacity of slender elements. In general, the older the concrete the greater the time to failure under a sustained high load.

Columns Failing Under a Short-Time Load Following a Period of Sustained Load. Although a constant sustained load will frequently occur in the columns in the lower stories of a building, the load level will only be high enough to cause failure under sustained loads if the column is under-strength. More frequently the loads in building columns consist of long-time (sustained) and short-time loads. In many investigations this loading sequence is idealized as shown by the long-short-time loading in Fig. 8.12. First the structure is subjected to the sustained load, and then after a set period of time it is quickly loaded to failure.

The carrying capacity of elements in such cases depends on the slenderness, on

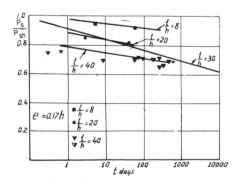

Fig. 8.15 Influence of slenderness on long-time load capacity of columns

the magnitude of long-time load, and on the duration of the sustained load on the element. In short elements, if the stress in concrete does not exceed the long-time strength, additional loading of the element after any duration of sustained loading does not reduce the capacity below the level of short-time capacity at initial time of loading the element with a sustained load. In many cases, the strength of concrete increases with age, and the carrying capacity will be even higher. On the other hand, if the slenderness of the column is moderate to large, the carrying capacity under additional loading will be lower than the initial short-time strength, but it is still higher than that under fully sustained loading for the same duration to failure. Consequently, the total load consisting of the long-time and short-time components acting on the element may vary from the magnitude equal to the carrying capacity of the element during short-time loading at the time t_0 to the magnitude equal to the carrying capacity during completely sustained loading, depending on the relationship between the magnitudes of the long-time and short-time components of the load and on the duration of loading.

In general, the strength of columns loaded in this manner is affected by the same variables as a column failing under sustained high loads, but to a lesser degree.

4   Effect of End Restraints

The behavior of compression members forming part of frame systems, which are connected monolithically to adjacent units, such as girders, thus obtaining elastic restraint, differs essentially from the behavior of a column hinged at both ends. This is because the deflections of the column are restrained by the adjacent members.

Fig. 8.16 shows a restrained column bent in single curvature in a braced frame. An axial load P and an unbalanced moment M_{ext} is resisted by the restraints M_r and the column M_c, as shown in Fig. 8.16(b). The maximum moment in the column is the sum of the column end moment M_c and the deflection moment M_d, as shown in Fig. 8.16(c). The column end moment is a direct function of the relative stiffnesses of column and beam. As the column deflects laterally under axial load and moment, the column stiffness is reduced so that more of the external moment at the joint is resisted by the restraints M_r and the column M_c as shown in Fig. 8.16(b). The maximum moment in the column is the sum of the column end moment M_c and the deflection moment M_d, as shown in Fig. 8.16(c). The column end moment is a direct function of the relative stiffnesses of column and beam. As the column

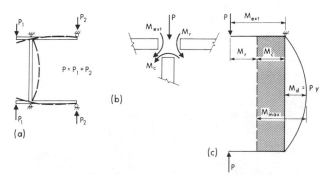

Fig. 8.16 Moments in restrained braced column: (a) Model of restrained column; (b) distribution of moments at joint; (c) moments in the column

deflects laterally under axial load and moment, the column stiffness is reduced so that more of the external moment at the joint is resisted by the beams and less by the column. Inelastic action in the column tends to hasten this reduction in the column stiffness, thus reducing the moment developed at the ends of the column still further. In a strong-column weak-beam frame, on the other hand, inelastic action in the beam tends to throw moment back into the column. The deflection moment is affected by the same variables that affect the column stiffness. An increase in the deflection moment tends to weaken the column.

Fig. 8.17(a) shows a frame tested with the columns bent in single curvature (Furlong and Ferguson, 1966). The columns had $l/h = 20$ ($kl/r = 57$). Failure occurred at Section A at midheight of one of the columns. In Fig. 8.17(b) the load and moment history at Sections A and B is superimposed on an interaction diagram for the column. The moment at B corresponds to the moment M_c at the end of the column in Fig. 8.16(c). Although the loads P and βP were proportionally applied, the variation in moment at Section B is not linear with increasing load, because the column stiffness decreased more rapidly than the beam stiffness. The moment at Section A, the failure section, is equal to the sum of the moment at Section B plus the moments due to the column deflection. The intersection of the interaction diagram and the line for Section A corresponded to column failure.

For short restrained columns, the reduction in the column end moment may be larger than the increase in moment due to deflections. As a result, the maximum moment in the column is decreased below the first-order value and the axial load capacity of the column increases. Generally, such an increase would be ignored in design. For a slender restrained column, however, the deflection moments tend to increase more rapidly than the restraint moments and the column is weakened (MacGregor et al., 1970).

Analyses based on various assumed values of the stiffness EI for the columns and beams are compared by Okamura et al. (1970). This paper shows that significant errors in column moments arise from the assumption of $EI = E_c I_g$ normally made in structural analysis.

The behavior of a column free to sway is markedly different from that of a column restrained against sway, because the swaying column and its restraining beams must resist any lateral shears. The resulting lateral deflections cause second-order P-Δ moments, which increase the tendency towards instability.

A column in a frame without lateral restraint must depend on the beams to prevent sidesway collapse. If the beams are quite flexible, the column will behave

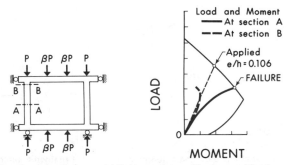

Fig. 8.17 Behavior of column in frame: (a) Test specimen; (b) measured load-moment response

essentially as a rigid body and the frame will deflect laterally due primarily to the bending of the beams. If the restraints are stiff, the column will resist some lateral deflection by bending of the column itself. In either case, however, the frame will form an unstable mechanism if the beams yield and can no longer restrain the columns. It is essential, therefore, that the design of these beams reflect the magnified column end moments which they will be called on to resist (MacGregor et al., 1970). With the presence of even a small amount of lateral restraint the behavior and capacity of the column change significantly, because part of the lateral load is resisted by the lateral restraint.

The effect of sustained loads on the behavior of columns in frames is discussed by Manuel and MacGregor (1967).

Although it does not adequately simulate the response of a column in a frame, the capacity of such a column may be approximately calculated from the capacity of the hinged column by means of an effective length, assuming the linear-elastically calculated effective length as the length of the hinged member. The effective length concept is extensively discussed in Chapter SB-4.

8.4   DESIGN OF INDIVIDUAL COMPRESSION MEMBERS

In developing design recommendations for columns it is customary to derive relationships for the behavior of a hinged ended column bent in single curvature (referred to in this chapter as the "basic column"), and then to introduce modifications to account for other curvature cases and other types of end restraint. This procedure will be followed in the following sections.

1   Hinged End Column Under Short-Time Loads

Moment Magnifier Method.   As the basic slender column is loaded, it deflects laterally as shown in Fig. 8.9(a) and the moments at midheight increase as shown in Fig. 8.9(b). This behavior can be represented by the basic equation $M = M_0 + P\Delta$ (Eq. 8.4), which can be written

$$M = \frac{M_0}{\left(1 - \dfrac{P\Delta}{M}\right)} \tag{8.13}$$

Introducing $\Delta = \phi l^2/\pi^2$ and $\phi = M_u/EI$, the behavior of a slender column can be represented by

$$M = \frac{M_0}{1 - \dfrac{P}{P_{cr}}} \tag{8.14}$$

and

$$P_{cr} = \frac{\pi^2 EI}{l^2} \times \frac{M}{M_u} \tag{8.15a}$$

It is important to introduce M, M_0, P, and EI from the same load level. The load level that is generally used is the ultimate load for the column. When this is done the last term in the equation for P_{cr} disappears, giving

$$P_{cr} = \frac{\pi^2 EI}{l^2} \tag{8.15b}$$

The major problem in presenting such an equation is the method used to define the flexural stiffness, EI, of the column cross section. Experimental, analytical, and statistical studies have shown that EI is a function of the shape and size of the cross section expressed in terms of the gross moment of inertia, I_g; the modulus of elasticity of the concrete, E_c; the reinforcement ratio, ρ_t; the cover on the reinforcement; the degree of cracking, expressed in terms of e/h; and the slenderness ratio l/h (MacGregor et al., 1975). The following equations proposed for EI for short-time loadings take these factors into account in varying degrees:

1. ACI Building Code (ACI Committee 318, 1971) which gives

$$EI = \frac{E_c I_g}{2.5} \tag{8.16a}$$

or

$$EI = \frac{E_c I_g}{5} + E_s I_s \tag{8.16b}$$

2. Soviet Building Code (Gosstroi USSR, 1972) which gives

$$EI = 0.65 E_c \left[I_g \left(\frac{0.11}{0.1 + \dfrac{e}{h}} + 0.1 \right) + \frac{E_s}{E_c} I_s \right] \tag{8.17}$$

Model Column Method. The Model Column Method, derived in Article 8.3.1, is a useful design procedure that utilizes either computer programs or tabulated moment curvature diagrams. Examples of its use are presented in the CEB Buckling Manual (CEB, 1972).

Additional (Complementary) Moment Method. The capacity M_0 of a slender column is given by the capacity tables (Table 8.2). Instead of using these tables directly, the capacity M_0 of a slender column can be referred to the capacity M_u of a short column ($l/h = 0$) using as design equations

$$M_u = M_0 + P\Delta \tag{8.4}$$

$$\frac{\Delta}{h} = C\lambda^2 \tag{8.18}$$

$$\lambda = \frac{l}{100h} \tag{8.19}$$

From the condition that the complementary moment method shall give the same result as the moment-curvature method, the deflection coefficient D is determined from Table 8.2 and given in Table 8.3 using

$$D = \frac{M_u - M_0}{Ph\lambda^2}$$ (8.20)

Usually l/h and P/P_c are known. From Table 8.3 a starting value of Δ/h can easily be found, for example, $\Delta/h \sim 6\lambda^2$. Then a first approximation for ω is determined, and a correct value of D is found from Table 8.3.

A procedure based directly on Eq. 8.4 with $P\Delta = P\phi l^2/10$ is included in the CEB Recommendations (CEB, 1970). Expressions are given in that document for the curvature, ϕ.

The British Standard Code of Practice (BSCP) (British Standards Institution, 1972; Cranston, 1972) has adopted this procedure, but expresses the curvature in terms of concrete strain term ϵ_{cu} modified to account for sustained loads, the yield strain of the steel, and the depth of the column.

The German DIN 1045 (1972) allows the use of an additional moment method for columns with kl/r from 20 to 70. The column is designed for the eccentricity $(e + e_a)$:
For $0 \leq e/h \leq 0.3$

$$e_a = \left[h \left(\frac{\frac{kl}{r} - 20}{100} \right) \cdot \sqrt{0.10 + \frac{e}{h}} \geq 0 \right]$$ (8.20a)

For $0.3 \leq e/h \leq 2.50$

Table 8.3 Deflection Δ computed from capacity table (Table 8.2) with $\Delta/h = D\lambda^2$

ω (1)	Rectangular section 1000 D					Circular section 1000 D				
	P/P_c = 0.1 (2)	P/P_c = 0.3 (3)	P/P_c = 0.5 (4)	P/P_c = 0.7 (5)	P/P_c = 0.9 (6)	P/P_c = 0.1 (7)	P/P_c = 0.3 (8)	P/P_c = 0.5 (9)	P/P_c = 0.7 (10)	P/P_c = 0.9 (11)
(a) $\lambda = 0.10$										
0.1	8.2	6.9	5.8	4.4	3.5	10.8	7.5	6.0	4.7	3.8
0.3	10.0	7.2	5.9	5.1	4.3	9.7	7.6	6.3	5.4	4.7
0.5	10.6	7.2	6.0	5.4	4.8	8.8	7.4	6.5	5.8	5.2
(b) $\lambda = 0.20$										
0.1	5.0	5.2	4.8	3.2	2.4	8.0	5.9	4.4	3.4	
0.3	6.6	5.7	5.8	4.3	3.2	9.0	6.9	6.0	4.7	3.7
0.5	7.6	5.9	6.0	5.0	4.0	8.8	7.3	6.3	5.7	4.6
(c) $\lambda = 0.30$										
0.1	4.3	4.6	3.5	2.6		6.2	4.0	3.0		
0.3	5.3	5.2	5.0	3.7	2.8	7.8	6.0	4.4	3.3	
0.5	5.8	5.4	5.3	4.3	3.5	8.2	6.4	5.6	4.3	

$$e_a = \left[h \left(\frac{\frac{kl}{r} - 20}{160} \right) \right] \geq 0 \qquad (8.20b)$$

For $2.50 \leq e/h \leq 3.50$

$$e_a = \left[h \left(\frac{\frac{kl}{r} - 20}{160} \right) \left(3.50 - \frac{e}{h} \right) \right] \geq 0 \qquad (8.20c)$$

Long Column Reduction Factors.   For many years slender columns have been designed for an amplified axial load P/R and an amplified moment, M/R. Although easy to use for a limited number of cases, such a design procedure does not correctly reflect the behavior of slender columns since only the moment should be amplified. For this reason, such design methods have generally been abandoned during the last decade, and will not be discussed further in this chapter.

Discussion of Basic Design Procedures.   It is important that a design procedure be based on an easily recognizable physical model that approaches the true behavior. Both the moment magnifier and additional moment procedures are based on the basic concept that the lateral deflections of a slender column increase the moments in the column.

Once a basic design model is selected it is necessary to present it mathematically. This involves a compromise between simplicity of application and accuracy of results. The differences between Eqs. 8.16a and 8.17, for example, simply reflect different opinions on the acceptable degree of complexity and different boundaries on the domain of acceptable solutions resulting from different economic conditions and different building traditions. In choosing the final form of design equations the code writer should also be guided by the actual range of variables encountered in the structures to be designed.

2   Modifications of Basic Design Solutions

Three methods of designing the basic hinged-ended column bent in single curvature have been presented. In the following articles the moment magnifier and complementary eccentricity methods will be extended to other deflected shapes and other types of end restraint. Since these two design procedures are closely related, the same modifications for restraints, etc., will generally be usable in both cases.

Effect of End Restraints.   For design purposes a column in a frame can be represented by an equivalent hinged column with a length equal to the "effective length" or "buckling length," kl. The effective length will be less than the actual length of the column in a frame braced against sway, and greater than the actual length in a frame free to sway laterally. If the column remains prismatic throughout the loading history (that is, no localized cracking or inelastic action, etc.), and if the relative stiffnesses of beams and columns are known and remain constant, it is possible to compute the effective length from the theory of elastic stability. In fact, however, the degree of cracking and inelastic action does vary from point to point along the column and its restraints, so that elastic values of k cannot truly be applied to reinforced concrete columns. More study of this problem is required. The concept of effective length factors is discussed more fully in Chapter SB-4.

For design use, effective lengths can be obtained using alinement charts (Johnston, 1966) or equations that approximate the effective lengths. The Jackson and Moreland alinement charts (Johnston, 1966), widely used in North America, are based on the assumption that the column for which the effective length is being computed is an interior column in an infinitely high and infinitely wide frame in which all columns have a constant cross section and axial load. Wakabayashi (1965) has discussed the errors involved in these assumptions.

The reinforcement ratios in the beam and column have a significant effect on the relative stiffness and hence on the effective length (Okamura et al., 1970; Breen et al., 1972). For columns with a slenderness ratio up to $kl/r = 60$ it is sufficiently accurate to use an elastically computed effective length based on Ψ values (see Eq. 8.22) evaluated considering 0.8 times the uncracked moment of inertia of the concrete in the columns, and 0.4 times the uncracked moment of inertia of the concrete in the beams. For longer columns Breen et al. (1972) give guidance.

Since it is difficult to estimate accurately the relative stiffnesses of the columns and restraints, the British Standard Code of Practice (1972; Cranston, 1972) gives simple upper bounds to the effective lengths using Eq. 8.21.

For braced columns use the smaller of

$$kl = l[0.7 + 0.05(\Psi_1 + \Psi_2)] \leq l \tag{8.21a}$$

$$kl = l(0.85 + 0.05\,\Psi_{min}) \leq l \tag{8.21b}$$

For unbraced columns use the smaller of

$$kl = l[1.0 + 0.15(\Psi_1 + \Psi_2)] \tag{8.21c}$$

$$kl = l(2.0 + 0.3\,\Psi_{min}) \tag{8.21d}$$

in which Ψ_1 and Ψ_2 refer to the relative stiffnesses at the two ends of the column given by

$$\Psi = \frac{\Sigma \dfrac{EI_{col}}{l_{col}}}{\Sigma \dfrac{EI_{beam}}{l_{beam}}} \tag{8.22}$$

For unbraced frames Furlong (1971) has proposed, for the effective length factor

$$k = \frac{20 - \Psi}{20}\sqrt{1 + \Psi} \qquad \text{for } \Psi < 2 \tag{8.23a}$$

$$k = 0.9\sqrt{1 + \Psi} \qquad \text{for } \Psi \geq 2 \tag{8.23b}$$

The Commentary to the ACI Code (ACI Committee 318, 1975) suggests the use of the Jackson and Moreland alinement charts and provides Eqs. 8.21a, 8.21b, 8.23a, and 8.23b as simplified approximations to the effective length factors.

For unbraced frames the BSCP (British Standards Institution, 1972) recommends that the average kl/r for all the columns in a story be used in calculating e_a. The

ACI Code (ACI, 1971) accomplishes the same thing by substituting ΣP and ΣP_{cr} for all the columns in a story into Eq. 8.14 when solving an unbraced frame.

For columns resting on foundations, a value of Ψ can be calculated from the moment-rotation response of the foundation by replacing the EI/l terms for the beams in Eq. 8.22 with an equivalent EI/l for the foundation (Prestressed Concrete Institute, 1971).

The problem of determining whether a structure is laterally braced or not will be discussed in Sections 8.5 and 8.6 of this chapter.

Effect of the Ratio of Initial End Moments. The derivation of the basic moment magnifier or additional moment relationships assumed that the column was bent in symmetrical single curvature so that the maximum deflection moments could be added directly to the maximum applied moments. If the maximum applied moment occurs at one end of the column, the maximum deflection and applied moments occur at different sections, and cannot be added directly. Massonnet (Campus and Massonnet, 1956) and others have shown that the design of such columns can be based on an equivalent, symmetrical, single-curvature bending moment diagram which would give rise to the same maximum moment as occurs under the actual loading. In the case of braced columns where no transverse loads are applied between the ends of the column a reduced moment, $C_m M_0$ (MacGregor et al., 1970) can be used in Eq. 8.14 or with the additional eccentricity method. Thus

$$M = \frac{(C_m M_2)}{1 - \dfrac{P}{P_{cr}}} \geq M_2 \tag{8.24}$$

$$C_m = 0.4 + 0.6 \frac{M_1}{M_2} \text{ but not less than } 0.4 \tag{8.25}$$

in which M_1 = the smaller initial end moment, taken as negative when the column is bent in double curvature, and M_2 = the larger initial end moment, taken as positive. For columns not braced against sway, $C_m = 1.0$.

The German concrete design standards (DIN, 1972) require that columns in braced frames be designed for the maximum eccentricity in the mid-third of the effective length. For a braced frame with average end restraints this gives essentially the same value of $(C_m M_2)$ as Eq. 8.25.

The British Standard Code of Practice (BSI, 1972) and the CEB (1970) suggest ways of adding M_0 and M_a at various points along the column so that reinforcement can be varied in very long members such as piers. This should be done with considerable care, since the stability of a concrete column with a variable moment of inertia has not been adequately studied and was not considered in the derivation of Eqs. 8.13 or 8.20.

The improved M_0 given by Eq. 8.7 serves as a means of incorporating this effect into the Model Column Method.

Effect of Load Duration. As discussed in Article 8.3.3, sustained loads have three significant effects on the strength of columns. First, the lateral deflections are increased due to creep, hence weakening the ability of the column to carry additional loads. Second, for very long columns, failure may occur due to "creep buckling" during the period of sustained load. Third, the lateral deflections cause a reduction in the rotational stiffness of the column which, if the column is in a braced frame, results in a reduction in the column end moments that tends to offset the deflection moments. For restrained columns up to $kl/r = $ about 20 in braced frames this will tend to cause an increase in the axial load capacity of the columns, while longer columns will be weakened (Manuel and MacGregor, 1967).

For design purposes there are essentially three major methods of accounting for sustained load effects. These will be discussed in the following paragraphs.

Dischinger procedure. As described in Article 8.3.3, Dischinger (1937) represented the creep deflections in slender unbraced viscoelastic columns by adding a creep eccentricity given by Eq. 8.8 to the actual deflections before calculating the effects of slenderness using Eqs. 8.13 or 8.4. For design use Warner (1974) has developed Eq. 8.26 for the 1972 German Code DIN 1045 to calculate the creep eccentricity $e_c = \Delta_k(t)$. This is

$$ e_c = e \left(\frac{0.8\phi}{\dfrac{P_{cr}}{P_\phi} - 1 - 0.4\phi} \right) \tag{8.26}$$

Effective modulus procedure. The effective modulus method, in which the modulus of elasticity in the EI equations is reduced to account for creep, is widely used in design relationships for the effect of sustained load due to its simplicity. Thus, the 1971 ACI Building Code uses

$$ EI_R = \left(\frac{EI}{1 + \beta_d} \right) \tag{8.27}$$

in which β_d = ratio of sustained load moment to total load moment. This reduces both the steel and concrete terms, because the load transfer from concrete to steel due to creep may cause a reduction in EI if the compression reinforcement yields prematurely. For columns containing moderate to high amounts of reinforcement this procedure tends to become conservative.

In the Soviet Code (Gosstroi USSR, 1972) only the concrete term in the EI equation (Eq. 8.17) is reduced. It is divided by $(1 + 0.5\phi\,\beta_d)$.

The CEB Recommendations (1970) and the British Standard Code of Practice (BSI 1972, Cranston 1972) account for creep by increasing the compression strain in the concrete. In the CEB the increase is a function of the ratio M_ϕ/M_0 and the amount of creep that is anticipated. This is simplified in the BSCP, which calculates curvatures for all loading conditions using $\epsilon_{cu} = (1.25 \times 0.003)$.

The CEB Buckling Manual (CEB, 1972) suggests the use of a stress-strain curve defined by

$$ \sigma_c = f_c' \left[2 \left(\frac{\epsilon}{\epsilon_0} \right) + \left(\frac{\epsilon}{\epsilon_0} \right)^2 \right] \quad 0 \leq \epsilon \leq \epsilon_0 \tag{8.28}$$

in which

$$ \epsilon_0 = 0.002(1 + \phi\beta) \tag{8.29}$$

and β = ratio between the sustained load and the ultimate load.

One major difference between Eqs. 8.27, 8.29, and the Soviet Code expression lies in the value of $\alpha\phi$ (see Eq. 8.11) assumed in each equation. Thus $\alpha\phi$ is taken as one in Eq. 8.27, to allow for considerable restraint of creep by the reinforcement, while α is taken as one in Eq. 8.29, assuming no such restraint. Work is continuing on this question.

Sustained load eccentricity method. Aas-Jakobsen (CEB, 1972) has suggested that column design for sustained loads could be based on

$$M = P(e + e_a + e_c) \qquad (8.30)$$

in which

$$e_c = \frac{\beta\phi l}{350} \qquad (8.31)$$

and β = ratio between the sustained load effect, S_g and the sum of all factored load effects, $\Sigma\gamma S$; thus $\beta = S_g/(\Sigma\gamma S)$.

3   Consideration of Imperfections in Column Design

Due to misalinement, unforeseen loading cases, dimensional errors, or variations in the concrete quality within columns, actual columns are seldom axially loaded and seldom have exactly the eccentricity computed in a structural analysis. As shown in Fig. 8.18, a small unintentional eccentricity causes a significant reduction in the strength of an axially loaded column regardless of the sign of the eccentricity. The same eccentricity has much less effect on the strength of a column with a large applied eccentricity. In slender columns, unintentional eccentricities will tend to be magnified by the effects of slenderness.

Investigations of the effects of the real imperfections are difficult because they must be based on a probabilistic concept and the statistical characteristics of all parameters must be known.

The effects of a number of variables on the strength of slender columns were studied by König and Heunisch (1972) and Heunisch (1973). The parameters varied and their statistical properties are summarized in Fig. 8.19(a). The scatter in the interaction diagram for this column is shown in Fig. 8.19(c). Fig. 8.19(b) shows the

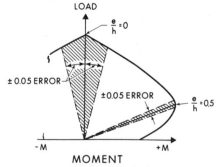

Fig. 8.18 Effect of errors in eccentricity on column strength

proportions of the total scatter due to the different parameters. Variations in the concrete strength and section size account for most of the scatter for compression failures, while variations in the reinforcement location and yield strength account for much of the variation in the tension failure region.

In design regulations the effects of imperfections are considered in two different ways (Kordina, 1969):

1. The effect is assumed to be included among other uncertainties covered by safety factors.

2. The effect of certain prescribed imperfections (such as eccentricity, curvature, and inclination) is supposed to be calculated and combined with the effect of other actions.

Principle (2) is generally used in combination with principle (1), so that when the code prescribes a distinct value of a geometrical imperfection it need not be a "representative" value of the imperfection itself, but may also include other uncertainties. Moreover, a geometrical magnitude is of statistical nature which cannot possibly be described by a single parameter. Under these circumstances any comparison between different regulations must be performed with care.

The following survey of regulations is limited to those instances in which numerical values for geometrical imperfections have been given explicitly. As will be seen, these instances are rare.

The following notation is used: l = buckling length; h = total depth of rectangular cross section in the buckling direction; and e = eccentricity of different forms.

According to the 1970 CEB-FIP Recommendations, sections subjected to

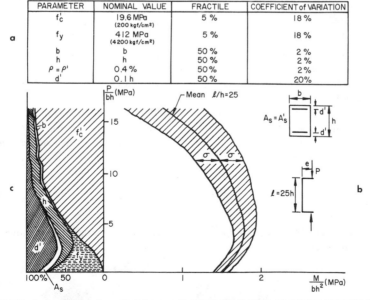

Fig. 8.19 Effect of variations in material properties and dimensions on column strength: (a) Variable parameters; (b) interaction diagram; (c) influences on total scatter

compression must be designed to take into effect the uncertainty of the point of application of the normal load, either by an extra safety factor $\gamma_c = 1.2$ on the material strengths, or by introducing an additional eccentricity e_a as

$$e_a = \frac{h}{30} \text{ but not less than 20 mm} \tag{8.32}$$

The CEB-FIP Recommendations also use a partial coefficient γs_3 on the design load which, among other things, is intended to allow for constructional discrepancies such as dimensions of cross section, deviation of columns from vertical, and accidental eccentricities. Thus the effect of imperfections on the over-all stability is considered by principle (1) given previously, while the effect on the individual element is taken into account partly by principle (1) and partly by (2).

The German concrete regulations (DIN, 1972) prescribe the use of an unintentional eccentricity

$$e_u = \frac{l}{300} \tag{8.33}$$

This unintentional eccentricity represents an important link within the safety philosophy of slender columns, because it is a compensation factor for all uncertainties not covered by the normal safety factors used for flexural members (Kordina, 1969). Primarily, it is intended to balance the uncertainties arising from dimension, direction, and point of application of the external forces; in addition it should cover inaccuracies with regard to the arrangement of reinforcement in the cross section and imperfections in the shape of the column axis.

Assumed distributions of the unintentional eccentricity along the column axis presented in the German Code are given in Fig. 8.20 and depend on the deflected shape of the column. The consequences of imperfections must be given attention also in connection with the whole structure.

The design of a multistory unbraced system taking into account such imperfections of single columns is troublesome. The problem can be simplified by assuming an inclination of the system to be investigated, as shown in Fig. 8.21. This is discussed more fully in Article 8.7.1.

The American Concrete Institute Code Regulations (ACI, 1971) prescribe that all members subjected to a compression load shall be designed for an eccentricity corresponding to the maximum moment that can accompany this loading condition, but not less than the eccentricity e given as

$$e = \frac{h}{20} \tag{8.34a}$$

for spirally reinforced or composite steel encased compression members with $d > 500$ mm, or

$$e = \frac{h}{10} \tag{8.34b}$$

for tied compression members with $h > 250$ mm. However, the eccentricity should not be less than $e = 25$ mm (1 in.) for cast-in-place columns, or $e = 15$ mm (0.6 in.) for precast members, provided that the manufacturing and erection tolerances are limited to $e/3$.

In addition, the material understrength factors for columns are 10% to 20% more severe than for flexural members in the ACI Regulations. Thus, the localized effect of unintentional eccentricity on the strength of columns with $e/h = 0$ is recognized by the minimum eccentricities given, while the effects of other variations are accounted for by the more severe material understrength factors.

In the Swedish Concrete Regulations (Statens Betongkommitte, 1968) the calculation of the load-carrying capacity for an individual column is based on an initial deflection e given as

$$e = \frac{l^2}{8000h} \tag{8.35}$$

Hinged columns are assumed to be up to 0.7% out of plumb. Thus, a hinged column is presumed to lean against its support with a horizontal force of 0.7% of the vertical load. However, the total horizontal force acting on bracing members in a structure is calculated with the columns in one row inclining 0.7% and the rest 0.35%. Thus, for a great number of column rows the average inclination will approach 0.35%. (This is a simplified way of considering both systematic and random errors.)

Structural members serving as bracing shall be designed for a proportion α of the normal force in the column in which

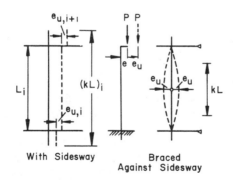

With Sideway

Braced
Against Sideway

Fig. 8.20 Code approximations to unintentional eccentricity

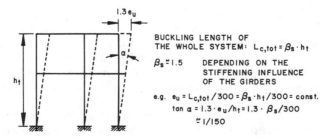

BUCKLING LENGTH OF
THE WHOLE SYSTEM: $L_{c,tot} = \beta_s \cdot h_t$

$\beta_s \simeq 1.5$ DEPENDING ON THE
STIFFENING INFLUENCE
OF THE GIRDERS

e.g. $e_u = L_{c,tot}/300 = \beta_s \cdot h_t/300 = const.$
$\tan \alpha = 1.3 \cdot e_u/h_t = 1.3 \cdot \beta_s/300$
$\simeq 1/150$

Fig. 8.21 System inclination to be substituted for unintentional eccentricity

$$\alpha = \frac{l}{6000h} \qquad (8.36)$$

In the Soviet Code (Gosstroi USSR, 1972) the magnitude of the initial eccentricity e_0 used in designing a column consists of the eccentricity obtained from structural analysis and the accidental eccentricity, which may appear as a consequence of the imperfections of construction. The magnitude of the initial accidental eccentricity is taken to be not less than $l/600$, $h/30$, or 1 cm (0.4 in.).

Construction practices may vary widely in different countries, and hence the uncertainties and imperfections in the structural systems may also vary widely. Therefore, it is important to exercise utmost care in comparing design standards adopted in different countries, particularly with respect to stability of slender elements and systems where the imperfections can play a critical role.

The fact that the sensitivity to imperfections increases with increasing slenderness is a strong reason in favor of selecting for the regulations an expression for the initial curvature that increases with increasing slenderness. Irrespective of whether measurements show a dependency on slenderness, the increased influence of a misjudgment of initial curvature with increasing slenderness ought to be limited.

4 Prestressed Concrete Columns

Columns, wall panels, or piles may be prestressed to resist handling stresses or to reduce service load deflections due to lateral loads between their ends. The behavior of prestressed concrete columns has recently been studied (Zia and Guillermo, 1967; Aroni, 1968). Tentative recommendations for their design have been prepared by a Commission of the Prestressed Concrete Institute (PCI, 1968). Based on the results of these studies the following conclusions may be drawn.

The interaction curves of prestressed concrete columns under combined bending and axial compression resemble the corresponding curves for ordinary reinforced concrete columns. Such curves can be derived by procedures involving stress and strain compatibility in essentially the same way as for reinforced concrete columns.

Wide variations of the column cross section, the concrete strength, and the arrangement of prestressing steel do not have any significant effect on the dimensionless interaction curve.

Partial prestressing increases slightly the load capacity of the column under a given bending moment for axial loads $N_U > 0.55 \cdot f_c' A_c$. For columns subjected to small axial loads, partial prestressing causes a slight reduction in the bending capacity compared with full prestressing. On the other hand, full prestressing reduces the load capacity for axial loads more than partial prestressing. The behavior of very slender prestressed columns is influenced by the fact that prestressing increases the cracking moment and consequently the bending stiffness at service loads. As the column approaches ultimate load, however, cracking will often lead to a large drop in stiffness and stability failures will result.

As Fig. 8.22 shows, prestressing is economic for compression members only in a very small range—roughly within prestress ratios $<0,3$ for medium eccentricities and medium percentage of prestressing steel.

The ACI Code (ACI, 1971) recommends the use of Eqs. 8.14 and 8.16a for the design of slender prestressed concrete, and there is good correlation between measured and calculated capacities using this procedure (MacGregor et al., 1970).

The Soviet Code (Gosstroi USSR, 1972) increases the concrete term in Eq. 8.17 slightly to account for prestressing.

In a prestressed building the prestress may delay the formation of cracks in the end restraints, leading to a more stable structure. It is important to consider the cracked state just prior to ultimate, rather than at service loads, in strength calculations, however.

There is no clear evidence as to the effect of prestress on the sustained load strength of a column. The increase in the compressive stress in the concrete, due to prestressing, causes larger creep deformations. The simultaneous effect of positive factors (the increase in the stiffness of the element, the delay of crack initiation and limitation of their width) and negative factors (increase in stress level in compressed concrete) may affect the carrying capacity of a slender element under long-time loading either favorably or unfavorably. More analyses and tests are required.

5 Lateral Buckling of Beams and Buckling of Plates

Sometimes, even in high-rise buildings, lateral buckling in precast beams may control their design. As yet, these problems are not fully understood, but some solutions have been proposed (Hansell and Winter, 1959; Rafla, 1969; Melhorn, 1970). The influence of concrete cracking in the tension zone may be particularly significant, as shown in Fig. 8.23.

Consideration of plate buckling may be essential to the design of the various sides of shear walls or in the design of precast panel structures. Linear elastic solutions have been well known for a long time. Buckling capacity diagrams for reinforced concrete plates in compression were published by Wiegand (1971) who calculated the buckling loads using an energy method with due regard for the nonlinear material behavior. Calculations based on Eq. 8.24 overlook anticlastic bending and the effects of restraints along the vertical edges. In addition, most equations for the

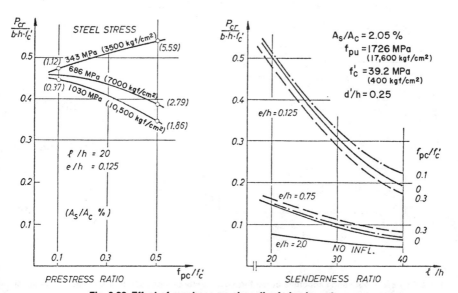

Fig. 8.22 Effect of prestress on strength of slender columns

EI of concrete columns do not apply when the reinforcement is in one layer in the wall. More study is needed in this area.

8.5 FRAME STABILITY

In design, evaluation of stability of the system as a whole traditionally has been approximated by considering stability (or slenderness effects) of individual members based on some estimated (approximate) effective length. Although from a practical point of view this approximation may be convenient and in some cases conservative, from a fundamental point of view it is not satisfactory, because one or more structural elements can become unstable without significant reduction in the stability of the system as a whole, or conversely, the system can become unstable at loads below those producing instability in the individual members with the estimated effective lengths.

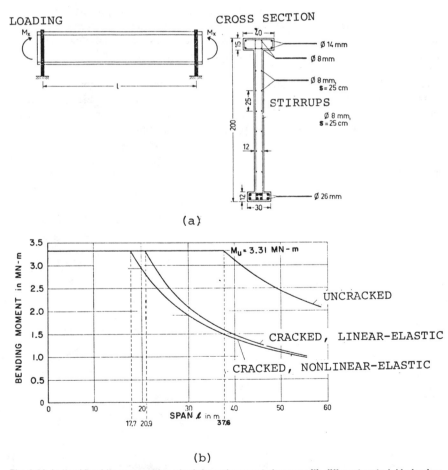

Fig. 8.23 Lateral buckling capacities of reinforced concrete beams with different material behavior: (a) Loading and beam section; (b) critical moments versus span

The problem of the stability of tall reinforced concrete frames has not been adequately studied. Although extensive research has been done on the stability of elastic frames, the strong effect of inelastic action on the critical load of a frame (Wood, 1958) along with the move to higher buildings, lower load factors, and less cladding, has made it essential to study the inelastic instability of practical frame structures.

This section presents a review of analyses of the stability of idealized elastic and elastoplastic frames. This is followed in Section 8.6 by an extensive discussion of the use of second-order analyses in the design of concrete buildings. Section 8.7 summarizes the findings of Sections 8.5 and 8.6 in a form suitable for design. These procedures are based primarily on the use of second-order analyses. Theoretical critical loads are presented in this section for three main reasons: (1) They provide necessary background material for any study of second-order effects; (2) some authors have used elastic stability theory to derive parameters indicating whether second-order effects can be ignored in frame analysis; and (3) for certain limited classes of structures a moment-magnifier solution based on elastic theory can be used.

1 Elastic Stability of Plane Frames

Two basic modes of frame instability must be considered when analyzing a plane frame. Under lateral loads, short moderate height frame buildings will deflect in the shear mode shown in Fig. 8.24(a). Such frames will become unstable in essentially the same mode. In tall slender buildings a part of the lateral deflection will result from cantilever bending of the entire frame involving lengthening and shortening of the columns as shown in Fig. 8.24(b). For such buildings a cantilever mode of instability should also be considered.

The mode of instability for shear wall-frame buildings will tend to lie between the flexural and shear modes.

It should be noted that occasionally an individual column in a frame may become unstable in a braced column configuration before the frame itself becomes unstable. Thus, over-all frame stability and individual column stability must be checked in design.

"Exact" Solutions. Solutions for the critical loads of structures have followed several main procedures:

1. The matrix formulation of the displacement method of analysis. Provided the formulation of the stiffness matrix includes the effects of the deflected shape

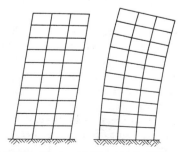

Fig. 8.24 Buckling of frame: (a) Shear mode; (b) flexural mode

of the structure and the reduction in member stiffness due to axial loads, the critical load is that load for which the determinant of the stiffness matrix vanishes (Goldberg, 1965). These methods can be extended to elastic-plastic structures by modifying the stiffness matrix to take the hinges into account (Jennings and Majid, 1965).

2. Various techniques based on the direct use of moment distribution or slope deflection have been proposed. Principally these are based on the use of stability functions and no-sway stability functions (Bleich, 1952; Goldberg, 1954; Merchant, 1956). Frequently a small lateral force is added to detect sway instability under gravity loads.

3. A conservative structure will be stable in a given state if the total potential energy is a minimum with respect to any change of deformation that satisfies the conditions of compatibility. For nonconservative structures the same principle can be applied if the energy absorbed in permanent deformations is included in the potential energy equation (Horne, 1961).

Approximate Solutions for the Critical Load of Tall Frames. The analyses described in the preceding article, while applicable in research projects, are generally not suited for design office use. For this reason some authors have proposed simplified approximate calculations of the critical loads of tall frames.

Shear mode. Based on simple second-order analyses, Rosenblueth (1965), Stevens (1967), and Goldberg (1973) have shown that the critical load of a story in a sway frame is approximately equal to

$$P_{ci} = \frac{K_{li}h_i}{\gamma} = \frac{H_i}{\gamma} \cdot \left(\frac{h_i}{\Delta_{1i}}\right) \tag{8.37}$$

Eq. 8.37 shows the strong relationship between the critical load, P_c, and the lateral stiffness, K_l; or alternatively the deflection index, Δ_1/h, for a given lateral load, H. The term γ ranges from 1.0 for flexible beams to 1.22 for rigid beams. Eq. 8.37 could also be applied to an entire building.

In a tall building the lateral deflections are limited, to prevent nonstructural damage to partitions and motion sickness of the occupants. These limits are independent of whether the building is braced or free to sway. If the lateral deflections of these two types of buildings are similar at a given load stage, as shown in Fig. 8.25, their P-Δ moments will be similar and, as shown by Eq. 8.37, their critical loads will also be similar.

Flexural or cantilever mode. In the design and analysis of buildings which are no more than moderately tall, it is usually sufficient to consider general or frame instability in terms of only the shear mode discussed in the preceding paragraph. In the case of tall slender buildings, however, frame instability may involve a mode combining both flexural and shear deformations. A safe approximation to the combined mode can be obtained by calculating the critical loads for the shear mode and flexural mode separately and then combining the results of the two cases.

Based on the model shown in Fig. 8.26, the critical load on an elastic cantilever column in which the flexural stiffness varied linearly from EI_0 at the base to $EI_0(1 - \beta)$ at the top may be taken as (Goldberg, 1973)

$$P_{0\,(cr)} = \frac{7.83\,EI_0}{L^2}(1 - 0.3\beta) \tag{8.38}$$

Eq. 8.38 could be applied to a cantilever wall or a frame. Unfortunately, there is no simple, direct way to arrive at the proper values to use for the effective flexural rigidity of a frame as an equivalent solid cantilever. However, for the present purpose, one may take the section as fully effective. In this case I is taken to be the sum of the second moments of area of all columns about the bending axis of the building. Knowing that this is unconservative, the engineer may wish to introduce a reduction factor so that the effective I is 70% to 80% of the fully effective value.

Other distribution of stiffness and loading could be considered using coefficients for tapered columns given by Timoshenko and Gere (1961).

Lateral buckling in the combined mode. To obtain an approximate formula for the critical magnitude of the loading in a mode that combines flexural and shear deformations, an analogy is drawn to the case of a uniform vertical cantilever subjected to an axial load applied at the tip. For this case a simple and slightly conservative solution exists (Goldberg, 1973). This solution gives the critical load including the combined effects of flexural and shear in terms of the critical loads for the two component cases, that is

$$\frac{1}{P_{cr}} = \frac{1}{P_{0(f)}} + \frac{1}{P_{0(s)}} \tag{8.39}$$

in which $P_{0(s)}$ = critical load (total load at the base of the frame) for the shear mode (Eq. 8.37), and $P_{0(f)}$ = corresponding critical load for cantilever buckling.

The critical load given by Eq. 8.39 must be assumed to be approximate, but may be useful in the early stages of design and in determining the importance of the flexural mode in comparison with the usually dominant shear or racking mode. It is important to note, however, that modern stiffness analyses include both shear mode and cantilever deflections as a matter of course. If such an analysis is used, Eq. 8.37 will give the critical load directly.

Effect of foundation rotations on the critical load. Assuming that the vertical load is equally distributed, that the flexural rigidity EI is constant, and the foundation rotates elastically in the building shown in Fig. 8.27, it can be shown (Dicke, 1974) that

$$P_{cr} = \Sigma H \times \frac{h_t}{\Delta_1} \tag{8.40}$$

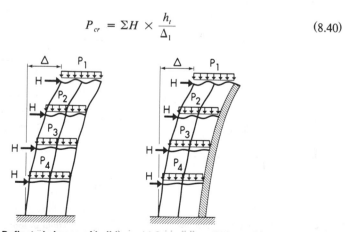

Fig. 8.25 Deflected shapes of buildings: (a) Sway frame; (b) braced frame

in which P_{cr} = critical load of the system; ΣH = total wind loading (equally distributed); and Δ_1 = displacement due to wind loading (first order). This is essentially the same as Eq. 8.37.

If P_0 = total vertical load of the building and $Q = P_0/P_{cr}$ then the total deflection (first and second order) is

$$\Delta_t = \frac{\Delta_w}{1 - \frac{P_0\Delta_1}{(\Sigma H \, h_t)}} \tag{8.41}$$

The total bending moment at the base of the wall is

$$M_t = \frac{1}{1 - Q} \cdot \frac{1}{2} \Sigma H \, h_t \tag{8.42}$$

One can decide if it is necessary to make a more precise calculation. That depends on the influences of the factor EI of the stiffening element and the rotation-stiffness of the foundation on the value of $1/(1 - Q)$.

Summary of Factors Affecting the Elastic Critical Load of Frames. Analyses of tall frames have suggested that the most important factors affecting their elastic stability are:

1. The lateral stiffness of the frame. Eq. 8.37 indicates that when the lateral stiffness of a frame increases, its critical load increases also. The lateral stiffness is strongly affected by the relative stiffness of the beams and columns (Merchant, 1956; Goldberg, 1973).

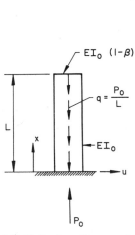

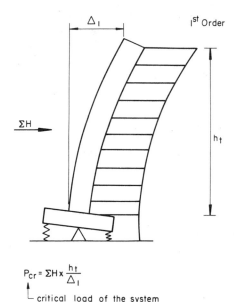

Fig. 8.26 Vertical cantilever model for instability considerations

Fig. 8.27 Effect of foundation rotations on instability

2. The number of bays. If a multibay frame is designed to satisfy the same drift requirement as a single-bay frame, the total lateral load on the frame remains constant while the total vertical load increases. Using Eq. 8.37 Stevens (1967) has shown that the critical load factor λ_c decreases as the number of bays increases until a lower limit of λ_c is reached due to stress limitations in the frame.

3. If gravity loads control the design of both beams and columns the critical load factor decreases as the number of stories increases (Stevens, 1967).

4. Total vertical load. Several studies have shown that the lateral instability of a frame or story is controlled by the total vertical load in the story rather than the load in a single column, since the entire story must fail as a unit. This is illustrated in Fig. 8.28. An exception to this would occur if one column buckled in a no-sway mode prior to the sway instability of the story.

5. Rotations of the foundations of the shear walls in a tall building may cause significant lateral deflections of the structure. As a result, the lateral stiffness of the building and hence its critical load may be reduced significantly.

2 Elastic Stability of Structural Systems

Shear Wall Frame Structures.

Hinged frames.   In the analysis of building frames the vertical loads are often assumed to be carried by the columns and walls, while the horizontal loads are assumed to be carried by only the walls, which act as slender vertical cantilever beams. This assumption is realistic for buildings in which the frame can be assumed

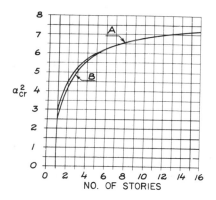

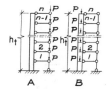

Fig. 8.28 Coefficient α_{cr}^2 for computing total buckling load, P_{cr}, for framework of multistory building of prefabricated beams and columns

to be hinged, as for example when a shear wall braces a steel or precast concrete frame.

When considering hinged frames braced by a shear wall, the total load in a story has more effect on the critical load than the distribution of the loads between the vertical members. Fig. 8.28 gives, for the critical load of the frameworks shown, values of the constant α_{cr}^2 in

$$P_{0cr} = \Sigma P = \alpha_{cr}^2 \frac{EI}{h_t^2} \qquad (8.43)$$

in which EI is constant over the entire wall height, h_t. As shown in Fig. 8.28, the critical load is a function of the total gravity load and is little affected by the distribution of these loads, except to the extent that the EI of the wall may be affected by the axial load in the wall. For a high building α_{cr}^2 becomes asymptotic to 7.83 and Eq. 8.43 converges on Eq. 8.38.

Continuous frames. In concrete shear wall-frame buildings, the frame may provide a significant amount of lateral load resistance and hence will tend to increase the buckling load. Glück and Gellert (1971) and Rosman (1974) have shown that the buckling load of a uniform cantilever wall coupled with a uniform shear resistant frame can be calculated using Eq. 8.43 with values of α_{cr}^2 given in Fig. 8.29. These plots assume the base of the wall is elastically supported and the base of the frame is on a separate foundation from the wall. Curves for other cases are given by Glück and Gellert (1971). The case of tapered walls and frames is discussed by Glück (1974). The terms in Fig. 8.29 are defined as follows: $K_w = EI$ of wall

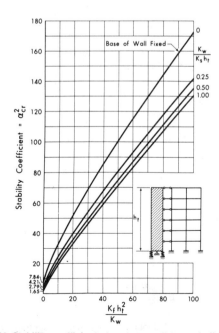

Fig. 8.29 Stability coefficients for shear wall-frame buildings

system; K_f = shear required to produce a unit slope of the deflection line of the frame; and K_s = rotational stiffness of the foundation.

As shown in Fig. 8.29, the presence of a moment-resisting frame can significantly increase the buckling load of a cantilever wall system.

Stability of three-dimensional buildings. Since all tall buildings are three-dimensional, it is desirable to consider instability due to torsional deformations as well as in the two principal directions. The phenomenon of torsional instability may be described as follows. When a structure is given an initial torsion, causing a constant specific rotation θ over the whole height (Fig. 8.30), the point of application of each column load will undergo a horizontal displacement that depends upon the total angle of rotation at the considered height and the distance from the center of rotation. At a height a_i the total angle of rotation is θa_i; with a distance b_j from the center of rotation the displacement of the column load under consideration is $\theta a_i b_j$; and the additional second-order torsional moment is $P_{ij}\theta a_i b_j$. This can be summed over all columns and over the total height.

The additional torsional moments will increase the initial torsional displacements, until either static equilibrium or collapse is reached. This process is analogous to lateral instability by horizontal displacement, and in both cases the total vertical load is involved in the second-order torsional moment.

The resistance to torsion depends largely on the arrangement and shape of the cores or shear walls, assuming the floors have sufficient strength to carry the loads to the cores. Shear walls in the shape of an angle or cross without parallel walls have very low torsional rigidity. Cores with at least two parallel walls can resist torsion mainly by the bending of the parallel walls. Closed core sections have the largest torsional resistance, although this is generally reduced severely by openings for doors, etc.

Cracking of the cores may greatly reduce their torsional stiffness. This should be considered in design. Thus, the CEB-FIP Recommendations (CEB, 1970) suggest

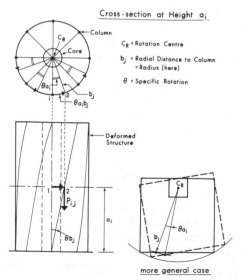

Fig. 8.30 Torsional instability of three-dimensional structure

that the torsional rigidity of normal beams after torsional cracking may drop to 15% to 20% of the uncracked rigidity. Cracking of the cores may be avoided by sufficient vertical loading or by prestressing.

Torsion of the cores is avoided in practice by using two or more cores near the ends of a building.

As a result of limited behavioral studies performed on three-dimensional structures, some general recommendations are proposed (Wynhoven and Adams, 1972):

1. Large degrees of asymmetry in structural arrangement should be avoided, as significant reductions in ultimate load-carrying capacity will result (particularly for heavily loaded, slender structures).

2. Significant increases in load-carrying capacity cannot be expected from increases (within the normal range) in the torsional resistance of the columns and walls. However, if the walls can be coupled so that an essentially closed section is formed, the ultimate strength will be increased.

3. In coupled frame-shear wall structures where the reinforced concrete shear walls form the main lateral load-resisting elements, hinging in the wall drastically reduces the stiffness of the structure and may, in fact, limit the height of the structure in which shear walls may be economically utilized. For this reason the forces and moments in the walls should be determined with all reasonable care, considering the influence of the twisting motion of the structure.

4. The ultimate load-carrying capacity is greatly influenced by the severity of the P-Δ effect caused by the vertical loads. This effect is more severe than in symmetrical structures of similar proportions, and must be considered to obtain a reasonable estimate of the ultimate strength.

Several analyses of the stability of three-dimensional buildings have been developed. Beck et al. (1968) assume a building can be represented by a core capable of resisting torsion, bending, and axial loads and a hinged frame carrying only vertical loads. They present parameters for determining whether torsional buckling must be considered. This analysis, while complex, can be applied to steel frames or precast beam and column structures with a shear core. It will tend to be conservative for cast-in-place structures, however, especially in the case of tube-in-tube structures.

The torsional resistance of the frame increases the torsional buckling load of a shear wall-frame structure. Rosman (1974b) has shown that the torsional buckling load can be computed using

$$P_{0cr} = \frac{\alpha_{cr}^2}{\phi} \cdot \frac{K_t}{h_t^2} \tag{8.44}$$

in which K_t = warping stiffness of the wall system; h_t = total height of the building; α_{cr}^2 is obtained from Fig. 8.29 using $K = K_t$ and K_f = torsional stiffness of the frame; and ϕ is a weight distribution factor defined as the weight moment of inertia about the rotation axis divided by the weight. If the weight is considered as a series of point load q_j located at distances r_j from the rotation axis, then

$$\phi = \frac{\Sigma_j q_j r_j^2}{\Sigma_j q_j} \tag{8.45}$$

3   Stability of Inelastic Structures

In virtually all practical structures a number of cross sections will be loaded inelastically prior to over-all structural instability. Because of the strong effect of plastic hinges on the critical load of frames it is essential to consider inelastic action in the stability analysis (Wood, 1958).

Horne and Merchant (1965) have suggested that the load factor λ_F corresponding to an inelastic sway instability failure can be approximated using

$$\frac{1}{\lambda_F} = \frac{1}{\lambda_c} + \frac{1}{\lambda_p} \tag{8.46}$$

in which λ_c and λ_p are the load factors against elastic buckling and rigid-plastic collapse mechanism, respectively. Eq. 8.46 gives reasonable results for elastic-plastic structures when the sway buckling shape and the plastic collapse shape are similar (Horne and Merchant, 1965; Korn, 1968).

Within any story of a building, a relationship can be derived between the relative story deflection, Δ, and the total story moment as

$$M = Hh + P\Delta \tag{8.47}$$

For most practical frames the solution of Eq. 8.47 can be carried out in two separate stages. First, the lateral deflections of the story caused by the first-order moments, Hh, can be computed for a given set of axial loads, including the effect of the axial load on the plastic moment capacities of the frame members but ignoring $P\text{-}\Delta$ moments. This relationship is plotted with the heavy solid line in Fig. 8.31(a). The term $M = P\Delta$ is a linear function of Δ, as shown by the dashed line in Fig. 8.31(a). The structure reaches a state of neutral equilibrium when these two lines are parallel (Bryson, 1972). It can be stated that a story in a structure will be stable at a given load increment, i, if at that instant the slope of the solid curve, relating Hh and Δ, exceeds the slope of the dashed, $P\text{-}\Delta$, curve or

$$K_j = \frac{dH_j}{d\Delta_j} \text{ exceeds } \frac{P\Delta_j}{h} \quad \Delta_j = \frac{P}{h} \tag{8.48}$$

In the case of a shear wall-frame structure, the lateral load-deflection diagrams for the wall and frame can be plotted as shown in Fig. 8.31(b) and (c), respectively.

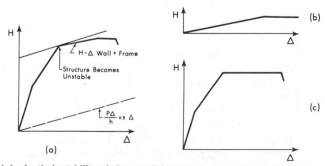

Fig. 8.31   Inelastic instability of shear wall-frame structure: (a) Structure; (b) frame; (c) wall

The solid line in Fig. 8.31(a) is the sum of the H-Δ curves for the frame and the wall. This story will become unstable when the slope of the solid curve drops to less than that of the dashed curve. In the bottom story of a multistory shear wall-frame structure, the relative widths and stiffnesses of the wall and frame for members are generally such that the shear wall will hinge before the frame. As shown in Fig. 8.31, hinging of the base of the wall will lead to over-all instability if the inequality in Eq. 8.48 is not satisfied. Thus, in this type of structure the frame must have a certain minimum stiffness to assure stability.

Because it is generally difficult to derive H-Δ curves for a story, it is desirable to have a stability check in terms of moments. If we consider a free-body diagram consisting of the portion of a building from the top down to a horizontal cutting plane at the base of the columns and wall in a given story, moment equilibrium about an axis in the cutting plane yields

$$M_H + (M_{P\Delta} - M_f) = M_w \qquad (8.49)$$

Once a hinge occurs in the wall in this story, M_w will remain constant for future load increments. Bryson (1972) has shown that the structure will be stable if the term in brackets is negative when the structure is given an imaginary additional sway deflection.

A step-by-step inelastic analysis of steel building frames considering sub-assemblages consisting of a half-story height column and one or more beams has been developed for design use by Lehigh University (Driscoll et al., 1970). Following a preliminary selection of members the strength of each story is checked by calculating a lateral load-deflection curve for each story including the effects of inelastic action and gravity loads. Such an analysis has been applied to concrete structures by Hage (1974).

4 Stability of Structures Subjected to Dynamic and Repeated Loadings

Stability under dynamic conditions will not be dealt with specifically in this chapter. In Chapter SB-4, Kato and Lu summarize problems related to dynamic instability, considering resonance, damping, impulsive loading, and strain rate. In practical structures under realistic dynamic conditions, such as earthquakes or tornadoes, these problems are usually of relatively little significance. Kato and Lu also discuss the more significant instability effects related to cyclic reversals of extreme loads in the inelastic range. Their discussion is focused primarily on steel structures. Cyclic reversal of extreme loads may be more significant for instability of reinforced concrete structures than for steel structures.

Two problems must receive special attention in the investigations of time-dependent effects on stability. First is the effect on stiffness of cyclic reversals of loading in the inelastic range. Tests show that stiffness varies during each cycle, as indicated by the typical hysteresis loops of load versus deformation characteristics. While for steel structures these loops may be defined by a simple elastoplastic law, for reinforced concrete structures excursions into inelastic range result in cumulative damage (increase in crack widths and local deterioration in bond or anchorage) and in degradation of stiffness, which effects are highly sensitive to prior history of loading. Consequently, stiffness cannot be defined by a simple elastoplastic law, and determination of stability of reinforced concrete frames under dynamic conditions requires proper modeling of variable stiffness and of loading history. This is discussed more fully in Chapter CB-6.

The second problem deals with initial conditions at the onset of extreme lateral loads. Two types of influences must be considered here: (1) Residual stresses and deformations in the structure, associated with previous service conditions —sustained loading and environment; and (2) residual stresses and deformations associated with previous confrontation with extreme overloads (hurricanes, earthquakes, and the like).

For example, in one case of a single-story one-bay portal frame studied by Bresler, creep under service load and shrinkage produced stresses in steel reinforcement and cracking in concrete which significantly reduced the frame stiffness. Under a lateral load, after several reversals, the sidesway displacement increased by 60% compared with that calculated for the same frame disregarding effects of creep and shrinkage.

A condition that may be even more important is the residual state of a reinforced concrete building which has been repaired after suffering moderate damage in a severe earthquake. Preliminary studies of typical repaired elements indicate that hairline cracks in concrete and damage due to slip between steel reinforcement and concrete were not repaired. Although typical repair may restore original load-carrying capacity or original stiffness, exposure of the repaired system to a severe earthquake is likely to cause rapid deterioration of stiffness, and consequently aggravate the danger of instability under recurring dynamic loadings.

8.6 SECOND-ORDER ANALYSIS OF FRAMES

In a second-order analysis the equilibrium equations are formulated for the deformed frame. Because this leads to a nonlinear relationship between loads and displacements, it is essential that the loads corresponding to the failure state be used in the analysis.

The displacements and hence the second-order effects depend on the assumed member stiffnesses which must correspond to the assumed failure state, considering nonlinear behavior. In the design phase it is desirable to check that each section has at least the stiffness assumed in the analysis.

Five separate procedures for computing second-order moments and deflections are presented in Articles 8.6.1 to 8.6.5. Limits on the use of second-order analyses are presented in Article 8.6.6.

1 Moment Magnifier Solution for Second-Order Effects

The method of analysis described in this article is approximate and is primarily of use in preliminary design. Generally the P-Δ analyses described in Article 8.6.2 are better than the moment magnifier solution.

The basic assumption in this method of analysis is that the shapes of the first- and second-order deflections are similar. The bending moment, M, at the base of the column shown in Fig. 8.32 is

$$M = Hh + \Sigma P\Delta_2 \qquad (8.50)$$

If the critical load for this column is P_{cr} and $Q = \Sigma P / P_{cr}$ then (Timoshenko and Gere, 1961)

$$\Delta_2 = \left(\frac{1}{1 - Q} \right) \Delta_1 \tag{8.51}$$

and

$$M = Hh + \Sigma P \left(\frac{1}{1 - Q} \right) \Delta_1 \tag{8.52}$$

But from Eq. 8.37 or 8.40

$$P_{cr} = \frac{Hh}{\Delta_1} = \frac{\Sigma P}{Q} \tag{8.40}$$

Therefore, the moment M is

$$M = Hh + \left(\frac{Q}{1 - Q} \right) Hh = Hh \left(\frac{1}{1 - Q} \right) \tag{8.53}$$

Thus, for a given loading pattern leading to first-order frame moments, M_0, the total second-order moment at any point in the frame is given by

$$M = M_0 F \tag{8.54}$$

in which

$$F = \left(\frac{1}{1 - \dfrac{P_0}{P_{0cr}}} \right) = \left(\frac{1}{1 - Q} \right) \tag{8.55}$$

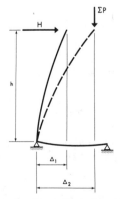

Fig. 8.32 Second-order moments in cantilever column

P_0 = total vertical load at the base of the frame, and P_{0cr} = corresponding critical load of the frame.

The critical load depends on the geometry of the frame, the distribution of the vertical loads, and the lateral stiffness of the frame. Once again it should be noted that the lateral stiffness must correspond to the failure state being considered, including any inelastic action that develops before failure.

The general procedure in using this method to compute second-order forces is to:

1. Compute first-order moments due to lateral loads throughout the structure.

2. Evaluate the critical loads of the frame and walls using the appropriate equations from Articles 8.5.1 and 8.5.2.

3. Evaluate the moment magnifiers for deflections in each principal direction and for torsional deflections.

4. Amplify the first-order moments as required and add to these the moments due to vertical loads.

The same moment magnifier can be applied to all sections of the frame, including beams, columns, and walls. This solution can be used for cast-in-place concrete structures, or steel or precast reinforced or prestressed concrete structures braced by a cast-in-place core.

2   The P-Δ Method

Iterative P-Δ Analyses.   For tall buildings designed for normal deflection limitations, an acceptable estimate of the second-order shears, moments, and forces in an elastic structure can be obtained by an iterative calculation including the "sway forces" induced by the P-Δ moments (Beck and König, 1966; Springfield and Adams, 1972; Wynhoven and Adams, 1972; MacGregor et al., 1972; Hage, 1974). The computation of sway forces for the combined loading case is relatively simple. The lateral and vertical loads are applied to the structure and the relative lateral displacements Δ_i in each story are computed by the first-order elastic analysis, ignoring P-Δ terms. The additional story shears due to the vertical loads are computed as $(\Sigma P_i \Delta_i)/h_i$ in which ΣP_i represents the sum of the axial forces in all the columns of the ith story, as shown in Fig. 8.33. At a given floor level, the sway force will be the algebraic sum of the story shears from the columns above and below the floor, as shown in Fig. 8.33. The sway forces are added to the applied

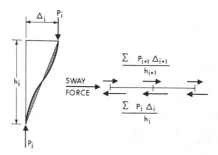

Fig. 8.33 Calculation of sway force

lateral loads and the total forces and moments in the structure can be computed. Generally, one or two cycles of iteration are adequate for elastic structures of reasonable stiffness. This procedure is also discussed in Chapter SB-4.

Limitations on the use of P-Δ analyses are discussed later in this section.

Direct P-Δ Analyses. Although the iterative P-Δ analysis just described has the advantage of being easily understood, several cycles of iteration may be required for convergence in very slender structures.

Fey (1966), Parme (1966), and Goldberg (1973) have all shown that the total second-order deflection, Δ_{2i}, in the ith story of an elastic structure can be computed using Eq. 8.51, which combines Eq. 8.40 and the traditional deflection magnifier equation giving

$$\Delta_{2i} = \frac{\Delta_{1i}}{1 - \dfrac{\Sigma P_i \Delta_{1i}}{H h_i}} \qquad (8.56)$$

in which H = shear in the story due to the applied lateral loads, and h_i = height of the ith story. A second-order analysis suitable for design would include:

1. A first-order analysis to determine Δ_{1i} in each story.

2. Computation of the second-order deflection in each story using Eq. 8.56.

3. Evaluation of the sway forces as outlined previously but using the story deflection, Δ_{2i}. The sway forces may be positive or negative.

4. Another first-order frame analysis for the frame subjected to the applied vertical and lateral loads, plus the sway forces from step 3, gives the second-order moments and forces.

Eq. 8.56 also provides an approximation to the critical load, which may be defined as the load at which the denominator of the equation vanishes. Thus an approximation to the magnitude of the critical load at the ith story is

$$P_{ci} \simeq \frac{H h_i}{\Delta_{1i}}$$

and this is essentially the same as Eq. 8.40 presented earlier.

Limitations on the Use of the P-Δ Analysis. The accuracy of the iterative P-Δ procedure and Eq. 8.56 was studied by Hage (1974) for a large number of free-to-sway reinforced concrete column-beam subassemblages. If the EI used to calculate the deflections corresponded to the column considered, Eq. 8.56 was found to give accurate results provided that the columns developed material failures and not instability failures. (See Fig. 8.9, Article 8.3.2.) The EI value is of major importance in any stability analysis and will be discussed more fully in Section 8.7.

All the stability failures studied by Hage (1974) developed at sway deflections greater than $\Delta/L = 1/200$ at ultimate or $\Delta/L = 1/300$ at working loads. Since both of these values exceed the deflection limits required for serviceability reasons, the P-Δ method and Eq. 8.56 can be used for practical high-rise buildings.

The iterative P-Δ procedure will tend to underestimate the deflections and moments since this calculation converges on the answer from below. When the iteration process converges slowly the deflections obtained from two successive cycles may not differ much, but they may still be 5% to 10% below the final deflection. If the iteration process is considered to have converged when the deflection in the nth cycle ($n = 0$ for the first-order analysis) is within 5% of the final deflection, Eq. 8.56 can be rearranged (Hage, 1974) to read

$$n + 1 = \frac{-1.30}{\log \left(\dfrac{\Sigma P_i \Delta_{1i}}{H_i h_i} \right)} \tag{8.57}$$

For the particular case where n is not to exceed 2

$$\left(\frac{\Sigma P_i \Delta_{1i}}{H_i h_i} \right) \leq 0.37 \tag{8.58}$$

must be satisfied.

Alternatively, the check of the iteration process may also be based on the convergence of the moments rather than the deflections, and for convergence of moments within 5% the convergence criterion may be expressed as

$$\left(\frac{\Sigma P_i \Delta_{1i}}{H_i h_i} \right)^{n+1} \leq 0.05 \tag{8.59}$$

3 Negative Bracing Member Method

The iterations required in the P-Δ solution can become tedious. Nixon et al. (1975) have shown that a direct solution of the second-order deflections and moments can be obtained using a standard first-order structural analysis program, by inserting a fictitious diagonal brace of negative area in each story as shown by the dashed lines in Fig. 8.34. The area of this brace can be obtained from an examination of the stiffness matrix for the column shown in Fig. 8.35. The slope-deflection equations for this column are

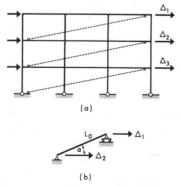

(a)

(b)

Fig. 8.34 Frame with negative bracing members

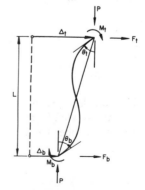

Fig. 8.35 Deflected column

$$\mathbf{M_t} = \frac{EI}{L}\left[4\theta_t + 2\theta_b - \frac{6\Delta_t}{L} + \frac{6\Delta_b}{L}\right] \tag{8.60a}$$

and

$$\mathbf{M_b} = \frac{EI}{L}\left[2\theta_t + 4\theta_b - \frac{6\Delta_t}{L} + \frac{6\Delta_b}{L}\right] \tag{8.60b}$$

From statics

$$\mathbf{F_t} = -\frac{[M_t + M_b]}{L} - \frac{P[\Delta_t - \Delta_b]}{L} \tag{8.61a}$$

$$\mathbf{F_b} = -\mathbf{F_t} \tag{8.61b}$$

Substituting Eq. 8.60 into Eq. 8.61 and writing the equations in matrix form gives

$$\begin{bmatrix} M_t \\ M_b \\ F_t \\ F_b \end{bmatrix} = \begin{bmatrix} \dfrac{4EI}{L} & \dfrac{2EI}{L} & -\dfrac{6EI}{L^2} & \dfrac{6EI}{L^2} \\[2mm] \dfrac{2EI}{L} & \dfrac{4EI}{L} & -\dfrac{6EI}{L^2} & \dfrac{6EI}{L^2} \\[2mm] -\dfrac{6EI}{L^2} & -\dfrac{6EI}{L^2} & \dfrac{12EI}{L^3} - \dfrac{P}{L} & -\dfrac{12EI}{L^3} + \dfrac{P}{L} \\[2mm] \dfrac{6EI}{L^2} & \dfrac{6EI}{L^2} & -\dfrac{12EI}{L^3} + \dfrac{P}{L} & \dfrac{12EI}{L^3} - \dfrac{P}{L} \end{bmatrix} \begin{bmatrix} \theta_t \\ \theta_b \\ \Delta_t \\ \Delta_b \end{bmatrix} \tag{8.62}$$

This is a second-order stiffness matrix because equilibrium is based on the deflected shape.

If a first-order program is used to analyze the frame shown in Fig. 8.34(a), the stiffness matrix for a column would contain all the terms in Eq. 8.62 except the four involving P/L. If the structure contained bracing members, as shown by the dashed lines in Fig. 8.34(a), the program would generate a stiffness matrix corresponding to the degrees of freedom shown in Fig. 8.34(b), that is

$$\begin{bmatrix} F_t \\ F_b \end{bmatrix} = \frac{AE}{L_0}\begin{bmatrix} \cos^2\alpha & -\cos^2\alpha \\ -\cos^2\alpha & \cos^2\alpha \end{bmatrix}\begin{bmatrix} \Delta_t \\ \Delta_b \end{bmatrix} \tag{8.63}$$

and add these terms to the over-all stiffness matrix in the same position that the P/L terms would occupy in the second-order matrix. The required area of fictitious bracing member for a given story is obtained by equating $AE/L_0 \cos^2\alpha$ and P/L, giving

$$A = -\frac{P}{L}\frac{L_0}{E\cos^2\alpha} \tag{8.64}$$

in which P would be the sum of the axial loads in the columns in the story.

The area found by Eq. 8.64 is generally very small and, as shown by Eq. 8.64, is negative. Ordinarily, bracing members stiffen the structure; the artificial bracing members make the structure more flexible. The increased flexibility is due to the P-Δ effect.

This analysis gives a direct calculation of the deflections and moments. Axial loads and shears are slightly in error, however, because of the horizontal and vertical components of the force in the bracing members, but can be easily corrected using statics. The effect of the vertical component can be reduced using long bracing members, as shown by the dashed lines in Fig. 8.34(a), since the horizontal component (that is, the $\Sigma P\Delta/L$ term) is constant for a given story.

4   Second-Order Finite Element Analysis

The solution of the second-order moments and forces can be obtained by means of the finite element method (Aas-Jakobsen and Grenacher, 1974).

A frame may be visualized as an assemblage of elements interconnected at their ends which are referred to as nodal points or nodes. If the force displacement relations for each element are known, the equilibrium configuration of the complete structure can be expressed in terms of the nodal displacements. The force-displacement relationship for the element shown in Fig. 8.36 can be written as

$$[K]\{w\} = \{P\} \qquad (8.65a)$$

in which $\{w\}$ is the displacement vector of the element and $\{P\}$ the corresponding force vector

$$\{w\} = \begin{bmatrix} w_1 \\ w_2 \\ w_3 \\ w_4 \\ w_5 \\ w_6 \end{bmatrix} \quad \{P\} = \begin{bmatrix} P_1 \\ P_2 \\ P_3 \\ P_4 \\ P_5 \\ P_6 \end{bmatrix} \qquad (8.65b)$$

Applying standard finite element techniques, the stiffness matrix $[K]$ can be written as

$$[K] = [K_1] + [K_2] \qquad (8.66)$$

in which $[K_1]$ is the first-order stiffness matrix, $[K_2]$ is the nonlinear geometrical stiffness matrix, and $[K_1]$ and $[K_2]$ are given in Fig. 8.37.

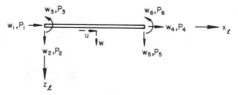

Fig. 8.36 Element in local coordinates

If the element is inclined at an angle θ with the x-axis, as shown in Fig. 8.38, the given stiffness matrix above relates to the local coordinates x_1-z_1. The global stiffness matrix $[K]$ in the x-z coordinate system is then given by

$$[K] = [R]^T[K_1][R] \tag{8.67}$$

in which $[K_1]$ is the local stiffness matrix given in Fig. 8.37, and $[R]$ is the transformation matrix relating local displacements $\{w_1\}$ and global displacements $\{w\}$, or local loads $\{P_1\}$ and global loads $\{P\}$ as follows:

$$\{w_1\} = [R]\{w\}$$
$$\{P_1\} = [R]\{P\} \tag{8.68}$$

and $[R]$ is given in Fig. 8.39. The global element stiffness matrix $[K] = [K_1] + [K_2]$ is given in Fig. 8.40.

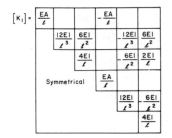

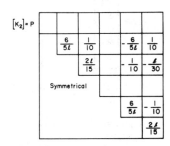

Fig. 8.37 Local element stiffness matrix $[K] = [K_1] + [K_2]$

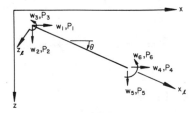

Fig. 8.38 Global forces and displacements

Similar to the force-displacement relationship for the element, the force-displacement relationship for the complete structure, or the complete system of elements, can be written as

$$[K]\{w\} = \{P\} \tag{8.69}$$

in which $\{w\}$ now contains all nodal displacements and $\{P\}$ all nodal loads.

The system stiffness matrix for the complete structure is obtained by superposition of the individual element stiffness matrices.

When the system stiffness matrix $[K]$ and the load matrix $\{P\}$ have been established, the system of equations is adjusted according to the given boundary conditions. If some displacement, for instance w_j, is identical to zero, this can be taken into account in a simple manner by replacing the diagonal stiffness coefficient K_{jj} by a large number, say 10^{50}.

The solution of the linear system of equations, Eq. 8.69, is most efficiently carried out taking into account the symmetry and the banded structure of the system stiffness matrix.

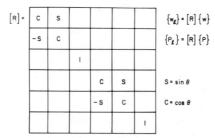

Fig. 8.39 Transformation matrix $[R]$

$[R] =$ matrix with entries c, s (row 1), $-s, c$ (row 2), 1, c, s, $-s, c$, 1

$\{w_\ell\} = [R]\{w\}$
$\{P_\ell\} = [R]\{P\}$

$S = \sin\theta$
$C = \cos\theta$

Fig. 8.40 Global element stiffness matrix $[K] = [K_1] + [K_2]$

It should be noted that the axial force P must be known in order to evaluate the element matrix $[K_2]$ in Fig. 8.37. The axial force is usually not known in advance, and an iterative procedure must be used. In the first cycle N is chosen equal to zero and the first-order forces are calculated. In the second cycle the axial forces found in the first cycle are used.

Usually the axial forces are practically not influenced by the second-order effects, such that two cycles are generally sufficient.

When the displacements have been determined, the element forces are found by substituting $\{w\}$ back into Eq. 8.65. It should be noted that $[K]$ in Eq. 8.65 is the local element stiffness matrix given in Fig. 8.37. The global displacements are transformed into local displacements according to Eq. 8.68.

The accuracy of the described method was studied by K. Aas-Jakobsen (1973). The calculated moments for frames permitted to sway were in excellent agreement with the exact ones when the columns were represented by one element.

For braced columns and frames, the errors in moments were as large as 10% when the columns were represented by one element, but vanished when the columns were divided into two elements.

5 "Exact" Second-Order Frame Analysis

The two main difficulties in the analysis of slender reinforced concrete frames are due to the influence of displacements on the equilibrium of the frame, and the nonlinear stress-strain relations for the materials. Such an analysis, while applicable in research projects, is generally not suited for design office use. Beck and Bubenheim (1972) and K. Aas-Jakobsen (1973) developed practical design procedures for multistory frames by slight modification of the procedure outlined in the following (taken from Aas-Jakobsen and Grenacher, 1974).

The load-carrying capacity of a frame with given cross sections and reinforcements is calculated in successive steps up to the maximum capacity.

Fig. 8.41 shows the flow chart used for determining a point on the load-displacement curve. The procedure starts with assumed rigidities for all elements. In a second-order elastic analysis, the elastic forces M and P, and the strain distribution expressed by middle strain ϵ_M and curvature $(1/r)$, are determined for all elements. The internal forces M_i and P_i are determined in a cross-sectional analysis based on the strain distribution found in the elastic analysis and the real material properties (see Section 8.2). If the elastic and internal forces differ by more than a predefined convergence criterion for any of the elements, the procedure is repeated based on improved (secant) rigidities.

The maximum load capacity of slender reinforced concrete frames is associated with instability, as indicated in Fig. 8.42. In a load controlled procedure where the external load is increased in steps, poor convergence develops near the maximum load. The unloading part of the curve cannot be calculated. In a displacement controlled procedure, where a characteristic displacement is increased step by step and the corresponding load is calculated, no problems of convergence are encountered.

An "exact" second-order frame analysis of a reinforced concrete structure would include the following factors, many of which can be disregarded in an analysis for design purposes:

1. Realistic axial load-moment-curvature $(P\text{-}M\text{-}\phi)$ relationships should be used

to define member properties at various loading stages. For practical engineering analyses the theoretical curves may be simplified to elastic-plastic or other similar diagrams.

2. The changes in the stiffnesses of individual members due to plastic hinging or inelastic action should be considered. Beck (1969) has modified the slope-deflection equations for members having elastic-strain hardening P-M-ϕ diagrams. Jennings and Majid (1965) and others have done the same for elastoplastic P-M-ϕ diagrams. Goel and Berg (1968) and others have used continuously curved Ramberg-Osgood functions to represent the P-M-ϕ diagrams for frame members.

3. The changes in the member stiffness coefficients C and S in the slope-deflection equations due to axial forces (Bleich, 1952; Goldberg, 1954)

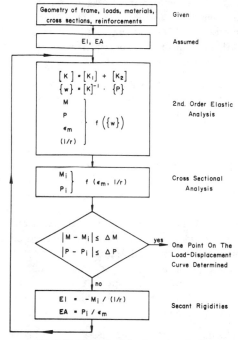

Fig. 8.41 Flow chart for frame analysis

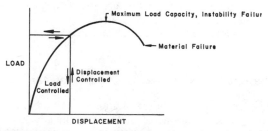

Fig. 8.42 Load displacement curve for slender reinforced concrete frame

theoretically should be considered, but in most practical analyses can be disregarded. The error due to disregarding this effect seldom if ever exceeds 8% in tall frames, and is less than 1% for more than 90% of all building columns.

4. The P-Δ moments resulting from the interaction of the lateral deflections and vertical loads are the major source of second-order moments. Techniques for including the P-Δ effect are presented for elastic and inelastic structures by a number of authors.

5. Changes in the lengths of members due to axial shortening and curvature shortening may be included. Korn and Galambos (1968) have shown that curvature shortening has a negligible effect. Axial shortening of the beams can also be disregarded, since this will lead to a slightly conservative solution. On the other hand, axial shortening of the columns may lead to significant lateral deflections in the elastic range. This effect becomes less pronounced after beam hinges occur. The ACI Tall Buildings Committee (ACI Committee 442, 1971) has suggested that axial shortening effects should be included directly in the member stiffness matrices, or may be accounted for approximately (Goldberg, 1973).

6. Beam moments due to gravity loads may have a significant effect on the stability of strong-column weak-beam structures. This is especially true if hinges occur at the leeward ends of beams due to combined gravity and wind loads.

7. In reinforced concrete structures the effects of the widths of joints on the stiffnesses and moments in the members entering the joints and the effects of joint distortions can also affect behavior. Neglect of joint width will tend to an overestimate of the lateral deflections which may be significant in modern concrete buildings. Methods of accounting for this are given by ACI Committee 442 (1971). At high lateral loads shear cracks and bond distress may occur in the beam-column joints in reinforced concrete structures. The resulting sway deflections will frequently be 5% to 10% of those due to bending of the columns and may lead to significant P-Δ moments, especially under seismic load reversals. If ties are provided in the joints the lateral deflections due to joint deformation will be reduced and can generally be ignored except in seismic regions.

8. Shearing deformations may sometimes be a problem (Goldberg, 1966) but are generally ignored in design analyses.

9. Rotations of the foundations of the shear walls in a tall building may cause significant lateral deflections of the structure. As a result, the lateral stiffness of the building and hence its critical load may be reduced significantly, as discussed in Article 8.5.1.

6 Limits on the Application of Second-Order Analyses

Since a second-order analysis requires additional analysis time and expenditures, it is desirable to have some means of determining in advance whether such an analysis is required. In addition, it is desirable to control the stiffness of a building such that the second-order effects are not too significant in the over-all response of the building. Some techniques proposed for handling these problems are examined in this article.

Eq. 8.54 expresses the second-order moment M as a function of the first-order M_0 and a moment magnifier, $F = 1/(! - Q)$ in which $Q = \Sigma P/P_{cr}$. As Q gets small, F approaches one and hence a lower limit on Q is not required although, if Q is less than 0.05, the second-order moments will not be more than 5% greater than the first-order moments and the second-order effects could be ignored in design.

On the other hand, Dicke (1974) has pointed out that an upper limit on Q is desirable since for large values of Q the factor $1/(1 - Q)$ is strongly affected by errors in calculating P_{cr} and Q. Such errors could result from using the wrong flexural rigidity, EI, or from a mistake in determining the rotational rigidity of the foundation. Based on assumed statistical distributions of loads and EI values, Dicke has shown that for Q smaller than 0.1 the probability of failure of a structure designed using a second-order analysis is relatively constant, while for Q greater than about 0.2 the probability of failure increases rapidly. For this reason he recommends an absolute upper limit on Q of 0.2.

In a similar manner, the value of Q based on the critical load for torsional instability (Eq. 8.44) should not be allowed to get too small, and torsional instability can be ignored if Q is less than about 0.05.

Based on analyses of hinged frames braced by a shear wall acting as a vertical cantilever similar to the frames shown in Fig. 8.28, Beck and König (1966) have proposed a test of the need to consider frame stability in the design of such a frame. This test uses the parameter α in

$$\alpha = h_t\sqrt{\frac{P_0}{EI_g}} \tag{8.70a}$$

If $\alpha \leq 0.6$ Beck and König suggest that a first-order analysis is sufficient, and if $\alpha > 0.9$ a second-order analysis is necessary. Using Eqs. 8.43 and 8.70 these limits can be shown to correspond to Q about 0.0475 and 0.01, respectively.

In Article 8.5.1 the effect of foundation rotations on critical load was discussed. This effect can be included (Dicke, 1974) in the test for over-all stability by rewriting Eq. 8.70a

$$\alpha = h_t\sqrt{\frac{\mu + 4}{\mu}\frac{P_0}{EI_g}} \tag{8.70b}$$

in which $\mu = (K_s h_t)/EI_g$, and K_s = rotational stiffness of the foundation. Again, the values of $\alpha = 0.6$ and 0.9 could be used in the stability check as suggested by Beck and König (1966).

A similar test can be derived considering the torsional instability of a hinged frame braced by one or more cantilever wall element. Thus, the torsional stability factor λ can be used to obtain the proper layout of walls (Beck et al., 1968). This characteristic value depends on the torsional stiffness (GI_{Pj}; EC_{Wj}) and the bending stiffness (EI_{xj}; EI_{yj}; EI_{xyj}) of each restraining element, on the height h of the building, on the distances between the lines of action of the vertical loads and the shear center of the building (r_k; r_j with its components x_j and y_j), as well as on the total vertical load of each restraining element P_j and each restrained column P_k (Fig. 8.43). It approximately can be represented by

$$\lambda^2 \simeq \frac{\sum\limits_{j=1}^{m} P_j \cdot r_j^2 + \sum\limits_{k=1}^{n} P_k \cdot r_k^2}{EC_W} \cdot h_t^2 \tag{8.71}$$

with

$$EC_W = \sum\limits_{j=1}^{m} \{ EC_{W,j} + EI_{x,j} x_j^2 + EI_{y,j} y_j^2 - 2EI_{xy,j} x_j y_j \} \tag{8.72}$$

in which $EC_{W,j}$ = warping rigidity of the restraining element j, related to its shear center; m = total number of restraining elements; and n = total number of restrained elements (columns).

If the value of λ exceeds the following values, stability should be checked:

$$\lambda \quad = 0.24\lambda_{Ki} \text{ for } \varkappa \leq 40$$

$$\lambda/\mu = 0.23 \text{ for } \varkappa > 40$$

in which λ_{Ki} = stability coefficient defined in Fig. 8.44, and

$$\varkappa = h_t \sqrt{\frac{GI_p}{EC_W}} \tag{8.73}$$

$$GI_P = \sum\limits_{j=1}^{m} GI_{P,j} \tag{8.74}$$

GI_{pj} = St. Venant's torsional rigidity of the restraining element, j.

This criterion is best if the shear center and center of gravity of the whole building coincide.

Still another estimate of whether second-order analyses are required can be obtained from Eq. 8.59. If it is assumed that the first-order moments will be

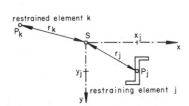

Fig. 8.43 Definition of dimensions in Eqs. 8.71 and 8.72

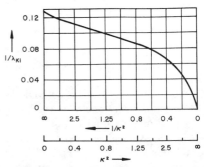

Fig. 8.44 Graph of values of stability coefficient λ_{Ki}

sufficiently accurate for design if they are within 5% of the second-order moments, a second-order analysis can be ignored if

$$Q = \left(\frac{\Sigma P_i \Delta_{1i}}{H_i h_i}\right) \leq 0.05 \qquad (8.75)$$

For values of Q greater than 0.05, sufficiently accurate moments will be obtained by adding $P\Delta$ to the first-order moments provided that

$$Q = \left(\frac{\Sigma P_i \Delta_{1i}}{H_i h_i}\right) \leq 0.22 \qquad (8.76)$$

To summarize, limitations based on Q and on dimensionless coefficients α and λ have been proposed for determining whether second-order analyses are required. Second-order effects can be ignored in design if Q is less than 0.05 for instability about all three axes of the building. Because of the variable nature of the loads and the term EI, Q should not be allowed to exceed 0.2. For Q between 0.05 and 0.2, the error in second-order moments will be less than 5% if $P \cdot \Delta_1$ is added to the first-order moments.

7   Second-Order Analysis—Summary

Five alternative procedures for carrying out second-order analysis have been presented in the preceding articles. The first may give considerable errors and is only justified for preliminary design. The P-Δ Method and the Negative Bracing Method seem well suited for office use in conjunction with standard computer analyses. The fourth and fifth methods are promising but, at the moment, are not ready for design office use.

8.7   DESIGN OF TALL REINFORCED CONCRETE BUILDINGS CONSIDERING STABILITY

1   Review of Current Code Requirements

Few national design codes adequately consider the stability of tall buildings. United States and Canadian codes specify details of individual column design but do not consider the over-all stability problem. Various codes and recommended practices require deflection limits at working loads ranging from $1/2000h$ (Gosstroi USSR, 1972) to $1/500h$ (ACI Committee 435, 1968) for the top of the structure and within any story. Building codes for the Netherlands and Denmark require the designer to consider a lateral load equal to the wind load or a horizontal force of 1.5% of the total vertical loads, whichever is greater.

Perhaps the most complete treatment of structural stability in a code is contained in the 1972 West German code for reinforced concrete, DIN 1045 (1972). This code requires the designer to pay special attention to the stability of buildings in both the final and the construction stages. If the stiffening elements are relatively flexible, deformations are to be considered in determining the internal forces. In structures with shear walls or concrete elevator cores the stability check can be omitted if

$$\alpha = h_{\bar{t}}\sqrt{\frac{P_t}{EI}} \leq 0.6 \text{ if } n > 4 \tag{8.70}$$

is satisfied (see Article 8.6.6). In Eq. 8.70, EI = total bending stiffness of all vertical stiffening elements, and h_t = total height of the building.

In analyses of buildings according to this code the designer must consider deflections caused by horizontal loads, eccentric gravity loads, and unintentional eccentricities of the vertical loads. In the case of the vertical stiffening elements the latter are designed assuming an unintentional inclination of all vertical elements as shown in Fig. 8.45 equal to

$$\frac{\Delta}{h_t} = \pm\frac{1}{100\sqrt{h_t(\text{in meters})}}$$

or $\tag{8.77}$

$$\frac{\Delta}{h_t} = \pm\frac{1}{55\sqrt{h_t(\text{in feet})}}$$

The individual floors must also be able to resist a horizontal force resulting from accidental inclinations of the columns above and below the floor equal to

$$\frac{\Delta}{h} = \pm\frac{1}{200\sqrt{h_{\text{avg}}(\text{in meters})}} \tag{8.78}$$

in which h_{avg} is the average of the two story heights. The inclinations in the two stories shall be oriented so that the resulting forces add together, as shown in Fig. 8.46.

The Swedish Building Code (Statens Betongkommitte, 1968) presents similar requirements, and requires that the forces caused by the imperfections act to cause the most dangerous loading in relation to the buckling mode, as shown in Fig. 8.47.

2 Review of Design Procedures

At the present time (1978) the most common design procedure is based on a first-order analysis of the structure, followed by the proportioning of the individual

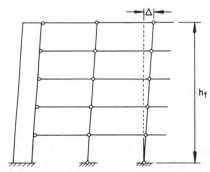

Fig. 8.45 Assumed imperfections in multistory building

columns based on their own effective lengths using a moment-magnifier expression or a long column reduction factor. This procedure is inadequate for "braced" frames because the second-order forces in the bracing and the frames are not accounted for. It is also inadequate for unbraced frames because it usually leads to overdesign of some columns and underdesign of others. Finally, the method errs on the unsafe side because it does not account for the increases in beam moments that result from slenderness effects.

Second-order frame analyses, as described in Articles 8.6.2 and 8.6.3 of this chapter, combined with column design according to Article 8.7.3, are currently the best available design procedures for tall buildings.

Some all-inclusive design methods have been proposed for steel structures. In these procedures solutions are made to satisfy strength and deflection requirements in a second-order frame. The three most promising of these are the Lehigh University Subassemblage Procedure (Driscoll et al., 1970), the computer design programs by Jennings and Majid (1965), and the frame design procedure derived by Holmes and his coworkers (1970). Hage (1974) has adapted the first of these for use in the design of concrete structures.

Nahhas and Yu (1972) have proposed a design procedure for sway frames based on assuring that the structure is still stable when enough plastic hinges have formed to reduce the structure to a statically determinate structure. Some other analyses are discussed in Chapter CB-6.

K. Aas-Jakobsen (1973) has presented the comprehensive design method given in Article 8.6.5. By an iterative procedure the cross-sectional properties are changed until a design criterion such as minimum cost is satisfied.

Two other papers are worthy of note here because they deal with the entire problem of design for slenderness. Wright (1965) has discussed the relationship between analysis, design, and design specifications as these apply to slender structures. Gregory (1966) points out that in choosing load factors for lateral and vertical loads the linear relationship between lateral loads and lateral deflections and the nonlinear relationship between vertical loads and lateral deflections must be considered.

3 Recommended Stability Analysis

Method of Analysis. The complexity of the method used to analyze and design the columns in a structure depends on the type of structure considered. If

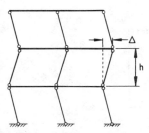

Fig. 8.46 Assumed imperfection acting on floor

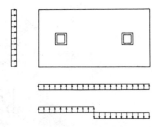

Fig. 8.47 Forces caused by imperfections placed to give most dangerous loading cases in relation to buckling mode

inspection, or the use of criteria such as Eqs. 8.70 and 8.75, suggest that the structure is not sensitive to second-order effects, design can be based on a first-order analysis. On the other hand, if lateral deflections approaching 1/500 occur at service loads, a second-order analysis should be considered even if the structure has shear walls or similar bracing.

Although an inelastic second-order analysis as presented in Article 8.6.5 is the best available method for determining the true deflections, moments, and strength of a reinforced concrete frame, such analyses are too complex and too expensive for everyday design use at the present time. It is conservative and sufficiently accurate for design purposes, however, to carry out a second-order elastic analysis for the factored ultimate horizontal and vertical loads provided that all critical sections are elastic or on the verge of yielding at the factored ultimate loads. The analytical procedure based on Eq. 8.56 or the procedure presented in Article 8.6.3 is recommended for this purpose.

This method of analysis, and the corresponding column design procedure presented in Article 8.7.3, is equally applicable for structures built of cast-in-place or precast concrete, steel or mixed forms of construction. In addition it can be applied to any structural form that can be analyzed, and has the advantage that the stability effects are clearly evident to the designer.

For structures with a height-to-width ratio greater than 3, deflections due to axial deformations of the columns should be considered. The effect of axial loads on the stiffness and carry-over factors of columns (that is, on C and S) can be disregarded if l/h is less than 15. The effect of joint width may be important, however.

Load Level Considered in Analysis. It is important that the second-order analysis be carried out at the ultimate load level. If one were dealing with first-order effects, an increase in the lateral load from $1.0H$ to $1.3H$ would increase the deflections to 1.3 times the initial deflections as shown by the dashed lines in Fig. 8.48. In the second-order case, however, the increase in deflections is greater, and they may approach 1.3 squared times those at $1.0H$ as shown by the solid lines in Fig. 8.48.

In terms of the CEB load factor format (1970) the design load, F^*, must be taken as

$$F^* = \gamma_s F_k \tag{8.79}$$

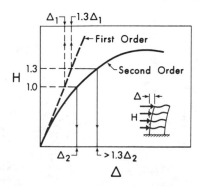

Fig. 8.48 Effect of load factors on second-order deflections

in which F_k = characteristic value of the load, and γ_s = corresponding load factor. The design member forces, S^*, are taken as

$$S^* = (\text{effects of } F^*) \qquad (8.80)$$

Because of the second-order effects described, the use of the relationship

$$S^* = \gamma_s (\text{effects of } F_k) \qquad (8.81)$$

will lead to an underestimate of the column and beam moments.

Flexural Stiffness of Frame Members.   The major problem in any stability or second-order analysis of concrete structures is the choice of a suitable mathematical model of the flexural stiffness, EI, under various loading conditions. Indeed, the errors resulting from the use of approximate methods of computing second-order deflections or critical loads will frequently be smaller than the errors resulting from the choice of EI values.

Ideally the EI value should reflect the amount of reinforcement, the extent of cracking, the effects of axial loads, the inelastic behavior of the steel and concrete, and the effects of creep. The EI values should reflect the variation of stiffness along the entire length of each member, taking into account cracked and uncracked regions, and should not merely represent the most highly loaded section. Clearly, however, when dealing with the highly statically indeterminate structural system of a tall building with more than 1500 members and more than 4000 critical sections (for a 20-story building), it is not economically feasible for designers to go into this detail.

If elastic second-order analyses are to be used in the design of columns in a building, it is important that the deflections be representative of those at the factored design loads. Thus the EI values required for such an analysis should be those at the stage immediately prior to the onset of yielding at the critical sections in the members. Article 8.2.3 explains how the secant stiffness can be calculated and tabulated for design purposes.

Kordina (1973) has presented the stiffness reduction factors given in Table 8.4 to represent the stage of loading immediately prior to the onset of yielding. These were derived considering the variation in properties along the full length of the member. The values given relate to short-time loading and do not take into account excessive rotations in the joints or connections between the particular members of the frame or the structure in question. However, they can be taken as representative of the stiffness at the factored design load level.

Hage (1974) has studied the variation in stiffness at the critical loading stage for beams subjected to gravity load, wind load moments, and combinations of the two for a limited number of beams. For the cases studied the effective EI for the beams near ultimate load varied from 0.45 to 0.6 $E_c I_g$, which corresponds reasonably well with the values given in Table 8.4.

The EI values used for design analyses should reflect the time-history of loading. For nonseismic regions the most practical loading history consists of a quick load to service load, a sustained period under service load and a quick loading to failure due to some unusual event. For this loading case it seems desirable to use an effective modulus of elasticity or effective EI value of the type given by Eq. 8.27 or 8.28.

Another source of stiffness reduction is exposure of the columns to fire. Bresler et al. (1976) discussed effects of fires of different intensity and duration showing that for 1-hr exposure the stiffness reduction may vary 30% to 80%; and for some types and locations of fires, 30% reduction in column stiffness may occur within about 0.4-hr fire duration. In framed buildings where fire safety is primarily dependent on structural integrity the response of columns to fire should be investigated.

Finally, the stiffness which should be used in such an analysis should not be based on the design strength ($F_c^* = F_c k/\gamma_c$), but rather should be the average stiffness which can be expected in the frame since the deflection of a tall frame depends on stiffnesses of many frame members. Thus, in computing the frame stiffness it is probably best to base the stiffnesses on a strength between the characteristic strength and the mean strength. Since concrete strengths are controlled in terms of the characteristic strength in the CEB-FIP Recommendations (1970), it is recommended that this value be used.

Once the structural analysis has been carried out, however, the design values of the strengths, R^*, should be used when proportioning individual members.

Based on Kordina's equations in Table 8.4 it is possible to derive simplified estimates of EI for use in design analyses for normal reinforcement ratios. Thus, the EI values used in the analysis can be based on the initial modulus of the concrete divided by about 1.25 to reflect sustained load action. For the beams I should be taken as $0.4I_g$ to $0.5I_g$ to account for inelastic action and cracking where I_g is the moment of inertia for the uncracked section ignoring the reinforcement. For the columns I should be taken equal to about $0.8I_g$.

Design of Columns. In the computation of the critical load of an axially loaded column in an elastic frame an effective buckling length, kl, is frequently used to account for the effect of end restraints on the critical load. In effect, the actual column is replaced by a hinged end column of length kl which is chosen so that the two columns have the same critical load. The extensive solutions available in the literature for the effective length of columns are reviewed in Section 4.3 of

Table 8.4 Stiffness of reinforced concrete members[a]

Kind of loading (1)	Rectangular cross section (2)	T-beam (3)
Bending and axial compression: (symmetrical reinforcement)[b]		
high overloads	$0.2 + 15(\rho + \rho')$	
service conditions	$0.6 + 15(\rho + \rho')$	
Bending: (tension reinforced only on one side)[b]		
high overloads	$0.3 + 10\rho$	0.45
service conditions	$0.6 + 10\rho$	0.65
Bending and axial tension: (symmetrical reinforcement)[b]		
high overloads	$15(\rho + \rho')$	
service conditions	$15(\rho + \rho')$	

[a] Reduction factor = $\dfrac{\text{effective stiffness } (EI)_{\text{eff}}}{\text{stiffness of uncracked plain cross section } (EI)_c}$.

[b] ρ, ρ' = reinforcement at restrained end; $\rho = A_s/A_c$; $\rho' = A_s'/A_c$.

Chapter SB-4. In Canada and the United States the effective length of columns is frequently estimated using nomographs (Johnston, 1966).

Because the behavior of completely braced and completely unbraced frames is so different, it is difficult to derive a single all-encompassing design rule for columns in both types of frames. For this reason it has been traditional to present one set of effective length factors for "completely braced frames" and another set of factors for "completely unbraced frames" (Johnston, 1966). However, no guidance is given for what constitutes bracing. This problem has recently been clarified in discussions of the design of steel columns (Springfield and Adams, 1972; Adams, 1972).

Fig. 8.49 shows columns with and without lateral displacements of the ends. If translation is prevented, the buckled shape is as shown in Fig. 8.49(a). The moments M_t and M_b are the applied end moments, while M_{rt} and M_{rb} are restraining moments caused by the rotations of the end restraints as the column deflects. Horizontal forces, H, are present if the end moments are unequal. At midheight there are secondary moments equal to the axial load times the deflections shown shaded. To account for the restraining moments M_{rt} and M_{rb} in the design of this "braced" column an effective length less than the real length is used to compute the lateral deflections.

If, however, the column is free to sway laterally as shown in Fig. 8.49(b), the moments M_t and M_b must equilibrate not only any horizontal load, H, but also a moment $P\Delta$. The secondary moments in this column can be divided into two components, one due to the additional horizontal reaction or sway force, $P\Delta/h$, necessary to resist the axial force in the deformed position, and the second equal to the axial load times the deflections from the chord line, shown shaded. If there is no bracing the sway force $P\Delta/h$ must be provided by increased column moments. Traditionally these have been accounted for in design by using the effective length factors for the unbraced case in designing the column.

On the other hand, if a "second-order" structural analysis is carried out including the effects of both the applied loads and the sway forces, the latter have been accounted for in the analysis and need not be considered a second time in evaluating the effective length. Under these conditions the design would be based

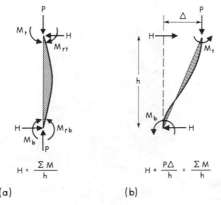

Fig. 8.49 Forces in deflected columns: (a) Sway prevented; (b) sway permitted

on the actual length of the column and the C_m factor corresponding to the second-order end moments to include the effect of the deflections of the column from the chord.

Once the structural analysis has been carried out, either the moment magnifier or the additional moment procedure can be used to calculate the slenderness effects for individual columns. If the frame is braced or if a second-order analysis has been carried out, column effective length factors for the braced case can be used.

Once the maximum forces and moments on a cross section in the column have been calculated including the effects of slenderness, an ultimate strength design procedure should be used to proportion the column.

In the design of slender structures, where moments depend on the deflections of the structure, one should check that the stiffness of the designed sections is at least equal to the assumed stiffness in the elastic analysis. The check can be carried out as explained in Article 8.2.3. The curvature ϕ corresponding to the calculated total moment M_t and assumed stiffness EI is given by

$$\phi = \frac{M_t}{EI} \tag{8.82}$$

Fig. 8.50 Marina City Twin Towers, Chicago, Ill., U.S.A. (Courtesy: Portland Cement Association; photo by Dudley, Hardin, and Yang, Inc.)

The moment capacity M_i of the section for this value of the curvature and the known axial load and reinforcement ratio is calculated as explained in Article 8.2.3. The moment capacity M_i should be equal to or greater than the moment M_i determined in the elastic second-order analysis.

8.8 CONDENSED REFERENCES/BIBLIOGRAPHY

The following is a condensed bibliography for this chapter. Not only does it include all articles referred to or cited in the text, but it also contains bibliography for further reading. The full citations will be found at the end of the Volume. What is given here should be sufficient information to lead the reader to the correct article: the author, date, and title. In case of multiple authors, only the first named is listed.

Aas-Jakobsen 1973, *Design of Slender Reinforced Concrete Beams*
Aas-Jakobsen 1974, *Analysis of Slender Reinforced Concrete Frames*
Adams 1972, *Design of Steel Beam-Columns*
ACI Committee 318 1971, *Building Code Requirements for Reinforced Concrete*
ACI Committee 318 1975, *Commentary on Building Code Requirements for Reinforced Concrete*

Fig. 8.51 Place Victoria, Montréal, Québec, Canada (J.V. Christiansen)

ACI Committee 435 1968, *Allowable Deflections*
ACI Committee 442 1971, *Response of Buildings to Lateral Forces*
Aroni 1968, *Strength of Slender Prestressed Concrete Columns*
Ballio 1973, *The Effect of the Process and Imperfections on the Load Bearing Capacity of Beam*
Baumann 1934, *Buckling of Reinforced Concrete Columns*

Bazant 1972, *Numerical Determination of Stress Response to a Given Strain History in Concrete*
Beck 1966, *Restraining Forces in the Analysis of Tall Buildings*
Beck 1968, *Characteristics Relating to the Torsional Stiffness of Multi-Story Buildings*
Beck 1969a, *The Relation Between Bending Moment and Curvature for Rectangular Sections*
Beck 1969b, *Stability & Material Behavior in Reinforced Concrete Construction*

Beck 1972, *A Procedure to Optimal Design of Planar Reinforced Concrete Frames*
Beck 1975, *Stability in the Design of Tall Concrete Buildings*
Bleich 1952, *Buckling Strength of Metal Structures*
Breen 1964, *Computer Use in Studies of Frames with Long Columns*
Breen 1972, *Determination of Effective Length Factors for Slender Concrete Columns*

Bresler 1976, *Response of Reinforced Concrete Frames*
Bresler 1976, *Limit State Behavior of Reinforced Concrete Frames*
British Standards Institution 1972, *Code of Practice for the Structural Use of Concrete*
Broms 1961, *Long Reinforced Concrete Columns*
Bryson 1972, *The Design of Shear Wall-Frame Structures*

Campus 1956, *Research on the Buckling of I-Columns in A37 Steel Obliquely Loaded*
Carpena 1972, *Stability, 6th Regional Conference*
CEB 1970, *International Recommendations for the Design and Construction of Concrete*
CEB 1972, *FIP-Handbook—Buckling-Instability*
Chen 1976, *Theory of Beam-Columns*

Chen 1975, *Design Formula for Biaxially Loaded Concrete Columns*
Cohn 1972, *The Flexural Ductility of Reinforced Concrete Sections*
Cranston 1966, *Determining the Relation Between Moment, Axial Load and Curvature*
Cranston 1972, *Analysis and Design of Reinforced Concrete Columns*
Dicke 1974, *Communication with Dr. Aas-Jakobsen*

Dickie 1974, *An Unusual Glass Tower Structure*
Dischinger 1937, *Investigations on Stability, Elastic and Time-Dependent Deflections of Concrete*
Driscoll 1970, *Plastic Design of Multi-Story Frames by Computer*
Fey 1966, *Approximate Second-Order Analysis of Reinforced Concrete Frames*
Furlong 1966, *Tests of Frames with Columns in Single Curvature*

Furlong 1971, *Column Slenderness and Charts for Design*
German Industrial Std. (DIN) 1972, *Reinforced Concrete Structures Design and Construction*
Glück 1971, *On the Stability of Elastically Supported Cantilever with Continuous Lateral Support*
Glück 1974, *The Buckling of Tier Buildings with Variable Lateral Stiffness Properties*
Goel 1968, *Inelastic Earthquake Response of Tall Steel Frames*

Goldberg 1954, *Stiffness Charts for Gisseted Members Under Axial Load*
Goldberg 1965, *Buckling of Multi-Story Buildings*
Goldberg 1966, *Analysis of Multi-Story Buildings Considering Shear Wall and Floor Deformations*
Goldberg 1973, *Approximate Methods for Stability and Frequency Analysis of Tall Buildings*
Gosstroi USSR 1972, *Structural Norms and Rules*

Gregory 1966, *Framed Structures, The Instability Problem*
Hage 1974, *The Second-Order Analysis of Reinforced Concrete Frames*
Hansell 1959, *Lateral Stability of Reinforced Concrete Beams*
Heunisch 1973, *Design and Safety of Reinforced Concrete Columns*
Holmes 1970, *Plastic Design of Multi-Storey Sway Frames*

Horne 1961, *Stability of Elastic-Plastic Structures*
Horne 1965, *The Stability of Frames*
Huddleston 1974, *Nonlinear Stability of Tall Buildings Under Combined Loads*
Iffland 1972, *Design for Stability in High-Rise Buildings*
Jennings 1965, *An Elastic-Plastic Analysis for Framed Structures Loaded up to Collapse*

Johnston 1966, *The Column Research Council Guide to Design Criteria for Metal Compression*

Kent 1971, *Flexural Members with Confirmed Concrete*
König 1972, *On the Statistical Safety Theory of Reinforced Concrete Structures*
Kordina 1959, *The Design of Buckling Sensitive Reinforced Concrete Members*
Kordina 1969, *Application of the Safety Theory to Stability Investigations*

Kordina 1973, *Cracking and Crack Control*
Korn 1968, *The Approximation of Stability Effects on Frames*
Korn 1968, *Behavior of Elastic Plastic Frames*
Kulicki 1973d, *Applications of the Finite Element Method to Inelastic Beam-Column Problems*
Kulicki 1974b, *Inelastic Analysis of Reinforced Concrete Beam-Columns*

Ku 1974, *On the Structural Stability of a Tall Building*
Lie 1974, *Fire Resistance of Reinforced Concrete Columns*
MacGregor 1970, *Design of Slender Concrete Columns*
MacGregor 1972, *The Approximate Analysis of Inelastic Shear-Wall Frame Structures*
MacGregor 1975, *A Re-Examination of the EI Value of Slender Columns*

Manuel 1967, *Analysis of Restrained Reinforced Concrete Columns Under Sustained Load*
Marinakis 1975, *The Philosophy of the Fundamental Propositions in the Theory for Buckling*
Marinakis 1975, *A Simple Practical Method to Study Buckling of Columns in Tall Buildings*
Mattock 1961, *Rectangular Concrete Stress Distribution in Ultimate Strength Design*
Mehmel 1964, *Bearing Behavior of Eccentrically Loaded Compression Members*

Melhorn 1970, *Lateral Buckling of Prestressed*
Merchant 1956, *Critical Loads of Tall Building Frames*
Migliacci 1972, *Geometric Second Order Effect on Tall R. C. Chimmeys*
Murashev 1968, *Design of Reinforced Concrete Structures*
Nahhas 1972, *The Elastic-Plastic Design of Reinforced Concrete Sway Frames*

Neville 1970, *Creep in Plain, Reinforced and Prestressed Concrete*
Nixon 1975, *Simplified Second-Order Frame Analysis*
Okamura 1970, *Elastic Frame Analysis*
Parme 1966, *Capacity of Restrained Eccentrically Loaded Long Columns*
PCI Commission on Columns 1968, *Tentative Recommendations for Design of Prestressed*

PCI 1971, *PCI Design Handbook*
Pfrang 1964, *Behavior of Restrained Reinforced Concrete Columns*
Pfrang 1964, *Load-Moment-Curvature Characteristics of Reinforced Concrete Sections*
Rafla 1969, *Approximate Calculation of the Critical Buckling Loading of Reinforced Concrete*
Rosenblueth 1965, *Slenderness Effects in Buildings*

Rosman 1974b, *Stability and Dynamics of Shear Wall-Frame Structures*
Rüsch 1967, *Parameters for the Behavior of the Compressive Zone of Reinforced Concrete*
Rüsch 1968, *Strength and Deformation of Non-Reinforced Concrete Under Constant Load*
Sargin 1971, *Stress-Strain Relationship for Concrete*
Schwarz 1967, *A Contribution to the Bearing of Eccentrically Loaded Concrete Columns*

Springfield 1972, *Aspects of Column Design in Tall Steel Buildings*
Statens Betongkommitte 1968, *Regulations for Concrete Structures*
Stevens 1967, *Elastic Stability of Practical Multi-Storey Frames*
Tal' 1952, *Experimental Investigations of Slender Reinforced Concrete Columns*
Tal' 1969, *Slender Axially Compressed Concrete Elements Under Long-Time Loading*

Tichý 1973, *Instability of Reinforced Concrete in Plastic Domain*
Timoshenko 1961, *Theory of Elastic Stability*
Van Langendonck 1975, *Critical Loads of Building Frames*
Wakabayashi 1965, *The Restoring Force Characteristics of Multi-Story Frames*
Warner 1963, *Creep Failure of Reinforced Concrete Columns*

Warner 1974, *Bearing Capacity of Slender Concrete Columns*
Wastlund 1972, *Stability of Concrete Structures*
Wiegand 1971, *A Contribution to the Buckling Stability of Reinforced Concrete Walls*
Wood 1958, *The Stability of Tall Buildings*
Wood 1976a, *Column Design by P-Delta Method*

Wood 1976b, *Further Aspect of Design by P-Δ Method*
Wright 1965, *Discussion of Rosenblueth 1965*

Wynhoven 1972a, *Analysis of Three Dimensional Structures*
Wynhoven 1972b, *Behavior of Structures Under Loads Causing Torsion*
Yashin 1970, *Deformation of Concrete Under Long-Time Loading at High Stresses*
Zia 1967, *Combined Bending and Axial Load in Prestressed Concrete Columns*

**Structural Design of
Tall Concrete and Masonry Buildings**

Chapter CB-9

Stiffness, Deflections,
and Cracking

Prepared by Committee 24 (Stiffness and Crack Control) of the
Council on Tall Buildings and Urban Habitat as part of the Monograph on the Planning and Design of Tall Buildings

Peter Gergely   Chairman
Mario Paparoni   Vice-Chairman
Joseph Schwaighofer   Editor

AUTHOR ACKNOWLEDGMENT

Special acknowledgment is due those individuals whose contributions and papers formed the substantial first drafts of the various sections of this chapter. First are the state-of-art reporters from the 1972 International Conference whose material was published in the Lehigh Proceedings. These individuals are:

P. Weidlinger, Section 9.1
P. Gergely, Section 9.2
J. Ferry Borges, Section 9.2
K. Kordina, Section 9.2
J. G. MacGregor, Section 9.2
N. Jackson, Section 9.2
Y. Higashi, Section 9.3
T. Takeda, Section 9.3
M. Paparoni, Section 9.5.

In addition to this, other sections were based on special contributions prepared by:

J. P. Colaco, Section 9.4
R. M. Libbey, Section 9.4
J. Schwaighofer, Section 9.4
B. Deschapelles, Section 9.4
P. W. F. Harris, Section 9.4
R. W. Turner, Section 9.4.

CONTRIBUTORS

The following is a complete list of those who have submitted written material for possible use in the chapter, whether or not that material was used in the final version. The Committee Chairman and Editor were given quite complete latitude. Frequently length limitations precluded the inclusion of much valuable material. The Bibliography contains all contributions. The contributors are: V. V. Bertero, J. P. Colaco, B. Deschapelles, J. Ferry Borges, M. Fintel, P. Funk, P. Gergely, P.W.F. Harris, Y. Higashi, M. Hirosawa, H. Holzenbein, N. Jackson, K. Kordina, F. Leonhardt, R. M. Libbey, T. Y. Lin, J. G. MacGregor, M. Paparoni, J. Schwaighofer, S. Soretz, M. Stamato, T. Takeda, R. W. Turner, R. F. Warner, P. Weidlinger.

COMMITTEE MEMBERS

E. Absi, T. Arakawa, A. L. L. Baker, O. Barsan, B. Deschapelles, J. Despeyroux, J. Ferry Borges, P. Funk, P. Gergely, J. Harvancik, Y. Higashi, M. Hirosawa, A. Hofsoy, H. Holzenbein, N. Jackson, K. Kordina, R. M. Libbey, J. C. Maldague, E. Mancini, J. G. MacGregor, M. Paparoni, J. Schwaighofer, N. F. Somes, S. Soretz, B. Stafford-Smith, T. Takeda, R. W. Turner, R. F. Warner, P. Weidlinger.

Stiffness, Deflections, and Cracking

9.1 INTRODUCTION

1 Scope of Chapter

Cracking of reinforced concrete elements (beams, slabs, prestressed beams) is discussed in terms of the maximum crack width as it affects appearance and corrosion of the reinforcement, and in terms of its effect on the stiffness of a tall building.

Various expressions for predicting the crack width in beams are in use; however, most of them lead to similar values for crack width. In spite of this, quite different limits are placed on allowable crack width in the building codes of various countries.

Cracking decreases the stiffness of a reinforced concrete member. Over-all stiffness reduction factors are given, and guidelines for their use in deflection and stability computations are provided.

Shear walls greatly affect the over-all stiffness of a tall building. The elastic stiffness of various shear-wall systems (shear walls with outriggers, nonplanar coupled shear walls, etc.) is discussed. The fundamental period of vibration as an indirect measure of stiffness and hence deflection is utilized for comparisons of actual and predicted behavior of buildings.

Finally, the performance of coupling beams and slabs is documented. Properly proportioned and reinforced coupling elements are able to meet stringent ductility requirements.

2 Basic Problems

The structural engineer, whether in his role as designer or analyst, addresses himself primarily to the task of assuring that criteria and requirements are complied with in terms of strength, stability, and displacements. Under ideal conditions each and every ramification is simultaneously considered and satisfied. Buildings, and especially tall buildings, are complex systems and this ideal procedure is never approached. Of necessity, these criteria are considered and their effects on the whole or on its parts examined one by one. The feasibility of such a sequence depends on familiar classical assumptions, but the fruitfulness and effectiveness of this method depends to a great degree on the recognition of the predominance of some of the phenomena which are to be investigated. It must be determined whether some other requirements might not override the results of the analysis: some structures, for instance, are obviously stable and sufficiently stiff if they are sufficiently strong. The danger lies, probably, in unduly depending on previous experience which may lead to procedures based on these assumptions. What might be true, or at least acceptable, for buildings of moderate height is frequently not so for tall buildings, simply because of the increased size of the structure or because of the cumulative effect of a very large number of components. Hence, the problem of stiffness, deflections, and crack control of tall concrete buildings is considered here as an isolated topic, but the strong interaction of this subject with numerous other topics should be kept in mind.

It might be useful to focus on stiffness and crack control by means of a somewhat arbitrary classification based on a simplified cause and effect relationship with regard to deformation, as shown in Table 9.1. The deformations can be static or dynamic, recoverable or permanent.

It might be noted that a reciprocal relation exists with respect to forces induced by displacements and vice versa. It can also be useful to divide structural elements by noting that there are those which function primarily to resist or control imposed forces or displacements, and those which are only indirectly affected by one of these primary functions. This is typically the case, for instance, in wind bracing elements designed for deflection control but affected by gravity loads. It is also important to consider the time scale of the duration of the phenomena (see Table 9.2). The unit of comparison of time should be the fundamental period or the period for the relevant mode of the structure. In this time scale one must also recognize the sequence in

Table 9.1 Causes of deformations

Forces (1)	Displacements (2)
Gravity Wind Inertial (seismic) Blast	Thermal Settlements Creep and shrinkage

Table 9.2 Time scale

Time (1)	Effect (2)
Short Long Cyclic Transitory	Dynamic Static, creep Fatigue, resonance Stresses due to construction loads

which the events occur, and especially distinguish the completed structure from the structure during construction.

The classification shown in Table 9.2 is quite obvious, but the last entry deserves special mention, since the effect of the construction cycle and locked-in stresses and deformations caused by it can frequently be neglected in buildings of moderate height. The distinction between the analysis of the complete structure and that of the partially completed structure is, however, significant in tall structures. More picturesquely, this idea is expressed by noting that gravity is not suddenly "turned on" after the building is completed. This consideration is well known to bridge designers but its importance to building construction has only become apparent in tall structures. The axial shortening of vertical elements subject to gravity load in tall buildings is an example. For instance, a slipformed concrete core is erected at each floor level to the theoretically finished elevation of that level. After the core has reached its maximum height the distribution of vertical displacements of the individual floor levels is quite different from the shortening of adjacent columns which are primarily subject to superimposed loads. The vertical displacement Δ_k, ignoring creep, of such a concrete wall due to its own weight at the kth floor is given by

$$\Delta_k = \frac{\gamma}{E} \sum_1^k \frac{h_i}{A_i} \times \sum_k^n h_i A_i \tag{9.1}$$

in which γ = unit weight of the concrete; h_i = story height at the ith floor; A_i = cross section at that level; E = elastic modulus; and n = total number of floors.

The problem becomes even a little more complicated if the variation of the elastic modulus E as a function of the age of the concrete and creep, during and after the slipforming, are also considered (Fintel and Khan, 1971; see also Chapter CB-10). In any case, the curve of the vertical displacements, as shown in Fig. 9.1(a), is quite different from the more usual one in Fig. 9.1(b), which represents vertical displacements of a column subject primarily to superimposed loads. The significant differential displacement pattern between a heavy wall and a lighter column, therefore, is a good illustration of some of the major differences in the emphasis which must be placed on the analysis of tall buildings with respect to deformation.

There are numerous other examples of phenomena common to all structures which become critical in tall buildings. One is the effect of temperature differentials between vertical elements situated on the outside and in the interior of the building. The temperature differential in these elements results in differential displacements which, in turn, induce bending in the floors. Temperature differences due to solar

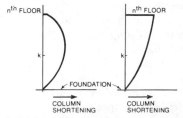

Fig. 9.1 Column shortening as function of height

radiation between exposed concrete exterior walls at right angles must also be considered. These effects, even in extreme climates, do not become really significant in buildings which are under 20 floors. This is discussed more fully in Chapter CB-10.

The most obvious critical phenomena relating to the stiffness of tall buildings are, of course, wind and seismic effects. It is only in relatively recent times that it has been generally recognized and accepted that not only seismic but also wind phenomena must be treated as primarily dynamic. The aerodynamics of tall slender buildings is a relatively new science, and results of research which are being obtained must be incorporated into the design and the analytical procedures. It must lead to a drastic revision in the concept of stiffness from that of a primarily static quantity to that of the dynamic stiffness of a nonconservative system.

Compared to the aerodynamic problem, seismic research and analysis is well advanced and better known in the scientific-engineering community. Current thinking both in wind and seismic design must, and does, take into account the essential inelastic properties of concrete, and the probabilistic nature of the phenomena.

Finally, the problem of "gravity drift" of tall buildings of unsymmetrical plan geometry might be mentioned. Such geometry results in differential shortening of columns, which in very tall buildings will induce significant lateral displacements. The manner of coping with this, in terms of construction procedures, details, and attachment of architectural cladding, is far from trivial. The analysis of secondary induced bending, of course, can be solved. The maximum allowable value or recommended value of the gravity drift is not known.

With respect to displacements, two pertinent comments should be made. First, the safety of the structure is rarely affected by displacements, although excessive displacements may very well be a sign of distress, indicating potential failure due to inadequate strength. On the other hand, generally, displacements that are due to loads of constant intensity should be eliminated by providing adequate cambers, that is, the geometry of the structure should be adjusted to eliminate these effects.

Excessive deflections do affect the useful service limit of the structure. The current problem here is the determination of the maximum acceptable values and the design of adequate details to permit these, without distress to the nonstructural elements.

The effect of displacements on human perception and tolerance is, at present, insufficiently understood. Considerable work exists in this field which explores acceleration-frequency effects in vehicles, such as ships, aircraft, and automobiles. From these studies (Goldman and von Gierke, 1961) it is known that, with rare exceptions, the displacement amplitude in itself does not affect the inhabitants of the building (except as mentioned in the previous paragraph). Only the dynamic component of the displacement is perceived and the level of perception is a function of the acceleration and of the associated frequency of the motion. In limiting wind drift of tall buildings, the mean amplitude must be controlled in order to eliminate distress in nonstructural elements, but the dynamic component is the one which needs to be considered in terms of human comfort requirements. The allowable sway deformations are discussed in Chapter CL-3 and Chapter SB-4.

The dynamic characteristics of floor structures also have an influence on human comfort. Recent experience in composite steel-concrete structures has shown that there are frequency ranges at which visual perception is affected, reducing the usefulness of certain spaces, such as operating rooms and display areas. This is discussed more fully in Chapter PC-13 and Chapter SB-5.

Modern high-rise structures differ from earlier buildings by the elimination of heavy nonloadbearing construction, among other things. In earlier tall buildings, a great deal of the stiffness was contributed by partitions. In current practice, the effect of partitioning is not taken into consideration, although it turns out that in some instances neglecting the stiffening effects of nonstructural elements might adversely affect the structure itself. This is so because the stiffness of such elements results in a deformation pattern which might be different from the one anticipated by analysis not taking these elements into account.

The prediction of distortion of concrete is, at best, an uncertain undertaking, but recent research taking into account the cracking of concrete has contributed significantly to the reliability of calculations. Control and prediction of crack width turn out to be significant, not only in terms of stiffness determination, but also in terms of fire and corrosion protection.

At the present time (1978) very little is known regarding the cost of providing adequate stiffness in tall concrete structures. In steel buildings, it is usually possible to separate those elements of the structure which are provided to assure sufficient lateral stiffness for wind or seismic effects from elements resisting gravity loads. In reinforced concrete structures, it is usually assumed that adequate stiffness is provided by the strength design of the members. The cost of resistance to lateral forces is measured by the cost of additional reinforcing provided for this purpose. Further developments in economical high-rise buildings in reinforced concrete should lead to design concepts in which lateral stiffness is provided by a conscious effort of the designer. This could result in economy in such buildings. The use of very high-strength concrete and prestressed concrete for gravity load carrying elements might well lead to structures requiring separate stiffening systems. Thus, the conventional rectangular beam and column framing system is not efficient for carrying lateral loads and, therefore, the premium cost for height is increasing so much beyond about 15 stories that such construction tends to be uneconomical. The additions of stiffening shear walls allowed the construction of 70-story high buildings. The framed tube system, consisting of closely spaced exterior columns with deep spandrel beams, is economical up to about 60 stories. The addition of a stiff core to the framed tube system has allowed the construction of even taller structures. This is discussed more fully in Chapter SC-1 and Chapter CB-3.

This brief review indicates the importance of recognition, identification, and definition of problems relating to the effects of stiffness. It appears that the well advanced experimental, analytical, and numerical techniques at the designer's disposal, together with the invaluable help of modern data processing equipment, almost guarantee that if these problems are identified, their solution will be forthcoming. The major tasks ahead are the identification of potential problems, the experimental work required in its support, and the definition of criteria for design.

9.2　CRACKING AND CRACK CONTROL

Two aspects of cracking are of concern in the design of tall buildings: the maximum crack width from the viewpoint of appearance and corrosion, and the effect of cracking on stiffness. The latter problem is not covered extensively because other chapters deal with the subject.

Cracking in reinforced concrete buildings or structural elements is usually classified according to the cause of cracking. There are four major types of cracks: (1) Flexural cracks in reinforced concrete (and prestressed concrete) beams, frames, and slabs; (2) diagonal tension (shear) cracks; (3) splitting cracks along the reinforcement in beams and in the anchorage zones of prestressed elements; and (4) temperature and shrinkage cracks. Although there may be some similarity in the basic cracking mechanisms in various types of elements, examination of the fundamental question of crack initiation and propagation has not been productive as far as design use is concerned.

This section focuses mainly on cracking in flexural reinforced or prestressed beams and slabs, since these are of primary importance in tall buildings. The problem has two aspects: serviceability and stiffness variation. The maximum crack width is important in the consideration of serviceability (appearance and corrosion). Although one can estimate the stiffness of cracked elements with reasonable accuracy, relatively little is known about the correlation between the extent of cracking (width and spacing of cracks) and the stiffness of concrete structures. Furthermore, various types of cracks affect stiffness to a widely varying degree; some of these problems are also discussed.

The definition of limit states of cracking in reinforced and prestressed concrete is still a controversial problem. Relatively few studies give indications on the influence of the crack width on the corrosion of bars embedded in concrete, or on the degree of fire protection. Surprisingly, other studies on corrosion only consider the influence of parameters such as permeability of the concrete, aggressive environment, and stress corrosion, and completely disregard cracking.

1 Factors Affecting Crack Width

Flexural crack width depends on geometrical factors and on loading. The width of a crack is restricted at the transverse bars in reinforced concrete members and it widens toward the surface of the member. Thus the concrete cover and the spacing of the bars are of primary importance. The steel bars should be well distributed and reasonably close to the sides and bottom of the beam.

Loading affects crack width in several ways. The crack width is proportional to f_s^n, in which f_s = steel stress, and $n = 1.4$; however, n can be taken as unity without significant error. The distribution and width of cracks also depend on the variation of moments along the member. For example, flexural cracking in negative moment regions is different from that in simply-supported beams. The loading history is also important: repeated or sustained loads increase the width of cracks, though these effects are less important in most tall buildings than in some other types of structures, such as bridges and warehouses.

The purpose of studies on cracking is not restricted to obtaining simple formulas for predicting crack widths. It is important to establish theories explaining how the different parameters influence the distance between cracks and the crack widths. Then from such theories it is possible to derive formulas and design rules conveniently compromising between accuracy and simplicity, according to the case considered.

The study of flexural cracking can be based on the following simple hypotheses (Ferry Borges, 1968): (1) The crack width equals the product of the distance between cracks and the difference of steel and concrete strains; (2) the distance between cracks is obtained by adding two terms, one proportional to the cover, the other proportional to the ratio of the area of concrete in tension to the perimeter of the bars; (3) in usual situations concrete strains at the face of a cracked element can be disregarded; and (4) the mean steel strain along a bar is proportional to the steel tensile stress in a cracked section. In case the effect of load repetitions is unimportant, the steel strain is reduced by the contribution of the restrictive effect of the concrete surrounding the bars. This effect is inversely proportional to the percentage of reinforcement.

The CEB-FIP Recommendations are based on these principles. The formulas presented in the Recommendations for the various conditions have all the same background. Recently, Beeby (1971) generalized CEB-FIP principles on cracking in order to derive an expression giving the depth of the cracks and their variable widths at any point of a cross section. The expressions thus obtained are complicated but they may serve for basic studies, for example, for optimizing the distribution of bars in the cross section of deep beams.

Since the late 1940s several theories on flexural cracking have been proposed. Although they have different aspects, they lead to results that are not too different. This is not surprising since all of them deal with the same reality. An instance of this analogy of results is given in Table 9.3, in which crack widths obtained by the ACI (American Concrete Institute) and the CEB (Comité Européen du Béton) formulas are given for three stress levels in five beams reinforced differently.

As compared to cracking in beams, the problem of cracking in reinforced and prestressed concrete slabs presents further difficulties resulting from: (1) The existence of biaxial state of stress, which may lead to cracking in a direction inclined to the direction of the bars; (2) the small percentages of reinforcement normally used in slabs; and (3) the control of the distance between cracks by the spacing of the transverse reinforcing bars. Extensive studies on the cracking of slabs have been recently performed in the United States (Nawy and Blair, 1972).

2 Cracking in Reinforced Concrete Beams

Several expressions have been developed for the prediction of flexural crack widths in reinforced concrete members. Most of these refer to the probable maximum crack width or to a value that will not be exceeded by a certain fraction

Table 9.3 Comparison of CEB-FIP and ACI rules for crack control

CROSS - SECTION	STEEL STRESS		COMPUTED CRACK WIDTH (mm)			
			c = 2.5cm (1")		c = 5.0cm (2")	
	N/cm²	p.s.i.	ACI	CEB	ACI	CEB
3#11	20 000	28 500	0.19	0.15	0.25	0.25
	30 000	42 700	0.28	0.24	0.38	0.41
	40 000	56 900	0.38	0.33	0.50	0.56
5#11	20 000	28 500	0.18	0.15	0.24	0.24
	30 000	42 700	0.27	0.24	0.36	0.38
	40 000	56 900	0.36	0.32	0.48	0.52
5#8	20 000	28 500	0.15	0.13	0.20	0.21
	30 000	42 700	0.22	0.21	0.30	0.35
	40 000	56 900	0.30	0.28	0.40	0.49
5#8	20 000	28 500	0.15	0.15	0.22	0.22
	30 000	42 700	0.22	0.24	0.33	0.38
	40 000	56 900	0.30	0.34	0.44	0.54
5#6	20 000	28 500	0.14	0.13	0.20	0.19
	30 000	42 700	0.21	0.21	0.30	0.35
	40 000	56 900	0.29	0.29	0.40	0.51

(say 10%) of the major cracks. An extensive summary was given by Ferry Borges (1968) and by Gergely and Lutz (1968). It seems unnecessary to derive complex expressions for the calculation of the maximum crack width, considering the uncertainties involved. The major aim is to enable the designer to avoid excessive cracks by limiting the steel stress or by distributing the steel bars. Crack width limitation is especially important if high-strength steels are used.

Only a few selected formulas are reported here for the estimation of the crack width at the tension face of flexural members. Gergely and Lutz (1968) give

$$w = 2.20R \frac{f_s}{E_s} \sqrt[3]{d_c A} \tag{9.2}$$

in which f_s = steel stress; $A = A_e/m$; A_e = area of concrete symmetrical about the center of gravity of steel; m = number of bars; d_c = the bottom cover, measured from the center of lower bars; and R is defined in Fig. 9.2.

Base, et al. (1966) give

$$w = \frac{Kt \, Rf_s}{E_s} \tag{9.3}$$

in which $K = 3.3$ for deformed bars, and t = the distance from the surface point to the surface of the nearest bar.

Ferry Borges (1968) gives, in inches

$$w = \frac{1}{E_s} \left(2.5d_c + 0.067\frac{d_b}{\rho} \right) \left(f_s - \frac{107}{\rho} \right) \tag{9.4a}$$

or, in millimeters

$$w = 10^{-6} \left(1.5d_c + 0.04\frac{d_b}{\rho} \right) \left(f_s - \frac{7.5}{\rho} \right) \tag{9.4b}$$

in which d_b = diameter of bars and ρ = steel ratio.

For low ρ-values, for example for beams of great height, the last fraction is too large. Rehm and Martin (1968) suggest a slightly modified form (in millimeters)

$$w = 10^{-6} \left(4 + 0.25\frac{d_b}{\rho} \right) f_s \left[1 - \left(\frac{3}{\rho f_s} \right)^2 \right] \tag{9.5}$$

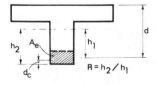

Fig. 9.2 Crack width—definition of symbols

The CEB Code proposal gives, for the mean crack width

$$w_m = \epsilon_s \left(2c + \frac{kd_b}{100\rho_t} \right) \tag{9.6}$$

in which ϵ_s = the steel strain; c = the concrete cover; and ρ_t = the steel ratio referred to the area A_e defined in connection with Eq. 9.2. (In one modification by Rehm the effective tension area A_e is bordered by a line that is four bar diameters above the main tension bars farthest from the tension face.) The coefficient k depends on the curvature and ranges from 20 for pure tension to less than 1 depending on the ratio of cover and the distance h_x between the neutral axis and the tension face; that is

h_x/c	0.05	0.10	0.15	0.20	0.30	0.40	0.50
k	15	9	5	3	1.6	0.9	0.6

The characteristic crack width, to be used in most design situations, is $1.7w_m$. Additional factors are applied for repeated loading, sustained loading, and for various corrosive effects.

The crack provisions of the ACI Building Code 318-71 are based on Eq. 9.2. Instead of requiring the evaluation of the maximum crack width directly, the provisions relate to an equivalent quantity that must be limited to assure that the expected maximum crack width remains below the limits specified for internal or external exposure. The ACI provisions are compared to the CEB provisions in Table 9.3.

3 Cracking in Prestressed Beams

Prestressed concrete beams are not often used in tall buildings but prestressed slabs are frequently employed. Cracking is of interest in partially prestressed beams, in unbonded post-tensioned members, or under overload conditions. Most of the time, prestressed concrete members are prestressed in one direction only. Therefore it frequently happens that there are cracks in the other two directions, which are not prestressed but are only reinforced or plain concrete. Cracking in these non-prestressed directions should be treated in the same manner as cracking in nonprestressed beams.

Where precast, prestressed members are joined together with reinforcement or grout, cracks may occur in such joints if they are not prestressed.

Prestressed concrete floors in high-rise buildings are not necessarily subject to shortening problems produced by shrinkage and creep. This is because all floors will tend to shorten more or less the same amount. Care must be taken with the first floor which will tend to shorten relative to the ground. Since the ground may prevent the first floor from shortening, prestress may be lost into the ground and cracking may result. Fortunately, the appearance of cracking may not be a sign of insufficient strength of that structural component; in fact, such cracking will usually relieve the stresses produced by strain. Therefore cracking, even in the first floor, may or may not be detrimental to the strength of that floor since often cracks occur where there is redundant support and restraint.

In order to minimize cracking due to shrinkage and creep under prestress, it is frequently desirable to place or locate the rigid elements or lateral force resisting elements near the center of the building rather than at the periphery. This will enable the building to shrink toward the center without producing undesirable cracks.

The significance of cracking as affecting corrosion depends on the kind of wrapping given to the tendon. For example, unbonded tendons enclosed in plastic wrapping may not be subject to corrosion from external air even if the concrete cracks up to the level of the tendons. Thus, the CEB (1977) classifies wires smaller than 6 mm (1/4 in.) in diameter and prestressing tendons subjected to a permanent tension of 400 MPa (58 000 psi) as highly corrosive.

Equations for the prediction of crack width in nonprestressed beams (for example Eq. 9.2) may also be used, with some modifications, for prestressed beams. The steel stress should be that caused by the difference between the acting moment and the decompression moment (that results in zero extreme fiber stress). Somewhat better correlation exists with data if the calculations are based, after appropriate modifications, on the cracking moment. Repeated load tests indicate that some residual crack width (about 0.02 mm or 0.0008 in.) is present in prestressed beams with limited prestress and this value is to be added to calculated crack widths (Lampert, 1971). The zero-load crack width is appreciable in prestressed beams with little or no nonprestressed steel because of the weaker bond properties of most prestressing steels.

Surface conditions of steels seem to affect cracking significantly. The calculated values for deformed bars should be increased by a factor of about 1.6 if strands are used, and by a factor of about 2.5 if smooth prestressing wires are employed (Lampert, 1971; Holmberg and Lindgron, 1970).

The addition of nonprestressed steel to beams is an excellent means of crack control. It is very effective in unbonded post-tensioned members where few large cracks would form otherwise. In some tests the nonprestressed steel close to the bottom of beams yielded and led to rapidly increasing crack widths; however this should not occur at service load levels in practice.

An alternative method is to limit the calculated fictitious stress (assuming the concrete can resist tensile stresses) at the tensile face. If the prestressing steel tendons and nonprestressed bars are well distributed, the magnitude of the fictitious stresses is a good indication of the expected maximum crack width (Abeles, 1967).

4   Crack Increase Due to Sustained or Repeated Loading

Limited information indicates that the maximum crack width will increase about 40% in reinforced concrete members with deformed bars subjected to sustained loads (Lutz et al., 1967). A small number of repeated loads increases the crack width by a factor of about 1.2, but a high number of cycles may increase the crack widths by a factor of up to 2. It seems that the effect of sustained and repeated loads is more pronounced in prestressed members, probably as a result of the inferior bond properties of prestressing steels. The increase may be as much as 100% under repeated loading. However, these effects are not likely to be important in tall buildings.

5 Cracking in Reinforced Concrete Slabs

The crack width in one-way slabs may be estimated by the formulas developed for beams. The most extensive study of cracking in two-way slabs reinforced with wire fabric has been conducted by Nawy and Orenstein (1969). They recommended

$$w = K\epsilon_s\sqrt{\frac{d_b s}{\rho}} \qquad (9.7)$$

in which s = spacing of reinforcement in the transverse direction; d_b = diameter of wires normal to the cracks; ρ = the corresponding active steel ratio per foot (per meter); and for an effective tension depth of $2d_c + d_b$, d_c = clear cover, K = about 1.0 for uniformly loaded interior slabs and K = 1.5 for simply-supported slabs, if w is in inches. The respective K values are 30 and 45 if w is in millimeters.

There is no information available on the cracking and crack control of two-way prestressed slabs.

6 Temperature and Shrinkage Cracks

Serious cracks may develop due to temperature or shrinkage in reinforced concrete members, especially in those that are prevented from free deformations. In some cases a more than minimal amount of reinforcement is necessary to restrict the size of the cracks. According to one approach, for a crack width of 0.3 mm (0.012 in.) the required reinforcement in a restrained member ranges from about 0.3% to 0.8% for bar diameters ranging from 5 mm (0.20 in.) to 25 mm (1.0 in.), respectively. For $w = 0.1$ mm (0.004 in.) the corresponding steel percentages are about double the above values (Falkner, 1969; Leonhardt, 1971).

The minimum shrinkage and temperature reinforcement in slabs recommended by the ACI Building Code varies with the strength of the steel and is about 0.18%. In walls the minimum amount of steel provided for strength is 0.25% and 0.15% in the horizontal and vertical directions, respectively.

The thermal strains in exterior columns of tall buildings may create distortions and cracking in partitions. Such cracks are to be restricted by proper reinforcement, but frequently it is more convenient to allow small movements of the partitions (Khan and Fintel, 1968).

Chapter CB-10 is concerned with creep, temperature, and shrinkage and contains information about the control of cracks due to these effects.

7 Crack Width Limits

Crack width limits are not well established. Several recent studies indicate that the maximum crack width depends strongly on the concrete cover. Obviously this does not mean that one should decrease the cover to zero. The width of the crack is not linear between the steel bars and the concrete surface (Lutz and Gergely, 1967). There is an optimum cover for corrosion protection. It is most likely that this value depends on the corrosive environment, type of steel and concrete, and on the type of loading. Little information is available on this important and interesting subject. In tall buildings the crack width may often be dictated by fire protection requirements or appearance rather than by the need for corrosion protection. This is especially true if the concrete is to be sand blasted to expose the aggregate, since sand blasting accentuates cracks.

One set of recommended maximum crack width values is given in the Commentary of the ACI Building Code 318-71. The magnitudes are 0.33 mm (0.013 in.) and 0.40 mm (0.016 in.) for exterior and interior exposure, respectively. For reinforced concrete the usual practice in Europe leads to crack width limits smaller than those accepted in the USA. The CEB-FIP Recommendations indicate for permanent loads maximum crack widths of 0.1 mm (0.004 in.), 0.2 mm (0.008 in.), and 0.3 mm (0.012 in.) for very exposed, unprotected, and protected members, respectively. For maximum loads these limits are increased to 0.2 mm, 0.3 mm in the two first cases. In the last case no value is given, because the limitation depends on appearance. The limiting crack width implied in DIN 4224 is 0.2 mm (0.008 in.). Leonhardt (1971) recommends 0.1 mm (0.004 in.) for prestressed members, 0.2 mm (0.008 in.) for wet conditions, and 0.3 mm (0.012 in.) for dry conditions.

There is in fact little reason for distinguishing crack limitations with respect to reinforced concrete, partially or fully prestressed concrete, provided corrosion protection is employed; obviously, corrosion of high-strength prestressing steels is more harmful than that of regular steels. The 1977 CEB-FIP Recommendations limit crack widths as a function of the susceptibility of the reinforcement to corrosion and the aggressiveness of the environment. Further research is needed to correlate crack width with concrete cover, corrosion, environmental conditions, loading types, stiffness, and fire damage.

8 Effect of Cracking on Stiffness

The stiffness of tall buildings is discussed in subsequent sections. Only a few comments about the relationship of cracking and stiffness are made here. The stiffness of a reinforced concrete member decreases as a result of cracking. This effect has been studied in detail mainly in beams and in simple frames. The stiffness deterioration caused by cracking occurs mainly at first cracking, and less during progressive cracking. Because the extent of cracking varies along the beam, neither the cracked nor uncracked moments of inertia are satisfactory when estimating the stiffness of a cracked beam.

Several good guidelines are available to estimate the effective moment of inertia of a cracked member. The ACI Building Code contains

$$I_e = \gamma^3 I_g + (1 - \gamma^3)I_{cr} \qquad (9.8)$$

in which $\gamma = M_{cr}/M$; M_{cr} = cracking moment; I_g and I_{cr} = the gross (uncracked) and cracked moments of inertia of the member, respectively; and M = maximum applied moment. Eq. 9.8 gives reasonable results even though the effective moment of inertia should also depend on the shape of the moment diagram.

The use of over-all stiffness reduction factors makes it unnecessary to consider the variation of properties along the member. Such factors are approximate but useful in the design of concrete frames. A tentative set of values for frame members under short-time loading has been proposed by Kordina (1972), as in Table 9.4.

For normal steel ratios and for factored (ultimate) load conditions the values in Table 9.4 suggest that I_e of beams is about $0.4I_g$ to $0.5I_g$ and that of columns is about $0.8I_g$.

Approximate values of stiffnesses are satisfactory for the calculation of deflections, but care must be exercised in using approximate values EI in calculating buckling loads or magnification. To arrive at conservative estimates of the buckling loads of a column in a frame, the stiffness of beams should be underestimated but the stiffness of the column must be overestimated to obtain a low value for the effective length of the column.

Crack widths at hinging regions have been found to increase significantly under cyclic loading (Gulkan and Sozen, 1971). After 100 cycles the maximum crack width was 0.50 mm (0.020 in.) as compared with 0.13 mm (0.005 in.) at the initial peak load. These cracks remained open across the entire cross section. The strength of the frames was not affected much by extensive cracking. The great reduction in stiffness as a result of repetitive loading at low levels indicates that cracking may be an important factor. Several informative load-deflection curves are presented by Bertero and McClure (1964), and Gulkan and Sozen (1971). The stiffness deterioration and energy absorption of a simple reinforced concrete model are discussed at length by Takeda et al. (1970).

The actual stiffness of frames is less than anticipated and the difference is caused primarily by shrinkage cracks at beam-column interfaces and by bond slip at joints (Gulkan and Sozen, 1971). Similar effects might be significant in slabs and should be studied. Little is known about the effect of cracking in shear walls on the stiffness of reinforced concrete structures. This question is of primary importance in design for wind loading and seismic forces.

The stiffness of structures is also influenced by microcracking (that is, by cracking at the mortar-aggregate interface and through the cement mortar). If microcracks

Table 9.4 Flexural stiffness of frame members just prior to onset of yielding

Loading (1)	I_e/I_g	
	Rectangular section (2)	T section (3)
Bending and axial compression for symmetrical reinforcement:		
Service loads	$0.6 + 15\,(\rho + \rho')$[a]	
Factored loads	$0.2 + 15\,(\rho + \rho')$[a]	
Pure bending of singly reinforced sections:		
Service loads	$0.6 + 10\rho$	0.65
Factored loads	$0.3 + 10\rho$	0.45
Bending and axial tension:		
Service and factored loads	$15\,(\rho + \rho')$[a]	

[a]The symbols ρ and ρ' represent the tension and compression steel ratios at the restrained ends of the member.

caused by prior loading or by creep exist, the stiffness of concrete may actually decrease by a factor as great as 2 because the softening effect of microcracking is delayed upon reloading. Not much work has been done on this interesting phenomenon.

Several studies have emphasized that the torsional stiffness is reduced significantly as a result of torsional cracking (Lampert, 1971; Rahles, 1970; Ojha, 1974). The cracked torsional stiffness ranges from about 5% of the uncracked stiffness for members with little reinforcement to about 20% for members with a large amount of steel. This reduction means that in many practical situations (Fig. 9.3), transverse beams lose most of their end fixity if the supporting (for example, spandrel) beams crack under the torsional effects.

Tests on reinforced concrete beams under combined flexure and torsion reported by Jackson and Estanero (1972) indicate that the presence of a twisting moment can result in a significant reduction of the postcracking flexural stiffness. This is another factor to be considered in the analysis of the nonlinear behavior of concrete structures.

9   Topics for Further Study

A number of aspects related to cracking, crack control, and stiffness in tall reinforced concrete buildings need detailed investigation. The more important ones are: (1) The effect of major cracks in regions of large moment gradient; (2) cracking at the column-beam and column-slab interface; (3) cracking in shear walls, stiffness loss due to bond slip of negative reinforcement; and (4) cracking (and force transmission) at the shear wall and frame interface. In all cases the problem has two parts: the control of cracking and the effect of cracking on stiffness.

9.3   STIFFNESS OF CONCRETE FRAMES

Modern tall buildings are generally built using light walls and partitions and high-strength materials. The deflections of such structures, especially for lateral loads, are important design criteria.

The knowledge of stiffness of concrete frames with or without filler walls is required in the calculation of deflections and dynamic response. Nonlinear stiffness characteristics are needed in a thorough design for severe earthquakes. This section is concerned mainly with linear stiffness properties; inelastic stiffness and ductility are discussed in Chapters CL-2 and CB-6.

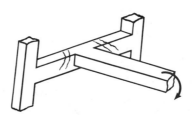

Fig. 9.3 Loss of torsional stiffness

1 Deflections

Fig. 9.4 shows the deflected shape of a rigid frame and a shear wall structure. The relative magnitude of the shear and flexural deformations depends on several factors, primarily on the slenderness of the structure. In open frames the shear deformation generally dominates, although as the slenderness of the building increases, the flexural deformation of the structure becomes appreciable.

Limit states of deflection should be considered with respect to cases in which the deflection may: (1) Hinder or even prevent the use of the structure; (2) affect the behavior of nonloadbearing elements; (3) render finishing operations more difficult; (4) affect the appearance of the construction; and (5) compromise the comfort of the occupants. The variety of these situations, directly related to the different types of materials, building techniques, and human sensitivities, makes it difficult to define limit states in general terms, although Working Group W23 from the International Building Committee, CIB, has been working towards that end. Generally speaking, the deflection limits indicated in codes should be taken merely as traditional values, tested by experience as leading to acceptable conditions in the normal situations. They obviously cannot express quantitatively the whole set of the various cases listed.

2 Drift Limitations

The limiting top deflection for building frames used to be about $1/300$ times the height, but old buildings usually have heavy partitions that limit deformations. Many modern structures are designed today in which the frame resists the entire lateral load. A wind drift limit of $1/500$ seems to result in a building without excessive deflections that could cause cracking of partitions, excessive vibrations, or large secondary effects. Motion discomfort has not been reported in concrete buildings.

Various approximate and refined analysis methods are available for calculating the forces and deflections in tall building frames. The drift limit to be used depends on the method used for deflection analysis and on the idealization. Most methods of

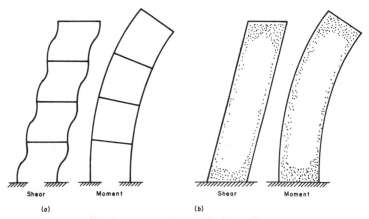

Fig. 9.4 Deflection components: (a) Open frame; (b) solid cantilever (shear wall)

analysis tend to overestimate the deflection, because they ignore the participation of nonstructural elements in the building. Chapter CB-5 and the report of ACI Committee 442 (1971) contain summaries of various approaches. Numerous computer programs are available for the determination of forces and deformations. It is generally recommended that axial deformation of columns should be included if the frame height-to-width ratio exceeds about 3:4. Sophisticated programs include foundation deformations, second-order geometry effects, and nonlinear behavior. If accurate analysis is used, the drift limit should probably be considerably smaller than 1/500.

The drift limit also varies with local ideas and customs. A square 32-story office building in Bratislava (Cizek, 1973) consists of a central square core and prefabricated frames along the outside edges. The core is very slender and the drift index was 1/810 for the core and 1/628 for the frames. Additional wall bracing was added to reduce the drift ratio to 1/2175.

Several earthquake regulations (Mexico, New Zealand, Chile, and Venezuela) include lateral sway and drift limitations (International Association for Earthquake Engineering, 1970). In Mexico the maximum drift between floors cannot exceed 0.002 or 0.003 according to the intended use of the buildings (public or housing). In New Zealand the corresponding value is 0.0025. This value can be doubled if convenient clearances for nonstructural elements are provided. Such clearances shall be at least three times the computed deflections under the design lateral forces. In Chile drift limitations are: (1) 0.002 if windows and filling walls can be damaged by the drift; and (2) 0.003 and 0.004 for soft and hard soils respectively, if clearances are provided to avoid damage of nonstructural elements. The same clearance limits as those of New Zealand are adopted. In Venezuela maximum drift between any two points on a vertical line of a building shall not exceed 0.002 (roofs and floors without live load being excepted). In any discussion of drift limitations under seismic loads it is important to distinguish between elastically computed drift and actual drift, which will be approximately equal to the elastic drift times the ductility factor.

The variation of deflection estimates between approximate and sophisticated approaches is great. Results obtained by two elaborate analyses may also differ considerably, by as much as 30%. Some of the reasons for the differences are: (1) The use of center-to-center dimensions versus analyses considering finite dimensions of the joints; (2) inclusion of axial deformations of columns; and (3) consideration of the stiffening effects of nonstructural elements.

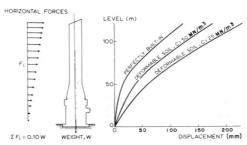

Fig. 9.5 Horizontal displacement of tall building

The magnification effect in columns may be considerable. Details of second-order analyses of concrete frames are presented in Chapter CB-8.

The horizontal stiffness of a tall building is often controlled by the stiffness of its foundation. Consequently studies of soil characteristics are recommended in order to define this deformability accurately. Fig. 9.5 shows the deformed line of a tall building on: (1) Rigid foundation; (2) elastic foundation with a modulus of compressibility $C = 50$ N/cm³, and (3) elastic foundation with a modulus of compressibility $C = 25$ N/cm³. These compressibilities correspond to normal conditions for dynamic loads in hard clays. It should be noted that an extensive discussion of allowable sway deflections is presented in Chapter SB-4.

3 Vertical Deflections

The interest of determining vertical deflections derives from two main reasons: (1) The need to limit these deflections in slabs and beams; and (2) the effect of vertical deflections on the over-all structural behavior.

In the first case deflections can be studied element by element. In a simplified way deflections are usually controlled by stipulating minimum thicknesses for both beams and slabs. Codes also include recommendations for computing deflections. As a general criticism of these recommendations it can be said that the effect of cracking is still taken into consideration in a very rough way. This is an area where improvement is urgently needed. Such improvement can be obtained by a conceptual unification of the theories of cracking and deformation leading to a suitable idealization of moment-curvature relationships. For computing deflections under service conditions sufficient accuracy can be assured by means of bilinear diagrams of the type recommended in the Portuguese Code for Reinforced Concrete (Fig. 9.6). Integration of these diagrams in typical cases (e.g., cantilever and simply-supported beams) yields diagrams giving the maximum displacement as a function of the modulus of elasticity of concrete, E_c, the maximum reduced bending moment, $m = M/bd^2$, and the percentage of tensile reinforcement, $\rho = A_s/bd$ (Fig. 9.7). Prestressed concrete floor systems in high-rise buildings are generally lighter and shallower than nonprestressed systems. However, such floor systems are usually stiffer than comparable steel systems and are generally considered stiff enough for

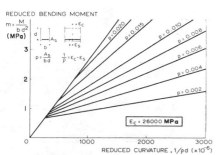

Fig. 9.6 Bilinear moment curvature diagrams for computing deformability of reinforced concrete beams

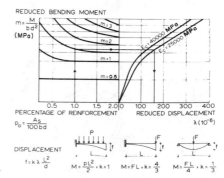

Fig. 9.7 Diagram for computing deflections of reinforced concrete beams

wind resistance. Since deflections in prestressed floors are controlled by pre-stressing, there should be little camber or deflection in a properly designed floor system. Of course, the long-time effects as a result of loss of prestress should be taken into account.

Effects of vertical deflections resulting from shortening of the columns and walls on the over-all structural behavior are referred to in the introduction to this chapter and in Chapter CB-10. Foundation settlements and differential shortening of vertical elements due to axial loading may considerably modify the distribution of bending moments, as exemplified in Fig. 9.8.

Acceleration records obtained in Los Angeles during the San Fernando earth-quake of February, 1971 show the important influence of vertical stiffness on the amplification of the vertical components of the soil vibration. Fig. 9.9 indicates a typical record (Muto, 1971) showing that from the basement to the top of the building vertical acceleration was amplified about four times. Note that this amplification, depending on the position of the accelerograph in the building, could also result from the over-all horizontal deflection of the total structure as a cantilever and from the vertical deformability of the members directly supporting the accelerograph. However in this and other cases amplification seems mainly to be due to the building vibrating as a vertical oscillator.

4 Torsional Deformations

In tall buildings, rotational deflections due to torsion about a vertical axis may be very important. This is particularly true in H-shaped buildings. The heavy damage due to the earthquake of July, 1967 suffered by the corner columns at the lower levels of Mene Grande Building in Caracas (Fig. 9.10) resulted from the torsional behavior of the building (Ferry Borges et al., 1969). In Caracas some other analogous cases were observed. Several earthquake regulations impose torsional stiffness and resistance studies. When designing a tall building it is also desirable to assure that the natural frequencies of bending and torsion are sufficiently different. If this condition is not satisfied beating may occur, leading to an undesirable amplification of oscillations (Fig. 9.11). This association of modes may be particularly inconvenient for earthquake loadings mainly due to the rotational component of soil vibrations (Newmark, 1969).

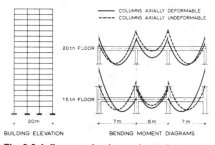

Fig. 9.8 Influence of column shortening on bending moments in beams

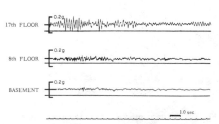

Fig. 9.9 Amplification of vertical vibration in tall building (San Fernando earthquake, 1971)

These considerations emphasize the desirability of a complete three-dimensional analysis taking as unknowns at each floor level, at least, the horizontal displacements in two orthogonal directions and the rotation around the vertical axis.

5 Bending Stiffness of Members

The bending stiffness of frame members is required in computer programs and in the calculation of deflections. Two approaches have been given in Section 9.2.

6 Unsymmetrical Buildings

In symmetrical structures the torsional effects due to lateral wind loads are generally small and are therefore neglected. However, due to site conditions or architectural design considerations or both, buildings may be unsymmetrical in floor plan and sometimes also in elevation. The following is a method for preliminary selection of the stiffness of an unsymmetrical tall concrete building subjected to wind loading. The stiffness computation is based on a preselected deflection criterion.

The first duty of the structural designer is to try to minimize the effects of torsion under wind forces; this is very difficult to accomplish sometimes. In general, the objective is to have the center of rigidity of the structure so located that the eccentricity with respect to the applied wind (or seismic) forces is kept to a minimum, and to arrange the stiffening elements to give adequate torsional stiffness. The approach is generally an intuitive one, with some preliminary calculations made to locate the center of rigidity of the structure so as to minimize eccentricity in the critical wind direction. Torsional effects are thereby minimized.

Fig. 9.10 Mene Grande Building in Caracas damaged by earthquake, 1967 (Courtesy: J. Ferry Borges)

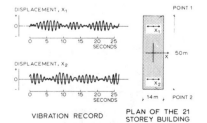

Fig. 9.11 Beating of vibration due to association of transverse and torsional modes

There are two types of noninteractive systems: (1) Systems with reinforced concrete frames around the perimeter of the building; and (2) reinforced concrete structures with only shear wall elements having stiffnesses which vary similarly over the height. In either case, the selection of the preliminary stiffness of the building can be isolated either on a floor-by-floor basis as in the case of frames, or in terms of the over-all deflection of the structure as in the case of shear-wall systems. This assumption requires that the structure should be regular with no abrupt changes in stiffnesses and reasonably similar floor-to-floor heights.

Procedures for the analysis of unsymmetrical buildings are presented in Chapter CB-5.

7 Nonlinear Behavior

Tall building frames ordinarily behave elastically during wind and minor earthquake loading, although the contribution of nonstructural secondary elements usually introduces nonlinear behavior even at low loads. Inelastic action is very important in coupled shear wall structures (see Section 9.5 of this chapter, and Chapter CB-6).

Nonlinear behavior is expected to occur during severe earthquakes. The following factors affect the nonlinear load-deflection characteristics of a concrete frame: (1) Yielding of the tension steel; (2) the P-Δ effect; (3) the amount of compression steel; (4) shear deterioration near and in rigid joints; (5) bond deterioration; (6) confinement; and (7) compression crushing. Recent tests of frames and joints under repeated reversed loading indicate that each of these factors is important.

Details must be designed with care to assure deformation (energy-absorption) capacity of the frame. The best way is to confine the concrete in and near joints and to delay shear and anchorage failures. Nonlinearity is beneficial because it represents energy absorption, but the hysteresis loop must be stable, that is, the force and deformation amplitude capacities should not decrease during cyclic loadings.

Although the deformation capacity of concrete frames reduces the forces created in a severe earthquake, excessive deformations may destroy secondary elements and the content of the building and thus produce an unacceptable economic loss. In such cases structural shear walls may be necessary to limit displacements (Fintel, 1974a).

Some idealized nonlinear load-deflection relationships have been proposed for analysis. One simple moment-rotation curve is shown in Fig. 9.12. Other load-displacement or moment-rotation curves were proposed by Takeda et al. (1970) and by Bertero and McClure (1964).

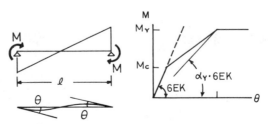

Fig. 9.12 Moment-rotation relationship of flexural member

Relatively few measured load-deflection relationships are available for reinforced concrete frames subject to reversed loading (Takeda et al., 1970). On this topic, see also Chapter CB-6.

9.4 EFFECTS OF SHEAR WALLS ON STIFFNESS

A study of buildings exposed to a recent earthquake (Fintel, 1973) has indicated that properly designed and detailed shear walls perform well under seismic loading. Their excellent behavior under wind loading has been proven over the years. The dual function of shear walls as vertical load-carrying and horizontal stiffening elements is well recognized. Herein only the second aspect is discussed, namely that of providing stiffness in tall concrete buildings against lateral loads.

1 Elastic Stiffness of Uncracked Shear Walls

For reasons of economy and performance shear walls in a building are generally provided, arranged and proportioned in such a fashion that the combined effect of lateral loads and minimum gravity loads yields none or only very small tensile stresses in the shear wall. When large tensile stresses are absent it is proper to assess the in-plane stiffness of a shear wall or an assembly of shear walls of a building on the basis of an elastic analysis. Normally linear elastic behavior is assumed in the computations. However, nonlinear elastic analysis could easily be employed, for example if the equivalent frame method were used.

Coupling beams and coupling slabs will rarely remain without appreciable tensile stresses. The loss in stiffness—due to cracking—of the connecting medium is considerable and should be accounted for in the analysis. The behavior and characteristics of coupling beams are discussed in Section 9.5 of this chapter, and in Chapter CB-6.

In tall buildings the elements that resist lateral loading should be, and commonly are, arranged symmetrically in plan with respect to the axes of the building. They are then subjected to axial load and to bending. On unusual sites, shear walls and columns may not follow perpendicular grid lines, or cores may be off center. Both these situations will lead to torsional stresses in the various elements, in addition to normal and flexural stresses.

Whereas rigorous and simplified elastic methods for the analysis of buildings with symmetrically arranged vertical elements are well established, there is—due to the complexity of the problem—still a considerable lack of reliable simplified methods for the analysis of shear-wall structures in which the walls are arranged in a random fashion. Examples of such structures follow.

Plane Coupled Shear Walls. These are widely used in apartment buildings (Fig. 9.13) and prove to be economical because they divide one apartment unit from another, carry gravity loading, and provide stiffness and strength against lateral loading. Height to width ratios H/B of up to 7 are quite common. The elastic stiffness of plane shear walls depends in addition on the over-all geometry and also on the span and cross-sectional dimensions of the connecting beams or slabs. In general, stiffness in the lateral direction is rarely if ever a problem with this particular layout for up to about 35 stories. However, in the longitudinal direction stiffening elements in addition to the stairwells and elevator shafts must frequently be provided to limit lateral deflections (Schwaighofer and Microys, 1974).

Shear Wall-Frame Buildings. In office structures, where shear walls rarely extend over the entire width of the building (Fig. 9.14), it is mandatory from a stiffness point of view that the interaction between frames, cores, and shear walls be considered. The familiar diagram (Fig. 9.15) shows that in the lower stories the shear walls lend lateral support to the frames, whereas in the top stories the frames restrain the lateral displacements of the shear walls. Structural systems in which shear walls and frames are combined have been used to about 75 stories. Stiffness considerations frequently govern the design of such systems. The equivalent frame method (Schwaighofer and Microys, 1969) directly supplies the elastic horizontal displacements of each individual story.

Shear Walls with Outriggers. In cases where excessive lateral displacements are encountered, outriggers at one or several levels may be provided (Fig. 9.16) to mobilize the axial stiffness of the exterior columns. These are effective in reducing the lateral deflection of the building usually only if they are one or several stories deep and assisted by extensionally rather stiff columns. Over-all reduction in lateral displacements and base moments of about 20% to 30% is common. The base shear is little altered by providing outriggers.

Tube Structures. In exceptionally slender (or very tall) buildings the tube concept is frequently employed (Fig. 9.17). Frames with closely spaced (sometimes wide) columns and deep spandrel beams form the periphery of the building, which is usually rectangular in plan. The elastic stiffness of such tubes is largely influenced by the spandrel depth and to a much lesser degree by the width of the columns. The stiffness of the tube can be adjusted in a fairly wide range by a judicious choice of column spacing, column size, spandrel depth, and the like. A three-dimensional analysis or a modified two-dimensional equivalent frame analysis (Coull and

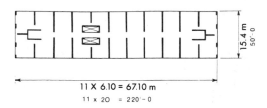

11 X 6.10 = 67.10 m
11 x 20 = 220'-0

15.4 m
50'-0

Fig. 9.13 Plan of typical apartment building

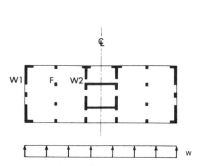

Fig. 9.14 Plan of shear wall-frame building

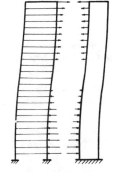

Fig. 9.15 Interaction of frame and wall

Subedi, 1971; Khan and Amin, 1973; Ast and Schwaighofer, 1974) will provide the floor displacements.

Nonplanar Coupled Shear Walls. Recently elastic methods of analysis for shear-wall structures which consider in-plane, out-of-plane, and torsional deformation have been advanced (Ricaldoni, 1958; Stamato, 1966; Winokur and Glück, 1968a; Rosman, 1969; Michael, 1969; Glück, 1970; Heidebrecht and Swift, 1971; Tso and Biswas, 1973; Vlasov, 1961). These are of particular importance when the location of the center of rotation and the line of action of the lateral loading differ appreciably (Fig. 9.18) and when the assembly of vertical elements is torsionally weak. Most of these methods involve considerable computational effort when applied to practical problems. Reliable simplified methods of analysis are needed. Table 9.5 shows representative results of the relative contributions of the torsional deflections of four buildings (Colaco and Banavalkar, 1974) to the over-all building deflection under the critical wind load. It can be seen that in general the contribution of the torsional deflection at a corner to the over-all lateral deflection of the building varies from 5% to 20% for eccentricity ratios (e/b) varying from 0.4 to 0.7.

Methods of Computations. For nonsymmetric buildings, if the structure consists of reinforced concrete frames around the perimeter of the building, or of shear wall elements having constant stiffness ratios over the entire height, a procedure has been suggested (Colaco and Banavalkar, 1974) for the preliminary selection of the stiffness. A preselected maximum deflection criterion is chosen.

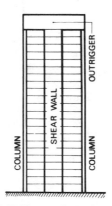

Fig. 9.16 Shear wall with outrigger

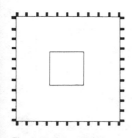

Fig. 9.17 Tube structure

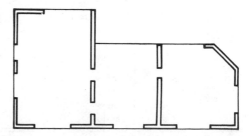

Fig. 9.18 Building with asymmetrically arranged shear walls

Then the center of rigidity $(\bar{x}, \bar{y})$ of the system of frames (or shear walls) is obtained by solving two simultaneous equations in $\bar{x}$ and $\bar{y}$ which expresses the equilibrium of the horizontal in-plane forces in two orthogonal directions. In Fig. 9.19 the equation of line AB is

$$y = x \tan\theta_i + c \tag{9.9}$$

$$x_1 = \frac{(\bar{y} - c)}{\tan\theta_i} \tag{9.10}$$

$$C_i = |\bar{x} - x_1| \tag{9.11}$$

$$R_i = C_i \sin\theta_i \tag{9.12}$$

Table 9.5 Relative magnitude of corner deflections due to torsion and total deflection of four buildings

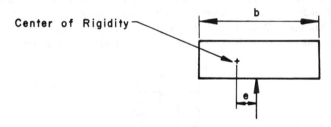

Center of Rigidity

Building (1)	Number of stories (2)	Type of system (3)	Eccentricity ratio, e/b_{max} (4)	Torsional deflection, Δ_t, in millimeters (inches) (5)	Total deflection, Δ, in millimeters (inches) (6)	$\dfrac{\Delta_t}{\Delta}$ (7)
A	31	Exterior frame	0.06	21.00 (0.83)	207.00 (8.14)	0.101
B	24	Shear wall frame inter-action	0.05	24.00 (0.95)	198.00 (7.80)	0.122
C	37	Shear wall frame inter-action	0.07	55.00 (2.16)	277.00 (10.92)	0.190
D	38	Shear wall frame inter-action	0.04	13.00 (0.52)	247.00 (9.72)	0.053

The computation of the center of rigidity is given by solving the two simultaneous equations which maintain equilibrium in the x and y directions. Hence

$$\sum_{i=1}^{n} K_i R_i \cos\theta_i = 0 \tag{9.13}$$

$$\sum_{i=1}^{n} K_i R_i \sin\theta_i = 0 \tag{9.14}$$

and

$$J = \sum_{i=1}^{n} K_i R_i^2 \tag{9.15}$$

in which $K_i = k_i L_i$; K_i = stiffness of a frame of length L; and k_i = stiffness of a frame per unit length.

To determine the stiffness of the various frames in an unsymmetrical structure, one simplifying assumption is made. For the general case of a n-sided figure, the assumption used is that the stiffness of each frame is proportional to its length. Hence the only unknown is the value of k, the frame stiffness per unit length.

Once the geometry of the building is defined, Eqs. 9.9 to 9.14 give the center of rigidity $(\bar{x}, \bar{y})$. For the wind force (V_i) acting on any face of the building, the eccentricity e_i is computed by geometry. Hence, the torsional moment $M_T = V_i e_i$ is known (Fig. 9.20).

The deflection of the structure under the specified wind force V_i is made up of two components: the direct deflection Δ_d for the wind force applied through the center of rigidity, combined with the torsional deflection Δ_t. The direct deflection Δ_d is

$$\Delta_d = \frac{V_i}{\displaystyle\sum_{i=1}^{n} kL_i \cos^2\gamma_i} \tag{9.16}$$

in which $\cos\gamma_i$ are the direction cosines of each frame with respect to the wind

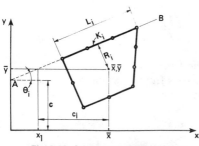

Fig. 9.19 Center of rigidity of frame

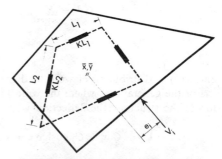

Fig. 9.20 Center of rigidity of wall system

direction. This deflection is in the direction of force V_i. The torsional rotation is given by

$$\beta_i = \frac{V_i e_i}{J} e_i \tag{9.17}$$

The torsional deflection of each frame in its own direction is then

$$\Delta_{ti} = R_i \beta_i \tag{9.18}$$

The maximum deflection Δ is then given by the vectorial addition of Δ_d and Δ_{ti}.

Since the maximum deflection Δ is specified for that story, the value of k is directly obtained. The total stiffness of each frame is then given by $K_i = kL_i$ in which L_i = length of the frame.

For a framed-type structure, this method can be utilized to determine frame stiffnesses on a floor-by-floor basis. For most buildings, architectural considerations will generally determine the depth of either the spandrel beam or the column. If the ratio of column-to-beam stiffness is known or can be reasonably estimated, or if the stiffness of either the spandrel beam or column is known, using the Maney-Goldberg equations (Parcel and Moorman, 1962), the member sizes in the frame can be determined.

For noninteractive systems which consist of shear walls only, if the variation of the stiffness of each individual wall over the height of the building is known and is the same for all walls, the only unknown is then the stiffness of the wall at its base. The method described for frame-type structures can then be used to determine the stiffness of the shear walls at the base.

For interactive systems, the determination of the preliminary stiffness values of the frames and shear walls is more complicated. Heidebrecht and Smith (1973) have developed a closed form differential equation for a symmetrical system with constant stiffness over the height of the structure. The governing equation is

$$\frac{d^4 y}{d x^4} - \alpha^2 \frac{d^2 y}{d x^2} = \frac{w(x)}{E_w I_w} \tag{9.19}$$

in which $E_w I_w$ are the EI values of the wall, $\alpha^2 = GA/E_w I_w$, and

$$GA = \sum_{\text{columns}} \frac{12 E_c I_c}{h^2} \left[\frac{1}{1 + \frac{2 I_c}{\left(\dfrac{I_{b1}}{L_1} + \dfrac{I_{b2}}{L_2}\right)}} \right] \tag{9.20}$$

and $w(x)$ = distribution of wind load over the height.

For the general case where the wind load varies from w_0 at the base to w_1 at the top of the structure, the deflection $y(x)$ is given by

$$y(x) = C_1 + C_2 x + C_3 \cosh \alpha x + C_4 \sinh \alpha x$$

$$- \frac{w_0 x^2}{2 E I \alpha^2} - \frac{(w_1 - w_0) x^3}{6 E I \alpha^2 H} \tag{9.21}$$

in which

$$C_1 = -\frac{w_1}{EI\alpha_4} - \frac{\beta \sinh \alpha H}{\alpha^3 EI} \qquad (9.22)$$

$$C_2 = \frac{\beta}{\alpha^2 EI} \qquad (9.23)$$

$$C_3 = \left(\frac{w_1}{EI\alpha^4} + \frac{\beta \sinh \alpha H}{\alpha^3 EI}\right)\frac{1}{\cosh\alpha H} \qquad (9.24)$$

$$C_4 = -\frac{\beta}{\alpha^3 EI} \qquad (9.25)$$

and

$$\beta = (w_1 + w_0)\frac{H}{2} - \frac{(w_1 - w_0)}{\alpha^2 H} \qquad (9.26)$$

In order to be able to determine the stiffnesses of the frames, the stiffness of the shear wall has to be known or assumed. For the case of constant stiffness of shear wall and of frames, the only unknown in the equation is the value of α. Since the maximum deflection of the building is prescribed, the value of α can be obtained from the above equations.

Figs. 9.21 and 9.22 show the variation of αH as a function of the value $\Delta_{final}/\Delta_{cant}$ where Δ_{final} is the prescribed maximum deflection and Δ_{cant} is the free deflection of the shear wall if it carries the entire wind load by itself. Fig. 9.21 is the curve for a constant wind load w_0 over the full height of the structure. Fig. 9.22 gives the curve for the case of $W_1 = 2W_0$.

For an unsymmetrical structure, the following steps are required (see Fig. 9.23):

1. For preliminary purposes, assume a value of primary deflection, Δ_{final}, excluding torsional effects.

2. Assume a value of EI of the wall.

3. For each direction of wind force the following computations are required: (a) Compute Δ_{cant} the deflection of shear wall, assuming it carries the wind load by itself; (b) from Fig. 9.21 or Fig. 9.22, compute the value of αH; (c) determine the value of equivalent frame stiffness $GA = E_w I_w \alpha^2$. Distribute the total GA value to each frame based on the length of the frame and direction cosine of each frame with respect to the applied direction of wind load, as $GA = \Sigma kL_i \cos^2\gamma_i$ in which k = the frame stiffness per unit length. Then the GA value of each frame is kL_i.

4. Compute the J value of the system at every floor by using Eq. 9.15, which neglects the torsional and warping stiffness of the walls. This is on the conservative side.

5. Compute the shear force distribution between walls and frames at each level for the critical wind direction. The shear in the wall at any level is given by

$$V_w(x) = -E_w I_w \frac{d^3y}{dx^3} \tag{9.27}$$

while

$$V_f(x) = GA\frac{dy}{dx} \tag{9.28}$$

gives the shear in the frame.

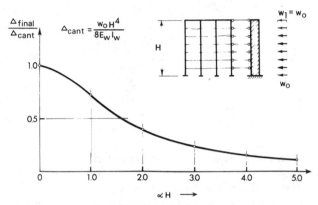

Fig. 9.21 Value of αH for $w_1 = w_0$

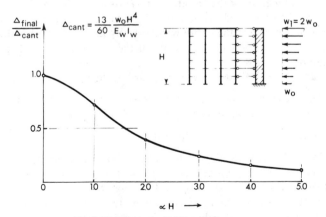

Fig. 9.22 Value of αH for $w_1 = 2w_0$

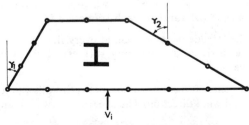

Fig. 9.23 Unsymmetrical interactive system

6. Distribute the shear in the frame to each frame in the same manner as the distribution of the *GA* values.

7. Compute the center of rigidity at each floor based on the force distribution between the various frames and shear wall.

8. Compute the eccentricity e_i by geometry.

9. Compute the torsional moment at each level $M_t = V_i e_i$ in which V_i = total external shear at that level.

10. Compute the torsional rotation at each level $\theta_i = M_i / J$.

11. Compute the torsional deflection $\Delta_{ti} = \theta_i R_i$.

12. Compute the maximum deflection as the vectorial sum of Δ_{ti} and Δ_d.

2 Deflections of High-Rise Shear Wall Buildings

The interest in determining lateral deflections is derived from the need to limit sway and interstory drift, as they may affect: (1) The stability of the structures; (2) the performance of nonstructural elements; and (3) the comfort of the occupants.

The 1973 National Building Code of Canada specifies that the maximum lateral deflection of the top of the building should be equal to or smaller than 1/500 of the total height of the building. This limitation, as similar ones in other codes, is arbitrary, but is based on the experience that tall reinforced concrete buildings designed in recent years which meet this requirement appear to have performed satisfactorily with respect to stability of individual members and the structure as a whole, the integrity of nonstructural elements, and the comfort of the occupants (Fintel, 1974b). Drift limits are also discussed in Chapter SB-4.

Frequently deflection measurements (Wiss and Curth, 1970) on actual structures indicate gross discrepancies between the actual and the computed displacements. These may be due to idealizations made in the mathematical model, on account of neglecting the increase in over-all stiffness, due to partitions, curtain walls, and the like.

Several studies have been conducted to check the accuracy of stiffness calculations of tall buildings. Since it is difficult to apply measurable loads for deflection measurements, most investigators have been concerned mainly with the determination of natural periods of vibration, which is an indirect measure of stiffness. Good agreement between calculated and observed values for the fundamental period of vibration for some recently completed tall reinforced concrete buildings has been reported (Libbey, 1974). Figs. 9.24 and 9.25 show typical floor plans and comparisons of measured and calculated fundamental periods for a 27-story and a 37-story building, respectively, for which the agreement is very good. It should be noted that the shear walls are arranged quite symmetrically and that the coupling between them is very definite. Because the fundamental period, T, and the top deflection, Δ_T, of the building are related by

$$T = 2\pi \sqrt{\frac{k.\Delta_T}{g}} \qquad (9.29)$$

good agreement of measured and computed fundamental period implies that the theoretical and actual deflections should agree well. In Fig. 9.26 values for k are given for several types of cantilevers.

Using Eq. 9.29, for a shear-wall building subjected to 1.45 kN/m² (30 psf) wind and using $T = 0.05 \ N$, the corresponding deflection index (H/Δ) is $H/\Delta = 8500/N$, which gives, for $N = 40$ stories, $H/\Delta = 2125$ (Libbey, 1974).

Another investigation (Wiss and Curth, 1970) was concerned with the deflections and natural period of a 56-story reinforced concrete building with plan dimensions of 27.2 m by 28.0 m (89 ft by 92 ft) and a height of 162.2 m (532 ft), including a 21.3 m (70 ft) high penthouse on top. Stiffness was provided by a core and shear walls up to the 42nd floor. Frame bracing was utilized above the 42nd floor. At a wind velocity of 112 km/hr (70 mph) at the top of the building the drift was 38 mm (1.5

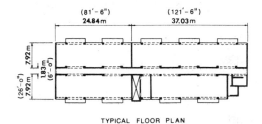

TYPICAL FLOOR PLAN

Method of determination	Fundamental period, in seconds	
	Longitudinal	Transverse
(1)	(2)	(3)
Empirical $T = \dfrac{0.05\ H^*}{\sqrt{D}}$ UBC	0.81	1.51
$T = 0.05\ N$ (Hawaiian experience)	1.35	1.35
Calculated	1.05	1.35
Measured by Taoka et al.	1.12	1.36

*In which D = over-all width of building, in feet, and H = height of building, in feet. When H and D are measured in meters, $T = 0.0906\,\dfrac{H}{\sqrt{D}}$.

Fig. 9.24 Kapiolani Manor (27 stories)

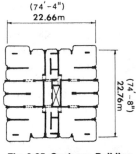

Fig. 9.25 Contessa Building (37 stories)

Method of determination	Fundamental period, in seconds	
	North-South	East-West
(1)	(2)	(3)
Empirical $T = \dfrac{0.05\ H}{\sqrt{D}}$ UBC	1.82	1.82
$T = 0.05\ N$ (Hawaiian experience)	1.85	1.85
Calculated	1.56	1.46
Measured by Taoka et al.	1.52	1.41

in.). The measured fundamental period was about 4.0 sec. The measured deflection is considerably less than the calculated value.

One set of measurements indicates that the stiffness of a building decreased with time. The fundamental period increased from 0.44 to 0.47 two years later. The stiffness varies as the square of the period; hence the decrease in stiffness is about 13%. Several small earthquakes occurred during the two years.

Sometimes, however, theoretical and actual natural frequencies may differ greatly, as Fig. 9.27 shows for a 40-story apartment building (Libbey, 1974). Note that the stiffnesses of the individual shear walls in this building vary greatly. Of considerable interest is also the influence which a base rotation has on the fundamental period and therefore on the top deflection.

3 Abrupt Changes in Stiffness of Shear Walls

Stiffness per se is neither good nor bad: it depends on the circumstances. Obviously a certain minimum amount of stiffness must be provided to limit lateral displacements and to achieve a satisfactory comfort level. In shear wall buildings of

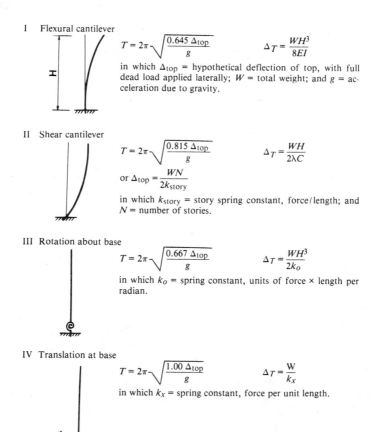

I Flexural cantilever

$$T = 2\pi \sqrt{\frac{0.645\,\Delta_{top}}{g}} \qquad \Delta_T = \frac{WH^3}{8EI}$$

in which Δ_{top} = hypothetical deflection of top, with full dead load applied laterally; W = total weight; and g = acceleration due to gravity.

II Shear cantilever

$$T = 2\pi \sqrt{\frac{0.815\,\Delta_{top}}{g}} \qquad \Delta_T = \frac{WH}{2\lambda C}$$

or $\Delta_{top} = \dfrac{WN}{2k_{story}}$

in which k_{story} = story spring constant, force/length; and N = number of stories.

III Rotation about base

$$T = 2\pi \sqrt{\frac{0.667\,\Delta_{top}}{g}} \qquad \Delta_T = \frac{WH^3}{2k_o}$$

in which k_o = spring constant, units of force × length per radian.

IV Translation at base

$$T = 2\pi \sqrt{\frac{1.00\,\Delta_{top}}{g}} \qquad \Delta_T = \frac{W}{k_x}$$

in which k_x = spring constant, force per unit length.

Fig. 9.26 Formulas for computing fundamental periods of tall structures of uniform stiffness

the type shown in Fig. 9.13 there is usually ample stiffnes provided in the lateral direction by the coupled shear walls, which extend ordinarily the entire height of the building. Intuitively a designer would be quite prepared to dispense with part or all of the shear wall in the top floors to achieve greater flexibility in architectural layout.

Fig. 9.28(a) shows a typical plane shear wall subjected to uniform loading (Schwaighofer and Microys, 1974). The shear wall is replaced by a frame in the upper stories. The changes which take place in the shear wall moments and the lateral displacements are shown in Fig. 9.28(b) and 9.28(c) as more and more frame is substituted for the wall. The moment at the base of the shear wall does not change if, at the top, a frame is substituted for the walls, as can be seen in Fig. 9.28(b) for $a = 6, 14,$ and 16 ($a =$ number of stories in which a frame replaces the shear wall). On the other hand, the top deflection of the bent increases rapidly with a as Fig. 9.28(c) demonstrates. It is important to note (but not shown in Fig. 9.28) that the shear forces in the connecting beams below the cut-off points are only affected to a minor degree, except that, at and immediately below this level, the shear forces in the beams increase—in this example by about 50%—above those which would occur at the same level in the shear wall if they were continued to the top of the bent. Therefore, additional shear reinforcing in the beams in the vicinity of the cut-off level may become necessary. In this example the change from a very stiff system, the shear wall, to a rather flexible system, the frame, occurs abruptly at one level. Less severe architectural layout requirements or necessary stiffness requirements may suggest other solutions.

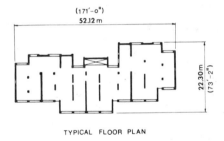

TYPICAL FLOOR PLAN

Method of determination	Fundamental period, in seconds	
	Longitudinal	Transverse
(1)	(2)	(3)
Empirical		
$T = \dfrac{0.05\,H}{\sqrt{D}}$ UBC	1.38	2.11
$T = 0.05\,N$ (Hawaiian experience)	2.00	2.00
Calculated		
cantilevered shear walls without base rotation		4.74
cantilevered shear walls with base rotation		6.66
dynamic analysis		4.45
Measured		
by Taoka et al.	2.05	2.10

Fig. 9.27 Yacht Harbor Towers

Fig. 9.29(a) shows an elevation of a typical shear wall where only one of the walls has been discontinued and replaced by a frame. The shear walls are interconnected by 165-mm (6.5-in.) thick floor slabs. The over-all characteristics of this system are similar to the one shown in Fig. 9.28; but while in that case ancillary problems were of a minor nature, here this configuration results in a drastically different shear interaction force distribution. This can be seen from Fig. 9.29(b) which shows the shear interaction forces in the connecting slabs in a solid line, and superimposed (in a dotted line) the interaction forces when both walls are carried to the top. It is significant that the maximum shear force in the slab for the case of a discontinued shear wall is more than double the maximum shear force if both walls are continued to the top. In the first case the shear force is largest at the cut-off level and decreases monotonically with decreasing elevation, whereas in the second case the shear force distribution follows the familiar pattern and displays its maximum at approximately one-third of the height of the building. In addition to this anomaly, note should be taken of the large horizontal forces in the connecting links at or near the cut-off level. Of particular interest is the reversal of sign of these forces which generally occurs [Fig. 9.29(c)].

From these two examples it can be concluded that sudden changes in cross section or configuration, or both, of the vertical load-carrying elements (staircases, shear walls, and the like) should be avoided and a more gradual transition, where possible, from stiffer to more flexible elements should be attempted.

4   Stiffness of Shear Walls with Cracked Sections

In tall buildings the individual wall sections in shear walls are usually slender members, two or several of which are coupled by aid of beams or slabs.

Normally these shear walls act as cantilever beams and are most highly stressed near the base. Frequently these wall sections have a constant cross section, though the axial force and the moment change appreciably with height. The extent of

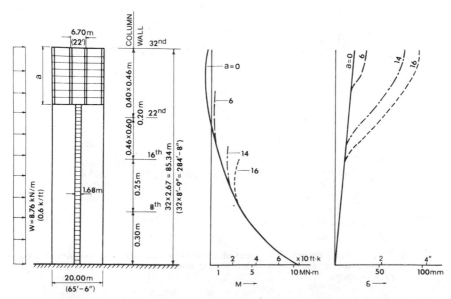

Fig. 9.28 Effect of abrupt changes in stiffness on moments and deflections of shear wall

cracking (due to external loading) in various sections of the wall will differ. The *EI*-value should reflect at each section the amount of reinforcing, the extent of cracking, the effects of axial loads, and the inelastic behavior of steel and concrete along the entire length of the shear wall. Usually the connecting beams are more highly stressed (see Section 9.5) and frequently their behavior differs markedly from that of flexural members because of small span/depth ratios. Economic restraints will limit designers of tall buildings to the use of the elastic methods of analysis. However, an attempt should be made to model the relative stiffness of interacting shear wall and shear wall-frame bents because the relative stiffness of the various bents influences the interaction forces between them greatly.

In some tall buildings, the shear walls which resist lateral forces may be post-tensioned vertically. The vertical tendons may extend to the bottom of the foundation. Such tendons will tie the elements together and will increase the resistance of shear walls or shafts to resist lateral forces. Under some circumstances, these tendons may also give a considerable amount of ductility to the shear walls or shafts.

9.5 COUPLING BEAMS

The problem of interaction between coupling beams and adjoining walls has received considerable attention from the theoretical point of view as well as from the experimental side. Studies by Rosman (1962), Michael (1967), Schwaighofer and Microys (1969), Hall (1969), and Schwaighofer (1969), are concerned with the point

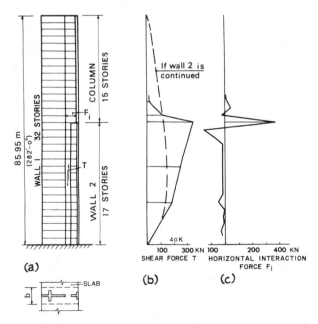

Fig. 9.29 Effect of abrupt changes in stiffness on shear force and axial force in connecting beam: (a) Elevation; (b) shear force in connecting beams; (c) axial interaction force in connecting beams

of contraflexure in and the end rigidity of coupling beams as they affect the elastic analysis of shear walls, whereas investigations by Paulay (1971), Paparoni and Holoma (1971), Luisoni et al. (1970), Schwaighofer and Collins (1976), and studies at the Laboratorio Nacional de Engenharia Civil (1971), relate to the actual behavior of coupling elements in coupled shear walls. Chapter CB-6 presents experimental studies and design recommendations for coupling beams.

1 Design Considerations

Connecting beams do not receive important loads other than those originating from the shear walls which they join and connect. As the name implies, the main function of coupling beams is to provide a path for transmitting forces between interconnected walls.

The dimensions of coupling beams are normally prescribed and cannot be changed easily, due to limitations either in the necessary door heights or on the wall thickness in a given story. Flexural and shear stresses in the coupling beams can attain high values even under moderate lateral design load, if these beams are arranged in vertical and continuous rows along the height of the pierced wall.

Paulay (1971) found that doubly reinforced coupling beams with span-to-height ratios of 1.02 to 1.29 having closely spaced stirrups develop tensile stresses in both top and bottom steel after diagonal cracks had developed over the entire face of the beam (Fig. 9.30). The shear strength of such beams is conservatively predicted by the ACI Code (1971) for monolithic static loading.

Paparoni and Holoma (1971) reported that doubly reinforced coupling beams with span-to-height ratios of 1.96 having closely spaced stirrups and additional diagonal reinforcing performed well under cyclic loading. Fig. 9.31 shows the geometry and reinforcing of these beams together with a load-deflection diagram. A coupling beam of the same geometry, however, reinforced with a structural I-section, displayed under identical loading about the same behavior (Paparoni and Holoma, 1971). The load-deflection curve as well as the reinforcing is shown in Fig. 9.32.

In apartment construction slabs frequently form the coupling element between shear walls. Usually a layer of top and bottom reinforcing is provided in a strip centered on and parallel to the shear wall. The load-deflection envelope for a typical

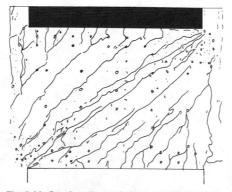

Fig. 9.30 Crack pattern of deep coupling beam

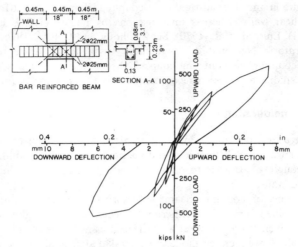

Fig. 9.31 Load-deflection curve of coupling beam

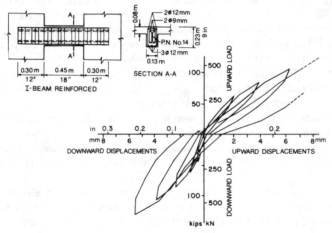

Fig. 9.32 Load-deflection curve of coupling beam reinforced with I-section

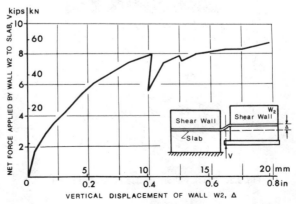

Fig. 9.33 Load–displacement diagram of coupling slab

connecting slab (Schwaighofer and Collins, 1976) under monotonically increasing load is shown in Fig. 9.33.

2 Ductility, Stiffness, and Crack Control

Coupling beams in shear walls, in particular when designed for seismic resistance, are required to possess adequate ductility. A specified over-all ductility for a shear-wall structure usually places a substantially higher ductility demand on the coupling beam.

Paulay (1971) and Paparoni and Holoma (1971) have shown that these high ductility demands can be met provided the beams are properly detailed.

For small span-to-height ratios diagonally reinforced coupling beams have shown substantially improved ductility and strength over conventionally reinforced ones when subjected to cyclic loading.

Tests (Paulay, 1971; Paparoni and Holoma, 1971; and Schwaighofer and Collins, 1976) indicate that the stiffness of coupling elements is considerably less than the predictions based on an uncracked section.

The formation of initial cracks in coupling elements results in some loss of stiffness. Coupling beams will experience progressive softening when subjected to cyclic loading (seismic loading) and further substantial loss of stiffness will result. The real goal of a good design, therefore, must be crack control and ductility; strength is a by-product.

By careful architectural planning excessive piercing of shear walls in the form of vertical rows of openings should be avoided. Ductility and strength requirements as well as crack control in deep coupling beams call for an approach different from that used in connection with slender beams. The conventional elastic analysis can be retained if simple changes in local parameters are incorporated.

More refined plastic design methods, no doubt, will predict much more realistic moment and shear force values in the individual connecting beam, and lead to more uniform reinforcing.

9.6 SUMMARY

Three main topics have been examined in this chapter: stiffness, deflection, and cracking as related to tall buildings.

At the present time (1978) there is a limited amount of information available on stiffness of partially cracked structural members (Kordina, 1970; MacGregor, 1972) but little is known about the magnitude of the flexural stiffness EI of an entire frame bent or a shear wall, accounting for cracked and uncracked portions of the wall and the connecting beams. This uncertainty regarding the flexural stiffness results in uncertain predictions of the horizontal displacements of tall buildings, which in turn may influence the computations of moments in columns if a second-order analysis is contemplated.

It is current practice to assess the agreement between actual and computed deflections on the basis of the measured fundamental period of vibration of the structure rather than by measuring the top displacement of the building due to known or prescribed loads. Though this procedure is of considerable merit it nevertheless is not a very sensitive indicator of the actual top deflection of the structure, because partitions and other nonstructural elements contribute to the general stiffening of the building. This increased stiffness is reflected in the measured period of vibration.

Considerable experimental work is still needed to base the prediction of the stiffness of a whole structure on a sound footing.

9.7 CONDENSED REFERENCES/BIBLIOGRAPHY

The following is a condensed bibliography for this chapter. Not only does it include all articles referred to or cited in the text, but it also contains bibliography for further reading. The full citations will be found at the end of the Volume. What is given here should be sufficient information to lead the reader to the correct article: the author, date, and title. In case of multiple authors, only the first named is listed.

Abeles 1967, *Design of Partially Prestressed Concrete Beams*
ACI Committee 435 1968, *Allowable Deflections*
ACI Committee 442 1971, *Response of Buildings to Lateral Forces*
ACI Committee 318 1971, *ACI Building Code 318-71*
AIJ 1974, *Proceedings of the National Conference on Tall Buildings*

ASCE-IABSE 1973, *Proceedings of the Twelfth Regional Conference*
ASCE-IABSE 1974, *Regional Conference on Tall Buildings*
Ast 1974, *Economical Analysis of Large Framed-Tube Structures*
Base 1966, *An Investigation of the Crack Control Characteristics of Various Types of Bar*
Beeby 1970, *Cracking in Partially Prestressed Members*

Beeby 1971, *The Prediction of Cracking in Reinforced Concrete Members*
Bennett 1971, *Calculation of the Width of Cracks in Class 3 Prestressed Beams*
Bertero 1964, *Behavior of Reinforced Concrete Frames Subjected to Repeated Reversible Loads*
Blume 1960, *Structural Dynamics in Earthquake-Resistant Design*
CEB 1977, *International System of Unified Technical Regulations for Structures*

Cizek 1973, *Some Systems of Tall Reinforced Concrete Buildings in Czechoslovakia*
Colaco 1974, *The Preliminary Selection of Stiffness in Unsymmetrical Tall Concrete*
Coull 1971, *Framed-Tube Structures for High-Rise Buildings*
Deschapelles 1973, *Three-Dimensional Analysis*
Eto 1976, *Inelastic Response of Reinforced Concrete Frames Under Earthquake Motion*

Falkner 1969, *About the Cracking in Restrained and Unrestrained Reinforced Concrete Members*
Ferry Borges 1966, *Cracking and Deformability of Reinforced Concrete Beams*
Ferry Borges 1968, *Cracking*
Ferry Borges 1973, *Summary Report, Planning and Design of Tall Buildings*
Ferry Borges 1969, *Behavior of Tall Buildings During the Caracas Earthquake of 1967*

Fintel 1971, *Effects of Column Creep and Shrinkage in Tall Structures*
Fintel 1973, *Quake Lesson from Managua*
Fintel 1974a, *Ductile Shear Walls in Earthquake Resistant Multistory Buildings*
Fintel 1974b, *Deflections of High-Rise Concrete Buildings*
Funk 1973, *Stiffness Requirements in Terms of Human Comfort*

Gergely 1968, *Maximum Crack Width in Reinforced Concrete Flexural Members*
Gergely 1973, *Cracking and Crack Control*
Gluck 1970b, *Lateral Load Analysis of Irregular Shear Wall Multistory Structures*
Goldman 1961, *Effects of Shock and Vibration on Man*
Gulkan 1971, *Response and Energy-Dissipation of Reinforced Concrete Frames*

Hall 1969, *Deformation and Stresses Within Joints of Frames*
Harris 1973, *The Resilient Mounting of RHM Center (Tower Block)*
Heidebrecht 1971, *Analysis of Asymmetrical Coupled Shear Walls*
Heidebrecht 1973, *Approximate Analysis of Tall Wall Frame Structures*
Higashi 1972, *Influence of Stiffness on Dynamic Analysis and Method*

Holmberg 1970, *Crack Spacing and Crack Widths Due to Normal Force on Bending Moment*
IAEE 1970, *Earthquake Resistant Regulations*
Jackson 1972, *Plastic Flow Law for Reinforced Concrete Beams Under Combined Flex and*
Jackson 1973, *Cracking and Control*
Khan 1968, *Effects of Column Exposure in Tall Structures*

Khan 1973, *Analysis of Tube Frame Structures for Tall Concrete Buildings*
Khan 1968, *Effects of Column Exposure in Tall Structures*
Kordina 1970, *Approximated Computation Method of Restraint Forces*
Kordina 1972, *Stability Analysis*
Kordina 1973, *Cracking and Crack Control*

Lampert 1971, *Postcracking Stiffness of Reinforced Concrete Beams in Torsion and Bending*
Leonhardt 1971, *Reinforcement of Concrete Structures*
Libbey 1974, *Calculated and Measured Deflections of Tall Concrete Buildings*
LNEC 1971, *Structural Studies of the Parque Central Buildings*
Luisoni 1970, *Experimental Verification of a Plastic and an Elastic Analysis of a Shear Wall*

Lutz 1967, *Mechanics of Bond and Slip of Deformed Bars in Concrete*
Lutz 1967, *Increase in Crack Width in Reinforced Concrete Beams Under Sustained Loading*
MacGregor 1972, *Flexural Stiffness*
MacGregor 1974, *Simple Design Procedures*
Michael 1967, *The Effect of Local Wall Deformations on the Elastic Interaction of Cross-Walls*

Michael 1969, *Torsional Coupling of Core Walls in Tall Buildings*
Muto 1971, *Strong Motion Records and Simulation Analysis of KII Building in the San Fernando*
Nawy 1968, *Crack Control in Reinforced Concrete Structures*
Nawy 1969, *Crack Width Control in Two-Way Concrete Slabs Reinforced with Welded Wire Fabric*
Nawy 1972, *Further Studies on Flexural Crack Control in Structural Two-Way Slab Systems*

Newmark 1969, *Torsion in Symmetrical Buildings*
Ojha 1974, *Deformations of Reinforced Concrete Rectangular Beams Under Combined Torsion*
Paparoni 1971, *A Model Study of Coupling Beams for the Parque Central Building*
Paparoni 1973, *Model Studies of Coupling Beams*
Parcel 1962, *Analysis of Statically Indeterminate Structures*

Paulay 1971c, *Coupling Beams of Reinforced Concrete Walls*
Rahles 1970, *About the Torsional Stiffness of Rectangular Reinforced Concrete Members*
Rehm 1968, *Concerning the Question of Limitation of Flaws in Reinforced Concrete*
Ricaldoni 1958, *Note About the Effect of Torsion on Tall Buildings*
Rosman 1962, *Photoelastic Investigation of a Shear Wall*

Rosman 1969, *Torsion of Perforated Concrete Shafts*
Schwaighofer 1969, *A Contribution to the Shear Wall Problem*
Schwaighofer 1969, *Analysis of Shear Wall Structures Using Standard Computer Programs*
Schwaighofer 1974, *Effects of Shear Walls on Stiffness*
Schwaighofer 1976, *Coupling Slabs in Shear Wall Buildings*

Soretz 1973, *Stiffness Requirements in Terms of Human Comfort*
Stamato 1966, *Distribution of the Wind Loads Among the Wind-Resistant Panels*
Stamato 1973, *Three-Dimensional Analysis of Tall Buildings*
Stiller 1965, *Distribution of Horizontal Forces on the Diaphragm System of Tall Buildings*
Takeda 1970, *Reinforced Concrete Response to Simulated Earthquakes*

Takeda 1976, *Inelastic Response of Reinforced Concrete Frames Under Earthquake Motion*
Taoka 1973, *Natural Periods of a Tall Shear Mall Building*
Tso 1973, *General Analysis of Nonplanar Coupled Shear Walls*
Vlasov 1961, *Thin-Walled Elastic Beams*
Weidlinger 1973, *Theme Report, Planning and Design of Tall Buildings*

Winokur 1968a, *Lateral Loads in Asymmetric Multistory Structures*
Wiss 1970, *Wind Deflections of Tall Concrete Frame Buildings*

**Structural Design of
Tall Concrete and Masonry Buildings**

Chapter CB-10

Creep, Shrinkage, and Temperature Effects

Prepared by Committee 25 (Creep, Shrinkage, and Temperature
Effects) of the Council on Tall Buildings and Urban Habitat as part
of the Monograph on the Planning and Design of Tall Buildings

Mark Fintel   Chairman
John Rankine Vice-Chairman
Amin Ghali   Editor

AUTHOR ACKNOWLEDGMENT

Special acknowledgment is due those individuals whose contributions and papers formed the substantial first drafts of the various sections of this chapter. First are the state-of-art reporters from the 1972 International Conference whose material was published in the Lehigh Proceedings. These individuals are:

> Mark Fintel, Section 10.1
> Clyde E. Kesler, Section 10.2
> Adam M. Neville, Section 10.4
> Frank A. Blakey, Section 10.5
> John L. Heiman, Sections 10.5 and 10.6
> Julian Karp, Section 10.7
> Eugene Holland, Section 10.8.

CONTRIBUTORS

The following is a complete list of those who have submitted written material for possible use in the chapter, whether or not that material was used in the final version. The Committee Chairman and Editor were given quite complete latitude. Frequently length limitations precluded the inclusion of much valuable material. The Bibliography contains all contributions. The contributors are: F. A. Blakey, M. Fintel, R. Frunza, A. Ghali, I. Gruner, J. L. Heiman, H. Hilsdorf, E. P. Holland, D. Jungwirth, J. Karp, C. E. Kesler, G. Macchi, A. M. Neville, J. Rankine, G. Rotaru, H. Rusch.

COMMITTEE MEMBERS

Z. Baczynski, V. V. Bertero, F. A. Blakey, D. Campbell-Allen, M. A. Chiorino, N. J. R. Christie, M. Fintel, R. S. Fling, F. Fluge, A. Garfinkel, A. Ghali, I. Gruner, J. L. Heiman, H. K. Hilsdorf, E. P. Holland, T. Huang, D. Jungwirth, S. Kajfasz, J. J. Karp, C. E. Kesler, S. Lichardus, C. A. Miller, A. M. Neville, J. Nutt, J. Rankine, I. Schousboe, Z. Smerda, J. Stigter, H. C. Visvesvaraya, H. Weigler.

CB-10

Creep, Shrinkage, and Temperature Effects

10.1 INTRODUCTION

In the 1950s, considering the effects of shrinkage and creep on the behavior of buildings was an academic subject. Although the researcher was familiar with some aspects of these subjects, the designer of buildings rarely considered them quantitatively. It was generally considered that creep has a beneficial effect in that it relieves overstressed sections and distributes the load to the less stressed sections. Shrinkage has been considered the necessary evil to which the users of concrete have become accustomed. The effect of temperature changes was accommodated over the years in the majority of structures by judicious arrangement of construction joints within long concrete structural units, combined with appropriate "temperature reinforcement," thus reducing the problem and partially relieving the stresses.

Creep and shrinkage are similar regarding their rate of progress with respect to time. The initial rate is the highest, and it diminishes with time. Average curves show that about 40% of the inelastic strains (creep and shrinkage) take place in the first 28 days. After 3 months and 6 months, 60% and 70%, respectively, of all the inelastic strains have taken place, while after 2 yr only about 10% is left over. Thus, several years after erection, a structure has experienced the majority of its eventual adverse effects from creep and shrinkage.

Temperature movements differ from creep and shrinkage in that they are a perennial occurrence for the life of the structure following the seasonal temperature fluctuations.

The recent advance in higher-strength materials with higher allowable stresses, resulting in more flexible structures and also reduction of the factors of safety, reduced the margin that was previously available to the stresses due to inelastic volume changes (shrinkage and creep) and to temperature change stresses. Thus, consideration of the effects of shrinkage, creep, and temperature ceased to be a secondary problem and became a primary problem, particularly in very tall structures.

Traditionally, the effects of creep, shrinkage, and temperature were considered in horizontal structures, such as long span bridges. The effects were usually

427

neglected in multistory concrete buildings, since, in the past, such structures seldom exceeded 20 stories. Some recent ultrahigh-rise buildings built without consideration of creep, shrinkage, and temperature effects in the vertical elements have developed partition distress, as well as structural overstress in horizontal elements. It has become necessary for the structural engineer to consider the various differential movements and to develop acceptable structural, as well as architectural, details for the satisfactory performance of the building.

In tall buildings, and in very long buildings, the effects of the time-dependent volume changes and temperature changes are cumulative and increase with the height or length of the building. This sensitivity of ultrahigh-rise buildings to the effects of volume changes has, in recent years, brought about the development of a number of procedures that consider these effects in the design of buildings. Also, architectural and mechanical details to accommodate the distortions of the building have been developed (Khan and Fintel, 1970). This section deals with the effects of creep, shrinkage, and temperature changes in an over-all discussion to introduce the subject. Subsequent sections in this chapter will relate to specific situations.

1 Control of Volume Changes Through Properties of Constituent Materials

The first step in minimizing the effects of shrinkage, creep, and temperature is to control these characteristics in the concrete, through either a proper choice or

Marina City Towers, Chicago, U.S.A. (Courtesy: Portland Cement Association)

proper proportioning of the constituent materials, or better curing of the concrete in its early ages. This is reviewed briefly here and is considered more fully in Section 10.2.

The magnitude of volume changes in concrete is directly related to the properties of the constituent materials. By careful selection of materials and the proportions in which they are used, volume changes can be kept to a minimum. The parameters affecting shrinkage and creep include: (1) Water-cement ratio of the cement paste; (2) physical characteristics of the aggregate; and (3) cement paste content and characteristics. It is important, therefore, to have proper control and supervision over the supply of specific materials and batching operations of concrete manufacturers. Too often engineers take for granted all the materials of concrete and check only such things as slump, workability, and strength—and find later that excessive shrinkage or creep has occurred, which with a little care could have been avoided.

With respect to the cement, the magnitude and rate of creep strain is influenced by the strength attained by the cement paste at the time of loading. This is controlled to some extent by the chemical composition and fineness of the cement. Cements of different composition and fineness also have variable effects on drying shrinkage. Such differences have been moderated considerably in recent years in most cements by providing optimum amounts of gypsum in the cement. At optimum gypsum content, the type of cement does not in itself significantly influence creep or drying shrinkage.

The role of the aggregate in concrete is to dilute the paste matrix and to restrain greatly the shrinkage and creep of the paste, thereby reducing the over-all shrinkage and creep of the concrete. The effectiveness of the aggregate in reducing shrinkage and creep increases as the volumetric fraction of coarse aggregate in the concrete increases. The mineralogical and physical properties of the coarse aggregate are important in providing restraint to shrinkage and creep. Because of the great variation in aggregate within any mineralogical or petrological type, it is not possible to make a general statement about the magnitude of shrinkage or creep of concrete made with aggregate of different types. Hard aggregates with high density and high modulus of elasticity coupled with moderate porosity or absorption produce concrete with the lowest drying shrinkage and creep. Other aggregate variables such as grading, maximum size, and particle shape have their main influence on shrinkage and creep in the effect they have on the paste content required for adequate workability.

Partial or full replacement of the lightweight fines by natural sand usually reduces shrinkage for concretes made with most structural lightweight aggregates. In terms of creep properties, there is little difference between normal and lightweight aggregate at equal compressive strengths. Information on the effect of admixtures can be found in Section 10.2. However, this information is limited because of the multiplicity of admixtures available and their frequent modification. At present, it is not possible to predict which combination of admixtures and cements will influence shrinkage or creep.

Chemical admixtures alter the rate at which early hydration reactions occur. This alteration of hydration is affected by a number of factors. The use of accelerators such as calcium chloride and triethanolamine results in substantial increases in drying shrinkage and creep of concrete. Some chemical admixtures of the water-reducing type also increase drying shrinkage and creep substantially (age of loading is important), particularly those containing an accelerator to counteract the retarding effect of the admixture. The materials commonly used to entrain air in concrete have little effect on shrinkage or creep.

Concrete containing pozzolanic admixtures which require more water may have increased shrinkage, but most low-carbon fly ashes will not appreciably affect shrinkage. However, pozzolans may increase creep because of the increase in paste content resulting from the increased volume of hydration productions brought about by the reaction of cement hydration products and the pozzolans.

The influence of proportions is best understood by considering interrelated factors such as water-cement ratio, cement content, aggregate content, and total water content. Both creep and shrinkage of concrete increase with an increase in water content. Shrinkage is approximately proportional to the percentage of water by volume in the concrete, while creep varies with the water-cement ratio. For mixtures of similar workability an increase in cement content decreases the water-cement ratio. The creep strains are reduced because of the increased strength resulting from the reduced water-cement ratio. If the aggregate-paste ratio is decreased, an increase in shrinkage and creep is to be expected.

The thermal properties of concrete are important in analyzing the effects of temperature variations. These properties include conductivity, diffusivity, specific heat, and coefficient of expansion.

Conductivity, k, and diffusivity are both greatly affected by the type of aggregate. Within narrow limits, however, conductivity is a function of the unit weight of the concrete. It is also affected by moisture content of the concrete. The water-cement ratio and strength have little or no effect on these properties. Specific heat is affected very little by the mineralogical character of the aggregates or the cement content of the mixture. In general, the specific heat varies directly with variation in the temperature and moisture content of the concrete.

The thermal expansion and contraction of concrete vary with such factors as type and amount of aggregate, richness of mix, water-cement ratio, temperature range, concrete age, and relative humidity (degree of saturation of concrete). Of these, aggregate type probably has the greatest influence.

Procedures for estimating the creep and shrinkage of concrete members are given in Section 10.3.

2   Vertical Effects in Buildings

Differential Creep and Shrinkage of Load-Carrying Elements.   It is known that columns with varying percentage of reinforcement and varying volume-to-surface ratio will have different creep and shrinkage strains (Fintel and Khan, 1968). An increase in percentage of reinforcement and in volume-to-surface ratio reduces strains due to creep and shrinkage under similar stresses.

In a multistory building, adjacent columns may have different percentages of reinforcement due to different gravity and wind loads. As a result, the differential inelastic shortening of adjacent columns will produce moments in the connecting beams or slabs and will cause load transfer to the element that shortens less. As the number of stories increases, the cumulative differential shortening also increases, and the related effects in the slab system become more severe. A common example is the case of a large, heavily reinforced column attracting additional loads from the adjacent shear wall, which has higher creep and shrinkage due to lower percentage of reinforcement and lower volume-to-surface ratio. Significant differential shortening may also occur due to a time gap between slipformed core and the columns. In such case the columns are subjected to the full amount of creep and shrinkage, while in the core most of the inelastic shortening may have occurred prior to casting of the adjacent columns.

For low and intermediate height structures, it is customary to disregard the effect on the frame of elastic and inelastic shortening of columns and walls. As buildings reach great heights, the differential *elastic* shortening should be considered in the analysis, together with the differential inelastic shortening due to creep and shrinkage. Under certain circumstances the latter may be higher than the elastic shortening. Neglecting the differential shortening in ultrahigh-rise buildings may lead to distress in the structure and in nonstructural elements of the building.

Although much research information is available on shrinkage and creep strains, it is not directly applicable to columns of high-rise buildings. The available shrinkage data cannot be applied without modifications, since they are obtained from small standard prisms or cylinders stored in a controlled laboratory environment. The available creep research is based on application of loads in one increment, and is applicable, therefore, to elements such as reinforced or prestressed flexural members. However, in the construction of a high-rise building, columns are loaded in as many increments as there are stories above the level under consideration. Only in recent years were results published of a number of investigations into the problem of inelastic effects in tall buildings (Magura et al., 1968; Pfeifer and Hognestad, 1968; Pfeifer, 1969, 1971).

The procedure recently suggested in the United States (Fintel and Khan, 1968,

Carl Sandburg Village, Chicago, U.S.A. (Courtesy: Portland Cement Association)

1970), to consider in tall structures the differential length changes of columns due to creep and shrinkage, incorporates determination of:

1. The amount of creep and shrinkage occurring in columns and shear walls with consideration of the loading history, size of member, percentage of reinforcement, and environment.

2. Analytical procedures to consider the structural effects on the frame due to the differential elastic and inelastic shortenings of vertical load-carrying members.

Obviously, several simplifying assumptions were made to arrive at a workable solution that can be economically implemented in a design office.

Although the magnitude of creep and shrinkage of plain concrete specimens may vary considerably depending on the concrete properties and climatic conditions, the final inelastic strains in reinforced concrete columns and walls have much less variation, due to the restraining effect of the reinforcement and to the larger size of structural concrete sections compared with the size of specimens used in laboratory

DeWitt-Chestnut Apartment Building, Chicago, U.S.A. (Courtesy: Portland Cement Association)

experiments. For structural engineering practice, it is convenient to consider specific creep, which is defined as the ultimate creep strain per unit of sustained stress. Specific creep is usually determined in laboratory testing of samples prepared in advance, or it can also, less reliably, be predicted from the initial modulus of elasticity at time of load application (Hickey, 1968).

Since a concrete specimen loaded at an early age exhibits a much larger specific creep than a specimen loaded at a later age (Ross, 1958), the loading history becomes particularly significant for columns of multistory buildings which are loaded in as many increments as the number of stories they carry. Creep decreases with age of the concrete at load application, and so each subsequent incremental loading contributes a smaller specific creep to the final average specific creep of the column. Thus an incrementally loaded column has considerably less creep than would be the case in a one-time loading. Consequently, duration of construction has a profound effect on the amount of creep to which the column will be subjected. For example, a 56-story column built at a rate of 1 floor every 5 calendar days will have only 50% of the creep that would result from the entire load applied to the column at the age of 7 days. The principle of superposition (McHenry, 1943) is applied to determine the total creep strains in a column subjected to a number of load increments by adding up creep strains caused by each of the incremental loadings.

Effects of Size on Creep and Shrinkage. The size of members has an effect on the amount of creep and shrinkage. Creep is less sensitive to member size than is shrinkage, since evaporation causing shrinkage occurs only from the surface of members. The relationship of creep and shrinkage to member size is best expressed by the volume-to-surface ratio, which represents an equivalent thickness in inches. Laboratory investigations show that the amount of creep and shrinkage decreases with increasing volume-to-surface ratio (Hansen and Mattock, 1965). Therefore, any creep data obtained on a 150-mm (6-in.) cylinder must be modified for the actual column size using curves developed for the relationship of creep to the volume-to-surface ratio. Also, much of the shrinkage data available in the literature is obtained on 279-mm (11-in.) long prisms of a 76-mm x 76-mm (3-in. x 3-in.) section [volume-to-surface ratio, $V/S = 19$ mm (0.75 in.)] or on 150-mm (6-in.) diam cylinders [$V/S = 38$ mm (1.5 in.)]. Obviously, such data cannot be applied to the usual size columns without considering the effect of size.

Effects of Reinforcement on Creep and Shrinkage. The amount of vertical reinforcing steel has by far the most pronounced restraining effect on the creep and shrinkage shortening of a concrete column.

Tests have shown that when reinforced concrete columns are subjected to sustained loads, there is a tendency for additional stress to be gradually transferred to the steel with simultaneous decrease in the concrete stress (Troxell et al., 1958; Pfeifer, 1969, 1971). It should, however, be noted that despite the redistribution of load between concrete and steel, the ultimate load capacity of the column remains unchanged.

Since creep and shrinkage in the concrete are restrained by the reinforcement, a portion of the load is shifted gradually from concrete to steel. As time progresses, the stress in the concrete progressively decreases, in addition to the progressively diminishing rate of creep.

By applying formulas developed by Dischinger (1937), the ultimate stress in the reinforcement and in the concrete can be determined for a particular column with a given shrinkage and creep coefficient. Also tables have been prepared (Fintel and

Khan, 1968; see also Section 10.4) to accommodate the quick solution of the exponential functions. These tables show that the residual creep and shrinkage of a reinforced column is between 35% and 90% of the total shrinkage and creep of the plain concrete column, depending upon the quality of the concrete, the ultimate specific creep, and the percentage of reinforcement.

Analysis for Differential Shortening of Columns. After the creep and shrinkage shortening of each vertical element has been computed, their differentials are determined to evaluate their effects on the multistory frame.

The differential elastic and inelastic shortenings are cumulative over the height of a structure. They start with zero at the top of footings and reach a maximum at the roof. Therefore, they become more critical with increasing height of a structure. For example, a realistic strain differential between an adjacent column and wall of 100×10^{-6} would produce the insignificant amount of about 0.26 mm (0.010 in.) per story of 2.62 m (8 ft 7 in.) height; which for an 80-story apartment building would mean a maximum cumulative differential shortening of 21 mm (0.83 in.) at the roof level. Such distortions can obviously not be neglected, either structurally or in architectural details.

Buildings of up to 30 stories with flexible slab systems, such as flat plate slabs of average spans, or long-span joist systems, are usually not adversely affected structurally by differential shortening of supports. In such cases, the *total inelastic strain* (unrestrained by frame action) of columns or walls should be computed and allowance made in the architectural details to avoid future distress of partitions, windows, cladding, and other nonstructural elements.

The differentially shortening supports cause the slab system to deflect. The deflecting slabs respond in turn with resistance shears acting back on the supports, thus decreasing the differential shortening. This decrease of the shortening is the

1000 Lake Shore Drive, Chicago, U.S.A.
(Courtesy: Portland Cement Association)

Astor Apartment Towers, Chicago, U.S.A.
(Courtesy: Portland Cement Association)

resistance of the frame and depends upon the slab stiffness and the axial stiffness of the columns. Detailed investigations show that this decrease can be minimal for flexible slabs, and can amount to up to 60% to 70% of the unrestrained differential movement for very stiff slab systems.

A relatively simple analysis for differential shortening of supports is considered sufficient, in view of the existing uncertainties in the assumptions of the magnitude of basic creep and the still uncertain dependence of creep on changes in relative humidity.

The analysis (Fintel and Khan, 1970) starts with the known differential settlements of supports (unrestrained by frame action) at each level. The analysis can be accomplished by a direct solution with a set of simultaneous equations. For manual operation or for small computers, use can be made of iterative methods. The analysis results in frame moments, shears, and axial forces for the columns due to differential creep and shrinkage.

While the columns shorten differentially over a period of years (at a progressively decreasing rate), the resulting slab moments are relaxed by the creep in the slabs. Limited studies by Ghali et al. (1969) indicate that for support settlements occurring during a period of more than 30 days, the amount of creep relaxation is about 50%. Therefore, based on this limited study, the design moments in the slabs and columns due to differential creep and shrinkage of columns may be only 50% of the calculated value.

The stresses due to differential shortening should be treated as equivalent dead load stresses with appropriate load factors before they are combined with other loading conditions. When choosing a load factor, it should be considered that the "design" shortening moments (after 50% creep relaxation) occur only for a short while during the life of the structure, and they continue to decrease after that (see Fig. 10.10 in Section 10.4).

Another entirely separate problem may result between structure and veneer due to vertical inelastic strain. Differential volume changes between vertical structural elements and nonstructural veneers may lead to buckling of the veneer if not properly detailed. While the structural element shrinks and creeps under load, the veneer may sometimes actually increase its volume because of moisture absorption, higher ambient temperatures, or solar radiation.

Providing horizontal soft joints at every floor, alternate floors, or every third floor eliminates the possibility of stress accumulation in the veneer. Such soft joints at the top of a panel [about 3 mm (0.125 in.) for each average story height] are placed under the lintel angle in masonry veneers of multistory structures. Lateral stability of the veneer is provided customarily with anchors.

3 Differential Temperature Shortening of Exposed Columns

In recent years some multistory apartment and office buildings have been built with exterior columns partially or fully exposed to the weather. When subjected to seasonal temperature variations, exposed columns change their length relative to the interior columns, which remain unchanged in a controlled environment. The length changes within a story are of secondary magnitude only. However, length changes are cumulative starting at the top of the footings and adding up to a maximum in the top story. For low buildings this causes insignificant structural problems which can be ignored. However, in taller buildings with partially or fully exposed exterior columns, temperature distortions become significant for the design of the structure.

The thermal movement of the exposed columns, similarly to the movement due to differential creep and shrinkage, causes a racking of floor slabs and consequently distortion of partitions. The column shortening within a story is only secondary in its effects on partitions. As can be seen in Fig. 10.1, the major effect on partitions is the rotation of the partition due to the cumulative change in length of the exposed column. The partition pivots around Point B when the exposed column shortens. The separation, w, is widest at Points A and C, decreasing gradually to zero.

Exposed columns are widely used for the following reasons: (1) Architectural expression of the structural system; (2) because substituting a part of the exterior elevation with an element already available reduces cost; and (3) to minimize the protrusion of columns on the inside. To consider the effects of temperature length changes in exterior columns, a procedure has been established in the United States (Fintel and Khan, 1965; Khan and Fintel, 1966, 1968) consisting of:

1. Determination of a realistic design temperature.

2. Determination of isotherms, temperature gradients, and average temperature of the exposed columns.

3. Determination of thermal length changes.

4. Frame analysis for differential length changes.

Design Temperature.   Before going into the structural analysis, the engineer must determine the lowest and the highest effective temperatures of all partially exposed columns or wall sections during the full seasonal cycle. The probability is remote that exterior temperature (ambient) will remain constant over a sufficient period of time; thus, an estimate of the thermal gradient based on the lowest recorded temperature is bound to be conservative. As steady-state heat conduction through any section is possible only if the boundary temperatures remain constant for a sufficient length of time, the chance of attaining true steady-state conduction is remote. Therefore, an equivalent steady state has to be derived.

To derive an equivalent steady state of heat transfer for the unsteady state, the

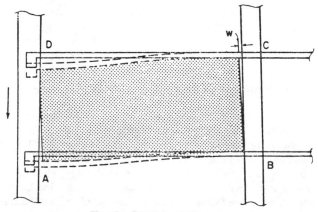

Fig. 10.1 Partition rotation

study (Fintel and Khan, 1965) has revealed two controlling factors: (1) The time lag; and (2) the attenuation of intensity (damping) of exterior amplitudes as the distance from the face increases. It is obvious from studies that rapid temperatures penetrate only skin deep. Only the amplitudes of slowly changing temperatures penetrate considerably into the depth of a member.

Based on studies of time lag and attenuation, it is considered adequate to use the minimum mean daily temperature with a frequency of recurrence once in 50 yr as the equivalent steady-state exterior winter temperature for design of reinforced concrete members of usual size range subjected to exterior temperature variations.

Isotherms, Temperature Gradient, and Average Temperature. After the equivalent steady-state temperature has been selected, the isotherms, the gradients, and the average temperature of the partially exposed columns have to be determined.

A graphical method, developed for construction of isotherms and gradients, is shown in Fig. 10.2 and described in detail in Section 10.7. The two basic effects caused by a temperature gradient through a column are bowing and axial length change (shortening or elongation). Each effect is considered separately, and the resulting stresses are then superimposed.

Bowing of exterior exposed columns of multistory buildings is principally prevented by the entire frame, which is connected to the exposed columns through the slabs. The length changes result in distortion of the slabs or beams of the exterior bay. The deflecting slabs in turn develop resistant shears which act on the exterior and interior column, decreasing the length changes. This rebound of

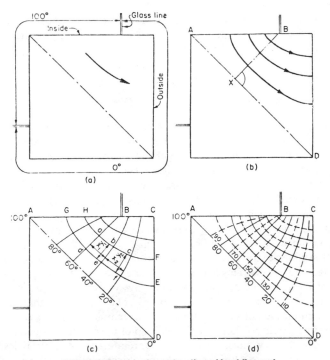

Fig. 10.2 Graphical construction of heat flow net

exterior and interior columns is the actual resistance of the structure to the thermal distortions, and depends upon slab or beam stiffness and upon the axial stiffness of the columns. Vertical shears generated in the deflected slabs cause transfer of load between the exterior column and the interior column.

In multistory frames with partially or fully exposed exterior columns, the effect of temperature movement of the exterior column is significant only in the elements of the exterior bay. These elements are the exterior column, the exterior bay slab, and the first interior column.

The stresses from temperature length changes of columns should be combined with the effects of gravity loads and lateral loads, such as wind or earthquake. Since it seemed too severe to combine full effect of temperature with the full effect of wind, the Chicago weather records (40 yr available) were studied to assess the coincidence of highest winds and lowest temperatures. The study indicated that, for a climate like Chicago's, a combination of vertical loads with 20% wind plus full temperature, or 25% of temperature plus full wind, should provide adequate safety.

A field survey of 15 tall structures with exposed columns (Khan and Fintel, 1968) in 1963-1964 revealed that: (1) No significant structural distress was observed despite known relative movement; and (2) the most frequent type of partition distress resulting from vertical column movement is separation at the vertical junction between the partitions and the columns, and that only partitions perpendicular to exposed columns in the exterior bay above floors 12 to 15 showed such separation. Measurements of movements of exposed columns on nine structures showed acceptable agreement with analytically computed movements. Tall buildings with exposed columns can be designed by providing structural and architectural details to accommodate the computed movement of the exterior columns; or if movement of the exposed columns is limited to a reasonable magnitude in relation to the slab span, only nominal additional structural and architectural details may be required.

4 Horizontal Effects

Horizontal effects, although not a specific problem of tall buildings, are a characteristic problem of long concrete elements, usually manifested by cracking due mainly to shrinkage and temperature changes. Creep plays a role only in axially stressed horizontal elements, such as prestressed concrete.

Shrinkage and temperature drop stresses occur when a member is prevented from shortening by exterior factors (such as columns, ground, etc.), or by interior restraining inclusions, such as reinforcement. If a member is not restrained from changing its length, it will have no stresses when uniform shrinkage causes shortening or when a shrinkage gradient causes bowing.

Most of the adverse structural effects of shrinkage and creep can be eliminated by proper design and details. This is true despite the fact that a full rigorous analytical treatment of inelastic volume changes is not always available. Present methods of construction and tolerances used in reinforced concrete suggest that knowledge of qualitative, and an idea of quantitative, volume changes may go a long way in the choice of proper details to eliminate the buildup of tensile stresses that may result in cracking. Since the low tensile strength of unreinforced concrete is less than the restrained stresses due to ultimate shrinkage, objectionable cracking will occur in restrained members unless a certain amount of well-distributed reinforcement is introduced. If this is done, the cracks can be kept small and harmless.

The four categories of joints are:

1. Expansion joint—complete separation of adjacent parts with a possibility that free movement can occur on each side of the joint.

2. Construction joints—a joint to accommodate the construction sequence with established continuity through the joint.

3. Control joints—created by weakening the concrete section, thus attracting eventual cracking into the joint.

4. Control strips about 0.6 m to 0.9 m (2 ft to 3 ft) wide, to be cast several weeks later to reestablish continuity.

In the United States in recent years expansion joints have been used less frequently in buildings, as it is recognized that concrete will normally never occupy a larger volume than at the moment of its casting. Control joints and control strips have largely replaced expansion joints in long buildings.

Although there are not generally uniform rules regarding the distance between joints to be maintained to eliminate shrinkage cracking, individual designers have their own "office" rules on the subject. Obviously climatic conditions play a significant part. Temperature drop has the same effect and is cumulative with shrinkage. Usually at the onset of the first cold temperature in the life of a structure, all the shrinkage cracking shows up, since shrinkage has been magnified by a temperature drop.

Shrinkage affects all slabs of enclosed multistory buildings. The roof slab may be subjected, in addition, to movements due to temperature changes if the thermal insulation is insufficient.

Experience has shown that temporary control strips in slabs of multistory buildings about 30 m to 46 m (100 ft to 150 ft) apart perform successfully in buildings up to 91 m (300 ft) long. In some cases buildings up to 122 m (400 ft) long with control strips have performed successfully. The control strips, which are strips several feet wide across the building, are cast later than the adjacent portions to reestablish continuity. Such strips divide the structure into parts that shrink independently until they are connected by casting the strip. The reinforcement running across the strip should be lapped within the strip to accommodate independent movements of the separated parts. To run the reinforcement continuously from one part through the strip into the other part would impede unrestrained shrinkage, thus defeating the objective of the temporary control strip. During the period when the control strip is open, the effects of the high rate of initial shrinkage on the adjacent slabs are substantially reduced. After the strip is cast, a certain amount of shrinkage will still take place in the adjacent parts. However, the concrete will have already built up a substantial tensile strength to resist this remaining shrinkage.

There is still a considerable need for development work in order to arrive at rational approaches to the location and spacing of expansion and construction joints. Unfortunately, the simplicity of the subject does not seem to attract the interest of the academic community.

5   Vertical Deflection of Slab Systems

Longtime deflections of reinforced concrete flexural members have been a troublesome problem for many years. In the last two decades in particular, with higher stresses, more slender elements, and considerably longer spans, the shrinkage and creep deflections require both a qualitative and quantitative knowledge in order to eliminate their adverse effects. Also, temperature deflections due to thermal gradient through the slab require the designer's attention. Such thermal gradient may occur when heating elements are embedded in structural slabs, or when the bottom surface of the slab is at a temperature different from its top surface.

It is usually not the creep and shrinkage deflections in themselves that are objectionable, but rather their effects on the nonstructural elements connected to the slabs, such as partitions and plaster—jamming of doors and cracking of windows, for example. On roofs, pounding of water may cause difficulties. The longtime creep and shrinkage deflection may be a multiple of the initial elastic deflection, depending upon the amount of compression reinforcement.

In concrete slab systems the immediate dead-load deflection (being a substantial part of the total elastic deflection) presents little problem, since it can usually be taken care of by sufficient camber.

Shrinkage deflection is caused in slabs and beams by:

1. Unsymmetrical reinforcement restraining shrinkage unsymmetrically. The higher rate of shrinkage of a slab cast over a partially preshrunk precast beam causes a deflection similar to that due to unsymmetrical reinforcement. Adding compressive reinforcement reduces shrinkage deflection by reducing asymmetry. An unsymmetrical deflection is also experienced with a steel beam and composite concrete slab.

2. Drying from only one surface, which causes a shrinkage gradient resulting in a deflection.

Creep deflections are caused by creep associated with the flexural stress gradient of the section. Compressive reinforcement also significantly reduces the creep deflection. Creep deflection can be materially reduced by a higher strength-to-stress ratio at the time of form removal. This can be achieved by using higher-strength concrete, delaying form removal, or effective reshoring.

Shrinkage deflection and creep deflection in flexural members are generally cumulative.

Several methods have been proposed for computing longtime deflections due to shrinkage and creep for concrete members. Common to most methods is the selection of coefficients for shrinkage and creep for use in the formulas. One of the difficulties is the correlation between shrinkage and creep of actual structural members and the shrinkage and creep of small concrete test prisms cured and stored under controlled temperature-humidity conditions.

The longtime deflection computation method mostly used in the United States is a multiplier of the elastic deflection originally developed by Yu and Winter (1960). It combines the effects of shrinkage and creep on deflection, making the longtime deflection a multiple of the immediate elastic deflection. This empirical method was developed from a considerable number of laboratory tests of simply supported flexural members. The multipliers include the effect of compressive reinforcement. The advantage of eliminating the need for shrinkage and creep coefficients in this method by far outweighs the inconsistencies of combining shrinkage and creep deflections, each of them depending upon different parameters.

Few field records are available of longtime deflections, to compare laboratory data with field performance of structural elements of various section sizes subjected to seasonal temperature and humidity.

Limits for longtime deflections to be imposed upon structural elements depend on the capacity for deformation of the supported nonstructural elements. The 1971 ACI Building Code suggests that the sum of longtime deflections plus the elastic live-load deflection be limited to $l/480$ when there is concern with brittle partitions and plaster, and $l/240$ where only appearance is considered.

It is important to note that computed deflection, to which deflection limits are applied, may vary greatly depending upon the assumption for the elastic stiffness of the section (cracked, partially cracked, or uncracked) and the method for computing longtime deflections. Therefore, a deflection limit without specifying the deflection computation method may be meaningless.

Considerable progress has been achieved in recent years in developing procedures to handle creep, shrinkage, and temperature effects in tall buildings. However, many problems still need further study in order to arrive at design procedures and details to produce ultrahigh-rise buildings which can accept all the distortions without ill effects.

Prestressed concrete slabs whose dead load is balanced by prestressing will have a very small amount of camber or deflection, even taking into account the effect of loss of prestress. In such floor systems, vertical deflection should not be a problem. However, the use of excessive prestress in the floor systems may result in undesirable horizontal shortening of the floor as a whole. Although such shortening will cause no problem for upper floors in tall buildings, attention should be given to the first floor and perhaps the second floor, for which the shortening is restrained by the foundation.

10.2 CONTROL OF CREEP, SHRINKAGE, AND TEMPERATURE VOLUME CHANGES

The commonly encountered volume changes in concrete are due to variations in humidity, stress, and temperature. Such volume changes may be partly or entirely reversible. Shrinkage—volume change due to loss of moisture—is generally undesirable because microcracking of the concrete and cracking of restrained members may occur. Creep—volume change due to load external to the concrete —may be undesirable if excessive deflections result, or if a large portion of the prestress is lost. On the other hand, creep can be beneficial in relieving stress concentrations and distributing loads in a desirable manner in a structure. For instance, creep reduces stresses induced by slow temperature changes. Volume change due to temperature change is not helpful and can cause cracking and loss of strength in structures, especially if there is a thermal incompatibility between the aggregate and the paste. Such volume changes also cause warping of slabs.

All volume changes in concrete are affected by the constituent materials, particularly the water, cement, admixtures, pozzolans, and aggregates. Careful selection of the constituent materials and their proportions, and subsequent handling of the concrete, can keep any volume change to an acceptable minimum. First, however, it is necessary to know how the constituents of the concrete affect its volume under various stimuli.

1   Material Properties Affecting Shrinkage

Drying shrinkage of concrete is caused by the contraction of the calcium silicate gel in the hardened paste as the moisture content is reduced. As concrete dries, the water lost first comes from the capillaries and causes little shrinkage. After the capillary water has been lost, the water is removed from the cement gel pores and noticeable shrinkage occurs. While many factors determine the magnitude of shrinkage, the materials that affect shrinkage are the water, cement paste, admixtures, and aggregates. The magnitude of drying shrinkage varies considerably, but for most structural concretes it is in the range of 400 to 900 millionths.

Shrinkage also occurs as the result of a reaction between carbon dioxide and certain constituents of the cement. The magnitude of carbonization shrinkage is dependent on the porosity of the concrete, the relative humidity, and the concentration of carbon dioxide. For very porous concretes at about 50% relative

Lincoln Park Towers, Chicago, U.S.A. (Courtesy: Portland Cement Association)

humidity, the magnitude of carbonation shrinkage may approach that of drying shrinkage. For concretes kept either continually wet or nearly dry, carbonation shrinkage will be small.

Water. One important factor affecting shrinkage is the unit water content. As the water content per unit volume of the fresh concrete is increased, the potential for shrinkage is increased. As an example, the shrinkage of concrete made with 270 kg of water per cubic meter (450 lb/yd^3) is about three times that of concrete made with 150 kg of water per cubic meter (250 lb/yd^3). A significant portion of the increase in shrinkage with increasing water content occurs because the additional water replaces aggregates which reduce shrinkage. In addition, the wetter concretes generally have a higher water-cement ratio and a larger volume of paste.

Any increase in water-cement ratio will cause a significant increase in shrinkage. For instance, increasing the water-cement ratio from 0.5 to 0.6 by weight in similar mixes may be expected to increase shrinkage by 30%.

Cement. Shrinkage is influenced by the composition and fineness of the cement. To minimize shrinkage, it is important that the cement contain the "optimum" amount of gypsum. The optimum amount is unique for each cement; it increases as the anticipated hydration temperature increases, and as the fineness of the cement increases.

Some chemical admixtures increase shrinkage by changing the gypsum content required for optimum. The length of time of mixing the concrete and also the size of the concrete member's cross section as it affects the concrete temperature may change the optimum gypsum content.

When portland cement contains the optimum gypsum content, the presumed detrimental effect of tricalcium aluminate, alkalies, and fineness on shrinkage is minimized and the difference between cements, except possibly those with an abundance of tricalcium aluminate, is greatly reduced.

Expansive cements can be used in concrete to overcome some of the undesirable aspects of shrinkage. Expansive cement concretes will shrink after curing and while drying approximately the same amount as other portland cement concretes. However, these concretes expand while curing and, if properly proportioned and restrained, the initial expansion will compensate for the subsequent shrinkage.

Admixtures and Pozzolans. Generally speaking, any admixtures that increase the unit water content increase shrinkage, and some that reduce the water content reduce shrinkage. However, many admixtures that reduce water content do not reduce shrinkage. When drying shrinkage is important, the admixtures should be evaluated using job materials, curing, and drying.

Air entraining agents do not significantly affect shrinkage, since the entrained air permits a decrease in water content for a given consistency.

The accelerators, calcium chloride and triethanolamine, usually increase shrinkage, in some instances as much as 50%.

Some pozzolanic materials requiring additional water, such as pumicite and raw diatomaceous earth, increase shrinkage of concrete. However, treated diatomaceous earth and low-carbon fly ash used in normal amounts do not appreciably affect shrinkage.

Aggregates. The drying shrinkage of concrete is only 7% to 20% of the shrinkage of cement paste, since the aggregates both replace a portion of the paste and restrain its shrinkage; that is, the larger the volume of aggregates in a concrete, the smaller the shrinkage. For the range of aggregate content generally used in structural concretes, increasing the volume of aggregates by 10% can be expected to reduce shrinkage by 50% or more.

The maximum size and gradation of the aggregate are important in reducing shrinkage only in that they affect the maximum volume of aggregate in a workable concrete.

Aggregates having low or virtually no shrinkage and a high modulus of elasticity result in concretes with low shrinkage. Such aggregates are granite, dolomite, limestone, and rocks rich in quartz and feldspar. Conversely, aggregates such as sandstone and slate, having a low modulus of elasticity and significant shrinkage, result in concretes which have comparatively high shrinkages. Aggregates which swell considerably as they take up water should not be used.

Lightweight aggregate concretes may have significantly greater shrinkage than concretes made with normal weight aggregate. Generally, lightweight aggregates with high absorption that require high cement contents for strength yield large shrinkages. However, with careful selection of materials and proportioning of the concrete, the drying shrinkage may be kept comparable to that of normal weight concrete. Lightweight structural concrete normally has drying shrinkage values of 0.04% to 0.15%.

Aggregates containing clay in any form will result in concrete having considerably more shrinkage than concrete made from aggregates free of clay.

2 Material Properties Affecting Creep

Creep is time-dependent deformation due to load. Concrete creeps under any tensile, compressive, or shear stress. The magnitude of creep in compression is approximately linearly proportional to the magnitude of the stress up to about 40% of its ultimate strength. Not all the creep that occurs is recoverable when the load is removed.

The mechanism of creep of concrete is not clearly understood; creep is probably due to a number of mechanisms. At the lower stresses, these mechanisms involve seepage, delayed elasticity, and viscous flow. At higher stresses, intercrystalline slip and microcracking probably contribute to the creep resulting in nonlinearity with respect to stress and nonrecoverable creep.

The magnitude of creep in concrete depends on the water, aggregates, cement, admixtures, pozzolans, and many other factors, such as age and temperature. Furthermore, any change—such as moisture, temperature, or load cycles—that disturbs the gel in any way increases the deformation in the direction of the load.

Concretes which have high shrinkage tend to have high creep.

Creep of structural concrete may vary from 30 to 300 millionths per MPa (0.2 to 2.0 millionths per psi). In effect, this corresponds to a variation of from 1 to 4 times the corresponding elastic strain.

Water-Cement Ratio.   The water content affects creep in that it affects the water-cement ratio. Also, as the concrete dries, it shrinks and thereby induces additional creep.

For a given stress, creep increases with an increase in water-cement ratio for a given paste content. Also, for a constant water-cement ratio, creep increases with increasing paste content. Generally speaking, for a particular stress, lean mixes creep more than rich mixes.

However, specimens loaded to the same stress-strength ratio and having the same paste content will have the same creep regardless of the water-cement ratio. Under this loading condition, a lean mix will exhibit less creep than a rich mix, although in a lean mix, a larger portion of the ultimate creep occurs at an early age.

Cement. The type and fineness of cement are important in determining the magnitude of creep in that they affect the rate of strength gain. If concretes similar except for cement type or fineness are stressed to the same level at the same age, those concretes made with cements that hydrate more rapidly will creep the least. High early strength cement, Type 3, concrete will creep less than general purpose, Type 1, cement concrete. Portland slag cement concretes creep more than those made with normal cements. Also, concrete with cements of the higher fineness will creep less.

If, however, concretes made with different cements are loaded to the same stress-strength ratio rather than to the same stress, the type of cement or fineness will be of considerably less importance.

If the gypsum content is not optimum, creep will be increased.

Admixtures and Pozzolans. The proper use of air entraining agents, including proper mix design, results in concretes whose creep is approximately the same as for nonair-entrained concretes.

The effect of water-reducing and set-retarding admixtures on creep is not clear. Apparently, though significant increases in creep (from 10% to 60%) in both lightweight and normal weight concrete can occur with both lignosulphonic and hydroxylated carboxylic acid admixtures, the effect is greater the richer the mix. Since some admixtures permit a reduction in paste content, which tends to reduce creep, the increased creep due to use of the admixtures may not be as great as indicated.

Pozzolans used as replacements for cements tend to increase creep; the amount of the increase becomes greater with increasing percentage of the replacement.

Aggregates. Aggregates provide restraint to creep as well as to shrinkage of concrete. With regard to creep, the most important property of the aggregate is the modulus of elasticity; other properties, such as shrinkage, creep, porosity, shape, and grading are also important.

Concretes made of aggregates with a high modulus of elasticity exhibit less creep than those made with aggregates of low moduli of elasticity. Sandstones have low moduli and, as a result, concretes made with sandstones as the aggregate may have three times as much creep as concrete with high modulus of elasticity aggregates, such as granite, quartz, limestone, and the usual gravels.

Generally speaking, as the porosity and absorption of aggregates increase, the modulus of elasticity decreases. Also, the porosity and absorption of aggregates influence the moisture movement in concrete which, in turn, affects creep. Thus, it can be expected that aggregates with high porosities and absorptions will result in concretes with large magnitudes of creep.

Aggregates such as sandstones, which show significant creep under load, will result in concretes with a high creep potential. Most aggregates creep very little under the stresses to which they are subjected in concrete.

As might be expected, clay particles or clay coatings on aggregates cause significant increases in creep, principally because of loss of bond, loss of restraint, and moisture movement.

There is no fundamental difference between the creep behavior of concretes made with lightweight aggregates and normal weight aggregates. The porosity of lightweight aggregates is directly reflected in their modulus of elasticity, which is the major factor in determining the amount of creep. The rate of creep of lightweight aggregate concrete does not decrease with time as fast as that of normal weight concrete, and ultimate creeps of lightweight concrete may be 20% to 50% higher than that of normal weight concrete, although the creep at early ages, less than 100 days, may be comparable.

The method of manufacture of the lightweight aggregate does not appear to affect the creep behavior of concrete in which it is used.

The shape of the aggregate particles and grading of the aggregates are important to the extent that they affect workability of the fresh concrete and, thus, its aggregate content.

3 Material Properties Affecting Temperature Volume Changes

Concrete, as most materials do, expands with rising temperatures and contracts with falling temperatures. The coefficient of expansion of concrete depends on the relative amounts of paste and aggregates, the type of aggregates, and the moisture content. The average coefficient of expansion for cement paste is higher and is influenced to a greater extent by moisture content than the average coefficient of expansion of the commonly used aggregates.

Moisture Content.   The coefficient of expansion of cement pastes ranges from 9.9 to 21.6 millionths per kelvin (5.5 to 12.0 millionths per 1°F, 9.9 to 21.6 millionths per 1°C). The exact value for a given paste depends on both the moisture content and the rate of the temperature change. The rate of temperature change affects the coefficient of expansion at any instant to the extent that the moisture has been redistributed and the moisture content changed as a result of changing vapor pressure. Paste porosity is an important factor in determining the time necessary for the paste to reach moisture equilibrium at any temperature.

Pastes that are oven dry or vacuum saturated have similar coefficients of expansion. Pastes with intermediate moisture contents may have different coefficients of expansion from oven dry or saturated pastes, usually higher but not always, with a maximum difference at relative humidities of 50% to 70%.

Since concrete is only partially paste, these effects, while evident, are moderated and the variation in the coefficient of expansion is smaller.

Aggregates.   The coefficient of expansion of the most commonly used aggregates varies from about 3.6 to 12.6 millionths per 1°C (2.0 millionths to 7.0 millionths per 1°F). Generally, chert, quartzite, and sandstones have coefficients above 4.5 (8.1), and limestone, granite, basalt, and gneiss have coefficients below 4.5 (8.1). Some crystalline rocks have different coefficients of expansion along different preferred orientation planes formed by the component minerals. Feldspar, for instance, has coefficients of about 17.1, 0.9, and 1.8 millionths per 1°C (9.5, 0.5, and 1.0 millionths per 1°F) along three different axes.

The coefficient of expansion of concrete depends to a large extent on the coefficient of the aggregate and the quantity of aggregate. Since the coefficient of the paste is higher than that of the aggregate, the coefficient of the concrete will be somewhat higher than that of the aggregate and, in general, ranges between 7.2 to 12.6 millionths per 1°C (4 to 7 millionths per 1°F) with a value of 9.9 millionths commonly used in design.

The coefficients of expansion of concrete can be estimated from the coefficients of the paste and aggregates if due consideration is given to their relative volumes in the concrete.

4 Control of Volume Changes

To keep volume changes of concrete to a minimum, the mixes should be designed to have the highest solids content and the lowest water content possible.

If moisture loss is kept to a minimum in the concrete, both shrinkage and creep will be reduced. However, if reduction in temperature volume change is a major consideration, either wet or dry concretes may have lower coefficients of expansion than concretes with intermediate moisture contents.

Portland cements should have optimum gypsum contents to reduce shrinkage and creep. For concretes loaded to a given stress, the creep will be less for a cement with the highest rate of strength gain. But, for concretes loaded to a particular stress-strength ratio, the type of portland cement or its fineness will be of less importance.

Expansive cement concretes may be used to overcome many of the undesirable effects of shrinkage, but careful attention should be given to the detailing of elements made with this cement (ACI Committee 223, 1970).

Air-entraining admixtures do not significantly affect creep and shrinkage because, for a given consistency of the fresh concrete, the water content can be reduced. Accelerators increase shrinkage and creep of concrete and should not be used when these volume changes are of prime importance. Some water-reducing and set-retarding admixtures increase shrinkage and creep substantially. They should not be used until evaluated with job materials and mixing and curing conditions. If such admixtures do increase volume changes, they should be used at the lowest possible dosage rate that will produce the desired degree of water reduction and set retardation.

Pozzolans such as pumicite and raw diatomaceous earth increase shrinkage since they require additional water. On the other hand, treated diatomaceous earth and low-carbon fly ash do not appreciably affect shrinkage. All pozzolanic materials tend to increase creep.

Aggregates that are hard, dense, and have a high modulus of elasticity keep shrinkage and creep to a minimum. Aggregates showing significant shrinkage and creep should not be used when creep and shrinkage are to be kept to a minimum. Aggregates should be free of clay particles and other deleterious materials.

Aggregates with a low coefficient of expansion will keep temperature volume changes of concrete to a minimum. However, if the temperature changes are large or frequent, consideration must be given to the thermal compatibility of the paste and aggregate.

10.3 RECOMMENDATIONS FOR PREDICTION OF CREEP AND SHRINKAGE

As described in the preceding section, creep and shrinkage characteristics are influenced by many factors, such as the composition of concrete, size of member, and the environment in which it is kept. Values of creep and shrinkage are required in design to evaluate their structural effects. The designer may resort to his own test results, or to recommended practices that are compiled from large numbers of tests.

For prestressed concrete members, creep and shrinkage will result in loss of prestress. Procedures for predicting this are given by Neville (1970), the PCI Committee on Prestress Losses (1975), and Tadros et al. (1975, 1977).

The most widely accepted recommendations are those reported by the ACI Committee 209 (1971) and by the CEB-FIP Committee (CEB, 1970). These prediction methods are not repeated here because they are fully reported in the two references just quoted. Rather, a revision of the CEB-FIP Recommendations, which is presently under review, is given in the following article. This new revision is based on a study by Rüsch et al. (1973).

1   Tentative CEB Recommendations (1976)

The coefficients given subsequently for creep and shrinkage form a working basis and are valid only for portland cement concretes of normal quality, hardening under normal conditions, and subject to stress not exceeding 40% of mean cylindrical strength.

Creep.   The effects of creep under working conditions may be evaluated using the theory of linear creep. Accordingly, the elastic-plus-creep deformation at time t, $\epsilon_{cc}(t, t_0)$ caused by a constant sustained stress, $\sigma_c(t_0)$, applied at time t_0, is

$$\epsilon_{cc}(t, t_0) = \sigma_c(t_0)\left[\frac{1}{E_c(t_0)} + \frac{\phi(t, t_0)}{E_{c28}}\right] \tag{10.1}$$

in which $E_c(t_0)$ and E_{c28} are the values of the secant modulus of elasticity of concrete at age t_0 and 28 days, respectively, and $\phi(t, t_0)$ is a coefficient expressed by

$$\phi(t, t_0) = 0.4\beta_d(t - t_0) +$$
$$\beta_{1c}\beta_{2c}[\beta_f(t) - \beta_f(t_0)] \tag{10.2}$$

In Eq. 10.2, β_{1c} = coefficient depending on the relative humidity of the ambient medium and on the consistency of concrete, Tables 10.1 and 10.2; β_{2c} = coefficient depending on the theoretical thickness h' of the member considered, Fig. 10.3 (h' is defined by Eq. 10.4); $\beta_d(t' - t_0')$ = coefficient depending on the theoretical ages t_0' and t', and varying between 0 and 1 (Fig. 10.4); and $\beta_f(t')$ = coefficient depending on the theoretical age t' (Eq. 10.3) and thickness h' (Eq. 10.4), and varying between 0 and 1 (Fig. 10.5).

The theoretical age t' is to be obtained from the actual age t by using

$$t' \text{ or } t_0' = \frac{\alpha_c}{30}\sum_0^{t \text{ or } t_0} \delta t(T + 10) \tag{10.3}$$

in which δt = number of days during which the average day temperature for concrete is T in degrees Celsius; and α_c = coefficient depending on the hardening speed of cement, Table 10.3.

The theoretical thickness h' is defined as

$$h' = \frac{2\lambda A_c}{u_c} \tag{10.4}$$

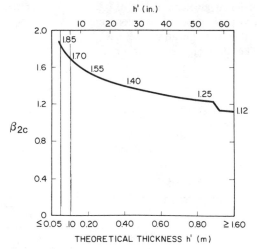

Fig. 10.3 Relationship between creep parameter β_{2c} and theoretical thickness

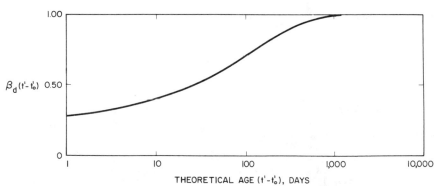

Fig. 10.4 Relationship between creep parameter β_d and theoretical age

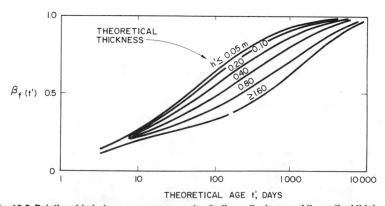

Fig. 10.5 Relationship between creep parameter β_f, theoretical age and theoretical thickness

in which λ = coefficient given in Table 10.1 to account for the effect of relative humidity; A_c = cross-sectional area of concrete; and u_c = perimeter of concrete cross section in contact with the atmosphere.

Shrinkage. The shrinkage strain in concrete $\epsilon_{cs}(t,t_0)$ which develops in the period $t - t_0$ is given by

Table 10.1 Effect of humidity on coefficients β_{1c}, β_{1s}, and λ

Position of concrete element (1)	Relative humidity of ambient medium, as a percentage (2)	Coefficients Creep, $\beta_{1c}{}^*$ (3)	Shrinkage, $\beta_{1s}{}^*$ (4)	λ (5)
In the water		0.8	$+10 \times 10^{-5}$	30.0
In very damp atmosphere immediately over water	90	1.3	-10×10^{-5}	5.0
Generally outdoor	70	2.0	-25×10^{-5}	1.5
In dry atmosphere or in dry interiors	40	3.0	-40×10^{-5}	1.0

*For the consistence fields C_1 and C_3, values must be respectively decreased or increased by 25%. Consistence fields are defined in Table 10.2.

Table 10.2 Effect of consistency of concrete

Consistence field (1)	Quality of concrete (2)	Slump[a], in millimeters (inches) (3)	Degree of compaction[b] (4)	Degree of compaction[c] (5)	Diameter of cone after 15 impacts,[d] in millimeters (inches) (6)	Number of impacts[e] (7)
C_1	stiff	0 to 20 (0 to 25/32)	1.45 to 1.26	1.40 to 1.19	50 (2)	more than 30
C_2	plastic	30 to 50 (1-1/8 to 2)	1.25 to 1.11	1.18 to 1.06	50 to 400 (2 to 16)	20 to 10
C_3	soft	70 to 150 (2-3/4 to 6)	1.10 to 1.04	1.05 to 1.0	410 to 500 (16 to 20)	6 to 3

[a]Slump test (Abrams, ASTM-C 143).
[b]Compaction test (Walz, DIN 1048).
[c]Compaction test (Fritsch).
[d]Slump test (Graf, DIN 1048).
[e]Deformation work test (Powers, 1968).

Table 10.3 Effect of type of cement on theoretical ages

Type of cement (1)	Coefficient α_c (2)
Normally and slowly hardening	1
Quickly hardening	2
Quickly hardening and high strength	3

$$\epsilon_{cs}(t, t_0) = \beta_{1s} \beta_{2s} [\beta_s(t') - \beta_s(t'_0)] \tag{10.5}$$

in which β_{1s} = coefficient depending on the relative humidity of the ambient air and on the consistency of concrete, Table 10.1; β_{2s} = coefficient depending on the theoretical thickness h' (Eq. 10.4) of the concrete element, Fig. 10.6; and $\beta_s(t')$ = coefficient depending on the theoretical time t' (Eq. 10.3 with $\alpha = 1$) and thickness h' (Eq. 10.4), and varying between 0 and 1, Fig. 10.7.

The values of $\phi(t, t_0)$ and $\epsilon_{cs}(t, t_0)$ calculated as shown are mean values. When the time-dependent behavior of concrete has a large effect on the limit state under consideration, a variation of $\pm 15\%$ should be considered, in order to cover the most unfavorable case.

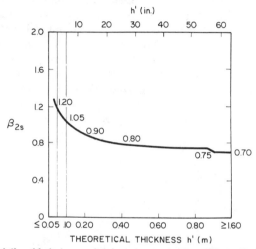

Fig. 10.6 Relationship between shrinkage parameter β_{2s} and theoretical thickness h'

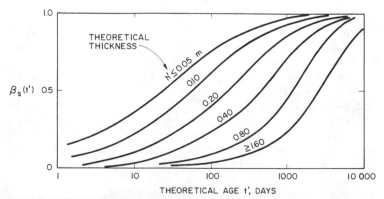

Fig. 10.7 Relationship between shrinkage parameter β_s, theoretical age and theoretical thickness

10.4 DIFFERENTIAL CREEP AND SHRINKAGE OF VERTICAL LOAD-CARRYING ELEMENTS

The nonelastic behavior of concrete is well known: under conditions of drying there is a decrease in volume, known as shrinkage, and under a sustained load there is a slow, time-dependent change in dimensions, primarily in the direction in which the load acts, known as creep. When the load is compressive (and this is of paramount importance in the case of load-carrying elements in tall structures), the creep is also compressive. Creep takes place whether or not concurrent shrinkage occurs, but the two phenomena are not simply additive because the action of shrinkage enhances creep. Thus the so-called drying creep occurs in addition to creep under conditions of hygral equilibrium, known as basic creep.

The nonelastic deformations considered have, in general, a magnitude that is significant and comparable with the magnitude of the elastic deformation. For instance, a stress of 7 N/mm² (1000 psi) in concrete whose modulus of elasticity is 28 000 N/mm² (4 × 10⁶ psi) would induce an elastic strain of 250 × 10⁻⁶.

Reasonably typical values of shrinkage and creep after a long time and under dry conditions would be 500 × 10⁻⁶ and 700 × 10⁻⁶, respectively. It can thus be seen that the nonelastic deformation of concrete (plain concrete being considered so far) is by no means a "second-order quantity," and it must not be ignored.

Nevertheless, the presence of nonelastic deformation in concrete would not be significant as far as vertical load-carrying elements are concerned if all the elements were subject to the same strain: all the columns and shear walls would simply shorten somewhat, but these strains would not induce any stresses. It is, in fact, the lack of equality of deformation of neighboring vertical members that lies at the root of the problem considered herein.

1 Sources of Differential Shrinkage

The subject of concern, therefore, is differences in the magnitude of shrinkage and creep within a given tall structure rather than the magnitude itself. Let us first consider shrinkage. In plain concrete, the magnitude of shrinkage of a given concrete is affected primarily by the humidity of the surrounding air and by the size of the member drying. If concretes of different composition are used in adjacent members, then the intrinsic shrinkage of the material may also be different.

In the simplest case, differential shrinkage effects may arise from the following causes. First, the humidity to which the vertical members are exposed may vary; for instance, the external columns of a structure may be wholly or partially exposed to a reasonably high relative humidity (say, 70% to 90%), while the interior columns in a heated building may be at a much lower humidity (say, 40% to 50%). The difference in the resulting shrinkage values is significant.

Second, the size of columns and shear walls near to one another may vary. The real parameter is the ratio of the volume of concrete enclosed to the drying surface, that is the volume-surface ratio; its inverse is sometimes used. It is important to be clear about which surface is able to allow evaporation of water and hence drying, as in some cases concrete is placed within or against an impermeable material, so that the effective volume-drying surface ratio is altered.

In addition to these factors, differential behavior may arise from two further causes, one connected with the speed of construction, and the other with structural design. The first is due to the fact that only that part of shrinkage is relevant to differential behavior which occurs after the given level of a structure has been constructed. Thus the position of supports of the nth floor of a structure is affected only by the differences in the shrinkage that occur after this floor has been placed. It follows that the slower the construction (provided the weather is sufficiently dry for shrinkage to occur), the greater the part of the total shrinkage that is realized before differential effects can enter the picture.

Finally, differential shrinkage is affected by design, in that steel reinforcement severely restrains the magnitude of the actual shrinkage developed. This statement is of considerable importance, as all that has been said so far was with reference to plain (unreinforced) concrete, and the usual values of shrinkage for various mixes and exposure conditions are invariably quoted for plain concrete.

2 Sources of Differential Creep

There is considerable similarity in the reasons for differential creep and differential shrinkage in a tall structure. Specifically, the relative humidity of storage and the volume-surface ratio affect creep qualitatively in the same way as they affect shrinkage. In general, the differential effects of these causes will include both creep and shrinkage, or neither.

Likewise, qualitatively, the influence of the composition of the mix on creep and on shrinkage is similar. For these reasons, the exposure of some columns and variation in column size will induce differential creep.

The speed of construction will also have some effect on differential creep, but the situation is more complicated because creep is affected by all the loads acting in other than a transient manner, and the dead load of the structure represents only a part of the loading which induces creep. Thus that part of creep which takes place before the nth floor has been placed does not affect the differential behavior at that level, but on the other hand there may be significant construction loads which, over a period of weeks, induce significant creep. This would be the case if large quantities of material were stored in the vicinity of some columns but not of others.

The relative rates of shrinkage and creep are similar, that is, the same proportion of deformation is developed in a given fraction of time required for total deformation. However, under continuous drying, shrinkage can be expected to be almost completed in under 2 yr, whereas creep would be stabilized, or nearly so, only after 20 yr to 30 yr. Furthermore, under practical conditions of exposure there is a variation in the relative humidity with an accompanying moisture movement of concrete.

The restraining effect of steel reinforcement on creep is similar to the effect on shrinkage so that, again, the laboratory data on creep of plain concrete have to be modified by the restraints involved.

In addition to the factors common to creep and shrinkage, there is one effect peculiar to creep: this is stress. Other things being equal, creep is proportional to the stress in the column, so that unequal stress in adjacent columns would lead to differential shortening. If, for instance, for architectural reasons, columns are of the same size but carry widely disparate loads, differential creep may occur. It is, however, possible to remedy this by reducing the reinforcement in the more lightly loaded columns.

It should be noted that creep is affected by the age when the load begins to act.

For the same mix and the same stress, the magnitude of creep developed decreases rapidly with an increase in the age of concrete. The speed of construction is therefore a significant factor in differential vertical movement: an incrementally loaded column has less creep than if the entire load were applied at the beginning. For instance, if the load is applied gradually over 1 yr, the creep would be one-half of that which would occur under a load applied at the age of 14 days. For the same reason the time gap between a slipformed core and a column greatly affects the differential creep developed.

It is perhaps worth stating clearly that creep influences stress distribution and deformation, which is the serviceability of the structure, but does not affect its strength, that is, its ultimate carrying capacity. Exceptions include buckling of long columns, fatigue of a member under repeated loading, and reduction in shear strength due to cracking. However, in the frame as a whole, differential creep may induce significant moments, shears, and stresses, and when load-induced stresses are added, failure can occur under a lower superimposed load than would be the case without differential creep.

3   Determination of Shortening

From what has been said in the preceding two articles, it is clear that, in general, in a tall structure there will exist differential shortenings in columns and shear walls. These have to be estimated so that it can be ascertained whether the differential effects are not significant, or whether they are significant and therefore have to be taken into account in the design of horizontal members, in the design of joints and in architectural features, or finally whether the differential effects are so large that a new design is desirable so as to produce smaller differential effects. An example of the last-mentioned case would be an avoidance of considerable disparity in exposure conditions of columns, in their size, spacing, or percentage reinforcement.

To determine the shortening of a reinforced concrete member, the inherent shrinkage of the mix under the given conditions of exposure has to be found, and this has to be corrected for the volume-surface ratio. Both of these operations can be done best with the aid of data such as those given in the CEB-FIP Recommendations (which were reproduced in Section 10.3).

Having found the shrinkage of plain concrete, one can proceed to consider the effect of reinforcement, with respect to both its amount and position. In the general case of a section with unsymmetrical reinforcement, in which A_{s1} is the area of tension steel, and A_{s2} is the area of compression steel, and $0 \leq A_{s2} \leq A_{s1}$, the axial shrinkage shortening is expressed in terms of the strains in the fibers of the two steel layers 1 and 2, assuming straight-line variation; thus

$$\epsilon(t_n) = \epsilon_1 + \frac{(\epsilon_2 - \epsilon_1)y_1}{y_1 - y_2} \tag{10.6}$$

in which $\epsilon(t_n)$ = axial shortening at time t_n; ϵ_1 and ϵ_2 = strains at the levels of steel 1 and steel 2, respectively; and y_1 and y_2 = respective distances of the two steels from the centroidal axis of the net concrete section.

If the reinforcement is symmetrically distributed about the centroidal axis, $A_{s1} = A_{s2}$, and $y_1 = -y_2$, so that $\epsilon_1 = \epsilon_2$. Assuming perfect bond between the steel and concrete, and using equilibrium equations, the following expression

$$\epsilon(t_n) = \frac{s}{1 + pn_0(1 + \eta\phi)} \tag{10.7}$$

can be derived for the axial strain (Neville, 1970), in which p = total steel area ratio; n_0 = modular ratio at the beginning of shrinkage; and

$$\phi = \frac{\text{creep}}{\text{initial elastic strain}} \tag{10.8}$$

and η = relaxation coefficient. This coefficient and ϕ recognize the fact that the stresses induced by the restraint of shrinkage are themselves relieved by creep. While ϕ refers to the creep properties of concrete at the beginning of shrinkage, η allows for the change in stress in concrete with the progress of shrinkage, that is on aging.

It may be convenient to represent the influence of $[1 + pn_0(1 + \eta\phi)]$ in graphical form as shown in Fig. 10.8 for different values of pn_0 and $\eta\phi$, the coefficient α_1 being defined as

$$\alpha_1 = \frac{1}{1 + pn_0(1 + \eta\phi)} \tag{10.9}$$

All this applies to symmetrical sections, symmetrically reinforced, and loaded axially.

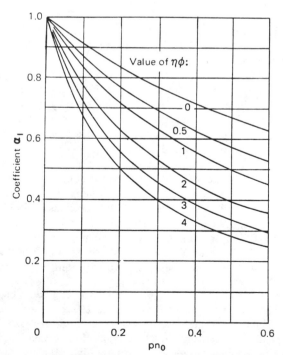

Fig. 10.8 Creep reduction coefficient α_1 for axially loaded symmetrically reinforced members as function of pn_0 for different values of $\eta\phi$

The basic Eq. 10.6 can be used to derive expressions for other special cases, for example, singly reinforced sections; but this is not of primary interest herein—the relevant data have been published (Neville, 1970).

A similar approach is possible for the calculation of shortening of a reinforced concrete member due to creep under an applied external moment and load. The general expression is inconveniently complex but can be simplified for symmetrical sections, see Neville (1970). Furthermore, where there is no external moment, that is when a symmetrically reinforced and axially loaded column is under consideration, the stress in concrete at time t_n is given by

$$\sigma(t_n) = \sigma_{av} \left[1 - \frac{\alpha\phi}{1 + \alpha\eta\phi} \right] \tag{10.10}$$

in which σ_{av} = average stress on the transformed area; ϕ is defined by Eq. 10.8; η = relaxation coefficient; and

$$\alpha = \frac{pn_0}{1 + pn_0} \tag{10.11}$$

is a stiffness coefficient which allows for the restraining effect of reinforcement.

Prestressed concrete, with or without nonprestressed steel, can be readily treated by similar methods.

4   Effects on Frame

The preceding article has indicated how the axial shortening can be calculated. The subsequent calculation of differential nonelastic shortening for any pair (or larger number) of supports is simple. It should be added that differential elastic shortening may also be significant in considering the frame behavior; it may be convenient to consider the elastic and nonelastic differentials together. (The elastic strains are calculated by established procedures.) Generally, the two effects vary in accord, that is run high or low together. This is of interest in that a design that minimizes elastic shortening differentials also minimizes the nonelastic differentials due to creep; shrinkage is of course independent of stress.

The differential shortening calculated on the basis of the preceding article is calculated for each story separately, but the effect is cumulative over the full height of the structure, with a maximum in the uppermost story. Thus the magnitude of the differential shortening, and probably its significance, increases with the height of the structure. For instance, if the differential strain is 150×10^{-6} (a value feasible in the case of a column and a shear wall), then over a height of 80 stories, say 300 m (1000 ft), the actual length (or level) differential would be $150 \times 10^{-6} \times 300 = 0.045$ m = 45 mm (1.8 in.). This value would have an important effect on the structural behavior as well as on architectural features.

Although the differential effects are cumulative, they do not rise in direct proportion to height. This is so because the creep effects depend on column sizes (which need not be constant) and also on loads: the loads are lower the higher the story. Creep depends also on the loading history, as already mentioned.

What value of differential shortening is structurally or architecturally significant depends on the details of support of horizontal members and on details of partitions, etc., but it seems that up to 91 m to 122 m (300 ft to 400 ft), the differential shortening is unlikely to be structurally serious, although architectural detailing must allow for the expected movement. However, with a rigid slab system, or when the elements which shorten differentially are close to one another, the structural effects can be serious even with lower heights.

The frame analysis is not the concern of this chapter, but we should note that as the differential shortening of supports causes deflections of slab (or beam) systems and induces moments, the slabs (or beams) in turn respond with resistance shears acting back on the supports, thus decreasing the differential shortening. In other words, the support that settles less will receive additional load from the support that settles more. This effect is the "resistance" of the frame and depends on the slab stiffness and axial stiffness of the columns (Fintel and Khan, 1970). Moreover, the moments in the slabs caused by differential settlement of supports cause a redistribution of loads between supports, which, in turn, create a new modified stress level for creep, but this is difficult to analyze (Fintel and Khan, 1970). The difficulty is not structurally important because the general level of accuracy of the data on creep and shrinkage does not warrant an accurate or elaborate analysis.

There is one other general point to be noted: the effects of any calculated differential shortening are smaller than would be expected because the effects are themselves subject to creep. As the effects arise gradually and are at all times being reduced by creep, the maximum effect is less than the sum of "increments." This has been demonstrated experimentally and analytically by Ghali et al. (1969). Specifically, if a given differential shortening occurs over a period of at least a month, the maximum effect is only about one-half of that with a sudden settlement, and is very little affected by the period of settlement (between one month and several years); see Fig. 10.9.

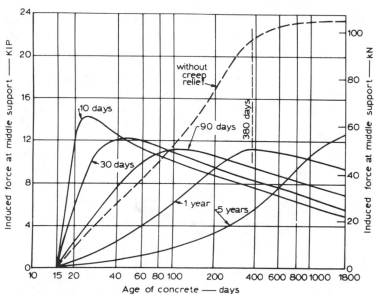

Fig. 10.9 Change in reaction of continuous beam of two equal spans due to settlement of middle support occurring during 10 days, 1 month, 6 months, 1 year, and 5 years

In general, therefore, differential shortening will exist in columns and shear walls or between different columns in a tall building. However, through proper care being taken on the design, this differential can be reduced to such an extent that the over-all effect on the building is minimized. However, the designer must be alive to the possibility and design against it. If it appears that it could be worrisome, then methods of evaluation are mentioned. Normally for a relatively symmetrical building up to 30 floors, where the concrete stresses are relatively uniform over the vertical cross section of the whole building and percentage of steel reasonably constant, little damage or distress is caused by differential shortening; however, over this height, or where there are conditions of unsymmetrical and nonuniform stress and marked variation in the percentages of steel in the vertical members of a building, troubles can occur. These effects are cumulative with height.

In a 13-story building in Australia, with an unsymmetrical cross section as shown in Fig. 10.10, built right up against an adjoining building, the building pulled away over 51 mm (2 in.) from the top of the next-door building, either due to differential creep of the outside columns which were more highly stressed than the shear walls of the core area, or due to differential foundation settlement between the columns and the walls.

This movement was known to occur from 6 months after the frame was completed (when cladding was fixed) up to a period of 18 months. The distress that occurred was in the cladding where it adjoined the existing next-door property.

5 Effects on Nonstructural Elements

A structure to be satisfactory has to be safe and serviceable. The former requirement is taken care of by the considerations of the preceding article; the serviceability problems merit equal attention.

One of the most common among these is partition distress: cracks may open in, above, or below partitions as a result of differential settlement of the supporting horizontal members. This is not only unsightly but also affects adversely the acoustical properties of the partitions.

Similarly, the cladding may spall off as a result of the shortening of the columns relative to the dimensions of the cladding material; this is especially likely when the cladding material has a high modulus of elasticity, as is the case with ceramic or glass. The effects of a separation of the cladding, with the possibility of its falling on the sidewalk below, are clearly very serious.

The remedy in both these cases (cladding and partitions) is to allow the

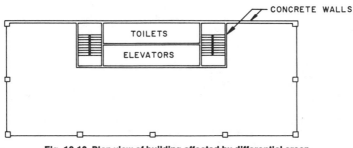

Fig. 10.10 Plan view of building affected by differential creep

movement to take place without inducing stresses in the nonstructural material, for example by the provision of compressible or flexible layers, or by support from above or below but not both.

Other adverse effects on nonstructural elements include damage to mechanical systems and especially to vertical pipes. These may be important and, if they are to be avoided, the mechanical engineer must be apprised by the structural designer of the anticipated movement.

A special case is that of elevators, of which the alinement and therefore proper functioning may be affected by the distortion of guide rails and the like. A solution similar to that in the case of vertical pipes applies.

A more general serviceability problem, possibly coupled with a safety aspect, is that of the twist of the entire structure off-center. This may be the result of complex nonuniform deformations. However, a proper consideration of structural movements would enable the designer to take the precautions necessary to avoid a major twist of the structure.

6 Design Criteria

It is not thought that quantified design criteria can be given at present. In general, a differential shortening of adjacent vertical members of about 6 mm (0.25 in.) is probably tolerable, but the exact limiting values are better expressed in terms of the ratio of relative movement to span; this would be analogous to the span-deflection limiting value. In relation to slabs, the use of a limiting angle of rotation may be most appropriate.

7 Methods of Control

Methods of control of differential vertical movement were mentioned when considering the various effects in the preceding articles, but it may be useful to collect them here.

To avoid structural overstress and nonstructural damage, the differential movement should be limited. This can be achieved by proportioning members so that there is no great disparity in nonelastic vertical movement of adjacent members, that is by the avoidance of greatly differing shrinkage and creep due to difference in the surface-volume ratio of members, axial stresses in them, relative humidity of exposure, percentage of reinforcement, age of placing, and loading. Some of these cannot be avoided but a balancing operation is possible, for example a more lightly loaded column should have a lower percentage of reinforcement (for the same column size), or should not be allowed to dry until a later age. In the case of columns close to a shear wall, a connection by a deep beam is desirable for load transfer from the shear wall to the column.

If significant differential movement cannot be avoided, it must be accommodated. The horizontal members must therefore be strong enough to resist the induced moments and shears; partitions must have a flexible or compressible layer or must be suspended or supported from below, but not both; mechanical systems and vertical pipes must allow axial contraction; and, in the case of elevators, special detailing of guide rails and stopping positions is necessary.

It seems that, provided the designer takes care to estimate the deformations induced by creep and shrinkage in a tall structure, he should be able to modify the structural design to minimize these effects to an acceptable level, or else assure that both the structural and nonstructural components can accommodate the anticipated movement.

10.5 TRANSVERSE DEFLECTION OF FLOORS

In the 1930s, and even in the 1950s, deflection of reinforced concrete was regarded as a completely academic subject, of no interest to practicing designers. Since then there has been a revolutionary change, and in many places it is now the designer's main concern.

What is of interest is rarely deflection in itself, but rather the effect that the deflection has on other, nonstructural, elements of a building. Generally this has taken the form of cracking of brick partitions (Fig. 10.11) in apartment buildings, but many other forms of trouble have been noted: along with cracking of partitions there have been jamming of doors and cracking of windows. In another interesting but distressing example, illustrated in Fig. 10.12, long-term deflection in an inner span of a floor caused an adjacent balcony to slope inwards. Rain falling on the balcony ran inwards under the doorway and formed a pool in the middle of the lounge floor, damaging carpets.

There is evidence to suggest that progressive deflections had been causing trouble in Sweden in the early 1950s. Early stripping of concrete floors was considered one of the causes, and this led to the first study of a rational approach to stripping of formwork for floors (Nielsen, 1952).

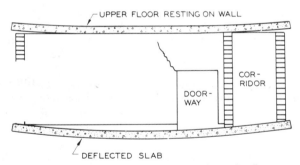

Fig. 10.11 Cracking of partition wall with sagging floor

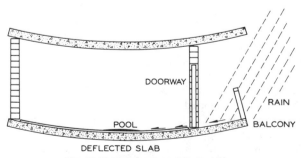

Fig. 10.12 Distress from deflected floor

Certainly the problem of deflection had appeared in Australia later in the 1950s, and was one of the main themes in an extensive study there of flat plates (Blakey, 1963a). Slightly later evidence also came from Germany (Mayer, 1966) and the United States (Portland Cement Association, 1965).

In a tall building, in which the size of the elements of the floor must be small to reduce the structure self-weight, and the formwork is usually stripped when the concrete is young, it is of importance that the deflection be predicted in a rational manner.

Design for deflection differs from design for strength in that the limits which must be set are external to structural engineering rather than internal. In calculating some aspect of strength the design engineer can interpret the result from knowledge of the loads and the properties of the materials in the structure. When he calculates deflection, the result will be incapable of interpretation unless the engineer has knowledge of, for example, the strength, stiffness, and location of partitions, the nature of the surface finishes, and the location and rigidity of door and window frames. It follows that the refinement in computing deflection cannot be justified unless it can be matched with equal precision in the establishment of allowable limits.

Deflection may be described as a low-key problem in design. Instances such as those cited must be regarded as failures of design or construction, but they do not bring the same headlines and widespread consternation as failure to meet a strength requirement, with attendant collapse.

Initial deflection is rarely a source of trouble. If a surfacing, or topping, layer of concrete is being applied to a long-span structural floor the deflection may be enough to require a substantial increase in the amount of material needed to bring the floor level, but unless there has been some error in design and construction it is seldom more serious than this. Again, long-term deflection is not always a problem that needs attention. In structures such as parking garages, and to an increasing extent in offices where "open planning" is in vogue, deflection is not an important criterion.

Shrinkage and creep are in themselves time-dependent phenomena, and in what follows it will be shown that they affect the long-term deflection directly and indirectly.

Temperature effects are seldom directly important but it will be shown that they may have important indirect effects.

1 Creep and Shrinkage

It has been long recognized that creep and shrinkage of concrete will contribute to long-term deflection of reinforced concrete flexural members (Glanville and Thomas, 1939; Miller, 1958). Rao (1951) claimed that all long-term deflection was due to shrinkage, but this is not generally accepted. Of the many studies of long-term deflection of beams that have been made in many countries, the pattern of behavior reported by Washa and Fluck (1952) may be regarded as typical (Fig. 10.13 and Table 10.4). The ratio of long-term deflection to initial deflection there is under 1.61 for beams with compression reinforcement, and roughly between 1.5 and 2.5 for beams reinforced only in tension. There is a sharp difference in the behavior of beams with and without compression reinforcement, but the amount of compression reinforcement has little effect, at least when it is more than one quarter of the tensile steel (Leong and Warner, 1970).

Two analytical studies (Lorentsen, 1968; Yu and Winter, 1960) have also demonstrated this pattern of behavior, and have shown that the multipliers 2 and 3 are reasonable idealizations of the actual relationship between total deflection and initial deflection under design load (Fig. 10.14). (In Fig. 10.14, ζ = total long-term

Table 10.4 Beam deflection[a]

Beam number [b] (1)	Immediate elastic deflection, A, in millimeters (inches) (2)		2½-year gross plastic flow deflection, B, in millimeters (inches) (3)		Ratio B/A (4)
A1, A4	13.46[c]	(0.53[c])	10.16	(0.40)	0.76
A2, A5	15.75[c]	(0.62[c])	16.51	(0.65)	1.05
A3, A6	17.02[c]	(0.67[c])	27.69	(1.09)	1.63
B1, B4	23.37	(0.92)	27.69	(1.09)	1.18
B2, B5	24.89	(0.98)	40.13	(1.58)	1.61
B3, B6	26.42	(1.04)	59.94	(2.36)	2.27
C1, C4	40.13	(1.58)	39.88	(1.57)	0.99
C2, C5	43.43	(1.71)	57.15	(2.25)	1.32
C3, C6	47.75	(1.88)	92.96	(3.66)	1.95
D1, D4	11.94	(0.47)	15.75	(0.62)	1.32
D2, D5	14.22	(0.56)	19.56	(0.77)	1.38
D3, D6	17.78	(0.70)	30.73	(1.21)	1.73
E1, E4	59.44	(2.34)	64.52	(2.54)	1.08
E2, E5	55.88	(2.20)	72.90	(2.87)	1.31
E3, E6	62.99	(2.48)	121.92	(4.80)	1.94

[a]After Washa and Fluck (1952).
[b]Beams 1 and 4 in each group have equal tension and compression; beams 2 and 5, half the amount in compression; and beams 3 and 6 have no compression steel.
[c]Because of an error in the initial readings of beams A1, A2, and A3 they are not included in the average.

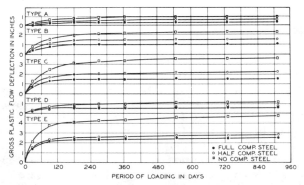

Fig. 10.13 Gross plastic flow deflection curves (Washa and Fluck, 1952)

deflection/initial deflection, and A_{s2}/A_{s1} = area of compression steel/area of tension steel.)

The extent to which these simple multipliers have found experimental confirmation (see for example Yu and Winter, 1960) has led to their widespread use in various standard Codes of Practice in the English-speaking world, and in the International Recommendations for Design and Construction of Concrete Structures (CEB, 1970). The multiplier value of 2 also finds confirmation in some field measurements (Table 10.5).

Table 10.5 Initial and final deflection of concrete floor systems

Floor system (1)	Initial deflection, in millimeters (inches) (2)		Final deflection, in millimeters (inches) (3)	
Flat slab	3.56	(0.14)	22.86	(0.90)
	3.30	(0.13)	13.21	(0.52)
	4.32	(0.17)	22.61	(0.89)
	4.06	(0.16)	17.78	(0.70)
	4.06	(0.16)	21.84	(0.86)
	3.81	(0.15)	22.35	(0.88)
	7.62	(0.30)	27.69	(1.09)
Beam and slab floors	0.25	(0.01)	11.94	(0.47)
	3.56	(0.14)	12.45	(0.49)
	2.03	(0.08)	12.19	(0.48)
	8.89	(0.35)	13.72	(0.54)
	3.56	(0.14)	9.40	(0.37)
	5.08	(0.20)	14.99	(0.59)
	7.87	(0.31)	10.92	(0.43)
	2.79	(0.11)	7.87	(0.31)
	1.02	(0.04)	8.64	(0.34)
	3.56	(0.14)	17.53	(0.69)
Flat plate slab	7.37	(0.29)	19.56	(0.77)
	8.64	(0.34)	17.27	(0.68)
	9.40	(0.37)	18.29	(0.72)

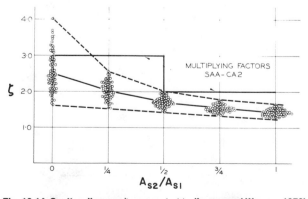

Fig. 10.14 Scatter diagram ζ versus A_{s2}/A_{s1} (Leong and Warner, 1970)

The higher long-term deflections of singly reinforced sections would seem to support the contention of Rao (1951) that long-term deflection is essentially a shrinkage phenomenon. Several authors have suggested that the deflection due to shrinkage be calculated directly (Leonhardt, 1959; Johnson, 1951) by some formula such as

$$\frac{1}{r} = \frac{\epsilon_s}{d} \qquad (10.12)$$

in which r = radius of curvature; d = depth of the tensile reinforcement from the compression face; and ϵ_s = shrinkage of the compression face.

Eq. 10.12 ignores any compression developed in the tensile reinforcement by the shrinkage, but this is likely to be small (Miller, 1958). The effect of this assumption will be to make the computed deflection larger than the actual. If the member is only reinforced on the tension face, ϵ_s will be the value of shrinkage appropriate to the size and exposure of the unit. For conventional members reinforced on both faces, ϵ_s must be reduced in accordance with the action of the steel restraining shrinkage in the compression zone.

The values of w/l (center deflection/span) derived from the previous equation have been presented graphically in Fig. 10.15 for a simply supported beam. It can be seen that even for a simple beam reinforced only in tension, it requires extreme conditions of slenderness and shrinkage before the w/l value from this source reaches commonly accepted limits like 1/360. It must be remembered that this type of computation applies directly only to one-dimensional members such as beams. For slabs and floor systems with bending in two directions it can be assumed that the deformations from shrinkage in each direction will be additive. This must be

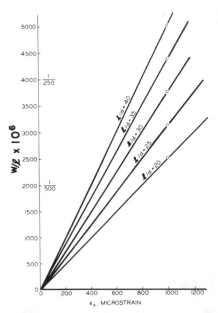

Fig. 10.15 Long-term deflection of simply supported beams due to shrinkage ($w/l = \epsilon_s l/8d$)

borne in mind when relating the acceptable deflection and slopes to the calculated movements.

For any such calculation, however, it is necessary to have basic information on shrinkage, and here seems to be one of the main gaps in knowledge in relation to the performance of structures. There is undoubtedly a vast amount of laboratory experimental data on shrinkage, but there is little evidence of the correlation of these data with field performance. What data are available on this point, in fact, suggest that the correlation is poor (Blakey, 1963b; Bate and Lewsley, 1970; Gamble, 1970), and that shrinkage under exposed or fluctuating conditions is probably less than under controlled or sheltered conditions (Blakey and Lewis, 1956). This strengthens the hypothesis that progressive cracking is largely responsible for the high deflections of exposed slabs, and also raises the question of how far air conditioning in practice has contributed to deflection through maintaining uniform drying conditions.

The processes of settlement and vibration in a freshly cast beam or slab produce a surface layer that is liable to shrink more than the mass of the concrete (Nylander, 1952), as shown by the figures in Table 10.6. This effect is aggravated if cement is trowelled into the surface during the finishing operation.

One approach attempting to take account of the many factors which can influence creep and shrinkage has been proposed by Ulitskii (1962) in a review of a number of Soviet studies. Instead of a single multiplier he proposes that the initial and final deformation be related by a series of multipliers as

$$w_\infty = \alpha_1 \, \alpha_2 \, \alpha_3 \ldots w_i \qquad (10.13)$$

in which α_1, α_2, etc. are parameters that vary with such matters as age of loading, humidity, and size of member. There is no doubt that this is a rational refinement, provided there can be precision in defining the functions for α_1, α_2, etc. This work has been quoted extensively (Blakey, 1963b), and a similar approach has been

Table 10.6 Shrinkage of concrete[a]

					210 days		250 days	
Beam (1)	30 days (2)	60 days (3)	90 days (4)	140 days (5)	ϵ_{mean} (6)	N (7)	ϵ_{mean} (8)	N (9)
A	0.25	0.16	0.14	0.15	0.35	0.17	0.37	0.16
B	0.37	0.35	0.40	0.37	0.33	0.36	0.35	0.34
C	0.22	0.21	0.22	0.23	0.35	0.23	0.36	0.25
D1	0.81	0.73	0.75	0.56	0.43	0.60	0.44	0.63
D2	0.84	0.74	0.71	0.65	0.33	0.67	0.36	0.61
G	0	0	0	0.05	0.39	0.08	0.41	0.10
H	0.19	0.16	0.14	0.15	0.35	0.20	0.37	0.19
I	1.10	1.0	0.90	0.84	0.48	0.92	0.51	0.90
J	0.24	0.27	0.25	0.28	0.35	0.31	0.37	0.30
F1	0.42	0.40	0.33	0.27	0.36	0.33	0.38	0.34
F2	0.50	0.48	0.49	0.44	0.33	0.42	0.45	0.40

[a]Values of $N = \Delta\epsilon/\epsilon_{mean}$ at various instants, in which $\Delta\epsilon$ = difference in shrinkage age between top and bottom surfaces of test beams, and ϵ_{mean} = mean amount of shrinkage. The columns for 210 days and 250 days also include the values of ϵ_{mean} in per thousand (Nylander, 1952).

suggested by Lorentsen (1968). Similar approaches to the calculation of total deflection, including that due to creep and shrinkage, have also been presented by Branson (1968) and Soretz (1971). While these methods may be expected to give a more accurate prediction of deflection, they are no different in concept from the ideas already discussed, and somewhat more elaborate in application. Because of the imprecise nature of any limits imposed on deflection it is reasonable to question whether anything more elaborate than a simple system of multipliers is justified for practical design, especially if the designer clearly understands the limits of such a system. More elaborate methods provide a means of examining differential shrinkage in members of different sizes or the effects of different ages of loading.

Insofar as long-term deflection is directly caused by shrinkage it should be independent of load, and therefore it seems illogical that its computation should be related to load by the initial deflection. There is, however, an indirect way by which shrinkage can influence deflection. The basic stiffness of a cracked reinforced concrete section is usually less, sometimes much less, than the stiffness of the surrounding gross concrete section. If a member is cracked by stresses caused by shrinkage or thermal change there will be a reduction in stiffness and increased deflection. As a time-dependent phenomenon shrinkage will act in this way to extend the zones of cracking in a member, and thus bring about increased deflection through reduction in stiffness. Table 10.7 shows the ratios of cracked and uncracked stiffnesses over a range of reinforcement and concrete.

It would appear that this change from uncracked to cracked section, which may be brought about and extended over a considerable period by thermal and

Table 10.7 Stiffness parameters for cracked reinforced concrete sections

n (1)	P (2)	Stiffness ratio, cracked to uncracked section (3)
5.0 $E = 41.368 \times 10^3$ MPa (6×10^6 psi, 4.218×10^9 kgf/m^2)	0.005 0.010 0.015 0.020 0.025	0.224 0.422 0.548 0.678 0.796
7.5 $E = 27.579 \times 10^3$ MPa (4×10^6 psi, 2.812×10^9 kgf/m^2)	0.005 0.010 0.015 0.020 0.025	0.315 0.546 0.738 0.903 1.044
10.0 $E = 20.684 \times 10^3$ MPa (3×10^6 psi, 2.109×10^9 kgf/m^2)	0.005 0.010 0.015 0.020 0.025	0.40 0.68 0.90 1.088 1.252
15.0 $E = 13.789 \times 10^3$ MPa (2×10^6 psi, 1.406×10^9 kgf/m^2)	0.005 0.010 0.015 0.020 0.025	0.546 0.900 1.170 1.382 1.572

shrinkage effects, offers potential for a corresponding continuing increase in deflection.

Insofar as creep can be isolated from shrinkage, and in the context that the distinction is admittedly artificial, it must usually be expected to have fairly minor importance (Constructional Review, 1961). There should be exceptions when the live load is large. Creep in the compression zone of a simply reinforced beam may be considered for calculation purposes as a time-dependent reduction in the modulus of elasticity. From one of the established formulas for stiffness of cracked reinforced concrete sections (Johnson, 1950) it follows that a twofold additional creep strain in the concrete regarded as a reduction of the elastic modulus by two-thirds will only reduce the section stiffness by about 30%. In the more common case with compression reinforcement the effect should be even less.

Throughout the world there is increasing use of lightweight aggregate concrete, and designers must be aware of differences between lightweight and normal concrete. The extent to which the shrinkage and creep of lightweight concrete are different from those of normal concrete of the same strength or the same cement content will depend very much on the particular aggregate and no useful generalization is possible. However, in one review (Blakey and Lewis, 1964) it was shown that there was no important difference from normal concrete in these properties, provided that the lightweight aggregate was a well coated expanded clay or shale with a volumetric absorption of less than 10% in 24 hr.

Before leaving the subjects of creep and shrinkage it is necessary to note that there have been several recorded instances (Constructional Review, 1961; Taylor and Heiman, 1970; Taylor, 1970; Blakey, 1963c) in which the long-term deflection has been much more than three times the initial value. It is not possible to explain these cases, in which the ratio of final to initial deflection has ranged up to 12 in conventional terms of creep and shrinkage, unless quite extraordinary levels are assumed for these properties. It is noteworthy that structures on which such high long-term deflections have been measured have been exposed to high temperature variation through direct solar radiation, and it is reasonable to consider that thermal stresses have with time substantially extended the regions of cracking so that the maximum effects of stiffness reduction from cracking, shrinkage, and creep have occurred simultaneously. In these cases initial deflections have usually been low, suggesting that the floor was largely uncracked.

The discussion so far has followed fairly closely the widespread current practice of expressing deflection limits, w, as a slope w/l in which l = span length. It is recognized that curvature, or some related factor, may be fundamentally a more correct basis for limiting movement, but it does not lend itself to such simple expression.

Again, it is recognized that for design purposes it would be much more convenient if the limits could be expressed in terms of span/depth ratio (l/d) instead of w/l. This matter has been considered at some length, but it is felt that the relation between these two parameters depends so much on the loading and degree of fixity at the bearing ends that to adopt the l/d ratios would mean setting a number of limits depending on support conditions which in a discussion like this might be confusing, and it has been simpler to consider w/l values.

Calculation of total deflection, if it is derived from a calculation of the initial deflection under load, is a somewhat complicated step; however, calculation of the long-term shrinkage deformation as given earlier is much less tedious, and it seems that a convenient compromise would be to calculate the long-term deflection due to creep and shrinkage by some multiplier (possibly 2) applied to the initial deflection. The point has already been made (and it will be discussed again later) that it is nearly always the long-term deflection, or some part of it, which is important, and not the initial or total deflection.

2   Temperature Effects

Rigorous analysis for the effects of temperature is normally beyond the limit of what is practically possible for most designs. The opportunity does not arise for temperature to influence transverse deflection, since floor systems are usually protected from large temperature changes soon after casting.

In those slabs that are not so protected, temperature changes can be quite important (Blakey, 1961), and the graphs in Fig. 10.16 show the temperature distribution through slabs of different thicknesses at 1400 hr on a summer day in Melbourne, Australia when the temperature variation was that shown in Fig. 10.17. (In Fig. 10.16, the solid lines represent inside air at constant temperature, and the broken lines represent inside air at variable temperature.) These curves have been derived analytically and confirmed in measurements on one slab 406 mm (16 in.) thick. Fig. 10.18 shows thermal deflection on another slab structure, in this case a waffle slab 381 mm (15 in.) thick spanning some 17.7 m (58 ft) each way. Temperature stresses have been known to cause distress in bridges (Maher, 1970).

For floor systems it seems that the main effect of temperature is the indirect one outlined in the previous article, although it should be noted that the modulus of elasticity decreases with increasing temperature (Blakey, 1955).

There are, of course, special instances in which temperature has contributed substantially to deflection. In one case, excessive deflections of suspended concrete floor slabs have been reported in Scotland by Jenkins et al. (1965), and were partly attributed to the effect of heating cables in the concrete screed above the structural slab. Exposure of concrete to high temperatures can lead to increased shrinkage and

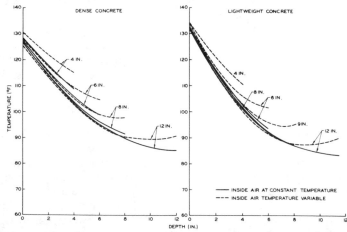

Fig. 10.16 Temperature gradients in slabs of dense concrete (left) and lightweight concrete (right)

creep associated with the accelerated drying-out of the concrete. Temperature stresses have also been shown to be responsible for cracking of roofs and masonry walls (Rosenhaupt, 1961).

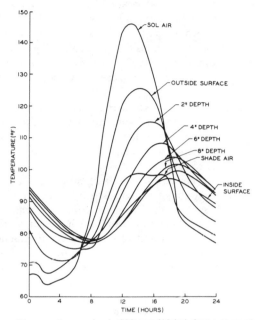

Fig. 10.17 Diurnal temperature cycles in 300-mm (12-in.) dense concrete on summer day

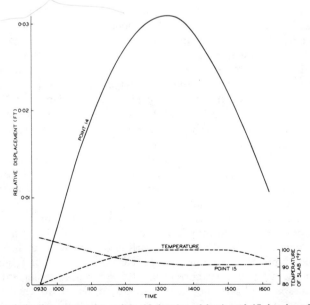

Fig. 10.18 Time-deflection curves for points 14 (center of bay) and 15 (center of column strip span), concrete slab in open deck garage and slab temperature 38 mm (1.5 in.) below surface

3 Effects on Nonstructural Elements

As stated earlier, design for deflection differs from design for strength in that the limits are not set intrinsically by the properties of the materials, but most often by the performance of other, nonstructural, components of a building.

An exception to this may be the limitation imposed by cracking. There has been extensive laboratory study in most parts of the world of crack spacing and crack width in concrete structures, and perhaps the most comprehensive review so far has been provided by Rehm and Martin (1968). However, in this case the uncertainty over limits to be set reappears when it is necessary to decide on acceptable crack widths.

The CEB Recommendations (1970) set three levels of maximum crack width, 0.3 mm, 0.2 mm, and 0.1 mm (0.012 in., 0.008 in., and 0.004 in.) in order of increasing severity of exposure, but studies to substantiate these limits have been few (CUR, 1956), especially when compared with those concerned with the calculation of maximum crack width and spacing.

Because a great deal of the concern with deflection has arisen over the associated cracking of supported brick walls, it is logical to try to derive the limits from the behavior of unreinforced brick walls. From tests on such walls (Wood, 1952) it would appear that cracking in the brickwork might begin at slopes as low as $w/l = 1/8000$. This would be a prohibitive figure to use in practice, and suggests that the walls do not follow completely the movement of the floors, or cracking would have been even more frequent than it has been. In many cases the wall must bridge over the deflected floor, and it does not crack unless the floor above deflects far enough to apply extra load to it. This would be less likely to happen if the mortar joint between the top of the brickwork and the upper floor has not been completely filled, as is frequently the case.

One authority (ASCE, 1961) has suggested that the limiting slope for a reinforced masonry wall is $w/l = 1/500$, although the evidence for this was not given. If this is accepted as a limit for the long-term deflection, a conservative design would set the limit for the immediate deflection/span ratio as $1/1000$. Although this is much more severe than the widely adopted $1/360$ it is not an impossible figure for design.

Other limits in the vicinity of $1/100$ and $1/180$ can be derived from the tolerances in doors and windows and the movements likely to cause jamming. Deflections of this order are fairly clearly visible, and it must be recognized that one of the most pressing objections to deflection is that it is esthetically disagreeable. Some casual observations suggest that slopes on the order of $1/100$ are detectable either visually or as one walks over them, but as far as the writers are aware no studies have ever been made to find how much deflection looks "wrong," and there would seem to be scope for work here. It would be just as legitimate an investigation as the subjective study of the levels of vibration that cause discomfort.

The problem of deflection has arisen in a slightly different form in relation to the differential movements from foundation settlements. Feld (1965) has discussed a number of such cases, but these in themselves do not seem to have led to any recommended limits on deflection or slope. He also presents for English readers a useful summary of Soviet rules current in 1965 on limiting settlement. Although a range of values is laid down they are not greatly different from those which have been discussed.

4 Limits and Control of Deflection

It has already been emphasized that precise limits on deflection are difficult, if not impossible, to set. The limiting deflection of a member is not to be determined from the properties of the steel and concrete in the same way as the strength of the member is derived from the strength of the steel or concrete.

Limits on deflection are nearly always set by the capacity for deformation of other usually nonstructural elements. In this the diversity is great and there is also a serious lack of quantitative data. In the face of such uncertainty it follows that: (1) Any attempt at precise computation of long-term deflection is unwarranted; and (2) design for deflection is a process calling for much greater engineering judgment and understanding than design for strength.

The measures for limitation or control of deflection can be fairly clearly defined. Undoubtedly the most effective is the use of prestressed members designed for zero deflection under sustained load (Brotchie, 1964). Another measure, frequently overlooked, is the establishment of the maximum degree of redundancy and continuity. Many influences, including economic ones, have led to a progressive simplification of structures in floor systems. A generation or more back, floors were usually two-way slabs supported on beams on all sides or flat slabs with large column capitals. In each case there was substantial interaction of the elements and a large measure of membrane action not considered in design or analysis. The other extreme today is a floor composed of precast planks spanning one way between supporting girders, or a lift slab with no capitals, drop panels, or continuity with the columns. Clearly, modern structures are intrinsically more flexible than those of the past.

Probably deflection first became a general design problem because the implications of using high-strength materials were not realized. The rules for the design of flat slabs which followed Westergaard's work in 1921 were adopted when the design stresses for steel and concrete were commonly 110 MPa and 4.1 MPa (16 000 psi and 600 psi, 1125 kgf/cm² and 42 kgf/cm²), respectively. Today in many countries stresses over 207 MPa (30 000 psi, 2109 kgf/cm²) for steel and 9 MPa (1300 psi, 91 kgf/cm²) for concrete are common. In the absence of any change in moduli of elasticity it is obvious that deformations must at least have doubled. When allowance is made for the greater region in which the concrete is cracked from higher steel stresses, deformations will be more than doubled.

Earlier it has been urged that progressive cracking plays a major role in long-term deflections, but that when members are fully cracked in accord with implicit design assumptions, then the multipliers provided in many codes for the computation of the long-term from the initial deflection are fairly reliable and have the advantage of simplicity. This contention has received some support in practice.

When deflection first created some difficulties in Australia, one office (Miller, 1959) adopted a practice of "precracking" the floors by loading them at an early age with all the bricks and other impedimenta subsequently to be used in nonstructural elements. This appeared to reduce difficulties from long-term deflection. Once a member is fully cracked under load the opportunity for further cracking due to restrained shrinkage or thermal movement with associated reduction in stiffness is greatly reduced, and the maximum long-term deflection likely can be more reliably predicted by the multipliers.

The evidence from laboratory and field, then, suggests that to control long-term deflection there should be no increase in the size of the cracked zones of a flexural member after it is first loaded. If stringent limitation of the absolute magnitude of deflection is required, perhaps for performance of some equipment, then the sections should be designed to remain uncracked, at midspan at least.

In flat plate structures the first loading is often that from the formwork shores carrying the upper floors (Blakey and Beresford, 1965), and the foregoing argument seems to lead to an interesting contradiction of common practice in that it encourages early stripping of formwork and shores. In this way the slab would be fully cracked in accordance with design assumptions, the probability of enlarging the zones of cracking later is greatly reduced, and the probability of a reliable prediction of the upper bound of the long-term deflection correspondingly increased.

Undoubtedly it is widely held that early stripping increases deflection, and it must certainly increase initial deflection. It is also well established that creep in plain concrete in compression (McHenry, 1943; Neville, 1963) is higher the earlier the age at which the specimens are loaded. However, the previous discussion suggested that creep in the concrete made only a relatively minor contribution to the long-term deflection of reinforced members.

One reference (Eriksson et al., 1962) claims that long-term (creep) deflection curves are essentially parallel, but the origin of the data on which this is based is not given. On this basis it follows that, provided the partitions are installed as late as possible after the floor is cast, the age of stripping of the floor is unimportant (Fig. 10.19).

Other measures that may be used to minimize the effects of deflection are:

1. Placing a compressible joint filler between the top of the partition and the soffit of the slab above.

2. Provision of upward camber in floor.

3. Provision of vertical joints at intervals along partitions and concealing the joints with cover strips.

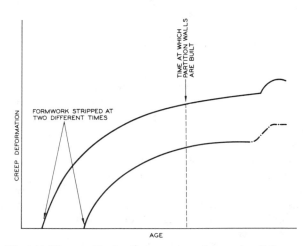

Fig. 10.19 Effect of different stripping times on creep deformation (Eriksson et al., 1962)

4. Delaying the construction and plastering or rendering of partition walls as long as possible after floors are constructed.

5. Reinforcing masonry partitions.

6. Extending door openings to ceiling level.

Temperature movements due to solar radiation may be reduced by insulation or merely by painting the surface white (Neumann et al., 1955). It has been reported (Constructional Review, 1961) that the surface of one experimental flat plate was up to 14°C (57.2°F) hotter than the body of the slab, and it was found that the flexural deformations associated with this thermal gradient were almost completely removed when the upper surface was painted white.

5 General

There is still scope for further research into the influence of creep, shrinkage, and temperature on the long-term deflection of reinforced concrete. Although the general pattern of behavior has been fairly well established, there is still need for further information on the interaction of the many factors that influence creep and shrinkage. Because of the time-dependent nature of these properties this information will not be readily obtained.

The information currently available suggests that for doubly reinforced beams and slabs shrinkage plays a minor direct role in contributing to increased deflection, but may indirectly contribute substantially by extending the zone of cracking by restrained shrinkage and thus reducing the stiffness below that of the gross concrete section.

For sections reinforced only in tension, shrinkage, creep, and cracking all contribute to the long-term deflection. It must be noted that if the top steel over supports is not securely held in place and is displaced towards the neutral axis, the stiffness over the support will be greatly reduced [if the effective depth is 180 mm (7 in.) instead of 200 mm (8 in.), as has been observed, the stiffness is reduced by 23%], and the member tends to behave as a simply reinforced one.

Reference has been made to a number of methods of calculating either long-term or total deflection, but no detailed presentation of these has been made here because it is considered that in design the most urgent problem is not the establishment of accurate methods of computation, but of establishing bases from which limits on deflection may be derived, and the expression of these limits in quantitative terms. There are remarkably few reliable data to assist in this direction.

Roughly, there seem to be two levels at which deflection may be limited:

1. When there is any concern with brittle partitions and claddings, $< l/500$.

2. Where appearance only is important, $< l/180$.

Each of these should be regarded as representative of a range, rather than as unique precise figures. The first limit is frequently applied only to the long-term deflection after the partitions or cladding have been put in place, but the second is applied to total deflection.

Control or reduction of deflection may be achieved by many steps that follow directly from elementary mechanics, namely, increased thickness and reinforcement, use of low shrinkage concrete, proper early curing, and so on. The most effective measure undoubtedly is to prestress the floor and design for zero deflection. It is often overlooked that the simplification of construction—in particular the use of precast flooring units—has removed many structural redundancies and interactions which added to the general rigidity.

The Future.   Concern with long-term deflection of floor systems seems likely to increase so long as the present trend to large clear floor areas continues. Such unobstructed areas provide a flexibility in the planning and use of internal space, which is currently architecturally attractive and economically desirable in a market economy. In such construction the risk to nonstructural elements of damage caused by the deflection of the floors is probably fairly slight, but there is an increased risk that the deflection will be evident and unsightly through lack of alinement in partitions or furniture.

Despite the pressing need for quantitative information on the amount of deformation that nonstructural elements can stand, there is no evidence that these data are going to be provided, and the prospects of neat quantitative criteria for the design for deflection do not seem good.

It therefore seems more likely that future interest will be directed to the development of structural floor systems that provide minimum deflection and maximum transverse flexural rigidity. Post-tensioned floors must be expected to play a larger role, as they can be designed to maintain zero deflection under sustained loads. However, end anchorage requirements or end shortening may at times introduce difficulties so that an alternative could be sought in different types of shallow shells. The possibilities here have long been recognized (Blakey, 1962; Milton and Brotchie, 1967) and the ideas have been tried in practice. Tall buildings are likely to provide opportunity for a large number of reuses of formwork for a floor system, so that the initial cost of a moderately complex form system should not be prohibitive.

No doubt there will also be an increasing use of composite systems in which the stiffness of steel is combined with the fire resistance, thermal capacity, and acoustic insulation provided by concrete. Since most of these steps would require the structure to show something nearer the classical linear elastic behavior, the interesting possibility arises that the risk of vibration discomfort may increase.

Where large fixed partitions are available, more use could be made of these to provide a composite construction in which the partition acts as a large girder web and the floors above and below it are the flanges. This is appropriate for certain situations, such as the floors immediately above a parking garage in an apartment building.

Up to about 1960 there had been a trend towards simplified structural forms, which were necessary if analysis and design of larger and larger structures were to be realistic. With the advent of the modern large computer there is no longer any urgent reason to avoid complexity and redundancy in structure, and an effective way of reducing nearly all deformations in any structure would be to allow all convenient redundancies to develop.

In brief, the forecast is that the problem of predicting long-term deflections will be bypassed by steps that will greatly enhance structural rigidity.

10.6 DEFLECTION OF LIGHTWEIGHT REINFORCED CONCRETE BEAMS

A comparison is here made between measured and calculated long-term deflections of lightweight concrete beams under service and test loads. The field measurements carried out on the Tower Building in Australia Square, Sydney, NSW, from 1966 to 1971 have shown that there can be considerable differences between measured deflections and those calculated by recently developed methods. Although this building was built with lightweight concrete, similar differences may also occur in buildings with normal weight aggregate.

1 Description of Structure

The Tower is a circular building of 50 stories and is 183 m (600 ft) high. It is 41 m (135 ft) in diameter and has a circular service core 19 m (62 ft) in diameter. The structural system used in most of the floors consists of 20 radial, tapered beams spanning 11 m (35 ft) between the core and the 20 external columns which project beyond the window line. The beams are spaced at approximately 4.6-m (15-ft) centers at midspan, and have an over-all depth of 521 mm (20½ in.). The slab thickness is 118 mm (4⅝ in.).

Construction and loading schedules, material properties, and measurement procedures have been reported by Heiman (1973).

Sydney Harbor, Australia: (left) Opera House; (right of center) Australia Square Tower (Courtesy: Ness Abdullah; photo by Max Dupain)

2 Calculated and Measured Deflections

The initial deflections were calculated using a 4.79-kPa (100-psf, 488-kgf/m²) live load obtained from the load cell measurements. The long-term deflections were calculated using a 0.72-kPa (15-psf, 73-kgf/m²) live load. This value was obtained from a live-load survey.

In the first method of calculation, the effective moment of inertia was determined at nine positions along the beam using Branson's formula (ACI Committee 435, 1966). In the second method, the deflections were calculated using a procedure developed by Neville (1970). In both methods, the deflections due to creep and shrinkage warping were determined separately. In the first method, the long-term deflection due to creep was determined by multiplying the initial deflection by a factor given by Branson. In the second method, a formula developed by Neville was used to determine the creep deflection. Neville's formula for determining the deflection caused by shrinkage warping was used in both methods.

In the third method, the long-term deflection was determined using the procedure given in the ACI Building Code (ACI, 1971).

The total long-term deflection calculated by the three methods is respectively 11.7 mm (0.46 in.), 8.7 mm (0.34 in.), and 8.9 mm (0.35 in.).

Graphs for eight of the 11 beams under observation, showing deflection plotted against time, are reproduced in Fig. 10.20. The graph of the deflections measured on B20, on floor 24, where the test load was applied, is also shown in Fig. 10.20, together with a graph of the calculated deflections.

The changes in the propping loads placed on part of floor 38 plotted against time are shown in Fig. 10.21.

3 Commentary

Beam Deflections. When the measured deflections for B20 on floor 16 [13.2 mm (0.52 in.)] and B15 on floor 20 [13.7 mm (0.54 in.)] are compared with the corresponding calculated, long-term deflections in Table 10.8, it can be seen that all three methods of calculation give results that are too small. There are several reasons for the discrepancies.

The long-term deflections caused by the 0.72-kPa (15-psf, 73-kgf/m²) live load are calculated without taking into account all the effects of the heavy construction loading applied on the beams soon after placement of the concrete. Because some cracking of the concrete must have occurred at this time, the subsequent creep deflection under the influence of 0.72-kPa (15-psf, 73-kgf/m²) live load was probably greater than the calculations indicate. However, when a comparison is made between the calculated creep deflections under a 4.79-kPa (100-psf, 488-kgf/m²) live load [3.0 mm (0.12 in.)] and under a 0.72-kPa (15-psf, 73-kgf/m²) live load [1.3 mm (0.05 in.)] using Neville's method, the difference in magnitude is not great.

The methods of calculating long-term deflections by means of a multiplier have been based partly on laboratory tests carried out by Washa and Fluck (1952) and by Yu and Winter (1960) in which narrow, reinforced concrete beams were subjected to continuously applied live loads that produced sustained stresses considerably higher than those likely to be produced by the actual service loading commonly associated with buildings of the type under investigation. Initial deflections of the beams in the

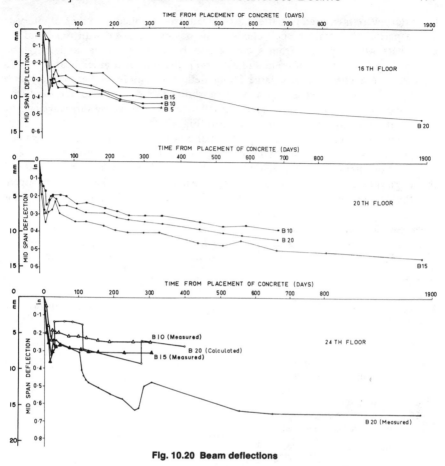

Fig. 10.20 Beam deflections

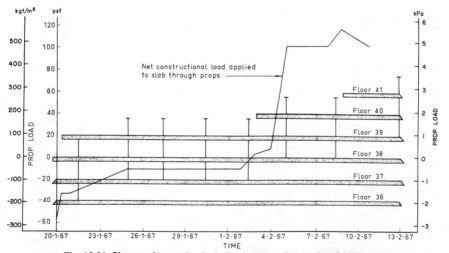

Fig. 10.21 Changes in prop loads during construction cycle—B14 floor 38

laboratory were measured just after the test loads were applied, and then at intervals over a period of years. The deflections of the beams increased with time, and the multipliers were obtained from a comparison between the initial and long-term deflections. This was a different situation from the one encountered at Australia Square, where comparatively large initial deflections under a heavy short-term construction loading were followed by a short period of creep recovery and shrinkage, and then by increasing long-term deflections caused by shrinkage and by creep under the influence of a small live load (Fig. 10.20).

The procedure of first calculating the initial elastic deflection under the assumed design live load, in order to obtain the long-term deflection, has little relevance to the situation that occurs commonly in practice, as it does not take any account of the magnitude of the construction loading, the length of time the floor is propped, and the way in which the props are struck. On many jobs, the props under a floor

Table 10.8 Calculated deflections

Type of deflection (1)	Amount of deflection, in millimeters (inches) (2)	
(a) Method 1		
Initial, determined from computer program based on effective moment of inertia and 4.8 kPa (100 psf) live load	6.1 (0.24)	
Long-term, caused by shrinkage warping during 5-year period	1.8 (0.07)	
Long-term, caused by creep due to dead load and 0.72 kPa (15 psf) live load during 5-year period using Branson's method	3.8 (0.15)	
Total long-term deflection	11.7 (0.46)	
(b) Method 2	Live load = 4.8 kPa (100 psf)	Live load = 0.72 kPa (15 psf)
Initial, due to 4.8 kPa (100 psf) live load using Neville's method	5.6 (0.22)	5.6 (0.22)
Long-term, caused by shrinkage warping during 5-year period	1.8 (0.07)	1.8 (0.07)
Long-term creep, due to live load during 5-year period	3.0 (0.12)	1.3 (0.05)
Total long-term deflection	10.4 (0.41)	8.7 (0.34)
(c) Method 3 (ACI Code)		
Initial, due to 4.8 kPa (100 psf) live load		5.6 (0.22)
Long-term, due to 0.72 kPa (15 psf) and obtained with an average value of the multiplier = 1.3		3.3 (0.13)
Total long-term deflection		8.9 (0.35)

are not all removed at one time. Consequently the initial loading can be applied in stages, during which time a combination of elastic and creep deflection takes place.

Some other factors that may have been partly responsible for the differences between the measured and calculated deflections, and for the variations in the measured deflections, were variations in ambient temperature during and soon after the placement of the concrete, differences in the strength of the concrete and propping times, and shakedown of the formwork and props after placement of the concrete.

The results of the shrinkage tests on prisms of plain lightweight concrete are higher than would normally be associated with normal weight concrete of similar mix proportions containing dimensionally-stable aggregate, such as quartzose river gravel or limestone. However, the calculated deflection for shrinkage warping formed only a small part of the total deflection, and suggests that the effect of the lightweight aggregate on the shrinkage of the beams was offset by the presence of a large amount of top steel. The top steel would have also had a beneficial effect in the reduction of the magnitude of the long-term deflection caused by creep. The deflection due to creep was also small.

The modulus of elasticity of the lightweight concrete was substantially lower than would be typical of normal weight concrete of similar strength. However, this disadvantage was offset by the reduction in weight associated with the use of lightweight concrete. The deflections measured on the two beams after 5 yr give a deflection-to-span ratio of 1/770, which is much lower than is generally required in building construction of this type.

Differential Movements Between Columns and Core. The levelling measurements on the beams also indicated that there was a long-term differential shortening of the core with respect to the columns. Levels taken on beams in the plant room, just under the roof of the building, showed a differential shortening of 28 mm (1.1 in.) from the time the roof slab was placed in April 1967 until September 1971.

There are no visible signs of distress in the structure as a result of the differential movement. However, the long-term absolute shortening of the core caused some problems with the elevators. During a period from September 1967, when the high-rise elevators were installed, until the end of 1971, it was necessary to shorten the elevator guide rails at level 48 by more than 76 mm (3 in.).

In conclusion, there is a need for more field investigations to increase the limited existing knowledge on the subject. In particular, more information is needed on the effects of construction practices on the long-term deflections of structural members.

10.7 TEMPERATURE EFFECTS

Within the last few decades some reinforced concrete high-rise buildings were designed with exterior columns partially or fully exposed. This was done mostly for architectural expression of the structural frame, or sometimes for economy. The exposure of structural frame to seasonal temperatures results in length changes of the exterior columns relative to the interior columns, thus creating distortions and structural overstress in the horizontal members of the exterior bays. Also, cracking of partitions occurred in the upper stories. After several buildings developed these problems (cracking of partitions being the more visible effect), structural engineers began to study and analyze temperature effects on tall buildings. Soon, a relatively simple computation method was developed for analysis of multistory building frames for length changes of exposed columns.

There are two basic approaches for designing structures with exposed columns:

1. With special details to accommodate large movements due to temperature exposure.

2. By proper design to limit temperature movement (limiting exposure, or adjusting the glass line).

Taller buildings designed without consideration of floor racking caused by temperature movement of the exterior columns may result in distress of partitions (Fig. 10.22) and reduced soundproofing between apartments or offices, and may create a continuous maintenance problem. In lower buildings the temperature movement of exterior columns is small and the structural problems are usually insignificant. Naturally, each building must be considered individually.

Height of the building may be the most important factor of the temperature effect on tall buildings, but it is not the only one. Other factors to be considered are: (1) The span of the exterior bays; (2) stiffness of the horizontal structural members (slab or beam); and (3) the relative stiffnesses of the exterior and the first interior columns. All of these factors will affect the final temperature movements of the frame. In lower floors of a high-rise building the length changes and the resulting distortions are of a secondary magnitude. This is because the length changes of the exterior column are cumulative starting at the ground level and adding up to a maximum in the top story. The length changes within one story are insignificant, but adding up 25 or more stories may produce a total movement of 19 mm (0.75 in.) or more. The purpose of the temperature computations and analysis for a high-rise structure is to establish the maximum height of multistory buildings beyond which the distortions of the frame become critical, and may require special partition details and possible additional structural considerations. This maximum height of multistory buildings, beyond which special details and strengthening of frame may be required, has an economic implication. If the required details prove too costly, the architectural design must be revised to limit temperature movements. In this case

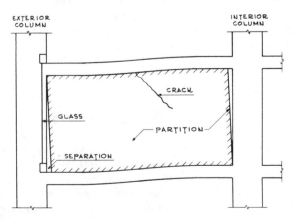

Fig. 10.22 Partition distortion

the exposure of exterior columns may be reduced, or the glass line may be adjusted without greatly changing the floor plan.

How does the structural frame affect the temperature movements of a high-rise structure? Consider a portion of a structural frame (Fig. 10.23), in which $\alpha = 9.9 \times 10^{-6}$ mm/mm/per 1°C (5.5×10^{-6} in./in./per 1°F). If the exterior and interior columns were not connected by floor slabs, and there were a temperature difference between the exterior and the interior, then the exterior columns would be free to move. This movement would be zero at the ground floor and maximum at the roof, and there would be no temperature stresses in the frame. However, the columns are interconnected by floor structure which resists this movement, and the resulting residual (final) movement is smaller than the theoretical free movement of the columns. The residual temperature movement of columns induces deflections, bending moments, and shears in the floor structure and the connected columns. The floor moments will also induce axial loads in the columns. (In addition to the above stresses, additional stresses induced by the effect of the temperature gradient between the cold and warm faces of the exterior column should be considered.) It is clear that, the stiffer the floor structure, the smaller will be the residual temperature movements. On the other hand, because the temperature-induced loads in columns counteract the column displacement, it is desirable to have "limber" (more elastic) columns. The less resistance the column offers against shortening and lengthening,

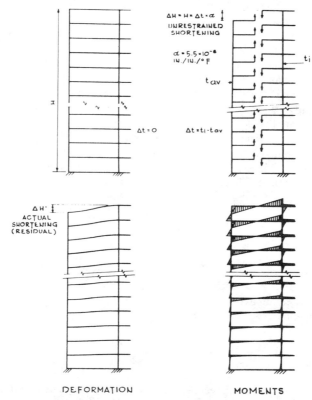

DEFORMATION   MOMENTS

Fig. 10.23 Axial shortening and its effects

the smaller the residual temperature displacement of the frame. However, all reductions of differential displacement are achieved after axial forces are induced in the columns, and bending and shear in the floor structure, which are to be combined with those caused by gravity and other loads. The additional stresses and column loads due to the differential displacement can be of appreciable magnitude, and careful attention must be paid to the design to arrive at a safe and also economical solution. All the foregoing indicates the obvious conclusion, that buildings subjected to the effect of differential temperature require more than routine attention in design and detailing.

1   Analysis for Length Changes of Exposed Columns

Design Temperatures.   Columns and members in the interior of the building are subject to relatively constant temperatures. These temperatures are in direct relation to the heating or cooling which normally maintain a temperature of about 21°C (70°F). Members on the outside of the building are subjected to constant temperature on their interior faces and a variable temperature on their exterior faces. The temperature of the exposed surfaces is influenced by the ambient air temperature and the effects of wind, solar radiation, and condensation. The lowest and the highest effective temperatures of all exposed members must be determined during the full seasonal cycle. It must be remembered that peak values selected must be of sufficient duration to produce an appreciable effect on massive structural members. Very thick members subjected to sudden temperature change on one side may approach a steady state only after many hours. Peak temperatures of a relatively short duration penetrate only skin deep and will have a small effect on the final movements. A study of temperature records should be made to establish the minimum and maximum temperatures for design purposes. For example, for the northeastern parts of the United States a minimum temperature of between $-18°C$ and $-29°C$ (0°F and $-20°F$) is indicated. In southern parts of the country the maximum differential may occur in summer, resulting in higher exterior surface temperature and lower interior temperature. Because the steady state of heat conduction through any section is only possible if boundary temperatures are assumed constant for a sufficient time, the chance of attaining true steady state of conduction is remote. Therefore, an equivalent steady state must be derived. The rate of heat flow, q, for the condition of steady state of conduction is defined by

$$q = -kA \frac{dT}{dx} = kA \frac{T_1 - T_2}{d} \qquad (10.14)$$

in which (dT/dx) = temperature gradient; A = area of material; k = conductivity of material; and d = thickness of section. Under the steady state of heat conduction when the two face temperatures are T_1 and T_2, the average temperature of the wall will be

$$T_{av} = \frac{T_1 + T_2}{2} \qquad (10.15)$$

and the gradient will be linear between the two faces. The estimate of thermal gradient based on the recorded temperature is bound to be conservative. This is because many hours are required to obtain a steady state of heat transfer in any sizable structural member. For lightweight concrete almost twice the time would be required to achieve the same penetration of the exterior temperature. Based on studies presented (Fintel and Khan, 1965) it is considered adequate to use the minimum mean daily temperature with a frequency of recurrence once in 40 yr as the equivalent steady-state exterior winter temperature for design purpose of reinforced concrete members. The recommended summer design temperatures are based on temperature charts used commonly by air-conditioning engineers. Some local weather bureaus or codes may be a good source to obtain the mean temperatures. A study of the highest temperatures ever recorded shows little fluctuation over the entire United States.

The effect of direct radiation on concrete surfaces may result in considerable increase in the surface temperature. The magnitude of this increase depends upon color, texture, density, and angle of incidence. The penetration of these temperatures into the member is limited to a few inches from the surface due to the relatively short cycle. The effect of direct radiation on concrete surfaces requires further study.

Temperature Gradient and Isotherms. After the equivalent steady-state temperature has been selected, the isotherms and the gradients through the partially exposed members have to be determined. Except for very long walls, the temperature gradient under a steady state of conduction is not linear. The gradient varies with shape of the section and the boundary conditions. The problem is to determine the realistic average temperature of the member. One of the better-known methods for solving two-dimensional and three-dimensional steady-state heat flow problems is the "relaxation method." The time involved in the analysis by the relaxation method may not always justify its use. A useful known graphical method of analysis may save time. This method developed for construction of isotherms and gradients is based on the concept of flow net known from soil mechanics. The heat flow is represented by two sets of intersecting lines, as shown in Fig. 10.2. One set of lines represents the heat flow lines; the other set, perpendicular to the first, is the set of isothermal lines. Isothermal line is a contour of equal temperatures. The two sets of lines intersect at right angles forming curvilinear squares with equal average sides in each direction. The difference in the final gradient, between a very accurately drawn flow net and a less accurate net, is insignificant. Usually, a few successive trial sketches are sufficient to construct a reasonably accurate flow net. The basic requirements are: (1) That the two sets of curves intersect at right angles; and (2) that each field be as nearly a curvilinear square as possible.

The actual heat flow through a column is probably somewhat different from that based on idealized assumption, for several reasons: (1) Concrete is a heterogeneous material; (2) the reinforcement having a coefficient of conductivity $k = 366$ as compared with $k = 4$ to $k = 15$ for concrete may change the theoretical heat flow; and (3) the design coefficients for thermal conductivity, heat capacity, and linear thermal expansion are average values. After the gradients and the isotherms have been constructed, the average temperature of the section can be established.

Average Temperature. The average temperature is represented theoretically by a horizontal plane that divides the total volume created by the isotherms in equal parts. In most cases of prismatic columns, this may be simplified. A mean gradient through a column is drawn and the average temperature computed by a numerical summation

$$T_{av} = \frac{\Sigma(\Delta d \times T)}{d} = \frac{\Sigma T}{n} \qquad (10.16)$$

in which Δd are vertical strips into which the column width, d, is subdivided. The graphically measured mean temperature of each strip is denoted T. If the column is subdivided into n equal strips, each d/n wide, the equation is simplified as indicated.

To account for the thermal properties of the applied finishes and surface conductances, equivalent column section instead of the actual section must be used. The finishes and surface conductances are converted into equivalent thicknesses of concrete (normal weight or lightweight) having the same thermal conductance. These equivalent thicknesses are added to the actual column section, to provide the equivalent column section used for construction of the isotherms. The equivalent thickness of concrete is

$$t_e = \frac{\text{conductivity of concrete}}{\text{conductance of finish or surface resistance}} \qquad (10.17)$$

The following are some of the commonly assumed thermal properties of the concrete, finishes, and surface conductances:

1. Conductance of inside surface (still air), $C = 29.84$ [kJ/(hr m² K)] = 1.46 [Btu/(hr ft² °F)].

2. Conductance of outside surface [winter 24.1 km/hr (15 mph) wind], $C = 122.65$ [kJ/(hr m² K)] = 6.00 [Btu/(hr ft² °F)].

3. Conductance of gypsum plaster 12.7 mm (0.5 in.) thick, $C = 63.78$ [kJ/(hr m² K)] = 3.12 [Btu/(hr ft² °F)].

4. Conductance of gypsum board 9.5 mm (0.375 in.) thick, $C = 63.78$ [kJ/(hr m² K)] = 3.12 [Btu/(hr ft² °F)].

5. Conductance of vertical spaces 19 mm to 102 mm (0.75 in. to 4 in.) (winter), $C = 21.05$ [kJ/(hr m² K)] = 1.03 [Btu/(hr ft² °F)].

6. Conductivity of lightweight concrete 5.27 kPa (110 psf, 536.8 kgf/m²), $k = 31.14$ [kJ/(hr m K)] = 5.0 [Btu/(hr ft °F)].

7. Conductivity of normal weight concrete, $k = 80.97$ [kJ/(hr m K)] = 13.0 [Btu/(hr ft °F)].

The equivalent column section is used only to construct the isotherms. The temperatures at the face of the plaster are along the line of the equivalent concrete thickness of the plaster. Similarly, the outside surface temperature is at the line of the equivalent concrete thickness of the outside surface conductance. The temperatures used in the formula for the computations of the average temperature are at the actual column faces and not of the equivalent column. Comparison of lightweight and normal weight columns indicates that the surface temperature drop for lightweight columns is much smaller than for normal weight columns. Consequently, the average temperature of lightweight columns is higher. Due to lower thermal conductivity, lightweight columns have better insulation capacity.

Condensation Control. The interior surface of an exterior column is much colder than the temperature inside the room. This is due to surface conductances which are producing a temperature drop. However, this may not be objectionable, since adjacent windows are usually much colder. Insulation, air space, or plaster are used to raise the temperature of the inside surface to avoid condensation. This may not always be the best solution as far as the thermal movement is concerned. Columns with insulation on the inside will have a lowered inside face temperature, resulting in a lower average temperature of the column and higher thermal movements and stresses. Because within any space condensation starts on the surface with the lowest temperature, no plaster or other finishes are required on columns in rooms with single glass windows. Plaster on columns may be required in rooms with double-glazed windows. Air spaces or rigid insulation may be necessary for windowless rooms.

Effect of Wind on Gradient. The effect of wind on the gradient is of secondary importance. The temperature drop at the exterior face amounts to only a few degrees, and the small drop in temperature due to higher wind will have almost no effect.

Effects of Temperature Gradient Through Wall and Column. For a freestanding wall subjected to a different temperature on both faces, a straight-line temperature gradient may be drawn in line with the previously discussed method. A strip of wall, if not restrained, will bow as a result of different temperatures at opposing faces of wall. The face with lower temperature shortens as compared with the warm face. If the wall is restrained, the bending moment required for this restraint would be

$$M = \frac{\delta T \, \alpha \, EI}{h_w} \qquad (10.18)$$

in which α = coefficient of thermal expansion and h_w = wall thickness. When the wall element is forced back by the applied moment M into the original shape, stresses will develop without strains. If the wall is freestanding with no bending moments, strains will develop without stresses.

In a building column with faces subjected to different temperatures, with the outside face subjected to a constant lower temperature, a linear gradient is assumed. If the column is restrained at the two ends, an axial force and a bending moment are created due to temperature variation. The axial force is determined by the change in strain due to temperature at the centroid of the column section multiplied by the axial elastic modulus times the area of the column EA, in which A = area of the column. The bending moment is calculated from Eq. 10.18.

Generalized Solution for Analysis. In multistory frames with exposed exterior columns, the effect of temperature movement of exterior columns is significant only in the elements of the exterior bay. The exposed columns change their length with temperature variations. This results in deflections and bending moments of horizontal floor members of the exterior bay. The distorted floor members in turn develop shears which act on the exterior and interior columns, reducing the original length changes. In frames with relatively flexible horizontal members, this statical problem may be solved with the use of the iterative method. This method will provide a fairly accurate solution within two or three cycles (Khan and Fintel, 1966). The success of the iterative procedure is due to the application of a forced-convergence technique. The computations are performed by the use of the following steps:

1. Compute the free vertical (initial) movement of the exterior column. These are the relative movements between the exterior and interior columns at each floor.

2. Compute fixed-end moments at horizontal floor members at each floor. Zero rotation of joints is assumed.

3. Distribute moments using moment-distribution or slope-deflection method.

4. Compute shears at columns.

5. Using shear forces as vertical loads at exterior and interior columns, compute the rebound of columns.

6. Compute total story rebound, consisting of the sum of exterior and interior column rebounds.

7. Apply convergence correction and compute corrected relative movements for next cycle. The analysis is repeated from the second step using the new corrected movements.

The method presented may be simplified if the distribution of moments at each joint is eliminated.

Simplified Design Method.   The simplified design method may be used provided the following three assumptions are fulfilled:

1. Sizes of columns and horizontal members do not change drastically from floor to floor.

2. Story heights are fairly constant.

3. Points of contraflexure in all columns are at midheight of each story.

In most buildings, these assumptions are fulfilled fairly well. Using the assumptions, the general iterative method is greatly simplified. The moments and shears at columns are computed directly without the use of moment distribution. In addition, to further simplify, the exterior and interior columns may be replaced by a single equivalent column which has the same rebound as the total story rebound of the two columns. The simplified design method has been used to develop diagrams with curves for direct prediction of relative movements between the exterior and interior columns (Khan and Fintel, 1966).

Residual Relative Movement.   Because the exterior and interior columns are interconnected by floor structure, the computed "free" movement of the exterior column will be reduced to a residual value, since the stiffness of the floors tends to equalize the floor levels. The resistance of the structure to length changes of the exterior columns depends not only upon the floor stiffness, but also upon the axial stiffness of the exterior and interior columns. The curves (Khan and Fintel, 1966) for prediction of relative movements between the exterior and interior columns present the residual movement as a percentage of the free movement. The residual movements as computed by the simplified design method differ only insignificantly from the more exact results of the iterative method. The differences increase towards the bottom of the structure, where they are less significant since the movements and the stresses due to bending moments decrease.

Load Transfer Between Exterior and Interior Columns. Vertical shears generated in the deflected slab (Fig. 10.23) cause transfer of loads from the shortened exposed column to the interior column. During the summer, when the exposed column elongates, the load transfer is reversed. The column loads due to temperature stresses are accumulative, starting at the roof level and proceeding downward with maximum loads at the bottom of the lowest level. The amount of load transfer can be substantial for very rigid connecting beams. Flexible slab systems follow the column length changes more easily, and therefore transfer only insignificant amounts of load from one column to the other. The bending stresses induced in connecting beams or slabs may be quite considerable. On the other hand, the shear stresses in the individual horizontal members are usually not critical. However, the accumulation of these stresses at the first floor of a 50-story building may produce a large column load sometimes in excess of 4.4 MN (1000 kips, 453.6 $\times 10^{-3}$ kgf). It must be remembered that the reduction of differential displacement is achieved at the cost of axial forces in the columns, and bending and shear stresses in the floor structure, which are over and above those caused by gravity and wind loads.

Stresses. Stresses in structural elements due to temperature length changes and bowing should be combined with effects of gravity loads and lateral loads, such as wind or earthquake. However, it would be unrealistic to design a structure for the full combined effect of extreme temperature, highest wind velocity, snow load, and gravity loads. To establish design criteria, consideration should be given to the following probabilities:

1. The highest stresses due to temperature and wind will not occur in the same member within the structure. While temperature effects are highest in the upper parts of the frame (except column loads), the wind stresses are highest in the lower parts.

2. Although extreme temperature conditions may exist for a longer period, coincidence of full temperature and highest wind effects is extremely improbable during the lifetime of a structure.

3. Some temperature effects, due to their occurrence over a longer period of time, are partially reduced by creep.

To assess the coincidence of high wind and extreme temperatures, local weather condition records should be studied. These conditions may be substantially different from one part of the country to another. Usually, severe temperatures are associated with milder winds; the stronger winds are associated with milder temperatures. The examination of local codes and the ACI Code, together with information from local weather bureaus and solid engineering judgment, will usually result in reasonable design criteria.

Behavior of Partitions. In high-rise buildings, the differential movement of columns of the exterior bay primarily affects partitions perpendicular to the exposed columns. Observation and studies of a number of existing structures with partially exposed columns indicate only insignificant distress in partition assemblies in buildings with less than 20 stories. Some government agencies limit building heights to 15 stories for which special temperature design and provisions are not required.

However, instead of deciding empirically on a critical height of multistory buildings, beyond which the effect of temperature differential produces a significant distress in partitions, a rational evaluation of individual buildings is suggested.

Thermal movements of the exposed column cause racking of floor slabs, which results in distress of partitions (Fig. 10.22) in upper floors. Column shortening within one story is only secondary in its effects on partitions. The major effect on partitions is rotation of the partitions due to the cumulative change in length of the exposed column. The partition pivots at the interior column when the exposed column changes its length. This rotation causes separation between partition and both columns. In winter, the separation is widest at the lower corner of exterior column and at the upper corner of interior column. In summer, the separation is opposite to that in winter. It is widest at the upper corner of exterior column and at the lower corner of interior column. Additional separation occurs at the ceiling and the partition. The width of separation depends on the amount of movement of the exposed column, and on the ability of the partition to distort. Drywall partitions, composed of a series of individual vertical panels attached flexibly to studs, can absorb at each joint a certain amount of displacement, which together with some distortion of each panel may provide sufficient adaptability to frame distortion. However, with large movements, hairline cracks may develop in the paint along the vertical joints of the panels. In completely rigid partitions, without any consideration of vertical floor movements, distress of partitions in the form of diagonal cracking may result due to shear generated by such movements. The width of the separation can be determined by geometry. Usually, because of some resilience and plasticity, the actual separation is smaller than expected by geometry. There is a significant difference in behavior of partitions in apartment and office buildings. In apartment buildings, partitions are usually stacked over the entire height of the building. They are tightly fitted into the frame. Unless intentionally separated from the frame, the partitions will distort with the building and contribute to the rigidity of the structure in resisting any movements of the frame. In apartment buildings, solid partitions because of their rigidity may reduce the residual movement to a small fraction of the free movement. The recorded actual movements are far short of the theoretical predictions. This results in additional stresses in partitions, which are usually not considered in the theoretical analysis.

In office buildings, on the other hand, partitions are mostly of the movable type and do not reach the underside of the slab. Consequently, they provide only insignificant resistance to distortions of the structure. Some of the other possible causes of partition cracking and separation from the frame are:

1. Volumetric changes of partition material due to moisture changes in partitions and in the air.

2. Failure to provide proper heat during and after completion of plaster operation.

3. Failure to meet the minimum plaster thickness requirements.

4. Other volumetric changes of the frame.

5. Roof slab movements due to temperature changes, and insufficient insulated roof slab.

6. Bending due to gravity loads.

Final partition design should therefore have adequate details to take care of these particular behaviors, which are not related to the differential movement of columns. Effects of thermal and other distortion of the frame on partitions can be predicted and consideration given in detailing.

Limitation of Movement. Structural distress, acceptable maximum tilt of slabs, effect on partitions, and economical considerations require limitation of thermal movements. Although it is feasible to accommodate structurally a considerable amount of movement of exposed columns, serviceability and economy will limit the thermal movements. The serviceability criterion is logically expressed as a ratio of the movement to the slab or beam length (angular distortion). Any movement limitation should relate to the type of structure and building materials used. It is clear that warehouses, industrial buildings, and similar structures will require movement limitations different from apartment buildings. Structures with brickwork, masonry partitions, and plaster walls will require more stringent limitations than buildings with metal cladding and no brickwork. Also, as discussed before, the movement of exposed columns is additive to gravity load deflections and other effects. Some publications recommend that to protect brickwork and plaster from cracking the thermal movement of exterior columns relative to interior columns be limited to 19 mm (0.75 in.) or $l/300$, whichever is smaller (Khan and Nassetta, 1970) as expressed by

$$[(w_e) - (w_i)] = \frac{l}{300} \text{ or } 19 \text{ mm } (0.75 \text{ in.}) \tag{10.19}$$

in which w_e = exterior column displacement; w_i = interior column displacement; and l = distance between columns.

For buildings without masonry and plastered partitions, the thermal movement of $l/200$ is considered tolerable. For a thermal movement limitation of $l/300$ (of exterior column relative to interior column) the center of the span may be subjected to a thermal movement of approximately $l/600$ only, which should be added to gravity load and other deflections. In addition, the criteria for maximum allowable deflections of the ACI Code must be satisfied.

2   Design Consideration

Buildings Designed for Large Temperature Movements. Building facades designed primarily on the basis of architectural considerations may result in large temperature movements. The location of the glass line with respect to the structural frame affects the percentage of column exposure. The effect of such design is that upper floors are expected to experience large movements and stresses due to temperature movements. Generally, this type of design is not advisable. Details that must be developed to relieve the bending stresses in the floor slab system may be costly and unsightly, may create maintenance problems, and may also reduce soundproofing and fire rating.

There are two alternative solutions to problems in buildings designed with large exposure: (1) To provide strength for accommodation of relatively large movements of exterior columns; and (2) to provide details to relieve the stresses in the floor structure.

To provide strength, heavy restraining girders connecting the exterior and interior columns may be provided at the roof, or at intermediate floors (mechanical floors). The restraining girders are generally one story deep and therefore very rigid. These girders may also be used for lateral sway control under wind loads. If located above the roof the girders should be designed for complete reversal of stresses (summer and winter) and stresses resulting from different temperatures on the faces of girders. In addition, the horizontal temperature movements of the girders should be considered.

The alternative is to provide details to relieve the stresses in the floor structure. Hinging of floors at the interior columns or shear walls for movement controlled by severe winter exposure, or at the exterior column if the movement of exposed columns is controlled by summer temperatures, may assure proper functioning of the structural system. The hinge details should include dowels to maintain lateral restraint of columns or walls. By using elastomeric material around a portion of dowels, the slabs are free to rotate, but provide lateral restraint of columns or walls at each floor level. In developing hinged type details, warping effect at the corner bays must be considered.

Buildings Designed for Controlled Movements.   The obvious method of compensating temperature effects would be to move the exterior enclosure outside the exterior column system so that, in effect, the exterior column is completely within the building environment. However, this is in some cases neither architecturally acceptable, nor is it economical for certain types of buildings, where the exposed exterior columns and spandrel beams may be part of the building fenestration. The economical implications must be considered when developing special details for the structure and the partitions. It is desirable to design the building components with controlled movements so that the maximum temperature movements will result in relatively simple and economical details. This means that, rather than use general limitations ($l/300$) of temperature movements, a more stringent criterion should be developed. This more stringent temperature criterion should generally result in acceptable stresses in the frame, usually requiring no special structural details, and in nominal partition details.

The simplest way to achieve this is to set the glass line on the basis of a temperature gradient analysis in a manner that the maximum average temperature difference between the exterior and the interior columns will not exceed a value equivalent to the maximum relative movement. It is reasonable to assume that in multistory office and apartment buildings a limited criterion of temperature movement corresponding to $l/600$ will minimize the need for special structural and partition details. If the glass line cannot be adjusted, then exterior columns may be "shaped" to keep the temperature movements within a specified limit. This may be a more costly solution because additional concrete and forming is involved. Another method is to provide cladding and insulation. It is worthwhile to consider that all tall buildings with columns protruding beyond the glass line, clad or unclad, should be designed for temperature movements. Some multistory apartment buildings with exterior columns completely within the building cladding developed temperature distress in partitions on upper floors. (Probable combination of a number of effects.) Here, the usually unaccounted contribution of partitions to the rigidity and resistance of the frame may have resulted in additional stresses in partitions.

Details.   Details of partitions and layout are a major influence on partition behavior. For example, door openings carried to the ceiling may eliminate common location of cracks. The distortion of structural frame induces shear and bending stresses in the partitions and, if not relieved by proper details, can cause unsightly as well as acoustically unacceptable cracking. In order to avoid such cracking of partitions, details around the edges of partitions should be provided to allow vertical as well as horizontal slippage. One of the simplest ways to achieve this is to provide a channel enclosure for partition walls, where the partitions meet columns and ceiling. The detail shown schematically in Fig. 10.24 has been effectively used in the design of some recent projects. This detail allows the partitions to "float" and provides the necessary restraint against lateral loads. Manufacturers of drywall partitions have developed a number of details, so temperature movements are absorbed. Details of the "floating" partitions are usually provided in upper floors only.

Although partition cracks seem to be the primary problem in some buildings, because they are visible, the structure itself can be considerably overstressed. Therefore, it is not sufficient to design and detail only the partition for the temperature movements; it is also necessary to design and detail the structural floors and columns for temperature deformations and stresses. For example, to reduce temperature effects on a column, a "sandwich" column detail has been effectively used in the design of some recent large projects. The exterior of 250-mm (10-in.) portion of column was separated from the structural portion of the column by 50-mm (2-in.) rigid insulation (Fig. 10.25). Horizontal joints were provided at each floor level to separate the nonstructural portion from the main portion of the column. It may also be desirable in tall structures to provide insulation at the outer faces of the columns if these columns are clad with stone or precast concrete panels.

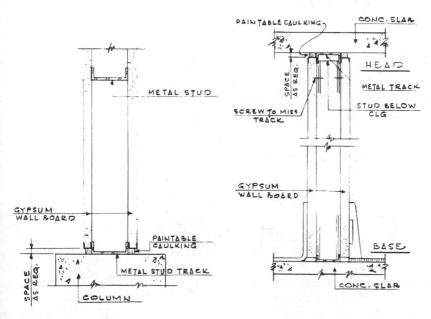

PLAN AT EXTERIOR COLUMN   SECTION THROUGH PARTITION

Fig. 10.24 Interior partition details

10.8 HORIZONTAL EFFECTS

There is a general disregard of the horizontal effects in structural elements due to volumetric changes. This is evidenced by the dearth of research on the subject by the academic community, resulting in a lack of input for mathematical techniques usable by the design profession. This means that the practitioner must rely on his judgment, which is based predominantly on experience with actual structures. Until a recent publication (ACI, 1971) this experience was limited to the engineer's own sphere of projects and their behavior. However, no two buildings are the same, and it is often incorrect to establish parameters based on experience with one building and extrapolate to another.

Changes in volume of concrete horizontal elements are due primarily to temperature variations and changes in moisture content. The volume change due to temperature variation is one of expansion and contraction movements, which may be cyclic daily or seasonally. In general, concrete structures continually lose moisture throughout their life. Therefore, the change in volume due to moisture variations is one of shrinkage. Seasonal increase in atmospheric humidity may cause a slight gain in moisture, but experience has shown that expansion due to moisture increase is not a practical consideration. The shrinkage of concrete due to loss of moisture is dependent primarily on the quantity of mixing water and cement used in the mix and the type and extent of curing. To a lesser degree the temperature of the concrete when cast and the environmental conditions affect the volume change. The amount of shrinkage may be substantially reduced with controls applied to the aforementioned elements. The amount of water used should be reduced to a minimum. The resulting low-slump concrete requires that the concrete design recognize this requirement in detailing reinforcement and allowing ample size

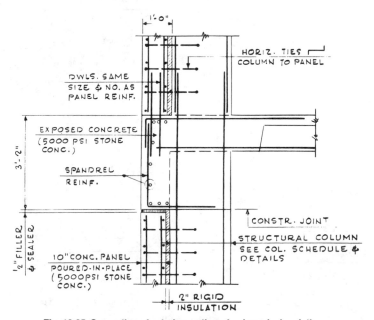

Fig. 10.25 Separation of exterior portion of column by insulation

members. Water content may be further reduced by utilizing a high quality plasticizing admixture. Some admixtures, however, increase shrinkage (see Sections 10.1 and 10.2). Lowering the concrete temperature will also allow reduction of mixing water required for a given slump. When these precautions are exercised, in addition to quality curing, drying shrinkage can be reduced by up to 40% (U.S. Bureau of Reclamation, 1956).

Cracking in horizontal concrete elements due to volumetric changes may occur in any building; it is not limited to "long" structures. When a slab is prevented from shortening or lengthening by relatively stiff building elements, such as shear walls, columns, and stair and elevator cores, cracks result in order to relieve the developed tension stresses. Abrupt changes in building plan also offer restraint to the slab movement within the slab's own plane. This condition, as well as slab openings, creates an environment that attracts cracking. The engineer cannot say with any degree of certainty that two structures even with identical contract drawings would behave the same when considering shrinkage and expansion conditions. This is due to the fact that the degree of contractor control of materials and construction sequencing is so variable. Most contractors prefer to use a very high-slump mix and avoid joinery in order to facilitate the scheduling, which many times is in contradiction of the engineer's program. The speed of construction seems to take precedence over the remedial work that is necessitated when volumetric change cracks develop. These cracks, once formed, continue to open and close with changes in temperature inside or out, and with lateral loads, etc. This requires expert cosmetic treatment and sometimes the crack is never successfully gapped. Attempts to use epoxies to reinstate the integrity of the slabs have been expensive and not too successful.

Assuming that proper precautions have been exercised with the mix design and curing, attempts by the design profession to minimize the effects of volumetric changes fall into two general categories: (1) Joinery with judgment and experience as the design parameters; and (2) providing equilibrium of the developed tension by internal or external means utilizing results of studies on laboratory specimens extrapolated to actual conditions. The former is used almost exclusively. Joints utilized are generally categorized as: (1) Expansion joints; (2) construction joints; (3) control joints; and (4) control strips.

1 Expansion Joints

Expansion joints completely separate adjacent concrete sections and allow free movement of the adjacent parts. They are used primarily in roof slabs and exposed elements, such as continuous balconies, spandrel beams, walls, etc., where the effect of differential temperature predominates. An indication of the amount of movement caused by temperature changes is obtained by multiplying the average thermal coefficient of expansion of concrete 0.000006 by length of the structure times the degrees change in temperature. For example, a building divided into 30.5-m (100-ft) sections for a temperature change of 33°C (60°F) would be expected to move at expansion joints approximately 13 mm (0.5 in.). The spacing of expansion joints in roofs is dependent to a great extent on the thermal roof insulation. The temperature change through the insulation and concrete for various conditions has been well established (Plummer, 1965). The temperature change to utilize in the aforementioned equation naturally depends on climatic conditions as well as many other variables. Therefore, it is foolhardy to presume that a blanket maximum spacing of expansion joints could be established. Because of this, designers have varying criteria for the placement of expansion joints. Requirements vary between 46 m and 61 m (150 ft and 200 ft) maximum spacing in roofs, and a smaller distance in exposed concrete, with particular attention paid to offsets. To be totally effective, expansion joints should extend entirely through the building. This is not required, however, when structural elements supporting the subjected concrete are flexible enough to deform with the temperature movement. For instance, slender columns supporting a concrete roof may be flexible enough to drift with the expansion of the slab without deleterious effects. Details of expansion joints for roofs, walls, etc., have been presented by the Portland Cement Association (PCA, 1953). Expansion joints are also used in roofs of buildings with nonlinear plan geometry. The prevalent Y, U, or L-shaped buildings with long or dissimilar wings are properly designed having expansion joints at the building core separating the wings.

Expansion joints for prestressed concrete floor systems will usually move more than those for conventional reinforced concrete floor systems. This is because the entire amount of shortening in prestressed floors will take place at the expansion joints, whereas the same will be spread throughout the conventional reinforced floor, which will have numerous cracks spaced throughout the entire floor.

2 Construction Joints

Construction joints are primarily used to accommodate the construction sequence and are designed to allow flexural and shear continuity through the joint (Fig. 10.26).

However, strategically located construction joints in conjunction with specific casting sequencing may be established such that individual slab areas will shrink independent of other slab areas and minimize shrinkage stresses. (Similar to the "checkerboard" pattern which is well recognized for grade slab construction.) Construction joint layout for the purpose of minimizing shrinkage depends on the extent of the slab and plan geometry. Long, narrow, rectangular structures would require construction joints spaced at approximately the narrow building dimension. Alternate areas are cast allowing as long a time as possible until the adjacent portions are cast, thus allowing shrinkage to occur and also providing time for the concrete to develop tensile strength. The nonlinear plan geometry requires construction joints at abrupt changes in plan, and at large openings such as elevation cores and stairwells. Alternate areas are cast as previously described,

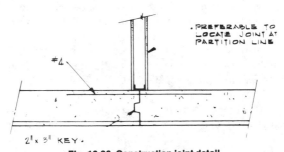

Fig. 10.26 Construction joint detail

allowing substantial time prior to casting the "infill" slabs. This procedure has been successfully used on a number of buildings. Two such plans are shown in Figs. 10.27 and 10.28. The numbers on the figures indicate the slab casting sequence, and the arrows indicate the direction of casting procedure. As with all other types of joinery, unfortunately, it often disrupts or curtails the speed with which a total slab may be cast.

Construction joints are needed in prestressed slabs in order to minimize frictional loss of prestress resulting from curvature of the tendons. Such construction joints

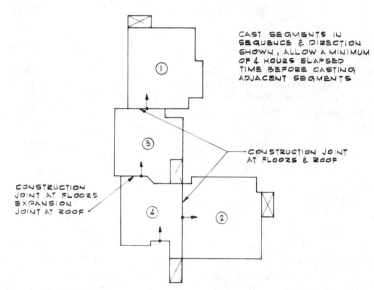

Fig. 10.27 Floor concrete placement sequence, L-shaped structure

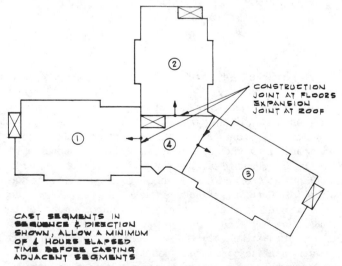

Fig. 10.28 Floor concrete placement sequence, Y-shaped structure

are often continued to the next slab pour by coupling the tendons. At other times, a closure strip would be left between two post-tensioned slabs and the strip then poured with concrete and joined with reinforcement protruding from the ends of the two adjacent slabs.

Post-tensioned slabs can be separated from their supports during construction by means of soft supports which would permit the slab to move freely under the effect of prestressing. Wrapped and greased dowels may protrude from supporting elements into slotted holes provided in the slab in order to permit slab movement. After elastic shortening and some shrinkage and creep have taken place, the slab can then be grouted to its supports, tying them together through steel dowels previously provided.

3 Control Joints

Control joints are created by weakening the concrete section, thus attracting eventual shrinkage cracking into the joint (see Fig. 10.29). A well-established analogous condition is that of sawed joints for slab cast on grade. Control joints are made by attaching to the forms, wood, plastic, or corrosive-resistant steel strips which leave narrow grooves in the concrete. It has been recommended that one-quarter to one-fifth of the concrete thickness be penetrated. The locations of the joints must be such that the structural integrity of the concrete element is not impaired, as this type of joint, unlike the construction joint, offers no prepared means of shear transfer. Also, the control joint more effectively serves its purpose if at least one-half of the reinforcing through the joint is made noncontinuous. This, therefore, reduces the flexural strength. In exposed concrete spandrels and walls, the spacing of control joints should range between 6 m and 9 m (20 ft and 30 ft) depending on the extent of the concrete, wall openings, offsets, etc. The fact that shrinkage movements will normally vary between 6 mm and 13 mm per 30 m (0.25 in. and 0.5 in. per 100 ft) points to the requirement of providing control joints in slabs at the same location but in place of the construction joints heretofore discussed (Figs. 10.26 and 10.27). If structurally possible, this will allow a greater amount of concrete to be cast in fewer operations.

4 Control Strips

Control strips are about 0.6 m to 0.9 m (2 ft to 3 ft) wide across the building, and are cast several weeks following adjacent slab casting (Fig. 10.30). The width of the strip is dependent only on the reinforcing lap distance required to reestablish continuity of the flexural reinforcing. Free shrinkage of the individual areas is allowed by not providing continuous reinforcement from one part through the strip into the other part. This would impede the independent movement of the individual parts and defeat the objective of the strip. The control strip is the most positive means of minimizing cracking due to shrinkage stresses. During the period the control strip is open the effects of the high rate of initial shrinkage of adjacent slabs are substantially reduced. After the strip is cast a minor amount of shrinkage will still take place. However, the concrete has already developed a substantial tensile strength to resist the remaining shrinkage stresses. The spacing of the control strips may be greater than the construction joint or control joints for a linear plan arrangement. Experience has shown that control strips in slabs of multistory buildings about 30 m to 46 m (100 ft to 150 ft) apart perform successfully in buildings up to 91 m (300 ft) long. However, they would still be required, as with control joints, at abrupt changes in plan geometry and at large openings which create a varying slab stiffness. The control strip scheme has similar pitfalls as the alternate slab pour but more seriously impedes construction progress. Shores and forms must be left in place for a great length of time following the main casting. The contractor returns at a later date to cast the strips. Several floors above may have been cast prior to casting the strips. Often wall enclosure follows closely after the slab pours, creating difficulties in depositing the strip concrete. In addition, extra reinforcement is required for the laps.

5 Need For Further Research

The means of minimizing the effects of volumetric changes require attempts to estimate the magnitudes of forces developed. The lack of laboratory-field inter-action has severely limited this approach. Much information is available on volumetric changes of small controlled laboratory specimens. However, the utilization of this information by the designer is possible only with very conservative and crude approximations. Many possible design techniques are available providing the forces to be used are adequately determined. Shrinkage compensating cement has been successfully utilized, to a great degree for slabs on grade, and to a lesser extent for supported slabs. Cost of the material has been a deterring factor. Providing reinforcing to transfer the shrinkage forces throughout the length of the slab has been attempted. The ACI Code prescribes reinforcement to be provided in structural floor and roof slabs for shrinkage and temperature control. Minimum

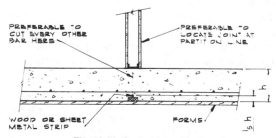

Fig. 10.29 Control joint detail

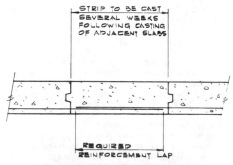

Fig. 10.30 Control strip joint detail

reinforcing is required as a percentage of the gross concrete area. For slabs, at least 0.18% to 0.25% steel is required, depending on the steel yield strength. Also spacing of the reinforcing by Code should be less than five times the slab thickness, or less than 457 mm (18 in.). This amount, however, appears to have no rational basis and in practice has not been adequate for many situations. On the other hand, it is often extremely conservative. Corners of openings and sudden changes of sections are susceptible to cracking due to large stress concentration. Cracks usually radiate from corners of openings. Additional reinforcing perpendicular to the potential cracks helps to minimize crack widths. Prestressing is another means to minimize cracking—not necessarily applied to volumetric change cracking, but serving that function as well as others. Directly post-tensioning or pretensioning slabs has been successful. In addition, attempts have been made to prestress peripheral beams, creating an equilibrium of the externally applied precompressing forces to the internal tensions developed from shrinkage and temperature changes.

The fact that distressed conditions due to volumetric changes are a common occurrence should provide the impetus necessary for further development work. Existing laboratory studies should be supplemented with further research projects and correlations made with actual in-place building behavior. This would, at the very least, provide a more rational approach to the use of joinery, and hopefully it would also allow development of more exacting mathematical techniques.

10.9 CONDENSED REFERENCES/BIBLIOGRAPHY

The following is a condensed bibliography for this chapter. Not only does it include all articles referred to or cited in the text, but it also contains bibliography for further reading. The full citations will be found at the end of the Volume. What is given here should be sufficient information to lead the reader to the correct article: the author, date, and title. In case of multiple authors, only the first named is listed.

ACI 1963, *Building Requirements Code for Reinforced Concrete*
ACI Committee 435 1966, *Deflections of Reinforced Concrete Flexural Members*
ACI Committee 223 1970, *Expansive Cement Concretes—Present State of Knowledge*
ACI Committee 209 Subcommittee 2 1971, *Prediction of Creep, Shrinkage, and Temperature Effects*
ACI 1971, *Designing for the Effects of Creep, Shrinkage and Temperature in Concrete Structures*

Ali 1964, *Mechanics of Creep in Concrete*
ASCE 1961, *Reinforced Masonry Design and Practice*
Avram 1975, *Effect of Restrained Shrinkage on Reinforced Concrete Shear Walls at Multistory*
Bate 1970, *Environmental Changes, Temperature Creep and Shrinkage in Concrete Structures*
Blakey 1955, *An Examination of the Effect of Atmospheric Temperature and Relative Humidity*

Blakey 1956, *Measurement of Dimensional Changes in Precast Concrete Walls*
Blakey 1961, *Deformations of an Experimental Lightweight Flat Plate Structure*
Blakey 1962, *A Commentary on Flat Plate Design*
Blakey 1963a, *Australian Experiments with Flat Plates*
Blakey 1963b, *Influence of Creep and Shrinkage on Structural Behaviour*

Blakey 1963c, *The Deflection of Flat Plate Structures*
Blakey 1964, *A Review of Elastic Deflection, Creep and Shrinkage of Expanded Shale Concrete*
Blakey 1965, *Stripping of Formwork for Concrete Buildings in Relation to Structural Design*
Blakey 1975, *Transverse Deflection of Floors—Creep Shrinkage and Temperature Effects*
Branson 1968, *Design Procedures for Computing Deflections*

British Standards Institute 1969, *The Structural Use of Reinforced Concrete*
Brotchie 1964, *Direct Design of Prestressed Flat Plate Structures*
Campbell-Allen 1963, *Creep and Shrinkage in Concrete as Influenced by Concrete Practice and*
CEB-FIP 1970, *International Recommendations for the Design and Construction of Concrete*
Constructional Review 1961, *Experimental Lightweight Flat Plate Structure—Part III, Long-Term*

CUR 1956, *Investigation of Admissible Crack Width in Reinforced Concrete Structures*
Dischinger 1937, *Investigations on Stability, Elastic and Time-Dependent Deflections*
Eriksson 1962, *Determination of Time to Form Removal*
Feld 1965, *Tolerance of Structures to Settlement*
Fintel 1965, *Effects of Column Exposure in Tall Structures, Temperature Variations and Their Effects*

Fintel 1968, *Effects of Column Creep and Shrinkage in Tall Structures—Prediction of Inelastic*
Fintel 1970, *Effects of Column Creep and Shrinkage in Tall Structures*
Fintel 1971, *Effects of Column Creep and Shrinkage in Tall Structures—Analysis for Differential*
Gamble 1970, *Field Investigation of Continuous Composite Prestressed I-Beam Highway Bridge*
Ghali 1969, *Time-Dependent Forces Induced by Settlement of Supports in Continuous Reinforced*

Glanville 1939, *Further Investigations on Creep or Flow of Concrete Under Load*
Gruner 1973, *Shrinkage Effect of Structural Concrete Walls in Multi-Story Buildings*
Hansen 1965, *Influence of Size and Shape of Member on the Shrinkage and Creep of Concrete*
Heiman 1973, *Long-Term Deformations in the Tower Building*
Hickey 1968, *Creep of Concrete Predicted from Elastic Modulus Tests*

Holland 1973, *Horizontal Effects—Length Changes Due to Shrinkage and Temperature*
Johnson 1950, *Calculation of Deformation in Reinforced Concrete Structures After Formation of*
Johnson 1951, *Deformations of Reinforced Concrete*
Karp 1973, *Temperature Effects in Tall Reinforced Concrete Buildings*
Kesler 1973, *Control of Shrinkage, Creep and Temperature Volume Changes Through Variations of*

Khan 1966, *Effects of Column Exposure in Tall Structures, Analysis for Length Changes of Exposed*
Khan 1968, *Effects of Column Exposure in Tall Structures, Design Considerations and Field*
Khan 1970, *Conceptual Details for Creep, Shrinkage and Temperature in Ultra High-Rise Buildings*
Khan 1970, *Temperature Effects on Tall Steel Framed Buildings*
Leong 1970, *Long-Term Deflections of Reinforced Concrete Beams*

Leonhardt 1959, *Initial and Time-Dependent Deflections of Cracked Reinforced Concrete Beams*
Lorentsen 1968, *Longitudinal Deformation of Slender Concrete Beams*
Macchi 1973, *Thickness Effects on Creep*
Magura 1968, *Time-Dependent Performance of Reinforced Concrete Columns—Field Investigation of*
Maher 1970, *The Effect of Differential Temperature in Continuous Prestressed Concrete Bridges*

Mayer 1966, *Structural Defects Due to Bending of Reinforced Concrete Members*
McHenry 1943, *A New Aspect of Creep in Concrete and its Application to Design*
Meloun 1973, *Results of Measurements of the Long-Term Strain of the Reinforced Concrete*
Miller 1958, *Warping of Reinforced Concrete Due to Shrinkage*
Miller 1959, *Private Communication*

Milton 1967, *A Proposal for Long-Span Shells as Floor Systems*
Moenaert 1965, *Researches About the Behavior of Reinforced Concrete Elements Under*
Neumann 1955, *Experiments in Thermal Protection of Concrete Roofs*
Neville 1963, *Properties of Concrete*
Neville 1963b, *Properties of Concrete*

Neville 1964, *Creep of Concrete as a Function of its Cement Paste Content*
Neville 1970, *Creep of Concrete: Plain, Reinforced, and Prestressed*
Nielsen 1952, *Loads on Reinforced Concrete Floor Slabs and Their Deformation During*
Nylander 1952, *Non-Uniform Shrinkage of Concrete Due to Segregation of Coarse Aggregate*
PCA 1953, *Expansion Joints in Concrete Buildings*

PCA 1965, *Deflections of Flat Plate Floors of Apartment Buildings*
PCI 1971, *Prestressed Concrete Institution Handbook*
PCI Committee on Prestress Losses 1975, *Recommendations for Estimating Prestress Losses*
Pfeifer 1968, *Incremental Loading of Reinforced Light-Weight Concrete Columns*
Pfeifer 1969, *Reinforced Lightweight Concrete Columns*

Pfeifer 1971, *Full-Size Lightweight Concrete Columns*

Philleo 1966, *Elastic Properties and Creep*
Plummer 1965, *Brick and Tile Engineering*
Powers 1968, *The Properties of Fresh Concrete*
Rankine 1973, *Summary Report: Creep, Shrinkage and Temperature Effects*

Rao 1951, *A Rational Conception of Creep in Concrete*
Rehm 1968, *On the Question of Crack Limitations in Reinforced Concrete Structures*
RILEM 1971, *Observations of the International "RILEM" Symposium on Concrete and Reinforced*
Rosenhaupt 1961, *A Study of Thermal Cracks in Masonry Walls*
Ross 1958, *Creep of Concrete Under Variable Stress*

Rüsch 1973, *Critical Review of the Method of Consideration of the Influences of Creep*
Sefton Jenkins 1965, *Investigations into the Causes of the Deflection of Heated Concrete Floors*
Sejnoha 1973, *Analysis of Mixed Wall Systems Composed of Concrete Elements of Different Age*
Sorete 1971, *Deformation: State of the Art in 1970*
Standards Association of Australia 1963, *Code for Concrete in Buildings*

Tadros 1975, *Time-Dependent Prestress Loss and Deflection in Prestressed Concrete Members*
Tadros 1977, *Effect of Nonprestressed Steel on Prestress Loss and Deflection*
Taylor 1970, *Initial and Long-Term Deflections of a Reinforced Concrete Flat Plate Structure*
Taylor 1970, *A Long-Term Investigation of Deflexions of a Flat Slab Structure*
Troxell 1958, *Longtime Creep and Shrinkage Tests of Plain and Reinforced Concrete*

Troxell 1968, *Composition and Properties of Concrete*
Ulitskii 1962, *A Practical Method for Computing Creep and Shrinkage of Concrete*
USBR 1956, *Concrete Manual*
Verbeck 1969, *Structures and Physical Properties of Cement Pastes*
Wallo 1968, *Prediction of Creep in Structural Concrete*

Warner 1975, *Axial Shortening of Reinforced Concrete Columns*
Washa 1952, *The Effect of Compressive Reinforcement on the Plastic Flow of Reinforced Concrete*
Washa 1956, *Plastic Flow (Creep) of Reinforced Concrete Continuous Beams*
Washa 1966, *Volume Changes*
Weidlinger 1964, *Temperature Stresses in Tall Reinforced Concrete Buildings*

Weil 1959, *Influence of Dimensions and Constraints on Shrinkage and Creep of Concrete*
Wood 1952, *Studies in Composite Construction, Part 1: The Composite Action of Brick Panel*
Yu 1960, *Instantaneous and Long-Time Deflections of Reinforced Concrete Beams Under Working*

Structural Design of
Tall Concrete and Masonry Buildings

Chapter CB-11

Design of
Cast-in-Place Concrete

Prepared by Committee 21D (Design of Cast-in-Place Concrete) of the Council on Tall Buildings and Urban Habitat as part of the Monograph on the Planning and Design of Tall Buildings

Ignacio Martin   Chairman
H. F. Microys   Vice-Chairman
I. Schousboe   Editor

AUTHOR ACKNOWLEDGMENT

Special acknowledgment is due those individuals whose contributions and papers formed the substantial first drafts of the various sections of this chapter. First are the state-of-art reporters from the 1972 International Conference whose material was published in the Lehigh Proceedings. These individuals are:

> J. P. Colaco, Section 11.2
> I. Martin, Section 11.3
> M. Tomii, Section 11.3
> J. O. Jirsa, Section 11.4.

In addition to this, other sections were based on special contributions prepared by:

> H. F. Microys, Section 11.1
> R. Walther, Section 11.2
> G. S. Ramaswamy, Section 11.2
> A. R. Cusens, Section 11.2
> F. Morán, Section 11.3
> G. König, Section 11.3
> L. G. Aycardi, Section 11.3
> O. Moretto, Section 11.5.

CONTRIBUTORS

The following is a complete list of those who have submitted written material for possible use in the chapter, whether or not that material was used in the final version. The Committee Chairman and Editor were given quite complete latitude. Frequently length limitations precluded the inclusion of much valuable material. The Bibliography contains all contributions. The contributors are: L. Aycardi, E. A. Calcagni, A. E. Cardenas, L. Cerny, T. Z. Chastain, J. Colaco, A. R. Cusens, A. Efsen, J. Grases, R. J. Hansen, Y. Higashi, J. O. Jirsa, M. Kavyrchine, G. König, K. Kordina, I. Martin, H. F. Microys, F. Morán, J. E. Monge, O. Moretto, Y. Owada, T. Paulay, M. Pommeret, G. S. Ramaswamy, R. Rosman, I. Schousboe, M. Stiller, M. Tomii, R. Walther, B. Zimmerli.

COMMITTEE MEMBERS

L. G. Aycardi, D. Brown, K. E. Bruinette, A. E. Cardenas, T. Z. Chastain, J. P. Colaco, A. R. Cusens, M. Fintel, A. Garcia-Meseguer, J. Grases, N. M. Hawkins, J. L. Heiman, J. O. Jirsa, G. König, I. Martin H. F. Microys, F. Morán, O. Moretto, T. Paulay, G. S. Ramaswamy, I. Schousboe, M. Stiller, M. Tomii, P. Vernescu, R. Walther.

CB-11

Design of Cast-in-Place Concrete

11.1 INTRODUCTION

1 Design Data Input

Input from Analysis. At the present time the distribution of load to the various elements in a tall concrete building is determined by an elastic analysis (see Chapter CB-5) regardless of the eventual method of design. Generally this analysis is dominated by the importance of providing resistance to lateral wind and seismic loads rather than gravity loads. Various simplifications and omissions made during the analysis phase have to be considered during the design process.

The increased use of high-strength and lightweight concrete and high-strength steel has resulted in more and more slender structures. Buckling of individual members and related failure mechanism, even stability of the structure as a whole, require scrutiny.

The capacity of available computers (invariably used in the analysis of tall buildings) or economic factors may force a size reduction of the actual problem. Consideration must be given to the suitability of this representation. Furthermore, the effect on elements not included in the analysis but undergoing the same deformations has to be assessed.

Quite frequently the analysis ignores such effects as creep, shrinkage, temperature, and nonlinear phenomena, unless they become of primary importance, such as in exposed columns in a hostile climate. A related problem is the differential shortening of columns near cores or exterior corner columns, which in tube structures have to carry high axial loads due to wind or earthquake but little gravity load. This is discussed in Chapter CB-10.

Finally, the fundamental behavior of a reinforced concrete structure has to be kept in mind, namely the limited range of a noncracking phase followed by a relatively extensive cracking phase (which depends on the reinforcement ratio). It may only become apparent during the design process that certain members will have entered that second phase. It may become necessary at this stage to reassess

503

the stiffness assumption made during the analysis. Finally, it must be confirmed whether the assumptions made during the analysis phase are valid. For instance, does the structure satisfy the ductility requirements on which the analysis was based?

It is thus evident that the bending moments, shears, torsions, and axial forces obtained from the analysis must be viewed in the light of the assumptions made. The design has to account for these forces and at the same time reflect the shortcomings of the analysis.

Design Limitations. The most common design limitations result from theoretical and practical considerations, construction practice, serviceability requirements, possible damage to nonstructural elements, the materials used, and the inexactitude of the design methods themselves. Many of these limitations are set down in building codes. The optimization of tall concrete buildings is discussed in Chapter CB-4.

Practical and economical aspects will guide the choice of the type of concrete, such as lightweight versus normal weight. The maximum compressive strength will influence the final member sizes and the amount of rentable space, but the available aggregate, the cost of cement, and the quality control expected on the project may be the limiting factors. Some thought should also be given to the actual concrete strength finally achieved in the structure.

Among the properties of the reinforcing steel, the strength sets the most rigid boundaries. The requirement for ductility and the penalties on other design parameters are often the deciding factors in setting an upper bound on yield strength and reinforcement percentages.

Deformations (such as differential shortening of adjacent members), deflection, and drift limitations need to be considered during the analysis phase, but a reassessment is necessary during the design stage. Additional moments may have to be accounted for because of local deformations. Although one of the inherent advantages of concrete is its stiffness, the desire for large column-free space results in spans where deflection problems have to be considered, such as long-term effects and cracking. Drift limitations control perceptibility of motion (though this is rarely a problem in concrete buildings), partition cracking, and sidesway buckling.(See Chapter CB-9.)

Buckling of a single member or of an entire section of a building has become an important aspect of design, because buildings are taller, safety factors are lower, and columns are smaller due to the introduction of high-strength steel and concrete. Design limitations result, for instance, because of stiffness changes in the columns, amount of reinforcement in connecting beams, and design eccentricities. The stability of tall concrete buildings is discussed in Section 11.3 of this chapter and in Chapter CB-8.

In zones of seismic activity ductility requirements may set certain limits. The yield strength of steel and the reinforcing ratio are generally restricted. The necessity for continuity and special detailing requirements may set limits to the reinforcing ratio in order to avoid congested areas.

Fire resistance may determine the cover to reinforcement and fix the slab thicknesses of waffle and joist floor construction.

It should be mentioned here that many of the aspects considered and dealt with in this chapter are not presented in research papers only. Various authors have covered much of this material in standard texts on concrete structures (Ferguson, 1973; Winter and Nilsen, 1972; Park and Paulay, 1975; Wang and Salmon, 1973).

Influences During Construction.   The intended construction process and the techniques used may profoundly affect the design of a building.

Temporary loadings of elements not at full strength and overloading of the structure invariably occur during construction. Because of the repetitive nature of the construction of tall buildings, such occurrences should be incorporated in the design process. Thus loadings from cranes and temporary hoists and elevators have to be included. Handling and storage of materials need to be planned. Because of the speed of construction, the removal of forms and the reshoring may put loads onto elements which have not attained sufficient strength. This is especially important in the use of flying forms when large sections of formwork are removed before reshoring can commence.

Other factors entering the design phase are construction tolerances; locations of construction, control, and expansion joints; splice locations of the reinforcing; variation in concrete strength of different elements; and permanent stresses induced during the construction process.

FOCSA apartment building, Havana, Cuba. Architects: Dominguez and Gómez Sampera; Structural Engineers: Sáenz, Cancio, Martin (Courtesy: I. Martin)

2 Classification of Building Members

For the purpose of this chapter, building members have been classified into horizontal members, vertical members, connections, and foundations. Subdivisions occur within each classification. The members discussed are obviously not confined to tall buildings; however, the aspect of tallness has been the main consideration in this presentation.

11.2 HORIZONTAL MEMBERS

1 Slabs and Beams

Types of Concrete Floors.   Concrete floors in tall buildings can be divided into the following types:

1. Two-way construction; namely, flat plate, flat slab, waffle slab, and two-way slab.

2. One-way construction; namely, solid slabs, pan joists supported on beams or bearing walls.

Concrete floor construction can also be categorized as follows:

1. All cast-in-place construction.

2. Precast forms (sometimes containing principal reinforcement) combined with cast-in-place concrete.

3. Precast structural members with cast-in-place concrete topping.

4. All precast floor framing members.

These various systems serve different functional purposes. Flat plate and solid slab constructions are commonly used for spans up to approximately 10 m (35 ft) in apartment, hotel, and short-span office buildings. Pan-joist and waffle construction, shown in Fig. 11.1, are prevalent for spans ranging from 6 m to 20 m (20 ft to 65 ft). The upper limits of span lengths indicated above generally would require prestressed construction rather than ordinary reinforced concrete construction. The most common use of pan-joist construction is in buildings requiring longer spans, such as office buildings, hospitals, and auto parking facilities.

Two-way beam and slab construction is less prevalent in the United States primarily due to the high cost of formwork and labor. Precast concrete units are becoming more common in order to reduce these high costs. The precast units take various shapes and sizes, the most common of which are the double tee system and the hollow cored slab system. Concrete topping slabs are generally cast over these precast units to obtain a monolithic floor. This type of construction is used in office buildings, apartments, hotels, and hospitals.

An all-precast concrete system can also be considered. This type of construction generally requires the use of post-tensioning or welded reinforcement to obtain continuity with the vertical supporting elements. In some precast construction, there is some difficulty in obtaining a uniformly level floor surface due to the tolerance in precast construction. Several solutions have been tried; among them, the use of concrete topping, or carpet with underlayment to cover irregularities, or the use of wide units ranging up to 3 m (10 ft) in width in order to minimize offsets at joints.

In the design of the floor system for a tall concrete building, a key consideration lies in the repetition of formwork and the speed with which the structure can be completed. "Gang-forming" for walls and "flying-forms" for slabs can speed the construction considerably and reduce on-site labor costs. A flying-form system is one that utilizes a plywood form resting on story-high trusses which are tied together to act as a unit. This form generally covers an area equal to the full bay dimensions. It, therefore, combines the horizontal formwork system with the vertical shoring elements required, and is moved from floor to floor as a unit. This type of flying-form system is most readily adaptable for flat plate or solid slab construction.

In pan-joist or waffle systems, it is sometimes advantageous to have beams the same depth as the joists. The uniform depth of construction reduces forming costs considerably and clears the ceiling area for mechanical services, and the resultant wide beam permits vertical passage of pipes and ducts. However, wide shallow beams impose a penalty on the primary lateral load-resisting frame.

For office buildings, a one-way system framing between the outside columns of the structure and the core of the building is frequently used in the United States. A special problem is encountered at the four corners, where it is desirable to equalize the loads on exterior columns in order to prevent large differential axial shortening between exterior columns under gravity loads. At least two solutions have been used

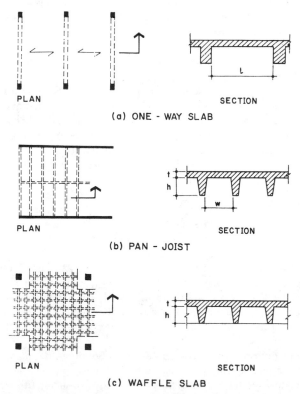

Fig. 11.1 Types of cast-in-place concrete floors

in the corners: namely, the use of the two-way system, or of a one-way system whose direction is reversed on every alternate floor. While either system will not completely equalize the loads on all columns, the load distribution will be more uniform than for a one-way, nonreversing system.

Other considerations that enter into the design of a flat slab floor system relate primarily to the width of the floor slab, which is part of the primary system resisting lateral loads (Black et al., 1976). Values less than the full width (Qadeer and Smith, 1969), equal to the full width (Barnard and Schwaighofer, 1967), and greater than the full width (Coull, 1966) have all been shown to be valid under certain circumstances. A similar problem is encountered in pan-joist floor construction where joists on either side of the center line of the column could be considered as part of the lateral resisting system, depending on the torsional stiffness of the spandrel beams into which they are framed (Colaco, 1970). In-plane action of the floor slab is required to distribute lateral loads to the various structural elements of the building that resist lateral forces. The actual in-plane deformation of the concrete floors has no significant effect on the distribution of this load, and the assumption that the floors are fully rigid in-plane is commonly used.

Design Criteria.

Stiffness and deformation. An inherent advantage of concrete floor construction is its stiffness, which results in less deflection under static loads and produces less floor vibration under moving loads. Concrete floors consequently are not susceptible to floor vibrations unless unusual conditions are encountered. Nevertheless, time-dependent creep and shrinkage deformations cause deflection problems that limit the slenderness of concrete floor framing. Although prestressed concrete members have smaller dimensions than comparable reinforced concrete members, generally prestressed concrete construction would still be stiff enough for most types of buildings.

In the design of concrete floors, both the short-term and the long-term deflection have to be considered (ACI Committee 435, 1968). Another factor that requires consideration is crack width under service load conditions. The American Concrete Institute Building Code Section 10.6 (ACI, 1971) specifies the average crack width at service load for interior and exterior exposure. Similar provisions are given in the Recommendations of the Comité Européen du Béton (CEB-FIP, 1970a). This subject is also discussed in Chapter CB-9.

Strength and ductility. Strength and ductility of concrete floor framing members can usually be obtained by careful detailing. Much research has examined this aspect of the problem and has resulted in the recommendations of the building codes. Openings in concrete floor beams for passage of mechanical ducts can be designed (Lorentsen, 1965; Nasser et al., 1967).

Fire rating. Concrete floors usually have an inherently high fire-rating capability which eliminates the necessity of fireproofing material except when using pan-joist or waffle construction with thin top slabs. The Underwriters' Laboratory (1971) has established the minimum thickness of concrete slabs required to obtain a given fire rating in the United States. Lightweight concrete requires less thickness than normal weight concrete.

Ceiling construction. In apartment and hotel buildings, flat plate construction has an economic advantage in that the underside of the slab can replace the finished ceiling. This reduces the floor-to-floor height, thereby producing further economies.

Dead loads and live loads. The dead weight of concrete floor construction is usually greater than comparable construction using other materials. This imposes a penalty on the vertical supporting elements and the foundation system which can be minimized by the use of lightweight concrete. However, the heavier the live load that has to be supported, the more economical concrete construction becomes, since the cost of formwork is almost unaltered. Under heavy live loads, moreover, the depth of the structure and hence the floor-to-floor height is almost always less in concrete construction than in any other type of construction. With light live loads, the loads imposed during construction due to shoring of freshly placed concrete, removal of formwork, and reshoring, must be considered in the design.

Acoustical ratings.   In general, concrete construction provides good acoustical ratings and transmits only surface noise. It is ranked much superior to most other types of construction in this regard.

Diaphragm action.   Diaphragm action comes into play in a floor system when transverse loads are transmitted into the frame and the laterally and torsionally stiff shear-wall core of the building. When the concrete floor system is monolithic in construction, diaphragm action will usually not prove to be critical for design purposes. In floors using precast units, the diaphragm action has to be provided for by means of welds between units.

Resistance to thermal movements and settlements.   The thermal movements become important in the design of exposed concrete structures. In monolithic reinforced concrete construction, there is greater resistance to movements due to the bending capability of floor framing members. These bending moments must be considered in the design of the concrete floor construction. Prestressed concrete's relatively more slender members can take settlement somewhat better than their stiffer reinforced concrete counterparts.

Types of Reinforcement.   Two types of reinforcement are currently in use: (1) Conventional reinforcement ranging in strength from 275 MPa (40 000 psi) to 520 MPa (75 000 psi); and (2) prestressed reinforcement ranging in strength up to 1860 MPa (270 000 psi). The choice between conventional reinforcing and prestressed concrete construction depends to a great extent on the spans and loads. In general, flat plate construction is economical with conventional reinforcement up to spans of 7 m to 8 m (21 ft to 25 ft), whereas for larger spans prestressing is more economical. For one-way pan-joist construction, conventional reinforcement has proved to be economical in the range of 9-m to 12-m (30-ft to 40-ft) spans. Spans larger than that demand prestressed reinforcement to obtain both the strength and deflection control required on long concrete spans. These prestressing elements are generally combined with conventional reinforcement to obtain the adequate ultimate moment capacity required, and also to obtain the shear strength.

2   Deep Beams

Definition.   According to the theory of elasticity, vertical plane members are defined as deep beams when the stress distribution of a cross section deviates appreciably from a straight line (Navier-Bernoulli's hypothesis that plane cross sections remain plane is not valid). This is usually the case when the ratio of the span l to the total depth h is smaller than 2 (Fig. 11.2); that is, $l/h < 2$ (slenderness).

In construction practice, beams with slenderness ratios up to 4 are sometimes referred to as deep beams, despite the fact that this is theoretically not justified.

Analysis. The elastic stress distribution of deep beams can be found by solving the differential equation

$$\Delta\Delta F = \frac{\partial^4 F}{\partial x^4} + 2\frac{\partial^4 F}{\partial x^2 \partial y^2} + \frac{\partial^4 F}{\partial y^4} \tag{11.1}$$

in which $F(xy)$ = Airy's stress function

$$\begin{aligned} \sigma_x &= \frac{\partial^2 F}{\partial y^2} \\ \sigma_y &= \frac{\partial^2 F}{\partial x^2} \\ \tau_{xy} &= \frac{\partial^2 F}{\partial x \partial y} \end{aligned} \tag{11.2}$$

When an analytical solution of this differential equation is too complicated, one can use methods of finite differences or of finite elements with the aid of electronic computers.

Such solutions are only valid for elastic, homogeneous bodies, as for example fully prestressed concrete beams at service loads. In conventionally reinforced deep

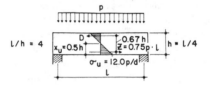

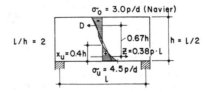

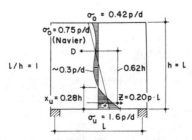

Fig. 11.2 Distribution of bending stresses σ_x **in beams of various slenderness ratios** l/h **according to theory of elasticity**

beams the distribution of internal forces changes considerably with the formation of cracks. Under the circumstances it is of little use to apply the complicated but inaccurate theory of elasticity. Extensive experimental investigations (Leonhardt and Walther, 1966) show that it is possible to dimension deep beams by assuming the lever arms of internal forces z as, in simply supported deep beams

$$\text{for } \frac{l}{h} > 1 \quad z \simeq 0.6\,h$$
$$\text{for } \frac{l}{h} < 1 \quad z \simeq 0.6\,l \tag{11.3}$$

and in continuous deep beams

$$z \simeq 0.5\,l$$
$$z \simeq 0.6\,h \tag{11.4}$$

whichever is smaller. Thus the forces T in the tension chord become approximately

$$T = \frac{M}{z} \tag{11.5}$$

in which M = maximum bending moment.

The concrete compression stresses and the shear stresses are usually not critical in deep beams. It should be noted, however, that the width of the inclined cracks may be significant unless closely spaced web reinforcement is provided (Kong et al., 1975; Rawdon de Paiva and Siess, 1965).

Detailing.   The essential problem of designing deep beams is in the detailing of the reinforcement. This is discussed at some length by the CEB-FIP (1970a). The following rules must be observed (Figs. 11.3, 11.4, and 11.5):

1. Main reinforcement must be well anchored over the supports either by horizontal hooks or special anchorage plates.

2. Reinforcing bars of the main reinforcement should be distributed over a depth of about $0.15\,h$ to $0.2\,h$ in order to prevent the formation of large cracks.

3. There is a very significant difference in the behavior of deep concrete beams depending on whether the loads are applied at the top or at the bottom (Figs. 11.6 and 11.7). In the latter case they must be carried to the compression zone by means of closely spaced stirrups and the same holds true for indirectly supported deep beams.

4. The entire deep beam should be provided with a closely spaced mesh of horizontal and vertical reinforcement to limit the width of inclined cracks.

5. Bent-up bars do not contribute anything to the "shear resistance"; they only weaken the tension chord.

6. Critical stress conditions in deep beams occur in the region of the supports. This zone must be carefully detailed and, if necessary, strengthened.

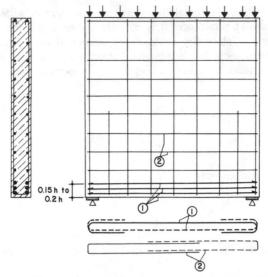

Fig. 11.3 Detailing of simply supported deep beams loaded at top (CEB-FIP, 1970a)

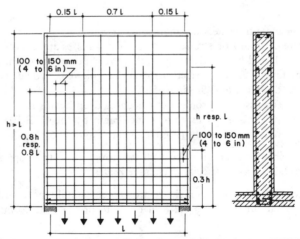

Fig. 11.4 Detailing of simply supported deep beams loaded at bottom (CEB-FIP, 1970a)

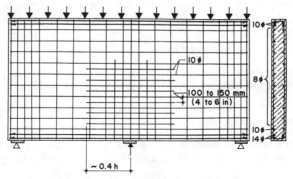

Fig. 11.5 Detailing of continuous deep beams (CEB-FIP, 1970a)

3 Shells

Although shells of single and double curvature are sometimes used as roofs of multistory complexes, their potential for use in load-carrying intermediate floors does not appear to have been fully appreciated and exploited. The funicular shell, an optimum structural form, carries loads in compression with little or no bending (Ramaswamy, 1961). Precast funicular shells, for example, have been used as permanent forms and structural elements for roofs and floors in high-rise buildings (George et al., 1973), resulting in reduced reinforcement quantities.

For floors, a waffle-shell arrangement with grid beams running in two directions is suitable (Fig. 11.8). This scheme is similar to the familiar waffle slab, with the difference that the interspace between beams is spanned by shells instead of slabs. This substitution results in remarkable improvement in rigidity, making the scheme suitable for long spans and heavy loads. Room-size waffle-shell units can be prefabricated and erected (Fig. 11.9). Alternatively, precast shells may be placed to form the grid beams, which subsequently are cast in place.

Vertical freestanding shells, parts of shells, or folded plates may be employed as the structural backbone of high-rise buildings to resist vertical and lateral loads. A high degree of rigidity is attainable. The use of such a structural scheme is described by Bandel (1964). If the resulting building is unsymmetrical, torsion effects caused by wind loads will demand special consideration. The behavior of such systems and their economics have not so far been fully explored.

4 Stairs

The stair is an indispensable component of all multistory buildings and it is usually treated as an inconspicuous detail of minor structural importance. On occasion, the architect and engineer have attempted to make a feature of the stair and the resulting structural form presents problems for the structural designer.

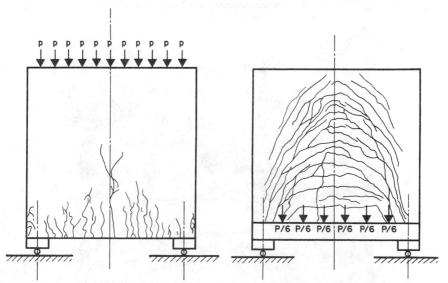

Fig. 11.6 Crack pattern of deep beam loaded at top (Leonhardt and Walther, 1966)   **Fig. 11.7** Crack pattern of deep beam loaded at bottom (Leonhardt and Walther, 1966)

The most common section for a cast-in-place reinforced concrete stair has a plane underside and may be designed as a slab. A second type has parallel upper and lower profiles resulting in a section which, for lack of a better name, may be designated saw-tooth or slabless.

The simplest form of stair is a straight flight between floors, or between floor and landing, in which the stair itself acts as a longitudinal beam or one-way slab, as shown in Fig. 11.10. Alternatively the stair may be supported on one or more longitudinal stringer beams. The principle of cantilevering the stair from a single

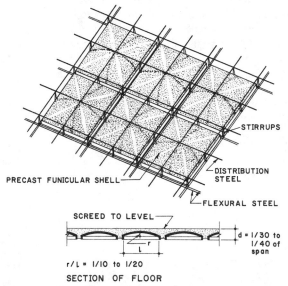

STIRRUPS

DISTRIBUTION STEEL

PRECAST FUNICULAR SHELL

FLEXURAL STEEL

SCREED TO LEVEL

$d = l/30$ to $l/40$ of span

r

L

$r/L = l/10$ to $l/20$

SECTION OF FLOOR

Fig. 11.8 Grid arrangement with funicular shells

Fig. 11.9 Prefabricated waffle-shell unit

stringer beam or from a wall may also be extended to helical stairs supported from the cylinder forming either the outer or the inner circumference of the helix (Fig. 11.11).

Freestanding stairs represent another recent development in cast-in-place stair construction. Such stairs are supported only at floor levels and may be curved in plan or rectilinear in plan with an unsupported landing (Fig. 11.12). Again the stair itself may act as the longitudinal beam, or the stair cross sections may have supporting stringer beams. Freestanding stairs are normally designed and constructed with fixed supports; this support condition reduces the maximum value of bending moment and normally results in a more economical design.

The dimensions and slopes of stairs are governed by architectural, economic, and

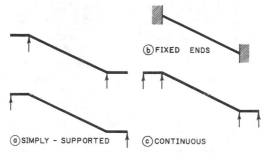

Fig. 11.10 Types of stair supports

Fig. 11.11 Helical stairway, Pine Grove Apartments, Isla Verde, Puerto Rico (Courtesy: I. Martin)

safety considerations. Schuster (1964) recommends that for each step $2R + T = 630$ mm (25 in.), in which R = height of the riser and T = length of the tread. National and city building regulations also specify dimensions. For example, the 1965 British Building Regulations (HMSO, 1965) give 570 mm (22 in.) $< (2R + t) < 635$ mm (25 in.) and a maximum permissible slope of 38°, with no more than 16 steps per flight and a minimum vertical headroom of 2 m (6.5 ft). Helical stairs are sometimes not acceptable as fire-escape routes.

The design of stairs is based on elastic analysis and conventional reinforced concrete detailing. The slabless stair should be analyzed as a rigid jointed frame; simple solutions are available for standard cases (Cusens, 1966). The reinforcing of the slabless section creates obvious difficulties due to stress concentrations at the re-entrant corners between treads and risers. A pattern of reinforcement [Fig. 11.13(a)] has been suggested by Saenz and Martin (1961), but in experimental tests this has been shown to have some weakness at the re-entrant corners. The arrangements suggested in Fig. 11.13(b) and (c) develop the full strength of the section.

Freestanding stairs may be analyzed by use of a space frame program. Approximate methods have been formulated for the rectilinear type, by Siev (1962), using a plate method, and by Cusens and Kuang (1965) using a simplified space frame technique. Helical stairs are usually analyzed as helical beams with fixed ends, and design charts (Cusens and Santathadaporn, 1966) are available for slab sections subtending angles in plan up to 360°.

In tall buildings, stairs are a highly repetitive element, and hence simple reinforcing details tend to give economy. Frequently, precast stairs will be used in conjunction with cast-in-place cores to save forming time and costs.

11.3 VERTICAL MEMBERS

1 Reinforced Concrete Columns

The present practice for the design of reinforced concrete columns consists in making an elastic analysis of the structure to determine the internal forces in its

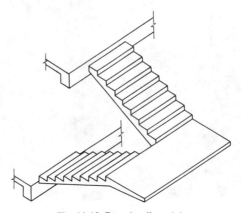

Fig. 11.12 Freestanding stairs

members, and then proportioning the section of the column according to the ultimate strength required of the cross section at each critical point.

Many design methods of elastic analysis and ultimate strength have been developed and are being used throughout the world. To illustrate the main trends of thought on the subject, reference will be made to the ACI Building Code (ACI, 1971) and to the CEB-FIP International Recommendations for the Design and Construction of Concrete Structures (CEB-FIP, 1970a), which cover present design practice in most of America and in Europe.

The design of columns by means of an elastic analysis of the structure and the ultimate strength of the member is complicated by the participation of the column in the possible instability of the structure, besides the possible instability of the column as a member.

The development of better construction materials such as high-strength reinforcing steel, large-diameter bars and high-strength concrete, new and more accurate methods of analysis and design, and better construction techniques have allowed reinforced concrete to participate in meeting the worldwide need of a better use of space by its utilization in multistory buildings. The use of better materials, shear walls, and flat plate floors has resulted in more slender columns and less restrained columns, bringing the possibility of instability failures to the design of columns.

A survey made of more than 20 000 columns in buildings in the United States (MacGregor et al., 1970) has shown that 98% of the columns had l_u/h less than 12.5 in braced frames and less than 18 in unbraced frames. This study showed that the upper practical limit of the slenderness ratio kl_u/r is about 70, and that slender columns seldom have e/h values in excess of 0.4. Research has been extended to columns with an effective slenderness ratio kl_u/r of 200.

Elastic Analysis.   ACI (1971) establishes that all members of structures of

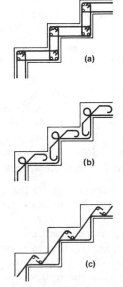

(a)

(b)

(c)

Fig. 11.13 Stair reinforcing details

continuous construction shall be designed for the maximum effects of the design loads as determined by the theory of elastic frames, but allows for the redistribution of the negative moments calculated by elastic theory within given limits.

CEB-FIP (1970a) states that the calculation of the effects of external loadings is traditionally carried out by the Theory of Elasticity, but warns that the appearance of nonlinear deformations (plastic deformations or local deformations due to cracking) can modify the elastic distribution (redistribution) of structural actions (such as bending moments, shear forces, etc.) at all stages, from the appearance of the first nonlinear deformations in concrete in tension to the final limit state, which requires taking into account these nonlinear deformations in the design. It recognizes that the available experimental data and theoretical knowledge are still inadequate to evaluate nonlinear deformations, and that therefore it is often necessary to use elastic values for the ultimate strength design of members.

Both the ACI and CEB design procedures are limit state design methods, because increased loads are compared with the strength of structure and the effects of service loads are compared with specific values.

The service loads are increased by means of load factors to provide for possible variations in loads, assumptions in structural analysis, simplifications in calculations, and effects of construction sequence and methods. The increased loads must be combined in such a way as to produce the most adverse conditions. These load factors combined with the design strengths of materials form the basis of the factor of safety of the structure. The main load factors for dead and live load are

$$\text{ACI:} \qquad 1.4D + 1.7\,L$$
$$\text{CEB:} \qquad 1.5D + 1.5\,L$$

When the dead load governs the design of a column, which is a common condition in a tall building, CEB requires higher ultimate strength than ACI.

CEB-FIP (1970a) is specific in the probabilistic nature of the safety of the structure through the determination of the loads and the design strength of materials, while ACI (1971), although using a similar approach, is silent in this respect.

The use of elastic analysis in the design of columns has the following shortcomings:

1. It does not take into account the inelastic action of a column or the restraining beams at joints. As the column deflects laterally under axial load and moment, the column stiffness is reduced, increasing the part of the external moment at the joint to be carried by the restraining beams. On the other hand, if the restraining beam section at the joint reaches the yield point of the steel, the moment in the column will increase.

2. Lateral deflections in columns generate moments due to the axial load, which must be added to the applied moments. In a short restrained column, the reduction in the column end moment may be larger than the increase in moment due to deflections, and the maximum moment in the column may be lower than the elastic analysis moment, which makes the axial load capacity of the column higher. In a slender column, the deflection moments tend to increase more rapidly than the restraint moments, reducing the axial load capacity because the maximum moment is increased.

3. Sustained loads increase column deflections with time, reducing the column

stiffness. For short columns, sustained loads may increase the strength of the column, while they may decrease it for slender columns (Manuel and MacGregor, 1967).

4. Slender columns bent in double curvature with large eccentricities may exceed the short column strength for the elastic analysis, because the reduced rotational stiffness of the column may make the end moments less than the elastic analysis end moments. For small eccentricities, the column deflections reduce the column strength below the short column value.

5. Slender columns in unbraced frames may form an unstable mechanism if the beams yield and cannot restrain the column. Therefore restraining beams must be designed to resist the column end moments, which may be higher than the elastic analysis end moments.

6. The nonlinear moment curvature characteristics of a column cannot be defined with a constant stiffness parameter EI.

Prila condominium, San Juan, Puerto Rico. Architects and Engineers: Capacete, Martin & Associates (Courtesy: I. Martin)

The study of the behavior of columns as members of frames has been made by means of tests and analytical studies in computers. Broms and Viest (1961) studied the inelastic stability of columns with linearly elastic restraints for the case of symmetrical single curvature bending, assuming a sine wave deflection. Pfrang and Siess (1964) developed a method of analysis considering linear elastic restraints that is not dependent on a predetermined deflected shape of the column. The effect of sustained loading is considered by modifying the stiffness of the end restraints and by doubling the concrete strains in the stress-strain curve.

Breen and Ferguson (1964) tested frames with the columns loaded in double curvature, and Furlong and Ferguson (1966) tested frames with the columns loaded in single curvature. MacGregor and Barter (1966) tested columns restrained by beams, and Manuel and MacGregor (1967) made an analysis of columns in frames for short-time and sustained loads by computing curvatures from the development of creep and shrinkage strains in individual fibers at individual cross sections.

The behavior of columns in frames free to sway laterally has been studied by Ferguson and Breen (1966) by testing frames with lateral loads. Green and Breen (1969) tested eccentrically sustained loaded columns free to sway laterally. Two columns loaded up to 160% of the service loading became unstable within 2 months of loading. For the small section tested, the Hognestad stress-strain diagram with the strain ordinates doubled for long-time loading underestimated the time-dependent curvature for a given moment. CEB (1973) recommends taking into account the creep effect by multiplying the concrete strains by a creep coefficient, which is a function of the relative humidity, the age at loading, the water-cement ratio, the thickness of the column, and the duration of the application of the load.

In analytical studies and experimental work carried out at the University of Texas (Pagay et al., 1970; Okamura et al., 1970; Ferguson et al., 1970) it has been found that the steel ratio in the beams is one of the most important variables influencing column strength. In tall buildings, the requirement of minimum eccentricity for lower story columns should be re-examined because the beam will not be strong enough to resist such column moment. Elastic frame analysis based on gross concrete sections generally leads to unsafe design of columns because of the lower stiffness of the cracked beam, the loss of stiffness of the column concrete near ultimate, and sometimes the yielding of the column compression steel on one face. It is necessary to consider the cracked section stiffness of the beams with low steel percentages in unbraced frames and increased eccentricities for short columns in braced frames.

For mechanical slenderness ratios up to 60 it has been recommended to compute the effective length of the column based on 80% of the uncracked moment of inertia of the concrete in the column and 40% of the uncracked moment of inertia of the beam (see Article 8.7.3, Chapter CB-8). It has also been proposed to use the cracked transformed section to determine the effective length (Breen et al., 1972). Cranston (1972) derived equations to determine the effective length of columns in frames.

Tall buildings are subject to gravity loads and lateral loads from wind and earthquake. Many methods of analysis have been developed to simplify or modify the elastic analysis. The analysis of tall structures is usually time-consuming, and this leads to the use of computer programs, which are capable of carrying out elastic analysis including the elastic axial deformation of members. Many simplifications have been proposed for the elastic analysis of tall shear walls combined with frames.

Chapter CB-5 presents a review of the main current methods available to the designer.

In summary, the present practice of design of reinforced concrete columns in tall buildings is the use of elastic analysis based on the gross section of members. Approximate methods of analysis which specify points of contraflexure in the columns should be avoided in tall building design, because in the case of relatively flexible beams compared to the columns, the first point of contraflexure may not be in the lower floors, which increases the slenderness of the lower columns. Computer programs are frequently used to perform the elastic analysis of tall buildings. In the use of elastic analysis results for the design of columns it is necessary to be familiar with the shortcomings of these methods and to apply the required limitations to the design to avoid unsafe situations. The following design limitations, pointed out by MacGregor (1967), must be considered:

1. Limitation of lateral drift to avoid sidesway buckling. Pfrang (1966) reports that relatively little lateral restraint is sufficient to develop a braced frame condition. A definition of the braced frame condition has been made stating that if the moment of inertia of the shear walls in each direction in a given story is six times the sum of the moments of inertia of all the columns, sidesway would not occur. This may prevent story sway but over-all stability should be checked.

2. For braced frames the design limitations of dimensions, concrete strength, steel reinforcing, and slenderness ratio tend to minimize the possibility of unsafe conditions due to the inaccuracies of elastic design.

3. In unbraced frames an entire story may buckle. Parme (1966) has developed an approximate procedure of analysis of this problem. The ACI Building Code (ACI, 1971) considers this situation by determining the magnifying moment factor, which amplifies the column moments to account for the effects of axial loads for the entire story (assuming all columns to be loaded) and for the individual column under consideration, and using the larger value obtained.

4. Design limitations are needed to make sure that the restraining beams have the necessary rotational capacity.

5. There should be design limitations to the stiffness parameter in the design of columns to approximate the stiffness variations due to cracking, creep, and the nonlinearity of the concrete stress-strain curve.

Strength Design. The traditional working stress design methods for the design of reinforced concrete columns were based on experimental investigations that led to the use of equations in which the load-carrying capacity of the short column was determined by the sum of the ultimate carrying capacity of the concrete and the steel, to which sum a factor of safety was applied. In essence the strength design principles were used in the design of reinforced concrete columns, even when working stress design methods were being used.

In the early days reinforced concrete columns were not slender; therefore the early investigations were concerned with short columns. The work of Considère, von Emperger, Mesnager, Bach, Graf, Rudeloff, Thullie, and Saliger in Europe and

Talbot, Withey, and Richart in the United States, and many others, established the basic principles of column design before 1930.

In 1930 ACI sponsored an extensive investigation on reinforced concrete columns carried out at the University of Illinois and Lehigh University. This investigation established the use of the design equation based on the sum of the load-carrying capacities of the concrete and the steel sections, which recognizes the transfer of stress from concrete to steel under sustained loading.

Properties of concrete. The ACI Code (ACI, 1971) permits the use of a stress-strain diagram with the shape of a rectangle, trapezoid, parabola, or any other shape that conforms to the results of comprehensive tests. It also limits the extreme concrete compression strain to 0.003. Fig. 11.14 shows the Hognestad stress-strain curve, which is widely used in the United States. A capacity reduction factor of 0.75 and 0.7 is applied to spiral and tied columns, respectively.

The CEB Recommendations (CEB-FIP, 1970a) permit the use of a second degree parabola to a strain of 0.002, followed by a rectangle to a maximum strain of 0.0035. It also permits the use of a simplified bilinear stress-strain block for the calculation of deformations in the analysis of buckling, limited to a maximum strain of 0.003. The maximum concrete strength in the stress-strain block is limited to 85% of the cylinder strength of the concrete. The design values are obtained by dividing the maximum strength by 1.5. Fig. 11.15 shows a typical rectangular parabola stress-strain curve used in Europe.

Properties of steel. Both ACI (1971) and CEB-FIP (1970a) use a bilinear stress-strain diagram for the steel, which consists of a straight line from zero strains to the yield point and a horizontal line at the yield strength after that point. ACI applies the same capacity reduction factor to the concrete and the reinforcing steel, while CEB divides the yield point of steel by 1.15. Fig. 11.16 shows the stress-strain diagram for as-rolled steel.

In the case of tied columns under compression failure the design strength of materials is, for the steel

$$\begin{aligned} \text{ACI:} \qquad & 0.700 f_y \\ \text{CEB:} \qquad & 0.870 f_y \end{aligned}$$

and for the concrete

$$\begin{aligned} \text{ACI:} \qquad & 0.700 f_c' \\ \text{CEB:} \qquad & 0.567 f_c' \end{aligned}$$

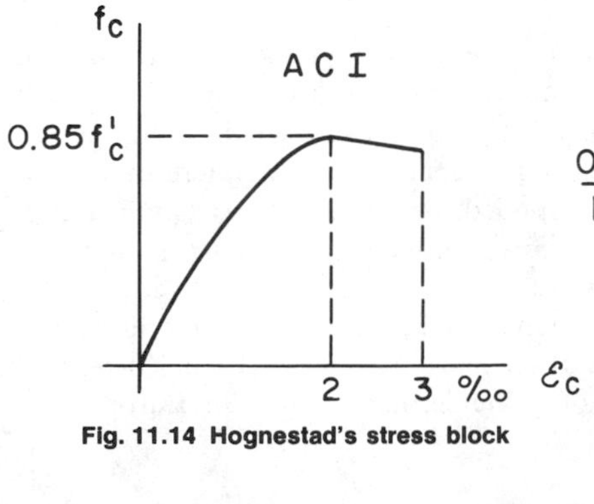

Fig. 11.14 Hognestad's stress block

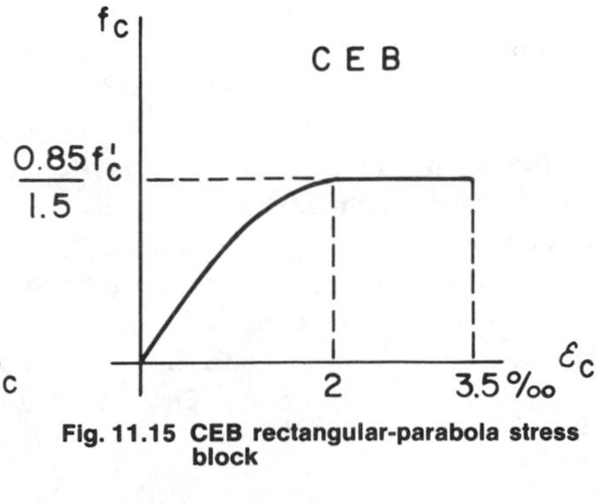

Fig. 11.15 CEB rectangular-parabola stress block

ACI permits higher concrete stresses than CEB, but the allowable steel stress is lower for ACI when compared with CEB. For higher steel percentages the ultimate strength of columns design by the ACI method may be lower than by the CEB method.

Design of short columns.   Short columns are analyzed through the properties of the cross section by means of load-moment interaction diagrams (Fig. 11.17). The ACI and CEB methods of determining the strength of eccentrically loaded short columns have been compared, taking into account the factors of safety implicit in the strength of materials, by Martín et al. (1966), and both methods show agreement in the short column design.

Pfrang et al. (1964) have made a comprehensive study of the behavior of tied columns, showing the effect of different cross-sectional properties on the load-moment-curvature relationship and the strength of the column.

From 1930 to 1960 tests on short columns made by Oengo and Moenaert in Europe and Richart and Hognestad in the United States have contributed to the development of knowledge on the subject.

Spiral reinforcement and ties increase the strength of concrete by restraining it laterally and preventing the buckling of the main bars. If the lateral reinforcement is closely spaced it increases the ductility of the column core. The restraining effect of spirals was studied experimentally in the 1930 ACI investigation, and more recently, Casillas (1963) tested 34 reinforced concrete spiral columns. Pfister (1964) and Bresler and Gilbert (1961) have studied the effect of ties in reinforced concrete columns.

In the case of biaxial bending an interaction surface may be obtained (Fig. 11.18). For biaxial bending and axial load, Bresler (1960) has presented an approximate expression for the capacity of columns. Farah and Huggins (1969) have tested reinforced concrete columns under biaxial bending and have proposed a method of analysis based on an integration method, and Warner (1969) has derived a method for determining the load-deformation characteristics of reinforced concrete column sections in biaxial bending. Fouré (1971) has found experimentally that bending in the most rigid direction reduces the stiffness of the column, which may decrease the buckling load in the less rigid direction. Nadal et al. (1970) have compared different design procedures with test results, and Morán (CEB, 1972) has compiled ten methods available to the designer to check rectangular sections under biaxial bending.

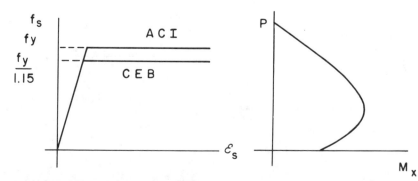

Fig. 11.16 Steel stress-strain diagram   Fig. 11.17 Interaction diagram

In America, biaxially loaded columns are designed by interpolating for the skew load line angle, between the values obtained from interaction diagrams for uniaxial load and for 45° biaxial load. In Europe (CEB, 1971), diagrams for different levels of axial load are used that permit the design of columns of given biaxial eccentricity (Fig. 11.19). These diagrams represent the section of the interaction surface by a plane parallel to the bending moment axes.

Hanson and Reiffentuhl (1960) tested ten columns with bundled reinforcement that showed no reduction in the load-carrying capacity, provided bond is not a problem. The availability of large-diameter bars and high-strength steel has made the use of bundled reinforcement in columns rare. Todeschini et al. (1964) tested columns reinforced with high-strength steel and found that strains of 0.003 can be developed in axially loaded columns with high-strength reinforcement. Sinha and Ferguson (1964) have reported columns with high-strength reinforcement and high eccentricities with measured concrete strains of 0.006. Similar tests were reported by Leonhardt and Teichen (1972). ACI (1971) limits the yield point of reinforcing steel to 550 MPa (80 000 psi) to assure that the yield point is reached before the concrete strain reaches 0.003 as suggested by Pfister and Mattock (1963).

Tall buildings may be subjected to high lateral loads due to wind and earthquake effects, which can induce shear and torsion in the columns. Investigations of combined axial loads and shear are limited. Capon and Díaz de Cossío (1965) tested spiral columns in shear and combined axial load and shear; Yamada and Furi (1968) tested tied columns subject to axial load and shear which showed explosive cleavage failure; and Bishara and Peir (1968) tested columns with axial load and torque, and found that the load-torque relation may be represented by an interaction diagram similar to the load-moment interaction diagram. Dynamic loading tests of reinforced concrete columns have been reported by Reinschmidt et al. (1964) showing that dynamically loaded short columns are 30% to 40% stronger than statically loaded columns. Hellesland and Green (1971) tested columns under cyclic loading and found a critical load at 90% to 95% of the load capacity prior to cycling which, if exceeded, may induce collapse. Based on observations of earthquake damage and experimentation, Hisada et al. (1972) recommend limiting the ratio of service axial load to the strength of the column section to no more than

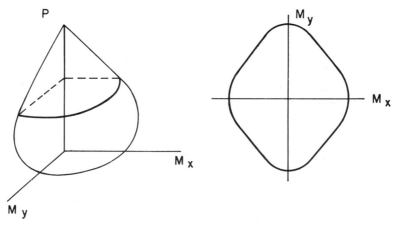

Fig. 11.18 Interaction surface   Fig. 11.19 Interaction rosette

one-third. Atkan and Pecknold (1974) have pointed out that the stiffness and therefore the bending moment capacity of columns is reduced under cyclic biaxial bending, when compared to uniaxial bending. After a few reversals beyond yielding of the reinforcement, the concrete contribution to the shear resistance may be considerably reduced.

Lightweight concrete columns have been tested by Pfeifer (1969, 1971) showing that the behavior of lightweight concrete columns is similar to normal weight concrete columns. Bresler (1971) has found that the reduction in ultimate strain capacity of lightweight concrete limits the effective use of high-strength steel and the ductility of columns; therefore, lightweight concrete columns with high-strength steel reinforcement under seismic loading should be subject to specific limitations.

Design of slender columns.   The methods for designing slender columns can be classified as follows:

1. The slender column is designed by means of a reduction factor that reduces the load-carrying capacity of the short column. This is the traditional approach and the reduction factor as a function of the slenderness has been treated in building codes as a curve, two straight lines, or a single straight line. ACI (1971) permits the use of this approach.

2. The moment magnifier method in which the column is designed for the axial load and a magnified moment. This is the approach used in steel design in the United States and the method recommended by ACI.

3. The complementary eccentricity method, originated by Aas-Jakobsen (1967) and used by CEB-FIP (1970a), in which the column is designed for the axial load and the moment from a first-order analysis plus the moment obtained by applying a complementary eccentricity to the axial load.

The behavior of slender columns has been studied in the past by numerous investigators. Von Kármán solved the stability problem of slender eccentrically loaded columns in 1910. Baumann, as early as 1934, was the first to apply Von Kármán's theory to the buckling of reinforced concrete columns. Other experimental work followed, such as the tests by Coyne, Thomas, Hanson, Rosentrom and Ramboll, Ernst, Hromadik and Riveland, Gehler and Hutter, Gaede, and Sáenz and Martín.

The analysis of slender columns was studied in depth by Broms and Viest (1961), when they presented a method of analysis based on Von Kármán's theory which assumes a sine wave deflected shape. Chang and Ferguson (1963) introduced a numerical integration procedure to determine the deflected shape of the column. Pfrang and Siess (1964) independently derived a numerical procedure by integrating the load-moment-curvature diagram along the column length. Later Pfrang (1964) extended the study to the case of sustained loading by the modified stress-strain curve. MacGregor and Barter (1966), Martín and Olivieri (1966), and Fouré (1971) tested slender tied columns in double curvature. The tests of slender columns as part of frames already mentioned in the section on elastic analysis also form part of the experimental work on slender columns. Drysdale and Huggins (1971) have tested slender columns under sustained biaxial bending. The effect of creep on the buckling of reinforced concrete columns has been studied by Mauch and Holley (1963), Distefano (1965), and more recently, by Dilger and Neville (1971), Creus (1971), and Goyal and Jackson (1971).

The complementary eccentricity method used by CEB has been compared by Aas-Jakobsen (1967) with 209 experimental test results and a mean value of test to computed load of 1.12 was found. MacGregor et al. (1970) have made the same comparison for the moment magnifier method with 60 columns and found a mean value of test to computed load of 1.13.

The CEB expression for the design moment in a slender column is (CEB-FIP, 1970a)

$$M_c = M_2 + P_u K \cdot \frac{(kl_u)^2}{10} \tag{11.6}$$

in which

$$K = \frac{M_c}{EI} \tag{11.7}$$

then, the value of M_c becomes

$$M_c = \frac{M_2}{1 - \dfrac{P_u}{[10\, EI / (kl_u)^2]}} \tag{11.8}$$

The critical load is

$$P_c = \frac{\pi^2 EI}{(kl_u)^2} \approx \frac{10 EI}{(kl_u)^2} \tag{11.9}$$

and

$$M_c = \frac{M_2}{1 - \left(\dfrac{P_u}{P_c}\right)} \tag{11.10}$$

The ACI magnified moment equation for the case of C_m equal to unity is (ACI, 1971)

$$M_c = \frac{M_2}{1 - \left(\dfrac{P_u}{\phi P_c}\right)} \tag{11.11}$$

which is the same as the CEB complementary moment except for the ϕ factor dividing the axial design load.

The CEB Buckling Handbook (CEB, 1973) has proposed the following approximate equation for the stiffness parameter EI

$$EI = \left(200 i_c^2 + \frac{\omega i_s^2}{\epsilon_s}\right) f_c A_c \tag{11.12}$$

If the following values are substituted

$$i_c^2 = \frac{I_c}{A_c} \qquad i_s^2 = \frac{I_s}{A_s}$$

$$\omega = \frac{A_s f_y}{A_c f_c} \qquad \epsilon_s = \frac{E_s}{f_y}$$

$$f_c = \frac{0.85}{1.5} f_c' \qquad E_c = 1000 f_c' \text{ (approx.)}$$

Eq. 11.12 becomes

$$EI = \frac{E_c I_c}{8.82} + E_s I_s \qquad (11.13)$$

This is more conservative than the expression given by ACI (1971) for the stiffness parameter, which is

$$EI = \frac{E_c I_c}{5} + E_s I_s \qquad (11.14)$$

MacGregor et al. (1975) have proposed a simple equation for the stiffness parameter based on the percentage of steel reinforcement.

Both methods reflect the behavior of slender columns by modifying the moment but not the axial load. The complementary eccentricity method is easy to apply and is well suited to predict the failure of concentric loaded columns or columns bent in single curvature—those are the conditions for which the method was originally derived. Tall buildings have columns bent in double curvature, and in some cases with sidesway. In these cases, the complementary eccentricity method may fail to predict the type of failure of the column.

The moment magnifier method is more rational in the prediction of failure, is easy to use, and has the advantage of being similar to the steel design method used in the United States. It has been claimed that the moment magnifier method is not rational in the prediction of failure of the concentric loading case, but this case is covered by the design requirement of the use of a minimum eccentricity.

The practicing engineer has at his disposal two methods to simplify the design of the complex behavior of slender columns as part of a structure. If second-order elastoplastic analysis methods for computer application are made available universally to the practicing engineer, both methods of analysis may be phased out to become historic landmarks in the knowledge of structural engineering.

The problem of slender column design and the use of second-order analyses in design are discussed more fully in Chapter CB-8.

Design and Construction Limitations. The approximate design methods currently in use require the application of limitations to avoid unsafe conditions that cannot be detected in the design calculations. Construction practices also impose limitations to the construction of columns. In tall buildings, the nature of column loads requires the consideration of further limitations to the design of columns. Some of these limitations may be summarized as follows.

Limitations due to approximations in design. Minimum longitudinal steel percentage is specified to prevent a buckling failure by creep and shrinkage, which is particularly dangerous in small-size sections. ACI (1971) specifies the minimum longitudinal reinforcement as 1% of the concrete section, while CEB (CEB-FIP, 1970a) specifies the minimum longitudinal steel percentage as a function of the ratio of the axial load to the load-carrying capacity of the member. It also has an additional limitation on the minimum ratio of steel for slender columns. ACI establishes a maximum steel percentage of 8% for practical reasons of placing the concrete in the sections where splices are needed. CEB does not have this type of limitation. ACI and CEB require the splice length to comply with the bond development length and requirements for the transverse reinforcement at splices. Butt welded splices, couplers, and end bearing splice devices are frequently used in columns to save space.

Both ACI and CEB specify the minimum bar diameter and the maximum spacing of ties, the lateral spacing of spirals, the spacing between longitudinal bars, and the minimum cover. CEB also limits the maximum cover.

ACI does not have limitations as to the size of columns to allow the use of concrete in light construction. In small-size columns the effect of shrinkage stresses must be carefully considered. CEB limits spiral column cores to at least 250 mm (10 in.). CEB has recommended minimum sizes for columns for fire protection starting with 150 mm (6 in.) for columns with a 30-minute rating.

Limitations due to construction practices. ACI (1971) has a provision to consider the effect of the weaker concrete in slabs and beams that may form part of the column at the joints. It has an expression to determine the equivalent concrete strength that is based on tests made by Bianchini et al. (1960). It also permits the use of concrete of the strength specified for the column in the slab about the column, a practice that requires close supervision, or the use of the weaker slab concrete strength by adding dowels and spirals as required.

Buildings must be built to conform with the construction tolerances anticipated in the design. The following construction tolerance limitations established by ACI are worth mentioning: maximum variation from plumb, 0.2% [25.4 mm (1 in.)]; maximum variation in plan of position of columns, 25.4 mm (1 in.); variation in cross section, minus 6 mm (0.25 in.) and plus 13 mm (0.5 in.). It is doubtful that these tolerances are currently being met by the American construction industry. CEB leaves the establishment of tolerances to the design engineer.

ACI requires the use of minimum eccentricities in the design, while CEB requires the use of an additional eccentricity. In both cases, these eccentricities are established to cover not only the inaccuracies in the elastic analysis, but also the eccentricities due to variations in the position of the axis of the column on account of misalinement, cracking, variations in the quality of concrete, tolerances in placing the steel reinforcement, and in the dimensions of members and the eccentricities due to unequal shrinkage and creep, which are not accounted for in the design methods.

The use of a minimum eccentricity by ACI (1971) is justified by the fact that the load capacity of a column is more sensitive to small applied eccentricities than to large applied eccentricities.

Limitations due to the nature of tall buildings. The use of reinforced concrete in very tall structures has made important the problem of differential temperature bending and length change of columns due to exposure, creep, and shrinkage that has been studied by Fintel and Khan (1965-1969). A differential shortening of columns with respect to the core amounting to 28 mm (1.1 in.) in four years in a 50-story, 183 m (600 ft) high building has been reported (Heiman, 1973).

Tall buildings under seismic effects are subject to dynamic loads that may require special provisions to give the structure the necessary ductility to resist the seismic loads, in the case that displacements are large enough to distort part of the structure beyond the elastic limit. ACI (1971) limits the longitudinal steel reinforcement from 1% to 6% in seismic resisting structures. The sum of the moments of the columns at the design axial load must be greater than the sum of the moment strength of the beams, unless the moment strength of the confined core of the columns is sufficient to resist the applied design loads. The concrete core must be confined by transverse reinforcement when the maximum design load is higher than 40% of the axial load capacity at balanced conditions. The column must be designed for the applied shears developed by the formation of plastic hinges in the frame. The yield strength of reinforcing steel shall not exceed 414 MPa (60 000 psi, 4200 kgf/cm^2), to avoid the risk of additional moments due to the greater load capacity of high-strength steel beyond the yield point. The strength of column to beam joints under seismic loads with grade 60 steel [yield strength 414 MPa (60 000 psi)] in seismic resisting frames has been studied by Hanson and Connor (1967) and Hanson (1971), and Blume (1971) has pointed out the need of designing first-story columns for strength, confinement, ductility, and shear capacity.

Lateral drift of tall buildings may induce the buckling collapse of the columns in a story. Although the limitations of lateral drift are not usually explicit in building codes, designers have limited the total drift per story from 1/300 to 1/600 of the story height to avoid undesirable perception by the users of the building to lateral displacements and to avoid cracking of partitions. It is also a safeguard against buckling collapse of columns. The relationship between drift and frame stability is discussed in Chapter CB-8.

Future Trends. The future trend of the design of columns in tall buildings seems to point in the direction of the development of more effective second-order, elastoplastic methods of analysis. While the methods of analysis are being developed, the complementary eccentricity and the moment magnifier methods will have to be developed further to establish all the limitations affecting the design of tall buildings.

The problem of column design in tall structures is not one of economics but of valuation of the consequences of failure. It is a problem of making better use of space by locating the columns in accordance with the architectural requirements and not in regular grid patterns, and of giving them shapes different from the circle and the rectangle. This can be done by using more powerful methods of analysis of structures with irregular column patterns, and designing columns with high-strength concrete and steel and high steel percentage ratios.

Reinforced concrete buildings of 100 stories may be built in the near future; therefore, the special features involved in the design of the columns of these structures, such as environmental exposure, dimensional changes, and response to lateral loads, will require the attention of designers and researchers. New materials with different properties, such as polymer concrete with compressive strengths over 70 MPa (10 000 psi, 700 kgf/cm^2) will be used in tall building columns in the future.

Needed Research. Research on reinforced concrete columns is needed in the following areas.

Analysis and design. The development is needed of new second-order elastoplastic methods of analysis for the design of columns as part of structures.

The accuracy of the present approximate methods of design has been determined by analytical computer models. The assumptions made in these analytical models need re-examination to determine how well they reproduce the behavior of columns.

The scope of application of the moment magnifier and complementary eccentricity methods requires exploration. The effect of cracking and plastic hinging of columns and beams must be carefully examined, as well as the applicability of the design limitations, such as a minimum eccentricity requirement to tall building columns.

In recent work, Ferry Borges and Castanheta (1971) have questioned the probabilistic soundness of the factor of safety for the combinations of loading required by ACI (1971). This area requires investigation.

Column members.   Investigations of columns in frames have been limited and made on reduced scale models. A more thorough knowledge of the behavior of columns in frames is needed, as well as more knowledge of the influence of the scale factor on the tests of columns in reduced model frames under sustained loading. Modern buildings require column sections that differ from the square or the circle. Testing of columns with other cross sections may explore the effect of the twisting of sections along the axis of the column.

Recent earthquakes have shown the shear, torsion, cyclic, and dynamic loading to be important features in the design of columns. The available research is limited and more tests are needed.

Los Olmos condominium, San Juan, Puerto Rico. Architects and Engineers: Capacete, Martin & Associates (Courtesy: I. Martin)

The use of high-strength steel in columns and frames has been investigated on a limited scale, and further investigation is necessary to determine whether the present design limitations are adequate for the use of this material. The use of lightweight concrete is a good way to save weight in tall buildings, and therefore it is to be expected that it will be more widely used. However, the behavior of this material in columns under sustained and dynamic loads, the effect of exposure to environmental conditions, and the effect of elastic and inelastic shortening require investigation. The code provisions regarding the effect of floor strength on the column strength are based on a single experimental work. More research is needed in this field.

Construction practices and building response. Load factors have been reduced in building codes based on experience and improved quality control in the concrete and steel production. The conformity of actual structures to the tolerances prescribed in codes is questionable; therefore a survey of the deviations from design in average construction will permit the evaluation of present tolerance requirements as well as of the design limitations.

Tall buildings in the future will require the use of every reserve of strength in the structure. Investigations on the design of columns for the concrete strength at the time the maximum load may be applied to the column, as the British Code permits, is desirable. Knowledge of the probability of loads to be applied on the columns during the lifetime of a tall building will contribute to the better use of the materials available. Actual measurements on tall structures under loads and exposed environment are limited. More research in this field will contribute to a better understanding of the behavior of tall buildings.

2 Shear Walls

This section deals primarily with shear walls in buildings in seismic regions. A further discussion of this topic is presented in Section 6.4 of Chapter CB-6.

In the Kanto Earthquake of 1923 much less damage was suffered by structural frames with infilled wall panels of reinforced concrete than by frames without such panels. Since that time, frames with infilled cast-in-place reinforced concrete walls, which can carry large shear forces, have been called "earthquake resisting walls" in Japan. The term "framed shear wall" is used in this section, up to and including the article on "Flexible Framed Shear Walls," as a short description of the combination of frames and infilled cast-in-place reinforced concrete walls. Reinforced concrete shear walls without boundary frames are called "frameless shear walls."

An uncracked shear wall has great rigidity and can carry large shear forces during an earthquake. The first diagonal crack occurs in the wall panel when the shearing deformation (shear angle) reaches approximately 0.25×10^{-3} rad. Following cracking the wall behaves as an anisotropic plate, setting up a compression field in the direction of one diagonal, while the expansion due to tension in the direction of the other diagonal is restrained by the wall reinforcement and the boundary frame. A properly reinforced boundary frame will suffer insignificant damage during an earthquake, while one shear crack after another occurs all over the wall panel as it resists an increasing shear force. The wall exhibits ductile shearing resistance, which cannot generally be expected of columns and beams, and acts as a damper by absorbing much energy due to the large shear strain.

If the boundary columns are designed to carry all vertical loads, and the wall panels (cracked or uncracked) are designed to carry shear only, the combination can resist severe earthquakes, provided the structure does not overturn. The energy from the horizontal forces is absorbed first by ductile shear damage in the wall panels, followed by ductile flexural damage in the frame members at their ends.

Ductile shear walls can be designed to resist fairly large earthquakes without large permanent deformations of the boundary frame. The structure can be rehabilitated for service merely by recasting the cracked or crushed wall panels. There are, however, still many unsolved problems connected with a rational seismic structural design of shear walls. Section 6.4 of Chapter CB-6 discusses the behavior of ductile walls under seismic actions.

According to recent investigations, very rigid structures with a very short natural period exhibit the largest seismic response. In order to control and reduce the great rigidity of shear walls, many devices have been investigated, such as the "slit shear wall" having a number of vertical slits built into the panel at appropriate intervals, and the "flexible shear wall" whose panel wall and boundary frame are connected by flexible shear connectors.

The shear failure of frameless reinforced concrete walls which carry vertical load is sometimes brittle, therefore the "frameless walls" should be used only when shear reinforcement is provided, or when their ultimate shear load is dominated by their yield in flexure. Section 6.4 of Chapter CB-6 extensively discusses the load-deformation response and design of frameless shear walls and coupled shear walls.

Shearing Resistance of Uncracked Framed Shear Walls. The coefficient for reduction of shear rigidity (= actual rigidity/elastic rigidity) due to the plastic properties of shear walls, just before the formation of the first shear crack, can be assumed to be

$$\beta_{cr} \simeq 0.9 \tag{11.15}$$

An uncracked shear wall can be analyzed elastically as an isotropic body. Strict elastic analyses of infilled wall panels by means of Airy's stress functions have been reported by Tomii and Hiraishi (1976a, 1976b). Stiffness matrix and flexibility matrix for shear walls are given by Tomii and Yamakawa (1974). The value of $\bar{\tau}_{cr}$ is the mean unit shear stress on horizontal sections in shear walls at initial cracking of the infilled panel. Experimentally obtained values of $\bar{\tau}_{cr}$ are shown in Fig. 11.20 and are given by

$$\bar{\tau}_{cr} = \frac{V_{cr}}{tl} \tag{11.16}$$

in which V_{cr} = shear force on a horizontal wall section at initial cracking; t = thickness of the infilled wall panel; and l = distance from center to center of the boundary frame's columns. The value of $\bar{\tau}_{cr}$ ranges from $0.15 f'_c$ to $f'_c/15$, with an average value of approximately

$$\bar{\tau}_{cr} \simeq 0.1 f'_c \tag{11.17}$$

in which f'_c = compressive strength of the concrete.

If shear cracks cannot be permitted, the allowable horizontal shear force V_1 is

$$V_1 = f_v tl \tag{11.18}$$

in which, for $f'_c \leq 21$ MPa (3000 psi)

$$f_v = 0.05 f'_c \qquad (11.19a)$$

or, for f'_c from 21MPa to 35 MPa (3000 psi to 5100 psi)

$$f_v = 7.5 + 0.015 f'_c \qquad (11.19b)$$

The shear deformation angle at incipient cracking, R_{cr}, ranges from 0.20×10^{-3} rad to 0.30×10^{-3} rad, with an average value of approximately

$$R_{cr} \simeq 0.25 \times 10^{-3} \text{ rad} \qquad (11.20)$$

Shearing Resistance of Cracked Framed Shear Walls. It is practical to express the behavior of shear walls in terms of the deformation angle R as the main parameter. The angle can be measured directly and removes scale effects in experiments.

The reduction coefficient β of the shear rigidity is

$$\beta = \beta_{cr} \left(\frac{R}{R_{cr}} \right)^{-(\log \beta_{cr} - \log \beta_u)/(\log R_u - \log R_{cr})} \qquad (11.21)$$

in which R = deformation angle of the shear wall, $R_{cr} \leq R \leq R_u$; R_u = deformation angle corresponding to ultimate (maximum) shear V_u for causing shear failure; β_u = ultimate shear rigidity reduction coefficient corresponding to R_u; and

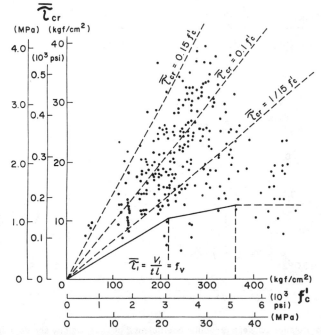

Fig. 11.20 Experimental relation between cracking mean unit shear stress $\bar{\tau}_{cr}$ in shear walls and compressive strength of concrete f'_c

$$\beta_u = \frac{\left(\dfrac{V_u}{R_u}\right)}{\left(\dfrac{V}{R}\right)_{\text{ini}}} \tag{11.22}$$

Eq. 11.21 is a straight line when plotted in orthogonal logarithmic coordinates (Tomii, 1957; 1963). Please see Fig. 11.21.

Analysis of many experiments on shear walls failed in shear yields approximately (Tomii and Takeuchi, 1968)

$$R_u = 4 \times 10^{-3} \text{ rad} \tag{11.23}$$

The equation for the straight line in Fig. 11.21 between points (R_{cr}, β_{cr}) and (R_u, β_u) is

$$\beta = 0.9(4R \times 10^3)^{\{2 + [\log V_u - \log(V/R)_{\text{ini}}]/1.2\}} \tag{11.24}$$

It is very difficult to evaluate V_u exactly. The value of $(V/R)_{\text{ini}}$ may be calculated by elastic analysis.

The restraining action of the boundary frame and the wall reinforcement on the expansion of the wall panel due to diagonal tension governs the ultimate horizontal shear force, V_u, resisted by the wall at failure in shear (Tomii and Hiraishi, 1976). The ultimate horizontal shear force, V_u, is given by

$$V_u = V_{ws \times u} + V_{bf \times u} \tag{11.25}$$

in which $V_{ws \times u}$ = contribution to V_u provided by the wall panel reinforcement, and $V_{fb \times u}$ = contribution to V_u provided by the restraining action of the boundary frame and the concrete in the cracked wall panel.

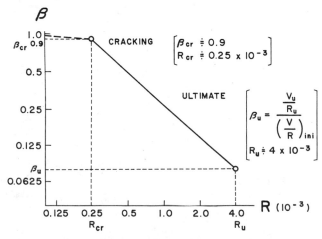

Fig. 11.21 Relation between reduction coefficient β of shear rigidity and deformed angle R

When a uniform expansion of the cracked wall panel can be assumed (Tomii, 1957; Tsuboi and Tomii, 1954) the first term in Eq. 11.25 is

$$V_{ws \times u} = \rho_w t l' f_y \tag{11.26}$$

in which ρ_w = reinforcement ratio for the horizontal and the vertical reinforcement in the wall panel, where the horizontal reinforcement ratio is equal to the vertical reinforcement ratio, $\rho_w \leq 0.012$; l' = clear span of the boundary frame (horizontal dimension of the infilled wall panel); and f_y = yield strength of the wall reinforcement, $f_y \leq 293$ MPa (42 500 psi).

For an evaluation of the second term, $V_{bf \times u}$ in Eq. 11.25, an analysis by a 45° orthotropic elastic plate theory (Tomii and Hiraishi, 1976b) is under study. However, at present it is still extremely difficult to estimate this term. For this reason an allowable shear force V_2 is established on the basis of experimental results, when cracking is permitted, that is, a shear force in excess of V_1 (Eq. 11.18) is desired.

In order to have enough ductility after shear cracking, the Japanese Code (AIJ, 1971) assumes that only the wall reinforcement, the concrete in the cross section of the columns, and the column hoops contribute to V_2. The contribution of the concrete in the horizontal cross section of the wall panel is not included. Hence

$$V_2 = V_{ws \times u} + \Sigma V_c \tag{11.27}$$

In Eq. 11.27, V_c is the contribution of each column in the boundary frame and is given by

$$V_c = \frac{7}{8} b_w d \left[1.5 f_v + 0.5 f_y (\rho_v - 0.002) \right] \tag{11.28}$$

in which b_w = width of the column; d = effective depth of the column (distance from extreme compression fiber to centroid of tension reinforcement); f_y = yield strength of the hoops $f_y \leq 293$ MPa (42 500 psi); and ρ_v = reinforcement ratio of the hoops, $0.002 \leq \rho_v \leq 0.012$.

Experimentally determined ultimate horizontal shear forces, $V_{u \times ex}$, have been used to plot the safety factors $\nu = V_{u \times ex}/V_u$ in Fig. 11.22. Although the safety factors are larger than one, the scatter is considerable. To find the ultimate horizontal shear force, V_u, it is necessary to investigate the restraining action of the boundary frame very carefully.

Shear force $V_1 < V_2$ is a necessary condition to assure good ductility after cracking, but not a sufficient condition when R exceeds 4×10^{-3} rad. The sufficient condition is not known, and additional research is needed.

A wall with embedded braces of structural steel plates or bars (see Fig. 11.23) is a ductile shear wall. The initial rigidity is as for ordinary shear walls. In the ultimate state the compression braces will buckle and the tension braces yield. Properly proportioned embedded braces can assure good ductility and prevent brittle shear failure.

Shear walls that will fail in flexure should be designed as flexural members of I-shaped cross sections, subjected to simultaneous bending and axial load.

Design of Framed Shear Walls With Small Openings. Shear walls with large openings can be analyzed approximately by frame theory, taking into consideration flexural and shear deformations and the rigid zones near the nodes. Shear walls with small openings are difficult to analyze. Instead, the rigidity and allowable horizontal shear force found by conventional design for a wall without openings are multiplied by experimentally-determined reduction coefficients. The coefficients (η or r) vary with the relative size of the openings, expressed by the opening coefficient

$$\xi = \sqrt{\frac{l_o h_o}{l' h'}} \tag{11.29}$$

in which l_o = width of the opening; h_o = height of the opening; l' = clear span of the boundary frame (horizontal dimension of the infilled wall panel); and h' = clear

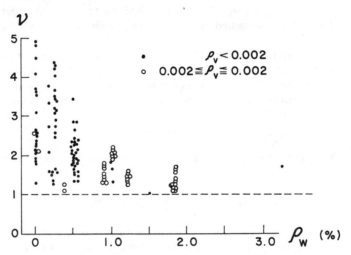

Fig. 11.22 Relation between safety factor v and wall reinforcement ratio ρ_ω

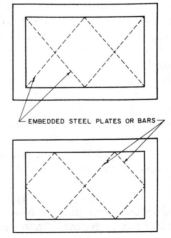

Fig. 11.23 Ductile shear wall with embedded plates or bars

height of the boundary frame (vertical dimension of the infilled wall panel). The reduction coefficient, η, is defined thus:

$$\eta = 1 \quad \text{when} \quad \xi = 0$$
$$\eta = 0 \quad \text{when} \quad \xi = 1 \tag{11.30}$$

$$\eta = \frac{V - V_{\xi=1}}{V_{\xi=0} - V_{\xi=1}} \tag{11.31}$$

in which V, $V_{\xi=0}$, $V_{\xi=1}$ are the horizontal shear forces in corresponding shear walls with equal deformation angles R. The experimental values of η in Fig. 11.24 are not much affected by the variations of R. The reduction coefficient, r, defined as

$$r = \frac{V}{V_{\xi=0}} \tag{11.32}$$

can be expressed in terms of η

$$r = \eta + (1 - \eta) \frac{V_{\xi=1}}{V_{\xi=0}} \tag{11.33}$$

When the second term in Eq. 11.33 can be disregarded

$$r \simeq \eta \tag{11.34}$$

Two experimental formulas for η have been proposed. Tomii's formula, derived from experiments with reinforced mortar models (Tomii and Miyata, 1960) is

$$\eta = 1 - 6\xi^2 + 10\xi^3 - 7.5\xi^4 + 3\xi^5 - 0.5\xi^6 \tag{11.35}$$

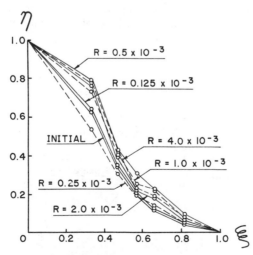

Fig. 11.24 Experimental relations between reduction coefficient η of shear rigidity of framed shear walls with openings and its opening coefficient ξ

Ban's formula, derived from experiments with rubber models (Ban, 1943) is

$$\eta = 1 - 0.5\xi - 2\xi^2 + 1.5\xi^3 \tag{11.36}$$

An experimental formula for r, derived from experiments with rubber models, proposed by Muto and Osawa (Muto, 1956) is

$$r = 1 - 1.25\xi \quad (\text{where } \xi \leq 0.4) \tag{11.37}$$

The limitation $\xi \leq 0.4$ corresponds closely to $\eta > 0.5$, from which is obtained minimum $\eta \simeq$ minimum $r \simeq 0.5$, or, by using Eq. 11.34

$$\eta = 1 - 1.25\xi \quad (\text{where } \xi \leq 0.4) \tag{11.38}$$

The three experimentally derived relationships are shown in Fig. 11.25.

The Japanese Code (AIJ, 1971) gives the reduction coefficient, r, as the lesser of r_1 and r_2, that is

$$r_1 = 1 - \frac{l_o}{l} \tag{11.39}$$

and

$$r_2 = 1 - \sqrt{\frac{l_o h_o}{l h}} \quad (\text{limitation:} \sqrt{\frac{l_o h_o}{l h}} \leq 0.4) \tag{11.40}$$

in which l = center to center spacing of the boundary frame columns, and h = center to center distance of the boundary frame beams.

Additional reinforcement should be provided to carry the diagonal tension stresses at each corner of the opening (see Fig. 11.26). In Fig. 11.26, $\sigma \alpha_w$ = normal stress on the 45° diagonal section of the infilled wall panel with opening; and $\sigma \alpha_w^*$ = normal stress on the 45° diagonal section of the infilled wall panel, without

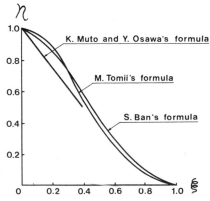

Fig. 11.25 Relation between reduction coefficient η of shear rigidity of framed shear walls with openings and its opening coefficient ξ

opening but similar in other respects to that with opening. When the opening is small and uniform shear stress distribution on the boundary of the wall panel is assumed, the additional tension force is (approximately)

$$T_d = \frac{(h_o + l_o)V_w}{2\sqrt{2l'}} \tag{11.41}$$

in which V_w = horizontal shear force carried by the wall panel.

The reinforcement around the opening resists vertical and horizontal tension forces T_v and T_h at each corner of the opening. These forces are found by assuming that the normal stresses on the horizontal and vertical sections through the center of the opening are equal to zero, and that the uniformly distributed shear stresses on the horizontal and vertical coupled sections adjacent to the opening are equal, that is

$$T_v = \frac{h_o V_w}{2(l' - l_o)} \tag{11.42}$$

$$T_h = \frac{l_o\left(\dfrac{h'}{l'}\right)V_w}{2(h' - h_o)} \tag{11.43}$$

The influence of many factors (such as the shape, proportions, and location of the opening; and reinforcement around the opening) must be investigated in detail for rational design of shear walls with openings.

Limitations on the Shape and Reinforcement of Framed Shear Walls. Limitations on the shape and reinforcement of cracked shear walls must be introduced to assure that they provide enough ductility and ultimately will fail in shear.

The following requirements, (1) through (8), pertaining to the relative dimensions of infilled wall panels, their boundary frames, and reinforcement ratios are taken from the Japanese Code (AIJ, 1971) or the commentary thereto. They are intended to assure that the first shear crack will occur in the wall panel (Tomii and Tokuhiro, 1970), and that the boundary frame will provide enough restraint on the wall panel.

Elastic analysis shows that compliance with (1) and (2) results in a maximum unit

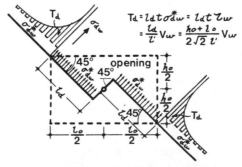

Fig. 11.26 Stress at corners of small opening in infilled panel wall subjected to pure shear at boundary

shear stress in the wall panel more than twice as large as the mean unit shear stresses in the boundary members.

1. The cross-sectional area $b_w D$ of the columns and beams of the boundary frame should be larger than $xt/2$, where t is the thickness, and x is the smaller of the clear height or the width of the infilled wall panel.

2. The web width b_w and depth D of the boundary frame members should be larger than $2t$.

From results of experiments:

3. The web width b_w and depth D of the boundary frame members should be larger than $\sqrt{xt/3}$.

A limitation on the wall panel thickness is given (similar to the 1971 ACI Code) to prevent buckling of the wall panel:

4. The thickness of the wall panel should be larger than $h'/30$, in which h' is the clear height of the infilled wall panel.

To assure the minimum restraining action of the boundary frame and the minimum ductility of the shear wall, requirements (5) through (8), as well as the computed requirements, should be satisfied.

5. The wall reinforcement ratio should not be less than 0.0025.

6. The flexural reinforcement ratio in the boundary frame members should not be less than 0.008.

7. The reinforcement ratio for hoops in the boundary frame members should not be less than 0.002.

8. The maximum spacing of hoops imposed on ordinary columns and beams should never be exceeded.

Elastic analysis (Tomii and Hiraishi, 1976a) shows that the maximum shear forces are found near the ends of the beams and columns. According to experimental results, most shear walls loaded to failure exhibit cracks, originating from the infilled wall panel, running diagonally across the boundary frame members near their ends. The particularly vulnerable parts are indicated by cross-hatched areas in Fig. 11.27.

Flexible Framed Shear Walls.   To reduce and control the initial rigidity of shear walls, several types of flexible shear walls have been developed. Such flexible wall panels together with frames, especially structural steel frames, can resist earthquake loadings.

One type of flexible shear wall, called the "Slit Shear Wall" (Ohmori, 1976), is shown in Fig. 11.28. It is a reinforced concrete wall panel with vertical slits made of embedded cement-asbestos plates.

The shear rigidity and ultimate horizontal shear force capacity of the slit shear wall can be adjusted by varying the wall reinforcement and the length and spacing of the slits. With many fine cracks distributed all over the wall panel, much strain energy can be absorbed. The deformation angle corresponding to the ultimate lateral shear force can amount to between 5×10^{-3} rad and 10×10^{-3} rad.

A wall panel connected to the boundary frame by flexible shear connectors also constitutes a flexible shear wall (see Fig. 11.29). The shear rigidity of this arrangement is less than that of an ordinary shear wall, even in the initial state. Very careful attention must be given to the details of the panel to frame connections.

Frameless Shear Walls.   Frameless shear walls carrying vertical loads together with horizontal shear forces are brittle when designed to fail in shear. Frameless shear walls should therefore be designed to fail in ductile flexure.

The flexural strength of frameless shear walls subjected to combined axial load and bending can be calculated according to the provisions of the ACI Code (1971). Interaction diagrams can be derived for such walls in the normal manner (see Section 6.4, Chapter CB-6). Alternatively

$$M_u = A_s f_y l_w \left(1 + \frac{N_u}{A_s f_y}\right)\left(\frac{1}{2} - \frac{\beta_1 c}{2l_w}\right) - \frac{c^2}{l_w^2}\left(1 + \frac{\beta^2}{3} - \beta_1\right) \qquad (11.44)$$

$$M_u \simeq 0.5 A_s f_y l_w \left(1 + \frac{N_u}{A_s f_y}\right)\left(1 - \frac{c}{l_w}\right) \qquad (11.45)$$

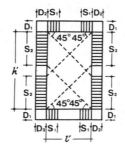

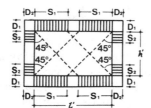

S_1: the larger of $\ell' - \hbar'$ and D_1

S_2: the larger of $\ell' - \hbar'$ and D_2

Fig. 11.27 Boundary frame parts particularly vulnerable to shear cracks on infilled panel wall

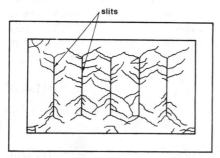

Fig. 11.28 Slit shear wall

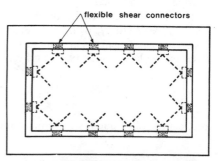

Fig. 11.29 Flexible shear wall with flexible shear connectors

in which

$$\frac{c}{l_w} = \frac{q + \alpha}{2q + 0.85\beta_1} \qquad q = \frac{A_s f_y}{l_w t f_c'}$$

$$\alpha = \frac{N_u}{l_w t f_c'} \qquad \beta = \frac{f_y}{E_s \epsilon_u}$$

and M_u = design resisting moment at section; A_s = total area of vertical reinforcement at section; f_y = specified yield strength of shear wall; c = distance from extreme compression fiber to neutral axis; t = thickness of shear wall; N_u = design axial load, positive if compression; f_c' = specified compressive strength of concrete; E_s = modulus of elasticity of steel; ϵ_u = limiting concrete compression strain; l_w = horizontal length of wall; β_1 = 0.85 for strength f_c' up to 28 MPa (4000 psi) and reduced continuously at a rate of 0.05 for each 7.0 MPa (1000 psi) of strength in excess of 28 MPa (4000 psi).

Test results of Portland Cement Association's investigation (Cardenas et al., 1973; Cardenas and Magura 1973; Barda et al., 1973) show that Eq. 11.44 or Eq. 11.45 can satisfactorily predict the flexural strength of shear walls with the span to height ratio l_w/h_w equal to or smaller than 1.0, if specified minimum horizontal reinforcement ρ_h = 0.0025 is provided.

The minimum shear strength is very important in order to design frameless shear walls to fail in flexure, rather than in shear.

In the design provisions, nominal shear stress is used as a measure of shear strength. Nominal unit shear stress is

$$\tau = \frac{V_{dt}}{\phi t d} \qquad (11.46)$$

in which V_{dt} = total applied design shear force on the horizontal section of the shear wall; ϕ = capacity reduction factor (ϕ = 0.85); d = distance from extreme compression fiber to resultant of tension force; and τ = nominal unit shear stress.

The design provisions of the ACI Code (1971) consider that ultimate nominal unit shear stress τ_u is made up of two parts. A portion of the shear is carried by the concrete while the remainder is carried by reinforcement, that is

$$\tau_u = \tau_c + \tau_s \qquad (11.47)$$

in which τ_c = nominal unit shear stress carried by the concrete, and τ_s = nominal unit shear stress carried by the reinforcement. However, τ_u should never exceed $0.831\sqrt{f_c'}$ MPa ($10\sqrt{f_c'}$ psi); and preferably not more than $0.50\sqrt{f_c'}$ MPa ($6\sqrt{f_c'}$ psi) if stress reversals can occur. The nominal shear stress τ_c carried by the concrete is given by the lesser value of τ_{c1} and τ_{c2}; that is, expressed in megapascals

$$\tau_{c1} = 0.27\sqrt{f_c'} + \frac{N_u}{4l_w t} \qquad (11.48a)$$

and, expressed in pounds per square inch

$$\tau_{c1} = 3.3\sqrt{f_c'} + \frac{N_u}{4l_w t} \qquad (11.48b)$$

Expressed in megapascals

$$\tau_{c2} = 0.050\sqrt{f'_c} + \frac{l_w\left[0.104\sqrt{f'_c} + 0.2\left(\dfrac{N_u}{l_w t}\right)\right]}{\dfrac{M_u}{V_{dt}} - \dfrac{l_w}{2}} \qquad (11.49a)$$

and, expressed in pounds per square inch

$$\tau_{c2} = 0.6\sqrt{f'_c} + \frac{l_w\left[1.25\sqrt{f'_c} + 0.2\left(\dfrac{N_u}{l_w t}\right)\right]}{\dfrac{M_u}{V_{dt}} - \dfrac{l_w}{2}} \qquad (11.49b)$$

in which τ_{c1} = nominal unit shear stress expected to cause inclined web-shear crack, and τ_{c2} = nominal unit shear stress expected to cause inclined flexure-shear crack. The flexure-shear cracks seldom occur in the framed shear walls. They mainly occur in the frameless shear walls. If N_u is zero or compression, the value of τ_{c1} or τ_{c2} need not be assigned a value less than $0.166\sqrt{f'_c}$ MPa ($2\sqrt{f'_c}$ psi) for reinforced concrete beams.

Based on "truss analogy," τ_s is computed by

$$\tau_s = \rho_h f_y \qquad (11.50)$$

in which $\rho_h = A_v/st$ = ratio of horizontal shear reinforcement; s = spacing of horizontal reinforcement in a wall; and A_v = area of shear reinforcement within distance s.

In order to prevent sudden failure, minimum shear reinforcement is provided. The specified minimum reinforcement, $\rho_h = 0.0025$, provides a shear stress contribution of about $0.166\sqrt{f'_c}$ MPa ($2\sqrt{f'_c}$ psi) to the strength of the shear wall. To develop shear strength computed by Eq. 11.50, the amount of vertical reinforcement shall be equal to the amount of horizontal reinforcement when the span to height ratio, l_w/h_w, is greater than 2.0. When l_w/h_w is less than 0.4, the required minimum vertical reinforcement area is 0.0025. When l_w/h_w is between 0.5 and 2.5, the required minimum vertical reinforcement is determined by

$$\rho_g = 0.0025 + 0.5[2.5 - (l_w/h_w)^{-1}](\rho_h - 0.0025) \qquad (11.51)$$

The shear capacity of shear walls containing minimum shear reinforcement is plotted in Fig. 11.30.

The proposed design provisions for shear strength of shear walls have been compared with the experimental results from Japan (Muto and Kokusho, 1953; Ogura et al., 1952) and America (Cardenas et al., 1973; Williams and Benjamin, 1952) in Fig. 11.31. Comparison of measured and calculated strengths indicates that the design provisions are satisfactory.

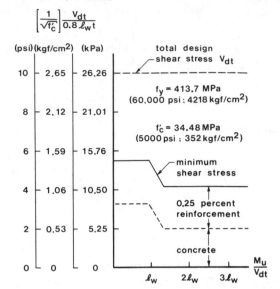

Fig. 11.30 Minimum shear strength of rectangular shear walls

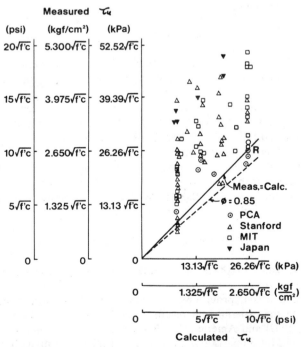

Fig. 11.31 Comparison of measured and calculated strength

Studies of tests on frameless shear walls, loaded axially to a stress of 1.97 MPa (285 psi) and subjected to cyclic shear forces, have shown that ductile flexural failure can be assured for any span ratio, provided the mean unit shear stress in the ultimate state is less than 2.41 MPa (350 psi) and the horizontal reinforcement ratio is 0.012.

In New Zealand, square shaped shear walls have been tested under reversed cyclic static loading, which was distributed along the top edge of the wall. According to the report (Paulay, 1974), it is suggested that the nominal unit shear stress must be less than $0.415 \sqrt{f_c'}$ MPa ($5 \sqrt{f_c'}$ psi), if a ductile flexure mechanism is desired in a low-rise shear wall. See also Section 6.8 of Chapter CB-6.

Frameless shear walls are often used as "coupled shear walls," where the connecting beams or slabs are weaker than the walls. Based on the report of Paulay (1974) the mean unit shear stress should be less than $0.415 \sqrt{f_c'}$ MPa ($5 \sqrt{f_c'}$ psi) if ductility in such conventionally reinforced coupling beams is desired under cyclic reversed loading. This is discussed extensively in Chapter CB-6 and design recommendations are given there.

Details of frameless shear walls require careful attention. Additional information may be sought in Galletly (1952) and Paulay (1969, 1973).

Needed Research. In the Japanese Code, the influence of bending is not considered in the computation of allowable horizontal shear force (see Eq. 11.26 and Eq. 11.27). In America, the influence of shear is not considered in the computation of flexural strength (see Eq. 11.44 and Eq. 11.45).

Further experimental and analytical studies are needed to clarify the shear-moment interaction relationships.

Nearly one thousand shear-wall specimens have been tested, but few experimental tests have been made under many cyclic reversed loadings or dynamic loading (Yamada et al., 1974a, 1974b; Shiga et al., 1971–1974). Experimental tests under cyclic reversed loading or dynamic loading are needed to clarify the influence of many factors on the following items:

1. The restraining action of the boundary frame on the expansion of the cracked infilled wall panel.

2. The mechanism of the failure.

3. The absorbed strain energy after cracking.

4. The ductility after cracking.

5. The ultimate shear force on the horizontal section.

The relevant factors are the shape (the span-height ratio, the cross sections of the columns and beams of the boundary frame, the thickness of the infilled wall panel, and openings in the infilled wall panel), reinforcement (the main reinforcement in the boundary frame, the hoops in the boundary frame, and the wall reinforcement), and devices (such as slits in the infilled wall panel, embedded steel braces, and flexible shear connectors between the boundary frame and the infilled wall panel).

These studies must be made not only for single-story shear walls, but also for multistory shear walls.

3   Three-Dimensional Shear Cores

This section deals with the problem of designing reinforced concrete cores of arbitrary cross section (Fig. 11.32).

An exact solution of this problem would imply the analysis of a folded plate of arbitrary cross section, which might be studied by a finite-element technique (see Chapter CB-5). In usual cases, however, a cantilever beam approach could serve the purpose.

It is assumed that a structural (elastic) analysis has been conducted and from it the action effects (stress resultants) are known at a number of horizontal cross sections of the core. These action effects are the axial force N, the bending moments M_x, M_y, the shear forces V_x, V_y and the torsional moment T (Fig. 11.33).

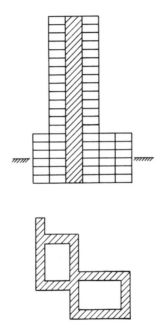

Fig. 11.32 Reinforced concrete core of arbitrary cross section

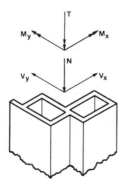

Fig. 11.33 Action effects

The problem is to design the reinforcement of the core. Usually the reinforcement required is studied at a number of cross sections, and from this the reinforcement of the core is selected. One must be aware of the fact that in many cases the reinforcement does not depend on the action effects, but rather on the minima required by construction conditions, cracking conditions, etc. In other cases, however, the resulting reinforcement may be excessive and an increase in the dimensions of the cross section might be convenient. In such cases a new structural analysis is usually required.

Design of Longitudinal Reinforcement for Bending and Compression. Normal action effects N, M_x, M_y are the resultants of normal stresses σ and require a certain amount of longitudinal reinforcement, which is designed independently of the other action effects.

It is assumed that the bending moments M_x, M_y already take into account second-order effects and supplementary eccentricities due to slenderness, if such exist.

Usually consideration is given to a number of cross sections at different heights, and for each different loading case, that is, sets of values N, M_x, M_y, without being able to foresee which one will be critical for the cross section.

A good solution is to select a number of possible distributions for the longitudinal reinforcement (A through H, Fig. 11.34), and to define the interaction surface for each of these distributions (Fig. 11.35). These interaction surfaces are conveniently represented, for design purposes, by their equal-load contours. A computer program making use of an automatic plotter is a logical way to draw such sets of contours. Representative interaction diagrams of this type are given in Section 6.4 of Chapter CB-6.

Design of Transverse Reinforcement for Shear. Transverse reinforcement is provided by closed horizontal stirrups in each of the individual walls constituting the core (Fig. 11.37). Transverse reinforcement area per unit height, A_t/s, is obtained in each individual wall by adding together the reinforcement required to resist shear in the x and y directions (V_x and V_y), and the reinforcement required to resist torsional moment, T.

To obtain the reinforcement required by shear at each individual wall, select the wall section X-X at which the maximum shear flow occurs (see Fig. 11.36). Then estimate the shear flow distribution between the different webs A, B, C of the cross

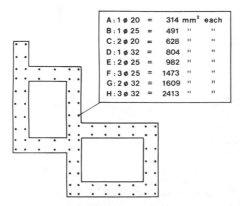

A : 1 ∅ 20	=	314 mm²	each
B : 1 ∅ 25	=	491 "	"
C : 2 ∅ 20	=	628 "	"
D : 1 ∅ 32	=	804 "	"
E : 2 ∅ 25	=	982 "	"
F : 3 ∅ 25	=	1473 "	"
G : 2 ∅ 32	=	1609 "	"
H : 3 ∅ 32	=	2413 "	"

Fig. 11.34 Possible solutions for longitudinal reinforcement

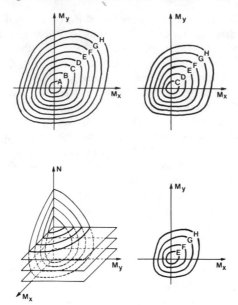

Fig. 11.35 Interaction surfaces

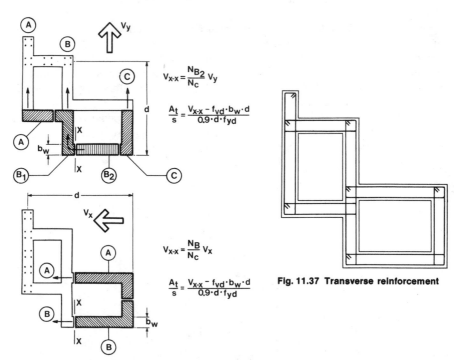

$$V_{x\text{-}x} = \frac{N_{B2}}{N_c} V_y$$

$$\frac{A_t}{s} = \frac{V_{x\text{-}x} - f_{vd}\cdot b_w\cdot d}{0.9\cdot d\cdot f_{yd}}$$

$$V_{x\text{-}x} = \frac{N_B}{N_c} V_x$$

$$\frac{A_t}{s} = \frac{V_{x\text{-}x} - f_{vd}\cdot b_w\cdot d}{0.9\cdot d\cdot f_{yd}}$$

Fig. 11.36 Design for shear

Fig. 11.37 Transverse reinforcement

section, and the shear flow at section X-X, $V_{X\text{-}X}$, as a percentage of total shear V_x or V_y. The shear flow percentages can be assumed to be equal to the ratios of the partial concrete stress-resultants N_A, N_B, N_C to the total concrete stress-resultant N_c. Once $V_{X\text{-}X}$ has been obtained, subtract from it the part resisted by the concrete, $f_{vd}b_w d$, which depends on the design value of the concrete shear strength, f_{vd}. The transverse reinforcement area A_t/s is obtained dividing the result by $0.9 f_{yd} d$, in which f_{yd} is the design value of the steel strength.

Design of Longitudinal and Transverse Reinforcement for Torsion. To resist a torsional moment, T, longitudinal and transverse reinforcement is required. The longitudinal reinforcement, A_1, must be added to the reinforcement required for bending and compression, and must be uniformly distributed over the perimeter of the cross section, u (Fig. 11.38). The transverse reinforcement per unit height, A_t/s, must also be added to the shear reinforcement at each wall of the cross section.

To compute these reinforcements, consider the equivalent hollow section (Fig. 11.38), taken halfway through the walls, whose area is A_o and whose perimeter is u.

If the torsion and shear forces are important, a check of the diagonal compressive stress in the concrete might be necessary.

Openings in Walls. Cores usually have openings in the walls, which can significantly reduce their cross section. In the case of openings of little importance in tension zones, the foregoing design procedure can be maintained, by providing supplementary bars near the borders of the opening with a cross section equivalent to the interrupted bars' cross section. A full, folded plate analysis might be necessary. Whether the opening shall be included in the analysis or not, and the degree to which the design procedure is correct, must be decided in each case.

The coupling beams between the openings transmit large shears. The design of such beams is discussed in Chapters CB-6 and CB-9.

4 Tension Supports (Roof-Hung Structures)

Tension supports have to carry only direct stresses apart from secondary bending effects. They have to be designed against yield of the tension material with an appropriate factor of safety. In addition, the design is governed by serviceability

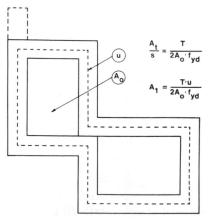

$$\frac{A_t}{s} = \frac{T}{2A_o \cdot f_{yd}}$$

$$A_1 = \frac{T \cdot u}{2A_o \cdot f_{yd}}$$

Fig. 11.38 Design for torsion

and durability criteria. Differences in the deformations of the tension supports and the stiffening core cause an inclination of the floor slabs, which must be limited in respect to cracking of partition walls. These differences result from: (1) Deformation of top supporting structure; (2) elastic and plastic (creep, shrinkage) strains of the core; and (3) strains of the tension supports.

The deformation differences caused by the dead load and the location of their maximum depend upon the construction sequence. Those caused by live load add up from top to bottom.

For tension supports steel or post-tensioned concrete members may be used. Post-tensioned concrete tension members may often be prestressed in stages to control the deformation of these members as additional loads are transferred to them. Steel tension supports are advantageously assembled from flat bars (flats), and connected with high-strength bolts. Thus changes in cross section corresponding to the loading are easily possible. Normally the design is governed by the joints. This results in an overdesign of a standard cross section, which is beneficial with regard to the deformation behavior.

For fire safety a special protective cover is necessary. To minimize the size of the cover, it may be useful to place the joints within the floor slabs.

The possible building heights are limited by the deformation differences due to live loads. The use of high-strength material in steel tension supports is less desirable, as high stress levels result in higher deformations.

For post-tensioned supports, the use of high-strength steel giving a considerable reduction of the necessary steel cross section is recommended. Though the deformations are small, as the steel and the concrete act together, it seems to be necessary to provide full post-tensioning considering primary loads.

The number of post-tensioning bars may be increased story by story. After construction of a floor the corresponding bars are post-tensioned. This results in a gradually increasing post-tensioning stress level, corresponding to the storywise load increase for the stories above. Very high stresses (referenced to concrete cross section) are obtained, which are much higher than those for nonslender compression members. The prestressing bars should be arranged concentrically to avoid an eccentric prestressing force.

The tension supports should be loaded concentrically and free of secondary stresses by the floor system. Rubber pad bearings between floor slab and the tension support have been succesfully used. If secondary stresses due to bending are unavoidable in the tension supports, the use of nonprestressed reinforcement for crack distribution may be necessary.

In summary, it may be pointed out that post-tensioned supports have a superior deformation behavior compared to that of steel tension supports; only the former may be used for very tall buildings. In addition, protection against corrosion and fire is guaranteed by the concrete.

The design and construction of a building with post-tensioned support trusses and post-tensioned support walls is described by Bliss and Herrera (1965).

5   Retaining Walls

Types of Walls and Stability.   In connection with tall buildings, retaining walls will generally be basement walls, often extending several stories below grade level. Design problems associated with such walls differ from those normally encountered for retaining walls which are not an integral part of a building, such as gravity walls, cantilever walls, and counterfort or buttress walls.

When dealing with the latter category, special attention must be paid to stability, overturning, and sliding of the walls.

In the former category, retaining walls in buildings, which are generally found in the basements, the instability problem either disappears, since the walls have support at the floor slabs, or the problem pertains to the building as a whole, as in the case of building basements dug into a slope.

Loads on Walls.   Because of the characteristics of basement walls of this type, they are generally subjected to bending and axial load. Bending is produced by the earth pressure, and the axial load by the part of the vertical load transmitted by the floor slabs.

Usually the walls have a considerable stiffness and can neither rotate nor move laterally. Therefore the design earth pressure must be greater than the active

Hato Rey Plaza condominium, San Juan, Puerto Rico. Architects and Engineers: Capacete, Martin & Associates (Courtesy: I. Martin)

pressure. In fact, it has been a common practice in these cases to use a pressure at least 20% greater than the active pressure.

Particular attention should also be given to the additional effects that may be caused by earthquakes. It has been established that the horizontal forces induced are obtained by the mass in the "Coulomb's Wedge" multiplied by the accelerations of the earthquake. The resulting dynamic pressure of the displaced soil is located at approximately 2/3 of the height of the wall from its base.

Design. In its final condition the wall will be subjected to both bending and axial load. The standard requirements for design of elements with this type of load combination must be met.

In the process of constructing basement walls, unfavorable loading conditions, different from the final conditions, may temporarily be obtained, as, for example, temporary loads from excavation bracing, or when backfill is placed and compacted before the full axial dead load is present.

A good protection against water infiltration may be obtained by tough, sealed membranes applied to the outside of the walls, and protected against puncture damage from the backfilling operation by pargeting. So-called "integral water-proofing" cannot be effective unless honeycombs and cracks in the concrete can be eliminated.

11.4 CONNECTIONS

The design of connections in reinforced concrete structures has generally been limited to satisfying anchorage requirements. With the increasing use of high-strength steels and concrete, large bar sizes and smaller sections, special attention must be given to connection details to assure the performance of the joint and to alleviate construction problems.

In a cast-in-place reinforced concrete structure, a large number of jointing situations may arise. Typical examples include the location in a structure where several members meet, where members change direction, or where changes in materials and geometry of members occur. This discussion will be limited to typical beam-column and slab-column connections. The beam-column connections may be planar or three-dimensional cases. The emphasis will be directed primarily toward moment-resisting connections, that is, connections subjected largely to flexural forces from the members meeting at the connection location. A typical beam-column connection is shown in Fig. 11.39 with the region of interest, the connection core, shaded.

In the United States, connections in most reinforced concrete buildings are not designed by the engineer, or they are designed, but not detailed, by the engineer. The general practice is for the structural engineer to design the member but to leave details, such as placement and layout of the reinforcement in both the members and the connection, to a detailer who may not understand the structural behavior intended by the designer. In many cases, placement of the reinforcement is not adequately considered and congestion of bars at the connection makes construction difficult. As a result, problems of congestion of reinforcement are alleviated by changes in bar placement on the job site. Since control of job-site practices is limited, such changes may impair the strength of the structure. Where seismic resistance is required, designers appear to spend more time detailing connections because of the importance of the connections to proper structural behavior under earthquake conditions. In some other countries all details must be designed and checked by an engineer (at least in New Zealand and most of Europe).

1 Types of Failures in Connections

To assess the problem of designing connections in cast-in-place reinforced concrete structures, it is essential to understand the reasons for failures in connections and the types of loading producing failure. Although a wide range of loadings could be considered, it is expected that in most tall buildings loadings generally will be either short-time overloads, possibly reversed due to lateral loadings, or sustained service loads. In seismic regions consideration must be given to reversal and repetition of overloads.

Beam-Column Connections. The forces acting on a typical beam-column connection are shown in Fig. 11.40. Depending on the location of the connection in the structure and the loading imposed, the beams would be likely to transfer shear and moment to the core, and the columns to transfer a combination of shear, bending, and axial load. If torsional moments are present in the beams or columns, or if beams frame into the connection in the transverse direction, the force diagram becomes more involved. It is relatively easy to determine the stress distribution resulting from member forces at any of the critical sections between the members and the core; however, within the core itself the states of stress are highly complex at failure. In planar or three-dimensional beam-column connections, failures are generally due to insufficient anchorage capacity, large shear forces in the connection core, or compressive failure of the concrete in the core.

Anchorage. Anchorage problems occur primarily at exterior connections. In this case (see Fig. 11.41) the beam moment must be developed by anchored bars. Because of the geometric limitations of the core, the anchorage usually consists of bent bars. If the development length from the face of the column is insufficient, the bar may pull out. Another possibility is that the hooked portion of the bar is placed

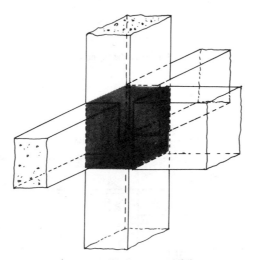

Fig. 11.39 Beam-column joint

too near the column face and the concrete at the face is pulled out with the bar. In any case, studies indicate that bent bar anchorages are less stiff than straight bar embedments and, even at low stress levels, bar slip at the column face will reduce the fixity at the end of the beam (Hribar and Vasko, 1969; Minor and Jirsa, 1971; Marques and Jirsa, 1972; Ismail and Jirsa, 1972). If repeated or reversed loads are imposed on the connection, there may be a gradual deterioration of bond, with a corresponding reduction in anchorage length as bond capacity is reduced at the face of the connection core (Bertero and Bresler, 1968; Ismail and Jirsa, 1972; Bertero and McClure, 1964).

In the case of interior connections, anchorage will generally not be a problem if beam bars are continuous through the connection core or are adequately spliced

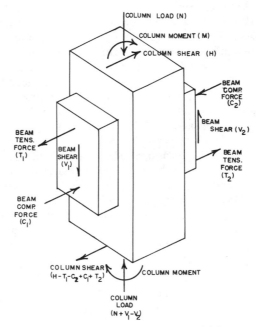

Fig. 11.40 Forces on beam-column joint

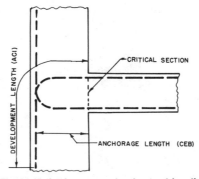

Fig. 11.41 Anchorage or development length

outside the core. Some problems may occur where the beams on opposite sides of the core are subjected to moments which produce tension on one side and compression on the other in the same bar. Under the high stress gradient developed, the application of several load reversals may destroy the interface between the bar and concrete, and the bar will be unable to transfer stress to the core. The designer should pay close attention to the anchorage requirements for post-tensioned tendons.

Shear. Perhaps the most difficult problem to be considered in designing a beam-column connection is shear in the connection core. The forces acting on the connection core produce a complex force and stress configuration. Resultant forces transmitted by the beams and columns to the connection core are shown in Fig. 11.42 considering a section through the core. The same pattern may exist in the orthogonal direction. In addition, the nature of stresses in the connection core is influenced by the manner in which stresses are transferred from the reinforcement to the concrete. Test results show that diagonal cracks are produced by the force couples acting on the core, and unless adequate transverse reinforcement is provided will lead to failure of the core (Hanson and Connor, 1967; Hanson, 1971; Corley and Hanson, 1969; Uzumeri and Seckin, 1974; Higashi and Ohwada, 1969; Park and Paulay, 1973).

Several approaches for determining the strength of the connection core have been proposed. One approach (Higashi and Ohwada, 1969) is to resolve the stresses into maximum principal values, using the tensile strength of the concrete to determine core strength. The concept of shear friction or the empirical equations for shear strength of deep beams (ACI, 1971) have been considered. However, none of these approaches appears to describe adequately the stress condition in the connection

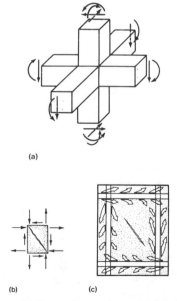

(a)

(b)   (c)

Fig. 11.42 Forces on joint core: (a) Forces in members at joint; (b) joint core; (c) transfer of forces within joint

core. At present, the use of equations derived to predict the shear force at diagonal tensile cracking appear to give the most reliable determination of the core strength (Corley and Hanson, 1969; Uzumeri and Seckin, 1974).

Compression. Compressive failures of the core concrete would be expected only in cases where the concrete in the core was of lower strength than the column above and below, or where lateral confinement in the form of ties or structural members framing in from the side is minimal (Bianchini et al., 1960). Combinations of moderate axial force and high moment in the core may also produce crushing along one side of the core.

Slab-Column Connections. The forces acting on a typical interior slab-column connection are shown in Fig. 11.43. In this case, bending moments in the slab produce bending on two opposite faces and torsion on the other two faces. The flexural and torsional forces combine with shear forces to produce failure. At exterior slab-column connections where spandrel beams are used, torsion may be predominant in producing failure. Therefore, in slab-column connections, the primary problem is one of providing sufficient shear capacity around the periphery of the support. As a result, flat plates and flat slabs present more difficulty than do other slab types. Exterior slab-column connections are subjected to torsional forces which may produce failure in the slab or in the spandrel beams.

Shear. Numerous tests have been conducted to determine the punching shear strength of slabs (ACI-ASCE, 1974). Tests of shearheads indicate that the shear strength is improved considerably with the addition of a structural shearhead in the presence of an unbalanced moment transferred to the column (Corley and Hawkins, 1968; Hanson and Hanson, 1968). Under these conditions, the shear force reduces the ductility of the section and produces punching failure under fairly low slab rotations. Therefore, ordinary flat plate structures should not be considered adequate for seismic resistant buildings, because of their low ductility unless shear walls or other lateral stiffening elements are incorporated into the design. In the

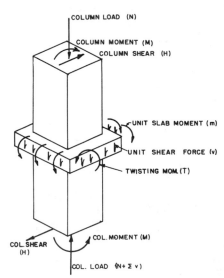

COLUMN LOAD (N)

COLUMN MOMENT (M)
COLUMN SHEAR (H)

UNIT SLAB MOMENT (m)

UNIT SHEAR FORCE (v)

TWISTING MOM. (T)

COL. SHEAR (H)

COL. MOMENT (M)

COL. LOAD (N+ Σ v)

Fig. 11.43 Forces on slab-column joint

case of slabs supported on rectangular columns, the shear will be concentrated toward the short sides of the column. For long thin columns or walls, a punching failure may occur at one edge without producing a general shear failure around the entire periphery of the column. A comprehensive report on the shear strength of slabs was presented by ACI-ASCE Committee 426 (1974).

Torsion. At exterior slab-column connections in flat plate and flat slab structures, torsion is the prevalent force producing failure. In the absence of spandrel beams the connection has low torsional strength. Torsional cracking may be quite severe under nominal overloads and very little moment is transferred to the exterior column with increasing loads on the slab. With spandrel beams the strength is improved somewhat. At exterior edges the mode of failure generally involves a flexural crack across the face of the column and torsional cracks in the beam (Jirsa et al., 1969). Tests indicate that it is virtually impossible and impractical to provide a spandrel beam of sufficient torsional strength to force the formation of a flexural yield-line at the slab beam interface, and nearly all failures involve torsion at the slab-beam-column connection (Jirsa, 1973).

Compression. Since certain economies may be realized by using low-strength concrete in floors, compressive failures may occur at the connection if the difference between floor and column concrete strengths is large and not considered in computing the axial load capacity of the columns (Bianchini et al., 1960).

Special Cases.

Knee joints. Where only two members join together, such as at corners of frames or where members change direction, the connections present special problems (Nilsson and Losberg, 1971; Mayfield et al., 1971, 1972; Taylor, 1974). The general mode of failure is tension in some portion of the connection which results in the outside surface of the connection being pushed off or the inside surface being pulled out. To prevent such failures, it is necessary to add supplementary reinforcement in the form of inclined bars or additional ties around the corner. Indications are that unreinforced fillets at the inside corner increase the strength of the connection.

Slab-to-wall or wall-to-footing connections. The main problem associated with slab-to-wall connections is the lack of thickness of the elements in which bars must be anchored. As a result the bar may tend to pull out of the element into which it is anchored and produce failure. This problem occurs where deep members frame into shear walls or thin columns. At present little research has been done on such connections.

2 Recommendations for Design

Design Philosophy. The underlying requirement of connection design is to provide a connection that will perform satisfactorily under the loading imposed on the structure. The connection must have sufficient strength to enable the strength of the members to be realized, and must maintain the integrity through the deformations imposed. In establishing design criteria for connections it is apparent that connections in all reinforced concrete buildings do not need to meet the same requirements. It is unrealistic to require the same performance of connections in a building designed according to strength design principles, where ductility is implied, as is required in a building subjected to seismic or blast loadings, where ductility requirements must be explicitly considered. It should be noted that the main difference in the effects of the loadings on the structure is in the deformations imposed on the members and on the connections. With large deformational requirements, as in blast or seismic loadings, the forces developed at the connections increase and, to maintain structural integrity, the connections must withstand the increase in force. It can be shown that in the presence of a moment gradient, increases in deformation can be achieved only if stresses are greater than yield (Wight and Sozen, 1973; ACI-ASCE, 1976).

The influence of deformation on the connection forces is illustrated in Fig. 11.44. A typical stress-strain curve for steel reinforcement is shown. As member deformation increases, steel strains also increase. If the steel has a well-defined yield point and only limited ductility is required, steel forces will remain at or near yield. Such a connection should perform satisfactorily if designed considering yield in the steel. However, with increased deformation and ductility requirements, steel stresses will be greater than yield as strains reach the strain-hardening region. Under these conditions, the forces at the connection must be based on stresses greater than f_y. To account for the increased stresses, it is necessary to specify design steel stresses that are greater than yield for connections subjected to certain loadings. The designer would be required to compute forces at the connection based on minimum stresses equal to Sf_y rather than f_y as is routine in most ultimate strength design procedures. The stress multiplier S would be based on severity of loading and type of reinforcement.

Classification of Types of Connections. As discussed previously, connections should be classified according to loading conditions imposed on the structure, and the stress multiplier varied accordingly. Thus, $S = 1.0$ for connections in continuous structures designed on the basis of strength without explicit consideration of ductility requirements. Stress multiplier $S = 1.25$ for connections required to dissipate energy through deformations into the inelastic range, such as might be imposed during any earthquake (SEAOC, 1973); and $S = 1.25$ to 1.8 for connections in structures where the energy dissipation through inelastic deformation

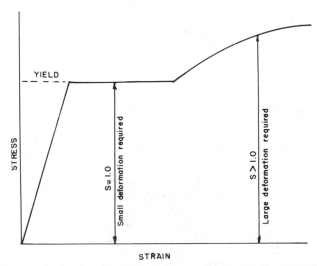

Fig. 11.44 Effect of strain or deformation on stresses (stress multiplier)

can be determined by the designer, and the associated stresses specified in a more rigorous manner. A typical example would be a connection in a structure designed for blast resistance.

Design Procedure. The design procedure listed below is intended to produce connections which develop the forces transferred from the members and retain structural integrity over the range of deformation imposed by the member.

1. Determine the forces at connections based on conventional analysis considering appropriate loading conditions. Such an analysis should include the effects of creep, shrinkage, temperature, and settlement. The forces to be carried by the connection should be taken from the calculations for the members being connected, selecting the combinations of bending, axial force, torsion, or shear which produce the maximum forces.

2. Proportion the members using conventional ultimate strength design considerations in accordance with standard codes, such as ACI 318-71 (ACI, 1971).

3. Compute the forces representing the reinforcement at the core-member interface using Sf_y. For some connections, the design forces on the connection will be greater than those used to design the members.

4. Using the bar stresses Sf_y, the development or anchorage lengths for the bars can be determined. The compressive and shear stresses in the concrete produced by the elevated bar stresses Sf_y should be compared with allowable values, and lateral reinforcement provided to develop the required capacity, or the cross section modified to reduce the stresses within allowable values.

Discussion of Design Procedure. Since research data are lacking with regard to the quantitative evaluation of connection behavior under many types of loading, beam-column connections must be designed according to provisions of current codes. In the following discussion the provisions of ACI 318-71 (ACI, 1971) will be used (see also PCI, 1973).

The strength of the members and the connection core are determined using the appropriate capacity reduction factors ϕ, and modifying where necessary to include the stress multiplier concept. For example, anchorage requirements are specified in Chapter 12 of the ACI Code. For connections the development length is controlled not by f_y but by Sf_y. Compressive stresses in the core may be increased by approximately 30% if confinement is provided by members framing into the connection on all four sides of the core, and the members are at least three-fourths the width of the core at the core-member interface (Corley and Hanson, 1969; ACI-ASCE, 1976).

It is important that the connection be adequately reinforced for shear in the core. The stresses in the core are determined from forces acting on the free body of the core with the forces at the critical sections determined using the stress multiplier. The critical sections for beam-column connections are generally the interfaces between the connection core and the members. As indicated in Fig. 11.42, the force couple transferred from the member to the core produces a shear force that is approximately equal to the steel tensile force in the member (area of steel multiplied by Sf_y). Allowable concrete shear stresses and reinforcing requirements may be computed using the provisions of Chapter 11 of the ACI Code. However, for all connection types a minimum amount of confining reinforcement should be provided in the core. The specifications of Section A6.4 to A6.6 of the ACI Code provide guidance in determining confinement requirements. The minimum spacing of spirals or hoops may be increased where reversed loading cycles are not anticipated. Some change in anchorage length and shear reinforcement requirements is to be expected as experimental data become available on which design recommendations can be based. In many cases the requirements for shear and anchorage will control the proportions of the connection, and, as a consequence, the proportions of the members (especially columns) framing into the connection.

The general requirements discussed for beam-column connections are applicable to slab-column connections; however, flat plate and flat slab construction does not appear to be adequate for seismic requirements unless lateral forces are carried by shear walls, or other stiffening requirements are carefully considered. The problem is alleviated somewhat if spandrel beams or shearheads are used. In the case of spandrel beams it is essential that the spandrel be reinforced to provide torsional capacity equal to or greater than the design exterior slab moment. Such reinforcement consists of both longitudinal reinforcement and closed ties. The longitudinal reinforcement must be anchored in the column to prevent premature torsional failure at the core-spandrel beam interface. In slab-column connections, where shear strength is critical, structural steel shearheads may be used.

3 Detailing Practice

The single most important factor regarding good practice is that details be worked out by the structural engineer and not relegated to subprofessional personnel. In designing the connection the structural performance of the connection must be considered and the resulting details should be reviewed to alleviate difficulties in construction and concrete placement resulting from congestion of reinforcement. This detailing process may necessitate the use of scale drawings to determine placement of bars in the connection. The detailing of connections is discussed by Somerville and Taylor (1972), Balint and Taylor (1972), Taylor and Clark (1976), and Park and Paulay (1973).

In detailing the connection it may become necessary to change the locations of bars to provide sufficient clearance. If the bar location is changed, a check should be made to determine whether the capacity as previously determined has been changed. Strength calculations should be based on actual dimensions and not on a preliminary bar layout. Detailing requirements are shown in Fig. 11.45.

To aid in construction, split ties may be used where strength only is required if sufficient length is provided to develop the tie strength. In connections where the concrete cover may spall under severe loading conditions and ductility is required, closed ties must be provided in both beams and columns. Intermediate tie legs may be used if the hooks are adequate to develop tie strength. Closed ties are also required in beams and columns if the members are subjected to torsional forces.

Where hooks are required to develop anchorage strength, the hook should be a 90° bend with straight extension past the bend. Research results indicate that 90° hooks are stiffer (slip less) than 180° hooks (Minor and Jirsa, 1971; Marques and Jirsa, 1972; Hribar and Vasko, 1969). The hook should always be placed within the portion of the core confined by lateral reinforcement. In addition, the hook should be placed as far as possible from the core-member interface at which maximum forces in the bar will be developed. Where members frame into the core and reinforcement in the member is not needed for strength, the bars should extend into the core at least 150 mm (6 in.) past the interface, as shown in Fig. 11.45. An example is the bottom reinforcement in a beam framing into a column.

4 Research Needs

It is apparent that additional research in a number of areas will need to be conducted before quantitative design specifications for all types of connections can be developed. The major areas of research need include:

1. Anchorage and development length requirements of deformed bars under various loading conditions and degrees of confinement. The influence of hook geometry, column axial load, concrete side cover, and tie spacing should be considered. Included here are the problems of deep beams framing into shear walls or other relatively thin supports.

2. Shear strength of the connection core. Nearly all present shear strength equations are for beam-type members. Tests should be conducted to determine shear strength of the core considering the influence of column axial load, percentage of column reinforcement, influence of confinement due to rectangular ties and cross ties or spirals and lateral members framing into the connection, type of anchorage from members framing into the core, and biaxial forces producing shear in both directions.

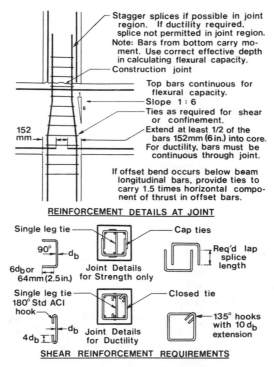

Fig. 11.45 Detailing requirements

3. Shear strength of slab-column connections. Tests have been conducted but more are needed to develop reinforcing details that will provide both strength and ductility at these connections.

5 Summary

Recommendations for designing connections for different loading conditions have been discussed. Prime consideration was given to moment-resisting beam-column and slab-column connections. To provide some understanding of the behavior of connections a brief review of different types of failures was presented. In beam-column connections failures are generally produced by deficiencies in anchorage or shear strength. In slab-column connections, shear or torsion are largely responsible for failure.

Design recommendations for connections in cast-in-place reinforced concrete structures were discussed. The design requirements vary according to the type of loading on the structure, which determines the deformation requirements of the members framing into the connection. Once the deformation requirements are established, forces to be carried at the connection can be estimated, and the connection designed accordingly.

Finally, the factors constituting good detailing practice for cast-in-place connections were discussed. Consideration was given to practices that will assure strength and at the same time minimize construction and bar placement difficulties.

11.5 FOUNDATIONS

1 Shallow Foundations

In shallow foundations the load transfer is mostly by end bearing and occurs close to the ground surface. Such foundations can be divided into spread footings, which support isolated loads of a structure (Figs. 11.46 and 11.47), and mat or raft foundations, which receive the loads of all columns and walls of a building.

Although it is a well-known fact that the stress distribution under a footing is not linear (Fig. 11.48), it is generally assumed, for practical reasons, that it is so.

Centrally Loaded Spread Footings. Centrally loaded spread footings may be wall footings (Fig. 11.49) essentially with one-way action, or column footings with two-way action (Fig. 11.50). In either case the footing may fail in shear, flexure, or bond.

Shear is checked at distance $d/2$ from the face of the wall or column. The maximum bending moment and bond stress occur at the face of the wall or column. Bond strength is an important factor in footing behavior which can generally be controlled by using small-diameter bars.

Eccentrically Loaded Spread Footings. Design generally follows the procedure outlined for centrally loaded footings, taking into account that the soil stress distribution is not uniform but varies linearly across the footing, and no tension stresses can develop at the contact face. The stress distribution is calculated from

$$\sigma_g = \frac{N}{A_f} \pm \frac{M}{R} \tag{11.52}$$

in which N = normal load; M = moment; and A_f and R = area and section modulus of the contact face, respectively.

For perimeter footings structural features are introduced to prevent column and footing rotation. Usually a uniform stress distribution is assumed but any other, more appropriate one, may be adopted.

One method to inhibit footing rotation is to provide a column of sufficient rigidity. This solution is applicable only to foundations on soils with a small modulus of deformation relative to the rigidity of the column. The column must be

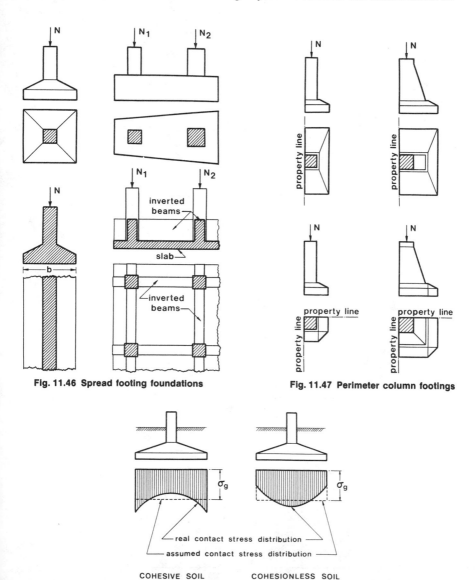

Fig. 11.46 Spread footing foundations

Fig. 11.47 Perimeter column footings

Fig. 11.48 Real and assumed distribution of contact stress reaction in cohesive and cohesionless soils

enlarged to absorb with only small deformations the moment Ne (Fig. 11.51). This moment is balanced by the moment resulting from the frictional force which develops at the contact face

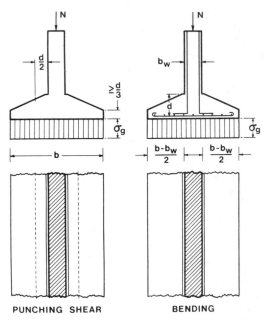

PUNCHING SHEAR   BENDING

Fig. 11.49 Centrally loaded one-way continuous footing

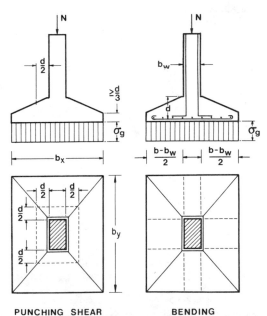

PUNCHING SHEAR   BENDING

Fig. 11.50 Centrally loaded rectangular footing

$$N \times e = \frac{F \times h \times \zeta}{\gamma_g} \qquad (11.53)$$

For cohesive soils the adhesion may also be considered. It is advisable to assume that only half of the adhesion is effective, because the water absorption from the wet concrete frequently softens a thin layer of the soil at the contact face. Substituting for F, including the adhesion, and rearranging Eq. 11.53 results in

$$\frac{N \times \tan\phi + C_a \times b_x \times b_y}{\gamma_g} \geq \frac{N \times e_{max}}{h \times \zeta} \qquad (11.54)$$

in which $F = N \times \tan\phi$, and ϕ may be taken as the angle of internal friction; for articulated columns $\zeta = 1$, while for a fixed end column $\zeta = 2/3$ (for partial fixity the value is somewhere between); γ_g is the factor of safety, at least 1.5; and e_{max} the maximum permissible eccentricity.

Thus, once the footing size has been selected for the appropriate stress distribution, e is determined, corresponding to this distribution with $e \leq e_{max}$. The footing design follows and finally the redesign of the column, taking into account the moment induced by the footing reaction.

Another method by which footing rotation can be controlled is to join the column to an adjacent one with a rigid beam (Fig. 11.52). The size of the footing, which acts one way because of the beam, is generally determined by assuming a uniform stress distribution.

Combined Footing. Combined footings support the load of two or more columns. Whether with or without linked beams (Fig. 11.46), they are assumed rigid. The contact stress distribution is uniform or linearly varying, and the design follows ideas outlined for centrally loaded footings.

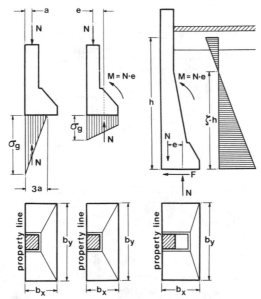

Fig. 11.51 Perimeter column footings with enlarged column

Footings on Elastic Foundations. In a flexible footing the contact stress distribution derives not only from its displacement and rotation as a rigid unit, but also from its bending deflection.

The theory of beams on elastic foundation, based on the assumption that the soil reaction of each point is proportional to the vertical displacement of the contact face at that point, is used to solve this problem. Solutions have been obtained for many practical cases for the well-known differential equation

$$\frac{EI}{b}\frac{d^4y}{dx^4} = -ky \tag{11.55}$$

in which k = modulus of subgrade reaction; y = deflection; b = width; EI = stiffness; and x = coordinate parallel to the length of the footing (Timoshenko, 1965; Hetenyi, 1946).

Although the theory is currently the most elaborate procedure available for the design of flexible footings it does have several drawbacks. There is no proportionality between deflection and ground reaction, and the value of k depends also upon stress level, load repetitions and duration of load. Furthermore, it is influenced by footing size and shape. Finally, it is difficult and costly to determine (Terzaghi, 1955).

The solutions obtained by this theory should only be used as guidance unless the coefficient has been determined with confidence. Real soil distributions will lie between two extremes which are easy to define (Fig. 11.53). The design should cover the maximum possible moment and shear envelopes located within those resulting from the two mentioned extreme stress distributions.

Mat Foundations. A mat or raft carries all columns or walls of a building and

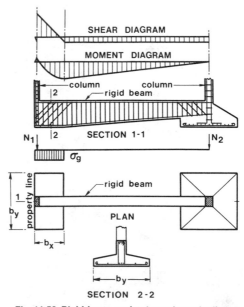

Fig. 11.52 Rigid beam perimeter column footing

consists of a single thick slab, with or without base enlargements, or the columns may be joined by beams which receive the ground reaction through the slab.

Although it is well known that the ground stress distribution under a rigid foundation is nonlinear (Fig. 11.48), mat design is generally based on a uniform or linearly varying stress distribution, as it is usually possible to make the mat sufficiently stiff to justify this assumption. For purely cohesive soils the errors in moments and shears are less than 20% and well within the provisions of the factor of safety, because no material under a footing behaves purely cohesively. For cohesionless soils the error due to the difference in the stress distribution is on the safe side.

The structural design of a mat follows the same procedure as a building floor. The ground reaction provides the distributed load, and the columns act as supports.

For a flexible mat foundation the stress distribution at the contact face is also a function of the deflection of the mat itself. A two-dimensional theory has been developed but it involves all the difficulties pointed out for beams on elastic foundations.

2 Deep Foundations

Deep foundations are divided into small-diameter or large-diameter piles and caissons. A pile is defined here as a solid or hollow structural element with a slenderness ratio larger than 10. Whether installed by driving or filling an excavation with concrete, provisions are generally made to assure good contact between the lateral surface of the pile and the surrounding soil.

Caissons are hollow with any cross section and a slenderness ratio less than 10. A caisson is excavated inside and under the edges, and sinks into the ground by its own weight or with the aid of additional dead weight.

Small-Diameter Piles. Precast or cast-in-place, small-diameter piles have a lateral dimension of 600 mm (23-5/8 in.) or less. After installation they are considered short columns because of the confining effect of the surrounding soil (even when buried in soft soil); however, they are weak in bending and must also be designed for handling stresses that occur prior to driving. The lateral loads should

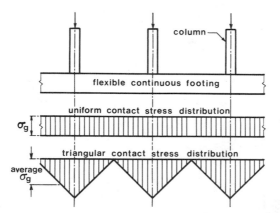

Fig. 11.53 Two extreme ground reactions for long rectangular footing carrying equally loaded columns

not exceed 1000 kg to 2000 kg (2205 lb to 4410 lb) depending on pile size. As a first approximation the load may be taken as (Moretto, 1971), for square piles

$$H(\text{kg}) = \frac{b^2}{100 \ (\text{mm}^2)} \tag{11.56a}$$

and for circular piles

$$H(\text{kg}) = \frac{(0.8b)^2}{100 \ (\text{mm}^2)} \tag{11.56b}$$

in which b = length of the side of a square pile or the diameter of a circular one. If a pile group is fully alined, bracing should be provided to give lateral stability to it.

Usually at least two piles are required to support a column. The piles are joined with a cap which serves as a link between columns and piles. The design of the cap should consider the displacement which may occur during driving. In a good installation the distance from the theoretical location usually does not exceed 100 mm (4 in.). The cap may fail by bending, splitting, or bond and is generally designed as a deep beam (Fig. 11.54), assuming a uniform load distribution over all piles for a centrally applied load. For three piles placed in an equilateral triangle pattern the maximum moments develop along the medians and the cap is reinforced parallel to them (Fig. 11.55). The same line of thought is followed for the design of caps with four or more piles (Moretto, 1970).

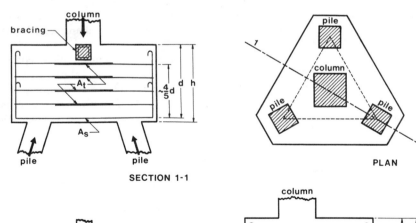

SECTION 1-1

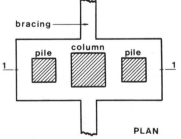

PLAN

Fig. 11.54 Pile cap for two piles

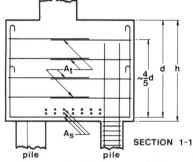

SECTION 1-1

Fig. 11.55 Pile cap for three piles

For an eccentrically loaded pile cap which allows only rotation and no deflection, the load per pile varies and is determined from

$$P = \frac{N}{n} \pm N \times e_y \times \frac{y}{\Sigma y^2} \pm N \times e_x \times \frac{x}{\Sigma x^2} \qquad (11.57)$$

in which n = number of piles and the other terms are defined in Fig. 11.56. The design of the cap follows the ideas outlined earlier.

For piles at the perimeter of the building along a property line a situation similar to the one for spread footings arises, as shown in Fig. 11.57. The design is essentially identical to this previous case.

The design of flexible pile caps requires an assessment of the deformation of the piles under load. The cap is assumed to be supported on elastic columns and a solution is obtained for the distribution of pile loading. The problem with this approach is that the settlements under load vary erratically from pile to pile. Consequently a flexible pile cap should be designed for all possible and reasonable pile load distributions.

Large-Diameter Piles.   Large-diameter piles, also called caissons in some locations, are always placed vertically. They can carry not only large normal load, but also substantial horizontal and eccentric loads. Because of their size and the relative precision with which they can be placed, it is possible to use one pile per column. Bracing in two nonalined directions is required.

Pile caps are placed for load transfer between columns and piles. Everything that was said for small-diameter pile caps is applicable here.

Caissons.   Typical caissons are used in building construction only where deep

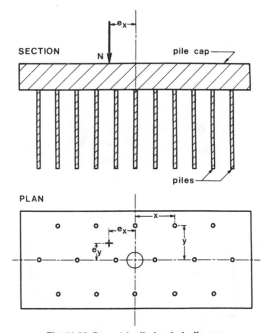

Fig. 11.56 Eccentrically loaded pile cap

basements are required in soft soils, and the caisson itself takes the place of the temporary and permanent bracing of the excavation. On reaching the final level the caisson is closed at the bottom with a concrete floor.

Because a caisson is always a rigid structure, the ground reaction may be taken as uniform for a centrally loaded caisson, or linearly varying for an eccentrically loaded one.

While a caisson is lowered into the ground it may be subjected to nonuniform lateral pressures by the surrounding soil. The distribution of this pressure depends upon the soil properties, and any deviation of the caisson from the vertical, which cannot be predicted. The structural design of the caisson is thus an empirical task in which these effects should be adequately assessed.

3 Bracing of Foundations

Whenever horizontal loads produced by wind and seismic action become important, spread footings (rafts excepted) and pile foundations are braced in two normal, or nearly normal, directions in order to distribute these loads among all foundation elements. The bracing struts are designed in compression and tension to adequately support the forces involved.

4 Suggestions for Further Research

Research should be directed to improve the existing knowledge on soil-structure interaction. Most of this information can only be obtained from field measurements. Only from a large mass of field data, that would indicate real general trends in the distribution of contact stresses, may the design of footings be improved.

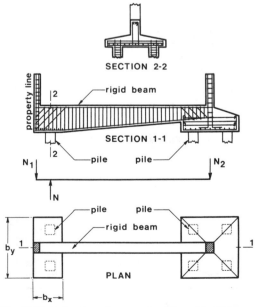

Fig. 11.57 Perimeter column on two piles with rigid beam

Analytical studies may also be made using finite-element analysis for various selected laws of soil reaction, both elastic and inelastic.

Pile foundations appear to lend themselves better to laboratory studies. However, the distribution of the load per pile in a multiple pile foundation is not only a function of the soil, but also of the shape and rigidity of the pile cap. It also depends upon minor construction details, such as variation in the refusal per pile, thus making laboratory studies questionable. Therefore, field measurements are also of major importance for the improvement of deep foundations. Again, analytical model simulation may provide useful insights.

11.6 CONDENSED REFERENCES/BIBLIOGRAPHY

The following is a condensed bibliography for this chapter. Not only does it include all articles referred to or cited in the text, but it also contains bibliography for further reading. The full citations will be found at the end of the Volume. What is given here should be sufficient information to lead the reader to the correct article: the author, date, and title. In case of multiple authors, only the first named is listed.

Aas-Jakobsen 1967, *The CEB Design Method for Reinforced Concrete Columns and Frames*
ACI-ASCE Committee 426 1962, *Shear and Diagonal Tension, Part 3, Slabs and Footings*
ACI Committee 435 1968, *Allowable Deflections*
ACI 1971, *Building Code Requirements for Reinforced Concrete*
ACI-ASCE Committee 426 1974, *The Shear Strength of Reinforced Concrete Members*

ACI-ASCE Committee 352 1976, *Recommendations for Design of Beam-Column Joints*
AIJ 1971, *Building Code Requirements for Reinforced Concrete*
Antebi 1960, *The Response of Shear Walls to Dynamic Loads*
Atkan 1974, *Response of a Reinforced Concrete Section to Two-Dimensional Curvature Histories*
Balint 1972, *Reinforcement Detailing of Frame Corner Joints with Particular Reference to Opening*

Ban 1943, *Experimental Study on the Seismic Resistance of Walls with Openings*
Bandel 1964, *Barrel Shells Form Structural Backbone of Multistory Buildings*
Barda 1973, *An Investigation of the Design and Repair of Low-Rise Shear Walls*
Barnard 1967, *Interaction of Shear Walls Connected Solely Through Slabs*
Bertero 1964, *Behavior of Reinforced Concrete Frames Subjected to Repeated Reversed Loads*

Bertero 1968, *Influence of Load History on Cracking in Reinforced Concrete*
Bianchini 1960, *Effect of Floor Concrete Strength on Column Strength*
Bishara 1968, *Reinforced Concrete Rectangular Columns in Torsion*
Black 1976, *Flat Plates Supported on Walls*
Bliss 1965, *Bacardi Building—An Unusual Structure for an Unusual Building*

Blume 1971, *Building Columns Under Strong Earthquake Exposure*
Breen 1964, *The Restrained Long Concrete Column as a Part of a Rectangular Frame*
Breen 1972, *Determination of Effective Length Factors for Slender Columns*
Bresler 1960, *Design Criteria for Reinforced Columns Under Axial Load and Biaxial Bending*
Bresler 1961, *Tie Requirements for Reinforced Concrete Columns*

Bresler 1971, *Lightweight Aggregate Reinforced Concrete Columns*
Colaco 1970, *End Moments for Floor Beams Framing into Spandrels*
CEB 1960, *Report on the 5th Working Session*
Cardenas 1973, *Strength of High-Rise Shear Walls—Rectangular Cross Sections*
Cardenas 1973, *Design Provisions for Shear Walls*

Casillas 1963, *Load-Deformation Characteristics of Spiral Concrete Columns*
Chang 1963, *Long Hinged Reinforced Concrete Columns*
Chow 1952, *Stresses in Deep Beams*

Colaco 1970, *End Moments for Floor Beams Framing into Spandrels*
CEB 1960, *Report on the 5th Working Session*

CEB-FIP 1970a, *International Recommendations for the Design and Construction of Concrete*
CEB-FIP 1970b, *International Recommendations for the Design and Construction of Concrete*
CEB 1971, *Contribution to the Preparation of the CEB-FIP Flexure-Compression Design Handbook*
CEB 1972, *Complementary Documentation to the CEB-FIP Flexure-Compression Design Handbook*
CEB 1973, *Lateral Buckling Handbook*

CRSI 1972, *CRSI Design Handbook*
Corley 1968, *Spearhead Reinforcement for Slabs*
Corley 1969, *Design of Beam-Column Joints for Seismic Resistant Reinforced Concrete Frames*
Coull 1966, *Tests on a Model Shear Wall Structure*
Coull 1967, *Tall Buildings, The Proceedings of a Symposium on Tall Buildings with Particular*

Cranston 1972, *Analysis and Design of Reinforced Concrete Columns*
Creus 1971, *Creep Buckling of Concrete Columns, Some Theoretical and Experimental Results*
Cusens 1965, *Analysis of Free Standing Stairs Under Symmetrical Loading*
Cusens 1966, *Analysis of Slabless Stairs*
Cusens 1966, *Design Charts for Helical Stairs with Fixed Supports*

Dilger 1971, *Creep Buckling of Long Columns*
Dischinger 1932, *A Contribution to the Theory of Semi-Infinite Plates and Wall-Like Beams*
Distefano 1965, *Creep Buckling of Slender Columns*
Drysdale 1971, *Sustained Biaxial Load on Slender Concrete Columns*
Farah 1969, *Analysis of Reinforced Concrete Columns Subjected to Longitudinal Load and Biaxial*

Ferguson 1966, *Investigation of the Long Concrete Frame Subject to Lateral Loads*
Ferguson 1970, *Computer Study of Long Columns in Frames*
Ferguson 1973, *Reinforced Concrete Fundamentals*
Ferry Borges 1971, *Structural Safety*
Fintel 1965–1969, *Effects of Column Exposure in Tall Structures*

Fintel 1974, *Ductile Shear Walls in Earthquake Resistant Multistory Buildings*
Foure 1971, *Study of Various Reinforced Concrete Column Buckling Problems*
Furlong 1966, *Tests of Frames with Columns in Single Curvature*
Galletly 1952, *Behavior of Reinforced Concrete Shear Walls Under Static Load*
George 1973, *Precast Concrete Doubly-Curved Funicular Shells Form Grid-Floors for Concrete*

Goyal 1971, *Slender Concrete Columns Under Sustained Load*
Green 1969, *Eccentrically Loaded Concrete Columns Under Sustained Load*
Hanson 1960, *Concrete Beams and Columns with Bundled Reinforcement*
Hanson 1967, *Seismic Resistance of Reinforced Concrete Beam-Column Joints*
Hanson 1968, *Shear and Moment Transfer Between Concrete Slabs and Columns*

Hanson 1971, *Seismic Resistance of Concrete Frames with Grade 60 Reinforcement*
Heiman 1973, *Long-Term Deformations in the Tower Building, Australia Square*
Hellesland 1971, *Sustained and Cyclic Loading of Concrete Columns*
HMSO 1965, *Building Regulations*
Hetenyi 1946, *Beams on Elastic Foundations*

Higashi 1969, *Failing Behaviors of Reinforced Concrete Beam-Column Connections Subjected to*
Hirosawa 1971–1973, *Strength and Ductility of Reinforced Concrete Members Subjected to Shear*
Hirosawa 1971, *Lateral Tests on Multistoried Full-Size Building of Reinforced Concrete Wall*
Hisada 1972, *Earthquake Design Considerations in Reinforced Concrete Columns*
Hribar 1969, *End Anchorage of High Strength Steel Reinforcing Bars*

Ismail 1972, *Bond Deterioration in Reinforced Concrete Subjected to Low Cycle Loads*
Jirsa 1969, *Torsional Strength of Spandrel Beams*
Jirsa 1973, *Torsion in Floor Slab Structures*
Johansen 1962, *Yield Line Theory*
Jones 1967, *Yield Line Analysis of Slabs*

Kong 1975, *Design of Reinforced Concrete Deep Beams in Current Practice*
Leonhardt 1966, *Wall-Like Beams*
Leonhardt 1972, *Reinforced Concrete Columns with High Strength Steel*
Lorentsen 1965, *Holes in Reinforced Concrete Girders*
MacGregor 1966, *Tests of Long Eccentrically Loaded Columns Bent in Double Curvature*

MacGregor 1967, *Recent North American Research and Design Developments in the Field of*
MacGregor 1970, *Design of Slender Columns*
MacGregor 1975, *A Re-Examination of the EI Value for Slender Columns*
Manuel 1967, *Analysis of Restrained Reinforced Concrete Columns Under Sustained Load*
Marques 1972, *A Study of Hooked Bar Anchorages in Beam-Column Joints*

Martin 1966, *Tests of Slender Reinforced Concrete Columns Bent in Double Curvature*
Martin 1966, *Critical Review of the Design of Reinforced Concrete Columns*
Mauch 1963, *Creep Buckling of Reinforced Concrete Columns*
Mayfield 1971, *Corner Joint Details in Structural Lightweight Concrete*
Mayfield 1972, *Strength and Stiffness of Lightweight Concrete Corners*

Minor 1971, *A Study of Bent Bar Anchorages*
Moretto 1970, *Reinforced Concrete Course*
Moretto 1971, *Deep Foundations—Selected Synthesis of the Present State of the Knowledge*
Muto 1953, *Experimental Study of Two-Story Reinforced Concrete Shear Walls*
Muto 1956, *Seismic Analysis of Reinforced Concrete Buildings*

Nadal 1970, *Experimental Investigation on 25 Prismatic Reinforced Concrete Parts Subjected to*
Naito 1924, *Theory of Earthquake-Proof Construction*
Nasser 1967, *Behavior and Design of Large Openings in Reinforced Concrete Beams*
Nilsson 1971, *Discussion of Opportunities in Bond Research*
Ogura 1952, *Tests to Failure of Two-Story Rigid Frames with Walls*

Ohmori 1976, *Studies on the Reinforced Concrete Slitted Shear Walls*
Okamura 1970, *Elastic Frame Analysis—Corrections Necessary for Design of Short Concrete*
Pagay 1970, *Importance of Beam Properties on Concrete Column Behavior*
Park 1973, *Behavior of Reinforced Concrete External Beam-Column Joints Under Cyclic Loading*
Park 1975, *Reinforced Concrete Structures*

Parme 1966, *Capacity of Restrained Eccentrically Loaded Long Columns*
Paulay 1969, *The Coupling of Shear Walls*
Paulay 1973, *Some Seismic Aspects of Coupled Shear Walls*
Paulay 1974, *Design Aspects of Shear Walls for Seismic Areas*
Pfeifer 1969, *Reinforced Lightweight Concrete Columns*

Pfeifer 1971, *Full-Size Lightweight Concrete Columns*
Pfister 1963, *High Strength Bars as Concrete Reinforcement (Part 5) Lapped Splices*
Pfister 1964, *Influence of Ties on the Behavior of Reinforced Concrete Columns*
Pfrang 1964, *A Study of the Influence of Creep on the Behavior and Capacity of Reinforced*
Pfrang 1964, *Behavior of Restrained Reinforced Concrete Columns*

Pfrang 1964, *Load-Moment-Curvature Characteristics of Reinforced Concrete Cross Sections*
Pfrang 1966, *Behavior of Reinforced Concrete Columns with Sidesway*
PCI 1973, *PCI Manual on Design of Connections for Precast, Prestressed Concrete*
Qadeer 1969, *The Bending Stiffness of Slabs Connecting Shear Walls*
Ramaswamy 1961, *Analysis, Design and Construction of a Shell of Double Curvature*

Rawdon de Paiva 1965, *Strength and Behavior of Deep Beams in Shear*
Reinschmidt 1964, *Dynamic Tests of Reinforced Concrete Columns*
Rosenhaupt 1961, *Elastic Analysis of Composite Walls*
Rosenhaupt 1964, *Stresses in Point Supported Composite Walls*
Saenz 1961, *Slabless Tread-Riser Stairs*

Sawczuk 1963, *Theory of Ultimate Load Carrying Capacity for Slabs*
Schleeh 1961, *The Rectangular Diaphragm with Arbitrary Load on the Short Edge*
Schleeh 1964, *A Simple Procedure for Solving Diaphragm Problems*
Schuster 1964, *Helical Stairs*
Shiga 1971–1974, *A Study on Dynamic Characteristics of Reinforced Concrete Shear Walls*

Siev 1962, *Analysis of Free Straight Multiflight Staircases*
Sinha 1964, *Ultimate Strength with High Strength Reinforcing Steel with an Indefinite Yield Point*
Somerville 1972, *The Influence of Reinforcement Detailing on the Strength of Concrete Structures*
SEAOC 1973, *Recommended Lateral Force Requirements and Commentary*
Taylor 1974, *The Behavior of In-Situ Concrete Beam-Column Joints*

Taylor 1976, *Some Detailing Problems in Concrete Frame Structures*
Terzaghi 1955, *Coefficients of Subgrade Reactions*

Timoshenko 1965, *Strength of Materials*
Todeschini 1964, *Behavior of Concrete Columns Reinforced with High Strength Steels*
Tomii 1957, *Studies on Shearing Resistance of Reinforced Concrete Plate*

Tomii 1960, *Study of Shearing Resistance of Earthquake Resisting Walls Having Various*
Tomii 1963, *Shear Wall*
Tomii 1968, *The Relations Between the Deformed Angle and the Shearing Force Ratio (0.80–1.00)*
Tomii 1970, *The Relation Between the Shape and the Location of the First Shear Crack on the*
Tomii 1974, *Relations Between the Nodal External Forces and the Nodal Displacements on the*

Tomii 1976a, *Elastic Analysis of Framed Shear Walls by Considering Shearing Deformation*
Tomii 1976b, *Elastic Analysis of Framed Shear Walls by Assuming Their Infilled Panel Walls*
Tsuboi 1954, *Analysis of Shearing Resistance of Cracked Shear Walls Based Upon 45-Degree*
UL 1971, *Building Materials List*
Uzumeri 1974, *Behavior of Reinforced Concrete Beam-Column Joints Subjected to Slow Load*

Wang 1973, *Reinforced Concrete Design*
Warner 1969, *Long Reinforced Concrete Columns in Biaxial Bending*
Wight 1973, *Shear Strength in Reinforced Concrete Columns Subjected to Large Deflection*
Williams 1952–1956, *Investigation of Shear Walls, Parts 1–2*
Winter 1972, *Design of Concrete Structures*

Wolfensberger 1964, *Optimum Dimensioning of Slabs for Given Loads*
Yamada 1968, *Shear Resistance and Explosive Cleavage Failure of Reinforced Concrete*
Yamada 1974a, *Reinforced Concrete Shear Walls Without Openings, Test and Analysis*
Yamada 1974b, *Reinforced Concrete Shear Walls with Openings, Test and Analysis*

**Structural Design of
Tall Concrete and Masonry Buildings**

Chapter CB-12

Design of Structures with Precast Concrete Elements

Prepared by Committee 21E (Precast Panel Structures) of the Council on Tall Buildings and Urban Habitat as part of the Monograph on the Planning and Design of Tall Buildings

Joseph J. Waddell   Chairman
Masatane Kokubu   Vice-Chairman
Adrian Pauw   Editor

AUTHOR ACKNOWLEDGMENT

Special acknowledgment is due those individuals whose contributions and papers formed the substantial first drafts of the various sections of this chapter. First are the state-of-art reporters from the 1972 International Conference whose material was published in the Lehigh Proceedings. These individuals are: A. P. Vasiliev, Y. D. Bychenkov and N. G. Matkov in Sections 12.1, 12.2, 12.3, 12.4 and 12.5; H. Sontag in Sections 12.1, 12.2, 12.4 and 12.5; M. Kavyrchine in Sections 12.1, 12.2, 12.3, 12.4 and 12.5; R. S. Fling in Sections 12.2, 12.3 and 12.4; A. Popoff, Jr. in Sections 12.1, 12.2 and 12.3; B. Thurlimann in Sections 12.5 and 12.6; F. R. Khan in Sections 12.1 and 12.2; B. Lewicki and A. Pauw in Sections 12.3 and 12.4; B. Lewicki, A. Cholewicki, J. Greszta, T. Henclewski, A. Pogorzelski, S. Wierzbicki and S. Zieleniewski in Sections 12.5 and 12.6.

In addition to this, other sections were based on special contributions prepared by J. Bobrowski, P. Abeles and B. Bardhan-Roy in Sections 12.1, 12.2, 12.3 and 12.4; A. Bruggeling in Sections 12.2, 12.3, 12.4 and 12.5; G. Rohm and K. von Wachter in Section 12.2; J. Stroband in Sections 12.2, 12.4 and 12.5; D. Ramesh, V. V. Nori, and T. R. Swami-Nathan in Section 12.3; J. Stigter in Section 12.2; U. Zeck in Section 12.5.

It is with deep regret that the Council notes the passing of Adrian Pauw on September 25, 1976, at a time when Chapter CB-12 was virtually complete. This chapter is largely the work of Dr. Pauw as he had worked diligently as Editor of Committee 21E obtaining material and preparing the text for the chapter. The Chairman and Members of Committee 21E and the Officers of the Council keenly regret that Dr. Pauw will not see the completion of his work. We are indebted to him for his dedication and perseverance in so ably bringing the work practically to fruition.

CONTRIBUTORS

The following is a complete list of those who have submitted written material for possible use in the chapter, whether or not that material was used in the final version. The Committee Chairman and Editor were given quite complete latitude. Frequently length limitations precluded the inclusion of much valuable material. The Bibliography contains all contributions. The contributors are: P. Abeles, B. Bardhan-Roy, J. Bobrowski, A. Bruggeling, Y. D. Bychenkov, A. Cholewicki, A. R. Cusens, F. Daschner, R. S. Fling, E. Grasser, J. Greszta, T. Henclewski, M. Kavyrchine, F. R. Khan, M. Kokubu, B. Lewicki, N. G. Matkov, V. V. Nori, A. Pogorzelski, A. Pauw, A. Popoff, Jr., D. Ramesh, G. Rohm, H. Sontag, J. Stigter, J. Stroband, T. R. Swami-Nathan, B. Thurlimann, A. P. Vasiliev, K. von Wachter, J. J. Waddell, S. Wierzbicki, U. Zeck, S. Zieleniewski.

COMMITTEE MEMBERS

A. L. L. Baker, B. K. Bardhan-Roy, J. M. Becker, T. Brondum-Nielsen, A. Cholewicki, A. R. Cusens, J. F. Cutler, M. Fintel, G. R. Fuller, J. Harvancik, M. Kokubu, B. Lewicki, G. Oberti, A. Pauw, D. Pume, G. Sebestyen, B. Stafford-Smith, M. Stiller, J. J. Waddell, R. F. Warner, M. Yorulmas, B. Zimmerli.

CB-12

Design of Structures with Precast Concrete Elements

12.1 INTRODUCTION

Prefabricated elements are now used in nearly all reinforced or prestressed concrete construction, at least as secondary elements, if not as structural parts. Precast concrete elements can be used for either a minor portion of the frame construction or nearly 100% of the structural components of the building. In precast concrete construction the structure is divided for manufacturing purposes into separate and distinct structural elements that are later assembled into the final structure (Kavyrchine, 1972; ACI-ASCE Committee 512, 1974).

Precast structural concrete elements can be either conventionally reinforced or prestressed. They are manufactured at a location (usually a factory) other than their final position in the structure.

The main structure may be of steel or concrete or of a mixed or composite system, but concrete appears in foundations, floor slabs, joists, beams, shear walls, partition walls, facade panels, and stairs. The concrete may be precast or cast-in-place, ordinary or lightweight, and used in structural or decorative units.

Multistory framed structures have been built in many countries using a wide variety of prefabricated reinforced concrete elements for the frame, floor systems, and walls. The efficiency of the use of prefabricated reinforced concrete is the result of standardization of these components and of their production in large mechanized factories (Vasiliev et al., 1972). Fig. 12.1 shows a 32-floor condominium apartment building in Oahu, Hawaii. Precast perimeter wall panels, tower stairs, garage columns, precast post-tensioned girders, beams, shear walls, and retaining walls were integrated with slipformed walls and cast-in-place flat slab floors in this structure constructed in eleven and a half months (Pankow, 1976).

Precast concrete system construction has made great progress in its 25-year history. Currently, in Great Britain, Denmark, Finland, and in other European nations, approximately 25% to 30% of all housing is constructed using precast systems. The Soviet Union projects that by 1980 over 80% of its housing construction will be of precast systems: an annual construction rate of 370 000 000 m^2 (4 billion ft^2) is projected for the period of 1976 to 1980.

577

Government-sponsored studies indicate that during the forthcoming decade some 26 000 000 new housing units will be required in the United States. This is nearly twice the number of housing units produced during the entire previous decade. The Secretary of Housing and Urban Development (HUD) has predicted that by the end of this decade at least two-thirds of all housing production in the United States will be factory-produced. Certainly, an appreciable amount of this production will involve precast concrete components and systems. Currently, however, the number of high-rise precast systems constructed in the United States is small, probably less than 2% of all housing construction (Popoff, 1972; Fuller, 1974).

The selection of appropriate building types for urban centers requires a thorough understanding of technical developments and their possibilities (Khan, 1973a). The objective of this chapter is to outline recent technological developments with respect to the use of precast concrete elements in tall building design and construction.

1   Usage of Precast Concrete

Precast reinforced and prestressed concrete elements can be utilized in nearly all tall buildings. Their use for structural systems in very tall buildings is limited by the weight and volume of the concrete element components. They require substantial foundations which interfere with functional utilization of the space. It is important to note the widespread use of lightweight concrete in tall building construction to

Fig. 12.1 Pearl Two condominium apartment building, Oahu, Hawaii (Pankow, 1976)

minimize weight. Precast concrete panels are economical in achieving stiff shear walls and cores, which provide good thermal and acoustical insulation and good damping of vibrations.

Entirely precast panel systems lend themselves best to apartment buildings due to the uniformity in dwelling modules. Such structures are presently limited to a maximum of 30 stories, but no greater height is reached with cast-in-place systems of bearing walls and flat slabs.

Moment-resistant frames, composed of precast posts and beams, necessitate heavily reinforced and costly element and joint details. They are therefore often constructed of precast elements combined with cast-in-place stiffening parts. Unusual shapes can be made efficiently by factory production methods, giving the architect great flexibility.

The attractive finish possible with precast elements makes them eminently suitable for use in facades. A curtain wall suspended from an independent bearing structure may be composed of precast concrete panels. A wide variety of architectural treatments can be provided for the same structural element. With current expertise the natural rugged character of the element can be enhanced or softened by the changes in surface texture and color possible with the use of different aggregates, cements, coloring admixtures, and surface finishes (Kavyrchine, 1972; ACI-ASCE Committee 512, 1974).

The increasing shift of emphasis on industrialization and precasting is, no doubt, a natural consequence of labor scarcity and rising wages which have overtaken the construction industry. Reduction of site work is directly associated with the over-all economy of a project, and has resulted in a tendency to aim at maximum prefabrication, ever increasing in size and complexity. Precasting is, however, only a means to an end and not the end itself. The success and efficiency of precast construction depends virtually in equal degrees on such factors as: (1) Standardization of elements; (2) ease of manufacture; (3) simplicity of assembly; and (4) speed of erection.

The important consideration in selecting an element is of course its suitability to fit into a particular architectural design, while assuring sufficient standardization to make economic sense. Many system buildings were unsuccessful because they were often found to restrict the freedom of architectural expression. Unlike in the car industry, complete standardization of buildings is still a long way away. Emphasis should therefore be put on a "method" rather than a "system." The method means standardizing components for the particular construction in such a way that these could be utilized in other applications, and at the same time assuring enough repetition in that particular construction for economic justification. For any structure there will be some frames and flooring. So by rationalizing the frame components and floor units a universal method could be evolved. Ease of manufacture depends on advances in manufacturing techniques. The ideal situation would be to develop a component that could be made with the required degree of accuracy without any special equipment or technical knowledge.

Simplicity of assembly would invariably require the minimum number of site connections and elimination of problems of dimensional tolerances. Sometimes these two requirements are contradictory, and a happy balance has to be achieved.

Speed of erection follows when the previous condition is satisfied, and is also influenced by the ease of connection, and by the use of minimum temporary work and minimum numbers of site workers (Bobrowski et al., 1974a).

2 Economics of Precast Concrete Construction

Innovations leading to more economic and efficient buildings can only be possible through a comprehensive understanding of the nature and behavior of various structural systems, of their relationship with other building functions such as those provided by the mechanical systems, and of the practical sense of construction problems (Khan, 1973b). It is also necessary to take into account society's preference for desirable types of living and working spaces in a building. Future societal needs and desires can be expected to change, and some consideration should therefore be given to incorporating in the design ease of demolition of the structure when it has become obsolete.

The use of prefabricated elements such as wall panels, floor slabs, and facades is normally justified if they are lighter than monolithic cast-in-place elements, and if multifunctional architectural and mechanical provisions can be incorporated in their manufacture.

With the use of standardized elements, economies are gained in the design of the elements, in mechanized production methods and speed of production, and through the repetitive use of high-quality forms. Structural efficiency, weight reduction, and deflection control may be enhanced by prestressing and by the use of lightweight concrete. With the increased accuracy that can be achieved with precasting, outlets for electrical services, water outlets, or other services can be built in before casting the elements. Inserts for furniture, such as bookshelves, laboratory tables, or seats for lecture halls can also be cast into the elements. Incorporating as much of the final installation of the building as possible at the plant contributes considerably to shortening the erection time of a building. The construction cost of precast-element structural frames is seldom less than that of monolithic frames. Over-all economy may be achieved, however, primarily through reduction in erection time and by the substitution of relatively unskilled factory labor for skilled site labor. Erection can often be performed during weather conditions that would halt other methods of construction. The construction period can thereby be shortened and construction costs reduced. To exploit these economies fully requires careful, detailed planning and scheduling. Thus an examination should be made during the preliminary planning of the economies possible with use of existing standard precast concrete products.

The type and availability of local products must be determined by consulting with local precasters. For those cases where standard products are not suitable, economical modifications can often be made. Where repetitive use justifies the construction of special forms, adequate lead time must be allowed in the job scheduling to permit the development and manufacture of those forms. Where there is little or no repetitive use of forms, the use of cast-in-place or a combination of precast and cast-in-place concrete may provide an economical solution (ACI-ASCE Committee 512, 1974).

Cast-in-place foundations or stiffening cores, or both, are often most economical for providing lateral stability. In other cases mixed structural systems using steel and concrete working together may be most economical. Steel buildings have the advantage of fast erection, relatively independent of weather conditions. The installation of the flooring should keep pace with the erection of the steel structure. The material most widely used for flooring is concrete. Precast concrete deck slabs may provide the best answer to meet the requirement for stiffening a steel skeleton.

They allow fast erection simultaneously with the steel structure. Composite action between the floor slabs and the floor girders increases the economy of the building and the stiffness of the floor structure. Precast concrete deck slabs can be tied to the floor girders after the erection by shear connectors, or by friction grip bolts, thus combining both fast erection and the structural efficiency of composite action. This operation requires very high accuracy of the precast slabs if it is intended that the flooring can be laid immediately on the structural floor slab without rendering with a leveling fill or topping.

Composite slabs may also be suitable for immediate use without further floor covering, as for example in building service areas or parking areas. In the latter case the surface should be roughened. For parking garages the floor should be watertight. Since prefabricated slabs are usually made of high-quality and well-vibrated concrete, the slabs themselves are generally waterproof. The joints can be waterproofed by using two-component plastic glue in place of cement mortar for grouting, or by applying waterproof adhesives to the edges of the concrete slabs before grouting. In this case the edges of the concrete slabs have to be cleaned carefully so that the aggregates of the concrete are exposed. This method requires careful execution on the site. Experience with this method has been encouraging (Sontag, 1973).

Where utilities and services cannot be directly incorporated in the factory, local mechanical trades can still find that working with precast structural concrete is more economical than other methods of construction, provided proper openings for utilities have been incorporated.

Where precast concrete is to be used throughout a structure, the precaster's manufacturing schedule may govern the time schedule for the project. The precaster's schedule should be consulted to decide if it affects the time to break ground and start the construction. Also this schedule should allow construction to proceed uninterrupted without a time gap prior to the availability and erection of the precast elements. Ideally, construction should be sequenced to permit erection of all precast concrete in one continuous operation. Expenses increase every time the erection crane is moved on and off the job site.

The erection schedule should be planned so that conduits, pipes, drains, or masonry are not installed above the bearing level of the precast material. Otherwise damage to one of these items can result when the precast components are placed (ACI-ASCE Committee 512, 1974).

Properly designed and detailed joints and connections are the single most important factor in assuring both safe and economical precast concrete structures. In a precast concrete system building, the instability of any one element may initiate a progressive collapse endangering the entire structure. Buildings with unreinforced, brittle joints are particularly prone to such failures. The failure of a London apartment house in 1968 focused attention upon the problem and initiated new code provisions (Popoff, 1972; Brondum-Nielsen, 1971; Griffiths et al., 1968; Fintel and Schultz, 1975; McGuire, 1974; Popoff, 1975; Speyer, 1976; Yokel et al., 1975).

Joints and connections in prefabricated concrete tall building structures must be designed and detailed to resist the forces to which they may be subjected. Not only should conventional loads, including wind and earthquake, be considered, but also the consequences of accidental overloads both during the construction phase and after completion of the building. Precast concrete structures are somewhat more prone to progressive failure than are monolithic structures. Special attention should therefore be given to the development of connection details which will provide the continuity and ductility required to assure general structural integrity. The cost of such connections places an economic limit on some prefabricated concrete systems. For systems where adequate lateral stability is provided by shear walls or a rigid core, joint and connection details can be devised to provide resistance against reasonably probable abnormal loads at relatively small cost. Over-all structural integrity must of course be developed regardless of load (Popoff, 1972).

For design concepts where future demolition is a design criterion, concrete should be omitted from the joints between elements and replaced with mechanical links. Construction with such prefabricated elements will be independent of the building season.

Future development in materials and production processes can be expected to result in further economies. Future construction materials and methods for prefabrication will include: wire-mesh reinforced concrete, lightweight concrete and concrete reinforced with glass fiber, and extensive application of such technologies as pressing and vacuuming, extrusion, and other thermodynamic processes (Kavyrchine, 1972).

3 Structural Design

In designing a tall building, the most important first step is to decide on the right structural system for each project. In an optimization approach to the design of a precast-element building system, the hierarchy of optimization starts from the selection of the total system, then the optimization of the subsystem, and finally the optimization of the members themselves. It is interesting to note that the hierarchy of optimization of the structure starts with the total system, whereas the hierarchy of the building standardization starts from members and moves upward, that is, standardization of the members first, subsystems second, and finally the total system (Pauw, 1976).

In a tall building, the structure becomes a subsystem of primary significance, and the effect of such major structures can often be so significant that they have strong influence on the final architectural expression. It is for this reason that in many recent tall buildings the path of load flow through the building has been expressed architecturally by the use of special structural forms (Khan, 1973a, 1973b).

The selection of an efficient and economical precast concrete structural system can be approached only through understanding of special design considerations, as well as of the significant factors affecting the economy and efficiency of any structural system. The most significant of these factors can be classified as follows:

1. Design lateral forces, such as wind or earthquake, and including forces resulting from accidental loadings and other exceptional loads of moderate probability.

2. Height-to-width ratio of the building, commonly known as the aspect ratio.

3. Criteria for lateral stiffness (drift ratio) and related perception of sway motion.

4. Types of occupancy (office versus apartment).

5. Local foundation considerations.

6. Local fire rating considerations.

7. Local availability and cost of main construction materials, including prefabricated concrete elements.

8. Local heating and air-conditioning load considerations.

9. Method of electrification—underfloor or punch-through or wall system.

10. Construction time schedule.

11. Cost of interim financing.

12. Relationship between construction labor and construction equipment.

It should of course be clearly understood that all of the mentioned factors must be tied together with the over-all considerations. For a developing country, item 12 makes the process of structural system selection distinctly different from that in a country with a highly developed technology.

Because the final choice of a structural system depends on these factors, it should be obvious that there cannot be any unique structural system valid for all locations in a country or in the world. It is this philosophic attitude that is essential for the engineer and the architect in evaluating the best possible structural system for a particular given project, for a particular given location, and at a particular given time. It is for this very reason that new structural systems constantly are being developed by the structural engineer together with the architect to satisfy the changing needs of time (Dunbar, 1973).

A structural system, to be valid for a given real estate and architectural program, must in a sense be a synthesis of the design considerations combined with confidence in analytical results and actual performance of such a system. Without going too deeply into the analytical problems, this chapter discusses the present state of the art (Khan, 1973a, 1973b).

12.2 CLASSIFICATION OF PRECAST-ELEMENT STRUCTURES

1 Classifications

Precast-element structures may be classified in a number of ways, the principal ones being based on:

1. The functional layout.

2. The type of elements used.

3. The framing system employed and the corresponding structural response.

Design optimization must begin with the early stages of the development of design concepts. This is the stage at which the greatest economies can be achieved compatible with local requirements and availability of resources. The over-all optimization of a design is far more sensitive to the selection of the design concept than it is to refinements in the final design after the basic layout has been frozen. For this reason, cooperation and consultation between engineer, architect, contractors, and suppliers are especially important in the early stages of a project.

The structural scheme should be consistent with the function of the building. For example, short spans and low story heights are generally more economical but are usually acceptable only in residential buildings. Similarly, precast floor units without a topping may be acceptable in buildings where carpet can be used as the finished floor to cover the unevenness between units. It should be noted, however, that in most cases a topping of some sort is necessary to prevent wear of the carpet at the joints between units.

Selection of the structural scheme should consider other elements of the construction. In some cases a small penalty on the structural system will result in substantial savings in other areas. For example, in residential buildings, concrete bearing walls may provide sound isolation, thermal insulation, and the necessary wall surfaces, as well as serve a structural function. In another case, wide, shallow beams rather than narrow, deep beams may provide the necessary mechanical distribution space between ceiling and floor without increasing story heights, and also allow vertical passage of piping through the beams. Thus, the saving in building height and mechanical services may more than offset any increase in the cost of structural framing.

Local conditions may influence the selection of a structural scheme. Examples are the availability of precast concrete elements, the experience of local contractors, the capability of local labor, and the cost of labor as compared to the cost of material.

Construction methods can influence the cost. The construction sequence, erection methods, adaptability of cranes and other material handling equipment to the project, and tolerances required for fitting of the structural frame between members and to other parts of the construction must be considered.

The building site itself may influence selection of a suitable framing system because of foundation conditions and because of accessibility for construction operations.

The most efficient use of material will minimize the cost when all other factors are constant. While true optimization does not consist of merely minimizing material quantities, this certainly will be a general objective in selection of a structural scheme, and a specific objective in the final selection of member sizes and reinforcing details.

It may be advantageous to make long span members in segments for economies in handling and transporting. Joints between the segments can be filled with concrete or high-strength epoxies, and post-tensioning used to prestress all the segments together to form the final member.

The structural and architectural functions required of the precast element must be clearly delineated during the preliminary planning stage. Precast elements can be used for slabs, beams, columns, walls, piling, or combinations such as a pile-column and wall-column (ACI-ASCE Committee 512, 1974).

In optimizing the selection of a precast structural system the proposed occupancy is a major factor. For example, the use of large precast concrete panel systems, while structurally efficient, is normally restricted to residential buildings where spans are limited and the numerous fixed partitions can serve as bearing and shear walls. On the other hand, for high-rise office buildings, it may be impractical and uneconomical for precast ductile moment-resisting frames to provide the stiffness required to avoid undesirable deflections for human occupancy.

From the structural engineering point of view, the primary aspects that are special to the design of tall buildings are:

1. Lateral loads effects: (a) Strength requirements for wind or earthquake loading; (b) stability under lateral loads; and (c) sway due to lateral loads resulting in possible perception of motion, as well as damage to architectural details.

2. Time-dependent behavior of columns and walls in reinforced concrete, such as creep and shrinkage.

3. Differential column movement due to variations in level of stresses.

4. Temperature effects on fully or partially exposed exterior columns or load-bearing wall panels.

5. Soil-structure interaction.

While these design aspects must be considered in addition to normal considerations in the design of any structure, their relative importance will depend on the system chosen. The less each of these factors actually affects the design of individual members of a system, the more efficient the system becomes (Khan, 1973a).

The designer may select an appropriate system from several basic categories, modified by an almost unlimited selection or combination of elements and construction details. As in cast-in-place construction, precast systems fall into three basic categories: rigid frame structures, shear wall structures, or shear wall-frame combinations. In the shear wall-frame combination, the utility core taking the lateral load is usually cast-in-place, while the beam-column frame is precast and takes vertical load only. In precast systems, the rigid frame structure and the shear wall-frame structure do not differ from conventional cast-in-place structures; the joints in framing members are so designed that points of inflection are predictable as to location and restraint capability.

The majority of precast systems falls into the shear-wall category. These are assembled from large panels or boxes. Precast-panel system buildings of well over 20 stories have been used extensively (Popoff, 1972).

In a rigid frame building, horizontal loads are transmitted by the floor system to the frames. The beams and columns of the frame may be made of one-bar (linear) or of frame components. The linear components are connected to each other at the column faces. To support the beams, the columns are provided with short brackets or corbels, projecting below, or concealed within, the depth of the beam. In housing and public buildings, hidden brackets or corbels are preferred, as for example in the classroom building shown in Fig. 12.2. When the components of the frame are made as linear elements (column and beams), fabrication in the factory and transportation to the site of construction are simplified. However, the connections between the girders and columns are, in this case, subjected to high forces, and this makes development of moment-resisting connections difficult. Lateral stability may be provided in braced or semibraced buildings. Horizontal loads are fully or partially transmitted by the floor system to the shear walls or to a rigid core formed around staircases or elevator walls, as shown in Fig. 12.3. In Fig. 12.3 (a), the left side shows socketed columns, and the right side shows use of multistory columns. Fig. 12.3(b) shows a precast office building in Oklahoma City, Oklahoma.

Although rigid cores and shear walls entail considerable expense, they permit substantial reduction of the weight of the frame members as well as standardization. It is for this reason that braced and semibraced systems, especially in tall buildings, have been widely adopted in the past few years.

Shear walls may be monolithic or assembled from large panels. In order not to delay construction of the frame and floor systems, assembled shear walls are often preferred, although their erection involves joints of great length.

Assembled shear walls are made of prefabricated panels of one-story height. Rigid connection between the panels and with the elements of the frame may be accomplished by welding steel plates anchored in the panel concrete and filling all the joints with concrete grout. Another commonly used method is to provide interlocking looped reinforcing bars projecting from the precast elements (Vasiliev et al., 1972).

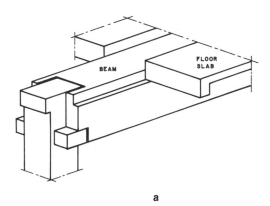

a

b

Fig. 12.2 Precast element framing (Courtesy: Stroband): (a) Concealed corbels; (b) classroom building, Technical University, Darmstadt

2 Frames

Precast-element framing systems may be divided into four categories, as shown in Fig. 12.4. Floor loads are transmitted to the foundations by means of beams and columns. In Category I the floor loads are transmitted to the spandrel beams of longitudinal frames, whereas in Category II transverse frames support the floor panels. Category III consists of skeleton space frames supporting two-way slabs, and in Category IV slabs are directly supported on a load-bearing facade (Bruggeling, 1972).

Moment-resisting frames can be constructed using linear elements or bilinear elements such as cross elements, T, H, and Π frames, or hollow panel frames.

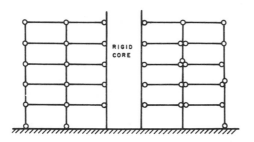

b

Fig. 12.3 Core stiffened framing: (a) Multistory skeleton frame; (b) precast office building, Okla-homa City, Oklahoma

Precast linear elements are readily fabricated, transported, and erected. In precast concrete frame systems their use may lead to congestion at points of intersection of beams and columns. Rigid moment connections in such systems are difficult if not impossible, as is illustrated in the Category I system shown in Fig. 12.5.

The interfacing of as many as five linear elements, as for example in Category III skeleton frames, can often be resolved by the use of bilinear frame components. With the use of T, Π, H, and cross components, beam joints can be made at points of contraflexure, thereby simplifying connection details (Bobrowski et al., 1974a).

When cross-shaped or H-shaped elements are used, fabrication and transportation are more complicated. However, connection of the beams to each other is considerably simplified, and consequently preference is often given to the use of components of this shape.

In seismic zones the use of the cross-shaped or H-shaped frame components is especially desirable. During earthquakes, the intersections between beams and columns are subjected to high forces. Shifting the beam connections into the span, therefore, is very advantageous (Vasiliev et al., 1972).

Bilinear frame subassemblies can be made on the site using linear precast segments. Prestressing provides a good method for connecting such precast segments. Element dimensions and deformations are reduced and cracks avoided. Pretensioning is widely used in factory-produced precast units (Kavyrchine, 1972; Brondum-Nielsen, 1975).

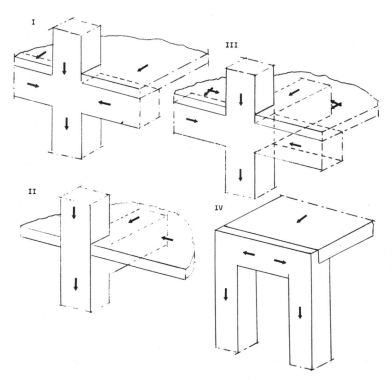

Fig. 12.4 Framing categories (Bruggeling, 1972)

Many novel and ingenious framing systems have been devised (Dunbar, 1973), for example the Yugoslavian IMS System. This unique prefabricated skeletal building system, designed to resist earthquakes, involves the use of heavily prestressed concrete floor beams and joints. Another example is the ingenious framing system shown in Figs. 12.6 and 12.7. This system was devised for the Transitorium III Laboratory building of the University of Utrecht, Netherlands, which was awarded the "Europe Prize 1974" by the European Institute of Prefabricators. Wide precast floor beams were combined with H- and T-elements using post-tensioning and a cast-in-place floor slab to produce a rigid skeleton (Bruggeling, 1972). A perimeter beam was produced by post-tensioning cables passing through the beams and T-column flanges. The cast-in-place floor slab acts as a compression flange for the wide floor beams.

3 Panel Building Systems

The construction of a number of building types may be implemented using large precast concrete panel elements. Large panel construction has been found to be economical especially for industrialized high-rise housing projects, and has been widely used for up to 20 or 30 stories in height (Kavyrchine, 1972; Fuller, 1974).

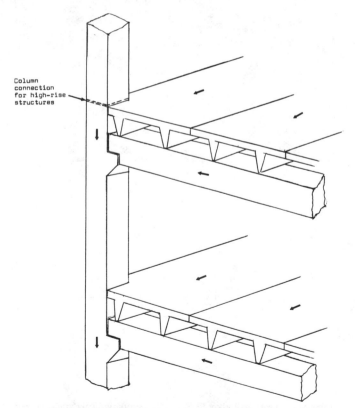

Column connection for high-rise structures

Fig. 12.5 Example—Category I—framing (Bruggeling, 1972)

The building blocks for large panel building systems are wall panels (provided with window and door openings as required) and floor panels. The basic construction principle is the "box," consisting of walls connected to a floor plate which doubles as ceiling for the unit below. Longitudinal and transverse walls provide lateral rigidity in two mutually perpendicular directions (Bruggeling, 1972).

An entirely prefabricated structure may be composed of panels, assembled to form flat slab plates and bearing walls (see Fig. 12.8). Such slab-and-wall systems are popular for apartment buildings and condominiums (Fintel and Schultz, 1975).

Normal room dimensions allow the use of one-piece panels for the floors (between walls) and for the walls (one story height, between floors). Bearing walls also serve the functional role of partitions; concrete panels provide excellent sound and thermal insulation between apartments. Architectural possibilities are con-

a

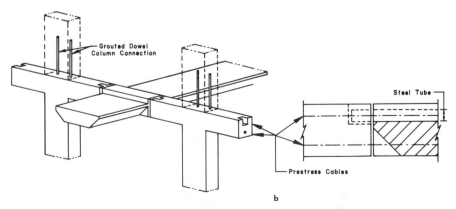

b

Fig. 12.6 (a) Framing system—Transitorium III (Courtesy: Stroband); (b) detail—beam connection to T-columns

strained by permissible wall layouts, and the limits imposed by the position and dimensions of holes for doors, windows, and ducts. Nevertheless, the utility and economy of panel systems have been demonstrated by the many successful applications in all parts of the world. Lewicki (1966) gives a good description of the use of precast concrete panels. Design recommendations for panel structures have

Fig. 12.7 Transitorium III, University of Utrecht (Courtesy: Stroband)

Fig. 12.8 Marshall Towers Apartments, Daly City, California: Challenge large panel system (Courtesy: Fintel)

been published by the Comité Européen du Beton (CEB, 1967).

In some systems, boxlike utility room elements are incorporated in some places in the structure, which otherwise remain mainly composed of panels. In other systems, the whole structure is made up of boxes. Such systems have been used in the United States and Eastern Europe. Many alternatives are possible; boxes may be prefabricated with four, five, or six faces. They may bear on all vertical faces, or on only two of them; or they may be supported on the corners, or on columns. Fig. 12.9 shows the installation of such a complete room element, a typical module (full building width) in an HUD Operation Breakthrough 18-story high-rise building (Fuller, 1974). The weight and assembly conditions of box systems make them ill-adapted at present for tall buildings (Kavyrchine, 1972).

For panel systems, the load capacity of standard panel walls and problems of tolerances and of hoisting also limit the height of entirely prefabricated slab-and-wall systems. At present it is unusual to construct buildings of more than 25 stories with panel systems.

Precast panel systems differ from cast-in-place structures in one paramount respect: precast systems have discrete and finite joints that are absent in cast-in-place structures. The detailed treatment of these joints may so effectively tie the individual panels forming the horizontal and vertical diaphragms that the building effectively becomes as monolithic as a cast-in-place wall and slab structure. On the other hand, the joints may be detailed so that the structural components are totally disconnected, the resulting structures depending solely on friction and gravity for stability. Such structures may exhibit a "house of cards" behavior when subjected to exceptional loads (Popoff, 1972).

Tall building structures are generally composed of cast-in-place transverse

Fig. 12.9 Box element, Shelley system, Jersey City, New Jersey (Courtesy: Fuller)

bearing walls, flat slabs, and precast facades, or of a slipformed core with a peripheral structure consisting of precast posts and beams.

4   Mixed Systems—Prefabricated and Cast-In-Place

It is often economical to use cast-in-place shear walls or stiffening cores, or both, to obtain lateral load resistant systems. The floors act as rigid diaphragms to transfer the lateral forces to these stiffening elements, as shown in Fig. 12.10. A stiff, slipformed central core, such as that shown in Fig. 12.11, surrounded by floors with precast units and a peripheral moment-resisting facade grid, is well adapted for tall building construction. Post-tensioning may be employed to tie elements to each other and to the core (Beck and Schneider, 1972).

Some important buildings in Moscow are of this last type, as for example the SEV Building (Council of Mutual Economic Assistance). The erection of the peripheral precast structure closely follows the advancement of the cast-in-place core (Kavyrchine et al., 1972).

Precast elements may be utilized in core-stiffened structures in a variety of ways. Such structures are not limited to a rectangular layout. In fact the core itself may be assembled of precast panels, as for example in the circular tower for the Holiday Inn Hotel in Augsburg shown in Fig. 12.12 (Bruckner and Popp, 1973). An isometric sketch of the framing details is shown in Fig. 12.13.

The Australia Square office building in Sydney is a round structure 184 m (604 ft) high of the core and perimeter frame type. In the erection, lightweight concrete, with a compressive strength of 24 MPa (3500 psi) was used. Precast elements were used as permanent formwork for columns and spandrel beams, as shown in the details in Fig. 12.14 (Stigter, 1966).

Fig. 12.15 shows the use of load-bearing precast panels in conjunction with cast-in-place concrete floors, columns, and elevator core in an office tower in Brisbane, Australia. The facade spandrel panels were precast with an exposed aggregate finish. The boundary shear walls were solid load-bearing walls constructed of two-story T-panels to minimize jointing and permit staggering of the joints to simplify erection. Panels were connected to each other by the use of grouted dowels (*Constructional Review*, 1974a).

Architectural precast concrete facade panels are commonly used with both

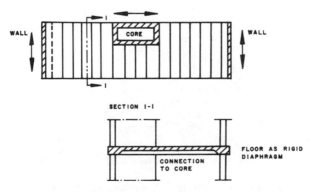

SECTION I-I

Fig. 12.10 Mixed systems, slipformed core and floor diaphragm

a

b

Fig. 12.11 University of Frankfurt, Academic Building (Courtesy: Beck and Schneider): (a) Construction view; (b) completed structure

Fig. 12.12 Holiday Inn, Augsburg (Courtesy: Bruckner and Popp)

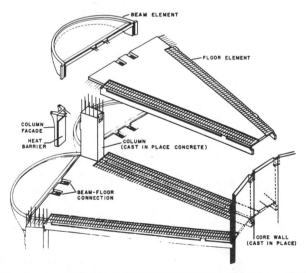

Fig. 12.13 Holiday Inn, Augsburg: tower structure frame details (Bruckner and Popp, 1973)

precast panel and cast-in-place floor slabs. A precast-element framing system consisting of precast facade panels, doubling as column formwork, precast beams and floor plank, and integrated with slipformed elevator and stair shafts is shown in Fig. 12.16 (*Western Construction*, 1969).

Prefabricated joists are often used for floors, with all kinds of main structures. Precast prestressed floors were used, for instance, for the suspended structure of Standard Bank Center of Johannesburg. Prefabrication of floors reduces erection time, as shoring is eliminated.

In the Massachusetts Blue Cross-Blue Shield Headquarters Office, precast concrete panels are in some parts structural elements and in other parts of the building only decorative. Wachovia Bank Building in Charlotte, North Carolina, has a precast concrete facade on a structural reinforced concrete frame (Vasiliev et al., 1972).

5 Mixed Systems—Steel and Precast Concrete

Steel and concrete are often used together, either in vertical load resisting systems, such as floors with steel beams and joists, or in lateral load resisting systems, such as shear walls made of a braced steel frame and a precast panel wall assembly. A widely used system consists of a stiff concrete core and a perimeter steel structure. Several towers in Paris, including the Maine-Montparnasse Tower, which has a slipformed concrete core 233 m (763 ft) high, have a concrete core to resist lateral loads, and a steel structure for the floors and facade columns, which carry only vertical loads. In such a system, special care has to be given to the calculation of

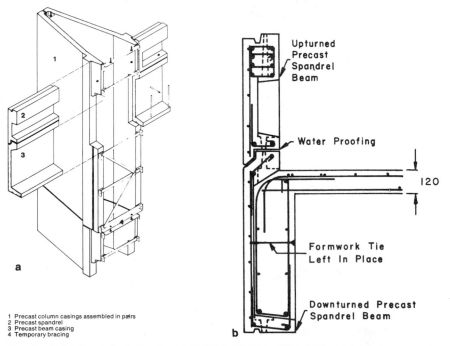

1 Precast column casings assembled in pairs
2 Precast spandrel
3 Precast beam casing
4 Temporary bracing

Fig. 12.14 Details of Australia Square Building (Stigter, 1966): (a) Precast facade assembly; (b) section through spandrel

vertical deformations, since shrinkage and creep affect only the concrete core.

The most important advantage of tall steel structures is that they can be built relatively quickly. Generally one floor can be completed every three days, whereas in cast-in-place concrete construction, even one floor every seven days is an optimistic projection. In steel buildings, the central cores are much more flexible than in concrete buildings, and any free area due to dropping off of the elevators can be immediately utilized as fully rentable area by adjusting the partition walls as necessary. In the SOM-Composite system, Khan (1973a) combined the advantages of a steel structure with the advantages of a concrete structure, thereby eliminating the disadvantages of both. The composite system consists of structural steel columns, beams, and floor construction, whereas, as shown in Fig. 12.17, the exterior closely-spaced columns and spandrels together with the curtain wall are formed of reinforced concrete. In order to keep the rate of construction equal to the normal rate for a steel building, and also to keep the structural steel trades separate from the reinforced concrete trades, the entire structure in steel should be built ahead of the exterior concrete structural cladding. In the CDC Building in Houston, an application of this system, precast concrete window panels were used to act also as the formwork for the reinforced concrete exterior system.

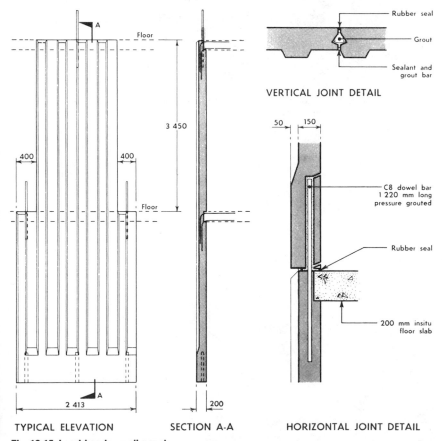

TYPICAL ELEVATION   SECTION A-A   HORIZONTAL JOINT DETAIL

Fig. 12.15 Load bearing wall panels

Fig. 12.16 Architectural facade panel frame, office building, Bellevue, Washington (Western Construction, May 1969)

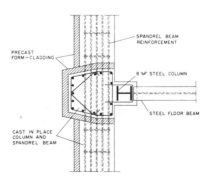

Fig. 12.17 Precast form-cladding: SOM-Composite system (Khan, 1973a)

The economy of multistory steel buildings depends largely on the suitability of their floor system. Precast concrete slabs on steel girders combine the advantages of prefabrication of the floor and composite construction. This system has not been widely used except by Krupp in Germany. Two different types of shear connection are used: (1) Welded studs; and (2) high tensile friction bolts.

A typical installation is shown in Fig. 12.18. The concrete slab acts as the compression zone of the composite section, and the lower part of the steel girder as its tension zone. The weight of the steel girder is reduced considerably by the composite action. The load deflection of a composite section is much smaller than that of a simple steel girder. Therefore the system is especially suitable for long spans (Sontag, 1973).

Precast concrete elements allow fast erection of the floor. According to its degree of prefabrication, the precast slab represents either the bearing core of the floor only, or the entire prefabricated floor system, including cast-in installation units and finished surfacing. Precast slabs are laid on either corrugated steel sheeting or steel floor girders. This floor system corresponds best to the prefabricated steel skeleton and offers many advantages:

1. The slabs can be manufactured in a factory, independent of weather conditions.

2. The simultaneous erection of concrete elements and the steel skeleton reduces total erection time.

3. The erection of the steel structure is simplified as no scaffolding is needed, and erection is less dangerous.

4. The quality of the precast deck slabs is much higher than that of cast-in-place slabs, with respect to both the quality of the concrete and manufacturing tolerances.

5. Bolted concrete slabs can be dismantled and re-erected.

6. The accuracy of prefabrication of the concrete deck slabs allows their immediate use without further layers of rendering or similar material.

7. This accuracy also allows cast-in fixings or outlets.

6 Floor Systems

The construction cost of floors is more than half the cost of the structural framework except in very tall buildings. Therefore, selection of the floor framing system deserves considerable study to provide the maximum resistance to lateral forces and gravity loads and to minimize cost.

Floor systems of buildings for human occupancy are often made of large standardized reinforced concrete slabs with cylindrical voids to reduce weight. Floor systems of industrial structures more commonly use prefabricated reinforced concrete ribbed slabs which are laid on the beams of supporting frames (Vasiliev et al., 1972).

Weight reduction is accomplished by the use of lightweight aggregate and thinner floors than would otherwise be used, or by prestressing. Serviceability requirements, rather than strength, usually limit floor thickness. Thinner floors can result from the use of shrinkage compensating cement (see Chapter CB-9) or prestressing to minimize cracking and deflection. The ideal minimum thickness is that required for fire protection, provided vibration and stiffness requirements do not govern. The slab thickness of ribbed slabs can be reduced to a minimum for structural purposes by applying sprayed-on insulation to achieve the required fire protection. Sprayed-on insulation can also be used on slabs cast on horizontal casting beds and inverted during erection. The finished contact surface of the casting bed eliminates the need for topping or rendering, and the rough-textured surface of the sprayed-on ceiling provides both thermal and acoustical insulation.

Precast panel floor systems should be enclosed in a perimeter framework, and continuity and transverse tie-beam reinforcement provided between panel ends over supporting beams or bearing walls. Such connections provide rigid diaphragm action of the floor to resist lateral loads. In seismic regions, the connection between the individual slabs may be strengthened by welding to steel plate inserts and by providing grooves along the junction sides which are filled with grout (Kavyrchine, 1972).

In addition to transmitting lateral forces it is usually assumed that horizontal slabs equalize the deformations of the vertical elements in the plane of the slab. Stress calculations should consider the effect of relative deformations, under bending, torsion, and compression of the shear walls and cores which cantilever vertically from the ground.

12.3 PRECAST STRUCTURAL SYSTEMS—DESIGN AND DESIGN CRITERIA

1 Preliminary Analysis

Analysis is a subset of design used to test the adequacy of one or more limit states of performance required. Likewise, member proportioning is another subset used to determine construction details. The simplest possible model should be used in preliminary analysis and member proportioning of potential framing systems. As the design process progresses and the number of alternate schemes is reduced, the analysis and member-proportioning procedures can become more refined. Until the structural system has been selected, neither a lengthy analysis nor detailed member proportioning will generally be justified (Fling, 1973).

2 Layout Criteria

The importance of a carefully considered layout cannot be overemphasized. The possibility and effects of differential settlement should be considered in determining the location of cores and shear walls. The risk of progressive collapse failure can also be minimized by strategic location of stiffening cores (Lewicki, 1966). Symmetry is generally desirable to avoid large torsional forces. While some redundancy in the structural system may be desirable to provide reserve resistance capacity against progressive collapse in the event of accidental overloads, excessive constraints above those required for lateral stability should be avoided. Especially in prestressed-precast frame elements, redundant constraints can cause excessive stresses, deformations, and even loss of prestress due to temperature, creep, and shrinkage effects. Ductile tensile continuity and peripheral ties should, however, be provided between components of the floor system and around the floor assembly, to assure stability in the event the structure is subjected to exceptional loading conditions.

3 Limit States Criteria: Serviceability—Drift

In tall buildings the deflection under lateral load should be given careful attention in selecting a precast-concrete system. The horizontal deflection of the building has to be restricted for the following reasons: (1) Effect on the structural element; (2) serviceability of the structure; (3) effect on nonstructural (cladding) elements; and (4) sensory acceptability. The ACI Committee on Deflections (ACI-435) recommends an upper limit for horizontal deflections at $H/500$, H being the height of the building. For large-panel precast construction this deflection may have to be restricted to $H/1000$ (Ramesh et al., 1973).

For low-rise buildings, the resistance to lateral forces is generally provided by the same framework designed for vertical forces, and the normal practice is merely to check its adequacy for lateral forces. With marginal strengthening of floor-column connections the structural framework is generally found to be sufficiently rigid for lateral stability. For high-rise buildings, however, the framed structure is impractical and uneconomical for resisting lateral forces, and often shear walls may be found necessary. The term "high-rise" in this context appears misleading because, for a flat-slab building, shear walls may have to be provided even for six to eight stories. If the building is not slender, shear walls may not be called for even if the structure is 15 to 20 stories high. Since the shear walls resist the major portion of the lateral

Fig. 12.18 Composite floor system (Sontag, 1973)

forces, they should be located in such a manner as to attract sufficient vertical load to minimize tensile stresses, and also to provide the required stability against overturning. In fact, the lateral force resisting system should be so planned that the structure is fully stressed under vertical forces, and yet the stresses due to lateral forces do not exceed the usual 25% to 33% stress increase normally permitted. Theoretically, there should be no addition to the structural cost which follows an optimum curve as shown in Fig. 12.19. This can only be achieved if there is a constant interaction between the structural engineer and the architect, even at the earliest stage of planning a building project.

While resistance to wind loads can be provided by stiff shear walls, they would, where seismic forces are involved, obviously give rise to larger inertia forces in comparison to a ductile frame. The latter may be acceptable for resisting seismic and wind forces but has undesirable deflections for human occupancy. Provision of deep planar walls does not present any complications from the functional viewpoint for apartments and hotel buildings. For office buildings, however, a deep shear wall is often unacceptable. For such situations, it may be necessary to depend on walls surrounding an inner service core to assure lateral stability. Since the size of the core is often governed by functional requirements rather than by the height of building, the core, by itself, may not be strong enough to resist these forces. The additional stiffness required is then provided by the external cladding, termed the "outer-tube," which acts in conjunction with the service core called the "inner-tube," and the framed structure, if any (Ramesh et al., 1973).

Another factor to be considered in the design of tall multistory buildings, especially those with a high aspect ratio, is the probability of developing vibrations due to wind gusts or vortex shedding, or both. The response of the structure to such actions needs to be considered, and, if necessary, some external damping provided. At eaves and corners high suction pressures may develop. These suction pressures may be as high as five times the positive pressure. The facade panels must be properly anchored to resist these suction pressures.

Precast systems also may differ from cast-in-place buildings in the amount of wall reinforcement used. Some structures rely on the dead-load weight to prestress the vertical members against tensile stresses due to wind forces. This may be the case with unreinforced panel structures and with portions of a building surrounding a narrow shear wall. Here, weight reduction would cause other problems that might increase the cost rather than reduce it.

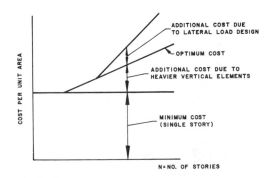

Fig. 12.19 Cost-height relationship

All cast-in-place buildings, including bearing-wall buildings, contain some continuous wall reinforcement. This reinforcement, even if only nominal, gives the building some degree of ductility. In some systems buildings, not only are the joints unreinforced, but the walls are also unreinforced. The building thus becomes a brittle "house of cards" when subjected to abnormal forces. To avoid the possibility of progressive collapse, tensile continuity reinforcement should be provided in the floor system and in the exterior walls. Such vertical and horizontal continuity reinforcement, adequately anchored at all floor levels, is essential to general structural integrity and will enhance the resistance of the structure to unforeseen eventualities.

4 Strength and Stability

Structural analysis of structural systems constructed with precast elements is basically no different from that of monolithic concrete systems, and is discussed in Chapter CB-5 (Elastic Analysis), Chapter CB-6 (Nonlinear Analysis), and Chapter CB-8 (Stability). Precast-element structures, however, are somewhat more subject to eccentricities in bearing walls and columns, and the rigidity of assembled panel shear walls is highly sensitive to vertical joint characteristics. These factors must therefore be considered in the mathematical models employed.

The strength and stability of large-panel structures is governed by the interaction of three important design details: (1) The design of the panel elements; (2) the joint filler; and (3) the connection details.

The wall elements of large-panel structures transmit to the foundation both vertical loads and horizontal forces, primarily through forces parallel to their planes. Flexural stresses are also induced into the walls due to lateral forces acting normal to their planes and to eccentricities of vertical loads. Wall elements may be analyzed as three-dimensional plates subjected to various combinations of loads parallel and normal to their planes. However, design is facilitated by considering the wall elements to be subjected separately to combined bending and axial load and combined shear and axial load (Bruggeling, 1972).

5 Stability of Precast System Buildings

To assure stability of a structure as a whole, it is at times necessary to analyze the structure in its deformed shape. Criteria for the necessity of such analyses and methods of analysis are presented in Chapter CB-8 and by Lorentsen (1972), Beck (1972), and MacGregor (1972). In this respect, the precast system building is analogous to the cast-in-place building. Similarly, necessary considerations for the design of slender wall panels have been presented by the Comité Européen du Béton (CEB, 1967). American design practice has been discussed by Raths (1974).

The brittle characteristics of some components and joints, however, introduce complex uncertainties. The lack of continuity through joints casts serious doubts on the restraint capability of the joints. Without known and predictable joint restraints, lower-bound assumptions must be made in stability analyses.

A structure may appear to be designed for all code-specified lateral loads, including loads caused by the deformation of the structure (second-order analysis per Chapter CB-8), and yet a local failure caused by an isolated imperfection (joint) may precipitate total collapse. Concern about progressive collapse in large-panel structures has been voiced since unreinforced joints appeared in medium-rise and high-rise construction. The partial collapse at Ronan Point dramatically focused attention to the urgency of the problem (Popoff, 1972).

There are three basic philosophies for avoiding progressive collapse in large-panel structures, namely:

1. Method A: By providing alternative paths of support to carry the load, assuming the removal of a critical section of the load-bearing walls.

2. Method B: By providing a form of construction of such stiffness and continuity as to assure the stability of the building against forces liable to damage the load-supporting members.

3. Method C: By providing a form of construction that avoids or reduces the probability that the main structural system can be subjected to exceptional or accidental forces; for example, "knock-out" panels to relieve accidental blast loading (Fuller, 1975). The effectiveness of this method has, however, been challenged by some building authorities. Furthermore, it would not alleviate the problem for accidental loads such as impact due to vehicular collision with a vital structural element.

The emerging philosophy concerning progressive collapse further embraces certain seismic design requirements of seismic codes. Seismic codes require that all concrete, including joints, be reinforced. This requirement extends to all seismic risk zones (Popoff, 1975).

Wind and seismic loads are specified by local building codes. Where specified seismic loads are low, the geometry of the structures may be such that wind loads are also very low. The problem of P-Δ stability may remain totally undetected (see Chapter CB-8). Hence, there is a need to develop general structural integrity. In an effort to meet this need, some codes specify a minimum lateral design load. Building codes in the Netherlands and Denmark require a minimum horizontal load of 1.5% of the total vertical loads (MacGregor, 1972). This has now been changed to require an increase in wind load. The introduction of a minimum lateral design load related to building mass will usually provide some assurance of over-all stability. As stability is a function of geometry and weight, a lateral load related to mass also provides a sense of direction and reality in designing diaphragms. This may well remove some objections raised against existing provisions to prevent progressive collapse (Popoff, 1972).

6   Design Criteria—Loads and Actions

The first step in preparing design criteria for precast concrete structures must be to identify and stipulate the loading conditions against which strength and serviceability must be measured. In keeping with the objective of achieving factors of safety and serviceability equivalent to those existing in monolithic concrete construction, most design loads and their configurations should be taken from existing standards and building codes (Fling, 1973).

Some design considerations and loadings not normally included in existing United States regulations are believed to represent a greater potential threat to the integrity of precast concrete structures than to the monolithic concrete frame structures commonly used in multistory buildings. At this time abnormal loadings such as explosions, partial collapse, severe windstorm, and flood can only be considered in qualitative terms and design criteria must be based on probability theory. Large-panel precast construction is especially sensitive to abnormal loads, due to lack of adequate details, resulting in limited continuity and ductility. Excellent summaries of the loading conditions that should be considered in the design of large-panel structures are given by Schultz and Fintel (1975) and by Speyer (1976).

The characteristics and range of dead load, live loads, wind load, snow load, and other service loads are specified by all model building codes. Gravity loads can be estimated fairly accurately. Were the wind loads also accurately predictable, discontinuous joints could be located judiciously and the resulting structure indeed would be stable. However, wind loads are not accurately known at every point on the surface of the structure. An unusual eddy current at the top of the structure, where gravity loads providing stability are small, may induce totally unforeseen vibrations and forces. For earthquake and other dynamic loads, the response of the structural system must be taken into consideration (Popoff, 1972).

In addition to the loads (including wind and seismic) specified by the building code, account must be taken of the loads and deformations caused by temperature and time-dependent deformations of the precast elements. The magnitude and even the nature of loads induced by volumetric changes resulting from shrinkage, creep, and temperature variations are not well understood. Particular attention should be given to loads caused by post-tensioned connections and by the rigid connections to supports for flexural members (ACI-ASCE Committee 512, 1974).

The ends of elements usually rotate due to shrinkage and creep deformations of the precast elements. Elastic deflection and creep deflection caused by sustained loads such as mechanical equipment, piping, walls, and partitions also contribute to the rotation of the ends of elements. End rotations also accumulate with repeated loading. If these rotations are restrained, forces are produced in the flexural and supporting elements. The effect of foundation settlement on the finished structure should be considered in the substructure design.

The effects of some loads are unpredictable: for example, forces arising from misalinement of wall elements as they are stacked upon each other, from differential gravity loads, as in the abutment of a bearing wall [possibly 7 MPa (1000 psi) stress] with a "nonbearing" wall [possibly 1.4 MPa (200 psi) stress], from vibration, from differential settlement, and innumerable other reasons. Reasonable assumptions as to the existence and magnitude of such forces should be made, including second-order (P-Δ) effects due to expected lateral displacements under load.

In precast concrete floor systems special consideration should be given to structural system criteria. In most precast systems the floors are assumed to function as rigid diaphragms with respect to in-plane forces. To realize this assumed condition, peripheral and cross tie beams, and continuity ties in panel joints over bearing supports (as shown in Fig. 12.20) are essential (Pauw, 1972). Where cross tie beams cannot be provided, some longitudinal joint reinforcement needs to be incorporated in the joint to confine panel end continuity connections.

These tie beams play a vital role, not only in connecting precast elements or element subassemblies to each other, but also in distributing loads and in equalizing deformations. Tie beams may be classified into functional categories as shown in Fig 12.21:

a. To tie structural nonbearing walls to the bearing walls.

b. To resist tensile forces in the floor diaphragms due to wind loads or other lateral forces, as well as to connect these diaphragms to the shear walls.

c. To supplement the shear resistance of the vertical joints.

d. To equalize vertical deformation of adjacent wall panels. Unequal deformation may result when loads are unequal, when panels are made of different materials (that is, concrete with different moduli of elasticity), or when precast wall panels are combined with a cast-in-place wall.

e. To restrain deformation and resist the forces induced by differential thermal expansion between stories.

f. To resist tensile forces in the wall diaphragms due to differential settlement.

Last, but not least, tie beams play a vital role in providing reserve strength to resist collapse due to accidental and unpredictable loads or to loss of member resistance capacity due to fire (Lewicki and Pauw, 1972).

In general, in design calculations it is assumed that the floor system is infinitely stiff in its own plane, and this assumption is justifiable if reinforcement is provided, particularly at the joints. For deciding on the necessary reinforcement in the floor system, a mode of buckling is generally used other than the one determined by the study of total stability. For example, in a long narrow building, stabilized at its ends by stairwell shafts, a buckling problem occurs when the floor systems deflect alternately in opposite directions between the towers so that the columns form a zigzag line. The floor-system cross sections are assumed to be cracked sections. If the floor system consists of elements without any embedded connecting reinforcement, the joints between the elements must be reinforced and filled with mortar such that a development length is assured by bond to anchor the reinforcement.

With a suitable arrangement of stabilizing elements the horizontal forces that originate in the floor system from shrinkage, and from creep, in prestressed concrete elements, can be limited. However, many times an arrangement must be accepted which is not suitable from this viewpoint. So that such forces do not affect the stabilizing structural elements detrimentally, thus endangering the total stability, it must be assured that the stabilizing elements can take up these forces. The forces still must not be large enough to crack the floor system at its weakest section. However, the forces resulting from creep, shrinkage, forced assembly, and other

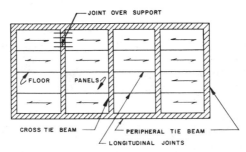

Fig. 12.20 Tie beams for precast floor system

constraining and secondary effects can sometimes be so large as to make special provisions for expansion and contraction necessary.

It has been observed in tests that the constrained deformation of a short column or bearing wall panel can be comparatively high without the capacity for vertical load being significantly affected. On the other hand, the ability of the element to provide lateral stability is reduced. The capacity to provide stability can actually be lost for large additional deformations caused by secondary phenomena, so that the element itself needs to be supported laterally by the floor system. The building must

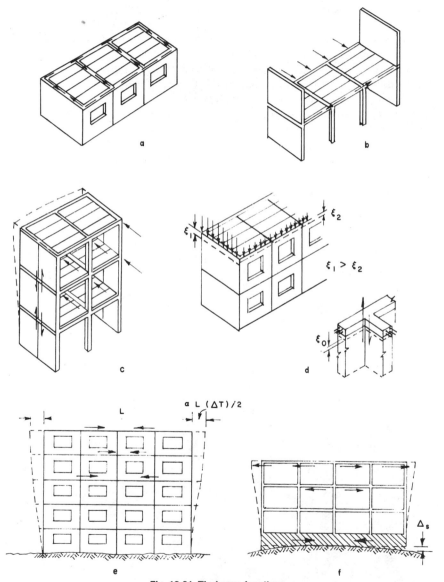

Fig. 12.21 Tie beam functions

be so designed with regard to these important factors that the intended stabilizing function is not endangered by uncontrolled secondary forces. In particular, large differences in deformation caused by differential shrinkage and creep can arise between the first-story system and the foundation system.

In summary, it should be noted that there is a marked conflict between the objectives of providing stability and of limiting constraining or secondary forces. A consistent system must be chosen and adequate measures taken, such as providing ductile reinforcement ties or support arrangements, so as to yield a system realizable in practice (Lewicki and Pauw, 1972).

Strength, stability, and serviceability depend upon the ability of the structure and its elements to accommodate the effects of each design consideration. The design process is one of controlling the anticipated response of the structure within acceptable limits. Consequently, design criteria for precast concrete systems must identify the response of the structure to each design consideration and load, including the effects on each primary structural element (Fling, 1973).

With respect to stability in the event of exceptional loads such as blasts, the effect of the possibility of the loss of one or more primary load-bearing elements, as shown

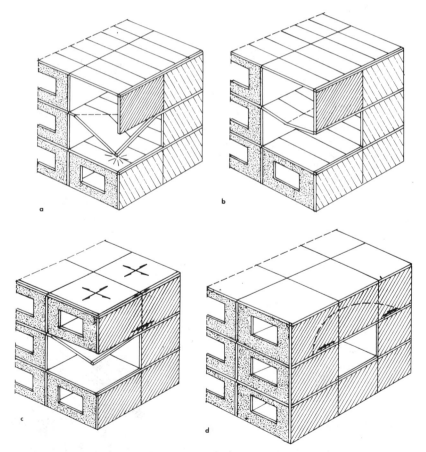

Fig. 12.22 Progressive collapse resistance mechanisms (Lewicki et al., 1974): (a) One-way floor panels untied to upper wall; (b) one-way floor panels tied to upper wall; (c) two-way floor panels; (d) wall beam action

in Fig. 12.22, should be considered (Lewicki et al., 1974). To prevent progressive collapse one can hardly overemphasize the absolute necessity of effectively joining the various components of the structure together to develop interaction between wall and floor elements to redistribute loads around damaged areas by wall cantilever or beam action. In this respect, it would appear to be of major importance to install mechanically continuous steel ties interconnecting opposite walls or facades and providing safeguards for all the vertical panels (Popoff, 1972). Unbonded tendons, either fully or partially or even nominally post-tensioned, have been successfully used as a practical and economical method to achieve this requirement.

As far as fire is concerned any measures that improve strength, load-bearing capacity, and over-all stability of a concrete structure at normal temperatures will invariably increase its resistance to fire damage. The reverse is also true (Institution of Structural Engineers, 1975).

7 Erection Considerations

Certain procedures must be established for the erection sequence of members. The elimination of welded connections or the use of bolted erection connections may simplify and speed up the erection operation in some instances. In many cases, however, welded joints at suitably designed points can save erection time and their cost offset the cost of pressure grouting or similar measures required for stability during erection. With suitable welded connections, stability during erection can often be achieved without the need for heavy propping or bracing, thus resulting in over-all economy. Stability of the building during the erection procedure should be built into the design. Connections should be designed to absorb the forces arising during erection from wind and the temporary forces caused by construction methods and equipment. Analysis must include consideration of forces which may be induced by differential loadings on members when the structure is partially erected. Temporary bracing must be carefully planned, because indiscriminate guying of the structure at the job site may create interference with other trades and encumber the progress of the project. Indiscriminate field cutting of precast structural members is extremely dangerous, and provisions should be made at the design and detailing stage of the project for all necessary cuts, holes, and notches. Where field cutting of small holes is advantageous for coordination with other trades, proper accommodation should be made during the design stage.

Another factor which should receive attention is the layout of the construction site. The contractor's layout can result in expensive operations around the buildings, costs invariably reflected in the over-all construction cost. His layout must be economical in terms of construction time. It is necessary, therefore, that the construction department concerned should give adequate attention to the layout of the site for building operations (ACI-ASCE Committee 512, 1974; Yee and Masuda, 1974).

The dimensional accuracy of the project should be verified as each phase is completed by a subtrade. It is more economical for the general contractor or owner to verify the work after each phase rather than to have the responsibility for accuracy passed on to the next subcontractor. The assurance of accuracy as work proceeds results in an economical and smoothly running project.

The size for precast concrete members may be limited by the permissible weight and dimensions permitted on highways. Special permits and routings are available in most cases. The precaster should deliver the fabricated precast concrete to the job site in such sequences as will permit the most efficient and economical erection directly from the vehicle.

The owner must provide adequate truck access to the job site and through to the crane. Good access can result in savings for all subcontractors. It may be advisable to place the base course of any roads or driveways to the project before the major portion of the building is started. Since the cost for the erection of the precast concrete can be a high percentage of the cost of the material, it is important to give proper consideration to this operation. The weight of the member and the distance to reach from solid ground determine the size necessary for the crane. If there are electric overhead wires within the swing radius of the crane boom, it may be necessary to relocate that service temporarily (ACI-ASCE Committee 512, 1974).

12.4 PRECAST ELEMENT DESIGN AND DETAILING

Prefabricated elements are cast and cured in a special yard depending on the job, or produced in a factory. They can be custom designed for the building to be erected, or selected from a factory catalog. They are then transported, erected, and connected to form the final structure. Connections can be provided by grouting, welding, bolting, prestressing, friction-gravity or cast-in-place concrete (ACI-ASCE Committee 512, 1974).

1 Concrete Strength

Concrete strengths used for precast structural elements are generally higher and more uniform than with cast-in-place concrete. The higher and more uniform strengths are the result of better quality control, better selection and proportioning of ingredients, and the use of lower slump concrete which can be more easily compacted at a plant due to mechanized vibration techniques. Higher-strength concretes lead to a more efficient use of concrete and steel, thus keeping the size and weight of the elements to a minimum.

The low water content, resulting from better selection of materials and from placement of the concrete at a drier consistency, lowers the concrete's shrinkage and creep. In addition, a large percentage of shrinkage takes place prior to erection since significant strengths are required before the member is erected. Creep values are less, due to the mix, use of accelerated curing techniques, and age of the elements when loaded.

Durability requirements will frequently dictate the section sizes and cover of the reinforcing steel. These requirements depend on the degree of exposure to weather, fire, and corrosive elements. Where corrosion from any cause is a problem, crack widths at service loads should be limited by limiting the amount of tension allowed by proper dispersion of the reinforcement.

Precasting permits great flexibility. Very complicated shapes, such as the precast spandrel beam in Fig. 12.23, can readily be produced in a factory provided there is sufficient repetitive use to warrant the investment in special forms. Architectural and production requirements for such shapes frequently dictate section sizes, fillets, and other details.

Large horizontal openings in floors and roofs may require special structural supports. Future as well as present use of the structure should be considered. Openings in the webs of members may seriously affect ultimate strength (ACI-ASCE Committee 512, 1974).

2 Production Methods

Production methods control some designs. It may be uneconomical to provide weld plates for connections in some standard elements, and alternate details may be necessary. Inserts on top surfaces should be avoided. Inserts with voids are subject to filling with debris and with water, which can damage an element if freezing occurs.

When large, heavy members or thin walls are used, special consideration should be given to adequate anchorage of the handling device for erection. The location of these devices can affect the ease of erection and also the fastening of the precast element to the structure (ACI-ASCE Committee 512, 1974).

3 Handling Stresses

The handling and stacking of precast members in storage and during transit should be considered in the selection and design of the members. Handling stresses can be higher than those experienced by the elements under service loads.

The location and capacity of all lifting inserts should receive careful consideration at the time of detailing. The location of lifting points should be distributed in such a way that during shipping, handling, and erection the stresses in the precast unit do not exceed those specified for the final condition, unless disposition of such stresses is satisfactorily included in the design.

The proper location of lifting points relative to the center of gravity of the unit will assure that no overstressing or failure occurs during erection. The location of

Fig. 12.23 Precast spandrel beam, Medical Faculty Building, Aachen, Germany (Courtesy: Manfred Stiller)

lifting point is especially critical for prestressed members. Lifting devices should be located on the architecturally less prominent surfaces. Otherwise, cutting off, patching, and filling operations may become an economic factor.

A minimum factor of safety of 4 is recommended for lifting devices. Where the possibility exists of directional changes in force occurring during the handling operation (for example, in the case of tilt-up construction), these changes must be considered in the design of the lifting device.

The avoidance of brittle materials for lifting loops is imperative for protection against shock loading; prestressing strand is preferable to cold bent reinforcing bars. The precaster is generally knowledgeable on the design of lifting devices. For delicate or complicated precast products, he should be consulted as to the best method of erection and type of lifting device (ACI-ASCE Committee 512, 1974).

4 Tolerances

Even though rigid tolerances and proper inspection are placed on the field portion of a precast concrete project, consecutive accumulated tolerances can cause conditions that are impossible to correct. This problem can be overcome by providing escape areas where accumulated tolerances or production errors can be absorbed. The problem of accumulated tolerances is not a condition peculiar to precast concrete structures, since it is impossible to achieve a zero variance condition in any type of member or material (ACI-ASCE Committee 512, 1974).

The size of members, the method of manufacturing, and the particular forms used are factors controlling the dimensional accuracy attained in precast construction. Double-T's, channels, hollow-core slabs, and small sections produced in fixed forms should be well within acceptable limits for dimensional tolerances. The dimensions of large single-T's and other members will vary more because of the size and the more complex forming involved. The design of the building should allow for the tolerance variations possible because of the forming methods, member type, and member size. The importance of tolerance variation depends on the location of the element in the structure and its method of connection to other materials or elements. Acceptable dimensional tolerances for precast prestressed concrete have been published by the Prestressed Concrete Institute (PCI 1970, 1971).

5 Member Proportioning

In tall buildings, the structural behavior and the cost of individual members as well as of the entire project require the investigation of forces and stresses that are frequently ignored in low buildings. For example, stresses resulting from differential creep, shrinkage, and thermal movements can usually be ignored in low buildings, but may be controlling factors in the design of tall buildings. Furthermore, the magnitude of a tall building project will make a more thorough analysis of all forces and stresses and a more refined proportioning of members economically feasible, so as to reduce the construction costs while maintaining a reasonable, uniform margin of safety. The same extensive design procedures would not be warranted for smaller projects.

Proportioning of members and connections after completion of the final analysis usually consists of sizing and detailing the reinforcement and selecting the required concrete strength, since revision of concrete outlines would modify the distribution of forces obtained in the analysis. At intermediate steps, such revisions may be necessary.

Changes in required concrete strength or reinforcing steel grade should be planned with great care to minimize construction errors which would endanger the safety of the structure. Likewise, reinforcement details, joints, and connections should be designed for easy, dependable, error-free execution.

The problems of joinery in precast linear structures (beams and columns) are quite different from those in panel structures. Precast linear members are frequently prestressed and hence experience significant volume reductions. This leads to large tensile forces in horizontal members and bending in the frame. Connections must resist tensile and horizontal shearing forces in addition to the shear and bending moment caused by gravity loads. The effects of creep and shrinkage should be considered for prestressed members (PCI, 1973). Panel structures experience these problems to a much smaller degree. Also, multistory structures are less influenced by the restraint of the foundations than are low, single-story structures.

Another difference between linear structures and panel structures is the method of carrying gravity loads in vertical members and joints. Columns must utilize the reinforcing steel to carry part of the load if they are to be kept to a reasonable size in tall buildings. The connection of precast column to precast column is relatively difficult if continuity of reinforcing steel is required. By contrast, panel structures usually do not require continuity of the vertical reinforcing steel across the joint to carry vertical load. Wall panels thick enough to satisfy other requirements, such as fire resistance, handling stresses, thermal insulation, and sound attenuation, are usually adequate to carry the vertical load without bearing on the reinforcing steel.

Panel structures arranged to resist all horizontal loads by in-plane bending of their wall elements are inherently very stiff. There may be little additional cost for resisting horizontal forces after the necessary panels for enclosing the building and subdividing the space are provided. On the other hand, precast linear structures resisting lateral forces by frame action must develop large moments at the connections. Such moments are difficult to resist in precast connections (Fling, 1972).

Bilinear elements such as T, Π, H, or cross frames may be used to move the connections away from high-moment areas. However, such frame elements require much more rigid fabrication and erection tolerances.

While strength is always an important consideration, the practical problems of production and field erection of precast concrete frequently dominate. That is, connection details must be economical and capable of production and implementation in the field with the tolerance conditions required. A careful balance should be drawn between loose tolerances, which may ease fabrication, and tighter tolerances, which may facilitate erection.

The use of shear walls is an efficient, economical method for resisting large lateral forces. Unfortunately, their primary mode of failure, especially if lightly reinforced, is usually a brittle shear failure which is unacceptable in seismic regions. The Japanese approach to this problem is to consider the concrete shear wall as infilling between columns of a frame capable of carrying the gravity loads. The wall is expected to remain uncracked in normal service, that is, to resist wind and mild earthquakes. In severe earthquakes, the shear wall becomes cracked but the boundary frame is designed as a ductile frame to resist propagation of the crack through the frame and to restrain expansion of the cracked infilled panel wall. Thus the wall exhibits a ductile shearing resistance and acts as a damper to the seismic forces by absorbing considerable strain energy. After damage by an earthquake the wall can be easily replaced (see Chapter CB-11).

Current column design procedures are based on laboratory tests of single-story columns that are extrapolated for the real situation in tall buildings. The stability of columns is discussed in Chapter CB-8. It has been observed that in the case of columns, as well as wall panels, precast in a horizontal position, the elastic modulus of the concrete may vary across the cross section due to differential compaction. Thus the geometric center line and the centroidal axis of resistance may not coincide. Some eccentricity may therefore be developed in elements which otherwise appear to be loaded concentrically. In most precast framing systems lateral forces are transmitted by diaphragm action of the floor system, and the entire lateral force resistance is provided by shear walls or a rigid core, or both. In such systems buckling instability of columns or bearing walls is greatly reduced although not completely eliminated (Bardhan-Roy, 1975).

Some of the considerations in the design of columns in tall buildings are:

1. The actual maximum eccentricity.

2. Generation of large horizontal forces due to deviation of columns from exact vertical position (Lorentsen, 1972).

3. The ultimate strain of concrete in columns as affected by using very high-strength concrete, lightweight concrete, high percentages of steel, massive sizes, or sustained stress at a high percentage of the concrete cylinder strength. An assumed ultimate compressive strain of 0.0030 or 0.0035 may be unnecessarily conservative in some cases and too liberal in other cases.

4. Method of transferring loads through a floor system when the column uses high-strength concrete in comparison to the strength of the concrete in the floor.

5. The shear capacity under high axial load, especially in columns resisting seismic forces.

6. Practical and theoretical upper limits on the quantity of longitudinal steel.

7. Variation in concrete strength, steel percentage, and size of columns along the height to achieve maximum economy (Fling, 1973).

6 Linear Elements and Frames

The principal linear elements used in precast concrete framing systems include beams, girders and one-way floor-slab elements, columns, and frame subassemblies including facade grids. An unlimited variety of cross sections is feasible for such members.

Beams and floor units may be rectangular, solid or cored, T, channel, double-T, or box sections. As shown in Fig. 12.24, I-profiles are often used for main girders, and channel sections are often used for spandrel beams as in Fig. 12.14.

Floor systems include thick slabs of constant thickness which give reduced story height and flexibility of internal planning, but are expensive in their use of concrete and reinforcing steel. They can be thin slabs on beams or slabs on a grid of beams forming a structural waffle, which are suitable for large spans and two directions of support.

Prefabricated floor units, with or without topping, are often used to avoid or simplify formwork. Commonly used sections include joists, rectangular or T-shaped; channel slab or double-T units; slab-panels, flat or ribbed, solid or cored. Holes or cores can be provided in appropriate places for service ducts. Linear floor elements, such as the channel slabs in Fig. 12.25, are often pretensioned (Kavyrchine, 1972).

A cast-in-place floor slab or topping slab is often used to tie precast-prestressed elements into a rigid diaphragm. When topping slabs are used the effect of differential shrinkage should be considered in the design.

The function of a floor system is to provide a usable horizontal flat surface capable of bearing the service loads. Also, mechanical equipment can be suspended from a floor.

Segmented precast units may also be used for girders, as for example the post-tensioned segment girders for the Gulf Life Center shown in Fig. 12.26. (The completed building is shown in Fig. 3.12 of Chapter CB-3.) Post-tensioning offers a good solution to the problem of building moment-resisting frames with precast segments. Prestressed joists have the advantage of faster erection than is possible with cast-in-place concrete joists. The economies of plant-produced precast elements and the quality of these elements are combined with a fast and efficient erection procedure in the use of segmental post-tensioned structures (Kavyrchine, 1972).

Fig. 12.24 Service building, Schiphol Airport: precast column and I-beam frames and precast double-T deck units (Manufacturer: Liesbosch Beton, Nieuwegein, The Netherlands) (Courtesy: Stroband)

7 Columns

Columns are traditionally used in reinforced concrete as vertical bearing elements. Structural systems made of concrete are relatively heavy, and concrete column sizes at the base may become so large as to be cumbersome. Many design schemes have been proposed to reduce the size of these columns; for example, steel sections encased in reinforced concrete columns can help reduce their dimensions. Partial prestressing may be desirable to increase column rigidity, especially in moment-resisting frames. Long columns, such as those in Fig. 12.27, are often economical since their use reduces the number of column splices required (Bruggeling, 1972).

Column connection and splicing details and beam supporting brackets or corbels

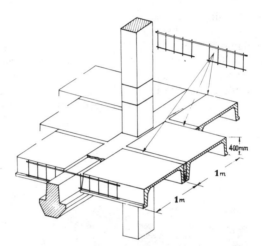

Fig. 12.25 Precast channel floor units supported on ledger beams (Kavyrchine et al., 1972)

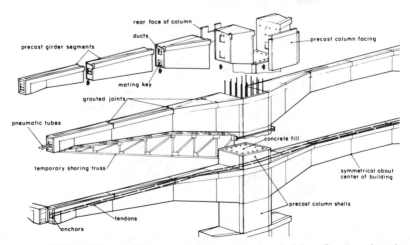

Fig. 12.26 Gulf Life Building, details of segmented post-tensioned girders (Courtesy: Jenny)

require special attention and should be designed and detailed to permit simple and fast erection. Brackets should be adequately reinforced to resist both vertical and horizontal forces to which they may be subjected. Standardized details have been developed by the Prestressed Concrete Institute, as for example the bracket detail in Fig. 12.28 (PCI, 1969).

8 Frames

To obtain adequate stiffness against lateral forces, it is necessary to create within the structure of a tall building two-dimensional systems which provide stability against forces acting within the plane of these systems. Such planar systems may consist of a grid of vertical columns and horizontal beams. Such frames are traditionally used in reinforced concrete, and provide good stability at an economical price for moderate heights (Kavyrchine, 1972).

For tall buildings, framed systems are less suitable because beams and column sizes become excessively large if stability depends on the flexural stiffness of beam and column elements and their connections. Cast-in-place moment connections in moment-resisting frames composed of precast columns and beams are usually complex and expensive. Field moment connections should therefore be avoided unless prestressing can be employed to construct frame subassemblies. More generally frame subassemblies are precast as cross, X, T, double-T, H, or pierced frame elements. Where architecturally acceptable, double-T, H, and frame elements are preferred since cross, X, and T elements require more elaborate temporary supports during erection. Such elements are especially appropriate for facade grids.

Fig. 12.27 Multistory "long" precast columns (Manufacturer: Liesbosch Beton, Nieuwegein, The Netherlands) (Courtesy: Stroband)

In this application they provide a good compromise between a shear wall and a grid of closely spaced columns and girders. A typical cross-element facade is shown in Fig. 12.29(a) (Kavyrchine, 1972), and multistory rectangular frame element in Fig. 12.29(b). The system shown in Fig. 12.29(a) was used for the facade of the Frantel Hotel in Rungis, near Orly, France. Fig. 12.29(b) shows how the use of precast-prestressed T floor beams provides a column-free building.

Precast pierced rectangular frames of various configurations are commonly used for bearing and curtain wall facades, as shown in Fig. 12.30. The precast pierced panels in this building served as formwork for the cast-in-place columns and spandrel beams. Such panels may be assembled into a moment-resisting frame and also serve as vertical load bearing elements. Such a system was applied in Erivan (Armenian SSR) for a 10-story building designed to resist seismic forces. Light-weight concrete was used for all parts of the building to provide good thermal insulation as well as to reduce total weight. Such systems have been proposed for 20-story buildings in seismic areas (Kavyrchine, 1972).

Precast Π and H frames, both with and without cantilevered beam elements, have been successfully used in a wide range of construction applications in various countries. They consist of two columns with an interconnecting beam cast as a single unit (Bobrowski et al., 1974a).

Connection of the cantilevered portions of these components with beams or to each other is accomplished by using simple butt joints, that is by welding or splicing the extended reinforcement bars and concreting the joint (Vasiliev et al., 1972). Where appropriate, H frames are preferred because column connections may be

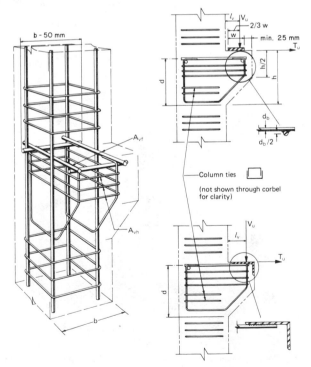

Fig. 12.28 PCI—standard bracket detail

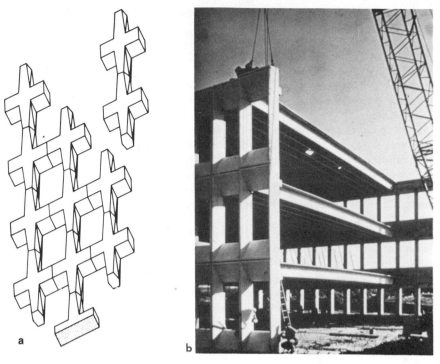

Fig. 12.29 Precast facade bearing wall elements: (a) Cross elements (Kavyrchine, 1972); (b) multistory frame elements (Courtesy: Kavyrchine)

Fig. 12.30 Pacific Telephone and Telegraph Headquarters, San Francisco (Courtesy: Pankow)

made in a low moment region. A typical example of the connection details required for such frames is shown in Fig. 12.31.

The ideal position of joints is at the midheight of a story where the point of contraflexure normally occurs. Sometimes, for architectural or manufacturing considerations, the position of the joints may vary. In any case it is away from the intersection of beam and columns, which is structurally the most sensitive area. Thus the connection design is primarily for compression, although sometimes a certain amount of bending has to be provided for to allow variations in position from the point of contraflexure. The horizontal beam connection between adjacent H frames, which occurs at midspan of alternate bays, is achieved either by welding of reinforcement or adding splice bars in the field-cast portion of the beam.

Shoes are fabricated by using steel channels or plates, or both, with some stiffeners and locating pins. The shoes are shop welded to the column reinforcement. The shoes could also be formed using standard square, rectangular, or circular hollow sections.

To assure a speedy erection sequence it is imperative that dimensional inaccuracies and their effect should be minimal. It is possible to use highly sophisticated optical instruments by which an accuracy within ± 2 mm (3/32 in.) in the positioning of shoes can be guaranteed. The normal procedure for specifying tolerances is shown in Fig. 12.32. All vertical frames of a bay (or several of the frames in the case of a very high building) are match cast against each other on the ground to form a chain of frames.

The advantages of H-frame construction are manifold. A frame requires propping in one direction only during erection, being stable in the other direction by itself. Locating pins assure proper positioning of successive vertical units, and connection is easily done by running weld along the perimeter of the shoes at the junction. Nominal runs of weld, or even spot weld, in most cases may be adequate during erection. Further welding can follow before the superloads are imposed. Because of match casting, constructional difficulties due to dimensional variations are for all practical purposes eliminated, and a rapid erection sequence can be maintained (Bobrowski et al., 1974a).

As may be seen in Fig. 12.33, H frames with an integral cladding panel are

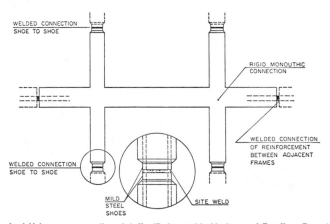

Fig. 12.31 Typical H-frame connection details (Bobrowski, Abeles and Bardhan-Roy, 1974a)

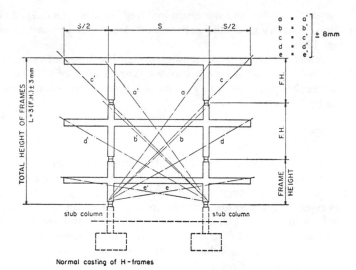

Fig. 12.32 H-frame match casting tolerances (Bobrowski, Abeles and Bardhan-Roy, 1974a)

Fig. 12.33 H-frame with integral cladding panels, Portsmouth Polytechnic biology block (Courtesy: Bardhan-Roy)

eminently suitable for office and apartment building facades. The integral cladding panel can also serve as a spandrel beam to support floor-beam or panel elements, as shown in Fig. 12.34.

Multistory frames, such as those shown in Fig. 12.35, are often economical, especially for buildings with a central corridor. The number of field connections required is markedly reduced by using such frames. Precast frame design procedures are discussed by Gensert et al. (1974).

9 Walls

Partitions of some type have to be built within a building. A logical idea is to use structural partitions, which can bear vertical loads and lateral forces; indeed, walls were thus used at the very beginning of the art of building. At that time their function was essentially to bear loads and assure separations. In tall buildings, walls are often used as stiffening elements against lateral forces and are called for that reason "shear walls." They are thinner than frames of equal resistance, but they are obstacles to communication, and have to be pierced by many holes for doors, windows, and ducts (Kavyrchine, 1972).

10 Wall Panel Elements

Interior bearing shear walls are generally solid walls, utilizing either normal-weight or lightweight concrete. Exterior walls are dual-purpose elements; in addition to serving as bearing walls or shear walls, or both, they should provide

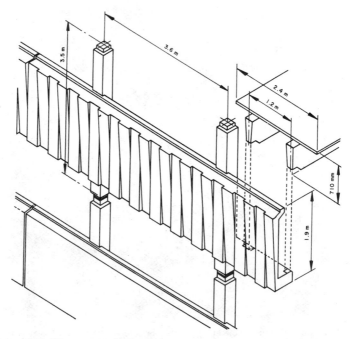

Fig. 12.34 Integral cladding as spandrel beam

thermal insulation. Sandwich construction is therefore often employed consisting of:

1. An exterior layer. Architectural precast concrete panels are used which may be textured to provide an esthetically pleasing surface. This layer is exposed to the elements and must be reinforced and of a quality adequate to inhibit deterioration due to corrosion and carbonation.

2. An insulating layer. Various products such as styrofoam, foam glass, or glass wool may be employed for this layer, and a vapor barrier may be incorporated.

3. An interior layer. This layer generally serves the structural function of bearing wall or shear wall, or both.

Since the exterior layer is subjected to temperature fluctuations and the interior layer is maintained at a relatively constant temperature, the intermediate insulating layer must permit differential movements without subjecting the nonstructural exterior layer to stress. The exterior must, however, be firmly tied to the interior layer so that it cannot peel off.

Sandwich panels must be detailed so that joints between adjacent panels can be made weathertight with appropriate plastic sealing compounds. The exterior layer must be free to expand and the attachments to the interior structural element so detailed that no undesirable "cold bridges" are created (Bruggeling, 1972).

11 Bearing Walls

The ACI Building Code specifies minimum reinforcement requirements for bearing walls subject to flexural stresses (ACI, 1971). European specifications are

Fig. 12.35 Multistory frames (Courtesy: Bardhan-Roy)

generally more liberal and require only such reinforcement as may be essential to resist temperature, shrinkage, and handling stresses (CEB/CIB/UEAtc, 1969; CEB, 1967; British Standard, 1970; Polish Standard, 1969; USSR Standard, 1965; Swedish Standard, 1967). Unreinforced panels are considered as plain concrete elements in computing static load bearing capacity (Lewicki, 1966; Finzi, 1965). In American specifications an effective safety factor (herein defined as the ratio of the mean bearing capacity divided by the expected mean load) of 4.5 is required for precast wall panels used as bearing walls (ACI Committee 533, 1971). The safety factors required by most European specifications are lower, being less than 3 in some East European specifications (Polish Standard, 1969; USSR Standard, 1965).

The wall bearing capacity to resist the combined effects of vertical and lateral forces should be checked for the two critical zones shown in Fig. 12.36. Zone I is at midheight of the wall panel, and Zone II encompasses the connection between floor and wall panels. Specific requirements for Zone II are given by Speyer (1976).

The ultimate load bearing capacity of Zone I may be expressed by

$$N_{uI} = \alpha_w A_w f_{wu} \tag{12.1}$$

in which α_w = wall capacity factor, a function of the load eccentricity, the slenderness ratio, modulus of elasticity of the concrete, and panel geometry including effect of end restraints; A_w = cross-sectional area of wall in zone checked; $f_{wu} = \alpha_c f_{cu}$ effective concrete compressive strength in the wall; α_c = capacity factor for compressive strength; and f_c' = ultimate (28-day) compressive strength. (See also the discussion at Eq. 12.6 in Section 12.5.)

The area A_w is the effective area subjected to an assumed uniform stress intensity. The capacity factor α_c may be assumed to have a value of 0.85 for plain walls if f_c' is from cylinder tests (ACI, 1971). For cored walls or walls with an intermediate horizontal joint this factor should be determined by test. The interaction of the eccentricity, slenderness ratio, and elastic modulus should be considered for an exact analysis of the bearing-capacity reduction factor for "beam-column" behavior

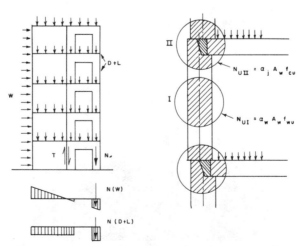

Fig. 12.36 Wall bearing capacity (Lewicki and Pauw, 1973)

(Lewicki, 1966). Some codes permit an approximate evaluation obtained by setting (Sahlin, 1959)

$$\alpha_w = (\alpha_e)(\alpha_{cw}) \qquad (12.2)$$

in which α_e = function of the eccentricity alone, and α_{cw} = function of the slenderness ratio and the modulus E_c.

The value of α_w may be approximated by analysis of an assumed behavior model. The structural model shown in Fig. 12.37 is conservative and therefore may always be used with safety. In this model the wall panel is assumed to be hinged, both top and bottom, at the intersection of the geometrical center lines of the wall and of the floor slabs. Floor-slab restraining moments do not affect the wall load eccentricity in this model. The maximum effective eccentricity then is the sum of three components, thus

$$e = d_e + d_p + e_{st} \qquad (12.3)$$

in which d_e = deviation of the elastic axis from the geometric center line; d_p = eccentricity of the transmitted axial load; and e_{st} = eccentricity due to floor loads.

Deviations of the elastic axis from the geometric axis may occur in sandwich panels as a result of unequal density and unequal elastic modulus in unsymmetrically placed layers. An allowance for possible eccentricity of the transmitted axial load is required to take into account tolerance errors in fabrication and in erection. For continuous floor slabs the third term should also include an allowance for the possibility of lack of symmetry due to dimensional tolerance errors as well as for unbalanced loads. The use of this model is consistent with the recommendations of ACI Committee 533 (1971).

For tall multistory buildings the conservative model is no longer satisfactory, and the interaction between floor and wall panels should be taken into consideration, as shown in Fig. 12.38. A satisfactory limit analysis taking into account the effect of plastic deformations and stress redistribution has yet to be developed and would

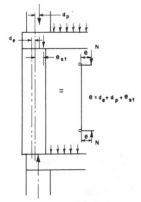

Fig. 12.37 Simplified behavioral model for wall panel (Lewicki and Pauw, 1972)

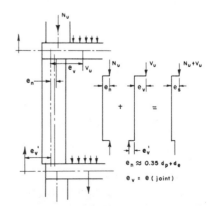

Fig. 12.38 Slab-wall interaction model (Lewicki and Pauw, 1972)

require for verification more experimental data than are now available. A few theoretical solutions based on simplifying assumptions have been proposed by Macchi (1969), Pagano (1968), Putkonen (1961), and Sahlin (1959).

These solutions have not gained wide acceptance because their complexity does not appear to be warranted until more reliable test data become available. In some of the European codes (such as the CEB/CIB/UEAtc Code and the Polish Standard PN-68) provisions are included for computing the eccentricities e_n and e_v based on the rigidity of the horizontal joint connecting the floor and wall panels. In these computations, the effect of construction inaccuracies is incorporated in the calculated value of e_n, the eccentricity of the transmitted axial load component. The effect of the interaction of the wall and floor panels is accounted for by e_v, the eccentricity of the shear force transmitted by the floor panel framing into the connection. While this empirical approach is still rather complex, it does result in a more realistic evaluation of structural behavior and more economical design dimensions (Lewicki and Pauw, 1972). A good example of American design practice is presented by Raths (1974)

12 Floor Panels

For short spans floor panels may be solid; cored prestressed panels are usually employed only for long spans. The end supports and connections should be so detailed as to prevent the accumulation of stress due to creep and shrinkage. Such accumulated stress was noted by Kist of the Delft Technological University and is termed the "Kist effect." When a prestressed member is "fixed" at the end supports, the member may develop a serious sag due to restrained creep and shrinkage of the bottom fibers.

Floor panels should be designed to support their own dead load in simple beam action; for superimposed loads and time-dependent creep and shrinkage effects a degree of continuity may be developed depending on the horizontal joint detail used. Lateral joints should be detailed to provide adequate lateral load distribution and to equalize deflection. Panels should be as wide as practical to reduce the number of longitudinal joints. Lightweight concrete is therefore often employed, because maximum panel size is commonly dictated by crane capacity (Bruggeling, 1972).

13 Boxes

Three-dimensional boxlike elements can also be prefabricated. They are often constructed by assembling several panels, but sometimes manufactured in special molds as monolithic castings (Kavyrchine, 1972).

14 Special Elements for Composite Construction

Special precast elements are often used for composite construction with steel frameworks. In one well-developed system precast floors serve both to support floor loads and as diaphragms.

The deck slabs generally are precast in a factory. Their size is limited by transport regulations on public roads. The width of the slabs ranges between 1.8 m (6 ft) and 3.0 m (10 ft); the average width is 2.4 m (8 ft). The longitudinal joints are located above the steel girders. The spacing of the floor girders therefore corresponds to the width of the concrete slabs. Statically the slabs are considered one-span beams. A live load between 2.9 kPA and 11.5 kPa (60 psf and 240 psf) requires a slab thickness of 100 mm to 127 mm (4 in. to 5 in.).

In order to economize on the handling of the slabs in the factory, in transit and on the site, the slabs should not be too large but on the other hand as large as possible to reduce the number of lifting operations, giving a suitable length of between 4.0 m and 8.0 m (13 ft and 26 ft).

The concrete slabs are cast in steel forms of very accurate manufacture. As welded forms tend to become distorted, either welding has to be avoided completely or the forms have to be planed after welding. The flatness tolerance for the lower surface of the slab (where it comes into contact with the steel girder) is 1 mm in 2 m (1/32 in. in 6 ft). The slab is 100 mm (4 in.) thick. The tolerance for the thickness is ± 1 mm (1/32 in.) (Sontag, 1973).

Two methods have been developed for fastening such slabs to the steel girders: welded studs and friction bolting. These connection systems are described in detail by Sontag (1973).

Precast spandrel panels can also be economically used to provide lateral stiffening in steel frames. They may be attached by friction bolting or by welding to insert plates or clips.

Systems using precast elements as "lost" forms have also been developed. Generally, in such systems the primary function of these elements is to provide architectural cladding; the structural function is performed by the field-cast concrete "filler." These systems are finding increased application for providing lateral stability in tall buildings for both steel and concrete frames (Khan, 1973a; Stigter, 1966).

Prefabricated elements may contain many erection accessories, for lifting, erection, and jointing, such as projecting bars, dowels, nuts, rods, and grouting ducts. Special holes and recesses also may have to be provided. All these accessories are an important factor in determining the cost of the element.

Tolerances are better than can be achieved for parts produced on site. Nevertheless, deformations of concrete during hardening and curing, under self-load and under prestress, have to be considered, and tolerances comparable to steel members cannot be expected. Careful curing and handling, and protection during storage, reduce undesirable deformations.

In any case, prefabricated elements using high-quality materials can be produced with greater care than cast-in-place parts. They can be easily checked and tested before erection, so that higher stresses can be allowed in precast elements, which may therefore be lighter than cast-in-place pieces (Kavyrchine, 1972).

12.5 JOINTS AND CONNECTIONS

Properly designed and detailed joints and connections are the single most important factor in assuring both safe and economical precast concrete structures. The strength, as well as economics, of precast construction is often governed by the connection of elements on site. The field connection should not only be efficient, but also assure simplicity of assembly and speed of erection (Lewicki and Pauw, 1972).

The proper assembly of prefabricated elements, to achieve a stable structure, is an important requirement; structural stiffness, insulation properties, watertightness, and durability depend on good execution (Kavyrchine, 1972).

The three principal design considerations are: (1) The load and actions to be resisted; (2) the structural function of the joint; and last but not least (3) the fabrication and erection procedures (Hanson, 1969).

The loads and actions to be resisted are a function not only of the size of the building but also of the structural system employed and the type of members joined at the connection. In addition to gravity and lateral loads due to wind and seismic forces, the effect of member volume changes due to creep, shrinkage, and temperature, the effect of differential column shortening and settlements, and the effect of fabrication and construction tolerance errors must be considered (Birkeland, 1966; PCI Handbook, 1971; PCI Manual, 1970; Khan and Fintel, 1971; Raths, 1974; Fintel and Khan, 1971; Popoff, 1972; Burton et al., 1967; PCI Connections Manual, 1973). There is always a probability that the structure may be subjected to abnormal loads, both during and after construction. Joints and connections must therefore be so detailed as to assure development of general structural integrity for all credible loading conditions.

Connections are invariably locations of stress concentration. Tolerance errors cause variations in the location and distribution of the forces acting at the connection (PCI Handbook, 1971). Quality of workmanship in field connections introduces another uncertainty. It is therefore common practice to use larger load factors or larger safety factors in the design of connections than are used for the precast elements connected (PCI Manual, 1970). With respect to their structural function, joints may be classified as simple bearing, bearing with axial continuity, and full moment-resisting connections. The structural performance required is primarily a function of the structural system employed to resist loads and forces. Functionally, precast structures tend to fall into one of three categories: rigid frames, shear-wall structures, and hybrid structures consisting of shear walls or shear cores combined with rigid frames. Full moment-resisting connections are required in rigid-frame structures to resist the lateral loads. In the other two categories lateral loads are transmitted by floor diaphragms to the shear walls or the shear core. In hybrid structures the lateral forces are resisted primarily by shear walls or shear cores and the frames are designed to resist gravity loads only.

In tall buildings, lateral loads tend to dictate the precast system selected. Since full-moment connections are expensive, precast rigid frame systems without shear walls are generally avoided if possible. Furthermore, in such frames, columns tend to become massive, thus occupying a large percentage of the floor area. The majority of tall precast concrete buildings, therefore, fall into either the shear wall or the hybrid shear wall-frame category. Precast shear wall structures are structures assembled of large precast panels or of precast boxes.

When the loads and actions to be resisted can be determined or estimated, joints can be designed on a rational basis using strength of materials principles. In American practice ultimate strength design principles are commonly employed. Load factors should be increased to reflect the greater uncertainty of loads and actions that must be resisted, and capacity reduction factors adjusted to reflect the field quality control of workmanship and the serious consequence of joint failure (PCI, 1971). Connections must be analyzed for possible failure modes, and reinforcement provided across potential failure planes. Such supplementary or confining reinforcement is usually designed on the basis of the shear friction theory (Birkeland, 1966, 1969). Volume change effects can be particularly troublesome, especially for prestressed elements. Shrinkage and creep in such elements as prestressed double-T beams can result in unrestrained axial strains of 0.06% to 0.11%. Joint restraint in continuous multiple-span frames can produce joint cracking or excessive loss of prestress (Raths, 1974). As a general principle no more stability connections should be provided than are required by the design system, since excess frame-stability conditions attract and result in a buildup of axial volume changes in columns and beams (Philleo, 1971).

The need for tensile continuity, not only for beams and slabs but also for columns and walls, cannot be overemphasized. This need was dramatically demonstrated in some of the structural failures in the San Fernando earthquake. Reinforcement for such tensile continuity should be sufficiently ductile to accommodate axial volume changes without excessive axial force buildup, yet have enough ultimate strength capacity to provide reserve strength to resist blasts or other unpredictable overloads (Lewicki and Pauw, 1972).

Finally, in designing joint and connection details, the problems of fabrication and erection should not be overlooked. Joints have to be located and detailed so as to facilitate erection. In many cases they have to sustain loads before grouting. Projecting steel sections, sometimes welded, in other cases bolted, threaded rods and nuts, dowels in sockets can be subjected to loads during the erection phase as well as in their final state. They help also initially to position the precast elements. The precision of this adjustment is essential in tall building construction, where accumulated errors can attain big values (Kavyrchine, 1972).

Minor design modifications can often result in significant fabrication and erection economies without jeopardizing the integrity of the design. In general the detail resulting in the simplest erection procedure will yield the greatest over-all economy (Lewicki and Pauw, 1972).

1 Joint Classifications

Joints and connections may be divided into "hard" and "soft" connections. In hard connections, movements and rotations within the connection are restrained. Such connections are normally used in rigid frames, such as beam to column, column to footing, and beam to girder connections, to resist lateral forces. Most hard connections employ steel plate or rolled shape accessories, such as bearing plates or confinement angles (Hanson, 1969; PCI, 1971). Clip angles or shear plates, anchored to the precast elements by welded studs or by reinforcement welded to the plates and oriented so as to resist tensile stresses, are often used (Birkeland, 1966, 1969). Alternately, structural shapes may be embedded, as for example in column connections. Industry standards have been developed for most of the commonly used frame connections, such as column-foundation, beam to column, and continuous beam to column connections (PCI, 1971). Post-tensioning and bonding with epoxy adhesives can also be effectively used to develop moment-resisting connections between elements (Hugenschmidt, 1974).

Soft connections permit a limited amount of movement in the connection. This is usually achieved by the use of elastomeric bearing pads. In actuality, most connections are neither fully soft nor fully hard.

Connections may also be classified on the basis of the mechanism employed

(Hanson, 1969). In gravity connections, lateral forces are resisted merely by the friction at the bearing surface. Positive connections may be achieved by bolting, welding, or post-tensioning. Gravity connections are commonly supplemented by dowels to resist lateral forces. Dowels may be fully grouted or they may only be partially grouted near the top to permit some lateral movement. Cast-in-place or grouted connections are commonly employed in panel construction, as will be discussed subsequently in more detail (Lewicki and Pauw, 1972).

A distinction is sometimes made between joints and connections, a joint being the interface between the adjoining or abutting elements, whereas a connection is a physical stress-resisting coupling or tie between such elements. Joints and connections may be further categorized as "wet" or "dry." A cast-in-place floor panel connection or a grouted or pointed mortar joint would be typical of the wet category, whereas an elastomeric bearing strip would be a dry connection. Where applicable, dry connections are preferred because they do not delay erection schedules.

It is virtually impossible to discuss all the various connection details that have been and could be developed for precast concrete structures. Some of the more important and commonly used details are described in what follows.

2 Design Criteria for Connections

The connections must sustain all of the imposed loads, both temporary (including erection) and sustained long term, without causing structural distress, either general or local. Connections must be carefully detailed if damage from local overstresses is to be avoided.

When possible, loads transferred through connections should be kept on the lateral center of gravity of the intersecting members to avoid torsional stresses. Consideration should be given to the effects on bearing conditions of dynamic loads caused by impact or earthquake. If the connections are too rigid, cracking of the concrete will occur, whereas ductile connections can be designed permitting some yielding under dynamic loading.

When selecting the type of connection to be used, it is desirable to eliminate welded connections if temperatures below -7°C (20°F) are likely at the time of erection, because of the possibility of fractured welds.

Where steel plates and shapes are used for connections the number of different sizes and shapes should be kept to a minimum. Such standardization assures maximum economy.

It is generally more economical to install in the field small 10-mm (3/8-in.) or smaller inserts for fastening windows, heating ducts, mechanical equipment, light fixtures, etc. The hole necessary for this type of anchor is approximately the same size as the bolt, and can be drilled directly through a hole in the fixture. This permits the use of predrilled fastening assemblies. Location tolerances for cast-in inserts are generally not adequate for use with predrilled multiple hole assemblies.

For adequate anchorage to precast T's with narrow stems, inserts should be installed in the vertical sides of the stem rather than the bottom. If fasteners are required deeper than 25 mm (1 in.), shop drawing fabrication sheets should be checked to assure that proposed locations do not coincide with those of reinforcing steel in the member. Power-driven fasteners are used on many precast concrete members, but caution must be exercised to assure the safety of personnel and also to prevent damage to the precast member. This is of special concern for precast-prestressed concrete members.

With precast structural concrete members, as with all building materials, it is impossible to provide bearing surfaces that match perfectly. The effects of surface variations can be minimized by placing some inert yielding material between the bearing surfaces. Suitable materials are neoprene, woven asbestos fabric, fiberglass, and roofing felt. Such materials can be impregnated with a two-component epoxy cement to produce a more rigid connection after the epoxy hardens. The use of a bearing filler is not a cure-all. When resilient bearing materials are used, due consideration should be given to the motion or breathing of the connection and its effect on the structure. An investigation should be made to assure that there is no possibility of minus tolerances accumulating so that the bearing length is reduced below the required minimum. The strength of cast-in-place joints should also receive careful attention from the design engineer (ACI-ASCE Committee 512, 1974).

A deficiency in joint design would not necessarily be serious in a low building where only gravity loads are of concern. However, in a tall building, where stability of the frame and the resistance to lateral forces depend on the transfer of moment between beams and columns or between beams and walls, joints always are of prime importance. In moment-resisting frames, field connections should therefore be made at points of contraflexure wherever possible.

The most serious problems in joint design are those of detailing the reinforcement within the joint to provide adequate shear and anchorage capacity, and at the same time minimize congestion of reinforcement, which makes construction difficult. In the design of joints, a distinction should be made between those required for strength only, those requiring limited ductility, those requiring energy absorption (blast), and those requiring greater ductility, as in seismic regions (Fling, 1973).

3 Connection Details for Precast Linear Elements

Typical connections for linear elements include column-base (CB), beam-to-column (BC), column-to-column (CC), and beam-to-beam (BB) connections. There are obviously many possible arrangements and a surprising variety of details for such connections. The detail selected for a given situation may be dictated by production or erection requirements; in other cases in-service design criteria or common local practice may determine the selection.

Detailed recommendations for the design of connections commonly used in the United States are contained in the report by ACI-ASCE Committee 512 (1974) and in the PCI Manual on Design of Connections for Precast-Prestressed Concrete (1973).

Column-Base Connections (CB). Fig. 12.39 shows several common arrangements for connecting a column to a foundation pier, wall footing, spread footing, or pile cap. All of the details use a nonshrink grout and double-nut system. If the connection is to be made at the top of a cast-in-place pier or wall, it is mandatory that sufficient ties be placed in the top of the pier or wall to confine the anchor bolts.

Typically, four anchor bolts are used with double nuts and there is a 50-mm to 60-mm (2-in. to 2-1/2-in.) gap for nonshrink grout between the top of the foundation and the bottom of the base plate. Anchor bolts are positioned either at the corners or at the middle of the sides depending upon erection requirements. Column reinforcement is welded to the base plate.

Column-base connections may also be made using grouted reinforcing bars. Two variations of this principle are encountered. In one case the foundation dowels project into voids cast into the column end, as shown in Fig. 12.40. Grout is injected or poured into a vent hole at the top of the void. (Nonshrinking grout is to be preferred.) When the height of grout is substantial, a two-stage grouting procedure as shown in detail in Fig. 12.40(b) is recommended to assure satisfactory pressure grouting, or the grout can be poured into a vent hole. In the variation shown in Fig. 12.40(c), the main column reinforcement is allowed to project and voids are cast into the foundation. The voids are partially filled with a thin mortar and the column is then lowered into position. An embedded metallic conduit is commonly used to form the required void, as shown in Fig. 12.40(d). Temporary bracing is required for the column until the grout has gained the desired strength. One method of bracing is to bolt an angle to inserts cast into the column and foundation.

This principle may also be employed for column-to-column (CC) connections. The primary objection to these connections is their inefficiency due to the relatively large anchorage length requirements. Several modified forms using short splicing sleeves and metallic, plastic, or other special fillers are under development but they have not yet been widely applied in practice.

A more economical system often encountered in European practice is the grouting of the column end into a specially prepared socket in the foundation, as shown in Fig. 12.41. With this system also, columns must be temporarily braced (fixed with wedges between the socket and the column) (Bruggeling, 1972).

Beam-to-Column Connections (BC). The connection types in Fig. 12.42 are but a few of the most typical simple beam connection combinations used for beams to columns in the United States. For simplicity, all the beams shown are rectangular, although they could be ledger beams, I-beams, or single T's.

The details shown may also be used for moment connections by using nonshrink grout between the ends of beam and the column and providing for tension at the top of the beam. Generally, field moment connections are inefficient and expensive and should be avoided if possible. Bearing pads are optional according to design requirements. The lapped-end connections in Fig. 12.42(b) and (c) usually require confinement angles because of high stresses, and they require care in detailing of the reinforcement in the connection zone.

Several different types of beam-column moment connections are shown in Fig. 12.43. In Fig. 12.43(a) the reinforcing bars are spliced by welding to angles. This

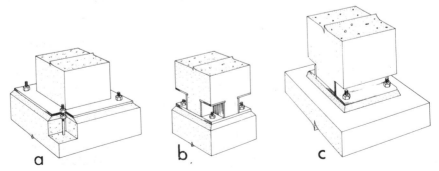

Fig. 12.39 Bolted base-column connections (PCI Connections Manual)

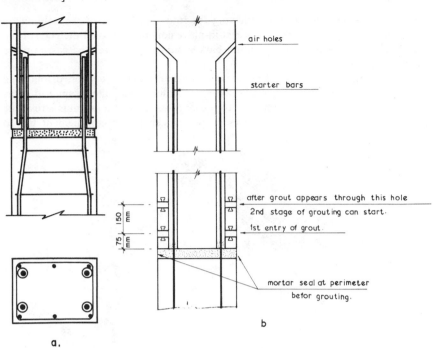

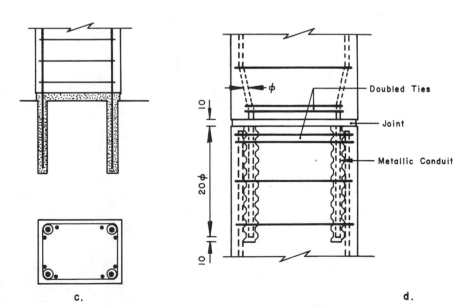

Fig. 12.40 Grouted base-column connections (b from Bardhan-Roy, 1975)

connection has the advantage of allowing for future extension of the column by placing anchor bolts or inserts in the cast-in-place concrete between the ends of the beams. When this is done, tied column bars should extend over the cast-in-place closure from the column below.

Fig. 12.43(b) shows a straight post-tensioning bar which is tensioned following placement of the nonshrink grout between the column and the beam end. This requires a good mechanical anchorage to prevent loss of post-tensioning stress due to seating or slippage. It also requires proper placement of confinement ties to

Fig. 12.41 Column base socket connection (Courtesy: Stroband)

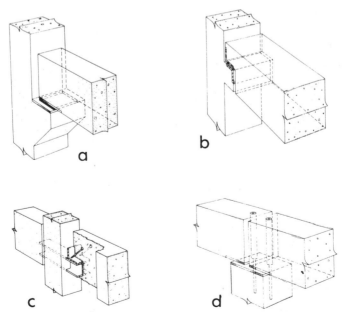

a

b

c

d

Fig. 12.42 Beam-to-column connections—simple bearing (PCI Connections Manual)

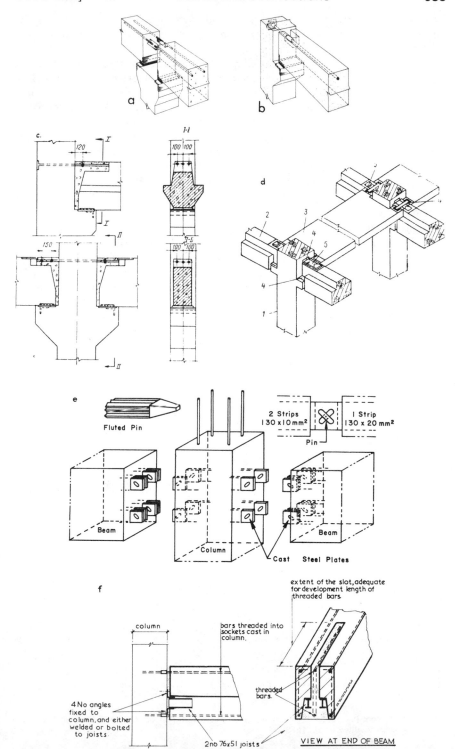

Fig. 12.43 Beam-to-column moment connections (a and b, Courtesy: PCI Connections Manual; f from Bardhan-Roy, 1975)

prevent excessive bearing stress under the end anchorage. The tendon may also be curved and anchored at the bottom of the beam, or be made continuous throughout the beam.

In Fig. 12.43(c) the column is pierced and the reinforcement extended through the column and anchored or spliced to adjacent beam reinforcement. The gap is filled with cast-in-place concrete or grout (Vasiliev et al., 1973). In Fig. 12.43(d) connections are executed by use of weld plates (1 = column; 2 = beam; 3 = floor slab; 4 = steel plates anchored in concrete; 5 = steel splice plates). Fig. 12.43(e) shows the so-called Engel connection. A hardened fluted pin is driven through the common square opening formed by overlapping diagonal slots. This connection was employed in the construction of the Medical School in Rotterdam. Yet another alternative is the moment connection detail shown in Fig. 12.43(f). The beam is erected on hidden stub joist brackets. Reinforcement is threaded into sockets cast into the column to develop a moment connection.

Column-to-Column Connections (CC). Some typical column-to-column splices are shown in Fig. 12.44. Most column splices use nonshrink grout between interfaces of the members to provide for dimensional variation due to construction tolerances. When base or cap plates are used, they may be of the same size as the column or recessed as much as 25 mm to 40 mm (1 in. to 1-1/2 in.), depending on the architectural requirements. Closely spaced confinement ties should be placed in the columns immediately above and below the joint. Connections can be made with anchor bolts, threaded reinforcing bars, or inserts. Provision should be made for erection and alinement, such as using the double-nut system.

In the details shown in Figs. 12.44(a), (b), and (c), anchor bolts are used. The column main reinforcement or dowels that lap the reinforcement are welded to the

a

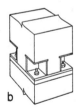
b

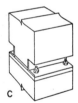
c

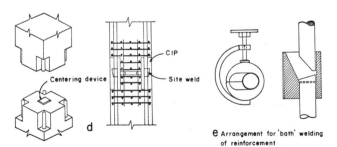
d

CIP

Centering device

Site weld

e Arrangement for 'bath' welding of reinforcement

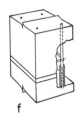
f

Fig. 12.44 Column-to-column connections (a, b, and c from PCI Connections Manual; d, e, and f from Vasiliev et al., 1973)

base plates. In Fig. 12.44(d), rigidity of the connection between the beam and column is achieved by welding the extensions of the reinforcement and of the steel plates anchored in the concrete and by filling the joint with concrete.

Fig. 12.44(e) shows how reinforcement extensions can be efficiently connected by "bath" welding in copper forms. The form encloses the ends of the bars and is taken off after welding. This type of welded connection does not require splicing plates and thus provides a compact connection. The bath welding is also notable for its low labor requirements and favorable transmission of forces. The detail shown in Fig. 12.44(f) is similar to that in Fig. 12.40(c) used for CB connections.

Beam-to-Beam Connections (BB).   Beam-to-beam connections occur primarily when H, Π, and T frames must be connected. In such connections the tensile reinforcement must be spliced by welding or by mechanical couplers. Several such coupling systems have been developed in recent years, including threaded couplers, forged sleeves, and couplers using a metallic filler. Standardization of connections is an important aspect of connection design. It improves quality control in the plant and contributes to production economies.

When welding reinforcement, weldability characteristics should be known; as a rule most low and intermediate grade bars can be welded. It is important not to weld reinforcing bars in the vicinity of a cold bend. This results in crystallization and unpredictable behavior of the reinforcing bar at the bend. Likewise, tack welding may produce similar crystallization and reduce bar strength, and should be carefully performed when required.

A connection detail that requires a large amount of added reinforcement in the ends of precast members can create production difficulties. Difficulty in placing and vibrating the concrete may lead to honeycombing within the connection. Congestion of reinforcing bars also may result in their being improperly positioned. A connection detail with reinforcing bars crossing each other requires careful dimensional checking to assure that sufficient clearances and tolerances are available for proper location of the steel. Coordination of the dimensions of the elements within connections is mandatory to produce satisfactory connection details.

4   Tolerances

Selection of tolerances for connections is as important as the structural analysis. Elementary, but frequently overlooked, is adequate clearance for making the connection; sufficient room for welding or adequate space to place a wrench to tighten a bolt must be provided. All connections should be provided with the maximum tolerance that is structurally or architecturally feasible.

Welded connections should not be used indiscriminately, since field welding is expensive and can produce undesirable results when the effects of welded connections are not fully considered. For example, additional forces due to restraint against volume changes may require increased strength in all the connections.

When making field-welded connections, the welding should be done in the downhand position whenever possible. Providing more weld than shown on the plans is not necessarily better, since it may result in unpredictable or undesirable behavior.

When welding in cold temperatures, preheating is required or special welding techniques such as thermite welding should be used. Moreover, welding in cold temperatures should be done carefully to prevent spalling of the adjacent concrete. In fact, with welded connections, potential damage to the concrete surrounding the connection must always be evaluated for possible effect upon performance of the connection.

5 Panel Wall and Floor Connections

Shear-wall construction offers significant structural and architectural advantages for tall buildings, especially for residential and institutional structures. Precast panel systems and precast boxes have therefore gained popularity (Kulka et al., 1975).

The stability of prefabricated concrete panel structures is dependent on diaphragm action of the horizontal floors and vertical walls. Adequate joints between prefabricates and properly designed tie and bond beams are required to assure that assembled individual panel elements act as rigid diaphragms. The tie and bond beams serve the additional function of joining these assembled diaphragms to each other. Slab joint details should be designed to provide for continuity between panels subjected to differential loads. The vertical joints between wall panels must be capable of transferring stresses due to the shear induced by lateral loads as well as shear due to nonuniform loads on adjacent panels. Joint details between floor and wall panels are particularly critical in tall buildings. These joints have a major effect on wall bearing capacity, and the quality of these joints may often constrain the dimensioning of the structure (Lewicki, 1966; Koncz, 1968; Lewicki and Pauw, 1972).

The ability of large-panel structures to perform satisfactorily under all conditions of loading depends upon the integrity of the connections. The connections must transmit gravity loads from floor to wall elements, from wall to wall, and from wall elements to the foundation. Horizontal and vertical connections must provide for interaction between the various elements in resisting lateral loads and in transmitting shear, tension, and compression forces. Where design against progressive collapse anticipates failure of a portion of the structure, the connections must have sufficient strength to assure alternate paths for loads on the rest of the structure. The necessary tensile and shear continuity required to prevent progressive collapse can be transmitted only through the reinforcement. The joints thus become the focal point (ACI-ASCE Committee 512, 1974). Bolted panel connections are discussed by Shemie (1973).

6 Floor Joints

Floor slabs should be tied together, as shown in Fig. 12.45. The slabs between bearing walls should be tied to each other by tie bars over the supporting wall to provide tensile continuity (Popoff, 1972). The longitudinal joints between panel elements should be keyed to permit shear transfer due to differential normal loads on the individual panels, and finally the whole diaphragm should be tied together by a peripheral tie or bond beam. Cross-tie beams should also be provided over all internal bearing walls to cross connect the longitudinal walls and to restrain longitudinal shear displacements between panel units.

The floor slab ties over the supports may be designed either as moment connections or as yield hinges. In either case, bars projecting from the precast elements should be firmly anchored in the tie beam to provide safety against the possibility of progressive collapse. For nonprestressed floor panels the rigid moment connection is preferred since it increases live-load resistance, reduces slab deflections, and increases the wall bearing capacity at the joint. A rigid connection may be achieved by one of the methods suggested in Fig. 12.45.

In Fig. 12.45(a) the connection is effected by anchoring hooked projecting panel bars over the longitudinal reinforcement in the tie or peripheral bond beam. A welded connection may also be used, either by welding overlapping projecting bars from the slab elements to each other, or by welding projecting bars to a structural angle as in Fig. 12.45(b). Alternately a strap may be welded to anchored plates cast into the panels, as shown in Fig. 12.45(c). Special precautions should be taken when reinforcement is welded. Carbon content should be less than 0.5% (other limits may apply in some countries—in Holland, for example, the limit is 0.29%) and low-hydrogen electrodes employed. Bars should not be welded closer than 200 mm (8 in.) to cold bends, and tack welding should be avoided because of the danger of brittle failure.

The end gap between panel elements in Figs. 12.45(a) through (c) should be at least 30 mm (1.25 in.) and preferably 50 mm (2 in.) wide. The joint should be filled with a high-quality mortar f_{cm} = 20 MPa (3000 psi) to resist the compressive stresses due to the support moments.

The connection shown in Fig. 12.45(d), consisting of overlapping loops anchored by the longitudinal tie beam bars, is an excellent connection, but requires a somewhat wider joint to accommodate an adequate loop overlap. A novel modification of the loop system is the joint detail used in the Polish WK 70 system shown in Fig. 12.45(c). In this joint the loops do not overlap but a coil is used to link them together (Lewicki et al., 1975).

Longitudinal confinement reinforcement is required in details (a) and (d) to resist the splitting tendency due to shear transfer between hooked or looped bars. All the connections in Fig. 12.45 will act as yield hinges when low-yield, high-ductility reinforcement is employed.

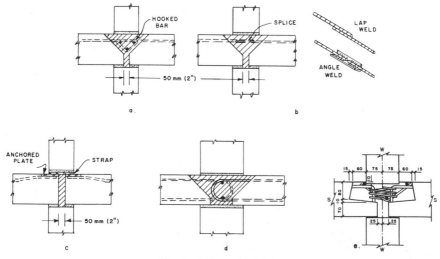

Fig. 12.45 Floor slab joints

Special precautions should be taken in the joint between floor panels and exterior walls or load-bearing facades to provide adequate anchorage and continuity to resist failure due to progressive collapse. Some typical connection details are shown in Fig. 12.46 (Kavyrchine, 1972).

In the detail shown in Fig. 12.46(a) the floor panel extends through the wall and continuity is provided by a dowel passing through the floor. The upper panel can be provided with a cast-in plate and the dowel threaded. A double-nut positive anchorage system can then be employed. In Fig. 12.46(b), the prefabricated facade provides a form for a cast-in-place edge beam with the floor slabs. Fig. 12.46(c) also uses a cast-in-place edge beam connecting the floor slab with the wall panels below. The panels above are set in a mortar grout and the joint is post-tensioned by the use of threaded rods passing through the wall panels.

Tie bars bonded in a slab leveling course or placed in the longitudinal joint between panels, as shown in Fig. 12.47, are used in a number of proprietary panel building systems. The behavior of such connections approaches that of a true hinge. Tie bars bonded in the leveling course are not recommended because of the danger that this course may peel away from the precast panels when subjected to shock or impact loads. When tie bars in the longitudinal joint between panels are used, high-strength mortar in the joints and confining reinforcement in the tie beams should be employed to avoid loss of bond. Straight deformed bars with adequate development length could be substituted for the hooked bars shown. This detail should be used with caution in zones of high seismic risk.

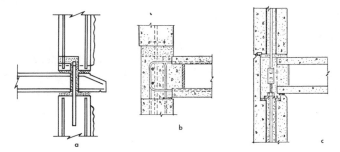

Fig. 12.46 Floor panel—facade joints

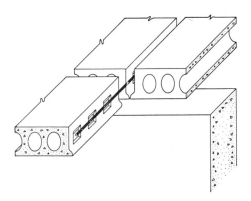

Fig. 12.47 Longitudinal joint ties

The longitudinal joint between edges of adjoining slab elements should be designed to transfer adequately the shear due to nonuniform floor loads. For normal load levels a grooved joint of the type shown in Fig. 12.48(a) will usually suffice. For heavy or concentrated, or both, live loads, keyed joints as shown in Fig 12.48(b) or welded clips are required. The joint shown in Fig 12.48(c) is popular in Belgium because it is easily formed and filled. The recommended minimum joint dimensions shown are required to assure that the joints can be properly filled with a high-quality mortar (Lewicki and Pauw, 1972). Bolted or welded connections are also recommended for flange joints between T and double-T beams. Typical details are shown in Fig. 12.49 (Zeck, 1976).

7 Composite Systems—Precast Floor to Steel Frame Connections

Two basic systems have been employed for developing composite action. Fig. 12.50(a) shows the use of stud welded shear connectors in a grouted joint. Coil reinforcement is used to distribute the stress in the joint. Composite action may also be achieved by the use of high tensile bolts, as shown in Fig. 12.50(b) (Sontag, 1973).

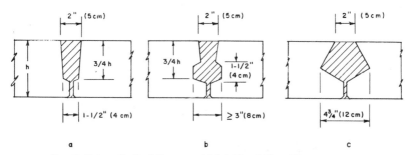

Fig. 12.48 Longitudinal floor-panel joints (Lewicki and Pauw, 1972)

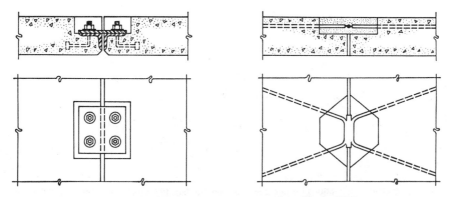

Fig. 12.49 Joints for flanged floor members (Zeck, 1976)

8 Vertical Wall Joints

Vertical joints between wall panels are extensively discussed in the literature (Lewicki and Pauw, 1972; Basler, 1966; Cholewicki, 1969, 1971; Cziesielski, 1966; Fric, 1969; Halasz and Tantow, 1966; Hansen, 1967; Hansen and Olsen, 1969; Polyakov and Szorochow, 1967; Pommeret, 1971; Pume, 1967; Lwow and Bluger, 1968). The three basic joint configurations shown in Fig. 12.51 are classified as plane, grooved, or keyed. Joints may further be classified as plain or reinforced. The horizontal tie beams interact with the vertical joints and their effect must be considered in determining the joint shear resistance. Their ultimate contribution to joint shear resistance may be estimated by the shear-friction principle (Birkeland, 1966)

$$\Delta V_u = A_t f_{yt} \mu \qquad (12.4)$$

in which ΔV_u = ultimate shear resistance contribution of the tie beam; A_t = area of longitudinal tie beam reinforcement; f_{yt} = yield strength of A_t; and μ = shear friction coefficient (1.4 to 1.7 for cast-in-place tie beams).

The most important properties of vertical wall joints are their strength and their shear deformability. The shear deformability influences the rigidity of the shear wall and consequently the distribution of vertical forces between individual shear-wall panels.

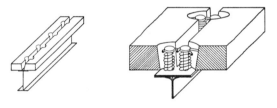

(a.) Composite section with precast concrete slab jointed above steel girder

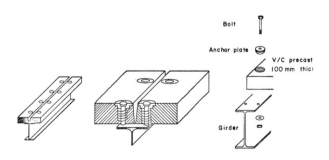

(b.) Precast concrete slabs bolted down with high-tensile bolts to cause composite action

Fig. 12.50 Shear connections for composite action (Sontag, 1973): (a) Shear studs in grouted joint; (b) high tensile bolt connection

Two distinct modes of joint behavior need to be considered: Mode I, elastic, and Mode II, elastoplastic. In the elastic mode the joint reinforcement is essentially unstressed and passive. Its primary function is to improve the bond between the concrete or mortar in the joint gap and the panels. Once the elastic strength of the joint mortar has been exceeded shear cracks develop, as shown in Fig. 12.52(a). The role of the joint reinforcement then is to resist the tensile stress component, while the role of the mortar is limited to resisting the compressive stress component. The joint reinforcement may be provided by bars projecting from the panel, or by longitudinal reinforcement in the tie beams, or both. Bars projecting from the panels provide a better structural joint but are not always essential.

The effect of the joint behavior on the vertical stress distribution is shown in Fig. 12.52(b). For Mode I, the panels act together and the wall behaves as a monolithic shear wall. Hence the vertical stress distribution is as shown. When the elastic shear capacity of the joint is exceeded, Mode II is activated and the shear between panels is limited by the elastoplastic capacity of the joint and the interacting tie beam. The effect of this limited shear capacity on the vertical stress distribution is shown by the discontinuity at the vertical joint.

Between the ideally elastic Mode I and the fully developed elastoplastic Mode II an intermediate joint behavior Mode I/II may be distinguished. At first small hairline cracks appear and there is some loss of bond between the panels and the joint filler due to shrinkage of the mortar. While there is some reduction in joint

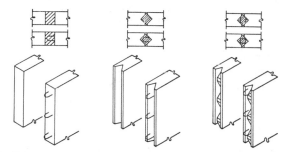

Fig. 12.51 Vertical wall-joint configurations (Lewicki and Pauw, 1972)

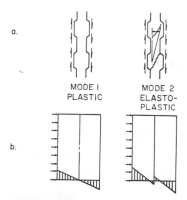

Fig. 12.52 Shear transfer modes (Lewicki and Pauw, 1972): (a) Joint behavior; (b) stress distribution

rigidity, this reduction does not significantly affect the vertical stress distribution in the shear wall. For purposes of analysis the wall may still be considered as monolithic with a resulting stress distribution as shown in Fig. 12.53. The shear-friction hypothesis with safe steel working stresses may be assumed to give a safe upper-bound shear capacity for Mode I/II behavior.

The rigidity of a vertical wall joint may be characterized by a rigidity coefficient K_j, defined as the ratio of an increment of shear stress $d\tau$ divided by the corresponding increment of shear displacement $d\Delta_h$, that is

$$K_j = \frac{d\tau}{d\Delta_h} \qquad (12.5)$$

The rigid-elastic mode (Mode I) is characterized by a value of K_j ranging from 400 GN/m³ to 500 GN/m³ (1500 k/in.³ to 1800 k/in.³). The deviation of the stress-displacement curve from the initial tangent represents the transition from Mode I to the intermediate Mode I/II behavior. It should be noted that even a relatively large decrease in the value of K_j does not significantly influence the rigidity of the composite shear wall. Assuming that shear-wall rigidity reduction of 5% can be tolerated, shear walls with joints characterized by a K_j-value as low as 7 GN/m³ (25 k/in.³) can be considered as rigid (Cholewicki, 1969).

The plane unreinforced concrete joint in Fig. 12.51(a), unrestrained by tie beams, has very low resistance. Due to shrinkage the bond between the joint filler and the panels is not dependable. Test results show a wide dispersion of shear resistance ranging from less than 10 kPa to 60 kPa (1.5 psi to 8.5 psi). Such joints are subject to a sudden brittle failure. Tie beams should always be provided regardless of the geometry of the joint detail. Plane, reinforced concrete joints are relatively ductile and do have considerable ultimate shear resistance.

The unreinforced grooved joint shown in Fig. 12.51(b) sometimes exhibits very high joint rigidity because the groove increases the bond surface. As in the case of unreinforced plane joints, such resistance is not dependable due to loss of bond

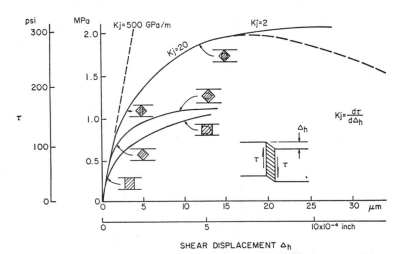

SHEAR DISPLACEMENT Δ_h

Fig. 12.53 Shear-displacement relationships (Lewicki and Pauw, 1972)

from shrinkage. Reinforced grooved joints exhibit higher elastic resistance than plane reinforced joints, but they have about the same ultimate shear strength.

The keyed joint shown in Fig. 12.51(c) develops elastic resistance by the interlocking action between keys rather than by bond. This type of joint exhibits the highest elastic resistance, and when reinforced is extremely ductile as compared to the other joint types.

The stress-deformation diagram for well reinforced keyed joints loaded at a uniform strain rate peaks well before ultimate deformations are reached. The large plastic deformations beyond the peak stress make these joints extremely ductile. They are therefore highly recommended for structures exposed to severe earthquake or other dynamic forces, or when foundations are subject to large differential settlements due to subsidence.

Large differences in the results of tests of vertical joints have been encountered (Koncz, 1968; Hansen and Olesen, 1969; Pume, 1967; Lwow and Bluger, 1968). These differences are attributed to such secondary effects as the maturity of the concrete or mortar joint filler, shrinkage as reflected by loss of bond, and temperature and moisture effects. The rather arbitrary definition of joint strength based on joint influence on shear-wall behavior also contributes to differences in allowable values specified in present codes. It should be emphasized that vertical joints should be designed and analyzed for both the elastic and elastoplastic modes for the appropriate limit states of behavior. For normal service loads and actions, such as gravity, wind, and dynamic loads and the effects of creep, shrinkage, and differential displacements, the joint shears should not exceed those for Mode I/II behavior. Enough reserve strength and ductility should be provided for Mode II behavior to resist the forces due to severe earthquake shocks and blast or other accidental loads. While some structural damage can be tolerated for such risks, the structure should have sufficient reserve strength to prevent complete collapse when vertical wall stresses are redistributed and increased due to plastic straining of these joints.

9 Horizontal Wall Joints

Horizontal joints in panel structures have been extensively studied (Lewicki and Pauw, 1972; Henclewski, 1969; Lugez and Zarzycki, 1969; Pogorzelski and Zielenieski, 1969; Pume, 1969; Shapiro and Sokolov, 1963; Spiridonov, 1957; Semencov, 1968).

The influence of the horizontal joint on the bearing capacity of the wall may be characterized by a wall bearing capacity factor, α_j, defined by

$$\alpha_j = \frac{N'_{uj}}{A_w f'_c} \qquad (12.6)$$

in which N'_{uj} = ultimate bearing capacity of the wall; A_w = area of the wall; and f'_c = compressive strength of the concrete in the wall.

Many factors influence the magnitude of the coefficient α_j, and an exact analysis is difficult, if not impossible. The specifications adopted by CEB-CIB consider α_j to be the product of four dimensionless parameters (Lugez, 1971)

$$\alpha_j = (\alpha_1)(\alpha_2)(\alpha_3)(\alpha_4) \qquad (12.7)$$

in which α_1 = joint stress distribution factor; α_2 = mortar layer strength and geometry parameter; α_3 = joint geometry form factor; and α_4 = floor edge moment factor. (See also the discussion at Eq. 12.1.)

The parameter α_1 takes into consideration the effect of thickness and modulus of elasticity of various parts of the joint on the stress distribution; α_2 reflects the effect of the resistance and thickness of mortar layers in the joint; α_3 reflects the increased strength of the concrete under local pressure and the confining action due to joint geometry; and α_4 takes account of the effect of the slab support moment. Empirical formulas have been developed to evaluate these parameters (Lewicki and Pauw, 1972).

No simple rational theory has been developed to date to satisfactorily explain the behavior of the great variety of horizontal wall joint details encountered in practice. The use of empirically determined capacity reduction factors supported by experience or test, or both, therefore remains the only practical alternative presently available.

Most horizontal wall panel joints are being designed as simple gravity connections. Dowels are generally used, but their primary function is to assist in positioning the panels during erection. Vertical continuity ties, such as in Fig. 12.46(c), between or in the wall panels are seldom provided because of practical difficulties and expense. Nevertheless the desirability of providing such ties, at least for exterior wall panels, was demonstrated by the Ronan Point tower collapse (Griffiths et al., 1968).

10   Tie-Beam Requirements

Concern over the brittle nature of joints in some types of precast concrete systems buildings has existed for some time. The Ronan Point apartment tower failure has dramatically focused attention on the possibilities of progressive failure (Popoff, 1972).

Design procedures to guard against progressive failure are available and used in seismic design. These procedures essentially demand continuous wall and slab and tie-beam reinforcement, and require minimum lateral design loads based on mass. Trends in the refinement of existing regulations and in the drafting of new regulations point to the adoption of these basic and cardinal procedures (Kavyrchine, 1972).

There is some variation in the minimum tie-beam requirements specified in various codes. The following minimum provisions are approximately equivalent to those specified by CEB-CIB (1969). Recommended minimum reinforcement requirements for the tie beams shown in Fig. 12.20 are listed below. These values may need to be increased to provide the strength requirements determined by design analysis. Peripheral bond beams and cross-wall ties should be reinforced with at least three 10-mm (#3) bars. Bars should be made continuous by providing adequate laps for tension splices or by welding. These beams should have a minimum cross-sectional area of 77 cm² (12 in.²). Tie beams may be provided by the cast-in-place portion of the joint or they may be incorporated as part of floor or wall panel edges. With cast-in-place tie beams the supporting edge of slab panels can be anchored by hooking projecting slab bars over the tie-beam bars, as shown in Fig. 12.45(a). These transverse ties should be anchored in the precast panels for 1/7 of the span length. To provide adequate tensile continuity over the supporting walls, a minimum reinforcement area of 1 cm²/m (0.05 in.²/ft) of tie beam is recommended. Tie-beam reinforcement may be incorporated in the panel edges. In that case the tie-beam reinforcement must be exposed at the panel corners and tensile continuity provided by mechanical splices, lapping or welding. For such joints the gap between floor panels over the supporting wall is relatively narrow and should be dry packed with a high-quality mortar.

The edges of floor panels and the supporting edges of the wall panels in these joints are particularly vulnerable to spalling. These edge details require careful design and good workmanship to assure uniform load distribution to reduce the risk of damage due to local stress concentrations (Lewicki and Pauw, 1972).

Inevitably, the cost of providing tensile and shear continuity throughout the structure must be reviewed. In 1970, when British building regulations were revised intending to localize failure and to prevent progressive collapse, claims were made that building costs would rise 2% or more. In Japan, cost data for 5-story large-panel systems were compared with similar traditional structures (Nakagawa and Yanase, 1971). Both designs are for severe seismic regions. The panel system design was 3% less than the conventional cast-in-place design. Included in this 3% saving was the joint work of the system building, which represented 3.75% of the total system building cost.

West Coast engineers emphasizing continuity and ductility in their design estimate that buildings designed for seismic Zone 3 cost from 0% to 1% of the total construction cost (or 0% to 5% of the structural work) more than similar buildings not designed for earthquakes.

Claims have been made that systems buildings cost up to 15% less than comparable cast-in-place buildings. Systems building with continuity would then cost 12% less than similar cast-in-place buildings (Popoff, 1972).

11   Tolerances for Large-Panel Construction

Tolerances between elements (especially exterior and facade panels) affect the proper procedure for sealing joints, and the likely gap must be carefully considered in the detailing and the selection of the type of joint sealant material. Generally, the desirable minimum width for construction joints is about 10 mm (3/8 in.). A gap of about that size prevents the possibility of capillary action and the joint is unlikely to become blocked by grit or other debris (ACI-ASCE Committee 512, 1974; Fiorato, 1973).

12.6   RESEARCH NEEDS

The current trend to the limit states design philosophy requires a better understanding of the behavior of joints and connections, with respect to not only their strength but also their deformability at various stress levels. From the point of view of economy it is not feasible to design structures to resist unusual or accidental overloads without some structural damage. Enough reserve strength and redundancy, however, should be provided so that such loads will not result in progressive collapse but that damage will be confined to the immediate neighborhood of the accident.

Both theoretical and experimental research, therefore, is needed to develop improved structural models for predicting joint resistance and deformability and the parameters that influence these characteristics. Alternate design details should be evaluated not only from the point of view of structural adequacy but also cost of fabrication and ease of construction, the ultimate goal being the development of reliable industry-wide standard designs. Additional research is also needed to determine the effect of joint behavior on the interaction between wall and floor slab elements at various load levels. Capacity reduction factors for wall panels appear to be unduly conservative. Research is needed to evaluate the effectiveness of providing lateral support by turning end panels and by providing adequate lateral shear resistance in vertical joints. International collaborations in research and exchange of experience have already provided much needed information in these areas and should be encouraged. For example, several agencies are engaged in experimental and analytical studies of walls consisting of precast panels, subjected to bending combined with axial load and shear combined with axial load. Data obtained from these studies along with information available in the literature should be analyzed to develop design procedures for walls in large-panel structures. Shear strength, axial load, flexural strength and slenderness effects, and effects of edge restraints should be included to the extent possible (Lewicki and Pauw, 1972; Lewicki et al., 1975).

Because of the scale and congestion of connections in large-panel structures, and judging from experience with connections in concrete frames, it would appear that connection design cannot be accomplished with a high degree of reliability by analytical means. A standardized set of simplified tests would result in less costly evaluation of connections. The use of scale-model tests should be studied as a more economical method for evaluating the comparative merits of different connection details (Pauw et al., 1976).

The state of the art of designing joints is presently still an "art of detailing," leaving much to the experience and intuition of the designer. Relatively few experimental data are available on the strength of the type of connections used in large-panel structures. No widely accepted design procedures for such connections are available.

Concerning the design of joints for ultimate strength, the development of appropriate physical models (for example, friction models, truss models) and their mathematical treatment on the principles of plastic analysis should again be stressed:

1. An equilibrium or kinematic model should describe the general behavior.

2. Details to avoid local failures should be observed, such as insufficient anchorage or insufficient splices of reinforcements, splitting of concrete due to local pressures of bent bars, or insufficient anchorage or compression diagonals.

Research on a systematic basis is needed to develop a commonly accepted basis for the design of such joints (Thürlimann, 1973).

In many instances an investigation of the individual joints should be followed by a study of an assembly of parts, as different failure modes may be governing. As an example the case of a floor slab consisting of precast elements may be cited. A frame surrounding all elements can provide sufficient strength against horizontal shear without elaborate joint details between the individual elements.

Research is urgently needed to obtain better information on the post-cracking load-deformation characteristics of tensile continuity configurations. Research is also needed on the mechanism of, and to develop design criteria for, the secondary structural system required to bridge the gap left by the loss of a primary load-bearing element due to a credible accident.

As a new floor type, partially prestressed slabs may come into use if the span exceeds 8 m to 10 m (25 ft to 32 ft) and supporting beams are to be avoided. Questions arise concerning bonded versus unbonded tendons, working and ultimate load behavior of the combined reinforcement, and punching shear around columns. As with prestressed slabs, the effect on joint behavior of time-dependent deformations needs to be given further study.

Design criteria for nonbearing interior partitions also need further study, not only with respect to their structural requirement but also with respect to acoustical and thermal isolation. With respect to frameworks, the state of the art is more advanced, but there are still areas deserving further study and research.

Concerning the structural and economical importance of columns in a tall reinforced concrete building the following considerations may put the problem into its proper perspective. Economically columns account for a rather small part of the total structural costs. Structurally they constitute a vital part of the structure. Depending on the structural system, a column failure may lead to a limited, an extended, or even a total collapse of a structure. In tall reinforced concrete buildings lateral forces are normally resisted by shear walls such that sway of the columns is prevented. Hence their effective slenderness ratios are rather low and second-order influences (P-Δ effect) are negligible.

It follows that future research should be concentrated on the strength of short columns, including the problems associated with high-strength reinforcement; with normal and lightweight concrete; high percentage of reinforcement; splices, encased structural shapes, and welded sections; with the influence of tie arrangements; and with redistribution of forces due to creep and shrinkage. The use of prestressing or partial prestressing to increase the flexural stiffness of columns also should be studied.

It has been hypothesized that high axial load on a beam-column joint will have a beneficial effect on the shear strength of the concrete and the bond strength of the reinforcement. Adequate test data to justify this hypothesis are still lacking. Post-tensioning could be used effectively to load and confine such beam-column joints.

Development of relatively simple and conservative design procedures and criteria would be preferable. Such criteria and procedures will not lead to an appreciable increase of the total structural cost, and will tend to reduce the likelihood of design errors.

12.7 CONDENSED REFERENCES/BIBLIOGRAPHY

The following is a condensed bibliography for this chapter. Not only does it include all articles referred to or cited in the text, but it also contains bibliography for further reading. The full citations will be found at the end of the Volume. What is given here should be sufficient information to lead the reader to the correct article: the author, date, and title. In case of multiple authors, only the first named is listed.

ACI 1965, *Precast Concrete Wall Panels*
ACI 318 1971, *Building Code Requirements for Reinforced Concrete*
ACI 533 1971, *Design of Precast Concrete Wall Panels*
ACI-ASCE Com 512 1974, *Precast Structural Concrete in Buildings*
Adam 1974, *Large Three-Dimensional Reinforced Concrete Elements*

ANSI A58.1 1972, *American National Standard Building Code Requirements*
Avram 1975, *Tall Buildings of Precast Space Elements*
Backler 1973, *Local Behavior of Shear Transfer and Compression Transfer Joints*
Bardhan-Roy 1975, *Precast Concrete Structures—Construction Details*
Basler 1966, *Connections in Prefabrication*

Battelle 1967, *The State of the Art of Prefabrication in the Construction Industry*
Beck 1972, *Stability in the Design of Tall Concrete Buildings*
Beck 1972, *Structural Frame of the AFE Faculty Tower of the University of Frankfurt*
Benedetti 1972, *Experimental Analysis of Horizontal Joints Between Large Panels*
Beresford 1970, *A Study of Concrete Panel Construction*

Birkeland 1966, *Connections in Precast Construction*
Birkeland 1969, *Relations Between Designer and Fabricator*
Birkeland 1972, *Dimensional Tolerance—Concrete*
Bljuger 1975, *Load-Bearing Capacity of Joints, Walls and Floor Slabs*
Bobrowski 1974a, *H-Frames—CIB-6th Congress*

Bobrowski 1974b, *The Impact of Research on the Use of Lightweight Concrete*
Borowiec 1973, *Stress and Deflection Analysis of Perforated Walls*
Bouda 1973, *Floors of Composite Thin-Walled Corrugated Sheet*
British Standard 1970, *Large Panel Structures*
British Standard 1972, *British Standard Code of Practice*

Brondum-Nielsen 1971, *Prevention of Structural Collapse*
Brondum-Nielsen 1975, *Precast Concrete Structures—Design Loads*
Brouwer 1972, *Prefabrication with Concrete*
Bruckner 1973, *Holiday Inn Hotel Tower in Augsburg*
Bruggeling 1972, *Prefabrication with Concrete*

Burnett 1972, *Influence of Joints in Panelized Structural Systems*
Burnett 1975, *The Avoidance of Progressive Collapse: Regulatory Approaches*
Burton 1967, *Connections in Precast Concrete Structures*
Cardenas 1973, *Design Provisions for Shear Walls*
CEB 1967, *International Recommendations for the Design and Construction of Large Panel*

CEB/CIB/UEAtc 1969, *International Recommendations for Panel Structures*
Cholewicki 1969, *Deformability of Vertical Joints and Its Effect on Behavior*
Cholewicki 1971, *Loadbearing Capacity and Deformability of Vertical Joints*
Cholewicki 1972, *Statical Role of Structural Connections in Concrete Shear Wall*
Cholewicki 1975, *Three-Dimensional Continuum Model of Building Structure*

Constructional Review 1974a, *Precast Shear Wall*
Constructional Review 1974b, *MCL Project, Sydney*
Corsmit 1968, *The Provisional Dutch Code of Practice for the Design of Precast Concrete*
Cusens 1975, *Precast Concrete Structures*
Cziesielski 1966, *Computations for Large Panel Walls Consisting of Individual Wall Elements*

Despeyroux 1968, *Structural Connection Problems and the Use of Special Materials*
Despeyroux 1975, *Construction of Prefabricated Panels in Tall Buildings*

Deutsche Bauzeitschrift 1973, *Town Hall*
Diamant 1968, *Industrialized Building*
Drossel 1976, *Double-Teaming Casting Techniques Erect Building Fast*

Dunbar 1973, *A Medley of Precast & Prestressed Concrete Systems*
Engineering News Record 1975, *Three Casting Techniques Cut Building's Cost*
Fauchart 1975, *Experimental Study of Horizontal Joints*
Fintel 1971, *Effects of Column Creep and Shrinkage in Tall Structures*
Fintel 1975, *Large Panel Structures*

Finzi 1965, *Design of Large Panel Prefabricated Buildings*
Fiorato 1973, *Geometric Variations in the Columns of a Precast Concrete Industrial Building*
Firnkas 1974, *Analysis of Precast Shear Wall Structures Subjected to Seismic Forces*
Fling 1973, *Optimization and Design of Concrete Frames*
Foure 1969, *Vertical Joints Resisting Shear Forces Between Large Perpendicular Panels*

Franz 1968, *The Connection of Precast Elements With Loops*
Frenzel 1974, *Some Basic Considerations for Prefabricated Long-Span Constructions*
Fric 1969, *Shear Resistance of Vertical Joints in Panel Construction*
Fric 1975, *The Compression Strength of Horizontal Joints in Panel Walls*
Fuller 1974, *Industrialized Concrete Construction for HUD*

Fuller 1975, *Precast Concrete Structures*
Gensert 1974, *Design of Frame*
Gerwick 1968, *Precast Prestressed Lightweight Aggregate Concrete*
Griffiths 1968, *Collapse of Flats at Ronan Point*
Groper 1975, *Bearing and Damping Capacity on Lock-Joints*

Halasz 1966, *Shear Resistance of Vertical Joints and Distribution of Horizontal Forces*
Hansen 1967, *Mortar Joints Between Concrete Elements in Shear Walls*
Hansen 1969, *Failure Load & Failure Mechanism of Keyed Shear Joints*
Hansen 1974, *Design of Vertical Keyed Shear Joints in Large Panel Buildings*
Hanson 1969, *The Structural Anchorage of Precast Prestressed Concrete*

Henclewski 1969, *Simplified Calculation Methods for Plane Joints*
Henclewski 1974, *Bearing Capacity of Partially Restrained Slender Concrete Walls*
Henclewski 1975, *Characteristics of Fixation of Continuously Analysed Wall*
Henclewski 1975, *Application of the Simplified Continuous Scheme in Analysis*
Hentschel 1975, *On the Calculation of Longitudinal Facade Walls*

Horacek 1973, *Recent Knowledge on the Theoretical and Experimental Solution*
Horacek 1975, *Determining the Flexibility of Warped Lintels*
HUD 1968, *Industrialized Building—A Comparative Analysis of European Experience*
HUD 1975, *Design & Construction of Large-Panel Structures*
Hugenschmidt 1974, *Epoxy Adhesives in Precast Prestressed Concrete Construction*

Informatie-Bulletin 1975, *Transitorium 3 on the Uithof Campus*
Institution of Structural Engineers 1975, *Fire Resistance of Concrete Structures*
Jensen 1975, *On the Ultimate Load of Vertical Keyed Shear Joints*
Jergling 1975, *Bearing Walls Balanced By Floors*
Karrholm 1974, *Progressive Collapse of Large Panel Buildings*

Kavyrchine 1972, *Reinforced, Precast and Prestressed Concrete*
Khan 1971, *Conceptual Details for Creep, Shrinkage and Temperature In Ultra High-Rise*
Khan 1973a, *Recent Development and Future of High-Rise Buildings*
Khan 1973b, *Newer Structural Systems and their Effect on the Changing Scale of Cities*
Koncz 1968, *System Building with Large Prefabricates*

Koncz 1970, *Manual of Precast Concrete Construction*
Kotlicki 1974, *Loadbearing Capacity and Deformability of Horizontal Joints*
Kotlicki 1975, *Application of the Frame Model in Evaluation of Forces*
Kotlicki 1975, *Behavior of Floor-to-Wall Connection Subjected to Horizontal Tensile Forces*
Krol 1975, *On Model Investigation of the Elastic Work of Building Walls*

Krol 1975, *On Model Investigations of Ultimate States in Apartment Buildings*
Krupinski 1975, *Arrangement of Reinforcement in Loadbearing Walls*
Kulka 1975, *Prestressed Concrete Building Construction Using Precast Wall Panels*

Larsson 1959, *Bearing Capacity of Plain and Reinforced Concrete Walls*
Leonte 1975, *Multistoried Frames with Precast Prestressed Concrete Beams*

Lewicki 1966, *Building with Large Prefabricates*
Lewicki 1968, *The Strength of Horizontal Joints in Large Panel Walls*
Lewicki 1972, *Structural Design of Tall Concrete Buildings*
Lewicki 1972, *Joints, Precast Panel Buildings*
Lewicki 1974, *Structural Requirements for Large Panel Buildings*

Lewicki 1974, *Interaction of Floor and Wall for the Prevention of Progressive Collapse*
Lewicki 1975, *Analysis of Work of Secondary Structural System*
Lewicki 1975, *High Rise Panel Buildings*
Lewicki 1975, *Limiting the Risk for Progressive Collapse*
Lewicki 1975, *Spacing of Expansion Joints in Prefabricated Buildings*

Lorentsen 1972, *Consideration of Imperfections in Design of Prefabricated Buildings*
Lugez 1969, *Influence of Horizontal Joints on the Resistance of Prefabricated Panel Elements*
Lugez 1971, *Strength of Horizontal Connections Between Concrete Wall Panels*
Lugez 1975, *Impact of Horizontal Joints on Working Diagram of Bearing Walls*
Lwow 1968, *Test Results on Strength of Multistory Buildings*

Macchi 1969, *Contribution to the Theory of Bearing Wall Construction*
MacGregor 1972, *Stability of Reinforced Concrete Building Frames*
Manson 1975, *Structural Joint Design in Large Panel Precast Concrete Structures*
Mathur 1973, *Technical Innovations for Eliminating Delays*
Mazzolani 1975, *Inelastic Stable and Unstable Behavior of Eccentrically Loaded Walls*

Mazzolani 1975, *Wall-Floor Interaction in Multistory Buildings Under Torsional Loads*
McGuire 1974, *Prevention of Progressive Collapse*
McMillan 1975, *African Eagle Life Centre*
Melhorn 1975, *Behavior of Panel Shear Walls*
Mihai 1975, *Continuity Connections in Precast Reinforced Concrete*

Murashev 1971, *Design of Reinforced Concrete Structures*
Muszynski 1972, *A Lightweight Curtain Wall*
Nakagawa 1971, *Efficiency of Large Panel System on Labor Saving*
Oberti 1968, *Special Design Problems*
Pagano 1968, *Theory of Buildings*

Palumbo 1968, *The Effects of Horizontal Forces on Prefabricated Panel Structures*
Pankow 1976, *Integrated Precast and Cast-in-Place Building Construction*
Pauw 1972, *Tensile Ties in Precast Concrete Systems*
Pauw 1976, *Precast Concrete Buildings*
Pauw 1976, *Wall-Floor Connections Between Prefabricated Elements*

PCI 1969, *Summary of Basic Information on Precast Concrete Connections*
PCI 1970, *Manual for Quality Control*
PCI 1971, *Design Handbook—Precast and Prestressed Concrete*
PCI Manual 1973, *Manual on Design of Connections for Precast-Prestressed Concrete*
PCI 1973b, *New Precast Prestressed System Saves*

Petersson 1974a, *Analysis of Loadbearing Walls*
Petersson 1974b, *Investigation of Vertical Joints Between Wall Panels*
Philleo 1971, *Summary of Symposium of Designing for Effects of Creep, Shrinkage and*
Pogorzelski 1969, *Method of Computing the Load Bearing Capacity of Horizontal Joints*
Pogorzelski 1975, *Eccentricities of Longitudinal Force in Walls*

Polish Standard 1969, *The Structures of Large Panel Buildings*
Polyakov 1967, *Shear Tests of Reinforced Concrete Joints*
Polyakov 1974, *Design of Earthquake Resistant Structures*
Pommeret 1971, *Shear Resistance of Vertical Joints in Coplanar Large Prefabricated Panels*
Pommeret 1974, *Structural Joints in Construction*

Popoff 1972, *Stability of Precast Concrete Systems Buildings*
Popoff 1975, *Design Against Progressive Collapse*
Pume 1967, *Shear Strength of Vertical Joints in Panel Walls*
Pume 1969, *Bearing Capacity of Joints Between Wall Panels and Floor Slabs*
Pume 1973, *Load-Bearing Capacity of Vertical Joints Between Wall Elements*

Putkonen 1961, *Analysis of Frames with Unreinforced Components*
Ramesh 1973, *Tall Buildings with Shear-Wall Systems*
Raths 1974, *Design of Load Bearing Wall Panels*
Reznik 1972, *Quality Control of Prefabricated Components for Tall Buildings*
Richardson 1973, *Precast Concrete Production*

Risarger 1969, *The Failure Load of Linear Elastic Walls Without Tensile Strength*
Rohm 1974, *Prefabricated Reinforced Concrete Construction with Large Elements*
Rosman 1974, *Analysis of Spatial Concrete Shear-Wall Systems*
Rosman 1975, *Response of Random Systems of Coupled Shear Walls*
Rozvan 1975, *Conclusions on the Design and Erection of an 11-Story Tall Building*

Sahlin 1959, *Structural Interaction of Walls and Floor Slabs*
Schultz 1975, *Design and Construction of Large-Panel Concrete Structures*
Schwing 1974, *Overall Behavior of Large Panel Shear Walls*
Sebestyen 1965, *Large-Panel Buildings*
Seddon 1956, *The Strength of Concrete Walls Under Axial and Eccentric Loads*

Sedo 1973, *Practical Application of New Methods of Calculation*
Sejnoha 1973, *Non-Linear Ultimate Strength of Three-Dimensional Wall Systems*
Sejnoha 1973, *Analysis of Mixed Wall Systems*
Semencov 1968, *Strength of Joints Between Wall and Floors in Large Panel Buildings*
Shapiro 1963, *On the Strength and Deformability of Horizontal Joints*

Shemie 1973, *Bolted Connections in Large Panel System Buildings*
Sontag 1973, *Precast Composite Flooring*
Speyer 1976, *Considerations for the Design of Precast Concrete Bearing Wall Buildings*
Spiridonov 1957, *Bearing Capacity of Horizontal Joints in Large Panel Buildings*
Stigter 1966, *Australia Square, Sydney*

Stiller 1975, *German Buildings with Precast Concrete Elements*
Suenaga 1974, *On Box-Frame-Type Precast Reinforced Concrete Construction*
Suzuki 1971, *The High-Rise Apartments & Silos Using Large Precast Panels*
Swedish Standard 1967, *Swedish Regulations on Large Panels*
Szoke 1973, *Quality Control of Buildings*

Szoke 1975, *Bearing Capacity of Welded Steel Joints Between Wall Panels*
Tani 1974, *Steel-Reinforced Concrete Structure-Prefabricated*
Thürlimann 1973, *Elastic Analysis-Strength of Members and Connections*
Tomii 1972, *Shear Wall*
Tsoukantas 1975, *Mechanical Behavior of Large Reinforced Concrete Panel Joints*

Tsuboi 1968, *A Study of the Strength Properties of Precast Reinforced Concrete Box-Frame Units*
USSR Standard 1965, *Regulations for Design of Large Panel Structures*
Vasiliev 1973, *Prefabricated Reinforced Concrete Multistory Frame Buildings in USSR*
Waddell 1974, *Precast Concrete: Handling and Erection*
Watson 1972, *Experiments for the Design of a System*

Western Construction 1969, *Bellevue Building Goes Up Fast*
Wierzbicki 1975, *Bearing Capacity and Deformability of Lintels*
Yee 1974, *Design for Erection Considerations*
Yokel 1975, *The Implementation of a Provision Against Progressive Collapse*
Zarzycki 1975, *The Influence of Supporting Length and Bearing Stiffeners*
Zeck 1976, *Joints in Large Panel Precast Concrete Structures*

Structural Design of
Tall Concrete and Masonry Buildings

Chapter CB-13

Design of
Masonry Structures

Prepared by Committee 27 (Masonry Structures) of the Council on
Tall Buildings and Urban Habitat as part of the Monograph on the
Planning and Design of Tall Buildings

Arnold W. Hendry   Chairman and Editor
Robert D. Dikkers   Vice-Chairman
Alan H. Yorkdale   Co-Editor

AUTHOR ACKNOWLEDGMENT

Special acknowledgment is due those individuals whose contributions and papers formed the substantial first drafts of the various sections of this chapter. First are the state-of-art reporters from the 1972 International Conference whose material was published in the Lehigh Proceedings. These individuals are:

> P. T. Mikluchin, Section 13.1
> R. J. M. Sutherland, Sections 13.1 and 13.2
> A. H. Yorkdale, Sections 13.1 and 13.2
> R. J. Mallet, Section 13.2
> H. K. Hilsdorf, Section 13.3.

In addition to this, other sections were based on special contributions prepared by:

> W. C. Bretnall, Sections 13.2 and 13.3
> W. L. Dickey, Section 13.2
> R. M. Gensert, Sections 13.2 and 13.3
> O. Pfeffermann, Section 13.2
> J. C. Scrivener, Section 13.2
> R. J. Mainstone, Section 13.3
> S. Sahlin, Section 13.3
> R. J. Young, Section 13.3.

CONTRIBUTORS

The following is a complete list of those who have submitted written material for possible use in the chapter, whether or not that material was used in the final version. The Committee Chairman and Editor were given quite complete latitude. Frequently length limitations precluded the inclusion of much valuable material. The Bibliography contains all contributions. The contributors are: W. C. Bretnall, W. L. Dickey, R. D. Dikkers, R. M. Gensert, A. W. Hendry, H. K. Hilsdorf, R. J. Mainstone, R. J. Mallet, P. T. Mikluchin, O. Pfeffermann, W. G. Plewes, S. Sahlin, J. C. Scrivener, R. J. M. Sutherland, K. Thomas, A. H. Yorkdale, R. J. Young.

COMMITTEE MEMBERS

M. Clauzon, J. F. Cutler, W. L. Dickey, R. D. Dikkers, R. Estrada, D. Foster, R. M. Gensert, A. Gerich, C. T. Grimm, J. Grogan, A. W. Hendry, H. K. Hilsdorf, M. Huet, W. J. LeMessurier, H. Lechner, G. Macchi, R. J. Mainstone, R. J. Mallet, M. Mathez, T. H. McNeilly, P. T. Mikluchin, C. B. Monk, L. Nevander, O. Pfeffermann, E. O. Pfrang, J. M. Prouve, D. Pume, G. S. Ramaswamy, T. Redmond, E. Reinle, S. Risager, R. Sagelsdorff, S. Sahlin, J. C. Scrivener, D. Serdaly, G. Shellbach, B. Sundara Rao, R. J. M. Sutherland, K. Thomas, P. K. Thomas, P. Vahakallio, M. Vallot, D. A. Wakefield, A. H. Yorkdale, M. Yorulmaz, V. A. Youl, R. J. Young.

Design of Masonry Structures

13.1 GENERAL DESIGN AND ARCHITECTURAL ASPECTS

1 Development and Application of Masonry Construction

Until the beginning of the twentieth century masonry in its various forms was the principal building material for tall buildings. Since then masonry has been largely superseded by structural steel and reinforced concrete for this purpose. Much theoretical and experimental research was devoted to the development of these new building materials and techniques. Refined methods of design, resulting from this research, brought about a veritable revolution in the architectural and structural fields. Building regulations and design codes were constantly updated, and helped to establish the wide use of these new materials.

Only quite recently has any progress been made in the use of structural masonry. Traditionally, masonry has not been treated as an engineered material, and has been hampered by outmoded regulations leading to buildings with excessively thick walls that were uneconomic in anything beyond 2-story or 3-story structures. However, research work was started in a number of countries in Europe and North America, and by the 1950s the Swiss had demonstrated the potentialities of engineered brick masonry. Since then, similar developments have taken place in many other countries and a substantial amount of research work has resulted in the evolution of design guides and codes of practice of steadily increasing sophistication.

This new movement in masonry construction includes among its achievements:

1. Creation of a modern theory of design of masonry structures founded on a solid experimental basis.

2. Codification of new theoretical and experimental results in the form of modern building codes.

3. Concentration of the creative efforts of progressive engineers and architects on developing the great potentialities of modern structural masonry.

4. Progress in manufacturing new masonry materials and in construction techniques.

657

Since the late 1960s, buildings ranging from 12 to 22 stories in height have been designed and built in plain and in reinforced masonry. Several 25-story buildings in plain masonry have been designed for nonseismic areas on the basis of modern engineering methods and the recommendations of new, progressive building codes. Investigations have shown that it would be possible to design and construct masonry buildings up to 50 stories in height. Following serious failures of masonry structures in earthquakes (for example, at Napier, New Zealand, in 1931), masonry structures met disfavor in seismic regions (Holmes, 1967). Recent research work (Scrivener, 1966 to 1976; Schneider, 1959, 1969; Esteva, 1966) and developments in design and construction techniques have overcome this limitation, and it is now possible to adopt reinforced masonry construction for tall buildings in seismic areas with confidence.

Modern structural masonry finds wide application in residential construction, including apartment buildings, student residences, and multistory hotels. Many hospital and office buildings are being designed with masonry as the principal structural material.

One of the main advantages of modern masonry structures lies in the fact that the walls serve simultaneously several functions of paramount importance. These include:

1. They provide a complete structural system supporting all the loads acting on them.

2. They define geometric space.

3. They provide a variety of architectural finishes with a wide choice of textures, patterns, and colors and a discernible scale.

4. They create weather resistant enclosures.

5. They provide thermal and acoustical insulation.

6. They provide fire resistance.

7. They require only simple erection techniques.

8. They reduce the number of materials to be handled and scheduled.

It is well known that for appropriate types of buildings, masonry bearing-wall construction is competitive with structural frame construction, and for some it costs less as a result of the multifunctional nature of the elements.

2 Design Considerations

It is impossible to give an exhaustive account of the various considerations that may arise during the process of design. The following is a brief outline of some design guidelines.

Functional space considerations, together with general structural requirements, characteristic for given materials and systems of construction, are the principal determinants of magnitudes and orders of basic physical dimensions of a building. These physical dimensions constitute the logical and natural matrix for establishing the size, order, and scale of the building.

Various geometric forms of basic masonry units, panels made of such units for use in various elevations, structural bays defined by a sequence of vertical bearing walls, and floor-to-floor spaces, provide a choice of geometric configurations which serve as basic visual modules or units. These units must be arranged in a certain order to create desirable architectural effects.

Such geometric forms can be combined in many ways to produce new expressions and give new insights into the architectural design of modern tall masonry buildings.

It is evident that the physical form of a masonry structure is greatly influenced by the geometry of a chosen basic masonry unit, extended in accordance with certain principles in a given direction in three-dimensional space. Such a form is a logical consequence of the inner arrangements of constituent masonry units. There is no limit to the complexity of forms that could be created from these masonry units.

In nature, form and structure are one. In the realm of architectural design, this unity of form and structure should also be the ultimate goal of the designer. In structures generally, realization of the balance between gravity forces, lateral forces, and reactive inner forces induced in the physical medium of the structure, is what dictates, to a great extent, the geometric configuration of the structural form.

Generally speaking, modern tall masonry buildings are three-dimensional structural systems satisfying all necessary space requirements, and resisting all loads by means of combined action existing between vertical masonry walls and structural floors. Arrangement and spacing of horizontal elements in the form of floors is determined mainly by functional space requirements. Arrangement and spacing of vertical elements in the form of bearing walls, supporting these floors, is a more complex problem of a topological and structural nature.

The basic types of structural masonry layouts are:

1. Transverse structural wall plan, in which main walls are perpendicular to the longitudinal axis of a building.

2. Longitudinal wall plan, in which main walls are parallel to the longitudinal axis of a building.

3. Composite wall plan, in which main structural walls are various combinations of transverse and longitudinal walls, forming L, T, cross and other similar shapes.

While it is possible to achieve great economy and variety of layout with masonry by careful design, such buildings are not always easy to alter to suit changing needs. This is particularly true where composite action has been used for lateral stability, and where headroom and floor thicknesses preclude the later addition of local framing. Masonry designers need to think about this when squeezing the last ounce of performance out of the material, and must discuss any restrictions with the client; otherwise, initial satisfaction can quickly turn sour, such as when a simple request for extra openings at ground level in a newly completed building could result in a large redesign estimate with no certainty of success.

3 Elevational Design of Tall Buildings

The process of designing the exterior elevations consists of establishing basic geometric forms as formal elements and organizing them into a sequence of specific relationships. This process requires a series of readjustments, ultimately resulting in the successful refinements of an original architectural concept.

These visual relationships, in the form of various proportional systems for the elevational treatment of tall masonry buildings, can be developed and analyzed as concrete mathematical and geometrical systems.

Openings in exterior surfaces of masonry walls play an important role. Their size, location, and shape are of great importance for the over-all visual impression which any particular design tries to achieve. The size of openings is instrumental in the characterization of the mass of a building. Relatively small openings give the impression of massivity. Large openings convey the feeling of lightness, transforming an elevation into almost a grid of vertical and horizontal linear elements.

The location of openings with respect to the main vertical surface of the wall is of importance, because if these openings are recessed considerably into the elevational surface, they create an impression of massivity. If they are projected beyond the elevational surface they introduce a special visual element creating new patterns of light and shadow effects, thereby affecting the over-all architectural design of the elevational surface.

The shape of openings also affects the architectural aspects of buildings, and must be taken into account during the process of design.

Monadnock Building, Chicago, Illinois (Courtesy: Chelsea Advertising, Inc.)

Thickness of walls or panels should be kept either constant or changing at certain strategic points (for example, at floor levels).

Any opening (a window or a door) should not be placed in such a manner as to give an impression of a hole, but must be arranged as logical and consistent interspace. Any discontinuity in bearing walls should be treated as a definite, clear division of over-all space that is esthetically justified, and not as an unwanted disturbance.

Modern masonry is notable for its range of colors. These colors are an important factor in the total architectural effect produced by an elevational surface. The latest developments in the technique of production of masonry units with various colors open up new possibilities for designers. Some of the newest colors have unique qualities found only in masonry materials.

The texture of masonry also plays an important role in the elevational design. Textural surface characteristics of various masonry units depend on the micro-topographic physical composition of the particular materials used in such units and the technique of their manufacture. A great variety of textures is available.

Surface characteristics of masonry elements, composed of individual masonry units, separated by joints, are the result of particular arrangements of such units within the body of the masonry element. Various treatments and patterns using textures as a design element are easily achieved.

Due to the prominence of joints in most masonry structures, masonry units always stand out. At the same time, such units provide clearly defined visual elements and become the basic unit of design, giving the human eye a definite sense of scale.

The geometry of the unit to a great extent determines the geometric order governing the design of the structure as a whole. Artful treatment of joints adds to the esthetic significance of the masonry. Light and shadow effects created by various types of joints also must be taken into account. The directional significance of joints is of great importance. In tall buildings the distance of an observer from the masonry surface influences the visual effect of joints.

Space, generally speaking, has no scale, and in order to appreciate and define it an appropriate referential yardstick must be provided by the context of architectural design of masonry structures; scale is established through the proper relationship between the dimensions of basic masonry unit and man, man and structure. The progression from small units, such as bricks and panels, to larger units, such as structural bays and floor-to-floor levels, and finally to the total building, perceived through the agency of the creative eye of man, reveals the subtle dynamism of controlled change in scale of the building and evokes, even without conscious rationalization, the esthetic association of the quality of design.

13.2 STRUCTURAL DESIGN OF MASONRY BUILDINGS

1 Basis of Structural Design

Buildings are at present designed in western countries by allowable stress design. Walls are normally designed for allowable stresses as vertical cantilevers by accepted principles of mechanics, with no moment transfer allowed for at floor-to-wall connections. Lateral loads are distributed to the shear walls according to their relative stiffnesses and locations by the diaphragm action of concrete floor slabs acting as horizontal beams, the walls in turn transferring the loads to the footing.

Loads acting result from floor or roof live loads, dead and self-weight loads including walls and construction loads, together with wind and any other lateral loads. In addition, stresses will result from temperature variations, characteristic dimensional changes of the materials, deflection and rotation of components in contact with or built into the masonry, foundation movements, and perhaps other specific conditions of loading (for example, snow loads). The result is wall and column elements with axial and eccentric loads applied at their ends, combined with localized lateral loads introducing intralength or height bending. These conditions of stress are then superimposed to establish statically equivalent vertical loads at an appropriate eccentricity. Component dimensions are then assumed and the stresses calculated.

The stresses are then checked against the allowable values from tabulated values for a chosen combination of brick strength and mortar type, or from actual prism tests of masonry.

According to Allen (1970) some of the shortcomings of these existing design procedures are that:

1. They should more directly reflect the conditions of failure of the structure. Some existing procedures tend to promote incorrect or uneconomical dimensions.

2. They should be more adaptable to new structures and different conditions of workmanship. This should be done on the basis of consistent over-all factors of safety against collapse.

3. The uniform safety factor does not mean uniform safety. The allowable stress based on a single safety factor on material strength is a misleading indicator of the actual safety of the structure. This is particularly true when tensions induced in walls by wind loads are counteracted by essentially constant dead-load compressive stresses. An unexpected increase in the wind load may lead to cracking.

4. Not all members should have the same safety. For example, nonstructural wall cladding should have lower factors of safety than, say, columns.

It is a commonly held opinion that the over-all load factor for buildings is unnecessarily high for most practical examples because of the tendency to apply limiting factors to each individual component. In addition, safety factors applicable to masonry structures in some cases greatly exceed those used for other types of structures. Some rational probabilistic analysis seems essential for better uniformity and more unified design.

It is noteworthy that the USSR, Poland, and Czechoslovakia have long since progressed to limit states design. This method had been preceded by the use of ultimate strength design method, in which the relation between load or load effect and load-carrying capacity of masonry element is assessed. The product of the nominal load and of the total safety factor should be less than the nominal load-carrying capacity. The nominal load corresponds approximately to service load. The values of total safety factor are given a priori, depending on the combination of the load effects taken into account. The nominal load-carrying capacities are, in most cases, directly means of statistical distribution.

The limit state design method is presently being introduced in the United Kingdom and in Europe generally for reinforced concrete design, and is becoming increasingly preferred to permissible stress design and ultimate strength design. A limit states code of practice for masonry will in fact be introduced in the United Kingdom, and a Model Code for Masonry based on limit states concepts is being prepared by CIB Commission W.23A.

The object is to economically design, construct, and maintain a structure that will serve without damage under the expected loads, without disquiet to the user and without loss of life. The likelihood of collapse from unusual loads, such as earthquakes or extreme winds, should be very small. Toward this end structural analysis is carried out to assure that the structure and its parts do not exceed the limit states during its expected life. Two kinds of limit states are defined:

1. Ultimate limit states, for which the maximum load-carrying capacity is reached.

2. Serviceability limit states, for which criteria governing normal use and durability are not satisfied.

The attempt to choose values for parameters such as loads and material properties is made on the basis of probability of occurrence, and the probability is represented by the characteristic value of the parameter where the characteristic material strengths are those which are exceeded say 19 times out of 20, while the characteristic loads are ones near the top of their range.

The variability of loads and load effects is expressed by considering the characteristic values, defined either on a statistical base or from an appraisal or experience. The variability of strengths is expressed by considering the characteristic values, estimated on a statistical base.

To take account of unfavorable deviations in practice the characteristic values are multiplied by partial safety factors (in most cases, greater than or equal to 1), which are related partly to the strength of materials and elements and partly to the loads and load effects. The design values are defined by applying dividing factors to the strength, and appropriate multiplying factors to the load and load effects.

The safety requirement for a masonry element is fulfilled if the design load effects are less than the design resistance of element.

For structural masonry buildings a rational definition of safety factor depends mainly, therefore, on a wide knowledge of the statistical data concerning both the basic strength of masonry and the effects of eccentricity and slenderness. The probabilistic approach shows that a considerable reduction of the safety factor can be obtained for structural brickwork, given wide statistical control of quality which would determine the characteristic strengths.

A notable advantage of the limit states method is that allowance can be made for the sometimes marked variation in workmanship of brickwork. It does this by means of clear separation into load factors, material and dimension factors, and performance factors, instead of using a single over-all factor as in allowable stress design. The change in workmanship is directly reflected by a change in the material or dimension factor, while other factors remain unchanged. The effect of quality of workmanship is immediately reflected in the calculation of structural safety.

In addition, limit states design differentiates between: (1) Dead loads which promote failure and are given an overload factor; and (2) dead loads which prevent failure and carry an underload factor. In regard to stability and stress reversal, safety is automatically assured without the need for special requirements.

Macchi (1970c) has suggested that, because of the variability of certain masonry elements, a probability of failure of masonry buildings may be 10^{-4} rather than the 10^{-7} expected in other structures.

2 Loading Effects

In addition to normal loading, including dead load, use and occupancy loads, and wind effects, various accidental forces should be considered in structural design including earthquakes, fire, bombing, explosions, and collisions.

Earthquake zones seem to be clearly defined: either one designs for earthquakes and the relevant codes state the requirements or one does not. Where earthquake resistance is required virtually all masonry becomes reinforced masonry. Good examples are the 17-story Park Mayfair East building and the later 20-story Park Lane Towers development, both in Denver, Colorado (Figs. 13.1 and 13.2)(Hanson, 1969; Sallada and Wakefield, 1970). Here the structural walls are 250 mm (10 in.) thick, consisting of two skins of brickwork of 100 MPa (14 000 psi, 980 kgf/cm²) strength with continuous vertical and horizontal reinforcement in a grouted cavity. Typical of single-wythe construction is the 15-story Catamaran Hotel in San Diego, California built with 200-mm (8-in.) reinforced concrete masonry bearing walls.

Other examples are found in New Zealand, including the Millbrook Apartments, Christchurch, which are nine stories in cavity-wall concrete blockwork with a 143-mm (5-5/8-in.) inner leaf and a 92-mm (3-5/8-in.) outer leaf.

Fig. 13.1 Park Lane Towers, completed block

Apart from grouted cavity construction, both in concrete block and brickwork, hollow concrete blockwork is frequently used with the hollows filled with concrete and reinforced as shown in Fig. 13.3, an example from New Zealand. (Note the shape of block for easy placing around the reinforcement.)

Also from New Zealand comes an application of prestressing to cavity walls in concrete block designed for earthquake resistance (Fig. 13.4). Here plastic-coated strand tendons run free in an open cavity, the anchorages and couplings at each floor level being protected by liberal applications of a bituminous sealer (Hanlon, 1970). This technique shows promise for much broader use.

After taking the required precautions against earthquakes, most other stability problems of masonry fade into comparative insignificance. One could reinforce the walls of all tall masonry buildings, but then a fair part of the economic advantage of the material would be lost. Having said this one must add that, even with reinforcement and a high strength brick, the Colorado buildings apparently compared favorably in cost with framed construction.

Fire is well covered as a danger in most countries' regulations, and masonry is better than most forms of construction in this respect.

Accidental damage from domestic gas explosions has been a known risk for at least 150 yr, but it has scarcely ever been considered a factor in structural design—that is, not until May 1968, when one corner of a 22-story precast panel

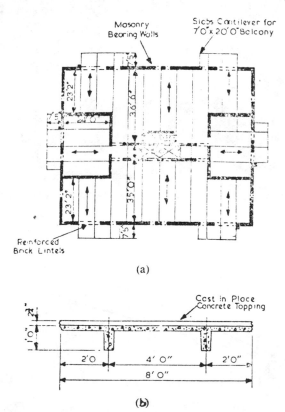

(a)

(b)

Fig. 13.2 Park Lane Towers, plan showing structural walls and floor system

apartment block in London collapsed from roof to ground due to a gas explosion on the 18th floor. This event had a traumatic effect in Britain, not just on system building but to varying extents on all forms of construction. After much uncertainty, legislation was passed covering not just gas explosions but any "incident." Broadly speaking each structural member and its connections must be just able to resist a force of 0.34 MPa (5 psi, 0.35 kgf/cm²) in any direction or the building must be designed so as to have a factor of safety against collapse of at least 1.05 if any one member is removed.

At first this legislation was thought to be an effective death warrant for high-rise masonry, but it has now been shown to add little to its costs and certainly not to limit its height (Haseltine and Thomas, 1971). Within the terms of the regulations, alternative paths of support for a masonry wall or column are not too hard to provide. Further, as Fig. 13.5 shows, masonry walls of normal story height will actually withstand pressure of 0.34 MPa (5 psi, 0.35 kgf/cm²) with relatively small

Fig. 13.3 Reinforced hollow concrete blockwork

Fig. 13.4 Prestressed blockwork

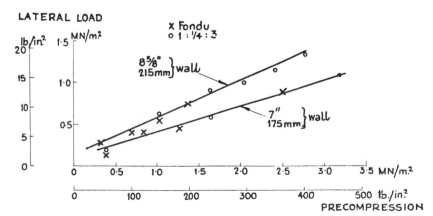

Fig. 13.5 Lateral resistance of masonry walls with precompression

precompression. These curves for resistance are based on air-bag tests by the British Ceramic Research Association, but can be verified approximately by simple arching checks and more exactly by rather full calculations (Morton and Hendry, 1973a, 1973b).

The problem of accidental loadings is discussed extensively in Chapter CL-5. The safety of masonry apartment buildings is statistically studied by Leyendecker and Ellingwood (1977).

Collisions of airplanes with tall buildings are comparatively rare, but heavy road vehicles out of control can cause severe local damage. In each case it is important to keep the damage local, and above all to prevent collapse. The same applies to alterations to buildings. "Price for price," a design that tolerates errors of judgment in alteration is preferable to one that might collapse with large loss of life just because someone thoughtlessly makes a new hole in a wall.

Many such dangers have been accepted quite calmly in the past but, with taller and taller buildings, the situation is changing. The question is whether accidental damage can be covered by building codes, or whether this is a design factor to which the codes should merely draw attention. Normal factors of safety are quite meaningless here.

Having listed some of the likely causes of accidental damage, one wonders what are the perils so far unrecognized. If we cannot cater successfully for the recognized risk, what hope is there with the unforeseen? Perhaps because of this dilemma, thinking in some countries has been more toward establishing arbitrary standards of stability, for masonry in particular, rather than catering for individual dangers.

For some time the Danish codes have required that at any level a building must be able to withstand a horizontal force up to 2-1/2% of the load above that level.

The present British load-bearing wall code (CP 111:1970) requires the local support to any wall or column to be capable of resisting a lateral load of 2-1/2% of the vertical load on it. In addition, the draft of the new code states that structures must be able to resist a lateral load of 1-1/2% of the dead plus superimposed load above the level considered, but this could be changed to 1-1/2% of the dead load only to come into line with the draft unified code for concrete.

It is hard to justify any of these arbitrary stability factors by logical argument. They certainly safeguard the building which becomes more exposed to wind than when it was designed, or is subjected to mild tremors in a zone thought free of earthquakes; they may usefully cover many, but certainly not all, of the other accidental forces already discussed. Alternatively, it could be said that they give more psychological help to the designer than necessary physical support to his buildings. In our present state of doubt, even if it is hard to justify such factors, it is equally difficult to argue against them.

3 Walls and Columns—Plain Masonry

Load Distribution. The structural behavior of walls and columns is normally judged by the ability of the component to resist vertical compressive loads or lateral loads, or both, either in the plane of the major dimension of the component or perpendicular to it.

With simple cross-wall structures load distribution between walls is seldom a problem, but the great advantage of masonry is that, without seriously increasing labor costs, it allows great variety and complexity of layout: this can be seen in Fig. 13.6, which shows some typical floor layouts of recently built masonry towers of 10 stories to 16 stories. With such layouts wall stresses due to floor loads alone may apparently vary by more than 50% at any one level, depending on the method of calculation.

Inaccuracy here can not only lead to large extra costs—especially in countries where the price of the material jumps sharply with strength—but it can also limit the maximum height or floor span quite severely. Methods of calculation were discussed by Sutherland (1969). Briefly, the simplest method, dividing the floor into triangular or trapezoidal sections along the walls as with beam and slab construction, gives the least accurate result, while equating larger irregular floor areas to whole wall units and checking the stress distribution often gives a more favorable spread, but is complex and still ignores over-all redistribution between units.

Instinct says that with tall buildings, arching of the structure as a whole will even out the stresses between wall units as well as within them, and this view is supported

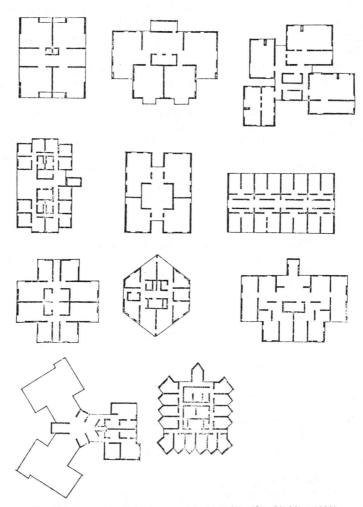

Fig. 13.6 Typical layouts of masonry tower blocks (Stockbridge, 1969)

by strain measurements taken by Stockbridge (1967). What is needed, if we are to design masonry buildings up to the optimum possible economy and performance, is some quick and cheap way of assessing the distribution of vertical loads throughout the walls, or proving that this is sensibly uniform. Technically it should not be difficult to develop a computer program that would give this load distribution, but it could be an expensive tool, and as with other complex programs, many jobs might prove unexpectedly to be just beyond its range.

Slenderness and Eccentricity. The structural behavior of vertical load-carrying components is dependent upon the capacity to provide: (1) Resistance to stress; (2) stiffness; (3) ductility; and (4) continuity.

It has been stated by Sahlin (1971) that for normal strength materials and a ratio of effective height to least lateral dimension less than 30, the load capacity of the component becomes a stress problem. For higher numerical values of slenderness ratio the failure is a buckling problem. To assure failure by stress, most western codes therefore control the maximum slenderness ratio of walls and columns by a figure which, for example, in the Australian Brickwork Code CA47, is 27 for walls and 12 for plain columns.

The calculation of slenderness ratio is in turn influenced by:

1. End conditions of lateral support and rotational restraint.

2. Effective thickness of the component as determined by its dimensions.

Although the distinction between eccentricity and fixity seems obvious (Fig. 13.7), it is curiously loosely treated in codes and handbooks. Eccentric loading is catered to in most codes, usually by stress reduction factors related to slenderness, but little guidance is given on fixity.

The question is whether exterior bearing walls (normally these are the only ones where the loading is seriously unbalanced) should be designed for fixity or for an assumed value of simple eccentricity, or instead whether the whole problem should be ignored and the wall loading considered as effectively axial. Many buildings exist where the problem has been successfully ignored, but this is illogical and could be dangerous.

Simple eccentricity is rare in multistory buildings, except where steel joists are used for floor systems. With concrete floors sandwiched between walls, as in Fig. 13.7(b), there must be some degree of fixity, and it remains to decide how much. It

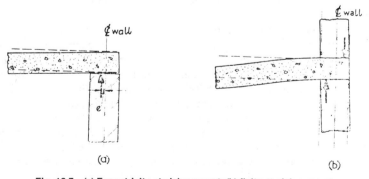

Fig. 13.7   (a) Eccentricity at slab support; (b) fixity at slab support

has been suggested that with axial stresses of 0.7 MPa (100 psi, 7 kgf/cm^2) the floor should be designed as fully clamped either for live load only or for the total load, depending on the method of construction (Thomas, 1970). If the designer plays safe and opts for such fixity for the total load, he can find in unfavorable circumstances that the flexural stress in the wall not only exceeds 0.7 MPa (100 psi), but that this stress alone approaches the allowable stress for the material. This is obviously an absurd situation. Almost regardless of how the building is constructed, the elastic deflection and a part of the creep deflection will have taken place before the load above it becomes great enough to achieve full clamping. These speculations have some interest, but they do not help the practical designer to decide what to do. Clearly there is no simple answer and this is probably why there is so little guidance available.

Perhaps the first point to remember is that with multistory buildings fixity and eccentricity are normally purely local effects and are not cumulative. They just form a constant ripple on the downward increasing axial stress. If the ripple is large, it is likely to be more serious at the upper levels, where it can cause cracking of the walls, than lower down, where it may or may not cause local overstressing. The possible range of this stress ripple is worth calculating. If the top limit is very high, it may indicate that the slab is too flexible anyway, which could cause other troubles as well.

If the slab cannot reasonably be made stiffer then it may be worthwhile prestressing it. If prestressing forces are provided to counterbalance the dead load, the problem with end rotation virtually vanishes. Unbonded cables in thin cast-in-place slabs are reputedly economical for the longer spans which are likely to cause trouble. The same applies to prestressed double T's as used recently in 20-story brick buildings in Denver (Sallada and Wakefield, 1971).

Surrounding the slab end in soft mortar (or, as has been suggested, bedding it on asbestos pads) gives greater freedom to rotate and probably has little effect on the over-all wall strength (Gensert and Kiris, 1969).

Having taken reasonable precautions the designer will probably find that the likely bending stresses in the walls are within the extra code limits for eccentricity or flexure. If so there need be no reduction in vertical load. The main point is to consider this problem in engineering terms rather than seek an answer in any country's code.

Most of the preceding remarks refer to the fairly stocky walls which predominate in high-rise masonry. However, with slender walls, where buckling dominates, the effects of fixity and slab rotation are both more important and more difficult to comprehend.

Local Stresses. Apart from the geometric aspects represented by factors already mentioned, the compressive strength capacity of plain masonry walls is most directly determined by the material properties of the masonry unit and the mortar type, as will be discussed in detail in Section 13.3.

Although mortar provides a bond between adjacent units, it does not produce a monolithic mass in itself. For this reason, the bonding or knitting of units by overlapping becomes important to the strength of the wall. When slabs and beams bear on the inside edge of a wall, local stresses are not necessarily uniform across the width of the wall. It then becomes desirable to continue the knitting of masonry in a transverse direction (headering) as well as in the longitudinal direction (lapped bonding). The use of metal ties between various wythes of a wall may be sufficient for some types of concentrated loading.

Bearing stresses will increase with height of building and span of floors. Bearing stresses are also directly related to the size of openings in the wall. To avoid compounding bearing stresses from successive wall openings, it is important to place openings directly above those in stories below (Fig. 13.8). In Fig. 13.9 the lower left pier receives a disproportionate load from upper levels. It is possible that the design of this pier could penalize the entire first story, since it is preferable to change wall thicknesses or masonry composition by stories rather than by piers.

Lintels over openings in masonry bearing walls can be critically loaded, depending upon the relationship of opening to floor level above and to the confinement of masonry at point of bearing of lintel. Fig. 13.10 shows the usual triangular load of wall on a lintel when the masonry is uninterrupted, thus allowing arching of masonry over the openings. The lintel is designed for the triangular weight of masonry only. Each arch creates a thrust at the spring line, and so a restraining force must be developed to maintain stability of the arch. If the opening is too close to the end of the wall, as in opening 1, the shear stress across the masonry pier to the left may be too much for the masonry. Should this be the case, the opening need not be moved, but the lintel should be designed for the full weight of wall and roof above it.

Opening 2 shows the effect of a floor load and wall opening just above a lintel. In this case, the triangular loading diagram is interrupted by the opening in the second story, and the arch action is destroyed. This lintel should be designed for the full floor load and the entire weight of masonry just above it.

Horizontal chases in bearing or shear walls greatly reduce the strength. Vertical chases, however, when properly located will not impair the strength of a wall.

Strength Capacity and Codes. Actual wall strengths range very broadly from 0.7 MPa (100 psi, 7 kgf/cm^2) to 48 MPa (7 000 psi, 490 kgf/cm^2) for normal masonry, although much higher strengths have been reported in exceptional cases.

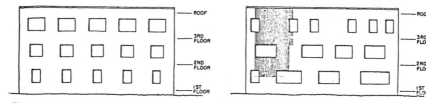

Fig. 13.8 Proper placement of openings   **Fig. 13.9 Improper placement of openings**

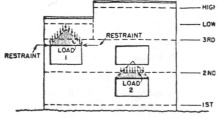

Fig. 13.10 Load distribution of lintels

For permissible stress design many national codes provide for:

1. An over-all safety factor that includes an allowance for the degree of eccentricity of vertical loads.

2. Slenderness factors that recognize the effect of changing slenderness ratio.

3. Factors providing reductions for members of small cross sections, less than 0.13 m² (200 in.²), as well as increases for highly concentrated loads such as bearing supports.

Comparing codes of practice in different countries is at best a frustrating business. Not only are the codes expressed differently, but there are omissions in some, or unique requirements in others, which subtly confuse comparisons. Gross and Dikkers (1969) made a comparison of the brickwork codes of Germany, Britain, Canada, Switzerland, and the United States, which they presented at the International Conference on Masonry Structural Systems in Texas in 1967.

In this they steered a creditably clear path through the code anomalies. Even so they had to qualify many statements and leave some questions unanswered. Good as this comparison is, it does not include concrete masonry units, and is already out of date in many respects. No new principles have emerged, but some of the changes in stress coefficients, and above all in the relative capabilities of masonry for use in tall buildings in different countries, are surprisingly large. Canada jumped from near the bottom of the table to allowing the highest permissible compressive stresses, while, for unreinforced brickwork, the United States has slipped back from where Canada is now to little above—and even below—Britain, where basic stresses are unchanged, but slenderness reduction factors are now more favorable.

A simplified comparison of the present allowable compressive stresses for the same five countries considered by Gross and Dikkers is given in Fig. 13.11. The following points are worth noting (the first three refer to brickwork only, but the rest to concrete masonry units as well):

1. In the range of slenderness most common in residential buildings, the codes allow comparable working stresses for the same middle-range unit strengths 41 MPa (6000 psi, 420 kgf/cm²) in Britain, the United States, and Germany, while substantially greater performance can be justified with these in Canada, and even more in Switzerland.

2. Switzerland is alone in taking advantage of the higher strengths of single-wythe walls, although tests in other countries as well clearly show that single-wythe walls fail at higher stresses for the same unit strength.

3. In Britain, Canada, and the United States, much higher compressive stresses are allowed for very high-strength clay units 83 MPa to 97 MPa (12 000 psi to 14 000 psi, 840 kgf/cm² to 980 kfg/cm²) than in Switzerland or Germany. In over-all allowable capacity of masonry, therefore, Switzerland gives way to Britain, Canada, and the United States, with Canada well in the lead.

4. Most countries specify allowable stresses for different unit strengths, mortars, and types of loading. In the United States and Canada, allowable stresses are selected in relation to a minimum ultimate 28-day strength of actual masonry (f'_m) derived from tests on prisms at least 400 mm (16 in.) high and with a height to thickness ratio of not less than 2 (more conservative

tabulated values of f'_m are given where tests are not thought worthwhile). One advantage of this method—apart from a direct performance benefit when quality is controlled by testing—is that the factor of safety in relation to the prism tests is always clear; this is generally 4 to 5 for direct compression (allowable $= 0.25\ f'_m$ to $0.20\ f'_m$), and a maximum of 3 for flexural compression (allowable $= 0.33\ f'_m$). It is interesting that Australia has adopted this method for its brickwork code and will shortly do so for its blockwork code.

5. Most codes allow the use of reinforcement to increase the compressive strength of walls, but this is of limited value in practice. Vertical bars in Quetta bond brickwork (Fig. 13.12), in filled cavities, or in hollow concrete

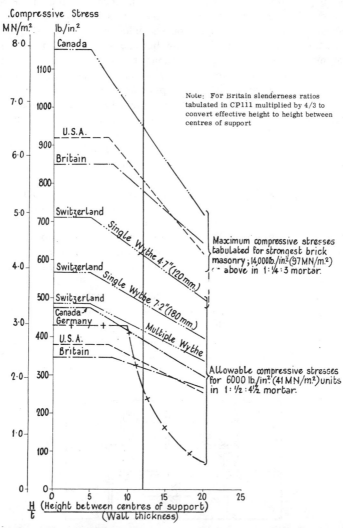

Fig. 13.11 Comparison of allowable stresses in clay brickwork for axial loading (unreinforced)

blocks, have all been extensively used, but mostly for tension rather than compression. It is difficult to get in enough steel to make a significant compressive contribution; even a 10% increase is hard to achieve. Such are the vagaries of codes that in the United States one is likely to gain more by changing to the reinforced masonry table in the code than by any calculated contribution of the steel.

4   Resistance to Wind Loading

As in the case of vertical loads, it is with complex towers rather than simple slab blocks that the calculation of wind resistance is difficult. The conventional method is to consider wall units as vertical cantilevers connected at each floor level by notionally hinged links; the horizontal load is then distributed between the cantilevers according to their stiffnesses and the resulting stresses calculated.

With the more widespread use of computers, fuller evaluation of composite action between the floor slabs and walls has now become practicable, and this has been used to varying extents in many recent masonry buildings. At the simple end of the scale, where walls in line are interrupted by corridors, standard pierced shear-wall programs have been employed. Elsewhere more ambitious computations have also been found necessary. In one such case a method based on interaction between three-dimensional groups of walls was developed initially in conjunction with Perspex model testing at Edinburgh University (Soane, 1967, 1969). With all such calculations appreciably greater wind resistance can generally be proved than by the connected cantilever method. However, virtually all these methods depend for their accuracy on what width of floor slab can effectively be considered as acting between the wall units, and what width of return walls can be taken as forming flanges to the wall units themselves. Recent tests, especially on a full-scale 5-story building in the Edinburgh University quarry test site, have indicated that some of the earlier assumptions on effective wall and slab widths were too optimistic. The horizontal deflections have proved greater than previously calculated for composite action, although less than those derived from the connected cantilever method (Hendry, 1971).

These remarks on wind loading are primarily directed toward unreinforced masonry designed for no tension and so that any flexural compression added to the maximum axial stress is still within the code limits (generally increased for wind). Tension, especially in rare extreme circumstances, is not necessarily harmful, but once one accepts it, one is encroaching on the factor of safety which in itself is uncertain. The size of this factor for lateral loads on masonry is something that

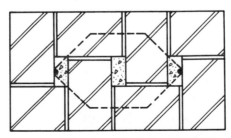

Fig. 13.12 Plan view of Quetta bond brickwork

designers would do well to know more about. It is difficult to visualize, let alone apply figures to, the sequence of events for a masonry tower subjected to an increasing lateral force through various load redistributions between the appearance of the first crack and ultimate collapse. Further, at what stage would perceptible movement or local damage become intolerable, and how much good would limited reinforcement do at critical points? With the present move toward limit states design and higher performance these matters are of more than academic interest. Further research may be needed, but in what form? Perspex or similar models with large tensile strengths are obviously useless.

For wind alone the need for this greater knowledge may not be too urgent, but other lateral forces are taking on special significance now that we are building higher, and all round there is a general questioning of stability not necessarily related to specific unbalancing forces.

Even with increased understanding of the behavior of unreinforced masonry buildings, the practical height of about 25 stories mentioned in Section 13.1 is not likely to be much exceeded, more because of the difficulty of avoiding tension than because of inadequate compressive strength.

Full-scale and model testing by Hendry and Sinha (1971) showed that failure of brick structures with and without openings under racking loads is generally due to the breakdown of the bond at the interface of the bricks and mortar, leading either to diagonal cracking or to cracks passing through bed joints. The effect of vertical loading on a shear wall is thought to have the greatest influence on the permissible shear stresses. That is, the shear strength of masonry is appreciably improved by simultaneous compressive stress. The factors critical to obtaining a high shear resistance in the absence of precompression are the initial rate of absorption of the masonry units, workmanship, and mortar strength and bond.

In work by Pieper and Trautsch (1970), clay brick walls had 22.6% more shear capacity than sand-lime brick walls. Shear stress capacity was found to decrease with length of wall and increase with thickness of wall using sand-lime bricks.

Tests by Grenley and Cattanneo (1970) confirmed that the racking strength of brickwork is appreciably increased by high-bond mortar.

The most usual test for estimating the shear strength of a masonry wall is the racking test. The boundary conditions produced in the test walls by this method are variable, and therefore it can only be considered a relative measure of the racking or shearing strength. The resulting apparent shear strength without precompression is anywhere between 0.17 MPa and 2.1 MPa (25 psi and 300 psi, 1.8 kgf/cm² and 21 kgf/cm²) under laboratory conditions. For concrete block walls, Fishburn as reported by Sahlin (1971) stated that the racking strength was 0.17 MPa to 0.34 MPa (25 psi to 50 psi, 1.8 kgf/cm² to 3.6 kgf/cm²) for walls having a compressive strength of 2.7 MPa to 3.2 MPa (390 psi to 470 psi, 27 kgf/cm² to 33 kgf/cm²), giving a racking strength of about 7% to 10% of the compressive strength. Tests by Rostampour on lightweight concrete-block masonry showed results similar to those obtained for clay brickwork (Rostampour, 1973). Turnsek and Cacovic (1970) propose that the mean shear stress value causing the first crack may be calculated by

$$v_0 = v_k \sqrt{1 + \frac{\sigma_0}{1.5 v_k}} \qquad (13.1)$$

in which v_0 = mean shear stress at failure with precompression; v_k = characteristic principal tensile strength = principal tensile stress at failure divided by 1.5; and σ_0 = normal compressive stress at failure when a wall is loaded also with a horizontal load.

Turnsek and Cacovic also found that for earthquake conditions the absorption of energy by shear deformation was greatest with 1:3:9 cement, lime sand, mortar than for other lime mortars or those of higher cement content.

A test program by Blume (1970), studying shear in grouted plain brick masonry wall elements, combined the properties of the mortar, grout, and brick in such a way as to produce homogeneous failure through the brick as well as the mortar and grout.

Testing by Hendry and Sinha (1969), using wire cut bricks set in 1:1/4:3 mortar, indicated that a formula for permissible working stresses in shear would appear to be 0.1 MPa (15 psi, 1 kgf/cm²) plus 1/6 of the precompression in the brickwork. Accordingly, the permissible shear stress in the Australian Code CA47 ranges from 0.1 MPa (15 psi, 1 kgf/cm²) for zero precompression to 0.5 MPa (75 psi, 5.3 kgf/cm²) for a vertical stress of 2.5 MPa (300 psi, 21 kgf/cm²).

With horizontal shear it is more difficult than with compression to find a logical connection between allowable stresses in the various codes. Some still specify fixed values unrelated to the state of loading, but in recent issues in several countries [for example, the United States (Brick Institute of America), Switzerland, and Britain], it is taken as proportional to precompression, with an over-all maximum in each case.

5 Seismic Performance

Because of the problems experienced with unreinforced lime-mortar masonry in the United States earthquakes of 1906 in San Francisco, 1933 in southern California, and others, masonry construction used in a structural manner received much unfavorable attention in the western states. It was primarily due to this experience and performance, plus a lack of forthcoming rational design information, that seismic design of masonry was and is now almost entirely empirical.

Rational design procedures based on structural performance research are a relatively recent development in the masonry industry; for example, the first United States Standard was adopted in 1966. Consequently, although some modern rationally designed masonry structures have experienced seismic events of some magnitude, seismic performance experience is minimal for this type of structural masonry.

Even in the early seismic events that occurred in the western United States, many masonry buildings, although unreinforced and built with relatively weak lime mortars, performed quite satisfactorily. However, there were also many masonry structures that suffered slight, and some quite severe, damage.

The Uniform Building Code, the traditional earthquake code in the United States, contains design requirements for masonry that are entirely empirically based. They grew and developed over the years as a long list of requirements, each individually addressed to a particular problem that had been experienced with masonry in seismically active areas.

The design requirements presently in force for masonry are believed by many engineers to be quite restrictive and very conservative. In recent years rationally designed buildings have performed quite well when subjected to earthquake loads. Failures and damage have occurred primarily where poor construction practices or poor design were involved. Where good construction practices and good design procedures were followed, the buildings performed well. Reports from the two most recent severe seismic events, the Alaska earthquake and the 1971 San Fernando earthquake, support these findings. Nevertheless, few masonry buildings that could be considered "tall buildings" have been built and put to this severe test.

Examples of masonry buildings that have been subjected to strong seismic actions and activity and have performed quite well are:

1. Veterans Administration Hospital, Sepulveda, California.

2. Towers Building, San Diego, California by J. V. Thompson and Associates, 13-story concrete masonry walls.

Other tall structural masonry buildings built in seismic zones and subjected to somewhat smaller seismic events have also suffered no damage. Among these are:

1. Park Mayfair East, Denver, Colorado. Architects—Andersons and Looms, AIA; Engineers—Sallada and Hanson. This building has been subjected to several minor and moderate seismic disturbances in the Denver area without suffering so much as cracked plaster.

2. Married Student Housing, Montana State University, Bozeman, Montana. Architect—McIver and Hess, AIA; Structural Engineer—Sallada and Hanson, Denver, Colorado.

3. Senior Citizens Apartments, London, Ontario, Canada. Architect—Hagarty, Buist, Breivik and Milics; Structural Engineer—B.A. Hastings.

4. Augustana College Dormitories, Sioux Falls, South Dakota. Architect/ Engineers—The Spitznagel Partners, Inc.

5. Library-Classroom Building, Eastern Montana College, Billings, Montana. Architect—Cushing, Terrell and Associates; Engineer—Wilbur J. Bennington.

6. Park Lane Towers, Denver, Colorado. Architect—Joseph T. Wilson Associates, AIA; Structural Engineers—Sallada and Hanson.

7. Housing for the Elderly, St. Paul, Minnesota. Architect—Brooks Cavin; Structural Engineer—Frank Horner Company.

Under the current Building Code Requirements and Design Procedures, structural and nonstructural masonry in seismic Zones 2 and above (moderate to severe seismic action) are required to be "reinforced." For the purpose of the code, reinforced masonry is defined as masonry

> ... in which reinforcement is embedded as required in such a manner that the two materials shall act together in resisting forces. The minimum area of steel shall be not less than 0.002 times the cross-sectional area of the wall, but with not more than two-thirds of the steel to be used in either direction. The maximum spacing of the principal reinforcement in general shall not be more than six times the wall thickness and no more than 48 inches.

In addition to these reinforcement requirements, structural masonry in general falls into the category of a structural "Box System" which, for code purposes, is defined as any structural system without a complete vertical load carrying space frame. For a box system the structural response factor or K factor is 1.33, leading to design seismic forces twice those for a moment resisting frame of equal mass [2312(d), UBC 1976].

Although more advanced analysis techniques, including dynamic structural analysis, are available and applied to other structural materials (steel and concrete), their application to masonry structures has been limited due to the lack of understanding of the behavior of masonry structural systems under dynamic excitation.

As previously stated, it is believed by many engineers that the seismic design requirements for masonry now contained in most building codes and standards are both restrictive and conservative. Many feel that masonry design technology has not progressed sufficiently to change the requirements. Because of this, masonry design is not able to use most of the newer analysis techniques.

Because of this lack of knowledge, and the need to improve the seismic design requirements for masonry, various research projects are now under way or proposed in this field in the United States. Much of this research is sponsored either partly or wholly by various segments of the masonry industry: materials, labor, and contracting; some is sponsored by the National Science Foundation; and some by various governmental agencies.

As the results of these structural investigations and testing research are examined by the engineering profession, it is anticipated that the technology for seismic design of masonry will become more rational in both concept and application. The anticipated result is that the excellent performance of masonry that has been previously experienced will be properly explained, and the performance and analysis techniques which are developed will be applied to new structures.

6   Walls and Columns—Reinforced

Tests on reinforced masonry elements all indicate that the behavior under static or alternating static loads is similar to that of reinforced concrete. Accordingly the well-known, and in many cases the well-researched, procedures of reinforced concrete design can be of much assistance in reinforced masonry design. Of course the designer must be aware of the differences between the two materials, in addition to differences in the allowable stress levels.

In reinforced masonry construction, it is more difficult to position reinforcing exactly where it is most needed. This applies particularly to confining reinforcement in compressive stress locations. The designer must assure that the reinforcing is surrounded by, and bonded to, grout or filling concrete so that he truly has a composite construction in which the component parts act together. He must remember that individual masonry units are brittle and when subjected to dynamic loads such as earthquake may show a tendency to separate from the rest of the structure or crack, and his design should restrain them. These minor differences are easily countered, and engineers are able to design with confidence in reinforced masonry.

Seismic resistant construction requires ductility of the structure and elements. Tests have shown that reinforced masonry can exhibit ductile flexural performance.

In any construction material squat elements behave in a shearlike manner, and masonry is no exception. The earthquake load to be resisted by a nonductile structure is larger than that required of a ductile structure. However, reinforced masonry has an advantage in that many walls are available to resist the shear load. Also, reinforced masonry appears to have high damping characteristics. The reinforced masonry structure can resist the earthquake load while remaining elastic and undamaged.

Resistance to lateral loads, such as wind and seismic loads, can be provided by using vertical reinforcement. Horizontal reinforcement should be used to resist differential foundation settlement and concentrated loads. Direct compression capacity is not much affected by the addition of reinforcement.

Nilsson and Losberg (1970) found that reinforced prefabricated masonry walls allow lateral loads to be raised appreciably after the cracking load has been reached until a gradual failure occurs after a large deflection. The yield-line theory for concrete could be used to estimate the failure loads of the walls tested. Tests by Cox and Ennenga (Sahlin, 1971) on laterally loaded reinforced masonry walls confirmed this.

In 1964, a Test Walls Committee was formed in Christchurch, New Zealand to consider the design and behavior of reinforced concrete-block walls. At this time, there was little information on the behavior of reinforced masonry in earthquakes or, for that matter, its behavior under the static loading used in design to simulate earthquake loading. The only information available pertaining to horizontal in-plane loading was of United States origin by Converse (1946) and Schneider (1959). These American tests were confined to the behavior under a monotonic racking load creating shear effects only. The flexural effect of the loading was counteracted in Schneider's tests by the provision of sufficient peripheral vertical reinforcing to preclude the steel being stressed beyond its yield point when subjected to the tensile forces induced by the maximum overturning moment. The loading in Converse's tests was effectively a diagonal compressive load causing diagonal tension cracking.

Flexural effects had not been investigated, and the first series of tests (Scrivener, 1966) was conducted to determine wall behavior due to a horizontal in-plane load applied at the top of the walls with no attempt to counteract the flexure. A second series (Scrivener, 1967) followed, in which the overturning moment of the horizontal load was counterbalanced by a vertical load at the loaded top corner, causing the walls to fail in shear. In both of these series, the aim was to determine the effect of varying the amount and distribution of vertical and horizontal reinforcing on cracking, stiffness, deflection, and failure. Only the reinforced cavities were grout filled.

A third series of tests (Moss and Scrivener, 1968) investigated the effect of filling all cavities of the hollow masonry units, and the results were compared with those of the partially filled walls of the first two series. Comparisons were also made with solid reinforced concrete walls equivalently reinforced.

The most significant results from the first series were that:

1. The walls behaved as vertical cantilevers, with the major cracks in the horizontal mortar joints at or near the base. These cracks eventually extended to the wall toe.

2. The load causing the onset of cracking, the wall stiffness, and the failure load

all increased as the percentage of vertical reinforcing increased. The most effective position in which to place the vertical steel was on the wall periphery, while the presence of horizontal reinforcing in bond beams had little influence on wall behavior.

3. The maximum load resisted by the wall could be closely predicted, usually to within 5%, assuming that all the vertical reinforcing had yielded and that the compression area was right at the wall toe. Accordingly, the resisting moment may be calculated as the sum of the moments of the yield force in each bar times the distance from the toe of the wall to the bar.

Where the behavior was essentially in shear, produced by just counterbalancing the moment of the horizontal load about the wall toe by a vertical load applied at the same corner as the horizontal load, tests indicated that:

1. The wall behavior was characterized by diagonal cracking from loaded corner to the toe of the wall, with most cracks in the mortar joints, but with many cracks across the concrete blocks.

2. No trend in wall stiffness values, calculated using the deflections, either at first cracking or at more serious cracking, was apparent even when the percentage of reinforcing was altered.

3. The load interval between severe cracking and failure increased markedly as the percentage of reinforcing increased.

4. The location of the reinforcing, whether horizontal or vertical, on the periphery or within the wall, had little effect on the failure load; however, even distribution of reinforcing delayed the onset of cracking.

These tests were conducted using a static horizontal in-plane load, applied at the top of the wall, which was increased from zero to maximum load in increments. Seismic load is essentially dynamic in character with reversed direction of loading occurring. The traditional manner of testing to simulate earthquake load is to subject the structure to a static load which cycles from a maximum load (or perhaps deformation) in one direction through zero to a maximum load or deformation in the opposite direction. It has been argued, certainly for reinforced concrete, that this loading is at least as severe in its effect on the structure as the seismic load which is of relatively low frequency.

Prompted by static cyclic tests by Meli and Esteva (1968) in Mexico, the behavior of reinforced masonry (both hollow concrete block and hollow brick) shear walls under static cyclic load was investigated in New Zealand by Williams and Scrivener (1973). These tests showed that for walls having a high aspect ratio, low quantities of vertical reinforcing, and a low bearing load, a flexural ductile behavior could be obtained characterized by relatively long yield plateaus in the hysteresis loops of load versus deformation (see Fig. 13.13). However, squat, heavily reinforced walls carrying large bearing loads exhibited a brittle shear behavior with initial diagonal cracking resulting in: (1) Reduced stiffness; (2) virtually no constant load plateau; (3) a tendency for the load to reduce sharply with increasing deformation; (4) extensive and sudden damage to the masonry; and (5) wall failure caused by distintegration of the masonry at the wall toe. Fig. 13.14 shows the load-deflection curves of such a wall.

In all cases of initial flexural behavior, the load to cause yielding of the wall could be predicted to within a few percent by the algebraic summation of the moments of the bearing loads and of the yield forces in the vertical reinforcing taken about the reaction corner.

For those walls in which shear determined the maximum load, the shear strength (ultimate shear stress based on the gross horizontal section) varied from 1.04 MPa to 1.8 MPa (150 psi to 260 psi). These values may be compared with a near constant value of 1.0 MPa (143 psi, 10 kgf/cm²) from Schneider's tests (1959) and 1.2 MPa (170 psi, 12 kgf/cm²) from Scrivener's tests (1967), where the reinforcing was 0.3% or greater. The higher values were associated with walls supporting large bearing loads.

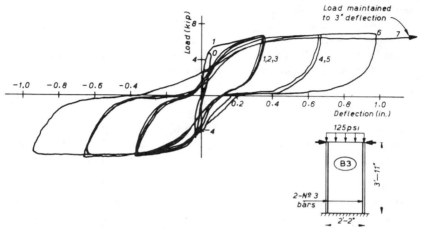

**Fig. 13.13 Load deflection curves for ductile reinforced masonry shear wall
(Courtesy: J. C. Scrivener)**

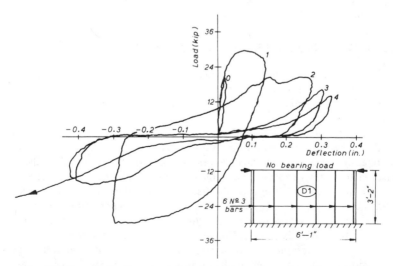

**Fig. 13.14 Load deflection curves for reinforced masonry wall failing in shear
(Courtesy: J. C. Scrivener)**

These static tests were followed by dynamic ones. Generally the walls with shearlike behavior performed dynamically as they had done statically. But flexural walls in the dynamic situation exhibited load deterioration and stiffness degradation with increasing deformation due to the walls sliding along the mortar bed above the second course. Because of this wall movement (which, of course, could not occur in the static tests), products of material crushing and splitting at the wall corner dislodged, and eventually the corner steel flexed and buckled. So the "steel couple" created by the peripheral reinforcing, and the basis of the ductile behavior, reduced with increasing deformation. It is apparent that, in order to achieve the inherent ductility of such flexural walls, means of reducing the corner material deterioration must be found, or some other means of retaining the confinement of the corner reinforcement must be incorporated.

Tests on reinforced masonry piers have been conducted in California by Schneider (1969).

Tests by Lyse (1933), reported by Sahlin (1971), showed that the strength of a reinforced brick masonry column may be computed from

$$P_{ult} = A(k \cdot f'_b + \rho' \cdot f_y) \tag{13.2}$$

in which P_{ult} = total strength of column; A = total area of column; k = efficiency factor, that is, the ratio between strength of masonry and strength of bricks; ρ' = ratio between area of longitudinal steel and of column; f'_b = compressive strength of bricks; and f_y = yield stress of steel.

Brettle (1971) has proposed a simplified ultimate-strength design procedure for proportioning reinforced brickwork piers subjected to compression and bending.

Testing has indicated that higher cement content mortars of, say, 1:1/2:4-1/2 give better results for reinforced masonry.

As an example of code provisions for reinforced elements, the Brick Institute of America Code for Engineered Brick Masonry presents the allowable stresses given in Table 13.1.

7 Out of Plane Loading of Reinforced Masonry Walls

Loading perpendicular to the masonry surface (out of plane loading), causing bending of the wall, has received much research attention for unreinforced walls. Combined bending and compressive loading of unreinforced walls has also been studied.

Two series of such tests on reinforced brick walls have been conducted in New Zealand (Scrivener, 1969). In the first series, monotonic uniformly distributed load was applied by air bag to one face of walls simply supported at their ends. A valid criticism of these tests was that the walls were rotated to lie in the horizontal plane so that the air bag reacted against the floor, the wall dead weight was incorrectly applied. Accordingly, in the second series, the walls were tested in the vertical orientation and a vertical platform was constructed for the air bag loading reaction. The base of the wall was mounted on roller bearings and the top of the wall was attached to the reaction platform by horizontal hinged rods allowing free rotation of the wall ends. A wall under test is shown in Fig. 13.15. A few cycles of static face load were conducted, the reverse loading being obtained by applying the air bag load to the other face of the wall.

Table 13.1 Allowable stresses in reinforced brick masonry[a]

Type of stress and type of wall or member (1)	Allowable Stresses, in megapascals (pounds per square inch, kilograms-force per square centimeter)	
	Without inspection (2)	With inspection (3)
(a) Compressive		
Axial: walls	$0.25 f'_m$	$0.25 f'_m$
Axial: columns	$0.20 f'_m$	$0.20 f'_m$
Flexural: walls and beams	$0.40 f'_m$	$0.40 f'_m$
Flexural: columns	$0.32 f'_m$	$0.32 f'_m$
(b) Shear		
Flexural members, no shear reinforcement	max. 0.17 (25, 1.76)	max. 0.34 (50, 3.52)
Shear walls, no shear reinforcement	max. 0.34 (50, 3.52)	max. 0.69 (100, 7.04)
Flexural members with shear reinforcement	max. 0.41 (60, 4.22)	max. 0.83 (120, 8.45)
Shear walls with shear reinforcement	max. 0.52 (75, 5.28)	max. 1.03 (150, 10.56)

[a]Brick Institute of America

Fig. 13.15 Test on face loaded reinforced brick masonry wall (Courtesy: J. C. Scrivener)

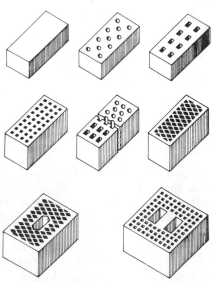

Fig. 13.16 Typical examples of clay bricks (DIN 105, 1957)

In both test series it was found that the test yield load (ultimate load) could be predicted to within a few percent by considering the reinforced brick section as a lightly reinforced wide beam and applying ultimate moment theory as for reinforced concrete.

8 Walls and Columns—Prestressed

Prestressing is a technique normally applied to concrete systems and sometimes to steel. It is used to great advantage with any material strong in compression and weak in tension. Post-tensioned brickwork, however, has been in use since 1825, when Brunel applied it to the Thames Tunnel Project.

Prestressed shear walls were tested by Henkley (1966), while Tasker (1975) has investigated prestressed walls on reactive soils. Gero (1969) reported a prestressed masonry reinforced concrete model space structure consisting of two thin, concrete floors with load-bearing masonry walls between. The walls were post-tensioned vertically, using the floors as anchors to enable a column-free area below of approximately 21 m × 21 m (70 ft × 70 ft).

9 Beams and Girders

The structural behavior of masonry beams is also quite similar to that of concrete. However, the orthogonal anisotropic nature of masonry causes some differences under certain types of loading. Overreinforced masonry beams are more brittle than overreinforced concrete beams, and the relative magnitudes of shear, tensile, and compressive strength of masonry are somewhat different from those for reinforced concrete.

Zelger (1970) observed from loading tests that plain brick lintels almost always break as a result of slip in the joints. A breakdown in bond is common in reinforced masonry beams, but the bond failure in this case is usually between steel and brickwork.

If one assumes that brickwork cannot absorb shear stresses in any direction, then the lintel must bear the load like an arch with a tie. The reinforcement in the bottom of the lintel acts as the tie with the plain brickwork above it acting as the arch. Lintel failures result from:

1. Compressive force destroying the arch.

2. Tensile force destroying the tie.

3. Horizontal shear destroying the bond between arch and tie at the springline.

Possibilities 1 and 2 are reduced by appropriate bending calculations, and possibility 3 by designing within the allowable shear or bond capacity. There are indications that the main concerns in designing reinforced masonry beams are shear and masonry bond strength and the quality of workmanship in the masonry.

Grogan (1970) has described reinforced masonry beams spanning 19.8 m (65 ft) and of section 3.1 m (10 ft 2-1/4 in.) deep and 432 mm (17 in.) thick, the former dimension being dictated by architectural requirements. The beams contain top, bottom, and shear stirrup reinforcement.

Flexure. Sahlin (1971) states that good agreement is found with the Whitney-type formula for the ultimate moment in a reinforced concrete beam, that is

$$m = q(1 - 0.59q) \leqq 0.4 \tag{13.3}$$

in which $m = M/bd^2f'_m$ and $q = \rho f_y/f'_m$; $b =$ width of beam for fully grouted beams or effective or equivalent solid width if the top blocks are hollow; $d =$ effective depth of beam; $M =$ ultimate moment; $f'_m =$ strength of masonry in compression; $\rho =$ steel area divided by masonry area (width times effective depth); and $f_y =$ steel yield stress.

The classical elastic theory of reinforced concrete beams will also give reasonable results for masonry.

From a survey of test data, Sahlin (1971) concludes that the bond strength is about 15% of the mortar strength for 10 mm (3/8 in.) round bars. Higher values are obtained for thinner bars, for square bars, and for deformed bars in grout.

As an example, the Australian Brickwork Code allows the following bond stresses:

Average bond stress on plain bars, 0.55 MPa (80 psi, 5.6 kgf/cm²).

Average bond stress on deformed bars, 1.10 MPa (160 psi, 11.3 kgf/cm²).

Allowable stresses as from the Brick Institute of America Code, given in Table 13.1, also apply for beam flexural compression.

Shear. Sahlin (1971) has suggested the following equation (due to Zelger) for nominal shear stresses in a masonry beam

$$v = \frac{V}{jdb}\left(1 - \frac{\mu}{\lambda}\right) \tag{13.4}$$

in which $v =$ shear stress; $V =$ shear force in a reinforced masonry beam; $jd =$ distance between the resulting force in the compression zone of a beam and the bars; $b =$ width of beam, or equivalent solid width if units are hollow; $\mu =$ "friction" coefficient $= 0.5$; and $\lambda =$ shear span ratio $= a/jd \geqq 0.8$.

He also referred to the shear strength of reinforced masonry beams as determined by Parsons, Stang and McBurney. As with reinforced concrete, the shear stresses were inversely proportional to the shear span ratio. The minimum nominal shear strength was 0.33 MPa (48 psi, 3.5 kgf/cm²) for bed joints perpendicular to the span, and 0.6 MPa (88 psi, 6.2 kgf/cm²) for bed joints parallel to the span.

Johnson and Thompson (1969) investigated reinforced masonry beams employing normal and high-bond mortar, and established definite relationships between the shear strength of the beams and the properties of the mortar. An increase in the water/cement ratio of the mortar was accompanied by a decrease in beam shear strength. The beams made with high-bond mortar developed shear strengths that ranged from 1.84 MPa (263 psi, 18.5 kgf/cm²) to 2.84 MPa (406 psi, 28.6 kgf/cm²), while normal mortar gave results ranging from 1.5 MPa to 2.37 MPa (214 psi to 338 psi, 15.1 kgf/cm² to 23.8 kgf/cm²).

The absorption of solid bricks influences the shear strength. The maximum shear strength occurs for 10% absorption; a "dusty" spalling brick surface can reduce the strength.

For brick with high suction rates, mortars with high water/cement ratios give increased shear strengths, according to Sahlin. Increased cement contents, however, also increase shear strength.

Additional shear resistance can be gained by the use of stirrups, as with reinforced concrete, although this solution can present practical problems. The shear strengths also increase with increasing percentages of tensile reinforcement, as with reinforced concrete, although work by Suter and Hendry (1975) suggests that this is not a significant factor in practical terms.

As an example, the Australian Code CA47 allows the following shear stresses:

In beams with no web reinforcement: 0.21 MPa (30 psi, 2.1 kgf/cm²).

In beams with web reinforcement: 0.84 MPa (120 psi, 8.45 kgf/cm²).

The Brick Institute of America Code maximum values for shear were given previously in Table 13.1.

10   Beams and Girders—Prestressed

Mehta and Pincher (1970) describe tests on six pretensioned masonry beams of nominal dimensions 250 mm wide × 300 mm × 2.1 m (10 in. wide × 12 in. × 84 in.). The recovery of deflection after cracking when unloaded was 95% and the cracks closed immediately. However, the magnitude of the deflections for an uncracked section was twice the predicted value. The beams failed in shear at an ultimate shear capacity not less than 80% of the predicted value.

The following observations were made as a result of the tests:

1. Coursing patterns of the bricks did not affect the behavior of the beam.

2. The bond between the clay brick and the grout, and between the prestressing steel and the grout, proved satisfactory.

Thomas and Plowman (1969) reported tests on small beams in soldier coursing which failed in tension at assumed principal tensile stresses between 0.6 MPa and 0.8 MPa (90 psi and 120 psi, 6.3 kgf/cm² and 8.4 kgf/cm²). The beams behaved in a manner similar to prestressed concrete beams, and shear failure was not a major concern. Local tensile failure was always in the bond between mortar and brick.

Creep and shrinkage are much less with clay bricks than with concrete or concrete masonry units, and this enhances the performance under prestressing.

Thomas reports tests by Ng using epoxy resin joints which gave a shear stress failure at 0.95 MPa (137 psi, 9.65 kgf/cm²). The modulus of rupture from flexural tests varied from 2.35 MPa to 4.67 MPa (341 psi to 677 psi, 24 kgf/cm² to 47.7 kgf/cm²), and the assumed tensile stress was 5.3 MPa approximately (763 psi, 53.7 kgf/cm²).

All of the tests indicate that large openings can be spanned with properly designed prestressed masonry beams.

Although there is a significant lack of test information, the known properties of masonry are sufficiently promising to assure much future development in the use of prestressed masonry beams as structural elements.

13.3   MASONRY MATERIALS AND CONSTRUCTION

The two components of masonry are prefabricated masonry units, normally of comparatively small size, and a joint material. The advantages of this masonry composite are mainly related to the economy and flexibility of fabrication of structural units rather than to the improvement of performance characteristics. It may be easier and often cheaper to join together comparatively small elements—the masonry units—than to produce a single monolithic element.

The properties of composite materials are controlled by the properties of the individual components and their interaction. Therefore, in the following section the interaction between masonry units and joint material leading to certain failure mechanisms of masonry will be discussed. Based upon this discussion, those properties of the individual components which have a particular effect upon the characteristics and performance of masonry will be identified and later treated in more detail.

Plain masonry structures are inherently weak when subjected to tensile stresses. This is, of course, a severe limitation of the applicability of masonry, particularly for tall structures. Therefore, steel reinforcement is often added. To assure sufficient bond and interaction between the masonry unit and the reinforcement, as well as to protect the reinforcing bars against corrosion, the reinforcement is often placed in joints or cavities which later are filled with grout or mortar. In reinforced blockwork masonry the steel can be placed in the core of the block.

Despite the general limitation of masonry for tall buildings, there have been some pilot studies (student thesis, Illinois Institute of Technology) on the architectural and structural feasibility of using masonry walls for tall apartment buildings up to 60 stories.

1 Description of Materials

Masonry Units. The oldest masonry units are clay bricks normally of rectangular dimensions. They are made of clay, shale, fire clay, or mixtures thereof by heating (sintering) them at temperatures between 750°C and 1300°C (1400°F and 2400°F). They consist of sand, aluminates, and various impurities. Bricks are available in a large variety of sizes and shapes, as well as with various coring patterns or perforations. For example (DIN 105, 1957), several types of clay bricks described in the German specification DIN 105 are shown in Fig. 13.16. The purpose of coring patterns may be numerous: improvement of thermal insulation characteristics, provision of spaces for reinforcing bars, reduction of weight, or ease of handling.

The maximum size of a clay brick is limited by the need to manufacture reasonably crackfree bricks, as well as by the weight and ease of handling of an individual brick. In addition to full-size bricks, also half-size or quarter-size bricks may be manufactured to facilitate masonry construction without cutting bricks at the site. Larger units may be employed if perforated clay blocks are used. These are units with relatively thin webs and shells. The cells may be parallel or perpendicular to the main direction of loading. Because of their continuous cavities clay blocks may have improved thermal insulation characteristics and reduced weight, as well as decreased material consumption. More recently ceramic units have been developed which may be story-high, thus eliminating bed joints and reducing costs of labor (West, 1970).

Masonry units are also made of normal or of lightweight concrete, depending on the type of aggregate. Typical aggregates for concrete blocks are crushed stone, expanded and air-cooled blast furnace slag, pumice, tuff, cinders, expanded clay or shale, scoria, or fly ash. Concrete blocks are often steam cured or autoclaved. Typical shapes and coring patterns of various types of concrete blocks are given in Fig. 13.17 (Sahlin, 1971; NCMA, 1965). The coring patterns may have a substantial effect on masonry strength even for a given net area of concrete. More recently concrete blocks have been in use which may be stacked without mortar. The concrete blocks contain cavities that can be filled later with concrete with or without reinforcement.

Sand-lime building bricks are made of siliceous sand and calcium hydroxide. They are formed under pressure and hardened at elevated temperatures in an autoclave. Their sizes and shapes are similar to those of standard clay bricks (Sahlin, 1971).

Lightweight cellular concrete blocks are made of hydraulic cementitious binders and ground sand. By adding various powders such as aluminum they may be of extremely high porosity. After casting and swelling in large containers, the blocks are cut into various sizes and shapes. Lightweight cellular concrete blocks are of comparatively low strength. This disadvantage, however, is partially offset by their small unit weight and dimensional stability.

Mortars. Conventional mortars are most commonly used as joint materials. They consist of a mixture of a cementitious material and aggregates for which, in most instances, natural sand is used. Gradation curves are specified in various national standards.

Portland cement may be used for mortars, the final strength of which depends mainly on the water-cement ratio of the mortar. Because of its faster rate of hardening portland cement mortars have a limited "pot life," which is the period of time during which the mortar maintains its workability.

Frequently, portland cement and lime are mixed to add hydraulic properties to lime mortar or to improve the workability of the mortar. Such mortars are frequently referred to using the ratio of their constituents—cement:lime:sand—as, for example, a 1:2:9 mortar, which is low strength, or a 1:1/4:3 mortar, which would be high strength. Air-entraining admixtures may be used for portland cement mortars to improve workability or frost resistance, but they are not generally encouraged for engineered masonry.

The low compressive strength and limited bonding characteristics of the joint material may significantly limit the range of applicability of masonry when subjected to compression, tension, or shear. Therefore, one of the most promising approaches to improve masonry, particularly for high-rise construction, is the development of high-strength, high-bond mortars. Polymer modified cement or lime mortars, or mortars containing only polymers as a cementation phase, are particularly well suited for this purpose. In the United States and elsewhere latex modified cement mortars are being used successfully as a joint material (Grenley, 1969; Schupak and McDonald, 1969). Also, epoxy resins with or without latex and cement additives are being used to an increasing extent (Gobel, 1971). Because of the high cost of such mortars, the joint thickness has to be kept to a minimum. A decrease of the joint thickness by itself will lead to improved masonry strength. However, this holds true only as long as the dimensions of the masonry units are controlled within close limits. The use of high-strength mortars is less advantageous for reinforced masonry where the reinforcement provides the improvement of tensile strength and ductility.

Mortar for reinforced masonry is generally of higher strength than the minimum allowed for unreinforced masonry. In the early years of reinforced masonry construction in New Zealand some difficulies were experienced with mortars in which adequate strength was difficult to obtain. This was probably due to poor sand grading requiring excessive quantities of plasticizer (lime) and water in order to achieve suitable workability and "fattiness" for the bricklayer, and a consequent

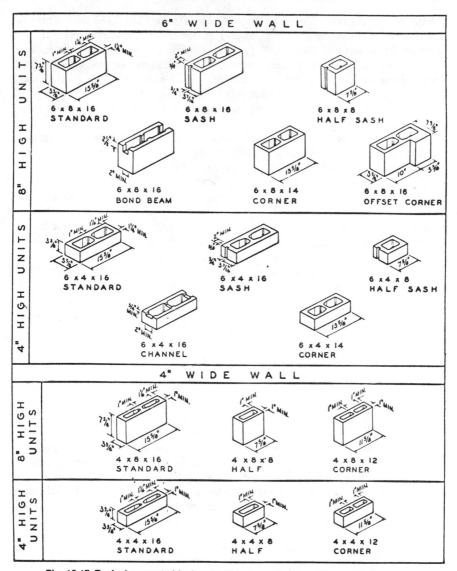

Fig. 13.17 Typical concrete block units (Courtesy: Concrete Masonry Association)

reduction in strength. This problem, in recent years, has been overcome due particularly to more rigorous control and inspection. In reinforced masonry, the supreme importance of assuring that grout, or filling concrete, fills all the required cavities or cells is evident in recent building codes. Insistence on adequate fluidity is given by specifying a minimum slump and a minimum spread (a New Zealand devised test to measure fluidity). Methods for grouting, either by low-lift or high-lift methods, are carefully specified and particular emphasis is given to cleaning-out procedures.

Damp-Proof Courses. When selecting a damp-proof course it is extremely important to consider the type of loading it will be subjected to, and also the likely temperature range. Damp-proof courses subjected to high vertical loading and normal temperatures might consist of brick, slate, or polythene, but if high lateral forces are imposed with little precompression the latter material may not be suitable. Bituminous felt-type damp-proof courses are satisfactory only for low-rise construction, and then only if the loading and temperature conditions are not too high. Cracking of brickwork is less likely to occur if horizontal movement is restrained by a suitable damp-proof course correctly positioned within a mortar joint. In conditions where the tensile strength of the wall is important, for example a free-standing wall, a brick damp-proof course is preferable near the base, as this provides the same order of tensile resistance to flexure and shear as the wall itself.

Wall Ties. The following materials are currently used for wall ties: galvanized mild steel; stainless steel; brass; bronze; manganese bronze (high tensile brass); hard-drawn copper; aluminum; gunmetal; and polypropylene. The choice of material must depend to a large extent upon the main functions that the wall tie will be required to perform, but due regard must be paid to the possibility of corrosion, damage by fire, and structural requirements.

Movement Joints. Movement occurs in all materials and may be due to variation in temperature or moisture content, physico-chemical or frost action, movement in adjacent structural material, or deflections and settlement. The inclusion of movement joints is essential in long runs of masonry, and failure to provide them, while rarely responsible for structural collapse, can be the cause of unsightly cracking that can be avoided if appropriate measures are taken at the design stage. The use of high-strength mortars enables masonry structures of greater load-bearing capacity to be built more rapidly, but less flexibility is present in masonry, and consequently allowance for movement must be made by suitably designed joints.

It is essential when designing a movement joint to consider the type of movement that may occur. Movements in brickwork may be due to expansion and contraction and, therefore, a material that is resilient and easily compressible should be used. Certain types of fiberboard and similar materials are not suitable for expansion joints. Tests have shown that in some instances a considerable stress can be reached up to 50% of the compression strength of the material, and on removal of the load the material does not return to its previous dimensions.

Strips of V-shaped copper have been successfully used for many years, but new materials such as premolded, extruded, closed-cell rubber or plastic sections can be used. Under certain circumstances, such as temporary joints, the use of lime-sand mortar may be considered sufficient for movement to take place (a 1:3 to 1:4-1/2 mix by volume of nonhydraulic lime and sand). The sealing of movement joints has always been a problem. Low grade butyl-based caulking compounds, with a backing such as nonrigid plastic foam, have been found satisfactory in buildings of up to nine stories in Australia. In more severe conditions, the more expensive poly-sulphide-based sealants may be required. It is also necessary to distinguish between closing joints in expanding materials and opening joints in shrinking materials.

2 Properties of Masonry Materials and Their Effect on Masonry Behavior

Masonry Units

Strength characteristics. The strength of clay bricks is primarily affected by the composition of the raw material, as well as by firing temperature, manufacturing process, and porosity. The compressive strength of clay bricks may range roughly between 10 MPa and 140 MPa (3000 psi and 20 000 psi, 210 kgf/cm^2 and 1400 kgf/cm^2) if related to the gross area of a particular brick. The modulus of rupture varies roughly between 10% and 30% of the compressive strength of a particular clay brick (Sahlin, 1971; Monk, 1967).

The coring patterns or perforations may have a significant influence on the load carrying capacity of clay bricks of given material properties. In Schellbach (1970) and West et al. (1968), it is shown that at the perforations of tiles which are embedded in mortar, high stress concentrations may be developed whose magnitude depends on the particular shape of the perforations. Well-rounded perforations reduce the stress concentrations and thus lead to improved masonry strength.

The compressive strength of hollow concrete blocks ranges from 3.5 MPa to 48 MPa (500 psi to 7000 psi, 35 kgf/cm^2 to 480 kgf/cm^2) based on the gross area of the block. It is most influenced by those factors that influence the strength of concrete, such as compaction, curing, and type of aggregate. In addition, however, the coring pattern may have an effect similar to the phenomena described for clay bricks. In many instances, concrete blocks are manufactured by a steam curing or autoclave process resulting in a rapid, early strength development. The effect of steam curing on the properties of lightweight aggregate concrete is discussed by Kuenning and Carlson (1956), and by Toennies and Redmond (1975).

The strength of lightweight cellular blocks may vary roughly from 1 MPa to 14 MPa (150 psi to 2000 psi, 10 kgf/cm^2 to 140 kgf/cm^2) and is most of all affected by the density of the particular material, which may range from 400 kg/m^3 to 700 kg/m^3 (25 lb/ft^3 to 45 lb/ft^3). Increasing porosity results in a reduction of strength and of unit weight. The modulus of rupture of lightweight cellular blocks is approximately 1/5 to 1/3 of the compressive strength.

The compressive strength of sand-lime building bricks may range from approximately 7 MPa to 100 MPa (1000 psi to 15 000 psi, 70 kgf/cm^2 to 1000 kgf/cm^2), with a modulus of rupture of approximately 20% of the compressive strength.

Based upon these strength characteristics, clay bricks, sand-lime building bricks, and concrete blocks may be suitable for load-bearing walls in tall buildings, while lightweight cellular blocks should be used primarily for nonload-bearing walls.

Various relations have been established between the strength of masonry and the strength of masonry units. They have been discussed in more detail by Sahlin (1971), and should be applied with due caution with regard to the type of unit for which a particular relationship was developed. In general, it can be said that an increase in the strength of the masonry units also leads to an increase of masonry strength (Fig. 13.18). However, even for a given joint material, other factors such as evenness and uniformity of dimensions of the masonry units or stress concentrations may be of equal importance. The "efficiency factor," that is, the ratio of the compressive strength of masonry to the compressive strength of masonry units, may be as low as 5% and rarely exceeds 60%, except where high-strength adhesives are used as a joint material or where high-strength grouts are used to fill hollow units. The efficiency factor is generally higher for concrete masonry than for brick masonry.

Modulus of elasticity and Poisson's ratio. The modulus of elasticity of clay bricks is influenced essentially by the same factors that influence the strength of bricks. As a rough estimate, modulus of elasticity of a brick E_b may be estimated from its compressive strength f_{bu} using an expression $E_b = 300 \, f_{bu}$ (Glanville, 1934). Poisson's ratio of clay bricks is on the order of 0.2 to 0.3 and increases slightly with increasing stress (Sahlin, 1971; Hilsdorf, 1965).

The modulus of elasticity E_b of concrete blocks ranges from $500 \, f_{bu}$ to $1500 \, f_{bu}$ (Sahlin, 1971; Kuenning and Carlson, 1956), in which f_{bu} is the compressive strength of the block. The values for lightweight cellular concrete depend on their unit weight and are approximately 1400 MPa (200 000 psi, 14 100 kgf/cm²) for blocks with a unit weight of 500 kg/m³ (31 pcf) and 2400 MPa (350 000 psi, 24 600 kgf/cm²) for blocks with a unit weight of 650 kg/m³ (40 pcf).

The modulus of elasticity of masonry depends on the modulus of the masonry units and the joint material, and can be estimated from the longitudinal strains of both components (Sahlin, 1971; Schubert, 1977).

Rate of absorption. The rate of absorption, also referred to as suction, is normally defined as the amount of water absorbed by a dry masonry unit when partially immersed in water for a given period of time. The rate of absorption is primarily a function of the porosity of the masonry units, as well as of the continuity of the pore system. In Fig. 13.19, the absorption after 24 hr to 28 hr of immersion of various types of masonry units is given as a function of the density of the masonry units (Sahlin, 1971). An increase in density leads to a reduction of absorption. A high rate of absorption of the masonry unit may substantially reduce the workability of the joint material and thus have a detrimental effect on masonry

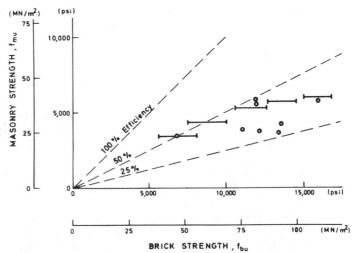

Fig. 13.18 Relationship between compressive strength of masonry f_{mu} and compressive strength of clay bricks f_{bu} (Sahlin, 1971)

strength. The strength of masonry loaded in compression may decrease substantially with increasing rate of absorption. This is particularly true for eccentrically loaded members, and is more pronounced for portland cement mortars than for cement-lime mortars (Haller, 1958). However, by prewetting the bricks the detrimental effect of high absorption may be reduced, but it must be remembered that this practice may result in efflorescence problems.

Shrinkage and creep. Most masonry elements exhibit a certain dimensional change as a result of moisture exchange with the surrounding environment. Shrinkage and swelling increase with increasing amounts of moisture gain, and are influenced by the porosity as well as by the internal surface area of the material. The total height of the joints seldom exceeds 20% of the height of a masonry wall (Sahlin, 1971), so masonry shrinkage is, therefore, mostly due to shrinkage of the masonry units. Shrinkage of burnt clay bricks may be reversible and normally does not exceed values of 2×10^{-4}. However, bricks may also undergo considerable permanent expansion as a result of a reaction between water and the fired clay (McDowell and Birtwistle, 1970). The consequences of this phenomenon vary from one part of the world to another; in Australia, it is known to have caused considerable damage to brickwork.

Shrinkage of concrete blocks may vary within rather wide limits and primarily depends on water-cement ratio, cement content, types of aggregates, and curing treatment of a particular block (ACI, 1969). Steam or autoclave curing normally reduces shrinkage. Also, precarbonation of steam cured blocks may substantially reduce shrinkage (Shiedeler, 1963).

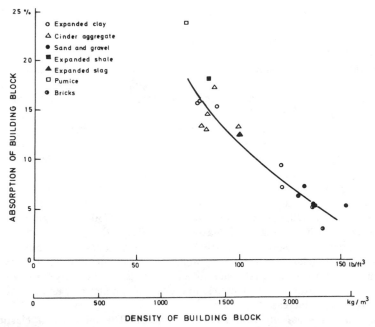

Fig. 13.19 Relation between absorption and density of various types of building blocks (Sahlin, 1971)

Creep of masonry has not been investigated extensively. Burnt clay bricks exhibit little if any creep. Nevertheless, creep strains of masonry were reported (Lenczner, 1970a, 1970b) which were 1.2 to 1.8 times the elastic strains. Creep of masonry made of concrete blocks may be up to three times the elastic strains (Nylander and Ericsson, 1957). The creep of brickwork has been investigated by Lenczner (1970, 1976) in the United Kingdom, who showed that full-size brickwork creep is appreciably less than laboratory tests would indicate. Mortar plays a major role in the creep characteristic of brickwork and, for equal strength, creep in brickwork is less than in concrete and ceases after a shorter time.

At working stress levels, according to this research, the temperature and moisture movement strains in brickwork can numerically exceed the creep strains, and as a result the total vertical strain in brickwork after a period under load could be less than the instantaneous strain obtained immediately after loading. On the other hand, the moisture expansion will add to the lateral creep strain caused by vertical loading, leading to a substantial increase in the over-all lateral strain. The ratio of maximum load strain to instantaneous strain obtained in these tests was found to be substantially lower than published values for concrete. In tests using $1:\frac{1}{4}:3$ and 1:1:6 mortars, the actual values of maximum creep strains at similar stress levels for the 1:1:6 mortar were approximately 2.5 to 3.5 times those obtained with the $1:\frac{1}{4}:3$ mortar.

The elastic modulus of brickwork using both mortars was approximately 240×10^3 MPa to 275×10^3 MPa (3.5×10^6 psi to 4×10^6 psi, 2.5×10^5 kgf/cm² to 4×10^5 kgf/cm²). The elastic recovery upon removal of the load was much better with the stronger mortar, and fell to only 31% recovery for a stress level 3.85 MPa (560 psi) using 1:1:6 mortar. The lower values are attributed to the more viscous nature of the weaker mortar. For 1:1:6 mortar the maximum load strain was reached after a period of 16 weeks for a stress level of 4.64 MPa (674 psi, 47.5 kgf/cm²). After this time no further creep occurred.

Joint Materials

Strength characteristics. The compressive strangth of lime mortar ranges from 0.1 MPa to 1 MPa (15 psi to 150 psi, 1 kgf/cm² to 10 kgf/cm²), while for cement or cement-lime mortars a compressive strength between 15 MPa and 30 MPa (2000 psi and 6000 psi, 140 kgf/cm² and 420 kgf/cm²) may be reached. The strength of cement and cement-lime mortars is highly influenced by the water-cement ratio as well as by age and curing conditions. The strength of lime-cement and masonry cement mortars also depends on the lime-cement ratio (Duhrkop, 1973). Little information is available on the tensile and compressive strength of polymer modified mortars, since such materials are tested mostly when used in large-scale masonry units. However, Grenley (1969) reports compressive strength values for latex modified cement mortars up to 50 MPa (7500 psi, 530 kgf/cm²).

The compressive strength of masonry is influenced by the strength of the mortar (Granholm, 1943). Particularly if high-strength adhesives are used as a joint material, the efficiency ratio may approach values of unity (Hilsdorf, 1965). The thickness of joints is an equally significant parameter, particularly for low-strength mortars. As the ratio of joint thickness to the height of a masonry unit decreases, the masonry strength increases.

Modulus of elasticity and Poisson's ratio. The modulus of elasticity of mortars E_1 can be related to its compressive strength f_{ju} and may be approximated by $E_1 = 100 f_{ju}$. Poisson's ratio of most hydraulic cement and lime mortars is on the order of 0.2 and increases rapidly as the uniaxial strength of the mortar is approached.

Workability and water retentivity. The workability of a mortar is measured in percentage flow, which is defined as the increase in the diameter of a cake of fresh mortar after it is dropped from a defined height for a given number of times. The flow of a mortar increases with increasing water content and increasing amount of lime. It may be further improved by air-entraining or water-reducing admixtures. Flow and workability may be highly influenced by atmospheric conditions, such as temperature and relative humidity. Under hot weather conditions, particularly if dry and high winds prevail, the moisture content of a mortar has to be increased in order to compensate for evaporation of water. Then, also, the period of time during which the mortar maintains its workability may be severely reduced.

Water retentivity is a measure of the ability of the mortar to retain water and thus prevent it from escaping into bricks or blocks with high suction. It may be measured, for example in accordance with ASTM C 109 and C 110. It is influenced to a large extent by the gradation of aggregates and the content of lime and water. Finer gradation, increased lime content, and a reduction in water content increase the water retentivity of a particular mortar.

Water retentivity of the mortar may influence the behavior of masonry in various ways: poor water retentivity may lead to a decrease of the water-cement ratio of a particular mortar, especially if the suction of the masonry units is high. Then the bond strength of masonry may be impaired. Too low a water retentivity may severely reduce the workability of a mortar, which often results in decreased masonry strength because the mortar joints may not support the masonry units uniformly, as discussed previously.

Shear strength and bond strength between joint material and masonry units. The bond strength between mortar and masonry units is not only dependent on certain properties of the mortar, such as its strength and water retentivity, but also on the physical characteristics of the material (Grandet, 1973), and suction of the masonry units. A very low rate of absorption may be due to low surface porosity, and consequently results in little mechanical interlock between masonry units and mortar. Under such conditions the bond strength is low. For masonry units with high absorption, too much water may be absorbed from the mortar, which thus loses its workability so that the area over which bonding is accomplished may be reduced.

For lime-cement mortars the shear strength increases considerably with an increase of the cement content (Granholm, 1943). In general, increased surface roughness of masonry units should improve the shear strength; however, dusty or spalling surfaces may severely reduce the shear or bond strength by values of up to 50%.

The tensile bond strength between masonry units and the joint material has been studied for conventional mortars as well as for polymer modified mortars. For masonry cement mortars the tensile bond strength may increase with the water-cement ratio because of the improved workability of the mortar (Isberner, 1969). The tensile bond strength between clay bricks and masonry cement mortars rarely exceeds values of 0.7 MPa (100 psi, 7 kgf/cm²). However, with polymer modified mortars, values larger than 3 MPa (250 psi, 17.6 kgf/cm²) may be achieved

(Grenley, 1969). If pure polymer mortars are used, the tensile bond strength may exceed the tensile strength of the masonry unit, so that tensile failure will occur in the masonry unit rather than in the joint.

Movement joints.   It is impracticable to produce a comprehensive specification for the position and spacing of movement joints for all structures. Each building must be considered as an individual unit and provision made accordingly. Opinion on the spacing of movement joints is varied, reflecting regional differences in climate and masonry material characteristics. Spacings varying from two to four times the height of the concrete block work with maximum values of 40 ft to 60 ft are recommended by NCMA for walls having amounts of joint reinforcement ranging from none to reinforcement in every course. In British practice, movement joints would be provided in clay brickwork at about 12-m (40-ft) intervals, and 7-m to 8-m (23-ft to 26-ft) intervals in the case of calcium silicate brickwork. A spacing of 1-1/2 to 2 times the height of a concrete blockwork wall has also been suggested. The Brick Development Research Institute of Australia (Occasional Publication 4, 1973) gives formulas for calculating the spacing of joints which seem to result in much greater spacing than usual in Britain. The Canadian Clay Masonry Manual (1965) also gives a formula, but as in all other design guides the necessity for consideration of each building is emphasized, rather than reliance on general rules.

3   Testing and Specification of Masonry Materials

Masonry Units.   In most codes relating to masonry, provisions are made with regard to size and dimensional tolerances of masonry units, their perforations and unit weight, compressive strength, freeze-thaw resistance, and water absorption characteristics.

In most specifications certain fixed dimensions are recommended for masonry, but certain deviations from such limitations are often allowed. Surprisingly, the maximum weight of a masonry unit is not limited in most codes.

Most specifications allow permissible variations in the dimensions of an individual masonry unit on the order of 3% to 4% of a particular dimension, whereas in the British Standard certain deviations of the total dimensions of 24 bricks are allowed. The specifications with regard to perforations are rather loose, leaving room for additional development. However, the detrimental effect of certain perforations is rarely mentioned.

One of the most problematic aspects of testing masonry units is the determination of their compressive strength. In most cases the masonry units are capped prior to testing and are then subjected to compressive stresses in a standard testing machine. Because of the restraining effect provided by the bearing platens of the testing machine, masonry units of different dimensions, particularly of different height-to-width ratios, yield different compressive strength values even for a given type of material. Such uncertainties in the determination of the compressive strength of a masonry unit are, at least in part, responsible for the wide scatter in experimental data for the relationship between masonry strength and standard compressive strength of a masonry unit. In addition, the stress state developed in a standard compression test of a masonry unit differs from the stress state in a masonry assembly. There, the masonry unit is subjected to stresses in the direction of the external load and lateral tensile stresses (Hilsdorf, 1969; Khoo and Hendry, 1973). The suggestion has therefore repeatedly been made to use the tensile strength of a masonry unit rather than its compressive strength as the basis on which to estimate the strength of masonry. It was also shown by Watstein (1971) that good correlation between masonry strength and strength of a masonry unit can be obtained if the restraining effect of the bearing platens in the testing of masonry units is eliminated.

Requirements with regard to freeze-thaw durability of masonry units are mostly limited to masonry units which may be exposed to such weather conditions. Most masonry units, particularly clay bricks, of reasonably high quality normally meet such requirements, but special care is necessary in adverse climates and in particularly exposed elements, such as parapet walls.

Though the significance of the absorption characteristics of masonry units upon the properties of masonry is well known, not all specifications require testing of such properties. Several different measurements of the absorption characteristics of brick are being used: ASTM C 67 specifies the initial rate of absorption (IRA), which is determined by measuring the amount of water initially absorbed by a dry brick when partially immersed in water to a depth of 3 mm (1/8 in.) for a period of one minute. Other methods or depths of immersion to determine the absorption characteristics of masonry units are specified in various countries. In general, however, different absorption tests yield values with similar tendencies, when related to the properties of masonry.

Joint Materials. In most specifications a determination of compressive strength, flexural strength, water retention, and flow before or after suction of mortars is required. Often, these requirements relate to laboratory procedures which are not suitable for field control. The compressive strength is determined either on mortar cubes of various sizes, or on the broken halves of prismatic specimens which had initially been subjected to a flexural load. The problems arising in the testing of the compressive strength of mortars are similar to those described for the testing of masonry units: the apparent compressive strength will be influenced by the particular type of specimen. In addition, the stress state developed in a mortar joint of masonry may differ from the stress state to which the specimen is subjected in a standard compression test. Furthermore, it has to be realized that the composition, particularly the water content and thus the water-cement ratio, of the joint material in masonry may differ from the composition of the material used in the test sample because of suction of the masonry units.

Sufficient workability of a fresh mortar is one of the prime requirements that must be satisfied to assure masonry of good quality. The flow is a good indication of this particular property.

In the United States it is measured as the increase, as a percentage, of the diameter of a molded cake of fresh mortar with a diameter of 100 mm (4 in.) after it is dropped 12.5 mm (1/2 in.) 25 times in 15 sec. Slightly different test parameters are specified in other codes. It may be determined before or after suction, thus simulating the conditions to which mortar in a masonry joint may be subjected.

The water retentivity of a mortar may be measured by draining water from a fresh mortar cake through vacuum. In this test the mortar cake rests on the perforated bottom of a form which is covered with filter paper. Then the flow is measured. This value is divided by the flow without suction, expressed as a percentage, and designated as water retentivity. In ASTM C 91 a minimum water retention of 70% is required.

Compression Tests on Masonry Prisms. Foster and Bridgeman (1973) report on prism tests for the design and control of brick masonry in New Zealand.

They looked for a prism that would give a reliable estimate of masonry performance in a structure, that is, where the failure was in splitting of the masonry normal to the horizontal mortar courses. This requires that the prism has a sufficient number of courses so that a masonry unit in the center of the prism is free of platen restraint and is therefore representative of masonry units in the structure. Foster and Bridgeman showed that the prism compressive strength decreases with increasing number of courses, and levels off to a constant value at five courses with the common size of New Zealand brick. Limited work on concrete masonry suggested that four courses were necessary with New Zealand concrete blocks. With at least these numbers of courses a vertical splitting failure was assured.

Similar work has been done in Australia and in the United States, and in both these countries prism tests are used to determine masonry strength. In the United

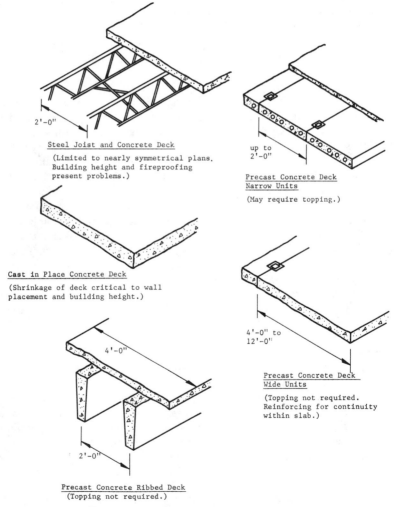

2'-0"

Steel Joist and Concrete Deck

(Limited to nearly symmetrical plans. Building height and fireproofing present problems.)

up to 2'-0"

Precast Concrete Deck
Narrow Units

(May require topping.)

Cast in Place Concrete Deck

(Shrinkage of deck critical to wall placement and building height.)

4'-0" to 12'-0"

Precast Concrete Deck
Wide Units

(Topping not required. Reinforcing for continuity within slab.)

4'-0"

2'-0"

Precast Concrete Ribbed Deck
(Topping not required.)

Fig. 13.20 Floor systems for load-bearing masonry

Kingdom, where cubes are used, although numerous prism tests have been carried out, it has been found difficult to establish a reliable correlation between cube strength and wall strength, and this form of test has not been adopted as a means of establishing masonry strength. Brickwork cubes have, however, been used as a means of site control.

4 Floor Systems in Masonry Buildings

Proper selection of the structural floor system depends on span, load-carrying capacity, ability to accommodate openings and cantilevers, deflection resistance, fire protection requirements, sound transmission, diaphragm action, and cost. Fig. 13. 20 shows several types suitable for wall bearing construction.

Steel Joist and Concrete Deck.   Simple spans and cantilevers are feasible for roof, but not for floor. This system is limited to nearly symmetrical plans. Building height and fireproofing present problems. Typical spans are 5 m to 8 m (15 ft to 25 ft). This system could also use metal decking with concrete fill.

Precast Deck, Narrow Units.   This system, of simple or multiple spans, may require topping to account for differential camber, provide a level surface, and

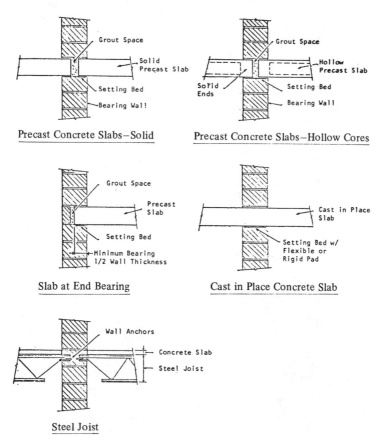

Precast Concrete Slabs–Solid   Precast Concrete Slabs–Hollow Cores

Slab at End Bearing   Cast in Place Concrete Slab

Steel Joist

Fig. 13.21 End conditions of various floor systems

provide continuity. Underside of units can be finished ceiling. Multiple spans are possible by reinforcing grout key over supports. Slab thickness should be modular with masonry wall. Roof and floor cantilevers are possible in one direction. Fill cells with grout at bearing walls. Continuity at bearing walls and diaphragm action may be problems. Typical spans are 5 m to 9 m (15 ft to 30 ft).

Precast Deck, Wide Units.   Simple or multiple spans. Frequently no topping is required. Underside of slab can be used as finished ceiling. Roof and floor cantilevers are feasible in one or two directions. Slab thickness should be modular with masonry wall. Typical spans are 2 m to 9 m (7 ft to 30 ft), one-way and two-way slabs.

Cast-in-Place Concrete Slab.   Multiple spans of 3 m to 6 m (10 ft to 20 ft). Roof and floor cantilevers are feasible in two directions. Underside of slab can be used as finished ceiling. Slab thickness should be modular with masonry wall. Shrinkage of slab during curing is critical to wall placement and building height.

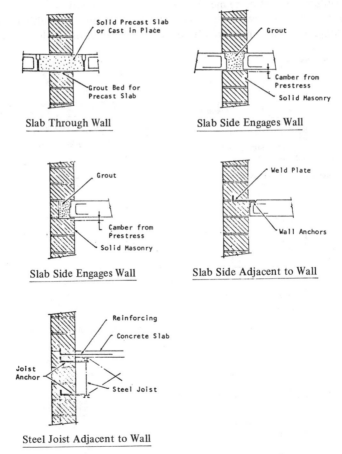

Slab Through Wall

Slab Side Engages Wall

Slab Side Engages Wall

Slab Side Adjacent to Wall

Steel Joist Adjacent to Wall

Fig. 13.22 Transfer of lateral shear forces to shear walls

Cast-in-place ribbed slabs are feasible for 5-m to 9-m (15-ft to 30-ft) multiple spans. Roof and floor cantilevers are possible in one direction.

Single-T and Double-T Units.   Spans with double T are 6 m to 12 m (20 ft to 40 ft); spans with single T are 12 m to 18 m (40 ft to 60 ft). Topping may be required. Continuity of bearing wall at point of support requires attention. High local stresses occur in wall at bearing.

Design Considerations.   A critical item regarding the interaction of bearing walls and large precast floor slabs lies at the point of bearing. Wide precast slabs require an extended mortar bed. It is virtually impossible to place the mortar bed and erect the slab before the mortar reaches its initial set. The preferred method is to place a slab on a bearing strip. Since masonry may be uneven at the point of bearing, this will avoid high concentrations of stress where it comes in contact with the slab, which could cause distress in either the slab or the wall.

Hollow precast floor slabs in the lower floors of a building must transmit the stresses in the bearing wall above them to the wall below. It is possible that the stresses within the precast slab from beam action and the stresses from the weight of wall above will be too high when combined. To overcome this problem, the usual practice is to provide solid ends in the precast slabs (Fig. 13.21).

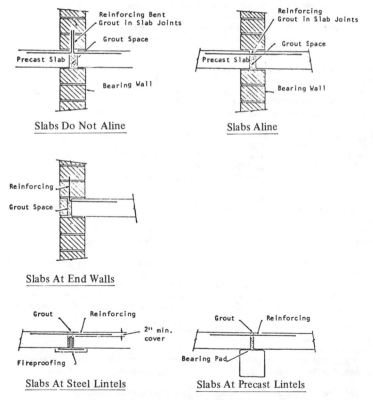

Fig. 13.23 Continuity reinforcing of precast floor systems

The transfer of horizontal forces from the floor system into the shear walls should be carefully considered. It may be necessary to grout reinforcing dowels from the precast elements into the masonry, or it may be necessary to provide steel shear lugs on the precast elements embedded in the shear walls (Fig. 13.22).

Certain configurations of shear and bearing walls may require tying the structure together over several spans. This may be accomplished by welding adjacent units together at their ends, or by grouting reinforcing bars into adjacent units, or by providing reinforcing in the topping continuous across the bearing point (Fig. 13.23).

13.4 CONDENSED REFERENCES/BIBLIOGRAPHY

The following is a condensed bibliography for this chapter. Not only does it include all articles referred to or cited in the text, but it also contains bibliography for further reading. The full citations will be found at the end of the Volume. What is given here should be sufficient information to lead the reader to the correct article: the author, date, and title. In case of multiple authors, only the first named is listed.

Adams 1970, *The Design of Brickwork Against Gas Explosions*
Albenque 1973, *The Prediliation of Ceramic Products*
Allen 1970, *Limit State Design—A Unified Procedure for the Design of Structures*
Allen 1973, *Effect of Direction of Loading on Compressive Strength of Brick Masonry*
Amrhein 1976, *A Tower with its top in the Heavens*

Anderson 1970, *Stack-Bonded Small Specimen as Design and Construction Criteria*
Anderson 1973, *Site Control of Structural Brickwork in Australia*
Anderson 1973, *The Interaction Between Walls and Floor in a Structure of Loadbearing Brickwork*
Anderson 1973, *Computer Design of Engineering Brick Masonry*
Astbury 1970, *Experiments to Determine the Resistance of Brick Buildings to Gas Explosions*

Astbury 1973, *Motion of Brickwork Structure under Certain Assumed Conditions*
Astbury 1973, *Gas Explosion Testing—Phrase IV*
Aylon 1976, *Highlights of the New Canadian Masonry Design Code—CSA Standard S304*
Baker 1973, *Flexural Strength of Brickwork Panels*
Beech 1977, *Some Problems in the Statistical Calculation of Safety Factors*

Berhmann 1973, *Damages in Masonry Caused by Perpendicular Deformation*
Bluck 1973, *The Need for a Strengthening Code*
Blume 1970, *The Shear Truth about Brick Walls*
Bradshaw 1969, *Preliminary Crushing Tests on Storey-Height Cavity Walls*
Bradshaw 1970, *Two Load-Bearing Brickwork Buildings in Northern England*

Brettle 1971, *Ultimate Strength Design of Reinforced Brickwork Piers in Compression and Biaxial*
Bryrup 1973, *The Future of Brick-Construction (With a Special View on the Danish Situation)*
Buckton 1970, *Modern Development Utilizing the Interaction of Deep Brick Panels and*
Burnham 1970, *Towards a Rational Aesthetic Criterion for the Selection of the Visual Properties of*
Cajert 1973, *Laterally Loaded Light Expanded Clay Block Masonry. The Effect of Reinforcement in*

Cantor 1970, *Three High-Bond Mortar Applications*
Carlson 1970, *Unit Masonry—Today and Tomorrow*
Converse 1946, *Tests on Reinforced Concrete Masonry*
Csekme 1973, *The Spreading of Monolithic, Prefabricated Parts (Walls and Ceilings) Made of*
Curtin 1968, *The Problems of Supervision of Calculated Load-Bearing Brickwork*

Cutler 1970, *The Development of the Canadian Building Code for Masonry*
Davey 1950, *The Structural Use of Brickwork*
Davies 1966, *Comparative Tests on Brickwork Panels Reinforced with Steelforce*
Davis 1976, *Philosophy and Practice of Job-Site Inspection*
Davison 1976, *Mortar Technology*

Dickey 1973a, *High Rise Load Bearing Concept*
Dickey 1973b, *Masonry Wall Beams*
Dickey 1973c, *Masonry and Earthquakes*
Dickey 1973d, *Masonry—Reinforced vs Partially Reinforced*
Dickey 1976, *History and Development of Hollow Brick for Reinforcement*

Dikkers 1970, *Strength of Brick Walls Subject to Axial Compression and Bending*
Drysdale 1976, *Design of Masonry Walls and Columns for Combined Axial Load and Bending*
Duhrkop 1973, *Influence of an Additional Compound on the Mechanical Characteristic of*
Dunstone 1970, *Comparative Prices of Load-bearing Brickwork and Concrete Walling*
Edwards 1973, *Recent Advances in Clay Brick Manufacture*

Ehm 1973, *Actual Position of the Standardization in Acoustic Insulation and Effects on the Masonry*
Erdmann 1973, *The Philadelphia National Bank—A Case Study in Prefabricated High Strength*
Esteva 1966, *Behaviour under Alternating Loads of Masonry Diaphragms Framed by Reinforced*
Falk 1973, *Deformations in Existing Masonry in Brick Skyscrapers*
Fattal 1976, *Structural Performance of Masonry Walls under Compressiona dn Flexural*

Fisher 1970, *The Effects of Wall-Ties on the Compressive Strength of Cavity Walls*
Fisher 1973, *The Effect of Chasing on the Compressive Strength of Brickwork*
Foster 1968, *Reinforced Brickwork and Grouted Cavity Construction*
Foster 1973, *Prism Tests for the Design and Control of Brick Masonry*
Francis 1969, *The S.A.A. Brickwork Code: The Research Background*

Francis 1970, *The Effect of Joint Thickness and Other Factors on the Compressive Strength of*
Funk 1973, *The Revision of the German Masonry Standard DIN 1053*
Gensert 1969, *Engineering Evaluation for East Liberty Plaza*
Gero 1969, *Prestressed Masonry-Reinforced Concrete Space Structure*
Glanville 1934, *Mechanical Properties of Bricks and Brickwork Masonry*

Gobel 1971, *New Development in Masonry Construction in Foreign Countries*
Gobel 1973, *Color, Shape and Structure of Construction*
Goffi 1973, *Research on the Deformation Characteristics of Ceramics to Allow Calculations at*
Grandet 1973, *Physico-Chemical Mechanisms of the Bond Between Cement and Ceramics*
Granholm 1943, *Reinforced Brick Masonry*

Green 1973, *Statutory Requirements and Site Control*
Grenley 1969, *Study of the Effect of Certain Modified Mortars on Compressive and Flexural Strength*
Grenley 1970, *The Effect of Edge Load on the Racking Strength of Clay Masonry*
Grenley 1970, *University Center Project*
Grimm 1973, *Field Quality Control Tests for Wetting Bricks in Masonry Construction*

Grimm 1974a, *Masonry Construction Operations*
Grimm 1974b, *Weather Effects on Mason Productivity*
Grimm 1975a, *Strength and Related Properties of Brick Masonry*
Grimm 1975b, *Colour of Structures*
Grimm 1975c, *Rationalized Aesthetics in Civil Engineering*

Grimm 1975d, *Principles of Composition in Building Art*
Grimm 1975e, *Design for Differential Movement in Brick Walls*
Grimm 1976, *Design of Brick Masonry Bearing Walls and Columns*
Grimm undated, *Quality Control in Brick Masonry Construction in the USA*
Grogan 1970, *Miscellaneous Reinforced Brick Masonry Structures*

Grogan 1973, *Standards of Quality for Materials used in Engineering Brick Masonry in the U.S.*
Gross 1969, *Building Code Requirements Relating to Loadbearing Brick Masonry*
Gross 1969, *Recommended Practice for Engineered Brick*
Haas 1973, *Planning, Costs and Calculation for a 10-Story Apartment Building in Jülich*
Haferkamp 1973, *Climatizing of our Archives by Brick Masonry*

Haferland 1973, *The Outside Wall—Element of Separation Between Interior and Exterior Climate*
Haller 1953, *Tall Buildings in Basel*
Haller 1958, *Technical Properties of Masonry Made of Clay Bricks and Used for High Rise*
Haller 1959, *The Technological Properties of Brick Masonry in Masonry in high Buildings*
Haller undated, *The Properties of Loadbearing Brickwork in Perforated Fire Brick for Multi-Storey*

Hanlon 1970, *Prestressed Concrete Masonry*
Hanson 1969, *Park Mayfair East*
Harding 1971, *Brick Making—Quality Control and Monitoring of Strength*
Hart 1973, *The Possibilities of Architectural Design with the New Techniques of Masonry*
Haseltine 1970, *Design and Construction of a Nineteen-Storey Load-Bearing Brick Building*

Haseltine 1971, *Loadbearing Brickwork—Design for the Fifth Amendment (to the Building*
Hatzinikolas 1976, *Shear Behaviour of Masonry Walls Subdivided by Floor Slabs*
Hauser 1973, *Efficiency Increase by Use of Large Wall Bricks*
Henclewski 1975, *Characteristics of Fixation of Continuously Analysed Wall*
Henclewski 1975, *Application of the Simplified Continuous Scheme in Analysis of Safety*

Hendry 1969, *Racking Tests on Storey-Height Shear-Wall Structures with Openings, Subject to*
Hendry 1971, *Wind Load Analysis of Multi-Storey Brickwork Structures*
Hendry 1971, *Shear Tests on Full-Scale Single-Storey Brickwork Structures Subjected to*
Hendry 1973, *Full Scale Tests on the Lateral Strength of Brick Cavity Walls*
Hendry 1976, *The Effect of Site Factors on Masonry Performance*

Hendry 1976, *Effect of Slenderness and Eccentricity on the Compressive Strength of Walls*
Henkley 1966, *Tests of One-Storey Pre-Stressed Brickwork Shear Walls*
Higgins 1970, *Reinforced Masonry Bearing Walls used in 13-Storey Buildings*
Hilsdorf 1965, *Studies of the Fundamentals of Masonry Strength*
Hilsdorf 1969, *Investigation into the Failure Mechanism of Brick Masonry Loaded in Axial*

Hoath 1970, *The Effect of Mortars on the Strength of Brickwork Cubes*
Hollings 1973, *A Philosophy for Improved Old Buildings to Resist Earthquakes*
Holmes 1967, *Masonry Buildings in High Intensity Seismic Zones*
Huet 1973, *Basic Formulations of the Evolution of the Constraints and Deformations in Ceramic*
Huizer 1976, *Measuring the Consistency of Masonry Mortars in the Laboratory and on the Job Site*

Huizer 1976, *The Effect of Brick Type on the Compressive Strength of Masonry*
Isberner 1969, *Properties of Masonry Cement Mortars*
Ilantzis 1973, *Deformations and Mechanical Resistance of Hollow Brick Walls and of Hollow Cement*
Irle 1973, *Wall Mortar, Resistant Against Stormwaters, Used for Dressing Masonry with Visible Bricks*
James 1969, *Review of the Methods of the SAA Brickwork Code—ASCA47—1969 for Determining*

James 1973, *Investigation of the Effect of Workmanship and Curing Conditions on the Strength*
Jenkins 1965, *Design and Economics of High Load-Bearing Brick Structures*
Jenkins 1968, *Recent Experiences with Calculated Load-Bearing Brickwork*
Johnson 1969, *Correlations of Tests of Masonry Assemblages with Strength Characteristics of*
Johnson 1970, *The Development of Structural Design Criteria for Clay Tile Assemblages*

Johnston 1973, *Specification, Testing and Site Control for Structural Brickwork*
Jones 1973, *The Present Situation About University Building in the United Kingdom*
Jung 1973, *Report on Tests on Walls Built out of Wall Stones of the Same Production, but with*
Kalita 1970, *An Experimental and Theoretical Investigation of the Stresses and Deflections in Model*
Kalita 1973, *An Investigation of the Stress and Deflections in a Model Cross-Wall Structure*

Kateiva 1970, *The Effects of the Meckering Earthquake on Engineered Brick Structures in Perth*
Khoo 1973, *A Failure Criterion for Brickwork in Axial Compression*
Kinniburgh 1968, *Claybricks and Concrete Blocks, Comparison of Building Times Required to Build*
Kirtschig 1973, *Determination of the Load Capacity of Masonry by the Help of Stress-Strain-Lines*
Klein 1965, *Multi-Storey Flat Buildings in Calcium Silicate Bricks and Blocks and the Testing of Wall*

Krahl 1970, *Case Study of Bricks used as Floor and Roof Structures*
Krantz undated, *Calculated Brick Bearing Wall Construction—What? Why? How?*
Krenek 1973, *The Use of Large Hourdesstones in Czechoslovakian Architecture*
Krupinski 1975, *Arrangement of Reinforcement in Loadbearing Walls*
Kuenning 1956, *Effect of Variations in Curing and Drying on the Physical Properties of Concrete*

Lee 1968, *The Design of Mortars for Calculated Load Bearing Brickwork*
Lefter 1976, *Evaluating the Earthquake Resistance of Existing Masonry Construction*
LeMessurier 1965, *Brick as a Structural Material*
Lenczner 1970a, *Creep in Model Brickwork*
Lenczner 1970b, *Creep in Brickwork*

Lenczner 1973, *Creep in Brickwork with and Without Damp Proof Course*
Lenczner 1976, *Creep and Moisture Movements in Masonry Piers and Walls*
Leuchars 1973, *Masonry Infill Panels*
Leyendecker 1977, *Design Methods for Reducing the Risk of Progressive Collapse in Buildings*
Lugez 1973, *Contribution to the Study of the Deformability of Joints Between Hollow Brick Masonry*

Lyse 1933, *Tests on Reinforced Brick Columns*
Macchi 1970c, *Saftey Considerations for a Limit-State Design of Brick Masonry*
Macchi 1973c, *Progress of the CIB-Guidelines for the Calculation and Execution of Masonry*
Mainstone 1971, *On the Stiffnesses and Strength of Infilled Frames*
Mathez 1973, *Calculation of Ceramic-Cement Complexes: Application to Prefabricated Ceramic*

Maurenbrecher 1970, *Aspects of the Strength and Fixity of the Joint Between a Brick Wall and a*
Maurenbrecher 1973, *Flexural Strains Due to an Applied Floor Moment in Single Leaf Brickwork*
Mazzolani 1975, *Inelastic Stable and Unstable Behaviour of Eccentrically Loaded Walls*
McDowell 1966, *The Strength of Brick Walls and Wallettes*
McDowell 1970, *Predicting the Long-term Moisture Expansion of Fired Clay Bricks*

McDowell 1971, *Arching Action Theory*
McIntosh 1970, *Specifying the Quality of Bedding Mortars*
McLaughlin 1976, *Earthquake Analysis in Design of Masonry Structures*
McNeilly 1976, *Serviceability*
McNicholas 1970, *Photoelastic Stress Analysis of Brick Masonry Systems*

Mehta 1970, *Structural Behaviour of Pretensioned Prestressed Masonry Beams*
Meli 1968, *Behaviour of Hollow Masonry Walls when Subjected to Alternating Lateral Load*
Meyer 1973, *Actual Position of Standardization in Heat Insulation and Effects on Masonry*
Mikluchin 1969, *Morphotectonics of Masonry Structures*
Mikluchin 1976, *Three Dimensional Static and Dynamic Analysis of Tall Masonry Buildings*

Monk 1958, *Resistance of Structural Clay Masonry to Dynamic Forces*
Monk 1965, *Old and New Research on Clay Masonry Bearing Walls*
Monk 1965, *European Clay Masonry Loadbearing Buildings*
Monk 1967, *A Historical Survey and Analysis of the CompressiveStrength of Brick Masonry*
Monk 1970, *Structural Action of Brick-Bearing Walls Exposed to Fire Temperatures*

Morton 1970, *The Stability of Load-Bearing Brickwork Structures Following Accidental Damage to a*
Morton 1973a, *An Experimental Investigation of the Lateral Strength of Brickwork Panels with*
Morton 1973b, *A Theoretical Investigation of the Strength of Brick Walls with Precompression*
Morstead 1976, *Construction Details and their Effect on Building Behaviour*
Moss 1968, *Concrete Masonry Wall Panel Tests—The Effect of Cavity Filling on Shear Behaviour*

Motteu 1973, *New Belgian Norms for Testing, Calculating and Erection of Masonry*
Motteu 1976, *International Recommendations for the Computation and Construction of Masonry*
Neumann 1973, *Measurements Comparing Temperatures on Standardized School Buildings*
Nilsson 1970, *The Strength of Horizontally Loaded Prefabricated Brick Panel Walls*
Nylander 1957, *Effects of Wall Deformation on Floor Slab Loads and Floor Slab Deformation in*

Pagano 1970, *On the Calculation of Bearing Masonry Buildings with the Help of the Electronic*
Peirs 1970, *The Measurement of Modulus in Brick Building*
Pfefferkorn 1973, *Design Principles for Reinforced Concrete Roof Decks*
Pfeffermann 1970, *The Behaviour of Brick Partitions with Deformation of Their Support*
Pfeffermann 1976, *Research of the Application of Reinforced Concrete*

Pfeffermann 1975, *Cracks of Partitions of Masonry Due to an Excessive Deformation of the Support*
Pieper 1976, *The Load Capacity of Thin Masonry Walls*
Pieper 1970, *Deformation Properties of Brickwork*
Pieper 1970, *Shear Tests on Walls*
Plowman 1965, *The Modulus of Elasticity of Brickwork*

Plowman 1968, *Damp-Proof Coursing in Load-Bearing Brickwork*
Plowman 1970, *The Selection of Damp-Proof-Course Material for Load-Bearing Structures*
Plummer 1965, *Brick and Tile Engineering*
Plummer 1965, *Reinforced Brick Masonry*
Pogonowski 1975, *Eccentricities of Longitudinal Force in Walls Seemed to be Continuously*

Pume 1962a, *Research on the Bearing Capacity of Masonry Walls*
Pume 1962b, *Buckling of Masonry Piers and Walls*
Pume 1963, *Bearing Capacity of Vibrated Masonry of Clay Tile Walls*
Pume 1967c, *Bearing Capacity of Clay Tile Wall Elements*
Pume 1970a, *Structural Performance of Clay Tile Wall Panels*

Pume 1970b, *Design Methods of Brick Masonry Structures in Czechoslovakia*
Ramaswamy 1970, *Funicular Brick Shell Roofs for Industrial Buildings*
Redmond 1975, *Compressive Strength of Composite Masonry Walls*
Reimitz 1973, *Effectiveness of Acoustic Bricks*
Reinders 1973, *The Influence of Porosity and Perforation on Heat Conductivity of Building Materials*

Risager 1969, *Structural Behaviour of Linear Elastic Walls Having No Tensile Strength*
Risager 1970, *The Buckling Load of Linear Elastic Walls Without Tensile Strength*
Risager 1976, *Brickwork: Strength, Statistics and Standards*
Ritchie 1973, *Water Penetration Tests of TTW Brick Walls*
Ritchie 1976, *Moisture Degradation in Masonry Walls*

Roberts 1976a, *The Effect Upon the Indicated Strength of Concrete Blocks in Compression of*
Roberts 1976b, *The Behaviour of Vertically Reinforced Concrete Blockwork Subject to Lateral*
Rose 1976, *Limit State Codes and Standards in the U.K. 1976—The Turning Point*
Rostampour 1973, *Aspects of the Design of Multistorey Buildings in Light-Weight Concrete*
Sahlin 1969, *Interaction of Brick Masonry Walls and Concrete Slabs*

Sahlin 1971, *Structural Masonry*
Sallada 1970, *Park Lane Towers Complex*
Schaub 1973, *Calculation of Two Shell Masonry with Insulation Between*
Schellbach 1970, *The Influence of Perforation on the Load-Bearing Capacity of Hollow Brick*
Schellbach 1973, *Construction and Dimensioning of Brick Masonry (Evaluation of Standards*

Schellbach 1976, *Recommendations for the Dimensioning and Construction of Masonry*
Schneider 1973, *Rigidity Against Wind by Masonry Tall Buildings*
Schneider 1959, *Lateral Load Tests on Reinforced Grouted Masonry Shear Walls*
Schneider 1969, *Shear in Concrete Masonry Piers*
Schubert 1977, *Deformations and Cracking Characteristics of Masonry*

Schupack 1969, *High Tension Adhesive Mortar in Concrete Masonry Structural Systems*
Scrivener 1966, *Concrete Masonry Wall Panel Tests—Static Racking Tests with Predominant*
Scrivener 1969a, *Face Load Tests on Reinforced Hollow Brick Non-Load-Bearing Walls*
Scrivener 1969b, *Static Racking Tests on Concrete Masonry Walls*
Scrivener 1971a, *Compressive Behaviour of Masonry Prisms*

Scrivener 1971b, *Behaviour of Reinforced Masonry Shear Walls Under Cyclic Loading*
Scrivener 1972, *Reinforced Masonry-Seismic Behaviour and Design*
Scrivener 1976a, *Comments on the New Code for New Zealand Masonry Buildings*
Scrivener 1976b, *Reinforced Masonry in a Seismic Area—Research and Construction Development*
Shiedeler 1963, *Carbonation Shrinkage of Concrete Masonry Units*

Sinha 1965, *The Effect of Brickwork Bond on the Loadbearing Capacity of Brick Walls*
Sinha 1970, *Model and Full-Scale Tests on a Five-Storey Cross-Wall Structure Under Loading*
Sinha 1973, *The Lateral Load Analysis of Brick Multi-Storey Shear-Wall Sructures*
Sinha 1976, *Test on a Three-Storey Cavity Wall Structure*
Smith 1968, *A 15-storey Tower Block in Load-Bearing Brickwork and its Problems*

Sneck 1976, *Winter Masonry Construction*
Soane 1967, *Model Analysis of Essex University Tower Block*
Soane 1968, *The Behaviour of Essex University Tower Blocks under Wind Loading*
Soane 1969, *Interaction of Brickwork Walls and Concrete Floors Under Lateral Load*
Stafford-Smith 1969, *A Method of Analysis for Infilled Frames*

Stafford-Smith 1973, *The Variation of Stresses in Brickwork Walls Subject to Shear Forces*
Stedham 1968, *Quality Control for Load-Bearing Brickwork 111 Wall Tests*
Stockbridge 1967, *A Study of High-Rise Load-Bearing Brickwork in Britain*
Stockbridge 1969, *Remarks on Paper 44*
Stockley 1973, *Case History—Recent "High-Rise" Load-Bearing Brick Construction in Sydney*

Suter 1975a, *Limit State Shear Design of Reinforced Brickwork Beams*
Suter 1975b, *Shear Strength of Reinforced Brickwork Beams*

Suter 1976a, *Shear Strength of Grouted Reinforced Masonry Beams*
Suter 1976b, *Shear Strength of Reinforced Masonry Beams and Canadian Code Implications*
Sutherland 1968, *The Development of the Design of the Brick Apartment Towers at Essex University*

Sutherland 1969, *Design Engineer's Approach to Masonry Construction*
Szabo 1973, *Influence of Stone Size over Load Capacity and Shear Strength of Masonry*
Tasker 1975, *Recommendations for the use of Prestressed Brick or Block Walls on Reactive Soils*
Thomas 1953, *The Strength of Brickwork*
Thomas 1966, *Movement Joints in Brickwork*

Thomas 1968, *Reinforced Brickwork*
Thomas 1969, *Current Post-Tensioned and Prestressed Brickwork and Ceramics in Great Britain*
Thomas 1970, *The Strength Function and Other Properties of Wall-Ties*
Thomas 1970, *The Effect of Pigment on Some Properties of Mortar for Brickwork*
Thomas 1970, *Tensile Strength Tests on Two Types of Brick*

Thomas 1972, *Structural Brickwork—Materials and Performance*
Thongcharoen 1973, *The Composite Action of Simply Supported Reinforced Brickwork Walls and*
Toennies 1975, *Siliceous Fines in the Cementing Medium of Steam-Cured Concrete Masonry Units*
Turkstra 1976, *The Moment-Magnifier Method applied to Brick Walls*
Turnsek 1970, *Some Experimental Results on the Strength of Brick Masonry Walls*

Ulmeanu 1973, *Contribution to the Optimization of Perforated Bricks*
Vahakallio 1973, *Concerning the Computations of Masonry Eccentricity*
Vahakallio 1976, *Method for Calculating Restraining on Joint Moments in Unreinforced Masonry*
Volkamer 1973, *Old-Fashioned Thoughts of an Architect*
Watstein 1969, *Experimental Determination of Eccentricity of Floor Loads Applied to a Bearing Wall*

Watstein 1970, *Structural Performance of Clay Masonry Assemblages Built with High-Bond Organic*
Watstein 1971, *Relation of Unrestrained Compressive Strength of Brick to Strength of Masonry*
Wesche 1976, *Comparison of Loadbearing Masonry in Some European Countries*
West 1968, *Experiments in the Use of the 9 Inch Brickwork Cube for Site Control Testing*
West 1968, *The Performance of Walls Built of Wirecut Bricks with and without Perforations*

West, 1970, *The Comparative Strength of Walls Built of Standard and Modular Bricks*
West 1973, *Mortar Modified with Sarabond*
West 1973, *Single Leaf Masonry: The Resistance to Rain Penetration of Some Composite Systems*
West 1973a, *Lateral Loading Tests on Walls with Different Boundary Conditions*
West 1973b, *The Resistance of Clay Brick Walls to Lateral Loading*

West 1976, *The Effect of Floor and Wind Loads Applied Separately or Simultaneously to a*
Wierzbicki 1975, *Bearing Capacity and Deformability of Lintels in Structural Walls*
Williams 1971, *Seismic Behaviour of Reinforced Masonry Shear Walls*
Williams 1973, *Response of Reinforced Masonry Shear Walls to Static and Dynamic Cyclic Loading*
Winkler 1973, *Acoustic Insulation as Part of Integrating Construction Physics*

Wolff 1973, *Pavement of Baked Material in Old and Modern Times*
Woodland 1973, *Preliminary Design Considerations for High-Rise Engineered Brick Masonry*
Yokel 1971, *Strength of Load Bearing Masonry Walls*
Yokel 1971, *Strength of Masonry Walls Under Compression and Transverse Loads*
Yorkdale 1973a, *Design and Construction Practices for Contemporary Brick Bearing Wall Buildings*

Yorkdale 1973b, *Contemporary Brick Bearing Wall Buildings in the U.S.—A Progress Report*
Yorkdale 1976, *Structural Research and Investigation for the Development of a Rational*
Zelger 1970, *Shear Design of Brick Lintels*
Zelger 1973, *Basics for the Dimensioning of Sederite Ceilings*
Zirpke 1976, *A Contractor Looks at Load-Bearing Masonry Design*

National Codes Referred To:

Australia

AS 1640-1974, *SAA Brickwork Code*
AS A 2-1969, *Burnt Clay and Shale Building Bricks*
CA 32-1967, *SAA Code for Concrete Block Masonry*

Britain

BS. 3679 1963, *Acid-Resisting Bricks and Tiles*
BS 2028 1968, *Precast Concrete Blocks*
BS 187 1970, *Part 2: Calcium Silicate (Sandlime and Flintlime) Bricks—Metric Units*
BS 1180 1972, *Part 2: Concrete Bricks and Fixing Bricks*
BS 3921 1974, *Specification for Clay Bricks and Blocks*
CP 111 1970, *Part 2: Structural Recommendations for Load-Bearing Walls*

Canada

Canadian Structural Design Manual 1970, *Supplement No. 4 to National Building Code of Canada*

Germany

DIN 105 1957, *Masonry Bricks; Solid and Perforated Bricks*
DIN 105 1969, *Masonry Bricks; Solid and Perforated Bricks*
DIN 18152 1971, *Solid Lightweight Concrete Blocks*
DIN 18554 1971, *Brick Work; Testing of Walls and Pillars*
DIN 106 1972, *Sand-Lime Bricks; Solid and Perforated Bricks*

DIN 18153 1972, *Hollow Concrete Blocks and Hollow Concrete Blocks with T-Section*
DIN 4165 1973, *Building Blocks Made from Steam Cured Cellular Light Weight Concrete*
DIN 1053 1974, *Masonry, Design and Construction*
DIN 18149 1975, *Perforated Light Weight Concrete Blocks*
DIN 18151 1975, *Hollow Light Weight Concrete Blocks*
DIN 398 1976, *Granulated Slag Aggregate Concrete Blocks*

Switzerland

SIA 113 1965, *Standard for the Calculation and Execution of Manufactured Blocks and Bricks*
SIA 177 1977, *Masonry Standard 177*

USA

ASTM C 73-67 1967, *Standard Spec. for Calcium Silicated Face Brick (Sand-Lime Brick)*
ASTM C 126-70 1970, *Ceramic Glazed Structural Clay Facing Tile*
ASTM C 404-70 1970, *Aggregates for Masonry Grout*
ASTM C 476-71 1971, *Mortar and Grout for Reinforced*
ASTM C 67-73 1973, *Brick and Structural Clay Tile, Sampling and Testing*

ASTM C 109-73 1973, *Compressive Strength of Hydraulic Cement Mortars (Using 2-in. or 50-mm*
ASTM C 270-73 1973, *Mortar for Unit Masonry*
ASTM C 212-74 1974, *Structural Clay*
ASTM C 34-74 1974, *Structural Clay Load*
ASTM C 55-75 1975, *Concrete Building Brick*

ASTM C 62-75a 1975, *Building Brick (Solid Masonry Units Made from Clay or Shale)*
ASTM C 90-75 1975, *Hollow Load-Bearing Concrete Masonry Units*
ASTM C 91-75 1975, *Masonry Cement*
ASTM C 145-75 1975, *Solid Load-Bearing Concrete Masonry Units*
ASTM C 216-75a 1975, *Facing Brick*

ASTM C 652-75 1975, *Hollow Brick*
ASTM C 62-75 1975, *Building Brick*
ASTM C 110-76 1976, *Physical Testing of Quicklime, Hydrated Lime and Limestone*
ASTM C 144-76 1976, *Aggregate for Masonry Mortar*
BIA 1969, *Building Code Requirements for Engineered Brick Masonry*

Miscellaneous Handbooks

ASTM 1964, *A Symposium of Testing of Masonry*
B. Ceram. R. A., *Model Specification for Loadbearing Clay Brickwork*
B. Ceram. R. A., *Design Guide for Reinforced and Prestressed Clay Brickwork*
BIA, *Contemporary Brick Bearing Wall, Case Study*
CIB 1964, *Methods of Design of Masonry Walls*

Lattbeton, 1965, *Handbook of Light Weight Cellular Concrete*
PCA 1976, *Concrete Masonry Handbook*
SCPI 1965, *Proceedings of the First National Brick and Tile Bearing Wall Conference*

Current Questions, Problems and Research Needs

This appendix identifies problem areas for further study and research. It constitutes an update of Council Report No. 5, first issued in 1972, as part of its mission to identify such problems for interested investigators and organizations. The sequence of headings is the same as that used in this Volume. Numbers in parentheses refer to the Committee responsible for the topic. Additional such study areas should be forwarded to Council Headquarters for transmission to the Committee for possible inclusion in the next revision of the Council's report on the subject.

DESIGN CRITERIA AND SAFETY PROVISIONS (26)

1. What are the limits of applicability and special problems in the application of safety theory to tall buildings?
2. What are the "serviceability" limit states, and how can the appropriate design factors be quantified?
3. What are the limit states of strength and durability, from both the serviceability and ultimate point of view, and what design concepts are suitable for each of them?
4. Development of the Level II approach to safety in view of the improvement of probabilistic codes.
5. Methods of considering load combinations and vectorial combinations of load-effects.
6. Problems of safety in nonlinear problems.

OPTIMIZATION OF TALL CONCRETE BUILDINGS (21B)

1. Determination of optimal structural systems to resist both vertical and horizontal forces.
2. Relative effects of optimization of structural material versus optimization of construction cost.
3. Relative effects of optimization of structure versus optimization of the entire system or other subsystems (such as energy or sound insulation).

709

ELASTIC ANALYSIS (21C)

1. Interaction between shear walls and floor slabs in buildings subjected to bending and torsion. Effective coupling stiffness of floor slabs, and mechanism of shear and moment transfer at slab-wall joint.
2. Soil-structure interaction in shear-wall structures. Influence of foundation flexibility on static and dynamic behavior.
3. Determination of effective widths of wide-flanged shear walls.
4. When can secondary influences of shear and torsion be disregarded?
5. Influence of joint stiffnesses in the analysis of precast buildings.
6. Influence of cracking of monolithic beam column joints on the analysis of such structures.
7. Representative stiffness (EI) values for the analysis of reinforced concrete frames approaching the ultimate limit state.
8. Frame analysis procedures for laterally loaded flat-plate structures.
9. Interaction of service core and "outer tube" of building frame.

NONLINEAR BEHAVIOR AND ANALYSIS (22)

1. What are the limits of applicability of limit design in tall concrete buildings?
2. Description of the yield surfaces of cross sections under generalized stresses.
3. Ultimate strength of shear walls under combined loading (shear, compression, bending, torsion).
4. To what extent do repeated excursions into the plastic range under seismic loadings reduce the capacity of the shear wall to resist future earthquakes?
5. What criteria can be used after an earthquake to assess repairability of a structure?
6. Limit analysis and optimum design of reticular space grids as floor structures in multistory buildings.
7. Limit design of multistory flat-slab and flat-plate buildings.
8. Ultimate resistance of a space frame system under combined transverse and torsional loading.

MODEL ANALYSIS (A38)

1. Development of appropriate modeling materials and fabrication techniques for small-scale reinforced and prestressed concrete structures, as well as masonry structures.
2. Study of similitude for bond and cracking in reinforced and prestressed concrete structures.
3. Correlation of model test results with prototype test results or analytical studies, or both.
4. All aspects of dynamic modeling.
5. What procedures should be followed to make ultimate strength models of complete tall buildings without incurring costs out of all proportion to the value of the model tests?

STABILITY (23)

1. Development of methods of second-order analysis suitable for design office use.
2. Development of methods for column design in frames that have been analyzed using a second-order analysis.
3. Clarification of the role of the effective length factor in the design of beam columns.

4. Development of practical methods of considering sustained load effects in the design of columns and frames.
5. Analysis of the capacity of slender walls with low tension strength (such as masonry, or lightly reinforced concrete).
6. Procedures for evaluating the effect of foundation deformations on frame stability.
7. Procedures for evaluating the effect of joints in precast construction on the over-all structural stability.

STIFFNESS, DEFLECTIONS, AND CRACKING (24)

1. What are realistic drift limits for various types of occupancy and various types of construction?
2. What are the effects of displacements (permanent and recoverable) on the integrity of the structure?
3. Development of stiffnesses (EI values, for example) that reflect cracking, reinforcement ratio, and other factors, and yet are sufficiently simple for use in the analysis of large frameworks.
4. What are realistic crack widths?
5. What mechanisms are available to control cracking?
6. Methods of calculation and limitation of cracking caused by thermal and shrinkage effects.
7. Studies of expansion, construction and control joints in tall building structures.

CREEP, SHRINKAGE, AND TEMPERATURE EFFECTS (25)

1. Development of methods for incorporating creep, shrinkage and temperature effects into structural analysis. The methods should be accurate yet simple enough to be adopted in practice.
2. What architectural and mechanical details are necessary to accommodate the effects of creep, shrinkage, and temperature? How may such details be used to control these effects?

DESIGN OF CAST-IN-PLACE CONCRETE (21D)

1. Development of practical ultimate strength procedures for the design of shear cores of buildings.
2. Development of practical ultimate strength procedures for the design of transfer girders.
3. Study of upper limits to the steel reinforcement ratio in reinforced concrete columns.
4. Reinforcing details in earthquake resisting structures.

DESIGN OF STRUCTURES WITH PRECAST CONCRETE ELEMENTS (21E)

1. Influence of joint or connection stiffnesses on the behavior of precast structures. Incorporation of these effects into elastic and inelastic analysis and design procedures.
2. Development of design details for panel structures in seismic regions.
3. Design details to control thermal cracking of panel walls.
4. Rational and practical design procedures to avoid progressive collapse.

DESIGN OF MASONRY STRUCTURES (27)

1. Identification of a constitutive law capable of leading to fairly accurate predictions of the carrying capacity of masonry walls. Development of rational height limits for load-bearing masonry walls and buildings.
2. The effect of interaction between floor slabs and walls on the effective compressive strength of the latter.
3. What are the long-term and short-term movement and cracking characteristics (creep, shrinkage, growth, etc.) in the elements of a composite, concrete masonry and clay masonry, bearing masonry element, and how will this affect the design?
4. What are the reliability and accuracy of methods of predicting load-deformation behavior of masonry walls?
5. What is the minimum area of steel reinforcing that will produce "ductility" in masonry structural elements?
6. Development of limit states design procedures for masonry structures under static and dynamic loadings.
7. Studies of the interaction of masonry walls and reinforced concrete floor slabs to form long-span beams or cantilevers (either intentionally or due to local collapse of supports).
8. Studies of means of avoiding progressive collapse of masonry buildings.

Nomenclature

GLOSSARY

Actions. Loads and imposed or constrained deformations which cause stresses and deformations in structural members.

Alinement chart. A nomograph for determining the effective length factor of a column from the joint bending stiffness ratios at each end of the column.

Allowable load. The ultimate load divided by factor of safety.

Allowable stress. Maximum permissible stress used in design of members of a structure and based on a factor of safety against rupture or yielding of any type.

Allowable stress design. See Working stress design.

Anchorage. Length of reinforcement, or mechanical anchor, or a hook, or combination thereof, beyond the point where the reinforcing is no longer required to resist calculated stresses.

Araldite. An epoxy resin.

Aspect ratio. In any rectangular configuration, the ratio of the longer dimension to the shorter dimension.

Asymmetric structure. A structure lacking corresponding points, signifying member geometry and properties, whose connecting lines are bisected by a given point or perpendicularly bisected by a given line or plane.

Beam. A structural member, usually horizontal, subjected primarily to flexure, on which the weight of a floor, partition, or other beam is carried.

Beam-and-slab floor. A reinforced concrete floor system in which the floor slab is supported by beams of reinforced concrete.

Beam-column. A beam that transmits an axial load along its longitudinal axis in addition to end moments or transverse loads, or both.

Bending resistant member. A connecting member with at least one of its ends rigidly connected to the adjacent members, so that it can resist bending, shear, and axial forces.

Bent. One of a series of parallel plane frame or wall and frame structures which comprise a complete building structure. Usually alined at right angles to the length of the building.

713

Bent bar. Longitudinal reinforcement in a beam, bent to pass from one face to the other of a member, anchorage of a bar.

Bifurcation. A term relating to a point in the load-deflection behavior of a perfectly straight and perfectly centered compression member at critical load at which two alternative load-deflection plots are mathematically valid.

Block. A concrete masonry unit.

Bond. Adhesion and grip of concrete or mortar to reinforcement or to other surfaces against which it is placed; also, the arrangement of units in masonry and brickwork so that vertical joints are discontinuous.

Bond strength. Resistance to separation of mortar and concrete from reinforcing steel and other materials with which they are in contact.

Box. A thin walled beam, typically an elevator or service core, whose cross section forms a closed contour.

Braced frame. A structural frame sufficiently braced against lateral force by shear walls or vertical trusses, or both, so that it cannot buckle in a sidesway mode.

Bracing panel. A structural element, such as a bent or a wall or a combination of these, which serves to resist horizontal loads on the building.

Buckling. A general term descriptive of the failure of a compression member or compression flange of a member due to loss of its original straight or nearly straight shape.

Cantilever buckling. The buckling mode of a multistory frame precipitated by the differential axial strains in the columns leading to collapse by cantilever bending of the frame.

Center of resistance. The intersection of the principal axes of inertia of a group of elements, members, or frames, capable of providing either shearing or flexural resistance to a disturbance to their original positions.

Bundled reinforcement. A group of up to four parallel reinforcing bars in contact with each other and enclosed in stirrups or ties and used as a reinforcing element.

Camber. A slight, usually upward, curvature of structural member or form to improve appearance or to compensate for anticipated deflections.

Cast-in-place. Mortar or concrete that is deposited in the place where it is required to harden as part of the structure, as opposed to precast concrete.

Cauchy number. The same as the Mach number.

Characteristic load. A load near the top of the distribution of similar loads that has an arbitrarily chosen probability of exceedance.

Characteristic strength. A material strength that will be exceeded with an arbitrarily chosen probability (usually 95%).

Coefficient of thermal expansion. The change in length per unit length of an unrestrained member caused by a rise or drop of temperature of one degree Celsius (or Fahrenheit). Its unit is degree^{-1}.

Column. A structural member whose prime function is to carry loads parallel to its longitudinal axis.

Column capital. An enlargement of the end of a column designed and built to act as an integral unit with the column and flat slab and to increase the shearing resistance or reduce the moments, or both.

Column, long, slender. A column whose axial load capacity is reduced because of its slenderness, due to moments induced by deflection of the column.

Column, short. A column whose axial load capacity need not be reduced because of its slenderness.

Composite construction. A type of construction made up of different materials (e.g., concrete and structural steel) or of members produced by different methods (e.g., cast-in-place concrete and precast concrete).

Compressive strength. The measured maximum resistance of a concrete or mortar specimen to axial loading; expressed in stress, or the specified resistance used in design calculations; in United States expressed in lbf per sq in. (psi) and designated f'_c.

Concrete. A composite material that consists essentially of a binding medium within which are embedded particles or fragments of aggregate; in normal portland cement concrete, the binder is a mixture of portland cement and water and the aggregate is sand and gravel.

Concrete, lightweight. Structural concrete made with lightweight aggregate; the unit density usually is in the range of 1440 kg/m³ to 1850 kg/m³ (90 lb/ft³ to 115 lb/ft³).

Concrete, normal-weight. Concrete having a unit density of approximately 2400 kg/m³ (150 lb/ft³) made with aggregates of normal weight.

Conductance. The heat energy transmitted per unit surface, per unit time, per unit temperature difference.

Conductivity. The heat energy flowing per unit time, per unit normal cross section, per unit temperature gradient.

Confinement. Concrete contained by various structural elements or by closely spaced special transverse reinforcement which restrains the concrete in directions perpendicular to the applied stress.

Connection. A physical stress-resisting tie between two adjoining or abutting elements. In Chapter CB-12 the following notation is used to describe particular types of connections:

    BB = beam to beam;
    BC = beam to column;
    CB = column base;
    CC = column to column.

Connection, hard. Movements and rotations within the connection are restrained.

Connection, soft. A limited amount of movement is permitted in the connection.

Construction joint. The surface where two successive placements of concrete meet.

Continuous medium. An analogy for a regular system of discrete connecting members in a structure. The analogy consists of a continuous connecting medium whose bending and shear properties are those of the discrete members distributed uniformly over the system.

Continuum. See continuous medium.

Control joint. Formed, sawed, or tooled groove in a concrete structure to regulate the location and amount of cracking and separation resulting from the dimensional change of different parts of a structure so as to avoid the development of high stresses.

Core. An assembly or group of shear walls, usually joined together to form an open or partially closed box structure, often used as a bracing element for a building structure.

Coupled frame-shear wall structure. A shear wall and frame structure in which the shear walls and the frame are coupled together for analysis purposes to determine the stiffness that the coupled structure provides against lateral movement under lateral loads.

Coupled walls. Shear walls that are connected together by bending resistant members.

Coupling beam, slab. A beam or floor slab connecting two sections of a shear wall.

Creep. The slow time-dependent change in dimensions of concrete under a sustained load, primarily in the direction in which the load acts. It is a dimensionless quantity having units of strain.

Critical load. The maximum load that can be sustained by a particular column, story, or frame without becoming unstable, taking into account the end restraints, etc.

Critical sustained load. The sustained load under which a particular concrete column will become unstable as time approaches infinity.

Curvature. The angle change per unit length of a loaded structural member.

Deep beam. A beam in which the elastic distribution of stresses is nonlinear and in which there are significant compressive forces between the loads and reactions.

Deflection. The horizontal or vertical movement of a point on a structure due to loads, creep, shrinkage, temperature changes, or settlements.

Deterministic. A quantity is said to be deterministic if its value is uniquely determined by specific causes. The opposite of probabilistic.

Development length. The length of reinforcement embedment required to develop by bond the design strength of the reinforcement at a critical section.

Diagonal tension crack. Crack in a reinforced concrete member caused primarily by a shear force.

Dial gage. An instrument for measuring deflection. A plunger operates a train of gears, and the last gear wheel rotates a pointer over a dial.

Diaphragm. A thin platelike structural element, whose in-plane rigidity may be used to stiffen the structure; for example, a floor slab which maintains the cross-sectional shape of the building.

Discrete (system). A set of structural elements with individual locations and defined properties, connected together at a finite number of nodes.

Dome. The square prefabricated pan form used in two-day (waffle) concrete joist floor construction.

Double tee slab. A precast, one-way slab element composed of a horizontal slab and two vertical webs. In cross section the member resembles the letter II.

Drift. The lateral deflection of a structure due to load.

Drift index. Ratio of the height of the building to the horizontal deflection of the top of the building.

Drift limit. The maximum permissible drift, usually expressed in terms of a drift index.

Drop panel. The structural portion of a flat slab which is thickened throughout an area surrounding the column, column capital, or bracket.

Drying shrinkage. The shrinkage which takes place due to the loss of water in hardened cement paste.

Ductility. That property of a material by virtue of which the material may undergo large permanent deformation without rupture.

Ductility factor. The ratio of the total deformation of a frame to the elastic limit deformation of the frame.

Edge beam. A stiffening beam at the edge of a slab.

Effective length. The equivalent length of a member which, in the Euler formula for a hinged end column, results in the same elastic critical loads as for the member or other compression element under consideration at its theoretical critical load.

Effective length factor. The ratio between the effective length of a member and the unbraced length of the member measured between the centers of gravity of the bracing members.

Elastic analysis. A method of analysis that satisfies equilibrium and compatibility based on a linear stress-strain relationship.

Elastic deformation. The change in dimensions of concrete occurring instantaneously at the time of load application.

Elastic model. A model made of a material different from that of the structure, and therefore capable of being used only within the elastic range.

Electric resistance strain gage. An instrument consisting of a zig-zag wire or thin foil, which is glued to a structure or structural model. As the element is strained, the wire or foil is also strained, and it consequently changes its electrical resistance, which can be related to strain.

Engel connection. A beam-column connection in precast construction in which a hardened fluted pin is driven through a common square opening formed by overlapping diagonal slots.

Epoxy resin. A thermosetting resin used for model-making. The uncured resin is mixed with a hardener, and the mixture is then cast in a mold.

Equivalent frame. A single-bay substitute frame used to replace one or more stories of a multibay, multistory building for the purpose of simplifying analysis.

Euler formula. The mathematical relationship expressing the value of the Euler load in terms of the modulus of elasticity, the moment of inertia of the cross section, and the length of a column.

Euler load. The critical load of perfectly straight, centrally loaded, pin-ended column that is slender enough to buckle at a stress less than the proportional limit of the material.

Expansion joint. A separation between adjoining parts of a concrete structure which is provided to allow small relative movements, such as those caused by thermal changes, to occur independently.

Factor of safety. The ratio of the ultimate strength (or yield point) of a material to the working stress assumed in design (stress factor of safety); or the ratio of the ultimate load, moment, or shear of a structural member to the working load, moment, or shear, respectively, assumed in design (load factor of safety).

Factored loads. The specified, working, or characteristic loads multiplied by appropriate load factors.

Falsework. See Formwork.

Fatigue failure. A fracture of material due to repeated cycles of loading.

Finite element. A single segment in an analogy developed for stress analysis, in which a continuous structure is subdivided into a number of discrete linear, two-dimensional or three-dimensional segments.

Fire resistance. The ability of a material or assembly to withstand fire or give protection from it; the ability to confine a fire or to continue to perform a given structural function, or both.

First-order analysis. An analysis in which equilibrium is formulated on the undeflected structure and which, as a result, ignores the interaction of vertical loads and lateral deflections.

First-order deflections, moments. Deflections or moments calculated by a first-order analysis.

Fixed ends. Support conditions at the ends of a member which prevent both displacement and rotation.

Flanges. The plates or elements located at the top and bottom of a beam cross section.

Flat plate. A flat slab without column capitals or drop panels (see Flat slab).

Flat slab. A concrete slab reinforced in two or more directions, generally without beams or girders to transfer the loads to supporting members.

Flexural crack. Crack in a reinforced concrete member caused by bending of the member.

Folded plate. A framing assembly composed of sloping slabs in a hipped or gabled arrangement.

Formwork. The total system of support for freshly placed concrete, including the mold or sheathing which contacts the concrete, as well as all supporting members, hardware, and necessary bracing. Falsework and Shuttering are also used with essentially the same meaning.

Foundation. The material or materials through which the load of a structure is transmitted to the earth.

Froude number. The ratio V/Lg, in which V = velocity, L = length, and g = acceleration due to gravity.

Fundamental period of vibration. Time necessary to complete one cycle of motion.

Gable wall. End wall of a building.

Grillage. A plane orthogonal set of beams rigidly connected together at their intersections.

High-strength steel. Concrete reinforcing bars generally having a minimum yield strength above 414 MPa (60 000 psi, 4220 kgf/cm^2).

Hook. A bend in the end of a reinforcing bar.

Hooked bar. A reinforcing bar with the end bent into a hook to provide anchorage.

Hysteresis loop. The graphical plot of the time-dependent load-deflection or moment-strain relationship of an element, member, or frame under dynamic loads.

Instability. A condition reached during buckling under increasing load in a compression member, element, or frame at which the capacity for resistance to additional load is exhausted and continued deformation results in a decrease of load-resisting capacity.

Interaction equation. An equation giving the relationship between two or more components of load or their equivalent stresses.

Interstory drift. The relative horizontal displacement of two successive floors of a particular building.

Joint. The interface between adjoining or abutting elements. In monolithic construction, the concrete between the ends of the columns and beams entering the joint.

Joist. One of a series of closely spaced horizontal structural members interacting with or supporting a deck.

Kist effect. Sag of a fixed-end prestressed member caused by restrained creep and shrinkage of the bottom fibers.

Lattice. A regular system of line members constituting a plane framework.

Lift slab. A method of concrete construction in which floor and roof slabs are cast on or at ground level and hoisted into position by jacking; also a slab which is a component of such construction.

Limit state. When a structure or structural element becomes unfit for its intended use due to collapse, lack of serviceability, or any other cause, it is said to have reached a limit state.

Limit states design. A design process that involves identification of all potential modes of failure (limit states) and maintaining an acceptable level of safety against their occurrence. The safety level is usually established on a probabilistic basis.

Linear creep. The value of creep calculated using the assumption that creep is directly proportional to the applied stress.

Link. See Pin-ended link.

Live load. Loads due to the use and occupancy of a structure.

Load effects. Moments, shears, and axial forces in a member due to loads or other actions.

Load factor. A partial safety factor to account for the probability of overloads.

Lost form. A form for cast-in-place concrete made of precast concrete. The form becomes part of the finished structure.

Lozenging. A deformation in which a rectangular-shaped structural section is distorted into a parallelogram shape.

Mach number. The ratio $V\delta/K$, in which V = velocity, δ = density, and K = bulk modulus of elasticity.

Masonry. Construction composed of shaped or molded units, usually small enough to be handled by one man and composed of stone, ceramic brick or tile, concrete, glass, adobe, or the like.

Material failure. A column failure occurring when the forces and moments at the failure cross section reach the capacity of that cross section.

Mean. The arithmetic average of a group of values.

Merit function. The criterion used to measure the desirability of a certain course of action.

Mesh reinforcement. Smooth or deformed wires welded into a two-way mesh in either sheets or rolls, and used to reinforce concrete.

Methyl methacrylate. An acrylic resin produced by the polymerization of monomeric derivatives of acrylic resins. It is thermoplastic and can be formed into a structural model by the application of heat and pressure (or vacuum). It is commonly marketed under the trade names of Plexiglas or Perspex.

Microconcrete. Concrete suitable for use in an ultimate-strength mode. The concrete may be scaled down by reducing either the size or the unit weight of the aggregate, or both.

Model analysis. Analysis of structure by means of measurements on an accurately scaled model.

Moment magnification. The increase in moment in a member resulting from the increase in the eccentricity of the applied axial load within the member due to deflections.

Moment redistribution. Moment transfer from section to section within a structure due to successive formation of cracking and plastic hinges.

Mortar. A mixture of cement paste, lime, and sand, used to bond together masonry elements. The proportions are expressed as a ratio (cement:lime:sand).

Natural frequency of a building. Number of cycles per second when the structure is vibrating in its most easily excited mode.

Node. A real or hypothetical joint between two or more structural elements, used for reference in structural analysis.

One-way construction. A structural system where the arrangement of the steel reinforcement is intended to resist stresses due to bending in one direction only.

Open section. A thin-walled structural member whose cross section does not form a closed contour.

Optimization. The process of maximizing the utility to be derived from a system.

P-Δ moments. Moments resulting from the lateral displacement of the vertical loads acting on a frame.

Pan. Prefabricated form unit, most commonly of steel or plastic, used in concrete joist floor construction.

Panel building system. A method of construction using precast wall and slab panels which are connected together at the building site to form the finished building structure.

Pan-joist. A horizontal structural concrete member usually supported by beams constructed by aid of prefabricated form units (pans).

Partial safety factor. A safety factor used to account for the variability of one aspect of structural safety.

Permanent form. Any form that remains in place after the concrete has developed its design strength. The form may or may not become an integral part of the structure.

Perspex. See Methyl methacrylate.

Photoelasticity. The property of certain transparent materials to break up the incident light into two components polarized in the directions of the principal stresses. Light waves are ordinarily oriented at random. By inserting a polarizing filter, only light in one plane is transmitted. A second polarizing filter is oriented at right angles to the first, and the model is placed between them. Since the filters are at right angles, no light is transmitted when the model is unstressed. When the model is stressed, colored fringes appear which connect points of equal difference between the two principal stresses. For numerical analysis, monochromatic light is used, which produces black fringes.

Pin-ended link. Structural members whose ends are hinged, and hence transmit axial forces only.

Pi theorem. Theorem used in dimensional analysis.

Plane coupled shear wall. A shear wall, where all elements (that is, wall sections and connecting beams) lie in one plane.

Plane frame. A framed structure that can be idealized as a two-dimensional structure.

Plexiglas. See Methyl methacrylate.

Point of contraflexure. A point in a structural member where the curvature changes sign and the bending moment is zero.

Polystyrene. A thermoplastic material made by the polymerization of styrene.

Post-tensioning. A method of prestressing reinforced concrete in which tendons are tensioned after the concrete has hardened.

Precast concrete. Concrete cast elsewhere than its final position in the structure.

Prestressed concrete. Concrete in which internal stresses of such magnitude and distribution are introduced that the tensile stresses resulting from the service loads are counteracted to a desired degree; in reinforced concrete the prestress is commonly introduced by tensioning the tendons.

Pretensioning. A method of prestressing reinforced concrete, in which the tendons are tensioned between fixed abutments before the concrete is placed, and are released after the concrete has hardened and bonded to the tendons.

Probabilistic. A quantity is said to be probabilistic if its value varies from occurrence to occurrence. The opposite of deterministic.

Progressive collapse. A situation in which the failure of one element causes failure of adjacent elements which spreads progressively through a large part of the structure. In general, the final amount of damage is many times that expected from the initial failure itself.

Reinforced concrete, masonry. Concrete or masonry containing reinforcement and designed on the assumption that the two materials act together in resisting forces.

Reinforcement. Metal bars, wires, or other slender members which are embedded in concrete in such a manner that the metal and the concrete act together in resisting forces.

Reinforcement ratio. Ratio of the effective area of the reinforcement to the effective area of the concrete at any section of a structural member.

Release. In structural analysis, the removal of a structural continuity at a section in a member which renders the member incapable of transmitting that particular force component across the section. In pretensioning, the time when the reaction between the tendons and the prestressing bed is removed.

Reshoring. The construction operation in which the original shoring or posting is removed and replaced in such a manner as to avoid damage to the partially cured concrete.

Resistance factor. A partial safety factor to account for the probability of understrength of materials or structural members.

Response spectrum. A set of curves or diagrams giving the maximum value of the response that can be expected for a given applied load or disturbance for a member or structure with prescribed values of mass, spring constants, and damping characteristics.

Reversed loading. A loading condition in which the load is first applied in one direction, then completely removed and reapplied in the opposite direction.

Rigid frame. A structure made up of beam and column members joined together at their intersections in such a manner that there is no relative rotation between the intersecting members at a joint under applied load or deformation.

Second-order analysis. An analysis which includes the effect on deflections and moments of the lateral displacement of the vertical loads on the structure.

Second-order deflections, moments. Deflections or moments calculated by a second-order analysis.

Semiprobabilistic safety factors. Discrete partial safety factors which approximate the results of a probabilistic safety analysis.

Serviceability limit state. A condition occurring in the service life of the building in which the structure becomes unfit for its intended use due to excessive deflections, cracking, vibrations, damage to contents, etc.

Service loads. Loads anticipated during the normal life of the building.

Set back. A reduction in the horizontal cross section of a building, causing the upper levels of the building to be narrower than the lower levels.

Shear. An internal force tangential to the plane on which it acts.

Shear buckling. The buckling mode of a multistory frame precipitated by the relative lateral displacements of joints leading to collapse by sidesway of the frame.

Shear head. A mechanical device introduced into the slab at a slab-column connection in order to increase the shear capacity of the connection.

Shear lag. An effect, which occurs in bending members with wide thin flanges, causing the axial flange stresses remote from the web to be less, and those close to the web more, than would be calculated on the basis of the proportionate distance from the neutral axis. The effect is due to in-plane shearing deformations of the flange.

Shear reinforcement. Reinforcement designed to resist shear or diagonal tension stresses; dowels are not considered to be shear reinforcement.

Shear wall. A structural wall which in its own plane carries shear forces resulting from lateral loads such as wind, earthquake forces, explosions, etc.

Shear wall, coupled. Two shear walls connected by beams or slabs which permit the two walls to act together as a load-resisting system.

Shear wall-frame structure. A structure in which shear walls and frames interact in resisting lateral loads.

Shear wall with outrigger. A shear wall from which a horizontal cantilever, one or several stories deep, projects extending to and engaging peripheral columns for the purpose of decreasing the lateral displacement of the structure.

Shore. Temporary vertical support for formwork and fresh concrete or for recently built structures which have not developed full design strength. Also called prop, tom, post, strut.

Shrinkage. Volume decrease caused by drying and chemical changes; a function of time but not of stress due to external load or thermal expansion. It is generally expressed in terms of a linear strain.

Sidesway. The lateral movement of a structure under the action of lateral loads, unsymmetrical vertical loads, or unsymmetrical properties of the structure.

Single tee. A precast, one-way slab member consisting of a wide top flange and a single web.

Slab. A flat, usually horizontal or nearly so, molded layer of plain or reinforced concrete usually of uniform thickness, but sometimes of variable thickness; as the flat section of floor or roof either on the ground or supported by beams, columns, or other framework. (See also Flat slab.)

Slenderness ratio. This term may refer to the geometric slenderness ratio or the mechanical slenderness ratio, generally the latter.

Slenderness ratio, geometric. The ratio of effective length to least dimension of the column cross section.

Slenderness ratio, mechanical. The ratio of the effective length of a column to the radius of gyration of the column, both with respect to the same axis of bending.

Slip form. A form which moves, usually continuously, during placing of the concrete. Movement may be either horizontal or vertical. Slip forming is like an extrusion process with the forms acting as moving dies to shape the concrete.

Soffit. The underside of a subordinate part or member of a building, such as a beam, stairway, arch, etc.

Space frame. A three-dimensional framework as contrasted to a plane frame.

Spandrel. That part of a wall between the head of a window and the sill of the window above it. (An upturned spandrel continues above the roof or floor line.)

Spandrel beam. Floor level beams in the faces of a building, usually supporting the edges of the floor slabs.

Spirally reinforced column. A column in which the vertical bars are enveloped by spiral reinforcement; i.e., closely spaced continuous hooping.

Splice. Connection of one reinforcing bar to another by overlapping, welding, mechanical end connectors, or other means.

Stability. The capacity of a member or structure to recover from displacement induced by an applied force or disturbance.

Stability function. Expressions used to compute stiffness factors, carry-over factors, and fixed-end moment coefficient factors, or similar corresponding terms in the slope deflection or three-moment equations, that are dependent upon the presence of axial load in the member, and evaluated by use of a parameter which is the ratio of the actual column load to the Euler buckling load.

Staggered wall beam system. A structural system for a building with frames in one direction and frames braced in the other direction by use of story-deep beams staggered in location at alternate frames on every other floor of the building.

Standard deviation. A quantity used to measure the dispersion of a set of values equal to the root-mean-square deviation of the values from their mean value.

Stiffness. The resistance to deformation of a member of structure measured by the ratio of the applied force to the corresponding displacement.

Stiffness matrix. An ordered set of quantities arranged in a rectangular array with values representing the coefficients of the correction rotation or displacement terms in the linear set of equations formulated for a structure under load or applied disturbance by the displacement method of analysis.

Strand. A prestressing tendon composed of a number of wires most of which are twisted about a center wire or core.

Strength design. A method of proportioning structures or members to have failure capacities equal to or greater than the elastically computed moments, shears, and axial forces corresponding to a specified multiple of the working loads and assuming a nonlinear distribution of flexural stresses.

Subassemblage. A truncated portion of a structural frame.

Subgrade. The soil beneath the foundation structure of the building.

Substructure. A part of a structure which may be analyzed apart from the remainder of the structure.

T-beam. A beam composed of a stem and a flange in the form of a T.

Temperature reinforcement. Reinforcement designed to carry stresses resulting from temperature changes; also the minimum reinforcement for areas of members which are not subjected to primary stresses or necessarily to temperature stresses.

Tendon. A steel element such as a wire, cable, bar, rod, or strand used to impart prestress to concrete when the element is tensioned.

Theoretical age. An adjusted age of concrete in days at the time of application of stress, or at the time at which creep or shrinkage are considered. The adjustment accounts for the effect of variation in the average day temperature.

Theoretical thickness. A variable affecting the amount of creep and shrinkage of a concrete member. Its value has the unit of length and is dependent upon the area and perimeter of the cross section and the relative humidity of the ambient medium.

Thin-walled beam. A beam whose cross section consists of platelike elements, whose width-to-thickness and length-to-width ratios are large, say greater than ten to one. Such a section is liable to warp under tension.

Tie. Closed loop of reinforcing bars encircling the longitudinal steel in columns.

Tied column. A column laterally reinforced with ties.

Time-dependent volume changes. The combined effect of creep, shrinkage, and temperature change.

Tolerance. The permitted variation from a given dimension or quantity.

Transfer girder. A large beam (normally situated at first or second story levels) used to redistribute vertical forces from the closely spaced columns above to the wider spaced ground floor columns.

Translation. A rigid body linear movement, in any specific direction, of the cross section of the building.

Transverse load. Horizontal lateral force applied at right angles to the vertical axis of the building.

Two-way construction. A structural system intended to resist stresses due to bending in two directions. The reinforcement is placed at right angles to each other.

Tube-in-tube system. A building with an inner core tube system and an exterior perimeter tube system.

Tube system. A building in which columns are closely spaced around the perimeter of the building and interconnected by stiff spandrel beams to optimize stiffness against lateral loads.

Ultimate limit state. A structure or structural element reaches an ultimate limit state when its useful life is terminated by collapse, fracture, overturning, instability, etc.

Ultimate strength design. See Strength design.

Ultimate strength model. A model made of the same material as the structure, or a material of a similar type. This model can be tested beyond the elastic range to destruction.

Unbraced frame. A structural frame that can buckle in a sidesway mode.

Utility. A function or measure of the desirability of a result.

Volume-to-surface ratio. A variable affecting the amount of creep and shrinkage of a concrete member. Its value has the unit of length and equals the volume of the member divided by its exposed surface area.

Waffle slab. A two-way concrete joist floor construction.

Warping. An out-of-plane deformation of a cross section whose plane is normal to the centroidal axis of a structural member, caused by flexural torsion.

Water-cement ratio. The ratio of the amount of water, exclusive only of that absorbed by the aggregates, to the amount of cement in a concrete or mortar mixture; preferably stated as a decimal by weight.

Web. The vertical plate, or its equivalent, that joins the top and bottom flanges in a beam.

Whiffle-tree loading system. A system of gravity loading, whereby a single load is applied at two points through distributing beam, where it is further subdivided into two point loads, etc. Thus a single weight or load can be used to produce a large number of point loads on a model.

Working load. The load for which a structure is designed under normal service and conditions.

Working stress. Maximum permissible design stress using working stress design methods.

Working stress design. A method of proportioning structures or members for prescribed working loads at stresses well below the ultimate, and assuming linear distribution of flexural stresses.

Wythe. Each continuous vertical section of a wall one masonry unit in thickness.

Yield point. The point during increasing stress at which the proportion of stress to strain becomes substantially less than it has been at smaller values of stress, below which the stress-strain curve may be assumed to be linear, and above which the curve is usually nonlinear.

Yield strength. The stress corresponding to the yield point.

SYMBOLS

The numerals in parentheses refer to the chapters in Volume CB in which the given symbol is used.

A	$= A_e/m$	(9)
A	= area of column	(13)
A	= cross-sectional area of bracing member	(8)
A_c	= concrete area	(8, 9, 11)
A_e	= effective tension area symmetric about centroid of steel	(9)
A_g	= gross area of a rectangular shear wall section	(6)
A_{s1}	= area of tension reinforcement	(10)
A_{s2}	= area of compression reinforcement	(10)
A_t	= specified over-all load factor of the structure	(6)
A_{vf}	= total vertical steel for the required clamping force	(6)
a	= depth of equivalent rectangular stress block = $\beta_1 c$	
a	= height of a point in the building	(8)
a	= shear span	(13)
B	= transformation matrix	(6)
B_1, B_2, etc.	= end slope at 1, 2, etc., in relation to jointed hinge	(6)
b	= width of beam	(9, 13)
b_w	= web width of beam and column	(11)
C	= constant	(2, 8)
C_a	= adhesion factor	(11)
C_m	= equivalent moment factor	(8)
c	= distance from extreme compression fiber to neutral axis	(11)
c_1	= distance	(9)
D	= deflection coefficient	(8)
D, L, Q, and T	= specified dead, live, wind, or earthquake loads and imposed deformations	(2)
D_d	= member stiffness	(10, 13)
d	= depth of tensile reinforcement from compression face	(10)
d_b	= bar diameter	(9)
d_c	= clear concrete cover	(9)
d'	= distance from compression face of column to centroid of compression reinforcement	(8)
E	= modulus of elasticity	(8)
E_b	= modulus of elasticity of a brick	(13)
E_c	= modulus of elasticity of concrete	(8)
E_{c28}	= modulus of elasticity of concrete at age of 28 days	(10)
E_R	= reduced modulus of elasticity	(8)
E_s	= modulus of elasticity of steel	(9)
E_1	= modulus of elasticity of a mortar	(13)
EI	= flexural stiffness	(11)
e	= eccentricity	(8)
F	= function	(7)
F	= moment magnifier	(8)
F_d	= γ_{f1}, F_k	(2)

F_k	= characteristic value of action or load	(2)
f	= member dimensions	(2)
f_{bu}	= compressive strength of a brick	(13)
f_{ck}	= compressive strength of concrete below which only 5% of all test values will fall	(8)
f_{ju}	= compressive strength of a mortar	(13)
f_s	= steel stress	(9)
f_s	= yield strength of steel	(13)
f_y	= yield stress of steel	(13)
f'_b	= compressive strength of bricks	(13)
f'_c	= 28-day compressive strength of concrete cylinder	(8)
f'_m	= compression strength of masonry	(13)
G	= dead weight	(2)
G	= shear modulus of elasticity	(7)
H	= height of building	(9)
H	= horizontal force or lateral load	(2, 8)
H	= transformation matrix	(6)
h	= distance from center to center of beams	(11)
h	= thickness of column	(8)
h_o	= height of opening in shear wall	(11)
h_t	= total height of building	(8)
h_w	= total height of wall from base to top	(11)
h'	= clear height of the boundary frame	(11)
I	= moment of inertia	(11)
I_c	= moment of inertia of concrete	(11)
I_{cr}	= moment of inertia of cracked section	(11)
I_e	= effective moment of inertia	(9)
I_g	= moment of inertia of uncracked gross section	(6)
I_s	= moment of inertia of steel reinforcement	(11)
i_c	= radius of gyration of concrete section	(11)
i_s	= radius of gyration of steel reinforcement	(11)
J	= torsional constant	(9)
j	= critical section	(6)
jd	= distance compression force—reinforcing bars	(13)
K	= coefficient depending on agreed probability of test values less than R_k	(2)
K	= coefficients in equation	(9)
K	= curvature of section	(11)
K	= efficiency factor, i.e., ratio of masonry strength to brick strength	(13)
K	= structural response factor	(13)
K	= term including stiffness parameters, axial load values, and bending moment distributions	(6)
K_j	= stiffness of a frame of length L_j	(9)
K_t	= lateral stiffness = H/Δ	(8)
k	= effective length factor	(11)
k	= efficiency factor (strength of masonry to strength of bricks)	(13)

k_j	= stiffness of frame j per unit length	(9)
L	= length of column, center to center of joints	(8)
L	= live loads, or their related internal moment and forces	(11)
L	= span	(7)
L_i	= length of frame i	(9)
L_0	= cracking limit (member or test specimen)	(6)
L_0	= length of brace	(8)
L_1	= yield limit (member or test specimen)	(6)
L_2	= ultimate limit (member or test specimen)	(6)
l	= distance from center to center of columns of the boundary frame	(11)
l	= span	(10)
l_o	= width of opening in shear wall	(11)
l'	= clear span of boundary frame	(11)
M	= applied moment	(9)
M	= bending moments in a structure	(6)
M	= ultimate moment	(13)
M,F,P	= factors representing respectively material properties, quality of the construction process, quality of design	(2)
M_c	= complementary bending moments	(11)
M_c	= the moment at which inelastic rotations become important	(6)
M_{cr}	= cracking moment	(9)
M_o	= maximum external moment capacity of a column when axial load is zero	(8)
M_p	= serviceability	(6)
M_{pj}	= unknown design plastic moment	(6)
M_r	= ultimate strength	(6)
M_t	= torsional moment	(9)
M_u	= design resisting moment at section	(11)
M_u	= ultimate moment	(6)
M_x	= bending moment about x-axis	(11)
M_y	= bending moment about y-axis	(11)
M_y	= yielding moment	(9)
M_1	= first-order moment	(8)
M_2	= total second-order moment equal to first-order moment plus P-Δ moment	(8)
M_2	= larger design end moment	(11)
M^E	= sum of the elastic moments	(6)
m	= number of tension bars of equal diameter	(9)
m	= $q(1.00-0.59\,q)$	(13)
m_r	= maximum reduced bending moment ($= M/bd^2$)	(9)
$\overline{m}$	= mean value of material properties	(2)
N	= member forces	(6)
N	= number of stories	(9)
N_u	= design axial load, positive if compression	(11)
N_{ul}	= ultimate load-bearing capacity at midheight of wall	(11)
N'_{uj}	= ultimate bearing capacity of the wall	(11)
n	= number	(7)

n	= total number of floors	(9)
n_0	= modular ratio at the beginning of shrinkage	(10)
O	= initial value	(6)
O_o	= rotation of imaginary hinge at the continuous section at the top left corner of the end bay	(6)
P	= axial load	(11)
P	= dimension of force	(7)
P	= live load	(2)
P	= reference column load	(6)
P_c	= critical axial load	(11)
P_c	$= f'_c A_c$	(8)
P_{cr}	= critical load in a story or in a frame in lateral buckling	(8)
P_E	$= (\pi^2 \cdot EI)/L^2 =$ Euler buckling load	(8)
P_o	= total vertical load in a building	(8)
P_s	= sustained load in column	(8)
P_{sh}	= short-time load capacity of a column	(8)
P_u	= axial design load	(11)
P_u	= ultimate load in column	(8)
P_{ult}	= ultimate load in column	(13)
P_v	= reinforcing steel ratio	(6)
P'_s	= reinforcing ratio	(13)
p	= steel area divided by masonry area (width times effective depth)	(13)
p'_s	= ratio between the area of the longitudinal steel and of the columns	(13)
Q	$= P/P_{cr}$ or $Q = \Sigma P \Delta_1 / H \cdot h =$ stability index	(8)
q	$= p f_y / f'_m$	(13)
q	= rate of heat conduction (heat energy per unit time)	(8)
R	= long column reduction factor	(8)
R	= ratio of distances	(9)
R	= redundant forces	(6)
R	= resistance	(2)
R	= shear deformation angle at shear walls	(11)
R_{cr}	= shear deformation angle corresponding to ultimate shear	(11)
R_d	$= R_k / \gamma_m$	(2)
R_k	= characteristic strength	(2)
R_m	= arithmetic mean of different test results	(2)
r	= coefficient in Eq. 9.4	(9)
r	= gap openings in a cut structure	(6)
r	= nominal value	(2)
r	= radius of curvature	(10)
r	= radius of gyration	(8, 11)
r	= ratio	(7)
r	= reduction coefficient	(11)
$\bar{r}$	= mean resistance	(2)
S	= force acting on the section	(2)
S	= structure stiffness	(6)
S	= surface area	(10)
S_d	= design load effect	(2)

s	= nominal value	(2)
s	= shrinkage	(10)
s	= spacing of horizontal reinforcement in a wall	(11)
s	= spacing of steel in slabs normal to crack	(9)
s	= standard deviation	(2)
s	= step	(6)
T	= fundamental period of vibration	(9)
T	= shear stress	(13)
T	= temperature	(10)
T	= total load	(2)
T_d	= additional diagonal tension force of corner opening	(11)
T_h	= additional horizontal tension force at corner opening	(11)
T_k	= principal tensile stress at failure divided by 1.5	(13)
T_o	= mean shear stress at failure with precompression	(13)
T_v	= additional vertical tension force at corner opening	(11)
t	= actual age in days	(10)
t	= construction completion	(4)
t	= thickness	(7)
t	= thickness of the infilled wall panel	(11)
t_e	= conductivity	(10)
t_s	= yield stress of steel	(13)
t'	= theoretical age of concrete—conductance of finish or surface resistance	(10)
U	= deformations	(6)
U_c	= perimeter of concrete cross section in contact with the atmosphere	(10)
V	= shear force	(13)
V	= shear force on the cross section of members	(11)
V	= volume	(10)
V_{bfu}	= ultimate horizontal shear force depending on the restraint action of the boundary frame on the expansion of the cracked infilled panel wall	(11)
V_c	= allowable horizontal shear force of each column in the boundary frame	(11)
V_{cr}	= shear force on horizontal wall section at initial cracking	(11)
V_{dt}	= total applied design shear force at section	(11)
V_E	= factor of uncertainties of structural analysis and of spatial distribution of loads	(2)
V_F	= fabrication coefficient of variation	(2)
$V_{f(x)}$	= shear in frame at level (x)	(9)
V_M	= material coefficient of variation	(2)
V_P	= professional coefficient of variation	(2)
V_R	= coefficient of variation of resistances	(2)
V_S	= coefficient of variation of loads	(2)
V_T	= coefficient of variation of total load	(2)
V_u	= ultimate horizontal shear force on the shear walls that fail in shear	(11)
V_{uex}	= experimental value of V_u	(11)
V_w	= horizontal shear force carried by the infilled panel wall	(11)

$V_{ws.u}$	= ultimate horizontal shear force, depending on the restraint action of the wall reinforcement on the expansion of the cracked infilled panel wall	(11)
$V_{w(x)}$	= shear in wall at level (x)	(9)
V_1	= allowable horizontal shear force on uncracked shear wall	(11)
V_2	= allowable horizontal shear force on cracked shear wall	(11)
v_{uf}	= average ultimate shear stress transferable across a well prepared rough construction joint	(6)
W	= load	(7)
w	= crack width	(9)
w	= total service load	(6)
w	= translational displacement	(10)
w_{ij}	= first yield load	(6)
w_u	= ultimate load	(6)
x	= distance from extreme fiber to neutral axis	(6)
x	= variable	(7)
x_j	= yield safety parameter	(6)
x_{ij}	= first yield load	(6)
x_1, x_2, etc.	= equal and opposite internal restraint moments acting at plastic hinges on the adjacent members	(6)
y_1, y_2	= respective distances of the two steels from the centroid axis of the net concrete section	(10)
z	= jd	(13)
z	= matrix of the influence coefficients	(6)
α	= coefficient in equations	(8)
α	= coefficient of thermal expansion	(10)
α	= curvature factor	(9)
α_a	= creep reduction coefficient	(10)
α_c	= capacity factor for compressive strength	(12)
α_c	= coefficient depending on hardening speed of cement	(10)
α_{cw}	= function of the slenderness ratio and the modulus E	(12)
$\alpha_D, \alpha_L, \alpha_Q$ and α_T	= load factors	(2)
α_e	= function of the eccentricity alone	(12)
α_j	= wall bearing capacity factor	(12)
α_r	= shrinkage coefficient	(10)
α_s	= stiffness coefficient allowing for the restraining effect of reinforcement	(10)
α_w	= wall capacity factor	(12)
α_y	= reduction factor for stiffness at yielding	(9)
$\alpha_1, \alpha_2, \alpha_3$	= parameters that vary with such matters as age at loading, humidity, and size of member	(10)
β	= a shape factor of the influence coefficients	(6)
β	= measure of the degree of reliability required	(2)
β	= reduction coefficient of shear rigidity	(11)
β_{cr}	= value of β before cracking	(11)
β_d	= coefficient depending on the theoretical ages t_0' and t', and varying between 0 and 1	(10)
β_f	= coefficient depending on the theoretical age t' and theoretical thickness h' varying between 0 and 1	(10)

β_r	= shrinkage coefficient for the composition of the mix	(10)
β_s	= coefficient depending on the theoretical time t' and the theoretical thickness h' and varying between 0 and 1	(10)
β_u	= ultimate shear rigidity reducing coefficient corresponding to	
β_1	= $a/c = 0.85$ for strength f'_c up to 4000 psi, and reduced continuously at a rate of 0.05 for each 1000 psi of strength in excess of 4000 psi	(11)
β_{1c}	= coefficient depending on the relative humidity of the ambient medium and on the consistency of concrete	(10)
β_{2c}	= coefficient depending on the theoretical thickness h' of the member considered	(10)
β_{1s}	= coefficient depending on the relative humidity of the ambient air and on the consistency of concrete	(10)
β_{2s}	= coefficient depending on the theoretical thickness h' of the concrete element	(10)
γ	= constant depending on the loading distribution and the degree of end restraint of adjoining spans	(6)
γ	= factor related to consequences of failure	(2)
γ	= M_{cr}/M	(9)
γ_c	= unit weight of concrete	(9)
γ_f	= load coefficient, function of partial coefficients $f1', f2$	(2)
γ_m	= unit greater than or equal to unity	(2)
Δ_d	= direct deflection of frame	(9)
Δ_k	= creep deflection	(8)
Δ_T	= deflection of top of building	(9)
Δ_t	= torsional deflection of frame	(9)
ΔV_u	= ultimate shear resistance contribution of the tie beam	(12)
Δ_1	= first-order deflection	(8)
Δ_2	= total second-order deflection equal to Δ_1 plus additional P-Δ deflections	(8)
δ_{ik}	= rotation at hinge k due to $x_i = 1$ acting	(6)
δ_{ok}	= rotation at hinge k due to external load	(6)
δ_t	= number of days during which the average day temperature for concrete is T, in degrees Celsius	(10)
ϵ	= strain	(8)
ϵ_c	= concrete strain	(11)
$\epsilon_{cc}(t_0,t)$	= elastic plus creep deformation at time t caused by a constant sustained stress $\sigma_c(t_0)$ applied at time t_0	(10)
ϵ_{cs}	= shrinkage strain in concrete which develops in the period $t-t_0$	(10)
ϵ_s	= shrinkage of the compression face	(10)
ϵ_s	= steel strain	(11)
$\epsilon(t_n)$	= axial shortening at time (t_n)	(10)
ϵ_1, ϵ_2	= strains at the levels of steel 1 and steel 2, respectively	(10)
ϵ_4	= limiting concrete compression strain	(11)
ζ	= total long-term deflection/initial deflection	(10)
η	= reduction coefficient of shear rigidity in shear walls with openings	(11)
η	= relaxation coefficient	(10)
θ	= function of the coefficients V_R and V_S	(2)

θ	= inelastic rotations	(6)
θ	= torsional rotation	(9)
θ_k	= rotation at hinge k	(6)
λ	= coefficient given to account for the effect of relative humidity	(10)
λ	= common load factor applied to all loads	(6)
λ	= shear span ratio = $a/z = a/jd \geqq 0.8$	(13)
λ_{ki}	= coefficient	(8)
λ_y	= yield load factor for section j	(6)
λ_0	= specific over-all load factor of a structure	(6)
μ	= friction coefficient = 0.5	(13)
ν	= safety factor	(11)
ξ	= opening coefficient	(11)
ρ	= ratio of creep strains to elastic strains	(8)
ρ	= ratio of steel area A_s/A_i	(8)
ρ	= tension reinforcement ratio A_s/bd	(9)
ρ_g	= flexural reinforcement ratio in walls	(11)
ρ_h	= horizontal shear reinforcement ratio in walls	(11)
ρ_l	= flexural reinforcement ratio in boundary frames	(11)
ρ_t	= steel ratio referred to tension zone	(9)
ρ_v	= shear reinforcement ratio in beams and columns of boundary frames	(11)
ρ_w	= reinforcement ratio for the horizontal of the vertical reinforcement in the wall panel	(11)
ρ'	= compression reinforcement ratio = A'_s/bd	(9)
σ	= steel stress	(9)
σ	= stress	(10)
σ_0	= compressive stress at failure when a wall is loaded also with a horizontal load	(13)
τ	= nominal unit shear stress	(11)
τ_c	= nominal unit shear stress carried by the concrete	(11)
τ_{c1}	= nominal unit shear stress expected to cause inclined web-shear crack	(11)
τ_{c2}	= nominal unit shear stress expected to cause inclined flexure-shear crack	(11)
τ_s	= nominal unit shear stress carried by the reinforcement	(11)
τ_u	= ultimate nominal unit shear stress on the horizontal section of frameless shear walls	(11)
$\bar{\tau}_{cr}$	= mean unit shear stress on horizontal sections in shear walls at initial cracking of the infilled panel	(11)
ϕ	= capacity reduction factor	(11)
ϕ	= curvature	(8)
ϕ	= performance factor = reduction factor for strength	(2)
ψ	= combination factor	(2)
ψ	= relative stiffness	(8)
ψ	= sway angle	(6)
ψ_h	= sidesway	(6)
ω	= $f_y A_s / P_c = \rho f_y$	(8)
ω	= mechanical steel ratio	(11)

ABBREVIATIONS

ACI	American Concrete Institute
AIPC	See IABSE (French)
ANSI	American National Standards Institute
ASCE	American Society of Civil Engineers
ASTM	American Society for Testing and Materials
BIA	Brick Institute of America
BOCA	Building Officials Council of America
BSCP	British Standard Code of Practice
CA	Australian Code (as in CA 47)
C and CA	Cement and Concrete Association, England
CB	Volume CB of Monograph, Concrete Buildings
CEB	Comité Européen du Béton (since 1976 Comité Euro-International du Béton), European Concrete Committee
CIB	Comité International du Bâtiment, International Committee on Building
CL	Volume CL of Monograph, Criteria and Loading
CP	Code of Practice (as in CP:110), United Kingdom
CSIRO	Commonwealth Scientific and Industrial Research Organization, Australia
DIN	Deutsche Industrie Normen, German Industrial Standards
FIP	Fédération Internationale de la Précontrainte, International Federation for Prestressing
HVAC	Heating Ventilating and Air Conditioning
IABSE	International Association for Bridge and Structural Engineering
ICE	Institution of Civil Engineers, England
ISE	Institution of Structural Engineers, England
ISO	International Standards Organization
IVBH	See IABSE (German)
LSD	Limit States Design
NCMA	National Concrete Masonry Association, U.S.A.
NPV	Net Present Value
PC	Volume PC of Monograph, Planning and Environmental Criteria
PCA	Portland Cement Association, U.S.A.
PCI	Prestressed Concrete Institute, U.S.A.
RILEM	International Association of Testing and Research Laboratories for Materials and Structures
SB	Volume SB of Monograph, Steel Buildings
SC	Volume SC of Monograph, Systems and Concepts
SEAOC	Structural Engineers Association of California
SIA	Schweizerischer Ingenieur- und Architekten-Verein, Swiss Engineers and Architects Association
UBC	Unified Building Code
UK	United Kingdom
UNESCO	United Nations Educational, Scientific and Cultural Organization
USA	United States of America
USD	Ultimate Strength Design
WSD	Working Stress Design

UNITS

In the table below are given conversion factors for commonly used units. The numerical values have been rounded off to the values shown. The British (Imperial) System of units is the same as the American System except where noted. Le Système International d'Unités (abbreviated "SI") is the name formally given in 1960 to the system of units partly derived from, and replacing, the old metric system.

SI	American	Old Metric
Length		
1 mm	0.03937 in.	1 mm
1 m	3.28083 ft	1 m
	1.093613 yd	
1 km	0.62137 mile	1 km
Area		
1 mm^2	0.00155 in.^{2}	1 mm^2
1 m^2	10.76392 ft^2	1 m^2
	1.19599 yd^2	
1 km^2	247.1043 acres	1 km^2
1 hectare	2.471 acres[1]	1 hectare
Volume		
1 cm^3	0.061023 in.^{3}	1 cc
		1 ml
1 m^3	35.3147 ft^3	1 m^3
	1.30795 yd^3	
	264.172 gal[2] liquid	
Velocity		
1 m/sec	3.28084 ft/sec	1 m/sec
1 km/hr	0.62137 miles/hr	1 km/hr
Acceleration		
1 m/sec^2	3.28084 ft/sec^2	1 m/sec^2
Mass		
1 g	0.035274 oz	1 g
1 kg	2.2046216 lb[3]	1 kg
Density		
1 kg/m^2	0.06428 lb/ft^3	1 kg/m^3
Force, Weight		
1 N	0.224809 lbf	0.101972 kgf
1 kN	0.1124045 tons[4]	
1 MN	224.809 kips	
1 kN/m	0.06853 kips/ft	
1 kN/m^2	20.9 lbf/ft^2	
Torque, Bending Moment		
1 N-m	0.73756 lbf-ft	0.101972 kgf-m
1 kN-m	0.73756 kip-ft	101.972 kgf-m

SI	American	Old Metric
Pressure, Stress		
$1\ N/m^2 = 1\ Pa$	0.000145038 psi	0.101972 kgf/m^2
$1\ kN/m^2 = 1\ kPa$	20.8855 psf	
$1\ MN/m^2 = 1\ MPa$	0.145038 ksi	
Viscosity (Dynamic)		
$1\ N\text{-}sec/m^2$	0.0208854 lbf-sec/ft^2	0.101972 kgf-sec/m^2
Viscosity (Kinematic)		
$1\ m^2/sec$	10.7639 ft^2/sec	1 m^2/sec
Energy, Work		
$1\ J = 1\ N\text{-}m$	0.737562 lbf-ft	0.00027778 w-hr
$1\ MJ$	0.37251 hp-hr	0.27778 kw-hr
Power		
$1\ w = 1\ J/sec$	0.737562 lbf ft/sec	1 w
$1\ kw$	1.34102 hp	1 kw
Temperature		
$K = 273.15 + {}^\circ C$	${}^\circ F = ({}^\circ C \times 1.8) + 32$	${}^\circ C = ({}^\circ F - 32)/1.8$
$K = 273.15 + 5/9({}^\circ F - 32)$		
$K = 273.15 + 5/9({}^\circ R - 491.69)$		

(1) Hectare as an alternative for km^2 is restricted to land and water areas.
(2) 1 m^3 = 219.9693 Imperial gallons.
(3) 1 kg = 0.068522 slugs.
(4) 1 American ton = 2000 lb.   1 kN = 0.1003612 Imperial ton.   1 Imperial ton = 2240 lb.

Abbreviations for Units

°C	degree Celsius (centigrade)	kw	kilowatt
cc	cubic centimeters	lb	pound
cm	centimeter	lbf	pound force
°F	degree Fahrenheit	MJ	megajoule
ft	foot	MPa	megapascal
g	gram	m	meter
gal	gallon	ml	milliliter
hp	horsepower	mm	millimeter
hr	hour	MN	meganewton
Imp	British Imperial	N	newton
in.	inch	oz	ounce
J	joule	Pa	pascal
K	kelvin	psf	pounds per square foot
kg	kilogram	psi	pounds per square inch
kgf	kilogram-force	°R	degree Rankine
kip	1000 pound force	sec	second
km	kilometer	slug	14.594 kg
kN	kilonewton	w	watt
kPa	kilopascal	yd	yard
ksi	kips per square inch		

CONVERSION TABLE FOR COMMITTEES AND CHAPTERS

The Council maintains an ongoing bibliography organized according to subject areas that are identified by the committee number. For this reason (and also because future editions of the Monograph may have different chapter numbers) the *committee* designations have been retained in the parenthetical information at the end of each bibliographic citation. The following conversion table is supplied for reference as is needed.

Committee	Chapter Number	Chapter Title
20	CB-1	Characteristics of Concrete and Masonry Tall Buildings
21A	CB-3	Concrete Framing Systems for Tall Buildings
21B	CB-4	Optimization of Tall Concrete Buildings
21C	CB-5	Elastic Analysis
21D	CB-11	Design of Cast-in-place Concrete
21E	CB-12	Design of Structures with Precast Concrete Elements
22	CB-6	Nonlinear Behavior and Analysis
23	CB-8	Stability
24	CB-9	Stiffness, Deflections, and Cracking
25	CB-10	Creep, Shrinkage, and Temperature Effects
26	CB-2	Design Criteria and Safety Provisions
27	CB-13	Design of Masonry Structures
A38	CB-7	Model Analysis

References/Bibliography

The citations that follow include both references and bibliography. The list includes all articles referred to or cited in the text and it also includes bibliography for further reading. The material is arranged alphabetically by author, followed by the year of publication. Since the citation in the text is to author and year, there will be instances in which reference is made to two different articles published in the same year by the same authors. In those instances it has been necessary to affix letters to the year to provide proper identification.

Where articles are published in a language other than English, the translation of the title is given first, followed by the title in the original language.

The numbers in parentheses designate the committee for which the citation is appropriate. (See facing page for committee/chapter conversion table.)

Additional bibliographies are available through the Council.

ACI, 1965
    PRECAST CONCRETE WALL PANELS, Proceedings of Symposium, ACI Publication No. SP-11, American Concrete Institute. (21E)
ACI, 1970
    LIMIT DESIGN OF REINFORCED CONCRETE STRUCTURES, Bibliography B.8, American Concrete Institute. (22)
ACI, 1970
    MODELS FOR CONCRETE STRUCTURES, Proceedings of Symposium held at Los Angeles, Calif., March 1968, ACI Publication No. 24, American Concrete Institute. (A38)
ACI, 1971
    DESIGNING FOR THE EFFECTS OF CREEP, SHRINKAGE AND TEMPERATURE IN CONCRETE STRUCTURES, Publication No. SP-27, American Concrete Institute. (25)
ACI, 1972
    MODELS FOR CONCRETE STRUCTURES, Proceedings of Symposium held at Dallas, Tex., March 1972. (A38)
ACI Committee 209 Subcommittee 2, 1971
    PREDICTION OF CREEP, SHRINKAGE, AND TEMPERATURE EFFECTS IN CONCRETE STRUCTURES, Publication No. SP-27, American Concrete Institute, pp. 51–93. (25)
ACI Committee 223, 1970
    EXPANSIVE CEMENT CONCRETES—PRESENT STATE OF KNOWLEDGE, *ACI Journal*, American Concrete Institute, Vol. 67, No. 8, pp. 583–610. (25)

ACI Committee 318, 1956
BUILDING CODE REQUIREMENTS FOR REINFORCED CONCRETE, ACI-318-56, American Concrete Institute. (26)

ACI Committee 318, 1963
BUILDING CODE REQUIREMENTS FOR REINFORCED CONCRETE, ACI-318-63, American Concrete Institute. (25)

ACI Committee 318, 1971
BUILDING CODE REQUIREMENTS FOR REINFORCED CONCRETE, ACI-318-71, American Concrete Institute. (21A, 21D, 21E, 22, 23, 24, 26)

ACI Committee 318, 1975
COMMENTARY ON BUILDING CODE REQUIREMENTS FOR REINFORCED CONCRETE (ACI 318-71), American Concrete Institute (see also revisions, *ACI Journal*, January 1976). (23)

ACI Committee 435, 1966
DEFLECTIONS OF REINFORCED CONCRETE FLEXURAL MEMBERS, *ACI Journal*, American Concrete Institute, Vol. 63, No. 6, pp. 637–674. (25)

ACI Committee 435, 1968
ALLOWABLE DEFLECTIONS, *ACI Journal*, American Concrete Institute, Vol. 65, No. 6, p. 433. (21D, 23, 24)

ACI Committee 442, 1971
RESPONSE OF BUILDINGS TO LATERAL FORCES, *ACI Journal*, American Concrete Institute, Vol. 68, No. 2. (21C, 23, 24, 26)

ACI Committee 444, 1972
STRUCTURAL CONCRETE MODELS, Proceedings of Symposium held at Dept. of Civil and Mechanical Engineering, McGill University, Montréal, Canada (Montréal, 1972). (A38)

ACI Committee 533, 1971
DESIGN OF PRECAST CONCRETE WALL PANELS, *ACI Journal*, American Concrete Institute, Vol. 68, No. 7, p. 504. (21E)

ACI-ASCE Committee 352, 1976
RECOMMENDATIONS FOR DESIGN OF BEAM-COLUMN JOINTS IN MONO-LITHIC REINFORCED CONCRETE STRUCTURES, *ACI Journal*, American Concrete Institute, Vol. 73, No. 7, pp. 375–393. (21D)

ACI-ASCE Committee 426, 1962
SHEAR AND DIAGONAL TENSION, PART 3, SLABS AND FOOTINGS, *ACI Journal*, American Concrete Institute, Vol. 59, No. 3, p. 353. (21D)

ACI-ASCE Committee 426, 1974
THE SHEAR STRENGTH OF REINFORCED CONCRETE MEMBERS, CHAPTER 5, SHEAR STRENGTH OF SLABS, *Journal of the Structural Division*, ASCE, Vol. 100, No. ST8, Proc. Paper 10733, pp. 1543–1591. (21D)

ACI-ASCE Committee 512, 1974
PRECAST STRUCTURAL CONCRETE IN BUILDINGS, *ACI Journal*, American Concrete Institute, Vol. 71, Title No. 71-35, pp. 537–549. (21E)

ACI-ASCE Committee on Limit Design, 1968
PROGRESS REPORT ON CODE CLAUSES FOR LIMIT DESIGN, *ACI Journal*, American Concrete Institute, Vol. 65, No. 9, pp. 713–719. (22)

AIJ, 1971
BUILDING CODE REQUIREMENTS FOR REINFORCED CONCRETE AND COMMENTARIES (in Japanese), Architectural Institute of Japan. (21D)

AIJ, 1974
PROCEEDINGS, National Conference on Tall Buildings, Architectural Institute of Japan. (24)

ANSI A58.1, 1972
AMERICAN NATIONAL STANDARD BUILDING CODE REQUIREMENTS FOR MINIMUM DESIGN LOADS IN BUILDINGS AND OTHER STRUCTURES, American National Standards Institute, New York. (21E)

AS A 2, 1969
BURNT CLAY AND SHALE BUILDING BRICKS, Standards Association of Australia, Sydney, N.S.W. (27)

AS 1640, 1974
SAA BRICKWORK CODE, Standards Association of Australia, Sydney, N.S.W. (27)
ASCE, 1961
REINFORCED MASONRY DESIGN AND PRACTICE, Report of the Task Committee on Reinforced Masonry Design and Practice, Albyn Mackintosh, Chmn., *Journal of the Structural Division*, ASCE, Vol. 87, No. ST8, Proc. Paper 3022. (25)
ASCE-IABSE, 1973
PROCEEDINGS, 12th Regional Conference on Planning and Design of Tall Buildings (held in Sydney, Australia, August 13–17, 1973), Lehigh University, Bethlehem, Pa. (24)
ASCE-IABSE, 1974
PROCEEDINGS, Regional Conference on Planning and Design of Tall Buildings (held in Kuala Lumpur, Malaysia, December 2–5, 1973), Institution of Engineers, Kuala Lumpur, Malaysia. (24)
ASTM, 1964
A SYMPOSIUM OF TESTING OF MASONRY, American Society for Testing and Materials, Philadelphia, Pa. (27)
ASTM C34—74, 1974
STRUCTURAL CLAY LOAD-BEARING WALL TILE, American Society for Testing and Materials, Philadelphia, Pa. (27)
ASTM C55-75, 1975
SPECIFICATION FOR CONCRETE BUILDING BRICK, American Society for Testing and Materials, Philadelphia, Pa. (27)
ASTM C62-75a, 1975
BUILDING BRICK (SOLID MASONRY UNITS MADE FROM CLAY OR SHALE), American Society for Testing and Materials, Philadelphia, Pa. (27)
ASTM C67-73, 1973
BRICK AND STRUCTURAL CLAY TILE, SAMPLING AND TESTING, American Society for Testing and Materials, Philadelphia, Pa. (27)
ASTM C73-67, 1967
STANDARD SPECIFICATION FOR CALCIUM SILICATED FACE BRICK (SAND-LIME BRICK), American Society for Testing and Materials, Philadelphia, Pa. (27)
ASTM C90-75, 1975
HOLLOW LOAD-BEARING CONCRETE MASONRY UNITS, American Society for Testing and Materials, Philadelphia, Pa. (27)
ASTM C91-75, 1975
MASONRY CEMENT, American Society for Testing and Materials, Philadelphia, Pa. (27)
ASTM C109-73, 1973
COMPRESSIVE STRENGTH OF HYDRAULIC CEMENT MORTARS (USING 2-IN. OR 50-MM CUBE SPECIMENS), American Society for Testing and Materials, Philadelphia, Pa. (27)
ASTM C110-76, 1976
PHYSICAL TESTING OF QUICKLIME, HYDRATED LIME AND LIMESTONE, American Society for Testing and Materials, Philadelphia, Pa. (27)
ASTM C126-70, 1970
CERAMIC GLAZED STRUCTURAL CLAY FACING TILE, FACING BRICK AND SOLID MASONRY UNITS, American Society for Testing and Materials, Philadelphia, PA. (27)
ASTM C144-76, 1976
AGGREGATE FOR MASONRY MORTAR, American Society for Testing and Materials, Philadelphia, Pa. (27)
ASTM C145-75, 1975
SOLID LOAD-BEARING CONCRETE MASONRY UNITS, American Society for Testing and Materials, Philadelphia, Pa. (27)
ASTM C212-74, 1974
STRUCTURAL CLAY FACING TILE, American Society for Testing and Materials, Philadelphia, Pa. (27)
ASTM C216-75a, 1975
FACING BRICK (SOLID MASONRY UNITS MADE FROM CLAY OR SHALE), American Society for Testing and Materials, Philadelphia, Pa. (27)

ASTM C270-73, 1973
SPECIFICATION FOR MORTAR FOR UNIT MASONRY (INCLUDING TENTA-
TIVE REVISION), American Society for Testing and Materials, Philadelphia, Pa. (27)

ASTM C404-70, 1970
AGGREGATES FOR MASONRY GROUT, American Society for Testing and Materials,
Philadelphia, Pa. (27)

ASTM C476-71, 1971
MORTAR AND GROUT FOR REINFORCED MASONRY, American Society for
Testing and Materials, Philadelphia, Pa. (27)

ASTM C652-75, 1975
HOLLOW BRICK (HOLLOW MASONRY UNITS MADE FROM CLAY OR SHALE),
American Society for Testing and Materials, Philadelphia, Pa. (27)

Aas-Jakobsen, A. A., 1964
BIAXIAL ECCENTRICITIES IN ULTIMATE STRENGTH DESIGN, *ACI Journal*,
American Concrete Institute, Vol. 61, No. 3. (22)

Aas-Jakobsen, A., 1967
THE CEB DESIGN METHOD FOR REINFORCED CONCRETE COLUMNS AND
FRAMES, Bulletin d'Information No. 62, Comité Européen du Béton, p. 41. (21D)

Aas-Jakobsen, K., 1973
DESIGN OF SLENDER REINFORCED CONCRETE FRAMES, Report No. 48, Institut
für Baustatik, ETH, Zurich, Switzerland. (23)

Aas-Jakobsen, K. and Grenacher, M., 1974
ANALYSIS OF SLENDER REINFORCED CONCRETE FRAMES, IABSE Publications,
Vol. 34-1, Zurich, Switzerland. (23)

Abdallah, N., 1973
THE M.L.C. CENTRE, Planning and Design of Tall Buildings, Proceedings of Australian
and New Zealand Conference, Sydney, pp. 316–321. (21A)

Abeles, P. W., 1967
DESIGN OF PARTIALLY PRESTRESSED CONCRETE BEAMS, *ACI Journal*, American Concrete Institute, Vol. 64, No. 10, pp. 669–677. (24)

Adam, M., 1974
LARGE THREE-DIMENSIONAL REINFORCED CONCRETE ELEMENTS (Des
grands elements en béton armé à trois dimensions), Proceedings of CIB 6th Congress, The
Impact of Research on the Built Environment, Vol. I/1, Theme II/4, pp. 564–575. (21E)

Adams, H. C., 1970
THE DESIGN OF BRICKWORK AGAINST GAS EXPLOSIONS, Proceedings of the
2nd International Brick Masonry Conference, H. W. H. West and K. H. Speed, eds.,
British Ceramic Research Association, Stoke-on-Trent, England, 1971, pp. 273–275. (27)

Adams, P. F., 1972
DESIGN OF STEEL BEAM-COLUMNS, Proceedings of Canadian Structural Engineering
Conference. (23)

Adams, P. F. and MacGregor, J. G., 1970
PLASTIC DESIGN OF COUPLED FRAME-SHEAR WALL STRUCTURES, *Journal of
the Structural Division*, ASCE, Vol. 96, No. ST9, Proc. Paper 7505, pp. 1861–1871. (22)

Ady, H. and Carpenter, J. E., 1970
MODELS FOR CONCRETE STRUCTURES (BIBLIOGRAPHY), ACI Publication No.
24, American Concrete Institute, pp. 449–487. (A38)

Ågårdh, L., 1968
ANALYSIS OF NON-LINEAR BEAMS, Chalmers University of Technology, Department
of Structural Mechanics, Göteborg, Sweden. (22)

Agaskar, V. L. and Weaver, W. J., 1972
AUTOMATED DESIGN OF TIER BUILDINGS, *Computer and Structures*, Vol. 2, No.
5–6, pp. 991–1011. (21A)

Air Force Design Manual, 1962
PRINCIPLES AND PRACTICE FOR DESIGN OF HARDENED STRUCTURES,
Technical Documentary Report No. AFSWC-TDR-62-138, Chapter 6. (22)

Albenque, M., 1973
THE PREDILIATION OF CERAMIC PRODUCTS (Le prédilatation des produits de terre
cuite), Proceedings of the 3rd International Brick Masonry Conference, Bundesverband
der Deutschen Ziegelindustrie e.V., Essen, Germany. (27)

Albiges, M. and Goulet, J., 1960
BRACING OF BUILDINGS (Contreventement des bâtiments), *Annales de l'Institut Technique du Bâtiment et des Travaux Publics*, H5. (21C)

Ali, I. and Kesler, C. E., 1964
MECHANICS OF CREEP IN CONCRETE, Publication No. 9, American Concrete Institute, pp. 35–57. (25)

Allen, D. E., 1970
LIMIT STATE DESIGN—A UNIFIED PROCEDURE FOR THE DESIGN OF STRUCTURES, Technical Paper 315, National Research Council of Canada. (27)

Allen, D. E., 1973
STRENGTH FACTORS FOR COMPOSITE MEMBERS, Planning and Design of Tall Buildings, Proceedings of 1972 ASCE-IABSE International Conference, Vol. III, No. 26-D4, ASCE, New York. (20, 26)

Allen, D. E., 1974
LIMIT STATES DESIGN IN CANADA, unpublished communication to the Joint Committee, July 1974. (26)

Allen, D. E., 1975
LIMIT STATES DESIGN—A PROBABILISTIC STUDY, *Canadian Journal of Civil Engineering*, Vol. 2, No. 1, pp. 36–49. (26)

Allen, M. H., 1973
EFFECT OF DIRECTION OF LOADING ON COMPRESSIVE STRENGTH OF BRICK MASONRY, Proceedings of the 3rd International Brick Masonry Conference, Bundesverband der Deutschen Ziegelindustrie e.V., Essen, Germany. (27)

Amaral, N. A., 1973
SOUTH AMERICAN STANDARDS FOR REINFORCED CONCRETE, Planning and Design of Tall Buildings, Proceedings of 1972 ASCE-IABSE International Conference, Vol. III, No. 20-3, ASCE, New York. (20, 26)

Amrhein, J. E., 1976
A TOWER WITH ITS TOP IN THE HEAVENS, Proceedings, 1st Canadian Masonry Symposium, E. L. Jessop and M. A. Ward, eds., University of Calgary, Canada. (27)

Anastasescu, D., Gidea, A. and Weisz, A., 1975
CONSIDERATIONS ON THE ANALYSIS OF REINFORCED CONCRETE MULTI-STORY ORTHOGONAL SPACE FRAMES IN INTERACTION WITH THE FOUNDATION SOIL THROUGH RAFT TYPE FOUNDATIONS (Consideratii Asupra Calculului Cadrelor Spatiale Ortogonale Multietajate din Beton Armat in Conlucrare Cu Terenul de Fundareprin Intermediul Fundatiilor de Tip Radire General), Reinforced Concrete Tall Buildings (Constructii Inalte De Beton Armat), Vol. 1, Consiliul National Al Inginerilor Si Tehnicienilor, Iasi, Romania, pp. 27–40. (21C)

Anderson, G. W., 1970
STACK-BONDED SMALL SPECIMEN AS DESIGN AND CONSTRUCTION CRITERIA, Proceedings of the 2nd International Brick Masonry Conference, H. W. H. West and K. H. Speed, eds., British Ceramic Research Association, Stoke-on-Trent, England, 1971. (27)

Anderson, G. W., 1973
SITE CONTROL OF STRUCTURAL BRICKWORK IN AUSTRALIA, Proceedings of the 2nd International Brick Masonry Conference, Bundesverband der Deutschen Ziegelindustrie e.v. Essen, Germany. (27)

Anderson, G. W., Dayeh, R. J. and Morgan, J. W., 1973
THE INTERACTION BETWEEN WALLS AND FLOOR IN A STRUCTURE OF LOADBEARING BRICKWORK, Proceedings of the 3rd International Brick Masonry Conference, Bundesverband der Deutschen Ziegelindustrie e.V., Essen, Germany. (27)

Anderson, R. P., 1973
COMPUTER DESIGN OF ENGINEERING BRICK MASONRY, Proceedings of the 3rd International Brick Masonry Conference, Bundesverband der Deutschen Ziegelindustrie e.V., Essen, Germany. (27)

Andrew, R. P. (ed.), 1956
SYMPOSIUM ON THE STRENGTH OF CONCRETE STRUCTURES, London. (22)

Ang, A. H. S. and Amin, M., 1969
SAFETY FACTORS AND PROBABILITY IN STRUCTURAL DESIGN, *Journal of the Structural Division*, ASCE, Vol. 95, No. ST7, Proc. Paper 6667, pp. 1389–1406. (26)

Antebi, J., Utuku, S. and Hansen, R. J., 1960
THE RESPONSE OF SHEAR WALLS TO DYNAMIC LOADS, Massachusetts Institute of Technology, Cambridge, Mass. (21D)

Aoyama, H., 1964
MOMENT-CURVATURE CHARACTERISTICS OF REINFORCED CONCRETE MEMBERS SUBJECTED TO AXIAL LOAD AND REVERSAL OF BENDING, Proceedings, ASCE-ACI Symposium held at Miami, Fla. (22)

Aoyama, H., 1967
RESTORING FORCE CHARACTERISTICS UNDER REVERSAL OF LOADING OF REINFORCED CONCRETE MEMBERS AND STRUCTURES, A Review of Japanese Research, Report of the U.S.-Japan Seminar on Basic Research in Concrete as Related to Behavior of Structures in Earthquakes, held in Tokyo, Japan. (22)

Aoyama, H., 1971
RESTORING FORCE CHARACTERISTICS AND EARTHQUAKE RESPONSE OF CONCRETE BUILDING STRUCTURES, Seminar under the Japan-U.S. Cooperative Science Program, Construction and Behavior of Precast Concrete Structures, held at Seattle, Wash., Reports by Japanese Participants, Part II, pp. 231–233. (22)

Aoyama, H., 1973
REPEATED AND CYCLIC LOADINGS, Planning and Design of Tall Buildings, Proceedings of 1972 ASCE-IABSE International Conference, Vol. III, No. 22-D2, ASCE, New York. (22)

Aoyama, H., Ito, M., Sugano, S. and Nakata, S., 1970
A STUDY OF DAMAGE TO THE HACHINOHE TECHNICAL COLLEGE DUE TO THE 1968 TOKACHI-OK EARTHQUAKE (PART I), Proceedings of the U.S.-Japan Seminar on Earthquake Engineering with Emphasis on Safety of School Buildings, held at Sendai, Japan, pp. 199–213. (22)

Arcan, M., 1964
CALCULATIONS AND METHODS FOR SHEAR WALLS WITH OPENINGS (Berechnungsverfahren für Wandscheiben mit einer Reihe von Öffnungen), Spannungsoptische Untersuchung, *Bautechnik*, H3. (21C)

Argyris, J. H. and Kelsey, S., 1963
MODERN FUSELAGE ANALYSIS AND THE ELASTIC AIRCRAFT, Butterworths, London, England. (22)

Argyris, J. H., Faust, G. and Willam, K. J., 1976
LIMIT LOAD ANALYSIS OF THICK WALLED CONCRETE STRUCTURES—A FINITE ELEMENT APPROACH TO FRACTURE, *Computer Methods in Applied Mechanics and Engineering*, No. 8, pp. 215–243. (22)

Aroni, S., 1968
STRENGTH OF SLENDER PRESTRESSED CONCRETE COLUMNS, *PCI Journal*, Vol. 13, No. 2, pp. 19–33; *Journal of the Structural Division*, ASCE, Vol. 94, No. ST4, Proc. Paper 5886, pp. 875–904. (23)

Aroni, S., Francis, A. J. and Brown, W. P., 1957
FULL-SCALE TESTS OF PRECAST MULTI-STORY FLAT CONSTRUCTION, Proceedings of ASTM Symposium on Full-Scale Tests of House Structures, Special Publication No. 210, ASTM, Philadelphia, Pa. (A38)

Ast, P. and Schwaighofer, J., 1974
ECONOMICAL ANALYSIS OF LARGE FRAMED-TUBE STRUCTURES, *Building Science*, Pergamon Press, Vol. 9, pp. 73–77. (21C, 24)

Astbury, N. F. and Vaughan, G. N., 1973
MOTION OF BRICKWORK STRUCTURE UNDER CERTAIN ASSUMED CONDITIONS, Proceedings of the 3rd International Brick Masonry Conference, Bundesverband der Deutschen Ziegelindustrie e.V., Essen, Germany. (27)

Astbury, N. F., West, H. W. H., Hodgkinson, H. R., Cubbage, P. A. and Clare, R., 1970
EXPERIMENTS TO DETERMINE THE RESISTANCE OF BRICK BUILDINGS TO GAS EXPLOSIONS, Proceedings of the 2nd International Brick Masonry Conference, H. W. H. West and K. H. Speed, eds., British Ceramic Research Association, Stoke-on-Trent, England, 1971. (27)

Astbury, N. F., West, H. W. H. and Hodgkinson, H. R., 1973
GAS EXPLOSION TESTING—PHASE IV, Proceedings of the 3rd International Brick Masonry Conference, Bundesverband der Deutschen Ziegelindustrie e.V., Essen, Germany. (27)

Atkan, A. E. and Pecknold, D. A., 1974
RESPONSE OF A REINFORCED CONCRETE SECTION TO TWO-DIMENSIONAL CURVATURE HISTORIES, *ACI Journal*, American Concrete Institute, Vol. 71, No. 5, p. 246. (21D)

Avantprojet, 1972
PROPOSAL FOR DANISH CODE OF CONCRETE DESIGN (Forslag til Dansk Ingeniorforenings Norm for Betonkonstruktioner), Avantprojet, May 1972. (26)

Avram, C., 1974
DESIGN OF CONCRETE STRUCTURES—DEVELOPMENT OF SPECIFICATIONS (Calcul des structures en béton—évolution des règlements), *Travaux*, Paris, No. 470. (26)

Avram, C. N. and Anastasescu, D. M., 1973a
GENERAL REVIEW OF STANDARDS FOR CONCRETE BUILDINGS IN EAST EUROPEAN COUNTRIES, Planning and Design of Tall Buildings, Proceedings of 1972 ASCE-IABSE International Conference, Vol. III, No. 20-4, ASCE, New York. (20, 26)

Avram, C. N. and Anastasescu, D. M., 1973b
PROBLEMS IN ANALYSIS, Planning and Design of Tall Buildings, Proceedings of 1972 ASCE-IABSE International Conference, Vol. III, No. 20-D2, ASCE, New York. (20, 26)

Avram, C. and Pop, A., 1975
A MATHEMATICAL MODEL TO CHOOSE THE OPTIMUM CONSTRUCTION SOLUTION (Model Matematic Pentru Alegerea Solutiei Constructive Optime), Reinforced Concrete Tall Buildings (Constructii Inalte De Beton Armat), Vol. 1, Consiliul National Al Inginerilor Si Tehnicienilor, Iasi, Romania, pp. 55–72. (21B)

Avram, C., Anastasescu, D. M. and Mirsu, O., 1973
RESEARCH REGARDING THE INTERACTION OF SHEAR WALLS AND FRAMES, Planning and Design of Tall Buildings, Proceedings of 1972 ASCE-IABSE International Conference, Vol. III, No. 21-D14, ASCE, New York. (21C)

Avram, C., Anastasescu, D., Mirsu, O. and Munteanu, I., 1970
RESEARCH REGARDING THE ANALYSIS AND THE BEHAVIOR OF TALL BUILDING FRAMES AND SHEAR WALLS SUBJECTED TO HORIZONTAL LOADS (in German), *Beton- und Stahlbetonbau*, Vol. 6, 7, p. 148, p. 171. (21C)

Avram, C., Bors, I., Grüner, I., Mihăescu, A., Friedrich, R., Rotaru, G., Frunză, R., Stoian, V., Moldt, M., Ianca, S. and Izverceanu, M., 1975
TALL BUILDINGS OF PRECAST SPACE ELEMENTS (Cladiri Multietajate din Elemente Spatiale Prefabricate), Reinforced Concrete Tall Buildings (Constructii Inalte De Beton Armat), Vol. 2, 34th National/Regional Conference, Iasi, Romania, pp. 29–50. (21E)

Avram, C., Frunza, R., Grüner, I., et al., 1975
EFFECT OF RESTRAINED SHRINKAGE ON REINFORCED CONCRETE SHEAR WALLS AT MULTISTORY BUILDINGS (Efectul Contractiei Impiedicate la Cladiri Etajate Cu Diafragme din Beton Armat), Reinforced Concrete Tall Buildings, Vol. 1, 34th National/Regional Conference, Iasi, Romania, pp. 41–54. (25)

Aylon, N. N., 1976
HIGHLIGHTS OF THE NEW CANADIAN MASONRY DESIGN CODE—CSA STANDARD S304, Proceedings of the 1st Canadian Masonry Symposium, E. L. Jessop and M. A. Ward, eds., University of Calgary, Canada. (27)

BIA, 1969
BUILDING CODE REQUIREMENTS FOR ENGINEERED BRICK MASONRY, Brick Institute of America, McLean, Va. (27)

BIA, undated
CONTEMPORARY BRICK BEARING WALL, CASE STUDY (a bimonthly publication), Brick Institute of America, McLean, Va. (27)

BS 187, 1970
CALCIUM SILICATE (SANDLIME AND FLINTLIME) BRICKS—METRIC UNITS (PART 2), British Standards Institution, London, England. (27)

BS 1180, 1972
CONCRETE BRICKS AND FIXING BRICKS, British Standards Institution, London, England. (27)

BS 2028, 1968
PRECAST CONCRETE BLOCKS, British Standards Institution, London, England. (27)

BS 3679, 1963
ACID-RESISTING BRICKS AND TILES, British Standards Institution, London, England. (27)

BS 3921, 1974
SPECIFICATION FOR CLAY BRICKS AND BLOCKS, British Standards Institution, London, England. (27)

Bachmann, H., 1971
INFLUENCE OF SHEAR AND BOND ON ROTATIONAL CAPACITY OF REINFORCED CONCRETE BEAMS, Report No. 36, Institut für Baustatik, ETH, Zurich, Switzerland. (22)

Bachmann, H. and Thürlimann, B., 1966
SHEAR DESIGN OF BEAMS (Schubbemessung von Balken), Report No. 8, Institut für Baustatik, ETH, Zurich, Switzerland. (22)

Bachmann, H. and Thürlimann, B., 1969
EXPERIMENTS ON THE PLASTIC BEHAVIOR OF TWO-SPAN CONTINUOUS REINFORCED CONCRETE BEAMS (Versuche über des Plastische Verhalten von Zweifeldrigen Stahlbeton Balken), Report No. 22, Institut für Baustatik, ETH, Zurich, Switzerland. (22)

Backler, A. P., Baylik, M. and Dill, M. I., 1973
LOCAL BEHAVIOR OF SHEAR TRANSFER AND COMPRESSION TRANSFER JOINTS, The Behavior of Large Panel Structures, CIRIA Report 45, London, England. (21E)

Bäcklund, J., 1972
LIMIT ANALYSIS OF REINFORCED CONCRETE SLABS BY FINITE ELEMENT, Proceedings of the Specialty Conference on Finite Element Method in Civil Engineering (McGill University, Montréal, Canada, June 1972), pp. 803–840. (22)

Baker, A. L. L., 1953
FURTHER RESEARCH IN REINFORCED CONCRETE AND ITS APPLICATION TO ULTIMATE LOAD DESIGN, Proceedings, Institution of Civil Engineers, London, Vol. 2, Paper No. 5894, pp. 269-310. (22)

Baker, A. L. L., 1956
THE ULTIMATE-LOAD THEORY APPLIED TO THE DESIGN OF REINFORCED AND PRESTRESSED CONCRETE FRAMES, Cement and Concrete Association, London, England. (22)

Baker, A. L. L., 1966
SIMPLIFIED BILINEAR LIMIT DESIGN, Structures hyperstatiques, Project d'annexe aux recommandations pratiques, Comité Européen du Béton, Paris, France. (22)

Baker, A. L. L., 1967a
THE INELASTIC SPACE FRAME, Concrete Publications, Ltd., England. (22)

Baker, A. L. L., 1967b
FRAME INSTABILITY, Concrete, Vol. 1, No. 1. (22)

Baker, A. L. L., 1970
LIMIT-STATE DESIGN OF REINFORCED CONCRETE, Cement and Concrete Association, London, England. (22)

Baker, A. L. L., 1973
FULLY PLASTIC ANALYSIS AND DESIGN, State of Art Report No. 4, Technical Committee No. 22, ASCE-IABSE International Conference on Planning and Design of Tall Buildings (Bethlehem, Pa., August 1972), Vol. III, No. 22-4, ASCE, New York. (22)

Baker, A. L. L. and Amarakone, A. M. N., 1964
INELASTIC HYPERSTATIC FRAMES ANALYSIS, Proceedings, International Symposium on Flexural Mechanics of Reinforced Concrete (Miami, Fla., November 1964), ASCE, New York. (22)

Baker, J. F., 1949
THE DESIGN OF STEEL FRAMES, The Structural Engineer, Vol. 27, October 1949. (22)

Baker, L. R., 1972
MANUFACTURE AND TESTING OF MODEL BRICKWORK WIND PANELS, Conference on Structural Models (Sydney, 1972), Cement and Concrete Assoc. of Australia in conjunction with Dept. of Architectural Science, University of Sydney, and Institution of Engineers, Australia, N.S.W. Division. (A38)

Baker, L. R., 1973
FLEXURAL STRENGTH OF BRICKWORK PANELS, Proceedings of the 3rd International Brick Masonry Conference, Bundesverband der Deutschen Ziegelindustrie e.V., Essen, Germany. (27)

Balint, P. S. and Shaw, F. S., 1965
STRUCTURAL MODEL OF THE AUSTRALIA SQUARE TOWER IN SYDNEY, *Architectural Science Review*, Vol. 8, No. 4, pp. 136–149. (A38)

Balint, P. S. and Taylor, H. J. P., 1972
REINFORCEMENT DETAILING OF FRAME CORNER JOINTS WITH PARTICULAR REFERENCE TO OPENING CORNERS, Technical Report 42.462, Cement and Concrete Association, London, England. (21D)

Ballio, G., Petrini, V. and Urbano, C., 1973
THE EFFECT OF THE PROCESS AND IMPERFECTIONS ON THE LOAD-BEARING CAPACITY OF BEAM COLUMNS, *Meccanica*, Vol. 8(16), N.1. (23)

Ban, S., 1943
EXPERIMENTAL STUDY ON THE SEISMIC RESISTANCE OF WALLS WITH OPENINGS (in Japanese), Transactions of the Architectural Institute of Japan, No. 30, September 1943. (21D)

Bandel, H., 1964
BARREL SHELLS FORM STRUCTURAL BACKBONE OF MULTISTORY BUILDINGS, Proceedings, World Conference on Shell Structures (San Francisco, Calif., 1962), National Academy of Sciences, National Research Council, Washington, D.C. (21D)

Barda, F., Hanson, J. M. and Corley, W. G., 1973
AN INVESTIGATION OF THE DESIGN AND REPAIR OF LOW-RISE SHEAR WALLS, Proceedings of the 5th World Conference on Earthquake Engineering held at Rome, Italy. (21D)

Bardhan-Roy, B. K., 1975
PRECAST CONCRETE STRUCTURES—CONSTRUCTION DETAILS, unpublished communications to the Joint Committee, September 1975. (21E)

Barnard, P. R. and Schwaighofer, J., 1967
INTERACTION OF SHEAR WALLS CONNECTED SOLELY THROUGH SLABS, Symposium on Tall Buildings (Univ. of Southampton, England, April 13–16, 1966), Pergamon Press, England, pp. 19–35. (21D)

Base, G. D., Beeby, A. W., Read, J. B. and Taylor, H. P. J., 1966
AN INVESTIGATION OF THE CRACK CONTROL CHARACTERISTICS OF VARIOUS TYPES OF BAR IN REINFORCED CONCRETE BEAMS, Report 18, Cement and Concrete Association, London, England. (24)

Basler, E. and Witta, W., 1966
CONNECTIONS IN PREFABRICATION (Verbindungen in der Vorfabrikation), Technische Forschungs und Beratungsstelle der Schweizerischen Zementindustrie, Wildegg. (21E)

Bate, S. C. C., 1968
WHY LIMIT STATE DESIGN? *Concrete*, Vol. 2, No. 3, pp. 103–108. (22)

Bate, S. C. C. and Lewsley, C. S., 1970
ENVIRONMENTAL CHANGES, TEMPERATURE CREEP AND SHRINKAGE IN CONCRETE STRUCTURES, Current Papers 7/70, Building Research Station, England. (25)

Battelle Memorial Institute, 1967
THE STATE OF THE ART OF PREFABRICATION IN THE CONSTRUCTION INDUSTRY, Report for the Building and Construction Trades Dept., AFL-CIO, Washington, D.C. (21E)

Baum, R., 1973
MUTUAL INFLUENCES BETWEEN BUILDING CONCEPT AND MECHANICAL SYSTEMS IN TALL STRUCTURES, Proceedings of the 12th Regional Conference (Sydney, Australia, August 14–17, 1973), Lehigh University, Bethlehem, Pa., pp. 483–498. (21B)

Baumann, O., 1934
BUCKLING OF REINFORCED CONCRETE COLUMNS (Die Knickung der Eisenbetonsaulen), EMPA, Bericht 89, ETH, Zurich, Switzerland. (23)

Bazant, Z., 1972
NUMERICAL DETERMINATION OF STRESS RESPONSE TO A GIVEN STRAIN HISTORY IN CONCRETE, Bulletin d'information no. 80, Comité Européen du Béton, Paris, France, pp. 79–112. (23)

Beck, H., 1959
CALCULATION OF FRAMES WITH SLENDER MEMBERS (Ein Beitrag zur Beruecksichtigung der Dehnungsverformungen bei Rahmen mit schlanken und gedrungenen Konstruktionsgliedern), *Bautechnik*, No. 36, p. 178. (21C)

Beck, H., 1962
CONTRIBUTION TO THE ANALYSIS OF COUPLED SHEAR WALLS, *ACI Journal*, American Concrete Institute, Vol. 59, No. 8, pp. 1055–1070. (21C, 22)

Beck, H., 1969a
THE RELATION BETWEEN BENDING MOMENT AND CURVATURE FOR THE RECTANGULAR REINFORCED-CONCRETE CROSS SECTION (Der Zusammenhang zwischen Biegemoment und Krummung für den Stahlbetonrechteckquerschnitt), *Berichte aus der Forschung und Praxis* (Rüsch-Festschrift), Ernst und Sohn, Berlin, Germany. (23)

Beck, H., 1969b
STABILITY AND MATERIAL BEHAVIOR IN CONCRETE CONSTRUCTION (Stabilität und Werkstoffverhalten im Stahlbetonbau), Vortrage, Betontag, p. 169. (23)

Beck, H., 1972
STABILITY IN THE DESIGN OF TALL CONCRETE BUILDINGS, Theme Report, Com. 23, ASCE-IABSE International Conference on Tall Buildings (August, 1972), Vol. III-23, pp. 1–16, ASCE, New York. (21E)

Beck, H., 1975
STABILITY IN THE DESIGN OF TALL CONCRETE BUILDINGS, Hellenic Conference on Tall Buildings, 33rd National/Regional Conference (Athens, Greece, October 1975), Technical Chamber of Greece, Athens. (23)

Beck, H. and Bubenheim, H. J., 1972
A PROCEDURE FOR THE OPTIMUM DESIGN OF REINFORCED CONCRETE FRAMES (Ein Verfahren zur optimaten Bemessung ebener Stahlbetonrahmen), *Der Bauingenieur*. (23)

Beck, H. and König, G., 1966
RESTRAINING FORCES IN THE ANALYSIS OF TALL BUILDINGS, *Proceedings*, Symposium on Tall Buildings, Pergamon Press, Oxford, England, p. 37; see also Halterkräfte im Skelettbau, *Beton- und Stahlbetonbau*, 62, 1967. (23)

Beck, H. and Schneider, K. H., 1972
STRUCTURAL FRAME OF THE AFE FACULTY TOWER OF THE UNIVERSITY OF FRANKFURT/MAIN (Tragwerk des Hochhauses AFE der Universitat Frankfurt/Main), *Beton- und Stahlbetonbau*, Vol. 67, H1. (21E)

Beck, H., König, G. and Rech, H., 1968
CHARACTERISTICS RELATING TO THE TORSIONAL STIFFNESS OF MULTI-STORY BUILDINGS, *Beton- und Stahlbetonbau*, Vol. 63. (23)

Beeby, A. W., 1971
THE PREDICTION OF CRACKING IN REINFORCED CONCRETE MEMBERS, thesis presented to the University of London, England, in partial fulfillment of requirements for degree. (24)

Beeby, A. W. and Taylor, H. P. J., 1970
CRACKING IN PARTIALLY PRESTRESSED MEMBERS, presented at 6th International Congress of the Fédération Internationale de la Précontrainte, Prague, Czechoslovakia, June 1970. (24)

Beech, D. G., 1977
SOME PROBLEMS IN THE STATISTICAL CALCULATION OF SAFETY FACTORS, Proceedings of the 4th International Brick Masonry Conference, Groupement National de l'Industrie de la Terre Cuite, rue de Poissoniers 13, Brussels, Belgium. (27)

Beekhuis, W. J., 1971
AN EXPERIMENTAL STUDY OF SQUAT SHEAR WALLS, M.E. Report, Dept. of Civil Engineering, University of Canterbury, Christchurch, New Zealand. (22)

Benedetti, D. and Ionita, V., 1974
NONLINEAR ANALYSIS OF SPACE TRUSSES, Politecnico di Milano, Technical Report No. 27, ISTC, Milan, Italy. (22)

Benedetti, D. and Vitiello, E., 1972
EXPERIMENTAL ANALYSIS OF HORIZONTAL JOINTS BETWEEN LARGE PAN-
ELS LOADED WITH NORMAL AND SHEAR FORCES, Politecnico di Milano,
Technical Report No. 1, ISTC, Milan, Italy. (21E)

Benjamin, F. R. and Cornell, C. A., 1970
PROBABILITY, STATISTICS AND DECISION FOR CIVIL ENGINEERS, McGraw-
Hill Book Co., Inc., New York. (26)

Benjamin, J. R. and Williams, H. A., 1958
BEHAVIOR OF ONE-STORY REINFORCED CONCRETE SHEAR WALLS, *ACI
Journal*, American Concrete Institute, Vol. 55, No. 11. (22)

Bennett, E. W. and Chandrasekhar, C. S., 1971
CALCULATION OF THE WIDTH OF CRACKS IN CLASS 3 PRESTRESSED BEAMS,
Proceedings, Institution of Civil Engineers, London, England, Vol. 49. (24)

Beresford, F. D., 1970
A STUDY OF CONCRETE PANEL CONSTRUCTION, PART 1, TESTS ON WALL-
TO-FLOOR CONNECTIONS, Report T12-1, Division of Building Research, Australia.
(21E)

Berg, V. B. and Straha, J. L., 1964
ANCHORAGE AND THE ALASKA EARTHQUAKE OF MARCH 27, 1964, American
Iron and Steel Institute, New York. (22)

Bergan, P. G. and Soreide, T., 1973
A COMPARATIVE STUDY OF DIFFERENT NUMERICAL SOLUTION TECH-
NIQUES AS APPLIED TO A NONLINEAR STRUCTURAL PROBLEM, *Computer
Methods in Applied Mechanics and Engineering*, Vol. 2, No. 2, pp. 185–201. (22)

Bergen, R. I., 1973
SHEARING STRENGTH OF CONCRETE GLUED JOINTS, *Beton i Zhelezobeton*, No.
11, pp. 23–24. (21E)

Bergmann, K. W., 1973
DAMAGES IN MASONRY CAUSED BY PERPENDICULAR DEFORMATION
(Schaden im Mauerwerk durch senkrechte Verformung), Proceedings of the 3rd Inter-
national Brick Masonry Conference, Bundesverband der Deutschen Ziegelindustrie e.V.,
Essen, Germany. (27)

Bertero, V. V., 1966
EFFECTS OF VARIABLE REPEATED LOADING ON STRUCTURES, A REVIEW,
University of California, Berkeley, Calif., July 1966. (22)

Bertero, V. V., 1968
INELASTIC BEHAVIOR OF BEAM-TO-COLUMN SUBASSEMBLAGES UNDER
REPEATED LOADING, Report No. EERC 68-12, Earthquake Engineering Research
Center, University of California, Berkeley, Calif., December 1968. (22)

Bertero, V. V., 1971
RESEARCH NEEDS IN LIMIT DESIGN OF REINFORCED CONCRETE STRUC-
TURES, Report No. EERC-71-4, Earthquake Engineering Research Center, University of
California, Berkeley, Calif., June 1971; CEB Bulletin, pp. 1367–1373. (22, 26)

Bertero, V. V., 1972
EXPERIMENTAL STUDIES CONCERNING REINFORCED PRESTRESSED AND
PARTIALLY PRESTRESSED CONCRETE STRUCTURES AND THEIR ELE-
MENTS, Introductory Report for Theme 4 of the IABSE Symposium on Resistance and
Ultimate Deformability of Structures Acted on by Repeated Forces (Lisbon, Portugal,
September 1972). (22)

Bertero, V. V., 1973
EFFECTS OF GENERALIZED EXCITATIONS ON THE NONLINEAR BEHAVIOR
OF REINFORCED CONCRETE STRUCTURES, Planning and Design of Tall
Buildings, Proceedings of 1972 ASCE-IABSE International Conference, Vol. III, No.
22-5, ASCE, New York. (22)

Bertero, V. V. and Bresler, B., 1968
INFLUENCE OF LOAD HISTORY ON CRACKING IN REINFORCED CONCRETE,
Report to California State Division of Highways, University of California, Berkeley,
August 1966; *Journal of the Structural Division*, ASCE, Vol. 94, No. ST6, Proc. Paper 6013,
June 1968. (21D)

Bertero, V. V. and Bresler, B., 1969
SEISMIC BEHAVIOR OF REINFORCED CONCRETE FRAMED STRUCTURES, Proceedings, 4th World Conference on Earthquake Engineering (Chile), Vol. I, pp. B-2, 109–124. (22)

Bertero, V. V. and McClure, G., 1964
BEHAVIOR OF REINFORCED CONCRETE FRAMES SUBJECTED TO REPEATED REVERSIBLE LOADS, *ACI Journal*, American Concrete Institute, Vol. 61, No. 10, p. 1305. (21D, 22, 24)

Bertero, V. V., Bresler, B. and Liao, H., 1969
STIFFNESS DEGRADATION OF REINFORCED CONCRETE MEMBERS SUBJECTED TO CYCLIC FLEXURAL MOMENTS, Report No. EERC-69-12, Earthquake Engineering Research Center, University of California, Berkeley, Calif., December 1969. (22)

Bertero, V. V., Rea, D., Mahin, S. and Atalay, M. C., 1972
RATE OF LOADING EFFECTS ON UNCRACKED AND REPAIRED REINFORCED CONCRETE MEMBERS, Report No. EERC-72-9, Earthquake Engineering Research Center, University of California, Berkeley, Calif., December 1972. (22)

Bianchini, C., Woods, R. and Kesler, C. E., 1960
EFFECT OF FLOOR CONCRETE STRENGTH ON COLUMN STRENGTH, *ACI Journal*, American Concrete Institute, Vol. 56, No. 5, p. 1149. (21D)

Birkeland, P. W., 1969
RELATIONS BETWEEN DESIGNER AND FABRICATOR—CONNECTIONS, The Prestressed Concrete Institute Convention, Boston, Mass. (21E)

Birkeland, P. W. and Birkeland, H. W., 1966
CONNECTIONS IN PRECAST CONSTRUCTION, *ACI Journal*, American Concrete Institute, Vol. 63, No. 3, p. 345. (21E)

Birkeland, P. W. and Westhoff, L. J., 1972
DIMENSIONAL TOLERANCE—CONCRETE, SOA Report 5, Committee 9, ASCE-IABSE International Conference on Tall Buildings (August 1972), Vol. Ib-9, pp. 69–74, ASCE, New York. (21E)

Bishara, A. and Peir, J. C., 1968
REINFORCED CONCRETE RECTANGULAR COLUMNS IN TORSION, *Journal of the Structural Division*, ASCE, Vol. 94, No. ST12, Proc. Paper 6305, p. 2913. (21D)

Biswas, J. K. and Tso, W. K., 1970
Discussion of LATERAL-LOAD ANALYSIS OF ASYMMETRIC MULTISTORY STRUCTURES by J. Glück, *Journal of the Structural Division*, ASCE, Vol. 96, No. ST11, Proc. Paper 7644, p. 2540. (22)

Biswas, J. K. and Tso, W. K., 1974
THREE-DIMENSIONAL ANALYSIS OF SHEAR WALL BUILDINGS SUBJECT TO LATERAL LOAD, *Journal of the Structural Division*, ASCE, Vol. 100, No. ST5, Proc. Paper 10537, p. 1019. (21C)

Black, D. C., Pulmano, V. A. and Kabaila, A. P., 1976
FLAT PLATES SUPPORTED ON WALLS, Mémoires, International Association for Bridge and Structural Engineering, 36-I, pp. 79–91. (21D)

Blakey, F. A., 1955
AN EXAMINATION OF THE EFFECT OF ATMOSPHERIC TEMPERATURE AND RELATIVE HUMIDITY ON THE ELASTIC PROPERTIES OF CONCRETE, Building Research Report C2.3-1, CSIRO, Australian Division. (25)

Blakey, F. A., 1961
DEFORMATIONS OF AN EXPERIMENTAL LIGHTWEIGHT FLAT PLATE STRUCTURE, *Civil Engineering Transactions*, CE3, Institution of Engineers, Australia. (25)

Blakey, F. A., 1962
A COMMENTARY ON FLAT PLATE DESIGN, *Architectural Science Review*, No. 5, p. 89. (25)

Blakey, F. A., 1963a
AUSTRALIAN EXPERIMENTS WITH FLAT PLATES, *ACI Journal*, American Concrete Institute, Vol. 60, p. 515. (25)

Blakey, F. A., 1963b
INFLUENCE OF CREEP AND SHRINKAGE ON STRUCTURAL BEHAVIOUR, *Constructional Review*, Vol. 36, No. 11, p. 15. (25)

Blakey, F. A., 1963c
THE DEFLECTION OF FLAT PLATE STRUCTURES, *Civil Engineering and Public Works Review*, Vol. 58, p. 1133. (25)

Blakey, F. A. and Beresford, F. D., 1965
STRIPPING OF FORMWORK FOR CONCRETE BUILDINGS IN RELATION TO STRUCTURAL DESIGN, *Civil Engineering Transactions*, CE7, Institution of Engineers, Australia, p. 92. (25)

Blakey, F. A. and Heiman, J. L., 1975
TRANSVERSE DEFLECTION OF FLOORS—CREEP, SHRINKAGE AND TEMPERATURE EFFECTS, Report 29, Division of Building Research, CSIRO, Australia. (25)

Blakey, F. A. and Lewis, R. K., 1956
MEASUREMENT OF DIMENSIONAL CHANGES IN PRECAST CONCRETE WALLS, *Constructional Review*, Vol. 29, No. 4, p. 23. (25)

Blakey, F. A. and Lewis, R. K., 1964
A REVIEW OF ELASTIC DEFLECTION, CREEP AND SHRINKAGE OF EXPANDED SHALE CONCRETE, *Constructional Review*, Vol. 37, No. 7, p. 19. (25)

Bleich, F., 1952
BUCKLING STRENGTH OF METAL STRUCTURES, McGraw-Hill Book Co., Inc., New York. (23)

Bliss, E. C. and Herrera, A., 1965
BACARDI BUILDING—AN UNUSUAL STRUCTURE FOR AN UNUSUAL BUILDING, *ACI Journal*, American Concrete Institute, Vol. 62, No. 12, pp. 1521–1532. (21D)

Bljuger, F., 1975
LOAD-BEARING CAPACITY OF JOINTS, WALLS, AND FLOOR SLABS IN MULTI-STORY BUILDINGS (Capacitatea Portanta a Impinarilor Intre Pereti si Plansee la Cladirele Inalte), Reinforced Concrete Tall Buildings, 34th National/Regional Conference, Iasi, Romania, October 1975, Vol. I, pp. 379–400. (21E)

Bluck, B. E., 1973
THE NEED FOR A STRENGTHENING CODE, Seminar on High Earthquake Risk Buildings, Wellington, pp. 117–122. (27)

Blume, J. A., 1960
STRUCTURAL DYNAMICS IN EARTHQUAKE-RESISTANT DESIGN, *Transactions*, ASCE, Vol. 125, pp. 1088–1139. (24)

Blume, J. A., 1970
THE SHEAR TRUTH ABOUT BRICK WALLS, Dickey, Harrington, Western States Clay Products Assoc. (27)

Blume, J. A., 1971
BUILDING COLUMNS UNDER STRONG EARTHQUAKE EXPOSURE, *Journal of the Structural Division*, ASCE, Vol. 97, No. ST9, Proc. Paper 8398, p. 2351. (21D)

Bobrowski, J., Abeles, P. W. and Bardhan-Roy, B. K., 1974a
H-FRAMES, The Impact of Research on the Built Environment, Proceedings of the CIB 6th Congress (October 1974), Vol. I/1, Theme II/4, pp. 585–591. (21E)

Bobrowski, J., Abeles, P. W. and Bardhan-Roy, B. K., 1974b
THE IMPACT OF RESEARCH ON THE USE OF LIGHTWEIGHT CONCRETE IN MAJOR STRUCTURAL WORK, The Impact of Research on the Built Environment, Proceedings of the CIB 6th Congress (October 1974), Vol. I/1, Theme II/4, pp. 576–584. (21E)

Borowiec, Z., 1973
STRESS AND DEFLECTION ANALYSIS OF PERFORATED WALLS, CIB 2nd International Symposium on Bearing Walls (Warsaw, Poland, September 1973), Theme 2, Paper No. 2, pp. 129–140. (21E)

Bouda, M. and Zofka, K., 1973
FLOORS OF COMPOSITE THIN-WALLED CORRUGATED SHEET AND WELDED-STUD-CONNECTED CONCRETE SLABS, Proceedings, 10th National/Regional Conference (Bratislava, Czechoslovakia, April 1973), pp. 433–444. (21E)

Bradshaw, R. E. and Foster, D., 1970
TWO LOAD-BEARING BRICKWORK BUILDINGS IN NORTHERN ENGLAND, Proceedings of the 2nd International Brick Masonry Conference, H. W. H. West and K. H. Speed, eds., British Ceramic Research Association, Stoke-on-Trent, England, 1971. (27)

Bradshaw, R. E. and Hendry, A. W., 1969
   PRELIMINARY CRUSHING TESTS ON STOREY-HEIGHT CAVITY WALLS, Design
   Engineering and Constructing with Masonry Products, F. Johnson, ed., Gulf Publishing
   Co., Houston, Tex. (27)
Braga Da Cruz, L., 1974
   COMPARATIVE STUDY OF SHEAR WALLS WITH OPENINGS BY THE FINITE
   ELEMENT METHOD AND AS A FRAME STRUCTURE, Regional Conference on
   Tall Buildings, 15th National/Regional Conference (Madrid, Spain, September 17–19,
   1973), Tipografia Artistica, Alameda 12, Madrid, pp. 111–127. (21C)
Brakel, J., 1972
   LIMIT STATES DESIGN, 6th Regional Conference Proceedings, 6th National/Regional
   Conference (Delft, The Netherlands, May 1972), Joint Committee on Tall Buildings,
   Lehigh University, Bethlehem, Pa., pp. 78–81. (26)
Brakel, J., 1973
   LIST OF LIMIT STATES, Planning and Design of Tall Buildings, Proceedings of 1972
   ASCE-IABSE International Conference, Vol. III, No. 26-2, ASCE, New York. (20, 26)
Branson, D. E., 1968
   DESIGN PROCEDURES FOR COMPUTING DEFLECTIONS, ACI Journal, American
   Concrete Institute, Vol. 65, p. 730. (25)
Breen, J. E., 1964
   COMPUTER USE IN STUDIES OF FRAMES WITH LONG COLUMNS, Flexural
   Mechanics of Reinforced Concrete, Proceedings of International Symposium (Miami, Fla.,
   1964), ASCE, New York, pp. 535–556. (23)
Breen, J. E., 1965
   STUDIES OF FRAMES WITH LONG COLUMNS, Proceedings of the International
   Symposium on Flexural Mechanics of Reinforced Concrete, Publication No. SP-12,
   American Concrete Institute. (22)
Breen, J. E. and Ferguson, P. M., 1964
   THE RESTRAINED LONG CONCRETE COLUMN AS A PART OF A RECTAN-
   GULAR FRAME, ACI Journal, American Concrete Institute, Vol. 61, No. 5, p. 563.
   (21D, 22)
Breen, J. E., MacGregor, J. and Pfrang, E. O., 1972
   DETERMINATION OF EFFECTIVE LENGTH FACTORS FOR SLENDER COL-
   UMNS, ACI Journal, American Concrete Institute, Vol. 69, No. 11, p. 669. (21D, 23)
Bresler, B., 1960
   DESIGN CRITERIA FOR REINFORCED COLUMNS UNDER AXIAL LOAD AND
   BIAXIAL BENDING, ACI Journal, American Concrete Institute, Vol. 57, No. 11, p. 481.
   (21D)
Bresler, B., 1971
   LIGHTWEIGHT AGGREGATE REINFORCED CONCRETE COLUMNS, Lightweight
   Concrete, Publication SP-29, American Concrete Institute, p. 81. (21D)
Bresler, B., 1976
   RESPONSE OF REINFORCED CONCRETE FRAMES TO FIRE, 10th Congress of
   IABSE (Tokyo, Japan, September 1976), Preliminary Report, pp. 273–280. (23)
Bresler, B. and Bertero, V. V., 1966
   REINFORCED CONCRETE PRISM UNDER REPEATED LOADS, RILEM Interna-
   tional Symposium on the Effects of Repeated Loading of Materials and Structural
   Elements (Mexico, September 1966). (22)
Bresler, B. and Gilbert, P. H., 1961
   TIE REQUIREMENTS FOR REINFORCED CONCRETE COLUMNS, ACI Journal,
   American Concrete Institute, Vol. 58, No. 11, p. 555. (21D, 22)
Bresler, B., Thielen, G., Nizzamuddin, Z. and Iding, R., 1976
   LIMIT STATE BEHAVIOR OF REINFORCED CONCRETE FRAMES IN FIRE
   ENVIRONMENTS, Proceedings, ASCE-IABSE Regional Conference on Planning and
   Design of Tall Buildings (Hong Kong, September 1976), pp. 310–325. (23)
Brettle, H. J., 1971
   ULTIMATE STRENGTH DESIGN OF REINFORCED BRICKWORK PIERS IN
   COMPRESSION AND BIAXIAL BENDING, UNICEF Report No. R49, University of
   New South Wales, Australia. (27)

British Ceramics Research Association, undated
DESIGN GUIDE FOR REINFORCED AND PRESTRESSED CLAY BRICKWORK, Special Publication No. 91, Structural Ceramics Advisory Group of the Structural Ceramics Research Panel, British Ceramics Research Association, Stoke-on-Trent, England. (27)

British Ceramics Research Association, undated
MODEL SPECIFICATION FOR LOADBEARING CLAY BRICKWORK, Special Publication No. 56, Structural Ceramics Advisory Group of the Building Science Committee, British Ceramics Research Association, Stoke-on-Trent, England (revised metric edition). (27)

British Standard, 1969
THE STRUCTURAL USE OF REINFORCED CONCRETE, Code of Practice 114, Council for Codes of Practice, British Standards Institution, London, England. (25)

British Standard, 1970
LARGE PANEL STRUCTURES, Code of Practice 116, Addendum No. 1, The Council for Codes of Practice, British Standards Institution, London, England, pp. 7–11. (21E, 26)

British Standard, 1972
CODE OF PRACTICE FOR THE STRUCTURAL USE OF CONCRETE—PART 1: DESIGN, MATERIALS AND WORKMANSHIP, Code of Practice 110, British Standards Institution, London, England. (21E, 23, 26)

Broms, B. B., 1965
CRACK WIDTH AND CRACK SPACING IN REINFORCED CONCRETE MEMBERS, *ACI Journal*, American Concrete Institute, Vol. 62, No. 10. (22)

Broms, B. B. and Viest, I. M., 1961
LONG REINFORCED CONCRETE COLUMNS—A SYMPOSIUM, *Transactions*, ASCE, Vol. 126, Part 2, p. 308. (21D, 23)

Brondum-Nielsen, T., 1971
PREVENTION OF STRUCTURAL COLLAPSE, Build International, September/October 1971, pp. 280–283. (21E)

Brondum-Nielsen, T., 1975
PRECAST CONCRETE STRUCTURES—DESIGN LOADS, unpublished communication to the Joint Committee, November 1975. (21E)

Brotchie, J., 1964
DIRECT DESIGN OF PRESTRESSED FLAT PLATE STRUCTURES, *Constructional Review*, Vol. 37, No. 1, p. 13. (25)

Brouwer, F., 1972
PREFABRICATION WITH CONCRETE, PART C (Prefabricage in Beton, Deel C), Lecture Notes, Dept. of Civil Engineering, Delft University of Technology, The Netherlands. (21E)

Brown, R. H. and Jirsa, J. O., 1970
REINFORCED CONCRETE BEAMS UNDER LOAD REVERSALS, Structural Research at Rice, Report No. 7, Rice University, Houston, Tex.; also *ACI Journal*, American Concrete Institute, Vol. 68, No. 5, May 1971, pp. 380–390. (22)

Bruckner, H. and Popp, C., 1973
HOLIDAY INN HOTEL TOWER IN AUGSBURG (Holiday-Inn-Turmhotel in Augsburg), *Beton- und Stahlbetonbau*, Vol. 68, H6, pp. 137–145. (21E)

Bruggeling, A. S. G., 1972
PREFABRICATION WITH CONCRETE, PART B (Prefabricage in Beton, Deel B), Lecture Notes, Dept. of Civil Engineering, Delft University of Technology, The Netherlands. (21E)

Bruinette, K. E., 1973
STRUCTURAL STANDARDS FOR REINFORCED CONCRETE IN SOUTH AFRICA, Planning and Design of Tall Buildings, Proceedings of 1972 ASCE-IABSE International Conference, Vol. III, No. 20-5, ASCE, New York. (20, 26)

Bruinette, K. E., 1975
OPTIMIZING SLABS, BEAMS, COLUMN SLAB STRIPS, COMPARATIVE SLAB PANELS, unpublished communication to the Joint Committee. (21B)

Bruinette, K. E. and Barnard, J. D. N., 1975
STRUCTURAL SYSTEMS, CONCRETE AND STEEL (INCLUDING THE ROLE OF PREFABRICATION), Proceedings of the National Conference on Tall Buildings

(Johannesburg, South Africa, November 18–20, 1975), National Building Research Institute of the CSIR, Hortors Printers, Johannesburg, South Africa. (21B)

Bryrup, J., 1973
THE FUTURE OF BRICK CONSTRUCTION, WITH A SPECIAL VIEW ON THE DANISH SITUATION (Die Zukunft des gemauerten Baues, in besonderem Hindick auf danische Verhaltnisse), Proceedings of the 3rd International Brick Masonry Conference, Bundesverband der Deutschen Ziegelindustrie e.V., Essen, Germany. (27)

Bryson, J., 1972
THE DESIGN OF SHEAR WALL-FRAME STRUCTURES, Structural Engineering Report No. 41, thesis presented to the University of Alberta, at Edmonton, Canada, in partial fulfillment of the requirements for the degree of Master of Science. (23)

Buckingham, E., 1914
ON PHYSICALLY SIMILAR SYSTEMS—ILLUSTRATIONS OF THE USE OF DIMENSIONAL EQUATIONS, *Physical Review*, Vol. 4, No. 4, pp. 345–376. (A38)

Buckton, G., 1970
MODERN DEVELOPMENT UTILIZING THE INTERACTION OF DEEP BRICK PANELS AND REINFORCED CONCRETE BEAMS TO SUPPORT MULTI-STOREY CONSTRUCTION, Proceedings of the 2nd International Brick Masonry Conference, H. W. H. West and K. H. Speed, eds., British Ceramic Research Association, Stoke-on-Trent, England, 1971. (27)

Building Research Institute, 1961
PREASSEMBLED BUILDING COMPONENTS, Proceedings of the 1960 Fall Conferences of the Building Research Institute, Publication No. NAS-NRC 911, National Academy of Sciences-National Research Council. (21E)

Burggrabe, A. Hilmar, 1972
MICROCONCRETE FOR STRUCTURAL MODEL INVESTIGATIONS (Mikrobeton für Modellstatische Untersuchungen), Berichte des Instituts für Modellstatik der Universität Stuttgart, Heft Nr. 1, Stuttgart, Germany. (A38)

Burnett, E. F. P., 1975
THE AVOIDANCE OF PROGRESSIVE COLLAPSE: REGULATORY APPROACHES TO THE PROBLEM, U.S. Dept. of Housing and Urban Development, Washington, D.C. (21E)

Burnett, E., Rajendra, R. and Clement, S., 1972
INFLUENCE OF JOINTS IN PANELIZED STRUCTURAL SYSTEMS, *Journal of the Structural Division*, ASCE, Vol. 98, No. ST9, Proc. Paper 9207. (21E)

Burnham, C. A. and Grimm, C. T., 1970
TOWARDS A RATIONAL AESTHETIC CRITERION FOR THE SELECTION OF THE VISUAL PROPERTIES OF ARCHITECTURAL SURFACES, Proceedings of the 2nd International Brick Masonry Conference, H. W. H. West and K. H. Speed, eds., British Ceramic Research Association, Stoke-on-Trent, England, 1971. (27)

Burton, K. T., Corley, W. G. and Hognestad, E., 1967
CONNECTIONS IN PRECAST CONCRETE STRUCTURES—EFFECTS OF RE-STRAINED CREEP AND SHRINKAGE, Journal of the Prestressed Concrete Institute, April 1967, p. 18. (21E)

CA 32, 1967
SAA CODE FOR CONCRETE BLOCK MASONRY, Standards Association of Australia, Sydney, N.S.W. (27)

CEB, 1960
REPORT ON THE 5TH WORKING SESSION, held at Vienna, April 1959, Bulletin d'information no. 25, Comité Européen du Béton, Paris, France, p. 21. (21D)

CEB, 1963
RECOMMENDATION FOR AN INTERNATIONAL CODE OF PRACTICE FOR REINFORCED CONCRETE, Comité Européen du Béton, Paris, France. (22)

CEB, 1964
METHODS OF ANALYSIS FOR REDUNDANT STRUCTURES (Méthodes de calcul des structures hyperstatiques), Bulletin no. 53, Comité Européen du Béton, Paris, France. (22)

CEB, 1966
NEWS BULLETIN NO. 53 (Bulletin d'information no. 53), Comité Européen du Béton, Paris, France. (22)

CEB, 1967
INTERNATIONAL RECOMMENDATIONS FOR THE DESIGN AND CONSTRUC-
TION OF LARGE PANEL STRUCTURES (Recommandations internationales unifiées
pour le calcul et l'éxécution des constructions en panneaux assemblés de grand format),
Comité Européen du Béton, Paris, France; Cement and Concrete Association, London,
England. (21E, 26)

CEB, 1970
INTERNATIONAL RECOMMENDATIONS FOR THE DESIGN AND CONSTRUC-
TION OF CONCRETE STRUCTURES, Comité Européen du Béton, Paris, France. (23)

CEB, 1971
CONTRIBUTION TO THE PREPARATION OF THE CEB-FIP FLEXURE-COM-
PRESSION DESIGN HANDBOOK (in French), Bulletin d'information no. 75, Comité
Européen du Béton, Paris, France. (21D)

CEB, 1972a
CEB-FIP HANDBOOK—BUCKLING (Manuel de calcul CEB-FIP—Flambement), Bulletin d'information no. 79, Comité Européen du Béton, Paris, France. (23)

CEB, 1972b
COMPLEMENTARY DOCUMENTATION TO THE CEB-FIP FLEXURE-COMPRES-
SION DESIGN HANDBOOK (Documentation complementaire au manuel de calcul
CEB-FIP flexion-compression), Bulletin d'information no. 83, Comité Européen du
Béton, Paris, France. (21D)

CEB, 1973
LATERAL BUCKLING HANDBOOK (Manuel de calcul flambement-instabilité), Final
Draft, Bulletin d'information no. 93, Comité Européen du Béton, Paris, France. (21D)

CEB, 1977
INTERNATIONAL SYSTEM OF UNIFIED TECHNICAL REGULATIONS FOR
STRUCTURES: MODEL CODE FOR STRUCTURES IN CONCRETE, Comité
Européen du Béton, Paris, France. (24)

CEB/CIB/UEAtc, 1969
INTERNATIONAL RECOMMENDATIONS FOR ANALYZING AND TESTING
LARGE PANEL STRUCTURES (Recommandations internationales pour le calcul et
l'éxécution des structures en panneaux), Comité Européen du Béton, Paris, France. (21E,
22)

CEB-FIP, 1970a
INTERNATIONAL RECOMMENDATIONS FOR THE DESIGN AND CONSTRUC-
TION OF CONCRETE STRUCTURES, Bulletin d'information nos. 72 and 73, Comité
Européen du Béton, Paris, France; 6th Congress of the Fédération Internationale de la
Précontrainte, Prague, Czechoslovakia; Cement and Concrete Association, London,
England. (21D, 25, 26)

CEB-FIP, 1970b
INTERNATIONAL RECOMMENDATIONS FOR THE DESIGN AND CONSTRUC-
TION OF CONCRETE STRUCTURES, APPENDIX 3—INTERNATIONAL REC-
OMMENDATIONS FOR THE DESIGN AND CONSTRUCTION OF DEEP BEAMS,
Bulletin d'information no. 73, Comité Européen du Béton-Fédération Internationale de la
Précontrainte, Paris, France, pp. 17–24. (21D)

CIB, 1964
METHODS OF DESIGN OF MASONRY WALLS, Transactions of the International
Building Council, Vol. 68. (27)

CP 110, 1972
See British Standard, 1972.

CP 111, 1970
STRUCTURAL RECOMMENDATIONS FOR LOAD-BEARING WALLS (PART 2),
with Amendment Slip No. 1 of 11 June 1971, British Standards Institution, London,
England. (27)

CRSI, 1972
CRSI DESIGN HANDBOOK, Concrete Reinforcing Steel Institute, Chicago, Ill. (21D)

CUR, 1956
INVESTIGATION OF ADMISSIBLE CRACK WIDTH IN REINFORCED CON-
CRETE STRUCTURES, Report No. 10, Netherlands Committee for Concrete Research
(Commissie voor uitvoering van research ingesteld door de betonvereniging), Amsterdam,
The Netherlands. (25)

Cajert, A. and Losberg, A., 1973
  LATERALLY LOADED LIGHT EXPANDED CLAY BLOCK MASONRY: THE
  EFFECT OF REINFORCEMENT IN HORIZONTAL JOINTS, Proceedings of the 3rd
  International Brick Masonry Conference, Bundesverband der Deutschen Ziegelindustrie
  e.V., Essen, Germany. (27)
Campbell-Allen, D., 1963
  CREEP AND SHRINKAGE IN CONCRETE AS INFLUENCED BY CONCRETE
  PRACTICE AND ENVIRONMENT, Constructional Review, Australia, No. 12, p. 6. (25)
Campus, F. and Massonnet, C., 1956
  RESEARCH ON THE BUCKLING OF I-COLUMNS IN A37 STEEL OBLIQUELY
  LOADED (in French), Bulletin no. 17, Comptes Rendus des Recherches, IRSIA,
  Brussels, Belgium, p. 219. (23)
Canadian Capitol Chapter ACI, 1972
  MODELS IN STRUCTURAL ENGINEERING, Proceedings of Symposium held at
  Montréal, Canada, in October 1972. (A38)
Canadian Structural Design Manual, 1970
  SUPPLEMENT NO. 4 TO NATIONAL BUILDING CODE OF CANADA. (27)
Cantor, I. G., Lombardi, M. W. and Dirkse, D., 1970
  THREE HIGH-BOND MORTAR APPLICATIONS, Proceedings of the 2nd International
  Brick Masonry Conference, H. W. H. West and K. H. Speed, eds., British Ceramic
  Research Association, Stoke-on-Trent, England, 1971. (27)
Capon, M. J. F. and Diaz de Cossio, R., 1965
  DIAGONAL TENSION IN CONCRETE MEMBERS OF CIRCULAR SECTION (in
  Spanish), Revista Ingenieria, Mexico, April 1965, p. 257. (21D)
Cardenas, A. E. and Magura, D. D., 1973
  STRENGTH OF HIGH-RISE SHEAR WALLS—RECTANGULAR CROSS SECTIONS,
  Response of Multistory Concrete Structures to Lateral Forces, Publication No. SP-36,
  American Concrete Institute, pp. 119–150. (21D, 22)
Cardenas, A. E., Hanson, J., Corley, W. G. and Hognestad, E., 1973
  DESIGN PROVISIONS FOR SHEAR WALLS, ACI Journal, American Concrete Institute,
  Vol. 70, No. 3, pp. 221–230. (21D, 21E, 22)
Carlson, E. Y., 1976
  UNIT MASONRY—TODAY AND TOMORROW, Proceedings of the 1st Canadian
  Masonry Symposium, E. L. Jessop and M. A. Ward, eds., University of Calgary, Canada.
  (27)
Carneiro, F. L. L. B., 1962
  REPORT OF BENDING EXPERIMENTS ON THREE SERIES OF REINFORCED
  CONCRETE BEAMS, National Institute of Technology, Brazil. (22)
Carneiro, L. L. B., 1965
  GALILEO, FOUNDER OF THE SCIENCE OF THE STRENGTH OF MATERIALS,
  RILEM Bulletin No. 27, pp. 100–119. (A38)
Carpena, A., 1972
  STABILITY, Proceedings, 6th National/Regional Conference (Delft, The Netherlands,
  May 1972), Joint Committee on Tall Buildings, Lehigh University, Bethlehem, Pa., pp.
  51–53. (23)
Casillas, J., 1963
  LOAD-DEFORMATION CHARACTERISTICS OF SPIRAL CONCRETE COLUMNS
  (in Spanish), Revista Ingenieria, Mexico, Vol. 33, October 1963, p. 373. (21D)
Castellani, A., 1966
  MODEL ANALYSIS OF SHEAR-TYPE BUILDINGS' RESPONSE TO EARTH-
  QUAKE, Meccanica, Vol. 1, No. 3-4. (22)
Castoldi, A., 1973
  NEW TECHNIQUES OF MODEL INVESTIGATION OF THE SEISMIC BEHAVIOR
  OF LARGE STRUCTURES, ISMES Bulletin No. 56, Istituto Sperimentale Modelli e
  Strutture, Bergamo, Italy. (A38)
Cement and Concrete Association of Australia, 1972
  STRUCTURAL MODELS, Proceedings of Conference on Structural Models (Sydney,
  1972), Cement and Concrete Assoc. of Australia in conjunction with Dept. of Archi-
  tectural Science, University of Sydney, and Institution of Engineers, Australia, N.S.W.
  Division. (A38)

Cervenka, V. and Gerstle, K. H., 1972
INELASTIC FINITE ELEMENT ANALYSIS OF REINFORCED CONCRETE PANELS, Publications of IABSE, Zurich, Switzerland. (22)

Chadha, J., 1970
WIND-EXCITED OSCILLATIONS OF CANTILEVER STRUCTURES, *Ontario Hydro Research Quarterly,* Vol. 22, No. 3, pp. 13–17. (21A)

Chamecki, S., 1969
CALCULATION OF PROGRESSIVE SETTLEMENTS OF FOUNDATIONS IN INTERACTION WITH STRUCTURES AND SOIL (in French), Annales de l'institut technique du bâtiment et des travaux publics, Paris, France, No. 251, p. 1321. (21C)

Chan, P. C. K. and Heidebrecht, A. C., 1974
STIFFENING OF SHEAR WALLS, *Canadian Journal of Civil Engineering,* Vol. 1, pp. 85–96. (21C)

Chang, W. F. and Ferguson, P. M., 1963
LONG HINGED REINFORCED CONCRETE COLUMNS, *ACI Journal,* American Concrete Institute, Vol. 60, No. 1. p. 1. (21D)

Charlton, T. M., 1966
MODEL ANALYSIS OF PLANE STRUCTURES, Pergamon Press, Oxford, England. (A38)

Chen, W. F. and Atsuta, T., 1976
THEORY OF BEAM-COLUMNS, VOL. 1, IN-PLANE BEHAVIOR AND DESIGN; VOL. 2, SPACE BEHAVIOR AND DESIGN, McGraw-Hill Book Co., Inc., New York. (23)

Chen, W. F. and Shoraka, M. T., 1975
DESIGN FORMULA FOR BIAXIALLY LOADED CONCRETE COLUMNS, Hellenic Conference on Tall Buildings, 33rd National/Regional Conference (Athens, Greece, October 1975), Technical Chamber of Greece, Athens. (23)

Cheng, H. K., 1973
CONCRETE DESIGN STANDARDS IN ASIA, Planning and Design of Tall Buildings, Proceedings of 1972 ASCE-IABSE International Conference, Vol. III, No. 20-7, ASCE, New York. (20, 26)

Chinn, J. and Zimmerman, R. M., 1965
BEHAVIOR OF PLAIN CONCRETE UNDER VARIOUS TRIAXIAL COMPRESSION LOADING CONDITIONS, Technical Report No. WL-TR-64-163, Air Force Weapons Laboratory, Kirkland Air Force Base, August 1965. (22)

Chitnuyanondh, L. and Campbell, T. I., 1976
SHEAR FAILURE DUE TO WEB CRASHING IN PRESTRESSED CONCRETE BEAMS, Proceedings of the National Structural Engineering Conference on Methods of Structural Analysis (Madison, Wis., August 1976), Vol. I, ASCE, New York, pp. 446–495. (22)

Cholewicki, A., 1969
DEFORMABILITY OF VERTICAL JOINTS AND ITS EFFECT ON THE BEHAVIOR OF PREFABRICATED SHEAR WALLS, CIB Symposium on Bearing Walls, Warsaw, Poland. (21E)

Cholewicki, A., 1971
LOAD-BEARING CAPACITY AND DEFORMABILITY OF VERTICAL JOINTS IN STRUCTURAL WALLS OF LARGE PANEL BUILDINGS, *Building Science,* Pergamon Press, Vol. 5. (21E)

Cholewicki, A., 1972
STATICAL ROLE OF STRUCTURAL CONNECTIONS IN CONCRETE SHEAR WALL OF TALL BUILDINGS, Proceedings of the National Conference on Tall Buildings, 7th National/Regional Conference (Warsaw, Poland, November 1972), Vol. II, pp. 263–277. (21E)

Cholewicki, A. and Galkowski, Z., 1972
DISTRIBUTION OF WIND FORCES ON SHEAR WALLS IN A SKELETAL TALL BUILDING, Proceedings of National Conference on Tall Buildings, Vol. II, 7th National/Regional Conference (Warsaw, Poland, November 27–30, 1972), Warsaw Technical University, Polish Group of IABSE, ASCE-IABSE Joint Committee on Planning and Design of Tall Buildings, pp. 279–287. (21C)

Cholewicki, A. and Galkowski, Z., 1975
  THREE-DIMENSIONAL CONTINUUM MODEL OF BUILDING STRUCTURE,
  Proceedings of CIB 2nd International Symposium on Bearing Walls (Warsaw, Poland,
  September 1975), Theme 2, Paper No. 3, pp. 141–155. (21E)
Chopra, A., Bertero, V. V., Mahin, S. and Collins, R., 1976
  RESPONSE OF THE OLIVE VIEW HOSPITAL MAIN BUILDING DURING SAN
  FERNANDO EARTHQUAKE, Report No. EERC-76-22, Earthquake Engineering
  Research Center, University of California, Berkeley, Calif. (22)
Choudhury, J. R., 1974
  ELASTIC ANALYSIS OF SPATIAL SYSTEMS OF INTERCONNECTED SHEAR
  WALLS AND FRAMES, Proceedings, Conference on Tall Buildings, Bangkok, Thai-
  land. (21C)
Chow, L., Conway, H. D. and Winter, G., 1952
  STRESSES IN DEEP BEAMS, Transactions, ASCE, Paper 2557. (21D)
Cizek, P., 1973
  SOME SYSTEMS OF TALL REINFORCED CONCRETE BUILDINGS IN CZECH-
  OSLOVAKIA, Proceedings, Regional Conference on the Planning and Design of Tall
  Buildings (Bratislava, Czechoslovakia, 1973). (24)
Clark, L. E., Gerstle, K. H. and Tulin, L. G., 1967
  EFFECT OF STRAIN GRADIENT ON THE STRESS-STRAIN CURVE OF MORTAR
  AND CONCRETE, ACI Journal, American Concrete Institute, Vol. 64, No. 9. (22)
Clark, W. J. and MacGregor, J. G., 1968
  ANALYSIS OF REINFORCED CONCRETE SHEAR WALL-FRAME STRUCTURES,
  Structural Engineering Report No. 16, Dept. of Civil Engineering, University of Alberta,
  Edmonton, Canada. (22)
Clough, R. W. and Johnston, S., 1966
  EFFECT OF STIFFNESS DEGRADATION ON EARTHQUAKE DUCTILITY RE-
  QUIREMENTS, Proceedings of Symposium on Earthquake Engineering, Tokyo, Japan,
  pp. 227–232. (22)
Clough, R. W. and King, I. P., 1964
  ANALYSIS OF THREE-DIMENSIONAL BUILDING FRAMES, Publications of
  IABSE, Zurich, Switzerland, Vol. 24, p. 15. (21C)
Clough, R. W., King, I. P. and Wilson, E. L., 1964
  STRUCTURAL ANALYSIS OF MULTISTORY BUILDINGS, Journal of the Structural
  Division, ASCE, Vol. 90, No. ST3, Proc. Paper 3925, p. 19. (21C)
Cohen, E., 1973
  U.S.A. STRUCTURAL STANDARDS FOR REINFORCED CONCRETE, Planning and
  Design of Tall Buildings, Proceedings of 1972 ASCE-IABSE International Conference,
  Vol. III, No. 20-1, ASCE, New York, (20, 26)
Cohn, M. Z., 1962a
  Discussion of "ULTIMATE LOAD DESIGN OF CONCRETE STRUCTURES (ICE
  Research Committee Report)," Proceedings, Institution of Civil Engineers, London, Vol.
  23, pp. 234–245. (22)
Cohn, M. Z., 1962b
  LIMIT DESIGN OF REINFORCED CONCRETE STRUCTURES FOR MAXIMUM
  YIELD SAFETY, Indian Concrete Journal, Vol. 36, No. 6, pp. 214–224. (22)
Cohn, M. Z., 1964
  ROTATION COMPATIBILITY IN THE LIMIT DESIGN OF REINFORCED CON-
  CRETE BEAMS, Proceedings of International Symposium on Flexural Mechanics of
  Reinforced Concrete (Miami, Fla.), Publication No. SP-12, American Concrete Institute,
  pp. 359–382. (22)
Cohn, M. Z., 1965
  OPTIMUM LIMIT DESIGN FOR REINFORCED CONCRETE CONTINUOUS
  BEAMS, Proceedings, Institution of Civil Engineers, London, Vol. 30, pp. 675–707. (21B,
  22)
Cohn, M. Z., 1966a
  DESIGN OF PLASTIC FRAMES FOR MAXIMUM YIELD SAFETY, Proceedings of
  the 5th U.S. National Congress on Applied Mechanics, p. 567. (22)
Cohn, M. Z., 1966b
  ON THE OPTIMUM LIMIT DESIGN METHOD, unpublished report to the Joint
  ACI-ASCE Committee 428 (Limit Design), February 1966. (22)

Cohn, M. Z., 1967
LIMIT-DESIGN SOLUTIONS FOR CONCRETE STRUCTURES, *Journal of the Structural Division*, ASCE, Vol. 93, No. ST1, Proc. Paper 5088, pp. 37–57. (22)

Cohn, M. Z., 1968
LIMIT DESIGN OF REINFORCED CONCRETE FRAMES, *Journal of the Structural Division*, ASCE, Vol. 94, No. ST10, Proc. Paper 6197, pp. 2467–2483. (22)

Cohn, M. Z., 1972a
OPTIMAL LIMIT DESIGN FOR CONCRETE STRUCTURES, Symposium on Inelasticity and Nonlinearity in Structural Concrete, Paper 15, SM Study No. 8, University of Waterloo Press, pp. 357–388. (21B, 22)

Cohn, M. Z., 1972b
ANALYSIS AND DESIGN OF INELASTIC STRUCTURES, Vol. 2, Problems, University of Waterloo Press, Waterloo, p. 273. (22)

Cohn, M. Z. (ed.), 1973
INELASTICITY AND NONLINEARITY IN STRUCTURAL CONCRETE, University of Waterloo Press, Waterloo. (22)

Cohn, M. Z., 1974
OPTIMAL DESIGN OF REINFORCED CONCRETE STRUCTURES, unpublished communication to the Joint Committee. (21B)

Cohn, M. Z. and Ghosh, S. K., 1972
THE FLEXURAL DUCTILITY OF REINFORCED CONCRETE SECTIONS, Publications of IABSE, Vol. 32-II. (23)

Cohn, M. Z. and Grierson, D. E., 1968
OPTIMAL DESIGN OF REINFORCED CONCRETE BEAMS AND FRAMES, Final Publications, 8th IABSE Congress, New York, pp. 215–226. (21B, 22)

Cohn, M. Z. and Grierson, D. E., 1970
FURTHER RESULTS ON THE EQUILIBRIUM METHOD OF LIMIT DESIGN, *Proceedings*, Institution of Civil Engineers, London, Vol. 46, pp. 143–168. (22)

Cohn, M. Z. and Petcu, V. A., 1960
ON THE INFLUENCE OF STEEL PERCENTAGE ON THE PLASTIC ADAPTABILITY OF REDUNDANT REINFORCED CONCRETE BEAMS, Bulletin de l'Academie Polonaise des Sciences, Série des Sciences Techniques, Vol. 8, No. 11–12, pp. 713–721. (22)

Cohn, M. Z. and Petcu, V. A., 1963
MOMENT REDISTRIBUTION AND ROTATION CAPACITY OF PLASTIC HINGES IN REDUNDANT REINFORCED CONCRETE BEAMS, *Indian Concrete Journal*, Vol. 37, No. 8, pp. 282–290. (22)

Cohn, M. Z., Burnett, F. P. and Grierson, D. E., 1969
SAFETY, SERVICEABILITY AND EFFICIENCY OF LIMIT DESIGN FOR REINFORCED CONCRETE BEAMS AND FRAMES, Publications of IABSE, Zurich, Switzerland, 29.I, pp. 17–32. (22)

Cohn, M. Z., Burnett, E. F., Grierson, D. E., Dutt, O., Francis, R., Parameswar, H. C. and Talwar, S., 1970
APPLICATION OF LIMIT DESIGN TO REINFORCED CONCRETE BUILDING STRUCTURES, *Proceedings*, Institution of Civil Engineers, London, Supplement xvii, pp. 375–414. (22)

Colaco, J. P., 1970
END MOMENTS FOR FLOOR BEAMS FRAMING INTO SPANDRELS, *ACI Journal*, American Concrete Institute, Vol. 67, No. 10. (21D)

Colaco, J. P., 1971
PRELIMINARY DESIGN OF HIGH RISE BUILDINGS WITH SHEAR WALLS, *ACI Journal*, American Concrete Institute, Vol. 68, No. 1, pp. 26–31. (21A)

Colaco, J. P., 1973
CONCRETE FLOOR SYSTEMS, Planning and Design of Tall Buildings, Proceedings of 1972 ASCE-IABSE International Conference, Vol. III, No. 21-6, ASCE, New York. (21A)

Colaco, J. P. and Banavalkar, P. V., 1974
THE PRELIMINARY SELECTION OF STIFFNESS IN UNSYMMETRICAL TALL CONCRETE BUILDINGS, presented at the ASCE Structural Engineering Conference (Cincinnati, Ohio, April 1974). (24)

Collins, M. P. and Lambert, P., 1971
REDISTRIBUTION OF MOMENT OF CRACKING, Publication No. 71-21, Dept. of Civil Engineering, University of Toronto, Canada. (22)

Constructional Review, 1961
EXPERIMENTAL LIGHTWEIGHT FLAT PLATE STRUCTURE—PART III, LONG-TERM DEFORMATIONS, Vol. 34, No. 4, p. 21. (25)

Constructional Review, 1974a
PRECAST SHEAR WALL, Vol. 47, February 1974. (21E)

Constructional Review, 1974b
MLC PROJECT, SYDNEY, Vol. 47, No. 3, September 1974. (21E)

Converse, F. J., 1946
TESTS ON REINFORCED CONCRETE MASONRY, *Building Standards Monthly*, February 1946. (27)

Corley, W. G., 1966
ROTATIONAL CAPACITY OF REINFORCED CONCRETE BEAMS, *Journal of the Structural Division*, ASCE, Vol. 92, No. ST5, Proc. Paper 4939, p. 121. (22)

Corley, W. G. and Hanson, N. W., 1969
DESIGN OF BEAM-COLUMN JOINTS FOR SEISMIC RESISTANT REINFORCED CONCRETE FRAMES, Proceedings of 4th World Conference on Earthquake Engineering (Santiago, Chile, January 1969), Vol. II, pp. B–3, 69–82. (21D, 22)

Corley, W. G. and Hawkins, N. M., 1968
SHEARHEAD REINFORCEMENT FOR SLABS, *ACI Journal*, American Concrete Institute, Vol. 65, No. 10, p. 811. (21D)

Cornell, C. A., 1969
A PROBABILITY BASED STRUCTURAL CODE, *ACI Journal*, American Concrete Institute, Vol. 66, No. 12. (26)

Corradi, L., DeDonato, O. and Maier, G., 1972
DEVELOPMENTS IN THE IMPOSED ROTATIONS METHOD FOR THE INELASTIC ANALYSIS OF REINFORCED CONCRETE FRAMES, Technical Report, ISTC, Politecnico di Milano, Italy. (22)

Corsmit, E. J. A., 1968
THE PROVISIONAL DUTCH CODE OF PRACTICE FOR THE DESIGN OF PRECAST CONCRETE STRUCTURES, AND SOME DETAILS OF RELATED RESEARCH, *Design Philosophy and its Application to Precast Concrete Structures*, Cement and Concrete Association, London. (21E)

Cortes, R., 1973
STRUCTURAL ANALYSIS AND DESIGN OF LAS AMERICAS (Puntos de Interes en el Diseno de Edificios de Altura), National Seminar on Tall Buildings (Memorias Del Seminario Nacional Sobre Edificios De Gran Altura), 16th National/Regional Conference (Bogotá, Colombia, September 24–29, 1973), Escuela Colombiana De Ingenieria, Bogotá, pp. 211–220. (21C)

Coull, A., 1966
TESTS ON A MODEL SHEAR WALL STRUCTURE, *Civil Engineering and Public Works Review*, London, Vol. 61, pp. 1129–33. (21D, A38)

Coull, A., 1971
STRENGTH OF SECTIONS AND CONNECTIONS—ULTIMATE STRENGTH DESIGN, 5th Regional Conference Proceedings, 5th National/Regional Conference (Chicago, Ill., November 29–December 1, 1971), Joint Committee on Tall Buildings, Lehigh University, Bethlehem, Pa., pp. 78–80. (21A, 21C)

Coull, A., 1974a
PIERCED SHEAR WALLS OF STEPWISE VARIABLE THICKNESS, *Journal of the Structural Division*, ASCE, Vol. 100, No. ST5, Proc. Paper 10536, p. 1157. (21C)

Coull, A., 1974b
STIFFENING OF COUPLED SHEAR WALLS AGAINST FOUNDATION MOVEMENT, *The Structural Engineer*, Vol. 46, pp. 23–26. (21C)

Coull, A. and Chantaksinopas, B., 1974
DESIGN CURVES FOR COUPLED SHEAR WALLS ON FLEXIBLE BASES, *Proceedings,* Institution of Civil Engineers, London, Vol. 57, Part 2. (21C)

Coull, A. and Choudhury, J. R., 1967
ANALYSIS OF COUPLED SHEAR WALLS, *ACI Journal*, American Concrete Institute, Vol. 64, No. 9, p. 587. (21C)

Coull, A. and Irwin, A. W., 1970
ANALYSIS OF LOAD DISTRIBUTION IN MULTI-STOREY SHEAR WALL STRUC-
TURES, The Structural Engineer, Vol. 48, p. 301. (21C)
Coull, A. and Irwin, A. W., 1972
MODEL INVESTIGATIONS OF SHEAR WALL STRUCTURES, Journal of the Struc-
tural Division, ASCE, Vol. 98, No. ST6, Proc. Paper 8936, pp. 1223–1237. (A38)
Coull, A. and Mukherjee, P. R., 1974
COUPLED SHEAR WALLS WITH GENERAL SUPPORT CONDITIONS, Proceedings
of Conference on Tall Buildings, 25th National/Regional Conference (Kuala Lumpur,
Malaysia, December 2–5, 1974), Institution of Engineers, Kuala Lumpur, pp. 4–24-4–31.
(21C)
Coull, A. and Stafford-Smith, B., 1967
TALL BUILDINGS, Proceedings of Symposium on Tall Buildings held at University of
Southampton in 1966, Pergamon Press, London, England. (21C, 21D)
Coull, A. and Stafford-Smith, B., 1973
TORSION ANALYSIS OF SYMMETRIC BUILDING STRUCTURES, Journal of the
Structural Division, ASCE, Vol. 99, No. ST1, Proc. Paper 9464, p. 229. (21C)
Coull, A. and Subedi, N. K., 1971
FRAMED-TUBE STRUCTURES FOR HIGH-RISE BUILDINGS, Journal of the Struc-
tural Division, ASCE, Vol. 97, No. ST8, Proc. Paper 8301, pp. 2097–2105. (21C, 24)
Cowan, H. J., 1961a
THE USE OF STRUCTURAL MODELS IN ARCHITECTURE, Bulletin, International
Council for Building Research Studies and Documentation (CIB), No. 3, pp. 19–20. (A38)
Cowan, H. J., 1961b
SOME APPLICATIONS OF THE USE OF DIRECT MODEL ANALYSIS IN THE
DESIGN OF ARCHITECTURAL STRUCTURES, Journal, Institution of Engineers,
Australia, Vol. 33, pp. 259–267. (A38)
Cowan, H. J., 1972
WHAT CAN WE DO WITH STRUCTURAL MODELS? Journal, Institution of Engi-
neers, Australia, Vol. 44, No. 9, pp. 15–22. (A38)
Cowan, H. J., Gero, J. S., Ding, G. D. and Muncey, R. W., 1968
MODELS IN ARCHITECTURE, Elsevier, London, England. (A38)
Cranston, W. B., 1965
A COMPUTER METHOD FOR INELASTIC ANALYSIS OF PLANE FRAMES,
Technical Report TRA 336, Cement and Concrete Association, London, England. (22)
Cranston, W. B., 1966
DETERMINING THE RELATION BETWEEN MOMENT, AXIAL LOAD, AND
CURVATURE FOR STRUCTURAL MEMBERS, Technical Report, Cement and
Concrete Association, London, England. (23)
Cranston, W. B., 1970
THE INFLUENCE OF SHEAR ON THE ROTATION CAPACITY OF REINFORCED
CONCRETE BEAMS, Technical Report TRA 439, Cement and Concrete Association,
London, England. (22)
Cranston, W. B., 1972
ANALYSIS AND DESIGN OF REINFORCED CONCRETE COLUMNS, Research
Report 20, Cement and Concrete Association, London, England. (21D, 23)
Cranston, W. B. and Chatterji, A. K., 1970
COMPUTER ANALYSES OF REINFORCED CONCRETE PORTAL FRAMES WITH
FIXED FEET, Technical Report TRA 444, Cement and Concrete Association, London,
England. (22)
Creus, G. J., 1971
CREEP BUCKLING OF CONCRETE COLUMNS, SOME THEORETICAL AND
EXPERIMENTAL RESULTS, Proceedings of RILEM International Symposium
(Buenos Aires, Argentina, 1971), Vol. 3, p. 65. (21D)
Crisfield, M. A. and Twemlow, R. P., 1971
EQUIVALENT PLATE APPROACH FOR THE ANALYSIS OF CELLULAR STRUC-
TURES, Civil Engineering and Public Works Review, Vol. 66, No. 776, pp. 259–263. (21A)
Csekme, I., 1973
THE SPREADING OF MONOLITHIC PREFABRICATED PARTS (WALLS AND
CEILINGS) MADE OF THIN-WALLED COARSE HOLE BRICKS IN HUNGARY
[Die Verbreitung monolithischer, vorgefertigter Bauteile (Wande und Decken) aus

dunnwandigen Grosslochziegeln in Ungarn], Proceedings of the 3rd International Brick Masonry Conference, Bundesverband der Deutschen Ziegelindustrie e.V., Essen, Germany. (27)

Curtin, W. G., 1968
THE PROBLEMS OF SUPERVISION OF CALCULATED LONG-BEARING BRICK-WORK, *Proceedings*, British Ceramic Society, No. 11. (27)

Cusens, A. R., 1966
ANALYSIS OF SLABLESS STAIRS, *Concrete and Constructional Engineering*, Vol. 61, No. 10, pp. 359–364. (21D)

Cusens, A. R., 1975
PRECAST CONCRETE STRUCTURES, unpublished communication to the Joint Committee, September 1975. (21E)

Cusens, A. R. and Kuang, J. G., 1965
ANALYSIS OF FREE STANDING STAIRS UNDER SYMMETRICAL LOADING, *Concrete and Constructional Engineering*, Vol. 60, No. 5. pp. 167–172. (21D)

Cusens, A. R. and Santathadaporn, S., 1966
DESIGN CHARTS FOR HELICAL STAIRS WITH FIXED SUPPORTS, Concrete Publications, Ltd., Cement and Concrete Association, London, England. (21D)

Cutler, J. F., Plewes, W. G. and Mikluchin, P. T., 1970
THE DEVELOPMENT OF THE CANADIAN BUILDING CODE FOR MASONRY, Proceedings of the 2nd International Brick Masonry Conference, H. W. H. West and K. H. Speed, eds., British Ceramic Research Association, Stoke-on-Trent, England, 1971. (27)

Cziesielski, E., 1966
COMPUTATIONS FOR LARGE PANEL WALLS CONSISTING OF INDIVIDUAL WALL ELEMENTS CONNECTED INTO A LARGE SHEAR WALL (Berechnung von Wanden des Grosstafelbaues die aus mehreren Einzelwanden zu einer grossen Wandscheibe zusammengeschlossen werden), *Die Bautechnik*, No. 3. (21E)

DIN 105, 1969
MASONRY BRICKS: SOLID AND PERFORATED BRICKS (Mauerziegel, Vollziegel und Lochziegel), Beuth-Vertrieb, Berlin, Germany. (27)

DIN 106, 1972
SAND-LIME BRICKS: SOLID AND PERFORATED BRICKS (Kalksandsteine: Voll-, Loch-, und Hohlbocksteine), Beuth-Vertrieb, Berlin, Germany. (27)

DIN 398, 1976
GRANULATED SLAG AGGREGATE CONCRETE BLOCKS (Huttensteine: Voll-, Loch-, und Hohlblocksteine), Beuth-Vertrieb, Berlin, Germany. (27)

DIN 1053, 1974
MASONRY, DESIGN AND CONSTRUCTION (Mauerwerk, Berechnung und Ausfuhrung), Beuth-Vertrieb, Berlin, Germany. (27)

DIN 4165, 1973
BUILDING BLOCKS MADE FROM STEAM CURED CELLULAR LIGHT WEIGHT CONCRETE (Gasbetonblocksteine), Beuth-Vertrieb, Berlin, Germany. (27)

DIN 18149, 1975
PERFORATED LIGHT WEIGHT CONCRETE BLOCKS (Lochsteine aus Leichtbeton), Beuth-Vertrieb, Berlin, Germany. (27)

DIN 18151, 1975
HOLLOW LIGHT WEIGHT CONCRETE BLOCKS (Hohlblocksteine aus Leichtbeton), Beuth-Vertrieb, Berlin, Germany. (27)

DIN 18152, 1971
SOLID LIGHT WEIGHT CONCRETE BLOCKS (Vollsteine aus Leichtbeton), Beuth-Vertrieb, Berlin, Germany. (27)

DIN 18153, 1972
HOLLOW CONCRETE BLOCKS AND HOLLOW CONCRETE BLOCKS WITH T-SECTION (Hohlblocksteine und T-Hohlsteine aus Beton mit geschlossenem Gefüge), Beuth-Vertrieb, Berlin, Germany. (27)

DIN 18554, 1971
BRICKWORK: TESTING OF WALLS AND PILLARS (Mauerwerk: Ermittlung der Tragfahigkeit von Wanden und Pfeilern), Beuth-Vertrieb, Berlin, Germany. (27)

Da Costa, A., 1974
CALCULATION OF HIGH BUILDINGS FOR LOADS DURING CONSTRUCTION, Regional Conference on Tall Buildings, 15th National/Regional Conference (Madrid, Spain, September 17–19, 1973), Tipografia Artistica, Alameda 12, Madrid, pp. 127–143. (21C)

Dally, J. W. and Riley, W. F., 1965
EXPERIMENTAL STRESS ANALYSIS, McGraw-Hill Book Co., Inc., New York. (A38)

Danay, A., Gellert, M. and Glück, J., 1974
THE AXIAL STRAIN EFFECTS ON LOAD DISTRIBUTION IN NON-SYMMETRIC TIER BUILDINGS, Building Science, London, Vol. 9, March, p. 29. (21C)

Darwin, D. and Pecknold, D. A., 1976
ANALYSIS OF RC SHEAR PANELS UNDER CYCLIC LOADING, Journal of the Structural Division, ASCE, Vol. 102, No. ST2, Proc. Paper 11896, pp. 355–369. (21C)

Davey, N. and Thomas, F. G., 1950
THE STRUCTURAL USES OF BRICKWORK, Structural and Building Paper No. 24, Institution of Civil Engineers, London, England. (27)

Davies, J. D. and Preece, B. W., 1966
COMPARATIVE TESTS ON BRICKWORK PANELS REINFORCED WITH "STEEL-FORCE," Civil Engineering and Public Works Review, Vol. 61, September 1966. (27)

Davis, R., 1976
PHILOSOPHY AND PRACTICE OF JOB-SITE INSPECTION, Proceedings of the 1st Canadian Masonry Symposium, E. L. Jessop and M. A. Ward, eds., University of Calgary, Canada. (27)

Davison, J. I., 1976
MORTAR TECHNOLOGY, Proceedings of the 1st Canadian Masonry Symposium, E. L. Jessop and M. A. Ward, eds., University of Calgary, Canada. (27)

De Donato, O. and Franchi, A., 1973
A MODIFIED GRADIENT METHOD FOR FINITE ELEMENT ELASTOPLASTIC ANALYSIS BY QUADRATIC PROGRAMMING, Computer Methods in Applied Mechanics and Engineering, Vol. 2, No. 2. (22)

De Donato, O. and Maier, G., 1970
MATHEMATICAL PROGRAMMING METHODS FOR THE INELASTIC ANALYSIS OF REINFORCED CONCRETE FRAMES ALLOWING FOR LIMITED ROTATION CAPACITY, Technical Report No. 487, ISTC, Politecnico di Milano, Italy. (22)

De Donato, O. and Maier, G., 1973
BOUNDS ON TOTAL DYNAMIC DEFLECTIONS OF ELASTOPLASTIC STRUCTURES ALLOWING FOR SECOND-ORDER GEOMETRIC EFFECTS, Technical Report No. 17, ISTC, Politecnico di Milano, Italy. (22)

De Paiva, H. A. R. and Siess, C. P., 1965
STRENGTH AND BEHAVIOR OF DEEP BEAMS IN SHEAR, Journal of the Structural Division, ASCE, Vol. 91, No. ST5, Proc. Paper 4496. (21D, 22)

Derecho, A. T., 1973
FRAMES AND FRAME-SHEARWALL SYSTEMS, Publication No. SP-36-2, American Concrete Institute, pp. 13–37. (21B)

Deschapelles, B., 1973
METHODS OF ANALYSIS, Planning and Design of Tall Buildings, Proceedings of 1972 ASCE-IABSE International Conference, Vol. III, No. 21-D12, ASCE, New York. (21C, 24)

DeSimone, V. J. and Camellerie, J. F., 1965
NOVEL STRUCTURAL FRAME COMBINED WITH SLIP-FORM RESULTS IN RECORD BREAKING CONSTRUCTION, ACI Journal, American Concrete Institute, Vol. 62, No. 10. (21B)

Despeyroux, J., 1968
STRUCTURAL CONNECTION PROBLEMS AND THE USE OF SPECIAL MATERIALS IN PRECAST CONCRETE CONSTRUCTION, Design Philosophy and its Application to Precast Concrete Structures, Proceedings of Symposium (London, England, May 1967), Cement and Concrete Association, London. (21E)

Despeyroux, J., 1973
THEME REPORT: COMMENTARY ON STRUCTURAL STANDARDS, Planning and Design of Tall Buildings, Proceedings of 1972 ASCE-IABSE International Conference, Vol. III, No. 20-Theme, ASCE, New York. (20, 26)

Despeyroux, J., 1975
CONSTRUCTION OF PREFABRICATED PANELS IN TALL BUILDINGS, Hellenic Conference on Tall Buildings, 33rd National/Regional Conference (Athens, Greece, October 1975). (21E)

Deutsche Bauzeitschrift, 1973
TOWN HALL OFFENBACH/MAIN (Rathaus Offenbach/Main), No. 9, pp. 1639–1644. (21E)

Diamant, R. M. E., 1968
INDUSTRIALIZED BUILDING, Iliffe Books Ltd., London, England. (21E)

Dicke, D., 1974
Communication with Dr. Aas-Jakobsen, September 1974. (23)

Dickey, W. L., 1973a
HIGH RISE LOAD BEARING CONCEPT, Proceedings of the 3rd International Brick Masonry Conference, Bundesverband der Deutschen Ziegelindustrie e.V., Essen, Germany. (27)

Dickey, W. L., 1973b
MASONRY WALL BEAMS, Proceedings of the 3rd International Brick Masonry Conference, Bundesverband der Deutschen Ziegelindustrie e.V., Essen, Germany. (27)

Dickey, W. L., 1973c
MASONRY AND EARTHQUAKES, Proceedings of the 3rd International Brick Masonry Conference, Bundesverband der Deutschen Ziegelindustrie e.V., Essen, Germany. (27)

Dickey, W. L., 1973d
MASONRY—REINFORCED VS. PARTIALLY REINFORCED, Proceedings of the 3rd International Brick Masonry Conference, Bundesverband der Deutschen Ziegelindustrie e.v. Essen, Germany. (27)

Dickey, W. L., 1976
HISTORY AND DEVELOPMENT OF HOLLOW BRICK FOR REINFORCEMENT, Proceedings of the 4th International Brick Masonry Conference, Groupement National de l'Industrie de la Terre Cuite, rue de Poissoniers 13, Brussels, Belgium. (27)

Dickie, J. F., Morris, M. C. and Poskitt, T. J., 1974
AN UNUSUAL GLASS TOWER STRUCTURE, Proceedings, 22nd National/Regional Conference (Bangkok, Thailand, January 1974), Asian Institute of Technology, Bangkok, Thailand, pp. 151–161. (23)

Dickson, M. G. T. and Nilson, A. H., 1970
ANALYSIS OF CELLULAR BUILDINGS FOR LATERAL LOADS, ACI Journal, American Concrete Institute, Vol. 67, No. 12, pp. 963–966. (21A)

Dikkers, R. D. and Yokel, F. Y., 1970
STRENGTH OF BRICK WALLS SUBJECT TO AXIAL COMPRESSION AND BENDING, Proceedings of the 2nd International Brick Masonry Conference, H. W. H. West and K. H. Speed, eds., British Ceramic Research Association, Stoke-on-Trent, England, 1971. (27)

Dilger, W., 1967
INITIAL AND SUBSEQUENT DEFLECTIONS DUE TO SHEAR (Anfangliche und nachtrögliche Infolge Querkraft), Beton- und Stahlbetonbau, Vol. 62, No. 9. (22)

Dilger, W. and Neville, A. M., 1971
CREEP BUCKLING OF LONG COLUMNS, The Structural Engineer, Vol. 49, May 1971, p. 223. (21D)

Dischinger, F., 1932
A CONTRIBUTION TO THE THEORY OF SEMI-INFINITE PLATES AND WALL-LIKE BEAMS (Beitrag zur Theorie der Halbscheibe und des Wandartigen Balkens), IVBH, Bd. I, Zurich, Switzerland. (21D)

Dischinger, F., 1937
INVESTIGATIONS ON STABILITY, ELASTIC AND TIME-DEPENDENT DEFLECTIONS OF CONCRETE BRIDGES (Untersuchungen über die Knicksicherheit, die elastische Verformung und das Kriechen des Betons bei Bogenbrucken), Der Bauingenieur. (23, 25)

Distefano, J. N., 1965
CREEP BUCKLING OF SLENDER COLUMNS, Journal of the Structural Division, ASCE, Vol. 91, No. ST3, Proc. Paper 4369. (21D)

Ditlevsen, O., 1973
STRUCTURAL RELIABILITY AND THE INVARIANCE PROBLEM, Report No. 22, Solid Mechanics Division, Waterloo. (26)

Driscoll, G. C., Jr., Armacost, J. O. and Hansell, W. L., 1970
PLASTIC DESIGN OF MULTISTORY FRAMES BY COMPUTER, *Journal of the Structural Division*, ASCE, Vol. 96, No. ST1, Proc. Paper 6995, p. 17. (23)

Drossel, M. R., 1976
DOUBLE-TEAMING CASTING TECHNIQUES ERECT BUILDING FAST, *Construction Methods and Equipment*, April 1976, pp. 57–60. (21E)

Drysdale, R. G., 1976
DESIGN OF MASONRY WALLS AND COLUMNS FOR COMBINED AXIAL LOAD AND BENDING MOMENT, Proceedings of the 1st Canadian Masonry Symposium, E. L. Jessop and M. A. Ward, eds., University of Calgary, Canada. (27)

Drysdale, R. G. and Huggins, M. W., 1971
SUSTAINED BIAXIAL LOAD ON SLENDER CONCRETE COLUMNS, *Journal of the Structural Division*, ASCE, Vol. 97, No. ST5, Proc. Paper 8103, p. 1423. (21D)

Duarte, T. T., Franca, V. and Carvalho, E. C., 1975
SEISMIC STUDY OF SOL-MAR BUILDING (Estudos Sísmicos do Edifício Sol-Mar), Report, Laboratório Nacional de Engenharia Civil, Lisbon, Portugal. (A38)

Duhrkop, H., 1973
INFLUENCE OF AN ADDITIONAL COMPOUND ON THE MECHANICAL CHARACTERISTIC OF WALL-MORTAR AND MASONRY (Einfluss eines Zusatzmittels auf die mechanischen Eigenschaften von Mauermortelm und Mauerwerk), Proceedings of the 3rd International Brick Masonry Conference, Bundesverband der Deutschen Ziegelindustrie e.V., Essen, Germany. (27)

Dunbar, N. F., 1973
A MEDLEY OF PRECAST AND PRESTRESSED CONCRETE SYSTEMS, *Journal of the Prestressed Concrete Institute*, Vol. 18, No. 2, pp. 78–86. (21E)

Dunstone, P. H., 1970
COMPARATIVE PRICES OF LOAD-BEARING BRICKWORK AND CONCRETE WALLING, *Proceedings*, British Ceramic Society, No. 17. (27)

Durelli, A. J. and Parks, V. J., 1970
MOIRÉ ANALYSIS OF STRAIN, Prentice-Hall, Inc., Englewood Cliffs, NJ. (A38)

Edwards, T., 1973
RECENT ADVANCES IN CLAY BRICK MANUFACTURE, Structural Brickwork Seminar, Macquarie University, Sydney, Australia, February 1973. (27)

Ehm, H., 1973
ACTUAL POSITION OF THE STANDARDIZATION IN ACOUSTIC INSULATION AND EFFECTS ON THE MASONRY CONSTRUCTION (Stand der Normung im Schallschutz und Auswirkung auf den Mauerwerksbau), Proceedings of the 3rd International Brick Masonry Conference, Bundesverband der Deutschen Ziegelindustrie e.V., Essen, Germany. (27)

Eiklid, G. E., Gerstle, K. H. and Tulin, L. G., 1969
STRAIN-HARDENING EFFECTS IN REINFORCED CONCRETE, *Magazine of Concrete Research*, Vol. 21, No. 69. (22)

Ellingwood, B. R. and Ang, A. H. S., 1972
A PROBABILISTIC STUDY OF SAFETY CRITERIA FOR DESIGN, Structural Research Series No. 387, University of Illinois. (26)

Eloseily, H., 1967
ULTIMATE STRENGTH OF RECTANGULAR REINFORCED CONCRETE SECTIONS, Report No. 15, Institut für Baustatik, ETH, Zurich, Switzerland. (22)

Elstner, R. C., 1970
TESTS OF ELASTIC MODELS OF FLAT PLATE AND FLAT SLAB FLOOR SYSTEM, Publication No. SP-24, American Concrete Institute, pp. 289-320. (21A)

Emilian-Davidovici, V. and Jalil, W. A., 1969
SLAB FLOORS, COMPARATIVE STUDY OF VARIOUS METHODS OF CALCULATION, *Annales*, Institut technique du bâtiment et des travaux publiques, Vol. 22, No. 264, pp. 1907–1950. (21A)

Engineering News-Record, 1974
ONE BISCAYNE TOWER, MIAMI'S TALLEST, April 1974. (21B)
Engineering News-Record, 1975
THREE CASTING TECHNIQUES CUT BUILDING'S COST, December 4, 1975, p. 16. (21E)
Erdmann, M. P., Eubank, J. P., Wood, A. W., Grenley, D. G. and Kirchner, H. W., 1973
THE PHILADELPHIA NATIONAL BANK—A CASE STUDY IN PREFABRICATED HIGH STRENGTH MASONRY, Proceedings of the 3rd International Brick Masonry Conference, Bundesverband der Deutschen Ziegelindustrie e.V., Essen, Germany. (27)
Ericksson, F., Hansen, T. and Holst, H., 1962
DETERMINATION OF TIME TO FORM REMOVAL, Report No. 83, National Swedish Council for Building Research (Svenska Statens Rad för Byggnadsforskning). (25)
Ernst, G. C., 1957
PLASTIC HINGING AT THE INTERSECTIONS OF BEAMS AND COLUMNS, ACI Journal, American Concrete Institute, Vol. 53, No. 12. (22)
Ernst, G. C., 1958
MOMENT AND SHEAR REDISTRIBUTION IN TWO-SPAN CONTINUOUS CONCRETE BEAMS, ACI Journal, American Concrete Institute, Vol. 55, No. 5. (22)
Estanero, R. A., 1972
MOMENT-ROTATION CHARACTERISTICS OF REINFORCED CONCRETE BEAMS UNDER COMBINED FLEXURE AND TORSION, thesis presented to the University of Dundee, Dundee, Scotland, in partial fulfillment of the requirements for the degree of Doctor of Philosophy. (22)
Esteva, L., 1960
BEHAVIOUR UNDER ALTERNATING LOADS OF MASONRY DIAPHRAGMS FRAMED BY REINFORCED CONCRETE MEMBERS, RILEM International Symposium on the Effects of Repeated Loading of Materials and Structural Elements (Mexico, September 1966). (27)
Estrada, J. E., 1973
USE OF COMPUTER FOR STRUCTURAL ANALYSIS IN BOGOTA (El Uso del Computador para el Analisis Estructural en Colombia), National Seminar on Tall Buildings (Memorias Del Seminario Nacional Sobre Edificios De Gran Altura), 16th National/Regional Conference (Bogotá, Colombia, September 24–29, 1973), Escuela Colombiana De Ingenieria, Bogotá, pp. 147–167. (21C)
Eto, H. and Takeda, T., 1976
INELASTIC EARTHQUAKE RESPONSE OF REINFORCED CONCRETE BUILDING, Part 3, (in Japanese), Ohbayashi-Gumi Technical Research Institute, Research Report No. 13. (24)

FIP, 1970
REPORT OF THE FIP COMMISSION ON DURABILITY, Proceedings of the 6th Congress of FIP, Prague, Czechoslovakia. (26)
FIP, 1975
FIP/CEB RECOMMENDATIONS FOR THE DESIGN OF REINFORCED AND PRESTRESSED CONCRETE STRUCTURAL MEMBERS FOR FIRE RESISTANCE, Fédération Internationale de la Précontrainte. (21A)
Falk, C., 1973
DEFORMATIONS IN EXISTING MASONRY IN BRICK SKYSCRAPERS (Deformationen in bestchendem Mauerwerk in gemauertem Hochhaus), Proceedings of the 3rd International Brick Masonry Conference, Bundesverband der Deutschen Ziegelindustrie e.V., Essen, Germany. (27)
Falkner, H., 1969
ABOUT THE CRACKING IN RESTRAINED AND UNRESTRAINED REINFORCED CONCRETE MEMBERS DUE TO TEMPERATURE EFFECTS (in German), Deutscher Ausschuss für Stahlbeton, Heft 208, Berlin, Germany. (24)
Farah, A. and Huggins, N. W., 1969
ANALYSIS OF REINFORCED CONCRETE COLUMNS SUBJECTED TO LONGITUDINAL LOAD AND BIAXIAL BENDING, ACI Journal, American Concrete Institute, Vol. 66, No. 7, p. 569. (21D)

Fattal, S. G. and Cattaneo, L. E., 1976
STRUCTURAL PERFORMANCE OF MASONRY WALLS UNDER COMPRESSION AND FLEXURE, NBS Building Science Series 73, U.S. Dept. of Commerce, Washington, D.C. (27)

Fauchart, J. and Cortini, P., 1975
EXPERIMENTAL STUDY OF HORIZONTAL JOINTS BETWEEN PREFABRICATED WALL PANELS, Annales de l'institut technique du bâtiment et des travaux publics, Paris, France, No. 325. (21E)

Faulkes, K. A., 1975
THE DESIGN OF FLAT PLATE BUILDINGS SUBJECTED TO LATERAL LOADS, Pan-Pacific Tall Buildings Conference Proceedings (Honolulu, Hawaii, January 1975), University of Hawaii, Honolulu, pp. 1–12. (21A)

Faupel, J. H., 1964
ENGINEERING DESIGN, John Wiley and Sons, New York, Chapter 9, pp. 556–564. (22)

Feld, J., 1965
TOLERANCE OF STRUCTURES TO SETTLEMENT, Journal of the Soil Mechanics Division, ASCE, Vol. 91, No. SM3, Proc. Paper 4336, p. 63. (25)

Fenwick, R. C. and Paulay, T., 1968
MECHANISMS OF SHEAR RESISTANCE OF CONCRETE BEAMS, Journal of the Structural Division, ASCE, Vol. 94, No. ST10, Proc. Paper 6167, pp. 2325–2350. (22)

Ferguson, P. M., 1973
REINFORCED CONCRETE FUNDAMENTALS, John Wiley and Sons, Inc., New York. (21D)

Ferguson, P. M. and Breen, J. E., 1966
INVESTIGATION OF THE LONG CONCRETE FRAME SUBJECT TO LATERAL LOADS, Symposium on Reinforced Concrete Columns, Publication No. SP-13, American Concrete Institute, p. 75. (21D)

Ferguson, P. M., Okamura, H. and Pagay, S. N., 1970
COMPUTER STUDY OF LONG COLUMNS IN FRAMES, ACI Journal, American Concrete Institute, Vol. 67, No. 12, p. 955. (21D)

Ferry Borges, J., 1966
CRACKING AND DEFORMABILITY OF REINFORCED CONCRETE BEAMS, Publications of IABSE, Zurich, Switzerland, Vol. 26. (24)

Ferry Borges, J., 1968
CRACKING, Preliminary Report to Commission IVa, Comité Européen du Béton, Paris, France. (24)

Ferry Borges, J., 1973
SUMMARY REPORT, Planning and Design of Tall Buildings, Proceedings of 1972 ASCE-IABSE International Conference, Vol. 3, No. 24–summary report, ASCE, New York. (24)

Ferry Borges, J., 1974
THE CHECKING OF NON-LINEAR STRUCTURES, Symposium on Nonlinear Techniques (Crawthorne, December 1974). (26)

Ferry Borges, J. and Castanheta, M., 1971
STRUCTURAL SAFETY, Bulletin d'information no. 78, Comité Européen du Béton, Paris, France. (21D, 26)

Ferry Borges, J. and Arantes e Oliveira, 1963
NON-LINEAR ANALYSIS OF REINFORCED CONCRETE BEAMS, Publications of IABSE, Vol. 23, Zurich, Switzerland. (22)

Ferry Borges, J., Grases, J. and Ravara, A., 1969
BEHAVIOR OF TALL BUILDINGS DURING THE CARACAS EARTHQUAKE OF 1967, presented at the 4th World Conference on Earthquake Engineering, (Santiago, Chile, January 1969). (24)

Ferry Borges, J., Arga, J. e Lima, Teixeira Coelho, A. and Monteiro, V., 1964
ANALYTICAL RESULTS CONCERNING THE NON-LINEAR BEHAVIOR OF REINFORCED CONCRETE STRUCTURE, Bulletin no. 53, Comité Européen du Béton, Paris, France. (22)

Fey, T., 1966
APPROXIMATE SECOND-ORDER ANALYSIS OF REINFORCED CONCRETE FRAMES (in German), Der Bauingenieur, June 1966. (23)

Fintel, M., 1968
STAGGERED WALL BEAMS OF MULTI-STORY BUILDINGS, *Civil Engineering*, ASCE, Vol. 38, No. 8, pp. 56–59. (21A)

Fintel, M., 1973
QUAKE LESSON FROM MANAGUA, *Civil Engineering*, ASCE, Vol. 43, No. 8, pp. 60–63. (24)

Fintel, M., 1974a
DUCTILE SHEAR WALLS IN EARTHQUAKE RESISTANT MULTISTORY BUILD-INGS, *ACI Journal*, American Concrete Institute, Vol. 71, No. 6, pp. 296–305. (21D, 24)

Fintel, M., 1974b
DEFLECTIONS OF HIGH-RISE CONCRETE BUILDINGS, presented at the ASCE Structural Engineering Conference (Cincinnati, Ohio, April 1974). (24)

Fintel, M. and Khan, F. R., 1965–1969.
EFFECTS OF COLUMN EXPOSURE IN TALL STRUCTURES, *ACI Journal*, American Concrete Institute, Vol. 62, December 1965, p. 1533; Vol. 63, August 1966, p. 843; Vol. 65, February 1968, p. 99; Vol. 66, December 1969, p. 957. (21D, 25)

Fintel, M. and Khan, F. R., 1971
EFFECTS OF COLUMN CREEP AND SHRINKAGE IN TALL STRUCTURES —ANALYSIS FOR DIFFERENTIAL SHORTENING OF COLUMNS AND FIELD OBSERVATION OF STRUCTURES, Publication SP-27, American Concrete Institute, p. 95. (21E, 24, 25)

Fintel, M. and Schultz, D., 1975
LARGE PANEL STRUCTURES, unpublished communication to the Joint Committee, November 1975. (21E)

Finzi, L., 1965
DESIGN OF LARGE PANEL PREFABRICATED BUILDINGS (La Statica Degli Edifice Prefabricati a Pannelli-Parete), *Construzioni in Cemento Armato*, Studi e Rendiconti, Vol. 2. (21E)

Finzi, L., 1972
ELASTIC ANALYSIS AND DESIGN OF STEEL FRAMES, Proceedings, 6th National/Regional Conference (Delft, The Netherlands, May 15, 1972), Joint Committee on Tall Buildings, Lehigh University, Bethlehem, Pa., pp. 46–48. (21C)

Fiorato, A. E., 1973
GEOMETRIC VARIATIONS IN THE COLUMNS OF A PRECAST CONCRETE INDUSTRIAL BUILDING, *Journal of the Prestressed Concrete Institute*, Vol. 18, No. 4, pp. 50–60. (21E)

Fiorato, A. E., Sozenmete, A. and Gamble, W. L., 1970
AN INVESTIGATION OF THE INTERACTION OF REINFORCED CONCRETE FRAMES WITH MASONRY FILLER WALLS, Technical Report to the Department of Defense, Contract DA HC 20-67-C-0136, Subcontract 12472 (6300 A-030) US OCD work unit 1127D, University of Illinois, Urbana, Ill. (22)

Firnkas, S., 1974
ANALYSIS OF PRECAST SHEAR WALL STRUCTURES SUBJECTED TO SEISMIC FORCES, ACI Symposium on Industrialized Construction (San Francisco, Calif., 1974). (21E)

Fisher, K., 1970
THE EFFECT OF WALL-TIES ON THE COMPRESSIVE STRENGTH OF CAVITY WALLS, Proceedings of the 2nd International Brick Masonry Conference, H. W. H. West and K. H. Speed, eds., British Ceramic Research Association, Stoke-on-Trent, England, 1971. (27)

Fisher, K., 1973
THE EFFECT OF CHASING ON THE COMPRESSIVE STRENGTH OF BRICK-WORK, Proceedings of the 3rd International Brick Masonry Conference, Bundesverband der Deutschen Ziegelindustrie e.V., Essen, Germany. (27)

Fling, R. S., 1973
OPTIMIZATION AND DESIGN OF CONCRETE FRAMES, Theme Report, Planning and Design of Tall Buildings, Proceedings of 1972 ASCE-IABSE International Conference, Vol. III-21, pp. 1–7, ASCE, New York. (21C, 21E)

Fling, R. S., 1973
THEME REPORT: ELASTIC ANALYSIS—STRENGTH OF MEMBERS AND CON-NECTIONS, Planning and Design of Tall Buildings, Proceedings of 1972 ASCE-IABSE International Conference, Vol. III, No. TC-21, ASCE, New York. (21A)

Forwood, B., 1975
A SYSTEMS APPROACH TO THE DESIGN OF TALL BUILDINGS, Pan-Pacific Tall Buildings Conference Proceedings (Honolulu, Hawaii, January 26–29, 1975), University of Hawaii, Honolulu, pp. 199–210. (21B)

Foster, D., 1968
REINFORCED BRICKWORK AND GROUTED CAVITY CONSTRUCTION, The Consulting Engineer, July 1968, pp. 46–50. (27)

Foster, P. K. and Bridgeman, D. L., 1973
PRISM TESTS FOR THE DESIGN AND CONTROL OF BRICK MASONRY, Technical Report No. 22, N.Z. Pottery and Ceramics Research Association; synopsis in Proceedings, Institution of Civil Engineers, London, England, Vol. 55, Part 2, March 1973. (27)

Foure, B., 1969
VERTICAL JOINTS RESISTING SHEAR FORCES BETWEEN LARGE PERPEN-DICULAR PANELS (Joints verticaux resistant aux efforts tangents entire grands panneaux perpendiculaires), Annales d'institut technique du bâtiment et des travaux publics, Paris, France, No. 258. (21E)

Foure, B., 1971
STUDY OF VARIOUS REINFORCED CONCRETE COLUMN BUCKLING PROB-LEMS (in French), RILEM International Symposium (Buenos Aires, Argentina, 1971), Vol. 1, p. 143. (21D)

Fox, A. J., 1955
CONCRETE APARTMENT HOUSE 39 STORIES HIGH, Engineering News-Record, 28 July 1955, pp. 34–37. (A38)

Francis, A. J., 1969
THE S.A.A. BRICKWORK CODE: THE RESEARCH BACKGROUND, Civil Engi-neering Transactions, Institution of Engineers, Australia, Vol. CEII, No. 2. (27)

Francis, A. J., Horman, C. B. and Jerrems, L. E., 1970
THE EFFECT OF JOINT THICKNESS AND OTHER FACTORS ON THE COMPRES-SIVE STRENGTH OF BRICKWORK, Proceedings of the 2nd International Brick Masonry Conference, H. W. H. West and K. H. Speed, eds., British Ceramic Research Association, Stoke-on-Trent, England, 1971. (27)

Fransson, B., 1973
UNSYMMETRICAL MULTI-STOREY BUILDINGS, Publication 73:4, Dept. of Struc-tural Mechanics, Chalmers University of Technology, Göteborg, Sweden. (21A, 22)

Franz, G., 1968
THE CONNECTION OF PRECAST ELEMENTS WITH LOOPS, Design Philosophy and its Application to Precast Concrete Structures, Cement and Concrete Association, London, England. (21E)

Frenzel, D., 1974
SOME BASIC CONSIDERATIONS FOR PREFABRICATED LONG-SPAN CON-STRUCTIONS (Einige grundsatliche Uberwegungen fur weitgespannte Konstruktionen aus Fertigteilen), Betonwerk + Fertigteil Technik, H9. (21E)

Fric, M., 1969
SHEAR RESISTANCE OF VERTICAL JOINTS IN PANEL CONSTRUCTION (La resistance aux efforts de cisaillement des joints verticaux dans les constructions en panneaux), Symposium on Bearing Walls (Warsaw, Poland, 1969). (21E)

Fric, M., Lishak, V., Horacek, E. and Sokolow, M., 1975
THE COMPRESSION STRENGTH OF HORIZONTAL JOINTS IN PANEL WALLS, CIB-2nd International Symposium on Bearing Walls (Warsaw, Poland, September 1975), Theme 1, Paper 2, pp. 13–19. (21E)

Fuller, G. R., 1974
INDUSTRIALIZED CONCRETE CONSTRUCTION FOR HUD, ACI Symposium on Industrialization in Building Construction (San Francisco, April 1974), Publication SP-48-2, American Concrete Institute, pp. 7–33. (21E)

Fuller, G. R., 1975
  PRECAST CONCRETE STRUCTURES, unpublished communication to the Joint Com-
  mittee, August 1975. (21E)
Fumagalli, E., 1973
  STATICAL AND GEOMECHANICAL MODELS, Springer, Vienna, Austria. (A38)
Funahashi, I., Kinashita, K. and Aoyama, H., 1969
  VIBRATION TESTS AND TEST TO FAILURE OF A SEVEN STOREY BUILDING
  SURVIVED A SEVERE EARTHQUAKE, Proceedings of 4th World Conference on
  Earthquake Engineering (Santiago, Chile), Vol. I, pp. B-1, 26–43. (22)
Funk, P., 1973a
  STIFFNESS REQUIREMENTS IN TERMS OF HUMAN COMFORT, Planning and
  Design of Tall Buildings, Proceedings of 1972 ASCE-IABSE International Conference,
  Vol. III, No. 24-D1, ASCE, New York. (24)
Funk, P., 1973b
  THE REVISION OF THE GERMAN MASONRY STANDARD DIN 1053 (Die
  Neubearbeitung der deutschen Mauerwerksnorm DIN 1053), Proceedings of the 3rd
  International Brick Masonry Conference, Bundesverband der Deutschen Ziegelindustrie
  e.V., Essen, Germany. (27)
Funnell, A., Pugh, A. and Young, R., 1972
  A SELECTIVE BIBLIOGRAPHY ON STRUCTURAL MODELS, Models Laboratory
  Report No. MR7, Department of Architectural Science, University of Sydney, Australia.
  (A38)
Furlong, R. W., 1970
  DESIGN OF CONCRETE FRAMES BY ASSIGNED LIMIT MOMENTS, *ACI Journal*,
  American Concrete Institute, Vol. 67, No. 4, pp. 341–353. (22)
Furlong, R. W., 1971
  COLUMN SLENDERNESS AND CHARTS FOR DESIGN, *ACI Journal*, American
  Concrete Institute, Vol. 68, No. 1, pp. 9–17. (23)
Furlong, R. W. and Ferguson, P. M., 1966
  TESTS OF FRAMES WITH COLUMNS IN SINGLE CURVATURE, Symposium on
  Reinforced Concrete Columns, Publication No. SP-13, American Concrete Institute, pp.
  54–74. (21D, 23)

Galletly, G. D., 1952
  BEHAVIOR OF REINFORCED CONCRETE SHEAR WALLS UNDER STATIC
  LOAD, Massachusetts Institute of Technology, Cambridge, Mass. (21D)
Gamble, W. L., 1970
  FIELD INVESTIGATIONS OF CONTINUOUS COMPOSITE PRESTRESSED I-BEAM
  HIGHWAY BRIDGE, Structural Research Series 360, University of Illinois Civil
  Engineering Studies. (25)
Gensert, R. M. and Kiris, U., 1969
  ENGINEERING EVALUATION FOR EAST LIBERTY PLAZA, Design Engineering
  and Constructing with Masonry Products, F. Johnson, ed., Gulf Publishing Co., Houston,
  Tex. (27)
Gensert, R. M., Peller, M., Parikh, K. and Fujita, R. Y., 1974
  DESIGN OF FRAME, Design Considerations for a Precast Prestressed Apartment
  Building, *Journal of the Prestressed Concrete Institute*, Vol. 19, No. 4, pp. 26–53. (21E)
George, Z. and Deshmukh, R. S., 1973
  PRECAST CONCRETE DOUBLY-CURVED FUNICULAR SHELLS FORM GRID
  FLOORS FOR CONCRETE TESTING LABORATORY, *Indian Concrete Journal*, June
  1973. (21D)
George, Z. and Mani, K., 1974
  PREFABRICATION TECHNIQUES IN INDIA, lecture delivered in advanced course on
  Design and Construction of Prefabricated Residential and Institutional Buildings
  conducted by Structural Engineering Research Centre (Council of Scientific and
  Industrial Research), Madras, India, December 9–17, 1974. (21A)
Gere, J. M. and Weaver, W., 1965
  ANALYSIS OF FRAMED STRUCTURES, Van Nostrand Reinhold Co., New York.
  (21C)

Gergely, P., 1973
CRACKING AND CRACK CONTROL, Planning and Design of Tall Buildings, Proceedings of 1972 ASCE-IABSE International Conference, Vol. 3, No. 24-1, ASCE, New York. (24)

Gergely, P. and Lutz, L. A., 1968
MAXIMUM CRACK WIDTH IN REINFORCED CONCRETE FLEXURAL MEMBERS, Publication SP-20, American Concrete Institute. (24)

German Industrial Standard (DIN), 1968
DIN 4224, DESIGN OF CONCRETE AND REINFORCED CONCRETE STRUCTURES (Bemessung von Beton und Stahlbetonbauten), Deutscher Industrie Normen, Berlin and Köln, Germany, 1959; Neubearbeitung, March 1968. (26)

German Industrial Standard (DIN), 1972
DIN 1045, REINFORCED CONCRETE STRUCTURES DESIGN AND CONSTRUCTION (Beton und Stahlbeton, Bemessung und Ausfuhrung), Deutscher Industrie Normen, Berlin and Köln, Germany. (23, 26)

Gero, J. S., 1969a
PRELIMINARY REPORT ON THE MODEL INVESTIGATION OF THE CENTRE-POINT TOWER FOR THE A.M.P., Models Laboratory Report MR2, Department of Architectural Science, University of Sydney, Australia. (A38)

Gero, J. S., 1969b
PRESTRESSED MASONRY-REINFORCED CONCRETE SPACE STRUCTURE, Design Engineering and Constructing with Masonry Products, F. Johnson, ed., Gulf Publishing Co., Houston, Tex. (27)

Gero, J. S., 1973
STRUCTURAL MODEL TESTING OF M.L.C. CENTRE TOWER BUILDING, Models Laboratory Report No. MR10, Department of Architectural Science, University of Sydney, Australia. (A38)

Gero, J. S., 1973
THE BEHAVIOR OF BUILDING STRUCTURES UNDER LATERAL LOADS, Proceedings of the 12th Regional Conference (Sydney, Australia, August 14–17, 1973), Lehigh University, Bethlehem, Pa., pp. 544–555. (21B)

Gero, J. S. and Cowan, H. J., 1970
STRUCTURAL CONCRETE MODELS IN AUSTRALIA, Publication No. 24, American Concrete Institute, pp. 353–386. (A38)

Gero, J. S. and Cowan, H. J., 1972
FEASIBILITY STRUCTURAL MODEL ANALYSIS: THE "CENTREPOINT" TOWER, SYDNEY, Conference on Structural Models (Sydney, 1972), Cement and Concrete Association of Australia in conjunction with Dept. of Architectural Science, University of Sydney, and Institution of Engineers, Australia, N.S.W. Division. (A38)

Gero, J. S., Rosenman, M. A. and Alexander, P. M., 1970
FEASIBILITY STRUCTURAL MODEL ANALYSIS OF A 700 FT HIGH TOURIST AND TELECOMMUNICATIONS TOWER, Proceedings, 4th International Conference on Stress Analysis, A. Myer, ed., Blackwell, Oxford, England, pp. 16–25. (A38)

Gerstle, K. H. and Tulin, L. G., 1971
INCREMENTAL DEFORMATIONS OF REINFORCED CONCRETE BEAMS, *Magazine of Concrete Research*, Vol. 23, No. 77. (22)

Gerwick, B. C., 1968
PRECAST PRESTRESSED LIGHTWEIGHT AGGREGATE CONCRETE—UTILIZATION, SPECIAL CONSIDERATIONS AND EVALUATION, Design Philosophy and its Application to Precast Concrete Structures, Cement and Concrete Association, London. (21E)

Gesund, H., 1973
COMPUTER ANALYSIS OF REINFORCED CONCRETE FRAMES, INELASTICITY AND NON-LINEARITY IN STRUCTURAL CONCRETE, University of Waterloo Press, Waterloo, pp. 289–314. (22)

Gesund, H. and Vandevelde, C. E., 1973
STIFFNESS OF REINFORCED CONCRETE COLUMNS IN BIAXIAL BENDING, Planning and Design of Tall Buildings, Proceedings of 1972 ASCE-IABSE International Conference, Vol. III, No. 22-D1, ASCE, New York. (22)

Ghali, A., Dilger, W. and Neville, A. M., 1969
TIME-DEPENDENT FORCES INDUCED BY SETTLEMENT OF SUPPORTS IN CONTINUOUS REINFORCED CONCRETE BEAMS, *ACI Journal*, American Concrete Institute, Vol. 66, No. 11, pp. 907–915. (25)

Ghosh, S. K. and Cohn, M. Z., 1970
CREEP OF CONCRETE COLUMNS, Preliminary Publication, IABSE Symposium on Design of Concrete Structures for Creep, Shrinkage and Temperature Changes (Madrid, Spain). (22)

Glanville, B., 1934
MECHANICAL PROPERTIES OF BRICKS AND BRICKWORK MASONRY, Building Research Special Report No. 22, Building Research Station (DSIR), Garston, Herts., England. (27)

Glanville, W. H. and Thomas, F. G., 1939
FURTHER INVESTIGATIONS ON CREEP OR FLOW OF CONCRETE UNDER LOAD, Studies in Reinforced Concrete, Building Research Technical Paper No. 21. (25)

Glück, J., 1969
LATERAL LOAD ANALYSIS OF MULTI-STORY STRUCTURES COMPRISING SHEAR WALLS WITH SUDDEN CHANGES OF STIFFNESS, *ACI Journal*, American Concrete Institute, Vol. 66, No. 9, p. 729. (21C)

Glück, J., 1970a
LATERAL-LOAD ANALYSIS OF ASYMMETRIC MULTISTORY STRUCTURES, *Journal of the Structural Division*, ASCE, Vol. 96, No. ST2, Proc. Paper 7089, p. 317. (21C, 22)

Glück, J., 1970b
LATERAL LOAD ANALYSIS OF IRREGULAR SHEAR WALL MULTI-STORY STRUCTURES, *ACI Journal*, American Concrete Institute, Vol. 67, No. 7, pp. 548–553. (21C, 24)

Glück, J., 1973a
ELASTIC ANALYSIS OF TALL CONCRETE BUILDINGS, Planning and Design of Tall Buildings, Proceedings of 1972 ASCE-IABSE International Conference, Vol. III, No. 21-D9, ASCE, New York. (21C)

Glück, J., 1973b
ELASTO-PLASTIC ANALYSIS OF COUPLED SHEAR WALLS, *Journal of the Structural Division*, ASCE, Vol. 99, No. ST8, Proc. Paper 9920, pp. 1743–1760. (22)

Glück, J., 1974
THE BUCKLING OF TIER BUILDINGS WITH VARIABLE LATERAL STIFFNESS PROPERTIES, *Building Science*, Pergamon Press, Vol. 9, pp. 39–43. (23)

Glück, J. and Gellert, M., 1971
ON THE STABILITY OF ELASTICALLY SUPPORTED CANTILEVER WITH CONTINUOUS LATERAL SUPPORT, *International Journal of Mechanical Sciences*, Pergamon Press, pp. 887–891. (23)

Glück, J. and Gellert, M., 1972
NON-LINEAR ANALYSIS OF AN ELASTIC SUPPORTED AND LATERAL RESTRAINED CANTILEVER, *Proceedings*, Institution of Civil Engineers, London, Vol. 51, Paper 7463, pp. 561–566. (22)

Glück, J. and Kalev, I., 1972
COMPUTER METHOD FOR ANALYSIS OF MULTISTORY STRUCTURES, *Computers and Structures*, Pergamon Press, Vol. 2, pp. 897–913. (21C)

Glück, J. and Krauss, M., 1973
STRESS ANALYSIS OF GROUP OF INTERCONNECTED THIN-WALLED CANTILEVERS, *Journal of the Structural Division*, ASCE, Vol. 99, No. ST10, Proc. Paper 10089, pp. 2143–2165. (21C)

Gobel, K., 1971
NEW DEVELOPMENT IN MASONRY CONSTRUCTION IN FOREIGN COUNTRIES, *Die Ziegelindustrie*, No. 12, p. 508. (27)

Gobel, K., 1973
COLOR, SHAPE AND STRUCTURE OF CONSTRUCTION (Farbe, Form und Struktur des Baues), Proceedings of the 3rd International Brick Masonry Conference, Bundesverband der Deutschen Ziegelindustrie e.V., Essen, Germany. (27)

Goel, S. C. and Berg, G. V., 1968
INELASTIC EARTHQUAKE RESPONSE OF TALL STEEL FRAMES, *Journal of the Structural Division*, ASCE, Vol. 94, No. ST8, Proc. Paper 6061. (23)

Goffi, L., 1973
RESEARCH OF THE DEFORMATION CHARACTERISTICS OF CERAMICS TO ALLOW CALCULATIONS AT RUPTURE OF COMPOSITE SLABS (Recherches sur les caracteristiques de déformation de la terre cuite pour permettre le calcul à la rupture des planchers mixtes), Proceedings of the 3rd International Brick Masonry Conference, Bundesverband der Deutschen Ziegelindustrie e.V., Essen, Germany. (27)

Goldberg, J. E., 1954
STIFFNESS CHARTS FOR GISSETED MEMBERS UNDER AXIAL LOAD, *Transactions*, ASCE, Vol. 119, p. 43. (23)

Goldberg, J. E., 1965
BUCKLING OF MULTISTORY BUILDINGS, *Journal of the Engineering Mechanics Division*, ASCE, Vol. 91, No. EM1, Proc. Paper 4223, pp. 51–70. (23)

Goldberg, J. E., 1967
ANALYSIS OF MULTI-STOREY BUILDINGS CONSIDERING SHEAR WALL AND FLOOR DEFORMATIONS, *Tall Buildings*, Pergamon Press, London, p. 349. (21C, 23)

Goldberg, J. E., 1973
APPROXIMATE METHODS FOR STABILITY AND FREQUENCY ANALYSIS OF TALL BUILDINGS, Proceedings, Regional Conference on Tall Buildings (Madrid, Spain, September 1973), pp. 123–146. (23)

Goldberg, J. and Richard, R., 1963
ANALYSIS OF NONLINEAR STRUCTURES, *Journal of the Structural Division*, ASCE, Vol. 89, No. ST4, Proc. Paper 3604, pp. 333–365. (22)

Goldman, D. E. and von Gierke, H. E., 1961
EFFECTS OF SHOCK AND VIBRATION ON MAN, Shock and Vibration Handbook, Vol. 3, Engineering Design and Environmental Conditions, p. 44–22. (24)

Goschy, B., 1974
TORSIONAL STIFFNESS OF "TUBE IN TUBE" SYSTEMS, unpublished communication to the Joint Council, June 1974. (21C)

Goschy, B., 1975
STRUCTURAL SYSTEMS (Tartoszerkezeti Kerdesek), 30th National/Regional Conference on Tall Buildings (Budapest, Hungary, May 1975), 200 Ivterjedelem 20, 25/A/5/IV, Budapest, Hungary, pp. 53–69. (21A)

Gosstroi USSR, 1972
STRUCTURAL NORMS AND RULES, Part II, Section V, Chapter 1, Concrete and Reinforced Concrete Structures, Design Norms, NIIZhb P-V.1-72, Moscow, USSR. (23)

Goyal, B. B. and Jackson, N., 1971
SLENDER CONCRETE COLUMNS UNDER SUSTAINED LOAD, *Journal of the Structural Division*, ASCE, Vol. 97, No. ST11, Proc. Paper 8544, p. 2729. (21D)

Grandet, M. B., 1973
PHYSICO-CHEMICAL MECHANISMS OF THE BOND BETWEEN CEMENT AND CERAMICS (Mécanismes physico-chimiques de l'adhérence entre la terre cuite et le ciment), Proceedings of the 3rd International Brick Masonry Conference, Bundesverband der Deutschen Ziegelindustrie e.V., Essen, Germany. (27)

Granholm, H., 1943
REINFORCED BRICK MASONRY, Chalmers University of Technology No. 16, Göteborg, Sweden. (27)

Green, H. and McNeilly, T., 1973
STATUTORY REQUIREMENTS AND SITE CONTROL, Structural Brickwork Seminar, Macquarie University, Sydney, Australia, February 1973. (27)

Green, R. and Breen, J. E., 1969
ECCENTRICALLY LOADED CONCRETE COLUMNS UNDER SUSTAINED LOAD, *ACI Journal*, American Concrete Institute, Vol. 66, No. 11, p. 866. (21D)

Gregory, M. S., 1966
FRAMED STRUCTURES, THE INSTABILITY PROBLEM, *Proceedings*, Institution of Civil Engineers, London, Vol. 35, pp. 451–473. (23)

Grenley, D. G., 1969
STUDY OF THE EFFECT OF CERTAIN MODIFIED MORTARS ON COMPRESSIVE AND FLEXURAL STRENGTH OF MASONRY, Design Engineering and Constructing with Masonry Products, F. Johnson, ed., Gulf Publishing Co., Houston, Tex. (27)

Grenley, D. G. and Cattaneo, L. E., 1970
THE EFFECT OF EDGE LOAD ON THE RACKING STRENGTH OF CLAY MASONRY, Proceedings of the 2nd International Brick Masonry Conference, H. W. H. West and K. H. Speed, eds., British Ceramic Research Association, Stoke-on-Trent, England, 1971. (27)

Grenley, D. G. and Terzes, J. G., 1970
UNIVERSITY CENTER PROJECT, AUSTIN, TEXAS, Proceedings of the 2nd International Brick Masonry Conference, H. W. H. West and K. H. Speed, eds., British Ceramic Research Association, Stoke-on-Trent, England, 1971. (27)

Grierson, D. E., 1968
OPTIMAL DESIGN OF REINFORCED CONCRETE FRAMES, thesis presented to the University of Waterloo, at Waterloo, Ontario, Canada, in partial fulfillment of the requirements for the degree of Doctor of Philosophy. (22)

Grierson, D. E. and Gladwell, G. M. L., 1971
COLLAPSE LOAD ANALYSIS USING LINEAR PROGRAMMING, Journal of the Structural Division, ASCE, Vol. 97, No. ST5, Proc. Paper 8127, pp. 1561–1573. (21B)

Griffiths, H., Saunders, O. and Pugsley, A., 1968
COLLAPSE OF FLATS AT RONAN POINT, Her Majesty's Stationery Office, London, England. (21E)

Grimm, C. T., 1973
FIELD QUALITY CONTROL TEST FOR WETTING BRICKS IN MASONRY CONSTRUCTION, Journal of the Construction Division, ASCE, Vol. 99, No. CO1, Proc. Paper 9839. (27)

Grimm, C. T., 1974a
MASONRY CONSTRUCTION OPERATIONS, Journal of the Construction Division, ASCE, Vol. 100, No. CO2, Proc. Paper 10630. (27)

Grimm, C. T., 1974b
WEATHER EFFECTS ON MASON PRODUCTIVITY, Journal of the Construction Division, ASCE, Vol. 100, No. CO3, Proc. Paper 10783. (27)

Grimm, C. T., 1975a
STRENGTH AND RELATED PROPERTIES OF BRICK MASONRY, Journal of the Structural Division, ASCE, Vol. 101, No. ST1, Proc. Paper 11066. (27)

Grimm, C. T., 1975b
COLOR OF STRUCTURES, Journal of the Structural Division, ASCE, Vol. 101, No. ST9, Proc. Paper 11547. (27)

Grimm, C. T., 1975c
RATIONALIZED AESTHETICS IN CIVIL ENGINEERING, Journal of the Structural Division, ASCE, Vol. 101, No. ST9, Proc. Paper 11546. (27)

Grimm, C. T., 1975d
PRINCIPLES OF COMPOSITION IN BUILDING ART, Journal of the Structural Division, ASCE, Vol. 101, No. ST9, Proc. Paper 11544. (27)

Grimm, C. T., 1975e
DESIGN FOR DIFFERENTIAL MOVEMENT IN BRICK WALLS, Journal of the Structural Division, ASCE, Vol. 101, No. ST11, Proc. Paper 11739. (27)

Grimm, C. T., 1976
DESIGN OF BRICK MASONRY BEARING WALLS AND COLUMNS, Proceedings of the 4th International Brick Masonry Conference, Groupement National de l'Industrie de la Terre Cuite, rue de Poissoniers 13, Brussels, Belgium. (27)

Griswell, M., 1970
STRENGTH AND BEHAVIOR OF REINFORCED CONCRETE SLAB-COLUMN CONNECTIONS SUBJECTED TO STATIC AND DYNAMIC LOADINGS, thesis presented to the University of Illinois at Urbana-Champaign, Ill., in partial fulfillment of the requirements for the degree of Doctor of Philosophy. (22)

Groper, M. and Pollner, E., 1975
BEARING AND DAMPING CAPACITY ON LOCK-JOINTS (Capacitatea Portanta si Amortizarea Imbinarilor Rigide), Reinforced Concrete in Tall Buildings, 34th National/Regional Conference (Iasi, Romania, October 1975), Vol. I, pp. 401–414. (21E)

Gross, J. G., Dikkers, R. D. and Grogan, J. C., 1969
RECOMMENDED PRACTICE FOR ENGINEERED BRICK MASONRY, Brick Insti-
tute of America, McLean, Va. (27)
Gruner, I., Rotaru, G. and Frunza, R., 1973
SHRINKAGE EFFECT OF STRUCTURAL CONCRETE WALLS IN MULTISTORY
BUILDINGS, Planning and Design of Tall Buildings, Proceedings of 1972 ASCE-IABSE
International Conference, Vol. III-25, ASCE, New York, p. 827. (21D)
Gulkan, P. and Sozen, M. A., 1971
RESPONSE AND ENERGY-DISSIPATION OF REINFORCED CONCRETE
FRAMES SUBJECTED TO STRONG BASE MOTIONS, Civil Engineering Studies,
SRS No. 377, University of Illinois. (22, 24)
Guy, E. D., 1970
DESIGN FOR MOVEMENT IN BUILDINGS, Proceedings of Symposium (October 14,
1969, London), Design and Development Divisional Committee of the Concrete Society,
London, England. (21A)
Gvozdev, A. A. and Krylov, S., 1964
STUDY OF REINFORCED CONCRETE STRUCTURES (Etude des constructions
hyperstatiques en béton armé au précontraint), Bulletin no. 53, Comité Européen du
Béton, Paris, France. (22)

HMSO, 1965
BUILDING REGULATIONS, Her Majesty's Stationery Office, London, England. (21D)
HUD, 1968
INDUSTRIALIZED BUILDING—A COMPARATIVE ANALYSIS OF EUROPEAN
EXPERIENCE, Division of Internal Affairs, U.S. Dept. of Housing and Urban
Development, Washington, D.C. (21E)
HUD, 1975
DESIGN AND CONSTRUCTION OF LARGE-PANEL STRUCTURES, Report 1,
Loading Conditions, Office of Policy Development and Research, U.S. Dept. of Housing
and Urban Development, Washington, D.C. (21E)
Haas, H., 1973
PLANNING, COSTS AND CALCULATION FOR A 10-STORY APARTMENT
BUILDING IN JÜLICH (Planung, Kosten und Kalkulation für zehngeschossiges
Wohnhochhaus in Jülich), Proceedings of the 3rd International Brick Masonry Confer-
ence, Bundesverband der Deutschen Ziegelindustrie e.V., Essen, Germany. (27)
Haferkamp, F., 1973
CLIMATIZING OF AN ARCHIVES BY BRICK MASONRY (Klimatisierung eines
Archivbaues durch Ziegelmauerwerk), Proceedings of the 3rd International Brick
Masonry Conference, Bundesverband der Deutschen Ziegelindustrie e.V., Essen, Ger-
many. (27)
Haferland, F., 1973
THE OUTSIDE WALL-ELEMENT OF SEPARATION BETWEEN INTERIOR AND
EXTERIOR CLIMATE (Die Aussenwand—Trennelement zwischen Raumklima und
Aussenklima), Proceedings of the 3rd International Brick Masonry Conference, Bundes-
verband der Deutschen Ziegelindustrie e.v. Essen, Germany. (27)
Hage, S. E., 1974
THE SECOND-ORDER ANALYSIS OF REINFORCED CONCRETE FRAMES, Struc-
tural Engineering Report No. 49, thesis presented to the University of Alberta, at
Edmonton, Canada, in partial fulfillment of requirements for the degree of Master of
Science. (23)
Halasz, R. and Tantow, G., 1966
SHEAR RESISTANCE OF VERTICAL JOINTS AND DISTRIBUTION OF HORI-
ZONTAL FORCES IN LARGE PANEL CONSTRUCTION (Schubfestigkeit der
Vertikalfugen und Verteilung der Horizontalkrafte in Grosstafelbau), Berichte aus der
Bauforschung, No. 45, Berlin, Germany. (21E)
Hall, A. S., 1969
DEFORMATION AND STRESSES WITHIN JOINTS OF FRAMES, UNICIV Report
No. R-51, University of New South Wales, Kensington, N.S.W., Australia. (24)
Haller, J. P., 1953
TALL BUILDINGS IN BASEL (Hochhaüser in Basel), Die Ziegel Industrie, Vol. 15. (27)

Haller, J. P., 1958a
TECHNICAL PROPERTIES OF MASONRY MADE OF CLAY BRICKS AND USED FOR HIGH-RISE CONSTRUCTION, *Schweizerische Bauzeitung*, No. 28, July 1958. (27)

Haller, J. P., 1958b
THE PROPERTIES OF LOADBEARING BRICKWORK IN PERFORATED FIRE BRICK FOR MULTI-STOREY BUILDINGS, translated from German by G. L. Cairns, Building Research Station Library Commun. 870, Garston, England. (27)

Haller, J. P., 1959
THE TECHNOLOGICAL PROPERTIES OF BRICK MASONRY IN HIGH BUILDINGS, Translation No. 792, National Research Council, Canada. (27)

Hanlon, J. R. C., 1970
PRESTRESSED CONCRETE MASONRY, *Concrete*, Vol. 4, No. 9. (27)

Hansell, W. and Winter, G., 1959
LATERAL STABILITY OF REINFORCED CONCRETE BEAMS, *ACI Journal*, American Concrete Institute, Vol. 56, p. 193. (23)

Hansen, H., 1967
MORTAR JOINTS BETWEEN CONCRETE ELEMENTS IN SHEAR WALLS, Norwegian Building Research Institute, Oslo, Norway. (21E)

Hansen, K. and Oleson, S., 1969
FAILURE LOAD AND FAILURE MECHANISM OF KEYED SHEAR JOINTS, Danmarks Ingeniorakademi, Report No. 69/22. (21E)

Hansen, K., Kavyrchine, M., Melhorn, G., Oleson, S. O., Pume, D. and Schwing, H., 1974
DESIGN OF VERTICAL KEYED SHEAR JOINTS IN LARGE PANEL BUILDINGS, *Building Research and Practice*, July/August 1974. (21E)

Hansen, T. C. and Mattock, A. H., 1965
INFLUENCE OF SIZE AND SHAPE OF MEMBER ON THE SHRINKAGE AND CREEP OF CONCRETE, *ACI Journal*, American Concrete Institute, Vol. 63, p. 267. (25)

Hanson, G. C., 1969
PARK MAYFAIR EAST, Design Engineering and Constructing with Masonry Products, F. Johnson, ed., Gulf Publishing Co., Houston, Tex. (27)

Hanson, N. W., 1971
SEISMIC RESISTANCE OF CONCRETE FRAMES WITH GRADE 60 REINFORCEMENT, *Journal of the Structural Division*, ASCE, Vol. 97, No. ST6, Proc. Paper 8180, pp. 1685–1700. (21D, 22)

Hanson, N. W. and Connor, H. W., 1967
SEISMIC RESISTANCE OF REINFORCED CONCRETE BEAM-COLUMN JOINTS, *Journal of the Structural Division*, ASCE, Vol. 93, No. ST5, Proc. Paper 5537, p. 533. (21D, 22)

Hanson, N. W. and Hanson, J. M., 1968
SHEAR AND MOMENT TRANSFER BETWEEN CONCRETE SLABS AND COLUMNS, *Journal*, PCA Research and Development Laboratories, Vol. 10, No. 1. (21D)

Hanson, N. W. and Reiffentuhl, H., 1960
CONCRETE BEAMS AND COLUMNS WITH BUNDLED REINFORCEMENT, *Transactions*, ASCE, Vol. 125, Paper 3-47, p. 889. (21D)

Hanson, T. A., 1969
THE STRUCTURAL ANCHORAGE OF PRECAST PRESTRESSED CONCRETE, Publication No. SP-22, American Concrete Institute, p. 105. (21E)

Harding, J. R., 1971
BRICK MAKING—QUALITY CONTROL AND MONITORING OF STRENGTH, G.L.C. Development and Materials Bulletin No. 50 (2nd series). (27)

Harris, R. W. F. and Turner, R. W., 1973
THE RESILIENT MOUNTING OF RHM CENTER (TOWER BLOCK), Planning and Design of Tall Buildings, Proceedings of 1972 ASCE-IABSE International Conference, Vol. III, No. 24-D2, ASCE, New York. (24)

Hartt, F., 1973
THE POSSIBILITIES OF ARCHITECTURAL DESIGN WITH THE NEW TECHNIQUES OF MASONRY (Die Möglichkeiten der architektonischen Gestaltung mit den neuen Techniken des Mauerwerkbaues), Proceedings of the 3rd International Brick Masonry Conference, Bundesverband der Deutschen Ziegelindustrie e.v. Essen, Germany. (27)

Haseltine, B. A. and Au, Y. T., 1970
DESIGN AND CONSTRUCTION OF A 19-STOREY LOAD-BEARING BRICK BUILDING, Proceedings of the 2nd International Brick Masonry Conference, H. W. H. West and K. H. Speed, eds., British Ceramic Research Association, Stoke-on-Trent, England, 1971. (27)

Haseltine, B. A. and Thomas, K., 1971
LOADBEARING BRICKWORK—DESIGN FOR THE FIFTH AMENDMENT TO THE BUILDING REGULATIONS, Technical Note No. 1, No. 3, Brick Development Association. (27)

Hasofer, A. M. and Lind, N. C., 1973
AN EXACT AND INVARIANT FIRST ORDER RELIABILITY FORMAT, Paper No. 119, Solid Mechanics Division, Waterloo. (26)

Hatzinikolas, M., 1976
SHEAR BEHAVIOUR OF MASONRY WALLS SUBDIVIDED BY FLOOR SLABS, Proceedings, 1st Canadian Masonry Symposium, E. L. Jessop and M. A. Ward, eds., University of Calgary, Canada. (27)

Hauser, K., 1973
EFFICIENCY INCREASE BY USE OF LARGE WALL BRICKS (Leistungssteigerung durch Verwendung grossformatiger Mauerziegel), Proceedings of the 3rd International Brick Masonry Conference, Bundesverband der Deutschen Ziegelindustrie e.v. Essen, Germany. (27)

Heidebrecht, A. C. and Stafford-Smith, B., 1973a
APPROXIMATE ANALYSIS OF TALL WALL-FRAME STRUCTURES, Journal of the Structural Division, ASCE, Vol. 99, No. ST2, Proc. Paper 9550, p. 199. (21C, 24)

Heidebrecht, A. C. and Stafford-Smith, B., 1973b
APPROXIMATE ANALYSIS OF OPEN-SECTION SHEAR WALLS SUBJECT TO TORSIONAL LOADING, Journal of the Structural Division, ASCE, Vol. 99, No. ST12, Proc. Paper 10234, p. 2355. (21C)

Heidebrecht, A. C. and Swift, R. D., 1971
ANALYSIS OF ASYMMETRICAL COUPLED SHEAR WALLS, Journal of the Structural Division, ASCE, Vol. 97, No. ST5, Proc. Paper 8100, p. 1407. (21C, 24)

Heiman, J. L., 1973
LONG-TERM DEFORMATIONS IN THE TOWER BUILDING, AUSTRALIA SQUARE, SYDNEY, ACI Journal, American Concrete Institute, Vol. 70, No. 4, p. 279. (21D, 25)

Hellers, B., 1967
ECCENTRICALLY COMPRESSED COLUMNS WITHOUT TENSILE STRENGTH SUBJECTED TO UNIFORMLY DISTRIBUTED LOADS, Report 35/67, National Swedish Institute for Building Research, Stockholm, Sweden. (22)

Hellesland, J. and Green, R., 1971
SUSTAINED AND CYCLIC LOADING OF CONCRETE COLUMNS, Journal of the Structural Division, ASCE, Vol. 97, No. ST4, Proc. Paper 8033, p. 1113. (21D)

Henclewski, T., 1969
SIMPLIFIED CALCULATION METHODS FOR PLANE JOINTS (Méthode simplifiée de calcul des joints plats), Symposium on Bearing Walls (Warsaw, Poland, June 1969). (21E)

Henclewski, T., 1974
BEARING CAPACITY OF PARTIALLY RESTRAINED SLENDER CONCRETE WALLS, CIB Commission W23A, Darmstadt, Germany. (21E)

Henclewski, T., 1975
CHARACTERISTICS OF FIXATION OF CONTINUOUSLY ANALYSED WALL, CIB 2nd International Symposium on Bearing Walls (Warsaw, Poland, September 1975), Theme 1, Paper 3, pp. 21–35. (21E, 27)

Henclewski, T. and Sliwonik, A., 1975
APPLICATION OF THE SIMPLIFIED CONTINUOUS SCHEME IN ANALYSIS OF SAFETY MARGIN IN A BEARING WALL OF A PREFABRICATED MULTI-STORY BUILDING, CIB 2nd International Symposium on Bearing Walls (Warsaw, Poland, September 1975), Theme 1, Paper 4, pp. 37–48. (21E, 27)

Hendry, A. W., 1966
PHOTOELASTIC ANALYSIS, Pergamon Press, Oxford, England. (A38)

Hendry, A. W., 1971
WIND LOAD ANALYSIS OF MULTI-STOREY BRICKWORK STRUCTURES, B.D.A. Research Note, Vol. 1, No. 3, January 1971. (27)
Hendry, A. W., 1976
THE EFFECT OF SITE FACTORS ON MASONRY PERFORMANCE, Proceedings of the 1st Canadian Masonry Symposium, E. L. Jessop and M. A. Ward, eds., University of Calgary, Canada. (27)
Hendry, A. W. and Hasan, S. S., 1976
EFFECT OF SLENDERNESS AND ECCENTRICITY ON THE COMPRESSIVE STRENGTH OF WALLS, Proceedings of the 4th International Brick Masonry Conference, Groupement National de l'Industrie de la Terre Cuite, rue de Poissoniers 13, Brussels, Belgium. (27)
Hendry, A. W. and Sinha, B. P., 1969
RACKING TESTS ON STOREY-HEIGHT SHEAR-WALL STRUCTURES WITH OPENINGS, SUBJECT TO PRECOMPRESSION, Paper 23, Design Engineering and Constructing with Masonry Products, F. Johnson., ed., Gulf Publishing Co., Houston, Tex. (27)
Hendry, A. W. and Sinha, B. P., 1971
SHEAR TESTS ON FULL-SCALE SINGLE-STOREY BRICKWORK STRUCTURES SUBJECTED TO PRECOMPRESSION, *Civil Engineering and Public Works Review*, December 1971. (27)
Hendry, A. W., Sinha, B. P. and Maurenbrecher, A. H. P., 1973
FULL SCALE TESTS ON THE LATERAL STRENGTH OF BRICK CAVITY WALLS, *Proceedings*, British Ceramic Society, No. 21. (27)
Henkley, A. T., 1966
TESTS ON ONE-STOREY PRESTRESSED BRICKWORK SHEAR WALLS, *New Zealand Engineering*, Vol. 21, No. 6. (27)
Hentschel, J., Richter, V. and Wolter, F., 1975
ON THE CALCULATION OF LONGITUDINAL FACADE WALLS WITH MANY OPENINGS WITH SPECIAL CONSIDERATION GIVEN TO THE BEARING CAPACITY OF LARGE PANEL BUILDINGS, CIB 2nd International Symposium on Bearing Walls (Warsaw, Poland, September 1975), Theme 2, Paper 7, pp. 169–180. (21E)
Hetenyi, M., 1946
BEAMS ON ELASTIC FOUNDATIONS, University of Michigan Press, Ann Arbor, Mich. (21D)
Heunisch, M., 1973
DESIGN AND SAFETY OF REINFORCED CONCRETE COLUMNS (Bemessung und Sicherheit von Stahlbetondruckgliedern), *Sicherheit von Betonbauten*, Deutscher Beton-Verein, Wiesbaden, Germany. (23)
Hickey, K. B., 1968
CREEP OF CONCRETE PREDICTED FROM ELASTIC MODULUS TESTS, Report No. C-1242, U.S. Dept. of Interior, Bureau of Reclamation, Denver, Colo. (25)
Higashi, Y. and Hirosawa, M., 1974
STIFFNESS AND CRACK CONTROL, unpublished communication to the Joint Council. (24)
Higashi, Y. and Ohwada, Y., 1969
FAILING BEHAVIOR OF REINFORCED CONCRETE BEAM-COLUMN CONNECTIONS SUBJECTED TO LATERAL LOAD, Memoirs of Faculty of Technology, Tokyo Metropolitan University, No. 19, pp. 91–101. (21D, 22)
Higashi, Y. and Takeda, T., 1972
INFLUENCE OF STIFFNESS ON DYNAMIC ANALYSIS AND METHOD, Technical Committee No. 24, State of Art Report 2, International Conference on Planning and Design of Tall Buildings, Lehigh University, Bethlehem, Pa. (24)
Higgins, R. F., 1970
REINFORCED MASONRY BEARING WALLS USED IN 13-STORY BUILDINGS, *Civil Engineering*, ASCE, November 1970, p. 40. (27)
Hilsdorf, H. K., 1965
STUDIES OF THE FUNDAMENTALS OF MASONRY STRENGTH, Report No. 40, Materialprufungsamt für das Bauwesen der Technische Hochschule München, Munich, Germany. (27)

Hilsdorf, H. K., 1969
INVESTIGATION INTO THE FAILURE MECHANISM OF BRICK MASONRY LOADED IN AXIAL COMPRESSION, Design Engineering and Constructing with Masonry Products, F. Johnson, ed., Gulf Publishing Co., Houston, Tex. (27)

Hirosawa, M., 1969
ULTIMATE STRENGTH OF REINFORCED CONCRETE WALLED FRAMES WITH AXIAL FORCE SUBJECTED TO LATERAL LOADING, *Transactions*, Architectural Institute of Japan, Tokyo, No. 108, pp. 8–14. (22)

Hirosawa, M., 1971
OTHER PROBLEMS CONCERNING SHEAR WALLS, Proceedings of 3rd Regional Conference on Planning and Design of Tall Buildings (Tokyo, Japan, September 1971). (22)

Hirosawa, M. and Goto, T., 1971–1973
STRENGTH AND DUCTILITY OF REINFORCED CONCRETE MEMBERS SUBJECTED TO SHEAR, MOMENT AND AXIAL LOAD, PART 1, 2, 3 (in Japanese), Summaries of Technical Papers of Annual Meeting of AIJ, November 1971–December 1973. (21D)

Hirosawa, M. et al., 1971
LATERAL TESTS ON MULTISTORIED FULL-SIZE BUILDING OF REINFORCED CONCRETE WALL CONSTRUCTION FOR EARTHQUAKE RESISTANT DESIGN, Building Research Institute, Ministry of Construction, Japanese Government Research Paper No. 49, May 1971. (21D)

Hisada, T., Ohmori, N. and Bessho, S., 1972
EARTHQUAKE DESIGN CONSIDERATIONS IN REINFORCED CONCRETE COLUMNS, *Earthquake Engineering and Structural Dynamics*, Vol. 1, No. 1, pp. 79–92; also, KICT Report No. 1, Kajima Institute of Construction Technology, Tokyo, Japan. (21D, 22)

Hoath, S. B. A., Lee, H. N. and Renton, K. H., 1970
THE EFFECT OF MORTARS ON THE STRENGTH OF BRICKWORK CUBES, Proceedings of the 2nd International Brick Masonry Conference, H. W. H. West and K. H. Speed, eds, British Ceramic Research Association, Stoke-on-Trent, England, 1971. (27)

Hoeland, G., 1969
ON THE ANALYSIS OF SHEAR WALLS ACTING AS FRAMES (in German), *Beton-und Stahlbetonbau*, No. 5, pp. 124–126. (22)

Hognestad, E., Hanson, N. W. and McHenry, D., 1955
CONCRETE STRESS DISTRIBUTION IN ULTIMATE STRENGTH DESIGN, *ACI Journal*, American Concrete Institute, Vol. 52, No. 4. (22)

Holister, S. C., 1967
EXPERIMENTAL STRESS ANALYSIS, Cambridge University Press, Cambridge, England. (A38)

Holland, E. P., 1973
HORIZONTAL EFFECTS—LENGTH CHANGES DUE TO SHRINKAGE AND TEMPERATURE; EXPANSION, CONSTRUCTION, AND CONTROL JOINTS—IN STRUCTURAL SLABS, Planning and Design of Tall Buildings, Proceedings of 1972 ASCE-IABSE International Conference, Vol. III, No. 25-5, ASCE, New York. (25)

Hollings, J. P., 1973
A PHILOSOPHY FOR IMPROVING OLD BUILDINGS TO RESIST EARTHQUAKES, Seminar on High Earthquake Risk Buildings (Wellington, New Zealand, October 1973). (27)

Holmberg, A. and Lindgren, S., 1970
CRACK SPACING AND CRACK WIDTHS DUE TO NORMAL FORCE OR BENDING MOMENT, Document D2: 1970, National Swedish Building Research. (24)

Holmes, I. L., 1967
MASONRY BUILDINGS IN HIGH INTENSITY SEISMIC ZONES, Design Engineering and Constructing with Masonry Products, F. Johnson, ed., Gulf Publishing Co., Houston, Tex., pp. 346–356. (27)

Holmes, M., Astill, A. W. and Martin, L. H., 1969
EXPERIMENTAL STRESSES AND DEFLECTIONS OF A MODEL SHEAR WALL STRUCTURE, *ACI Journal*, American Concrete Institute, Vol. 66, No. 6, pp. 667–677. (A38)

Holmes, M. and Sinclair Jones, H. W., 1970
PLASTIC DESIGN OF MULTI-STOREY SWAY FRAMES, *Proceedings*, Institution of Civil Engineers, London, England, Paper 7332. (23)

Hongladaromp, T. and Lee, S. L., 1974
AN APPROXIMATE ANALYSIS OF SHEAR WALL-FRAME BUILDINGS, Proceedings of the Conference on Tall Buildings, 25th National/Regional Conference (Kuala Lumpur, Malaysia, December 2–5, 1974), Institution of Engineers, Kuala Lumpur, pp. 4.44–4.53. (21C)

Hongladaromp, T., Lee, S. L. and Wang, Y. C., 1972
APPROXIMATE ANALYSIS OF TALL BUILDINGS FRAMES, Proceedings of the National Conference on Tall Buildings, Vol. II, 7th National/Regional Conference (Warsaw, Poland, November 27–30, 1972), Warsaw Technical University, Polish Group of IABSE, ASCE-IABSE Joint Committee on Planning and Design of Tall Buildings, Warsaw, pp. 123–138. (21C)

Hongladaromp, T., Pithyachariyakul, P. and Lee, S. L., 1974
ANALYSIS OF ASYMMETRIC SHEAR WALL-FRAME BUILDINGS, Proceedings of the Regional Conference on Tall Buildings, 22nd National/Regional Conference (Bangkok, Thailand, January 23–25, 1974), Asian Institute of Technology, Bangkok, pp. 353–365. (21C)

Horacek, E., 1973
RECENT KNOWLEDGE OF THE THEORETICAL AND EXPERIMENTAL SOLUTION OF THE LOAD-BEARING WALL SYSTEM OF HIGH-RISE BUILDINGS, Proceedings, 10th National/Regional Conference (Bratislava, Czechoslovakia, April 1973), pp. 361–372. (21C)

Horacek, E., Lishak, V. and Sokolov, M., 1975
DETERMINING THE FLEXIBILITY OF WARPED LINTELS, CIB 2nd International Symposium on Bearing Walls (Warsaw, Poland, September 1975), Theme 2, Paper 8, pp. 181–185. (21E)

Horne, M. R., 1961
STABILITY OF ELASTIC-PLASTIC STRUCTURES, Chapter 8, *Progress in Solid Mechanics*, Sneddon and Hill, eds., North Holland Publishing Co., Amsterdam, The Netherlands. (23)

Horne, M. R. and Merchant, W., 1965
THE STABILITY OF FRAMES, Pergamon Press, England, pp. 146–151. (23)

Hossdorf, H., 1971
MODEL ANALYSIS (Modellstatik), Bauverlag, Wiesbaden, Germany. (A38)

Hribar, J. A. and Vasko, R. C., 1969
END ANCHORAGE OF HIGH STRENGTH STEEL REINFORCING BARS, *ACI Journal*, American Concrete Institute, Vol. 66, No. 11, p. 875. (21D)

Huddleston, J. V., 1974
NONLINEAR STABILITY OF TALL BUILDINGS UNDER COMBINED LOADS, Proceedings of the Regional Conference on Tall Buildings, 22nd National/Regional Conference (Bangkok, Thailand, January 1974), Asian Institute of Technology, Bangkok, Thailand, pp. 129–138. (23)

Huet, C., 1973
BASIC FORMULATION OF THE EVOLUTION OF THE CONSTRAINTS AND DEFORMATIONS IN CERAMIC-CEMENT COMPLEXES (Formules de base pour l'évolution des contraintes et déformations dans les complexes céramique-béton), Proceedings of the 3rd International Brick Masonry Conference, Bundesverband der Deutschen Ziegelindustrie e.v. Essen, Germany. (27)

Hugenschmidt, F., 1974
EPOXY ADHESIVES IN PRECAST PRESTRESSED CONCRETE CONSTRUCTION, *Journal of the Prestressed Concrete Institute*, Vol. 19, No. 2, pp. 112–124. (21E)

Huizer, A. and Ward, M., 1976
THE EFFECT OF BRICK TYPE ON THE COMPRESSIVE STRENGTH OF MASONRY, Proceedings of the 4th International Brick Masonry Conference, Groupement National de l'Industrie de la Terre Cuite, rue de Poissoniers 13, Brussels, Belgium. (27)

Huizer, A., Jessop, E. L., Morstead, H. and Ward, M. A., 1976
MEASURING THE CONSISTENCY OF MASONRY MORTARS IN THE LABORATORY AND ON THE JOB SITE, Proceedings of the 1st Canadian Masonry Symposium, E. L. Jessop and M. A. Ward, eds., University of Calgary, Canada. (27)

IABSE, 1969
SYMPOSIUM ON SAFETY CONCEPTS IN STRUCTURES (Symposium sur les notions de sécurité dans les structures), Proceedings of symposium held in London, IABSE, Zurich, Switzerland. (26)
IAEE (International Association for Earthquake Engineering), 1970
EARTHQUAKE RESISTANT REGULATIONS: A WORLD LIST, Association for Science Documents Information, Tokyo, Japan. (24)
ICE, 1964
ULTIMATE LOAD DESIGN OF CONCRETE STRUCTURES, Report of the Research Committee, Institution of Civil Engineers, London, England. (22)
Iffland, J. S. B., 1972
DESIGN FOR STABILITY IN HIGH-RISE BUILDINGS, State of Art Report No. 2, Committee 16, ASCE-IABSE Joint Committee on Planning and Design of Tall Buildings. (23)
Ilantzis, A., 1973
DEFORMATIONS AND MECHANICAL RESISTANCE OF HOLLOW BRICK WALLS AND OF HOLLOW CEMENT BLOCKS MADE OF LIGHT AND COARSE AGGREGATE, UNDER ECCENTRIC AND NONECCENTRIC LOADS (Déformations et résistance mécanique des murs en briques creuses et en blocs de béton creux de cranulats légers et lourds sous charges centrées et excentrées), Proceedings of the 3rd International Brick Masonry Conference, Bundesverband der Deutschen Ziegelindustrie e.v. Essen, Germany. (27)
Informatie-Bulletin, 1975
TRANSITORIUM 3 ON THE "UITHOF" CAMPUS OF THE UNIVERSITY OF UTRECHT (Transitorium 3 in het Universiteits-Centrum "de Uithof" Utrecht), Systeembouw, 1975/1. (21E)
Inomata, S., 1969
COMPARATIVE STUDY ON BEHAVIOUR OF PRESTRESSED AND REINFORCED CONCRETE BEAMS SUBJECTED TO REVERSED LOADING, Journal of Prestressed Concrete Engineering Association, Japan, Vol. 11, No. 1. (22)
Institution of Structural Engineers, 1975
FIRE RESISTANCE OF CONCRETE STRUCTURES, Report of Joint Committee of the Institution of Structural Engineers and the Concrete Society, August 1975. (21E)
International Standard Organization, 1973
GENERAL PRINCIPLES FOR THE VERIFICATION OF THE SAFETY OF STRUCTURES, ISO Norm 2394, International Organization for Standardization, Geneva, Switzerland. (26)
International Standard Organization, undated
GUIDE FOR THE EVALUATION OF HUMAN RESPONSE TO WHOLE BODY VIBRATION, TC-10B WG, International Organization for Standardization, Geneva, Switzerland. (26)
Irle, W., 1973
WALL MORTAR, RESISTANT AGAINST STORM WATERS, USED FOR DRESSING MASONRY WITH VISIBLE BRICKS (Mauermortel für schlagregensicheres Ziegelsicht- und Verblendmauerwerk), Proceedings of the 3rd International Brick Masonry Conference, Bundesverband der Deutschen Ziegelindustrie e.v. Essen, Germany. (27)
Isberner, A. W., 1969
PROPERTIES OF MASONRY CEMENT MORTARS, Design Engineering and Constructing with Masonry Products, F. Johnson, ed., Gulf Publishing Co., Houston, Tex. (27)
Ishikawa, N. and Grierson, D. E., 1972
ITERATIVE OPTIMAL LIMIT DESIGN OF REINFORCED CONCRETE FRAMES, Symposium on Inelasticity and Nonlinearity in Structural Concrete, Paper 16, SM Study No. 8, Solid Mechanics Division, University of Waterloo, (21B)
Ismail, M. A. F. and Jirsa, J. O., 1972a
BOND DETERIORATION IN REINFORCED CONCRETE SUBJECTED TO LOW CYCLE LOADS, ACI Journal, American Concrete Institute, Vol. 69, No. 6, pp. 334–343. (21D, 22)

Ismail, M. A. F. and Jirsa, J. O., 1972b
BEHAVIOR OF ANCHORED BARS UNDER LOW CYCLE OVERLOADS PRODUC-
ING INELASTIC STRAINS, *ACI Journal*, American Concrete Institute, Vol. 69, No. 7,
pp. 433–438. (22)

Iyengar, H., 1973
PRELIMINARY DESIGN AND OPTIMIZATION OF STEEL BUILDING SYSTEMS,
Planning and Design of Tall Buildings, Proceedings of 1972 ASCE-IABSE International
Conference, Vol. II, No. 14-2, ASCE, New York. (21B)

Iyengar, K. T. and Narayanaswamy, V. P., 1967
INCREMENTAL LOAD ANALYSIS OF CONTINUOUS BEAMS WITH NONLIN-
EAR BEHAVIOR, Proceedings of the Symposium on Ultimate Load Design of Concrete
Structures, PSO College of Technology, Coimbatore, India. (22)

Jackson, N., 1973a
CRACKING AND CRACK CONTROL, Planning and Design of Tall Buildings,
Proceedings of 1972 ASCE-IABSE International Conference, Vol. III, No. 24-4, ASCE,
New York. (24)

Jackson, N., 1973b
TORSION/FLEXURE INTERACTION, Planning and Design of Tall Buildings, Pro-
ceedings of 1972 ASCE-IABSE International Conference, Vol. III, No. 22-D3, ASCE,
New York. (22)

Jackson, N. and Estanero, R. A., 1971
PLASTIC FLOW LAW FOR REINFORCED CONCRETE BEAMS UNDER COM-
BINED FLEXURE AND TORSION, *Magazine of Concrete Research*, Vol. 23, No. 77,
December 1971, with discussion Vol. 24, No. 81, December 1972. (22, 24)

James, J. A., 1969
REVIEW OF THE METHODS OF THE SAA BRICKWORK CODE—ASCA47-
69—FOR DETERMINING THE PERMISSIBLE COMPRESSIVE FORCE OF AXI-
ALLY-LOADED BRICKWORK, Report No. S/CA47-1969/2, Building Development
Laboratories Pty. Ltd., Perth, Australia. (27)

James, J. A., 1973
INVESTIGATION OF THE EFFECT OF WORKMANSHIP AND CURING CON-
DITIONS ON THE STRENGTH OF BRICKWORK, Report No. W/Work/1, Building
Development Laboratories Pty. Ltd., Perth, Australia; Proceedings of the 3rd Inter-
national Brick Masonry Conference, Bundesverband der Deutschen Ziegelindustrie e.v.
Essen, Germany. (27)

Janney, J. R., Breen, J. E., Geymayer, H., Lockman, W. T. and Rocha, M., 1970
THE USE OF MODELS IN SRUCTURAL ENGINEERING, Publication No. 24,
American Concrete Institute, pp. 1–18. (A38)

Jenkins, R. A. S., 1965
DESIGN AND ECONOMICS OF HIGH LOAD-BEARING BRICK STRUCTURES,
Proceedings, British Ceramic Society, No. 4. (27)

Jenkins, R. A. S. and Haseltine, B. A., 1968
RECENT EXPERIENCES WITH CALCULATED LOAD-BEARING BRICKWORK,
Proceedings, British Ceramic Society, No. 11. (27)

Jenkins, W. M., 1969
MATRIX AND DIGITAL COMPUTER METHODS IN STRUCTURAL ANALYSIS,
McGraw-Hill Book Co., Inc., London, England, pp. 189, 193. (22)

Jennings, A. and Majid, K. I., 1965
AN ELASTIC-PLASTIC ANALYSIS FOR FRAMED STRUCTURES LOADED UP TO
COLLAPSE, *The Structural Engineer*, Vol. 43, p. 407. (23)

Jennings, P. C., 1971
ENGINEERING FEATURES OF THE SAN FERNANDO EARTHQUAKE, FEB-
RUARY 9, 1971, Report EERL 71-02, California Institute of Technology, Pasadena,
Calif. (22)

Jensen, C. C., 1975
ON THE ULTIMATE LOAD OF VERTICAL KEYED SHEAR JOINTS IN LARGE-
PANEL BUILDINGS, CIB 2nd International Symposium on Bearing Walls (Warsaw,
Poland, September 1975), Theme 2, Report 9, pp. 187–195. (21E)

Jergling, A., 1975
  BEARING WALLS BALANCED BY FLOORS, CIB 2nd International Symposium on
  Bearing Walls (Warsaw, Poland, September 1975), Theme 2, Paper 10, pp. 197–224. (21E)
Jirsa, J. O., 1973
  TORSION IN FLOOR SLAB STRUCTURES, Analysis of Torsion in Reinforced Concrete
  Structures, Publication No. SP-35, American Concrete Institute. (21D)
Jirsa, J. O., Baumgartner, J. L. and Mogbo, N., 1969
  TORSIONAL STRENGTH OF SPANDREL BEAMS, *ACI Journal*, American Concrete
  Institute, Vol. 66, No. 11, p. 926. (21D)
Johansen, K. W., 1962
  YIELD LINE THEORY, Cement and Concrete Association, London, England. (21D)
Johnson, A. I., 1950
  CALCULATION OF DEFORMATION IN REINFORCED CONCRETE STRUC-
  TURES AFTER FORMATION OF CRACKS (Baräkning av deformationer i armerade
  betongkonstruktioner efter sprickbildningen), Bulletin No. 6, Division of Building Statics
  and Structural Engineering, Royal Institute of Technology, Stockholm, Sweden. (25)
Johnson, A. I., 1951
  DEFORMATIONS OF REINFORCED CONCRETE, Publications of IABSE, 11, Zurich,
  Switzerland, p. 253. (25)
Johnson, F. B. and Thompson, J. N., 1969
  CORRELATION OF TESTS OF MASONRY ASSEMBLAGES WITH STRENGTH
  CHARACTERISTICS OF REINFORCED MASONRY BEAMS, Design Engineering
  and Constructing with Masonry Products, F. B. Johnson, ed., Gulf Publishing Co.,
  Houston, Tex. (27)
Johnson, F. B., Thompson, J. N. and Matthys, J. H., 1970
  THE DEVELOPMENT OF STRUCTURAL DESIGN CRITERIA FOR CLAY TILE
  ASSEMBLAGES, Proceedings of the 2nd International Brick Masonry Conference, H.
  W. H. West and K. H. Speed, eds., British Ceramic Research Association, Stoke-on-Trent,
  England, 1971. (27)
Johnson, L. P. and Sawyer, H. A., 1958
  ELASTIC-PLASTIC ANALYSIS OF CONTINUOUS BEAMS AND FRAMES, *Journal
  of the Structural Division*, ASCE, Vol. 84, No. ST8, Proc. Paper 1879. (22)
Johnston, B. C. (ed.), 1966
  THE COLUMN RESEARCH COUNCIL GUIDE TO DESIGN CRITERIA FOR
  METAL COMPRESSION MEMBERS, 2nd ed., John Wiley & Sons, Inc., New York, p.
  217. (23)
Johnston, V. R. and McNeilly, T. H., 1973
  SPECIFICATIONS, TESTING AND SITE CONTROL FOR STRUCTURAL BRICK-
  WORK, Proceedings of the 3rd International Brick Masonry Conference, Bundesverband
  der Deutschen Ziegelindustrie e.v. Essen, Germany. (27)
Jones, L. L. and Wood, R. H., 1967
  YIELD LINE ANALYSIS OF SLABS, Thames and Hudson, London, England. (21D)
Jones, P. E., 1973
  THE PRESENT SITUATION ABOUT UNIVERSITY BUILDING IN THE UNITED
  KINGDOM, Proceedings of the 3rd International Brick Masonry Conference, Bundes-
  verband der Deutschen Ziegelindustrie e.v. Essen, Germany. (27)
Jorgensen, D. W., 1972
  INVESTMENT BEHAVIOR IN U.S. MANUFACTURING, *Econometrica*, Vol. 35, No. 2.
  (21B)
Jorgensen, I. F., 1962
  INFLUENCE OF REINFORCEMENT STRESS-STRAIN CURVES ON A CONCRETE
  MEMBER OF ULTIMATE LOAD, *ACI Journal*, American Concrete Institute, Vol. 59,
  No. 3. (22)
Jumikis, T., 1973
  THE ROLE OF STRUCTURAL CONSULTANTS IN THE DESIGN OF TALL
  BUILDINGS, Proceedings of the 12th Regional Conference (Sydney, Australia, August
  14–17, 1973), Lehigh University, Bethlehem, Pa., pp. 156–170. (21B)
Jung, E., 1973
  REPORT ON TESTS ON WALLS BUILT OF WALL STONES OF THE SAME
  PRODUCTION BUT WITH DIFFERENT HEIGHTS (Bericht über Versuche an

Wanden hergestellt aus Mauersteinen gleicher Produktion, jedoch mit unterschiedlichen Hohenmassen), Proceedings of the 3rd International Brick Masonry Conference, Bundesverband der Deutschen Ziegelindustrie e.v. Essen, Germany. (27)

Jurica, M., Sobota, J. and Zvara, J., 1973
STATICAL ANALYSIS AND BEHAVIOR OF THE REINFORCED CONCRETE CORE OF THE TV-TALL BUILDING, BRATISLAVA, Proceedings, 10th National/Regional Conference (Bratislava, Czechoslovakia, April 9–12, 1973), Lehigh University, Bethlehem, Pa., pp. 475–482. (21C)

Kalita, U. C. and Hendry, A. W., 1970
AN EXPERIMENTAL AND THEORETICAL INVESTIGATION OF THE STRESSES AND DEFLECTIONS IN MODEL CROSS-WALL STRUCTURES, Proceedings of the 2nd International Brick Masonry Conference, H. W. H. West and K. H. Speed, eds., British Ceramic Research Association, Stoke-on-Trent, England, 1971. (27)

Kalita, U. C. and Hendry, A. W., 1973
AN INVESTIGATION OF THE STRESSES AND DEFLECTIONS IN A MODEL CROSS-WALL STRUCTURE SUBJECTED TO LATERAL LOAD AND TORSION, Proceedings of the 3rd International Brick Masonry Conference, Bundesverband der Deutschen Ziegelindustrie e.v. Essen, Germany. (27)

Kano, Y. and Nakayama, T., 1969
SHEAR STRENGTH OF REINFORCED CONCRETE BEAMS UNDER MANY CYCLIC ALTERNATE LOADINGS (in Japanese), Proceedings, Annual Conference of the Architectural Institute of Japan (August 1969), pp. 887–888. (22)

Kármán, T., 1973
LOAD FACTORS, Planning and Design of Tall Buildings, Proceedings of 1972 ASCE-IABSE International Conference, Vol. III, No. 26-3, ASCE, New York. (20, 26)

Karp, J., 1973
TEMPERATURE EFFECTS IN TALL REINFORCED CONCRETE BUILDINGS, Planning and Design of Tall Buildings, Proceedings of 1972 ASCE-IABSE International Conference, Vol. III, No. 25-4, ASCE, New York. (25)

Kärrholm, G. and Petersson, H., 1973
STRESSES IN WALLS DUE TO VERTICAL LOADS, Planning and Design of Tall Buildings, Proceedings of 1972 ASCE-IABSE International Conference, Vol. III, No. 21-D10, ASCE, New York. (21C)

Kärrholm G. and Petersson, H., 1974
PROGRESSIVE COLLAPSE OF LARGE PANEL BUILDINGS, CIB 6th Congress, *The Impact of Research on the Built Environment*, Vol. I/1, Theme II/3, pp. 482–487. (21E)

Karsan, I. D. and Jirsa, J. O., 1969
BEHAVIOR OF CONCRETE UNDER COMPRESSIVE LOADINGS, *Journal of the Structural Division*, ASCE, Vol. 95, No. ST12, Proc. Paper 6935, p. 2543. (22)

Kateiva, G. A., 1970
THE EFFECTS OF THE MECKERING EARTHQUAKE ON ENGINEERED BRICK STRUCTURES IN PERTH, WESTERN AUSTRALIA, Proceedings of the 2nd International Brick Masonry Conference, H. W. H. West and K. H. Speed, eds., British Ceramic Research Association, Stoke-on-Trent, England, 1971. (27)

Kavyrchine, M., 1972
REINFORCED, PRECAST AND PRESTRESSED CONCRETE, SOA Report 1, Tech. Comm. 3, ASCE-IABSE International Conference on Tall Buildings (August 1972), Vol. Ia-3, pp. 13–34. (21E)

Kazinezy, G., 1933–34
THE DESIGN OF NOT FULLY RESTRAINED STEEL "I" FLOOR BEAMS CONSIDERING PLASTIC DEFORMATIONS (Die Bemessung unvollkommen eingespannten Stahl "I" Deckenträgen unter Berücksichtigung der plastischen Formänderungen), Publications of IABSE, Vol. 2, Zurich, Switzerland. (22)

Kemp, E. L., 1973
SUMMARY REPORT: COMMENTARY ON STRUCTURAL STANDARDS, Planning and Design of Tall Buildings, Proceedings of 1972 ASCE-IABSE International Conference, Vol. III, No. 20-Summary, ASCE, New York. (20, 26)

Kent, D. C. and Park, R., 1971
FLEXURAL MEMBERS WITH CONFINED CONCRETE, *Journal of the Structural Division*, ASCE, Vol. 97, No. ST7, Proc. Paper 8243, pp. 1869–1890. (23)

Kesler, C. E., 1973
CONTROL OF SHRINKAGE, CREEP AND TEMPERATURE VOLUME CHANGES THROUGH VARIATIONS OF MATERIAL PROPERTIES, Planning and Design of Tall Buildings, Proceedings of 1972 ASCE-IABSE International Conference, Vol. III, No. 25-1, ASCE, New York. (25)

Khan, F. R., 1967
ON SOME SPECIAL PROBLEMS OF ANALYSIS AND DESIGN OF SHEAR WALL STRUCTURES, *Tall Buildings*, Pergamon Press, London, p. 321. (21C)

Khan, F. R., 1972
THE FUTURE OF HIGHRISE STRUCTURES, *Progressive Architecture*, Vol. 53, Reinhold Publishing, Inc., Stamford, Conn., pp. 78–85. (21A)

Khan, F. R., 1973a
RECENT DEVELOPMENT AND FUTURE OF HIGH RISE BUILDINGS, Theme III Report, 8th National/Regional Conference on Tall Buildings (New Delhi, India, January 1973), pp. 106–128. (21E)

Khan, F. R., 1973b
NEWER STRUCTURAL SYSTEMS AND THEIR EFFECT ON THE CHANGING SCALE OF CITIES, Schweizerischer Ingenieur und Architekten Verein, Berichte 1, Hochhauser, Zurich, Switzerland, pp. 195–201. (21E)

Khan, F. R. and Amin, N. R., 1973
ANALYSIS AND DESIGN OF FRAMED TUBE STRUCTURES FOR TALL CONCRETE BUILDINGS, Publication SP-36-3, American Concrete Institute. (21B, 24)

Khan, F. R. and Amin, N. R., 1973
ANALYSIS AND DESIGN OF FRAMED TUBE STRUCTURES FOR TALL CONCRETE BUILDINGS, *The Structural Engineer*, Vol. 51, p. 85. (21C)

Khan, F. R. and Fintel, M., 1966
EFFECT OF COLUMN EXPOSURE IN TALL STRUCTURES—ANALYSIS FOR LENGTH CHANGES OF EXPOSED COLUMNS, *ACI Journal*, American Concrete Institute, Vol. 63, No. 8, pp. 843–864. (22, 25)

Khan, F. R. and Fintel, M., 1968
EFFECTS OF COLUMN EXPOSURE IN TALL STRUCTURES, DESIGN CONSIDERATIONS AND FIELD OBSERVATIONS OF BUILDINGS, *ACI Journal*, American Concrete Institute, Vol. 65, No. 2, pp. 99–110. (24, 25)

Khan, F. R. and Fintel, M., 1971
CONCEPTIONAL DETAILS FOR CREEP, SHRINKAGE AND TEMPERATURE IN ULTRAHIGH-RISE BUILDINGS, Publication No. SP-27, Paper 9, American Concrete Institute, p. 215. (21E, 25)

Khan, F. and Iyengar, H. S., 1973
OPTIMIZATION APPROACH FOR CONCRETE HIGH-RISE STRUCTURES, Publication SP-36-4, American Concrete Institute, pp. 61–74. (21B)

Khan, F. R. and Nassetta, A. F., 1970
TEMPERATURE EFFECTS ON TALL STEEL FRAMED BUILDING, *Engineering Journal*, American Institute of Steel Construction, New York. (25)

Khan, F. R. and Sbarounis, J., 1964
INTERACTION OF SHEAR WALLS WITH FRAMES, *Journal of the Structural Division*, ASCE, Vol. 90, No. ST3, Proc. Paper 3957, pp. 285–335. (21A, 21C, 22)

Khan, M. A. H. and Stafford-Smith, B., 1975
RESTRAINING ACTION OF BRACING IN THIN-WALLED OPEN-SECTION BEAMS, *Proceedings*, Institution of Civil Engineers, London, Vol. 59, Part 2, p. 67. (21C)

Khoo, C. L. and Hendry, A. W., 1973
A FAILURE CRITERION FOR BRICKWORK IN AXIAL COMPRESSION, Proceedings of the 2nd International Brick Masonry Conference, Bundesverband der Deutschen Ziegelindustrie e.v. Essen, Germany. (27)

Kinniburgh, W., 1968
CLAYBRICKS AND CONCRETE BLOCKS, COMPARISON OF BUILDING TIMES REQUIRED TO BUILD WALLS, *Building*, Vol. 215, No. 6543. (27)

Kirk, C. L., 1970
NATURAL FREQUENCIES OF STIFFENED RECTANGULAR PLATES, *Journal of Sound and Vibration*, Vol. 13, No. 4, pp. 375–388. (21A)

Kirtschig, K., Cordes, R. and Schoner, W., 1973
DETERMINATION OF THE LOAD CAPACITY OF MASONRY BY THE HELP OF
STRESS-STRAIN LINES (Zur Ermittlung der Tragfahigkeit von Mauerwerk mit Hilfe
von Spannungsdehnungslinien), Proceedings of the 3rd International Brick Masonry
Conference, Bundesverband der Deutschen Ziegelindustrie e.V., Essen, Germany. (27)
Kitagawa, Y., 1972
A STUDY OF THE SOIL-BUILDING INTERACTION SYSTEM BY SIMULTANE-
OUS OBSERVATION OF EARTHQUAKE MOTIONS, Building Research Institute,
Tokyo, Japan. (22)
Klein, A., 1965
MULTI-STOREY FLAT BUILDINGS IN CALCIUM SILICATE BRICKS AND
BLOCKS AND THE TESTING OF WALL PANELS OF BRICKS, BLOCKS AND
MORTAR FOR CALCULATED MASONRY, Proceedings of the International Sym-
posium on Autoclaved Silicate Building Products, p. 239. (27)
Koizumi, Y., Hirosawa, M., Okamoto, S., Matsushima, Y. and Endo, T., 1970
LATERAL LOAD TESTS ON MULTI-STORIED FULL-SIZE BUILDINGS OF RE-
INFORCED CONCRETE WALL CONSTRUCTION FOR EARTHQUAKE RESIS-
TANT DESIGN, BRI Research Paper No. 49, Building Research Institute, Tokyo, Japan.
(22)
Kokusho, S. and Hayashi, S., 1971
STRENGTH REDUCTION OF REINFORCED CONCRETE MEMBERS DUE TO
ALTERNATELY CYCLIC LOADING, Proceedings of the Tokyo Meeting of ASCE-
IABSE Joint Committee on Tall Buildings, Technical Report TC-26. (22)
Kokusho, S. and Ogura, K., 1970
SHEAR STRENGTH AND LOAD DEFLECTION CHARACTERISTICS OF REIN-
FORCED CONCRETE MEMBERS, Proceedings of the U.S.-Japan Seminar on
Earthquake Engineering with Emphasis on the Safety of School Buildings, Sendai, Japan,
pp. 364–389. (22)
Koncz, T., 1968
SYSTEM BUILDINGS WITH LARGE PREFABRICATES, Bauverlag GmbH, Germany.
(21E)
Koncz, T., 1970
MANUAL OF PRECAST CONCRETE CONSTRUCTION, VOL. 3: SYSTEM BUILD-
ING WITH LARGE PANELS, Bauverlag GmbH, Germany. (21E)
Kong, F. K., Robins, P. J. and Sharp, G. R., 1975
DESIGN OF REINFORCED CONCRETE DEEP BEAMS IN CURRENT PRACTICE,
The Structural Engineer, Vol. 53, No. 4, pp. 173–180. (21D)
König, G. and Heunisch, M., 1972
ON THE STATISTICAL SAFETY THEORY OF REINFORCED CONCRETE STRUC-
TURES (Zur statistischen Sicherheitstheorie im Stahlbetonbau), Mitteilungen aus dem
Institut für Massivbau der Technischen Hochschule Darmstadt, Heft 16, Ernst & Sohn,
Berlin, Germany. (23)
Koor, P. H., 1957
STRESSES IN CENTRALLY LOADED DEEP BEAMS, Proceedings, Society for Exper-
imental Stress Analysis, Vol. 15, No. 1. (22)
Kordina, K., 1959
THE DESIGN OF BUCKLING SENSITIVE REINFORCED CONCRETE MEMBERS
(Die Bemessung Knickgefahrdeter Stahlbetonbauteile), Arbeitstagung, Deutscher Beton-
Verein, Wiesbaden, Germany. (23)
Kordina, K., 1969
APPLICATION OF THE SAFETY THEORY TO STABILITY INVESTIGATIONS IN
CONCRETE CONSTRUCTION (Zur Anwendung der Sicherheitstheorie bei Stabilitäts-
untersuchungen im Stahlbetonbau), aus Theorie und Praxis des Stahlbetonbaues, Franz-
Festschrift, Ernst & Sohn, Berlin, Germany. (23)
Kordina, K., 1970
APPROXIMATED COMPUTATION METHOD OF RESTRAINT FORCES, presented
at IABSE Symposium, held at Madrid, Spain. (24)
Kordina, K., 1972
STABILITY ANALYSIS (Knicksicherheitsnachweis), Beton-Kalender, Wilhelm Ernst &
Sohn, Berlin, Germany. (24)

Kordina, K., 1973
CRACKING AND CRACK CONTROL, Planning and Design of Tall Buildings, Proceedings of 1972 ASCE-IABSE International Conference, Vol. III, No. 24-D2, ASCE, New York. (23, 24)

Koreishi, I., 1970
TEST OF REINFORCED CONCRETE BEAM-COLUMN CONNECTION, Umemura Laboratory Report, University of Tokyo, Japan, pp. 185–194. (22)

Korn, A., 1968
THE APPROXIMATION OF STABILITY EFFECTS ON FRAMES, Publications of IABSE 28-II, Zurich, Switzerland, pp. 101–112. (23)

Korn, A. and Galambos, T. V., 1968
BEHAVIOR OF ELASTIC-PLASTIC FRAMES, *Journal of the Structural Division*, ASCE, Vol. 94, No. ST5, Proc. Paper 5942, p. 1119. (23)

Kostem, C. N., 1970
THE STRESSES IN FOLDED PLATE ROOF TRAVERSES, Proceedings of Symposium, Association for Shell and Spatial Structures, Vienna, Austria, Vol. 2. (21A)

Kostem, C. N., 1972
THERMAL STRESSES AND DEFORMATIONS IN PNEUMATIC CUSHION ROOFS, Proceedings of Symposium, International Association for Shell and Spatial Structures, Delft, The Netherlands, Vol. 2. (21A)

Kostem, C. N., 1973a
OPTIMIZATION OF FOLDED PLATE ROOFS, *Computers and Structures*, Pergamon Press, London, Vol. 3. (21A)

Kostem, C. N., 1973b
OPTIMUM SHAPED PNEUMATIC ROOFS, Proceedings of International Symposium on Industrialized Spatial and Shell Structures, Kielce, Poland. (21A)

Kostem, C. N., 1976
LOAD-CARRYING CAPACITY OF RIBBED PRESTRESSED CONCRETE ROOF PANELS, Proceedings of World Congress on Space Enclosures (Montréal, Canada), International Association for Shell and Spatial Structures. (22)

Kostem, C. N. and Kulicki, J. M., 1975
INELASTIC ANALYSIS OF BEAM-COLUMNS, Proceedings of 2nd International Conference on Space Structures, Guildford, England. (22)

Kotlicki, W., 1974
LOADBEARING CAPACITY AND DEFORMABILITY OF HORIZONTAL JOINTS IN SZCZECIN AND W-70 SYSTEMS, CBSRD, Warsaw, Poland. (21E)

Kotlicki, W., 1975
APPLICATION OF THE FRAME MODEL IN EVALUATION OF FORCES IN-DUCED BY NONUNIFORM SETTLEMENT IN BUILDINGS WITH TRANS-VERSAL BEARING WALLS, CIB 2nd International Symposium on Bearing Walls (Warsaw, Poland, September 1975), Theme 5, Paper 1, pp. 387–401. (21E)

Kotlicki, W. and Bociaga, A., 1975
BEHAVIOR OF FLOOR-TO-WALL CONNECTION SUBJECTED TO HORIZONTAL TENSILE FORCES, CIB 2nd International Symposium on Bearing Walls (Warsaw, Poland, September 1975), Theme 5, Paper 2, pp. 403–415. (21E)

Krahl, N. W. and Ransom, R. R., 1970
CASE STUDY OF BRICKS USED AS FLOOR AND ROOF STRUCTURES, Design Engineering and Constructing with Masonry Products, F. Johnson, ed., Gulf Publishing Co., Houston, Tex. (27)

Krantz, D., undated
CALCULATED BRICK BEARING WALL CONSTRUCTION—WHAT? WHY? HOW? Advance Press, Perth, Australia. (27)

Kratky, R. J. and Puri, S. P. S., 1971
Discussion of MODIFIED BEAM METHOD FOR ANALYSIS OF SYMMETRICAL INTERCONNECTED SHEAR WALLS, by B. Stafford-Smith, *ACI Journal*, American Concrete Institute, Vol. 68, No. 6, p. 472. (21C)

Krawinkler, H., Popov, E. P. and Bertero, V. V., 1972
CYCLIC BEHAVIOR OF THREE REINFORCED CONCRETE FLEXURAL MEM-BERS WITH HIGH SHEAR, Report No. EERC 72-5, Earthquake Engineering Research Center, University of California, Berkeley. (22)

Krenek, J. and Sirhal, H., 1973
THE USE OF LARGE HOURDESSTONES IN CZECHOSLOVAKIAN ARCHITEC-
TURE (Die Verwendung grossformatiger Hourdissteine in tschechoslowakischen Bauwesen), Proceedings of the 3rd International Brick Masonry Conference, Bundesverband
der Deutschen Ziegelindustrie e.v. Essen, Germany. (27)

Krishnaswamy, K. T. and Gharpure, S. V., 1974
ANALYSIS OF COUPLED SHEAR WALLS SUBJECTED TO CONCENTRATED
LOADS AT FLOOR LEVELS, Proceedings of 25th National/Regional Conference on
Tall Buildings (Kuala Lumpur, Malaysia, December 1974), Institution of Engineers,
Kuala Lumpur, pp. 4.54–4.60. (21C)

Krol, W. and Kania, A., 1975
ON MODEL INVESTIGATION OF THE ELASTIC WORK OF BUILDING WALLS
ON MINING GROUNDS, CIB 2nd International Symposium on Bearing Walls
(Warsaw, Poland, September 1975), Theme 5, Paper 3, pp. 417–424. (21E)

Krol, W. and Malek, E., 1975
ON MODEL INVESTIGATIONS OF ULTIMATE STATES IN APARTMENT BUILD-
INGS LOCATED ON BENDING MINING GROUND, CIB 2nd International
Symposium on Bearing Walls (Warsaw, Poland, September 1975), Theme 5, Paper 4, pp.
425–434. (21E)

Krupinski, P. and Pawlikowski, J., 1975
ARRANGEMENT OF REINFORCEMENT IN LOAD-BEARING WALLS, CIB 2nd
International Symposium on Bearing Walls (Warsaw, Poland, September 1975), Theme 1,
Paper 8, pp. 67–75. (21E, 27)

Ku, A. B., 1974
ON THE STRUCTURAL STABILITY OF A TALL BUILDING, Proceedings of the
Regional Conference on Tall Buildings, 22nd National/Regional Conference (Bangkok,
Thailand, January 1974), Asian Institute of Technology, Bangkok, Thailand, pp. 139–149.
(23)

Kuenning, W. H. and Carlson, C. C., 1956
EFFECT OF VARIATIONS IN CURING AND DRYING ON THE PHYSICAL
PROPERTIES OF CONCRETE MASONRY UNITS, Development Dept. Bulletin D13,
Portland Cement Association. (27)

Kulicki, J. M. and Kostem, C. N., 1972
THE INELASTIC ANALYSIS OF REINFORCED AND PRESTRESSED CONCRETE
BEAMS, Fritz Engineering Laboratory Report No. 378B.1, Lehigh University, Bethle-
hem, Pa. (22)

Kulicki, J. M. and Kostem, C. N., 1973a
NONLINEAR ANALYSIS OF CONCRETE FLEXURAL MEMBERS, Planning and
Design of Tall Buildings, Proceedings of 1972 ASCE-IABSE International Conference,
Vol. DS, ASCE, New York. (21A, 22)

Kulicki, J. M. and Kostem, C. N., 1973b
FURTHER STUDIES ON THE NONLINEAR FINITE ELEMENT ANALYSIS OF
BEAMS, Fritz Engineering Laboratory Report No. 378A.5, Lehigh University, Bethle-
hem, Pa. (21A, 22)

Kulicki, J. M. and Kostem, C. N., 1973c
USER'S MANUAL FOR PROGRAM BEAM, Fritz Engineering Laboratory Report No.
378B.2, Lehigh University, Bethlehem, Pa. (21A, 22)

Kulicki, J. M. and Kostem, C. N., 1973d
APPLICATIONS OF THE FINITE ELEMENT METHOD TO INELASTIC BEAM-
COLUMN PROBLEMS, Fritz Engineering Laboratory Report No. 400.11, Lehigh
University, Bethlehem, Pa. (21A, 22, 23)

Kulicki, J. M. and Kostem, C. N., 1974a
THE EFFECTS OF DISCRETIZATION ON THE INELASTIC ANALYSIS OF PRE-
STRESSED CONCRETE BEAMS, Proceedings of the International Conference on
Discrete Methods in Engineering, Etas Libri, Milan, Italy. (22)

Kulicki, J. M. and Kostem, C. N., 1974b
INELASTIC ANALYSIS OF REINFORCED CONCRETE BEAM-COLUMNS, Pre-
liminary Report, IABSE Symposium on the Design and Safety of Reinforced Concrete
Compression Members (Quebec City, Canada). (22, 23)

Kulicki, J. M. and Kostem, C. N., 1975a
ANALYTICAL MODELING OF MATERIAL NONLINEARITIES, Proceedings of International Conference on Cable Structures (Bratislava, Czechoslovakia), International Association for Shell and Spatial Structures. (22)

Kulicki, J. M. and Kostem, C. N., 1975b
INELASTIC RESPONSE OF PRESTRESSED CONCRETE BEAMS, Publications of IABSE, Vol. 35-II, Zurich, Switzerland. (22)

Kulka, F., Liu, T. Y. and Yang, Y. C., 1975
PRESTRESSED CONCRETE BUILDING CONSTRUCTION USING PRECAST WALL PANELS, Journal of the Prestressed Concrete Institute, Vol. 20, No. 1, pp. 62–73. (21E)

Kupfer, H., Hilsdorf, H. K. and Rüsch, H., 1969
BEHAVIOR OF CONCRETE UNDER BIAXIAL STRESSES, ACI Journal, American Concrete Institute, Vol. 66, No. 8. (22)

Kuske, A., 1970
PHOTOELASTICITY IN THE DESIGN OF BUILDINGS (Spannungsoptik im Bauwesen), Werner, Düsseldorf, Germany. (A38)

LNEC, 1971
STRUCTURAL STUDIES OF THE PARQUE CENTRAL BUILDINGS (Estudos estructurais dos edificios de Parque Central), Seismic Tests of Transverse Walls (Ensaios Sismicos de Paredes Transversais), Laboratorio Nacional de Engenharia Civil, Lisbon, Portugal. (24)

Lampert, P., 1971
POSTCRACKING STIFFNESS OF REINFORCED CONCRETE BEAMS IN TORSION AND BENDING, Publication 71-20, Department of Civil Engineering, University of Toronto, Canada. (22, 24)

Laredo, M., 1969
GENERAL THEORY FOR THE BEHAVIOR OF LARGE STRUCTURES (Théorie général du comportement des grandes structures spatiales), Annales de l'Institut Technique du Bâtiment et des Travaux Publics, Paris, No. 254. (21C)

Larsson, L. E., 1959
BEARING CAPACITY OF PLAIN AND REINFORCED CONCRETE WALLS, Chalmers Technical University, Göteborg, Sweden. (21E)

Larsson, L. E., 1967
ANALYSIS OF WIND BRACING WALL PANELS IN TALL BUILDINGS (in Swedish), CTH Handlingar No. 315, Chalmers Technical University, Göteborg, Sweden. (22)

Lattbeton, 1965
HANDBOOK OF LIGHT WEIGHT CELLULAR CONCRETE (Tlattbetonghadboken), A. B. Lattbeton, Stockholm, Sweden. (27)

Lauletta, E. and Castoldi, A., 1970
EARTHQUAKE SIMULATION BY A SHAKE TABLE, ISMES Bulletin No. 48, Istituto Sperimentale Modelli e Strutture, Bergamo, Italy. (A38)

Lee, H. N. and Pyle, M. A., 1968
THE DESIGN OF MORTARS FOR CALCULATED LOAD BEARING BRICKWORK, Proceedings, British Ceramic Society, No. 11. (27)

Lefter, J. and Colville, J., 1976
EVALUATING THE EARTHQUAKE RESISTANCE OF EXISTING MASONRY CONSTRUCTION, Proceedings of the 1st Canadian Masonry Symposium, E. L. Jessop and M. A. Ward, eds., University of Calgary, Canada. (27)

LeMessurier, W. J., 1965
BRICK AS A STRUCTURAL MATERIAL, Proceedings of the 1st National Brick and Tile Bearing Wall Conference, Washington, D.C. (27)

Lenczner, D., 1970a
CREEP IN MODEL BRICKWORK, Design Engineering and Constructing with Masonry Products, F. Johnson, ed., Gulf Publishing Co., Houston, Tex. (27)

Lenczner, D., 1970b
CREEP IN BRICKWORK, Proceedings of the 2nd International Brick Masonry Conference, H. W. H. West and K. H. Speed, eds., British Ceramic Research Association, Stoke-on-Trent, England, 1971. (27)

Lenczner, D., 1973
CREEP IN BRICKWORK WITH AND WITHOUT DAMP PROOF COURSE, *Proceedings*, British Ceramic Society, No. 21. (27)

Lenczner, D. and Salahuddin, J., 1976
CREEP AND MOISTURE MOVEMENTS IN MASONRY PIERS AND WALLS, Proceedings of the 1st Canadian Masonry Symposium, E. L. Jessop and M. A. Ward, eds., University of Calgary, Canada. (27)

Leong, T. W. and Warner, R. F., 1970
LONG-TERM DEFLECTIONS OF REINFORCED CONCRETE BEAMS, *Civil Engineering Transactions*, Institution of Engineers, Australia, Vol. CE12, p. 21. (25)

Leonhardt, F., 1959
INITIAL AND TIME-DEPENDENT DEFLECTIONS OF CRACKED REINFORCED CONCRETE BEAMS: SUGGESTIONS FOR LIMITATIONS AND SIMPLIFIED ANALYSIS (Anfängliche und nachträgliche Durchbiegungen von Stahlbetonbalken im Zustand II, Vorschläge für Begrenzungen und vereinfachte Nachweise), *Beton und Stahlbeton*, Vol. 54, p. 240. (25)

Leonhardt, F., 1965
NEWS BULLETIN NO. 65, Bulletin d'information no. 65, Comité Européen du Béton, Paris, France. (22)

Leonhardt, F., 1971
REINFORCEMENT OF CONCRETE STRUCTURES (Das Bewehren von Stahlbetontragwerken), *Beton-Kalender*, Wilhelm Ernst & Sohn, Berlin, Germany. (24)

Leonhardt, F. and Teichen, K.-T., 1972
REINFORCED CONCRETE COLUMNS WITH HIGH STRENGTH STEEL (Druck Grosse von Bewehrungsstaben Stahlbeton Stutzen mit Hochfestem Stahl ST 90), Deutscher Ausschuss für Stahlbeton, Heft 222, Berlin, Germany. (21D)

Leonhardt, F. and Walther, R., 1962
SHEAR TEST OF SINGLE-SPAN REINFORCED CONCRETE BEAMS (Schubversuche an einfeldrigen Stahlbetonbalken), Bulletin 151, Deutscher Ausschuss für Stahlbeton, Berlin, Germany. (22)

Leonhardt, F. and Walther, R., 1966
WALL-LIKE BEAMS (Wandertige Träger), Bulletin 178, Deutscher Ausschuss für Stahlbeton, Berlin, Germany. (21D, 22)

Leonte, C., 1975
MULTISTORIED FRAMES WITH PRECAST PRESTRESSED CONCRETE BEAMS FOR RESISTANCE STRUCTURES OF STORIED INDUSTRIAL BUILDINGS (Cadre Multiplu Etajate cu Rigle Prefabricate de Beton Precomprimat Pentru Structurile de Resistenta ale Unor Cladire Industriale Etajate), Reinforced Concrete Tall Buildings, 34th National/Regional Conference (Iasi, Romania, October 1975), Vol. II, pp. 263-279. (21E)

Leuchars, J. M., 1973
MASONRY INFILL PANELS, M.E. Report, University of Canterbury, Christchurch, New Zealand. (27)

Levi, F., 1968
THE PROBLEM OF SAFETY IN HYPERSTATIC STRUCTURES (Il problema della sicurezza nelle costruzioni iperstatiche), *Giornale del Genio Civile*, No. 4. (26)

Levi, F., 1970
GRADUATED INTRODUCTION OF SEMI-PROBABILISTIC CORRECTION CO-EFFICIENTS (L'introduction graduée des coefficients de correction semi-probabilistes), Costruzioni in Cemento Armato, Studi e Rendiconti, Vol. 7. (22, 26)

Levi, F., 1973
THEME REPORT: LIMIT STATES DESIGN, Planning and Design of Tall Buildings, Proceedings of 1972 ASCE-IABSE International Conference, Vol. III, No. 26-Theme, ASCE, New York. (20, 26)

Lewicki, B., 1966
BUILDING WITH LARGE PREFABRICATES, (originally published by Arkady, Warsaw, 1964), Elsevier Publishing Co., New York. (21E)

Lewicki, B., 1968
THE STRENGTH OF HORIZONTAL JOINTS IN LARGE PANEL WALLS, Design Philosophy and its Application to Precast Concrete Structures, Cement and Concrete Association, London, England. (21E)

Lewicki, B. and Cholewicki, A., 1972
STRUCTURAL DESIGN OF TALL CONCRETE BUILDINGS, Proceedings of the 7th
National/Regional Conference on Tall Buildings (Warsaw, Poland, November 27–30,
1972), Warsaw Technical University, Polish Group of IABSE, ASCE-IABSE Joint
Committee on Planning and Design of Tall Buildings, Warsaw, pp. 235–276. (21C, 21E)

Lewicki, B. and Galkowski, Z., 1975
SPACING OF EXPANSION JOINTS IN PREFABRICATED BUILDINGS, CIB 2nd
International Symposium on Bearing Walls (Warsaw, Poland, September 1975), Theme 5,
Paper 5, pp. 435–455. (21E)

Lewicki, B. and Pauw, A., 1972
JOINTS, PRECAST PANEL BUILDINGS, SOA Report 2, Committee 21, ASCE-IABSE
International Conference on Tall Buildings, Vol. III-2, pp. 25–43. (21E)

Lewicki, B., Deuar, K. and Kapron, M., 1975
ANALYSIS OF WORK OF SECONDARY STRUCTURAL SYSTEM IN BUILDING
CORNER, CIB 2nd International Symposium on Bearing Walls (Warsaw, Poland,
September 1975), Theme 3, Paper 1, pp. 285–307. (21E)

Lewicki, B., Deuar, K. and Zieleniewski, S., 1974
INTERACTION OF FLOOR AND WALL FOR THE PREVENTION OF PROGRES-
SIVE COLLAPSE IN LARGE PANEL BUILDINGS, CIB 6th Congress, The Impact of
Research on the Built Environment, Vol. I/1, Theme II/3, pp. 494–499. (21E)

Lewicki, B., Kukulski, W. and Pawlikowski, J., 1972
COMMENTARY ON DESIGN SAFETY MARGINS FOR TALL CONCRETE BUILD-
ING, Proceedings of National Conference on Tall Buildings, Vol. 1, 7th National/Re-
gional Conference (Warsaw, Poland, November 1972), Warsaw Technical University,
Polish Group of IABSE, ASCE-IABSE Joint Committee on the Planning and Design of
Tall Buildings, Warsaw, Poland, pp. 297–307. (26)

Lewicki, B., Odgard, A. and Olesen, S. O., 1975
LIMITING THE RISK FOR PROGRESSIVE COLLAPSE, CIB 2nd International
Symposium on Bearing Walls (Warsaw, Poland, September 1975), Theme 3: Response of
Buildings Subjected to Abnormal Loadings, pp. 49–70. (21E)

Lewicki, B., Rao, A. G. M. and Murthy, D. S. R., 1974
STRUCTURAL REQUIREMENTS FOR LARGE PANEL BUILDINGS, UNDP/SERC,
Structural Engineering Research Centre, Madras, India. (21E)

Lewicki, B., Cholewicki, A., Greszta, J., Henclewski, T., Pogorzelski, A., Wierzbicki, S. and
Zieleniewski, S., 1975
HIGH-RISE LARGE PANEL BUILDINGS—PROBLEMS OF STRUCTURAL ANAL-
YSIS AND CONSTRUCTION, Research and Development Report, Center for Building
Systems, Warsaw, Poland. (21E)

Leyendecker, E. V. and Ellingwood, B. R., 1977
DESIGN METHODS FOR REDUCING THE RISK OF PROGRESSIVE COLLAPSE
IN BUILDINGS, Report No. NBSIR 76-1106, Center for Building Technology, National
Bureau of Standards, Washington, D.C. (27)

Liauw, T., 1972
MODERN DEVELOPMENT IN STRUCTURAL DESIGN CONCEPTS FOR TALL
BUILDINGS, *Indian Concrete Journal*, Vol. 46, No. 11. (21A)

Libbey, R. M., 1974
CALCULATED AND MEASURED DEFLECTIONS OF TALL CONCRETE BUILD-
INGS, presented at the ASCE Structural Engineering Conference, held at Cincinnati,
Ohio, in April 1974. (24)

Lie, T. T. and Allen, D. E., 1974
FIRE RESISTANCE OF REINFORCED CONCRETE COLUMNS, IABSE Symposium
on Design and Safety of Reinforced Concrete Compression Members, Preliminary
Publication, pp. 245–254. (23)

Lin, T. Y., 1965
DESIGN OF PRESTRESSED CONCRETE BUILDINGS FOR EARTHQUAKE RE-
SISTANCE, *Journal of the Structural Division*, ASCE, Vol. 91, No. ST5, Proc. Paper
4488, pp. 1–7. (22)

Lind, N. C., 1971
CONSISTENT PARTIAL SAFETY FACTORS, *Journal of the Structural Division*, ASCE,
Vol. 97, No. ST6, Proc. Paper 8166, pp. 1651–1670. (26)

Linzey, M. P. T., Brotchie, J. F. and Nicholas, J. F., 1973
A SYSTEMS APPROACH TO BUILDING PLANNING AND DESIGN, Proceedings of the 12th Regional Conference (Sydney, Australia, August 14–17, 1973), Lehigh University, Bethlehem, Pa., pp. 590–604. (21B)

Lorentsen, M., 1965
HOLES IN REINFORCED CONCRETE GIRDERS, Portland Cement Association, February 1965. (21D)

Lorentsen, M., 1968
LONGITUDINAL DEFORMATION OF SLENDER CONCRETE BEAMS (Longtidsdeformationer hos slakarmerade Betongbalkar), Byggmästaren 12. (25)

Lorentsen, M., 1972
CONSIDERATION OF IMPERFECTIONS IN THE DESIGN OF PREFABRICATED BUILDINGS, SOA Report 6, Committee 23, ASCE-IABSE International Conference on Tall Buildings, Vol. III-23, pp. 87–105. (21E)

Lugez, J., 1971
STRENGTH OF HORIZONTAL CONNECTIONS BETWEEN CONCRETE WALL PANELS AND FLOORS (Résistance des joinctions horizontales entre panneaux de mur en béton et plancher), Document annexe no. 5 to Bulletin d'information no. 77, Comité Européen du Béton, Paris, France. (21E)

Lugez, J., 1973
CONTRIBUTION TO THE STUDY OF THE DEFORMABILITY OF JOINTS BETWEEN HOLLOW BRICK MASONRY AND FLOORS (Contribution à l'étude de la résistance et de la déformabilité des joints entre maçonnerie de briques creuses et plancher), Proceedings of the 3rd International Brick Masonry Conference, Bundesverband der Deutschen Ziegelindustrie e.V., Essen, Germany. (27)

Lugez, J. and Zarzycki, A., 1969
INFLUENCE OF HORIZONTAL JOINTS ON THE RESISTANCE OF PREFABRICATED PANEL ELEMENTS OF BEARING WALLS (Influence des joints horizontaux sur la resistance des elements prefabriques de murs porteurs), Cahiers du Centre Scientifique et Technique du Bâtiment, No. 103. (21E)

Lugez, J., Zieleniewski, S. and Henclewski, T., 1975
IMPACT OF HORIZONTAL JOINTS ON WORKING DIAGRAM OF BEARING WALLS IN LARGE PANEL BUILDINGS, CIB 2nd International Symposium on Bearing Walls (Warsaw, Poland, September 1975), Theme 1: Behavior of Bearing Walls Resisting Vertical Loads, pp. 5–22. (21E)

Luisoni, C. J., Somenson, H. M. and Ungaro, M. A., 1970
EXPERIMENTAL VERIFICATION OF A PLASTIC AND AN ELASTIC ANALYSIS OF A SHEAR WALL (Verificacion experimental de un calculo plastico y otro elastico de una pared de corte), XIV Jornadas Sudamericanas de Ingenieria Estructural y IV Simposio Panamericano de Estructuras, Vol. 5, Buenos Aires, Argentina, pp. 230–286. (24)

Lutz, L. A. and Gergely, P., 1967
MECHANICS OF BOND AND SLIP OF DEFORMED BARS IN CONCRETE, ACI Journal, American Concrete Institute, Vol. 64, No. 11. (24)

Lutz, L. A., Sharma, N. K. and Gergely, P., 1967
INCREASE IN CRACK WIDTH IN REINFORCED CONCRETE BEAMS UNDER SUSTAINED LOADING, ACI Journal, American Concrete Institute, Vol. 64, No. 9. (24)

Lwow, I. A. and Bluger, F. G., 1968
TEST RESULTS ON STRENGTH OF MULTISTORY BUILDINGS (Resultaty Naucno-isledovatielskich Rabot v Oblasti Procnosti Konstrukstiyi Mnogoetaznych Zdaniy). MNIPITEP, Moscow, USSR. (21E)

Lyse, I., 1933
TESTS ON REINFORCED BRICK COLUMNS, Journal of the American Society of Ceramics, Vol. 16. (27)

Macchi, G., 1954
STRENGTH AND DEFORMATION OF CONCRETE JOINTS (Résistance et déformation des noeuds des ossatures en béton armé), No. 15, Atti 1st. Universitorio di Architettura, Venice, Italy. (22)

Macchi, G., 1955
EXPERIMENTAL INVESTIGATIONS ON CONTINUOUS PRESTRESSED CON-
CRETE BEAMS IN THE PLASTIC RANGE AND ULTIMATE STRENGTH (Etude
expérimentale de poutres continues précontraintes dans le domaine plastique et à la
rupture), Proceedings of 2nd Congress (Amsterdam, The Netherlands), Fédération
Internationale de la Précontrainte. (22)
Macchi, G., 1956
REDISTRIBUTION OF MOMENT IN INELASTIC FIELD AND RUPTURE IN
PRESTRESSED CONCRETE BEAMS, Proceedings of Symposium on Plasticity in the
Science of Construction. (22)
Macchi, G., 1959
A PROPOSED METHOD OF ANALYSIS BASED ON THE THEORY OF IMPOSED
ROTATIONS (Proposition de calcul basée sur la théorie des rotations imposées), Bulletin
no. 21, Comité Européen du Beton, Paris, France. (22)
Macchi, G., 1961
REDUNDANT STRUCTURES (Structures hyperstatiques), Note pour la discussion à
Monaco, Bulletin no. 30, Comité Européen du Béton, Paris, France. (22)
Macchi, G., 1964a
ELASTIC DISTRIBUTION OF MOMENTS ON CONTINUOUS BEAMS, Proceedings
of ACI-ASCE International Symposium on the Flexural Mechanics of Reinforced
Concrete (Miami, Fla., November 1964), ASCE, New York. (22)
Macchi, G., 1964b
A PROPOSED METHOD FOR CALCULATING THE DEFORMATIONS IN RE-
DUNDANT CONCRETE STRUCTURES (Proposition pour le calcul des déformations
du béton armé en vue des calcules hyperstatiques), Bulletin no. 52, Comité Européen du
Béton, Paris, France. (22)
Macchi, G., 1966
THE METHOD OF IMPOSED ROTATIONS (Méthode des rotations imposées), Struc-
tures hyperstatiques, Projèt d'annexe aux Recommandations Pratiques, Comité Européen
du Béton, Paris, France. (22)
Macchi, G., 1969a
CONTRIBUTION TO THE THEORY OF BEARING WALL CONSTRUCTION ON
THE ASSUMPTION OF CONTINUITY (Contribution à l'étude des constructions à
murs porteurs avec l'hypothèse de la continuité), CIB Symposium on Bearing Walls
(Warsaw, Poland, June 1969). (21E)
Macchi, G., 1969b
LIMIT-STATES DESIGN OF STATICALLY INDETERMINATE STRUCTURES
COMPOSED OF LINEAR MEMBERS, Costruzioni in Cemento Armato, No. 6. (22)
Macchi, G., 1970a
PRELIMINARY DESIGN OF CONCRETE FRAMES ACCORDING TO THE LIMIT-
STATES METHOD, No. 14, Atti Ist. Universitorio di Architettura, Venice, Italy. (22)
Macchi, G., 1970b
THE METHOD OF IMPOSED ROTATIONS (Méthode des rotations imposées), Struc-
tures hyperstatiques, Annexe aux Recommandations Pratiques, Comité Européen du
Béton, Paris, France. (22)
Macchi, G., 1970c
SAFETY CONSIDERATIONS FOR A LIMIT-STATE DESIGN OF BRICK MASON-
RY, Proceedings of the 2nd International Brick Masonry Conference, H. W. H. West and
K. H. Speed, eds., British Ceramic Research Association, Stoke-on-Trent, England, 1971.
(27)
Macchi, G., 1973a
THEME REPORT: NON-LINEAR ANALYSIS AND LIMIT DESIGN, Planning and
Design of Tall Buildings, Proceedings of 1972 ASCE-IABSE International Conference,
Vol. III, No. 22-Theme, ASCE, New York. (22)
Macchi, G., 1973b
THICKNESS EFFECTS ON CREEP, Planning and Design of Tall Buildings, Proceedings
of 1972 ASCE-IABSE International Conference, Vol. III, No. 25-D3, ASCE, New York.
(25)
Macchi, G., 1973c
PRACTICAL RECOMMENDATIONS FOR MASONRY STRUCTURES PRINCIPLES
(Stand der CIB-Richtlinien für die Berechnung und Ausführung von Mauerwerk),

Proceedings of the 3rd International Brick Masonry Conference, Bundesverband der Deutschen Ziegelindustrie e.V., Essen, Germany. (27)

MacGregor, J. G., 1967
RECENT NORTH AMERICAN RESEARCH AND DESIGN DEVELOPMENTS IN THE FIELD OF REINFORCED CONCRETE COLUMNS, Bulletin d'information No. 63, Comité Européen du Béton, Paris, France, p. 1. (21D)

MacGregor, J. G., 1972a
STABILITY OF REINFORCED CONCRETE BUILDING FRAMES, SOA Report 1, Com. 23, ASCE-IABSE International Conference on Tall Buildings (August 1972), Vol. III-23, pp. 19–35. (21E)

MacGregor, J. G., 1972b
FLEXURAL STIFFNESS, Discussion No. 5, Technical Committee 24, International Conference on Planning and Design of Tall Buildings, Lehigh University, Bethlehem, Pa. (24)

MacGregor, J. G., 1973a
LOAD FACTOR VARIABLES, Planning and Design of Tall Buildings, Proceedings of 1972 ASCE-IABSE International Conference, Vol. III, No. 26-D1, ASCE, New York. (20, 26)

MacGregor, J. G., 1973b
DESIGN FOR THE LIMIT STATE OF INSTABILITY, Planning and Design of Tall Buildings, Proceedings of 1972 ASCE-IABSE International Conference, Vol. III, No. 26-D2, ASCE, New York. (20, 26)

MacGregor, J. G., 1974
SIMPLE DESIGN PROCEDURES, presented at the IABSE Symposium on the Design and Safety of Reinforced Concrete Compression Members held at Québec, Canada. (24)

MacGregor, J. G., 1976
SAFETY AND LIMIT STATES DESIGN FOR REINFORCED CONCRETE, Canadian Journal of Civil Engineering, Vol. 3, No. 4, pp. 484–513. (26)

MacGregor, J. G. and Barter, S. L., 1966
TESTS OF LONG ECCENTRICALLY LOADED COLUMNS BENT IN DOUBLE CURVATURE, Symposium on Reinforced Concrete Columns, Publication No. SP-13, American Concrete Institute, p. 139. (21D)

MacGregor, J. G., Breen, J. E. and Pfrang, E. O., 1970
DESIGN OF SLENDER COLUMNS, ACI Journal, American Concrete Institute, Vol. 67, No. 1, p. 6. (21D, 23)

MacGregor, J. G., Oelhafen, U. and Hage, S. E., 1975
A RE-EXAMINATION OF THE EI VALUE FOR SLENDER COLUMNS, Reinforced Concrete Columns, Publication No. SP-50, American Concrete Institute, pp. 1–40. (21D, 23)

MacGregor, J. G., Majumdar, S. N. G., Nikhed, R. P. and Adams, P. F., 1972
THE APPROXIMATE ANALYSIS OF INELASTIC SHEAR WALL-FRAME STRUC-TURES, Journal of the Structural Division, ASCE, Vol. 98, No. ST11, Proc. Paper 9351, p. 2351. (23)

MacLeod, I. A., 1967
LATERAL STIFFNESS OF SHEAR WALLS WITH OPENINGS, Tall Buildings, Pergamon Press, London, England, pp. 223–244. (21C, 22)

MacLeod, I. A., 1970
SHEAR WALL-FRAME INTERACTION—A DESIGN AID WITH COMMENTARY, Portland Cement Association, Chicago, Ill. (21C)

MacLeod, I. A., 1973
ANALYSIS OF SHEAR WALL BUILDINGS BY THE FRAME METHOD, Proceedings, Institution of Civil Engineers, London, Vol. 55, pp. 593–603. (21C)

MacLeod, I. A. and Green, D. R., 1973
FRAME IDEALIZATION FOR SHEAR WALL SUPPORT SYSTEMS, The Structural Engineer, Vol. 51, pp. 71–74. (21C)

Magura, D. D., Pfeifer, D. W. and Hognestad, E., 1968
TIME-DEPENDENT PERFORMANCE OF REINFORCED CONCRETE COLUMNS —FIELD INVESTIGATION OF A 70-STOREY BUILDING, Proceedings of 8th Congress of IABSE (September 1968), pp. 1019–1026. (25)

Maher, D. R. H., 1970
THE EFFECT OF DIFFERENTIAL TEMPERATURE IN CONTINUOUS PRE-STRESSED CONCRETE BRIDGES, *Civil Engineering Transactions*, Institution of Engineers, Australia, CE12, p. 29. (25)

Mahin, S. A. and Bertero, V. V., 1974
NONLINEAR SEISMIC RESPONSE EVALUATION—CHARAIMA BUILDING, *Journal of the Structural Division*, ASCE, Vol. 100, No. ST6, Proc. Paper 10614, p. 1225. (22)

Maier, G., De Donato, O. and Corradi, L., 1972a
INELASTIC ANALYSIS OF REINFORCED CONCRETE FRAMES BY QUADRATIC PROGRAMMING ALLOWING FOR SECOND-ORDER EFFECTS, Symposium on Inelasticity and Non-linearity in Structural Concrete, S.M. Study No. 8, Waterloo University, Ont., Canada. (22)

Maier, G., De Donato, O. and Corradi, L., 1972b
INELASTIC ANALYSIS OF REINFORCED CONCRETE FRAMES BY QUADRATIC PROGRAMMING, International Symposium on Inelasticity and Non-linearity in Structural Concrete, Study No. 8, Paper 10, University of Waterloo Press. (22)

Mainstone, R. J., 1971
ON THE STIFFNESSES AND STRENGTHS OF INFILLED FRAMES, *Proceedings*, Institution of Civil Engineers, London, England, Paper No. 7360 S. (27)

Majid, K. I. and Croxton, P. C. L., 1970
WIND ANALYSIS OF COMPLETE BUILDING STRUCTURES BY INFLUENCE COEFFICIENTS, *Proceedings*, Institution of Civil Engineers, London, Vol. 47, p. 169. (21C)

Maldague, J. C., 1965
STUDIES ON THE DEFORMATION OF CONCRETE BEAMS (Etude de la déformation des poutres en béton armé), Annales de l'institut technique du bâtiment et des travaux publics, No. 209. (22)

Maldague, J. C., 1973
IMPOSED ROTATIONS METHOD, Planning and Design of Tall Buildings, Proceedings of 1972 ASCE-IABSE International Conference, Vol. III, No. 22-Summary, ASCE, New York. (22)

Mancini, E., 1974
CONTINUOUS ANALYSIS OF TALL BUILDINGS STRUCTURES SUBJECT TO LATERAL LOADS, unpublished communication to the Council, February 1974. (21C)

Mancini, E. and Savassi, W., 1975
THREE-DIMENSIONAL ASSOCIATION OF GENERAL PANELS, unpublished communication to the Council, April 1975. (21C)

Manson, E. R., 1975
STRUCTURAL JOINT DESIGN IN LARGE PANEL PRECAST CONCRETE STRUCTURES, Hellenic Conference on Tall Buildings, 33rd National/Regional Conference (Athens, Greece, October 1975). (21E)

Manuel, R. F. and MacGregor, J. G., 1967
ANALYSIS OF RESTRAINED REINFORCED CONCRETE COLUMNS UNDER SUSTAINED LOAD, *ACI Journal*, American Concrete Institute, Vol. 64, No. 1, pp. 12–23. (21D, 22, 23)

Manuzio, C., 1973
PRESENT TRENDS IN PROBABILISTIC STUDIES OF STRUCTURAL SAFETY, Italian National Conference on Tall Buildings, 19th National/Regional Conference (Sorrento, Italy, October 1973), Collegio dei Tecnici dell Acciaio (CTA), 20121 Milano, Italy, Pizzale R. Morandi, 2, pp. 79–85. (26)

Marcal, P. V., 1972
FINITE ELEMENT ANALYSIS WITH MATERIAL NON-LINEARITIES—THEORY AND PRACTICE, Proceedings of the Specialty Conference on Finite Element Method in Civil Engineering, June 1972, McGill University, Montréal, Canada, pp. 35–69. (22)

Marinakis, K., 1975
A SIMPLE PRACTICAL METHOD TO STUDY BUCKLING OF COLUMNS IN TALL BUILDINGS, Reinforced Concrete Tall Buildings, Vol. I, 34th National/Regional Conference (Iasi, Romania, October 1975), Consiliul National al Inginerilor si Technicienilor, Iasi, Romania, pp. 427–437. (23)

Marinakis, K., 1975
THE PHILOSOPHY OF THE FUNDAMENTAL PROPOSITIONS IN THE THEORY FOR BUCKLING OF COLUMNS, Reinforced Concrete Tall Buildings, Vol. I, 34th National/Regional Conference (Iasi, Romania, October 1975), Consiliul National al Inginerilor si Technicienilor, Iasi, Romania, pp. 439–450. (23)

Marinov, R., 1975
THE TORSIONAL BEHAVIOR OF REINFORCED CONCRETE CORES OF TALL BUILDINGS (Studiu Privind Comportarea la Torsiune a Nucleilor din Beton Armat la Cladirile Inalte), Reinforced Concrete Tall Buildings (Constructii Inalte De Beton Armat), Vol. I, 34th National/Regional Conference (Iasi, Romania, October 14–16, 1975), Consiliul National al Inginerilor si Technicienilor, Iasi, Romania, pp. 245–263. (21C)

Marques, J. G. L. and Jirsa, J. O., 1972
A STUDY OF HOOKED BAR ANCHORAGES IN BEAM-COLUMN JOINTS, University of Texas, Austin, Tex., July 1972. (21D)

Martin, I., 1973
REINFORCED CONCRETE COLUMNS, Planning and Design of Tall Buildings, Proceedings of the 1972 ASCE-IABSE International Conference, Vol. III, No. 21-5, ASCE, New York. (21C)

Martin, I. and Olivieri, E., 1966
TESTS OF SLENDER REINFORCED CONCRETE COLUMNS BENT IN DOUBLE CURVATURE, Symposium on Reinforced Concrete Columns, Publication No. SP-13, American Concrete Institute, p. 121. (21D)

Martin, I., MacGregor, J. G., Pfrang, E. O. and Breen, J. E., 1966
CRITICAL REVIEW OF THE DESIGN OF REINFORCED CONCRETE COLUMNS, Symposium on Reinforced Concrete Columns, Publication No. SP-13, American Concrete Institute, p. 13. (21D)

Mathez, J., 1969
REPORT ON PERMISSIBLE DEFORMATIONS IN BUILDINGS (Rapport sur les déformations admissibles dans les constructions), Commission W23, International Council for Buildings. (26)

Mathez, J., Gensburger, F. and Huet, G., 1973
CALCULATION OF CERAMIC-CONCRETE COMPLEXES: APPLICATION TO PREFABRICATED CERAMIC BASED FLOORS (Calcul des complexes céramique-béton: Application aux planchers préfabriqués à base de terre cuite), Proceedings of the 3rd International Brick Masonry Conference, Bundesverband der Deutschen Ziegelindustrie e.V., Essen, Germany. (27)

Mathieu, H., 1975
THE CEB MANUAL OF STRUCTURAL SAFETY (Manuel de sécurité du Comité Européen du Béton), Bulletin no. 106–107, Comité Européen du Béton, Paris, France. (26)

Mathur, G. C., 1973
TECHNICAL INNOVATIONS FOR ELIMINATING DELAYS IN THE EXECUTION OF MULTISTORIED BUILDING PROJECTS, National Conference on Tall Buildings, 8th National/Regional Conference (New Delhi, India, January 1973), pp. V–39–45. (21E)

Matsushita, K., Kokusho, S. and Matsumura, A., 1971
STRENGTH AND BEHAVIOR OF AUTOCLAVED LIGHTWEIGHT CONCRETE PANEL WALL WITH JOINT UNDER SHEAR FORCE, Seminar under the Japan-U.S. Cooperative Science Program, Construction and Behavior of Precast Concrete Structures, Reports by Japanese Participants (Seattle, Wash., August 1971), Part I, pp. 31–42. (22)

Mattock, A. H., 1965
ROTATIONAL CAPACITY OF HINGING REGIONS IN REINFORCED CONCRETE BEAMS, Proceedings of the International Symposium on Flexural Mechanics of Reinforced Concrete, Publication No. SP-12, American Concrete Institute. (22)

Mattock, A. H., Kriz, L. B. and Hognestad, E., 1961
RECTANGULAR CONCRETE STRESS DISTRIBUTION IN ULTIMATE STRENGTH DESIGN, ACI Journal, American Concrete Institute, Vol. 57, pp. 875–928. (23)

Mauch, S. and Holley, M. J., 1963
CREEP BUCKLING OF REINFORCED CONCRETE COLUMNS, Journal of the Structural Division, ASCE, Vol. 89, No. ST4, Proc. Paper 3610, p. 451. (21D)

Maurenbrecher, A. H. P. and Hendry, A. W., 1970
ASPECTS OF THE STRENGTH AND FIXITY OF THE JOINT BETWEEN A BRICK WALL AND A FLOOR SLAB, Proceedings of the 2nd International Brick Masonry Conference, H. W. H. West and K. H. Speed, eds., British Ceramic Research Association, Stoke-on-Trent, England, 1971. (27)

Maurenbrecher, A. H. P. and Hendry, A. W., 1973
FLEXURAL STRAINS DUE TO AN APPLIED FLOOR MOMENT IN SINGLE LEAF BRICKWORK WALLS, Proceedings of the 3rd International Brick Masonry Conference, Bundesverband der Deutschen Ziegelindustrie e.V., Essen, Germany. (27)

Mayer, H., 1966
STRUCTURAL DEFECTS DUE TO BENDING OF REINFORCED CONCRETE MEMBERS (Bauschäden als Folge der Durchbiegung von Stahlbetonbauteilen), Bericht No. 68, Materialprufungsamt für Bauwesen der Technischen Hochschule München, Munich, Germany. (25)

Mayer, H., 1967
DETERMINATION OF DEFLECTION OF REINFORCED CONCRETE MEMBERS (Die Berechnung der Durchbiegung von Stahlbetonteilen), *Deutscher Ausschuss für Stahlbeton*, Report No. 194, Berlin, Germany. (22)

Mayfield, B., Kong, F. K. and Bennison, A., 1972
STRENGTH AND STIFFNESS OF LIGHTWEIGHT CONCRETE CORNERS, *ACI Journal*, American Concrete Institute, Vol. 69, No. 7, pp. 420–427. (21D)

Mayfield, B., Kong, F. K., Bennison, A. and Twiston Davies, J. C. D., 1971
CORNER JOINT DETAILS IN STRUCTURAL LIGHTWEIGHT CONCRETE, *ACI Journal*, American Concrete Institute, Vol. 68, No. 5, pp. 366–372. (21D)

Mazilu, P., Baubec, S., and Softoiu, E., 1972
THE USE OF PHOTOELASTICITY FOR DIMENSIONING THE STRUCTURE OF A TALL BUILDING (L'utilisation des essais optiques en vue du dimensionnement de la structure d'un grand bâtiment à Bucarest), Final Report, 9th Congress of IABSE (Amsterdam, The Netherlands, 1972), pp. 315–320. (A38)

Mazzolani, F. M. and Faella, C., 1975
INELASTIC STABLE AND UNSTABLE BEHAVIOR OF ECCENTRICALLY LOADED WALLS, CIB 2nd International Symposium on Bearing Walls (Warsaw, Poland, September 1975), Theme 1, Paper 6, pp. 53–61. (21E, 27)

Mazzolani, F. M. and Palazzo, B., 1975
WALL-FLOOR INTERACTION IN MULTI-STOREY BUILDINGS UNDER TORSIONAL LOADS, CIB 2nd International Symposium on Bearing Walls (Warsaw, Poland, September 1975), Theme 2, Paper 12, pp. 229–239. (21C, 21E)

Mazzolani, F. M. and Ramasco, R., 1971
STATIC OF FRAMED SPACE SYSTEMS WITH WALLS VARIOUSLY SHAPED (Statica dei Sistemi Intelaiati Spaziali con Irrigidimenti di Forma Qualsiasi), *Giornale del Genio Civile*, No. 3, p. 195. (21C)

McArthur, A. J., Codella, F. L. and Knapp, R. L., 1973
ARCHITECTURE OF TALL BUILDINGS, Planning and Design of Tall Buildings, Proceedings of the 1972 ASCE-IABSE International Conference, Vol. Ia, No. 1–8, ASCE, New York. (21B)

McCormick, C. W., 1963
PLANE STRESS ANALYSIS, *Journal of the Structural Division*, ASCE, Vol. 89, No. ST4, Proc. Paper 3581, p. 37. (21C)

McDermott, J. F., Abrams, J. I. and Cohn, M. Z., 1972
COMPUTER PROGRAM FOR SELECTING STRUCTURAL SYSTEMS, Preprint No. 1863, ASCE Annual and National Environmental Engineering Meeting, October 16–22, 1972. (21B)

McDowell, I. C. and Birtwistle, R., 1970
PREDICTING THE LONG-TERM MOISTURE EXPANSION OF FIRED CLAY BRICKS, Proceedings of the 2nd International Brick Masonry Conference, H. W. H. West and K. H. Speed, eds., British Ceramic Research Association, Stoke-on-Trent, England, 1971. (27)

McDowell, E. L., McKee, K. E. and Sevin, E., 1956
ARCHING ACTION THEORY, *Journal of the Structural Division*, ASCE Vol. 82, No. ST2, Proc. Paper 915. (27)

McDowell, I. C., McNeilly, T. H. and Ryan, W. G., 1966
    THE STRENGTH OF BRICK WALLS AND WALLETTES, Special Report No. 1, Brick
    Development Research Institute, Melbourne, Australia. (27)
McGuire, W., 1974
    PREVENTION OF PROGRESSIVE COLLAPSE, Proceedings of the Regional Conference
    on Tall Buildings, 22nd National/Regional Conference (Bangkok, Thailand, January
    1974), pp. 851–865. (21E)
McHenry, D., 1943
    A NEW ASPECT OF CREEP IN CONCRETE AND ITS APPLICATION TO DESIGN,
    Proceedings, American Society for Testing and Materials, Vol. 43. (25)
McIntosh, J. D., 1970
    SPECIFYING THE QUALITY OF BEDDING MORTARS, *Proceedings*, British Ceramic
    Society, No. 17. (27)
McLaughlin, R. H. B., 1976
    EARTHQUAKE ANALYSIS IN DESIGN OF MASONRY STRUCTURES, Proceedings
    of the 1st Canadian Masonry Symposium, E. L. Jessop and M. A. Ward, eds., University
    of Calgary, Canada. (27)
McMillan, C. M., 1975a
    AFRICAN EAGLE LIFE CENTRE—A HIGH-RISE PRECAST LOAD BEARING
    FACADE, Pan-Pacific Tall Buildings Conference Proceedings, 28th National/Regional
    Conference (Honolulu, Hawaii, January 1975), pp. 258–266. (21E)
McMillan, C. M., 1975b
    OPTIMUM DESIGN OF HIGH-RISE BUILDINGS, A MULTIDISCIPLINARY EN-
    GINEERING APPROACH, Pan-Pacific Tall Buildings Conference Proceedings (Hono-
    lulu, Hawaii, January 26–29, 1975), University of Hawaii, Honolulu, pp. 211–224. (21B)
McNeilly, T., 1976
    SERVICEABILITY, Proceedings of the 1st Canadian Masonry Symposium, E. L. Jessop
    and M. A. Ward, eds., University of Calgary, Canada. (27)
McNicholas, J. B., 1970
    PHOTOELASTIC STRESS ANALYSIS OF BRICK MASONRY SYSTEMS, Proceedings
    of the 2nd International Brick Masonry Conference, H. W. H. West and K. H. Speed,
    eds., British Ceramic Research Association, Stoke-on-Trent, England, 1971. (27)
Megget, L. M. and Park, R., 1971
    REINFORCED CONCRETE EXTERIOR BEAM-COLUMN JOINTS UNDER SEIS-
    MIC LOADING, *New Zealand Engineering*, Vol. 26, No. 11, pp. 341–353. (22)
Mehmel, A., Schwarz, H., Kasparek, K. and Makovi, J., 1964
    BEARING BEHAVIOR OF ECCENTRICALLY LOADED COMPRESSION MEM-
    BERS OF REINFORCED CONCRETE (Tragverhalten ausmittig beanspruchter Stahl-
    betondruckglieder), Documentation of DAfStb, No. 204, Berlin, Germany. (23)
Mehta, K. C. and Fincher, D., 1970
    STRUCTURAL BEHAVIOUR OF PRETENSIONED PRESTRESSED MASONRY
    BEAMS, Proceedings of the 2nd International Brick Masonry Conference, H. W. H. West
    and K. H. Speed, eds., British Ceramic Research Association, Stoke-on-Trent, England,
    1971. (27)
Melbourne, W. H., 1972
    MODELLING OF STRUCTURES TO MEASURE WIND EFFECTS, Conference on
    Structural Models (Sydney, 1972), Cement and Concrete Assoc. of Australia in
    conjunction with Dept. of Architectural Science, University of Sydney, and Institution of
    Engineers, Australia, N.S.W. Division. (A38)
Melhorn, G., 1970
    LATERAL BUCKLING OF PRESTRESSED CONCRETE, (Kippen von durch reine
    Biegung beanspruchten Spannbetonträgern mit einfach-symmetrischen I-Querschnitten),
    6th Congress of FIP, Prague, Czechoslovakia. (23)
Melhorn, G. and Schwing, H., 1975
    BEHAVIOR OF PANEL SHEAR WALLS, CIB 2nd International Symposium on Bearing
    Walls (Warsaw, Poland, September 1975), SOA Reports, Theme 2: Behavior of Shear
    Walls Resisting Vertical and Horizontal Loads, pp. 23–47. (21E)
Meli, R. and Esteva, L., 1968
    BEHAVIOUR OF HOLLOW MASONRY WALLS WHEN SUBJECTED TO ALTER-
    NATING LATERAL LOAD, presented at 2nd National Congress of Seismic Engi-
    neering (Veracruz, May 1968). (27)

Meloun, V., 1973
RESULTS OF MEASUREMENTS OF THE LONG-TERM STRAIN OF THE REINFORCED CONCRETE COLUMNS IN A TEN-STORY BUILDING, 10th Regional Conference Proceedings, 10th National/Regional Conference (Bratislava, Czechoslovakia, April 1973), Lehigh University, Bethlehem, Pa., pp. 483–491. (25)

Merchant, W., 1956
CRITICAL LOADS OF TALL BUILDING FRAMES, *The Structural Engineer*, Vol. 33, March 1955; Vol. 34, June, August 1956. (23)

Meyer, H. G., 1973
POSITION OF STANDARDIZATION IN HEAT INSULATION AND EFFECTS ON MASONRY CONSTRUCTION (Stand der Normung im Warmeschutz und Auswirkung auf den Mauerwerksbau), Proceedings of the 3rd International Brick Masonry Conference, Bundesverband der Deutschen Ziegelindustrie e.V., Essen, Germany. (27)

Michael, D., 1967
THE EFFECT OF LOCAL WALL DEFORMATIONS ON THE ELASTIC INTERACTION OF CROSS-WALLS COUPLED BY BEAMS, Symposium on Tall Buildings held at University of Southampton, England, in April 1966; Pergamon Press, Oxford, England. (24)

Michael, D., 1969
TORSIONAL COUPLING OF CORE WALLS IN TALL BUILDINGS, *The Structural Engineer*, Vol. 47, No. 2, pp. 67–72. (21C, 24)

Migliacci, A. and Castellani, A., 1972
GEOMETRIC SECOND-ORDER EFFECT ON TALL R.C. CHIMNEYS (Considerazioni sugli effetti del 2° ordine e secondari nelle alte ciminiere in C.A. e sulla sicurezza che ne consegue), Costruzioni in Cemento Armato, Vol. 10. (22, 23)

Mihai, E., Tertea, I., Onet, T., Păcurar, V. and Socaciu, N., 1975
CONTINUITY CONNECTIONS IN PRECAST REINFORCED CONCRETE MULTISTORIED STRUCTURES (Imbinari de Continuitate la Structurile Etajate Prefabricate din Beton Armat), Reinforced Concrete Tall Buildings, 34th National/Regional Conference (Iasi, Romania, October 1975), Vol. II, pp. 315–329. (21E)

Mihailescu, M., Pocanschi, A., Olaru, I. and Boder, M., 1975
TALL BUILDINGS WITH PERIPHERIC SHEAR WALLS (Cladiri Inalte cu Diafragme Perimetrale), Reinforced Concrete Tall Buildings, Vol. I, 34th National/Regional Conference (Iasi, Romania, October 1975), Consiliul National Al Inginerilor Si Tehnicienilor, Iasi, Romania, pp. 373–378. (21A)

Mikluchin, P. T., 1969
MORPHOTECTONICS OF MASONRY STRUCTURES, Proceedings of International Conference on Masonry Structural Systems, Texas. (27)

Mikluchin, P. T., 1976
THREE-DIMENSIONAL STATIC AND DYNAMIC ANALYSIS OF TALL MASONRY BUILDINGS, Proceedings of International Conference on Masonry Structural Systems. (27)

Miller, A. L., 1958
WARPING OF REINFORCED CONCRETE DUE TO SHRINKAGE, *ACI Journal*, American Concrete Institute, Vol. 54, p. 939. (25)

Miller, P. O., 1959
Private communication, P. O. Miller, Milston & Ferris, Sydney, Australia. (25)

Miller, P. O., 1972
MODEL ANALYSIS OF THE QANTAS CENTRE, Conference on Structural Models (Sydney, 1972), Cement and Concrete Assoc. of Australia in conjunction with Dept. of Architectural Science, University of Sydney, and Institution of Engineers, Australia, N.S.W. Division. (A38)

Milton, H. J. and Brotchie, J. F., 1967
A PROPOSAL FOR LONG-SPAN SHELLS AS FLOOR SYSTEMS, Proceedings of 3rd Australian Building Congress, Melbourne, Australia, p. 287. (25)

Ministerial Decree, 1974
TECHNICAL NORMS FOR COMPOSITE STEEL-CONCRETE STRUCTURES UTILIZING PLAIN AND PRESTRESSED CONCRETE (Norme tecniche alle quale devono uniformarsi le costruzioni in conglomerato cementizio, normale e precompresso ed a struttura metallica), Decreto Ministeriale, May 30, 1974, Rome, Italy. (26)

Ministry of Public Works, 1973
INSTRUCTION FOR THE PROJECTION AND EXECUTION IN BUILDING ALL CONCRETE STRUCTURES (Instrucion para el proyecto y la ejecucion de obras de hormigon en masa y armado), EH 73, Ministry of Public Works, Madrid, Spain. (26)

Minor, J. and Jirsa, J. O., 1971
A STUDY OF BENT BAR ANCHORAGES, Report No. 9, Structural Research at Rice University, Houston, Tex. (21D)

Moenaert, P. and Pfeffermann, O., 1965
RESEARCHES ABOUT THE BEHAVIOR OF REINFORCED CONCRETE ELE-MENTS UNDER LONG-TIME LOADING (Essais sur des éléments en béton armé soumis à une sollicitation de longue durée), Presses Universitaires de Bruxelles, Belgium. (25)

Monk, C. B., Jr., 1958
RESISTANCE OF STRUCTURAL CLAY MASONRY TO DYNAMIC FORCES, Research Report 7, Structural Clay Products Research Foundation, Geneva, Ill. (27)

Monk, C. B., Jr., 1965
OLD AND NEW RESEARCH ON CLAY MASONRY BEARING WALLS, Proceedings of 1st National Brick and Tile Bearing Walls Conference (Pittsburgh, May 1965). (27)

Monk, C. B., Jr., 1967
A HISTORICAL SURVEY AND ANALYSIS OF THE COMPRESSIVE STRENGTH OF BRICK MASONRY, Research Report No. 12, Structural Clay Products Research Foundation, Geneva, Ill. (27)

Monk, C. B., Jr. and Gross, J. G., 1965
EUROPEAN CLAY MASONRY LOADBEARING BUILDINGS, Structural Clay Products Institute. (27)

Monk, C. B., Jr., Goldberg, J. E. and Jearkjirm, V., 1970
STRUCTURAL ACTION OF BRICK-BEARING WALLS EXPOSED TO FIRE TEM-PERATURES, Proceedings of the 2nd International Brick Masonry Conference, H. W. H. West and K. H. Speed, eds., British Ceramic Research Association, Stoke-on-Trent, England, 1971. (27)

Moretto, O., 1971
REINFORCED CONCRETE COURSE (Curso de Hormigon Armado), 2nd ed., Libreria El Ateneo, Buenos Aires, Argentina. (21D)

Moretto, O., 1971
DEEP FOUNDATIONS—SELECTED SYNTHESIS OF THE PRESENT STATE OF THE KNOWLEDGE ABOUT SOIL INTERACTION, Revista Latinoamericana de Geotecnia, Caracas, Venezuela, July–September 1971. (21D)

Morstead, H., 1976
CONSTRUCTION DETAILS AND THEIR EFFECT ON BUILDING BEHAVIOR, Proceedings of the 1st Canadian Masonry Symposium, E. L. Jessop and M. A. Ward, eds., University of Calgary, Canada. (27)

Morton, J. and Hendry, A. W., 1973a
AN EXPERIMENTAL INVESTIGATION OF THE LATERAL STRENGTH OF BRICKWORK PANELS WITH PRECOMPRESSION UNDER DYNAMIC AND STATIC LOADING, Proceedings of the 3rd International Brick Masonry Conference, Bundesverband der Deutschen Ziegelindustrie e.V., Essen, Germany. (27)

Morton, J. and Hendry, A. W., 1973b
A THEORETICAL INVESTIGATION OF THE STRENGTH OF BRICK WALLS WITH PRECOMPRESSION, Proceedings, British Ceramic Society, No. 21. (27)

Morton, J., Davies, S. R. and Hendry, A. W., 1970
THE STABILITY OF LOAD-BEARING BRICKWORK STRUCTURES FOLLOWING ACCIDENTAL DAMAGE TO A MAJOR BEARING WALL OR PIER, Proceedings of the 2nd International Brick Masonry Conference, H. W. H. West and K. H. Speed, eds., British Ceramic Research Association, Stoke-on-Trent, England, 1971. (27)

Moss, P. J. and Scrivener, J. C., 1968
CONCRETE MASONRY WALL PANEL TESTS—THE EFFECT OF CAVITY FILL-ING ON SHEAR BEHAVIOUR, N.Z. Concrete Construction, April 1968, pp. 60–63. (27)

Motteu, H., 1973
NEW BELGIAN NORMS FOR TESTING, CALCULATING AND ERECTION OF MASONRY (Nouvelles normes belges pour les essais, le calcul et l'éxecution des

maçonneries), Proceedings of the 3rd International Brick Masonry Conference, Bundes-verband der Deutschen Ziegelindustrie e.V., Essen, Germany. (27)

Motteu, H., 1976
INTERNATIONAL RECOMMENDATIONS FOR THE COMPUTATION AND CON-STRUCTION OF MASONRY (Recommandations internationales pour le calcul et l'éxécution des maçonneries), Proceedings of 4th International Brick Masonry Confer-ence, Groupement Nationale de l'Industrie de la Terre Cuite, rue des Poissoniers 13, Brussels, Belgium. (27)

Mufti, A. A., Mirza, M. S., McCutcheon, J. O. and Spokowski, R., 1972
A STUDY OF NON-LINEAR BEHAVIOR OF STRUCTURAL CONCRETE ELE-MENTS, Proceedings of the Specialty Conference on Finite Element Method in Civil Engineering, June 1972, McGill University, Montréal, Canada, pp. 767–802. (22)

Müller, R. K., 1961
PHOTOELASTIC INVESTIGATION OF A SHEAR WALL UNDER WIND LOAD FOR THE W1 SKYSCRAPER (Spannungsoptische Untersuchung einer Querwind-schweibe unter Windbelastung für das Hochhaus W1 der Farbenfabriken Bayer A.G., Leverkusen), unpublished report, Institut für Spannungsoptik und Modellmessungen der Technischen Hochschule Stuttgart, Germany. (A38)

Müller, R. K., 1971
HANDBOOK OF MODEL ANALYSIS (Handbuch der Modellstatik), Springer, Berlin, Germany. (A38)

Munro, J., 1965
THE ELASTIC AND LIMIT ANALYSIS OF PLANAR SKELETAL STRUCTURES, Civil Engineering, ASCE, May 1965. (22)

Munro, J., Krishnamoorthy, C. S. and Yu, C. W., 1972
OPTIMAL DESIGN OF REINFORCED CONCRETE FRAMES, The Structural Engi-neer, Institution of Structural Engineers, London, Vol. 50, No. 7, pp. 259–264. (21B, 22)

Murashev, V., Sigalov, E. and Baikov, V., 1971
DESIGN OF REINFORCED CONCRETE STRUCTURES, MIR Publishers, Moscow, USSR. (21E, 23)

Murzewski, J., 1972
SAFETY OF TALL BUILDINGS AND PROBABILISTIC METHODS, Proceedings of National Conference on Tall Buildings, Vol. 1, 7th National/Regional Conference (Warsaw, Poland, November 1972), Warsaw Technical University, Polish Group of IABSE, ASCE-IABSE Joint Committee on the Planning and Design of Tall Buildings, Warsaw, Poland, pp. 267–385. (26)

Muszynski, W. and Ruppert, J., 1972
A LIGHTWEIGHT CURTAIN WALL, Proceedings of the National Conference on Tall Buildings, 7th National/Regional Conference (Warsaw, Poland, November 1972), Vol. II, pp. 295–301. (21E)

Muto, K., 1956
SEISMIC ANALYSIS OF REINFORCED CONCRETE BUILDINGS, Proceedings of the 1st World Conference on Earthquake Engineering, June 1956. (21D)

Muto, K., 1969
NEWLY DEVISED REINFORCED CONCRETE SHEAR WALLS FOR HIGH-RISE BUILDING STRUCTURES, Proceedings, Structural Engineers' Association of Cali-fornia, 38th Annual Convention, Hawaii, pp. 39–47. (22)

Muto, K., 1971
STRONG MOTION RECORDS AND SIMULATION ANALYSIS OF KII BUILDING IN THE SAN FERNANDO EARTHQUAKE, Muto Institute of Structural Mechanics, Tokyo, Japan. (24)

Muto, K. and Kokusho, S., 1953
EXPERIMENTAL STUDY OF TWO-STORY REINFORCED CONCRETE SHEAR WALLS (in Japanese), Transactions, Architectural Institute of Japan, No. 47, September 1953. (21D)

NB-1, 1960
DESIGN AND CONSTRUCTION OF REINFORCED CONCRETE STRUCTURES (Calculo e execucao de obras de concreto armado), Associacao Brasileira de Normas Tecnicas (partially revised in 1967). (26)

NBN 15, 1972
CONCRETE STRUCTURES, INITIAL DRAFT OF THE 7TH EDITION (Ouvrages en béton, avant projet de la 7e édition), Brussels, Belgium. (26)

NEN 3861, 1973
SPECIFICATIONS FOR CONCRETE TYPE A, B, AND E (Voorschriften Beton Deel A, B, en E), The Netherlands. (26)

NITU 3-39, 1939
CODES AND TECHNICAL RECOMMENDATIONS FOR DESIGN OF REIN-FORCED CONCRETE STRUCTURES (Normi i techniceskie usloviia proektirovaniia jelezobetonnie konstruktii), Moscow, USSR. (26)

Nadal, J., Martínez-Calzón, J., Morán, F. and Verde, A., 1970
EXPERIMENTAL INVESTIGATION OF 25 PRISMATIC REINFORCED CON-CRETE PARTS SUBJECTED TO SKEW BENDING (in Spanish), Istituto Eduardo Torroja, Research Working Paper No. 26, January 1970. (21D)

Nahhas, U. and Yu, C. W., 1971
THE ELASTIC PLASTIC DESIGN OF REINFORCED CONCRETE SWAY FRAMES AGAINST INSTABILITY, Commission XI paper, Comité Européen du Béton, Paris, France. (22)

Nahhas, U. and Yu, C. W., 1972
THE ELASTIC-PLASTIC DESIGN OF REINFORCED CONCRETE SWAY FRAMES AGAINST INSTABILITY, Proceedings, Institution of Civil Engineers, Part 2, Vol. 53, Paper 7458. (22, 23)

Naito, T., 1924
THEORY OF EARTHQUAKE-PROOF CONSTRUCTION (in Japanese), Publication Dept. of Waseda University, Japan, September 1924. (21D)

Nakagawa, T. and Yanase, S., 1971
EFFICIENCY OF LARGE PANEL SYSTEM ON LABOR SAVING, Seminar, Coop-erative Japan-U.S. Science Program (Seattle, Wash., August 1971), p. 201. (21E)

Nakano, K., Okamoto, S. and Kameda, Y., 1971
STRUCTURAL BEHAVIOR OF MULTI-STORIED PRECAST REINFORCED CON-CRETE CONSTRUCTION ASSEMBLED WITH POST-TENSIONING METHOD, Seminar under the Japan-U.S. Cooperative Science Program, Construction and Behavior of Precast Concrete Structures, Reports by Japanese participants (Seattle, Wash., August 1971), Part I, pp. 91–102. (22)

Narayanaswami, R. and Girija Vallabhan, C. V., 1972
STATIC AND DYNAMIC ANALYSIS OF SHEAR WALLS BY FINITE ELEMENT, Proceedings of the Specialty Conference on Finite Element Method in Civil Engineering (sponsored by McGill University, Canadian Society of Civil Engineers, Engineering Institute of Canada, June 1–2, 1972, Montréal, Canada), pp. 513–547. (21C)

Nasser, J., 1973
CONCRETE DESIGN STANDARDS IN ARAB COUNTRIES, Planning and Design of Tall Buildings, Proceedings of 1972 ASCE-IABSE International Conference, Vol. III, No. 20-6, ASCE, New York. (20, 26)

Nasser, K. W., Acavalos, A. and Daniel, H. R., 1967
BEHAVIOR AND DESIGN OF LARGE OPENINGS IN REINFORCED CONCRETE BEAMS, ACI Journal, American Concrete Institute, Vol. 64, No. 1, p. 25. (21D)

National Printing House, 1970
SPECIFICATIONS FOR REINFORCED CONCRETE STRUCTURES (Regulamento de estruturas de betao armado), Imprensa Nacional, Lisbon, Portugal. (26)

National Research Council, 1975
LIMIT STATES DESIGN, National Building Code of Canada 1975, Supplement No. 4, Commentary F, NRCC 13989, National Research Council, Ottawa, Canada. (26)

Nauman, W. and Walter, H., 1961
CALCULATION OF HORIZONTALLY LOADED SHEAR WALLS (Bericht zur statis-chen Berechnung waagrecht belasteter Querwaende bei Hochbauten), Die Bauingenieur, H8. (21C)

Nawy, E. G., 1968
CRACK CONTROL IN REINFORCED CONCRETE STRUCTUERES, ACI Journal, American Concrete Institute, Vol. 65, No. 10. (24)

Nawy, E. G. and Blair, K. W., 1972
FURTHER STUDIES ON FLEXURAL CRACK CONTROL IN STRUCTURAL TWO-WAY SLAB SYSTEMS, Special Publication No. 30, American Concrete Institute. (24)

Nawy, E. G. and Orenstein, G. S., 1969
CRACK WIDTH CONTROL IN TWO-WAY CONCRETE SLABS REINFORCED WITH WELDED WIRE FABRIC, Engineering Research Bulletin No. 47, Rutgers University, N.J. (24)

Nawy, E. G., Danesi, R. F. and Grosko, J. J., 1968
RECTANGULAR SPIRAL BINDERS EFFECT ON PLASTIC HINGE ROTATION, ACI Journal, American Concrete Institute, Vol. 65, No. 12. (22)

Negoita, A. and Pop, I. G., 1973
SEISMIC ANALYSIS OF EXPANDED CLAY LIGHTWEIGHT CONCRETE FRAMES, Planning and Design of Tall Buildings, Proceedings of 1972 ASCE-IABSE International Conference, Vol. III, No. 21-D1, ASCE, New York. (22)

Nervi, P. L., 1955
BUILDING THE RIGHT WAY (Costruire Corretamente), Hoepli, Milan, Italy. (A38)

Neumann, N., Peleg, M. and Robinson, N., 1955
EXPERIMENTS IN THERMAL PROTECTION OF CONCRETE ROOFS, Report No. 4, Israel Institute of Technology. (25)

Neumann, W., 1973
MEASUREMENTS COMPARING TEMPERATURES ON STANDARDIZED SCHOOL BUILDINGS (Temperaturvergleichsmessungen an typisierten Schulbauten), Proceedings of the 3rd International Brick Masonry Conference, Bundesverband der Deutschen Ziegelindustrie e.V., Essen, Germany. (27)

Neville, A. M., 1963a
PROPERTIES OF CONCRETE, Isaac Pitman, London, England. (25)

Neville, A. M., 1963b
PROPERTIES OF CONCRETE, John Wiley & Sons, Inc., New York. (25)

Neville, A. M., 1964
CREEP OF CONCRETE AS A FUNCTION OF ITS CEMENT PASTE CONTENT, Magazine of Concrete Research, Vol. 16, No. 46, pp. 21–30. (25)

Neville, A. M., 1970
CREEP IN PLAIN, REINFORCED AND PRESTRESSED CONCRETE, North Holland Publishing Co., Amsterdam, The Netherlands; Elsevier Publishing Co., New York. (23, 25)

Newmark, N. M., 1969
TORSION IN SYMMETRICAL BUILDINGS, Proceedings, 4th World Conference on Earthquake Engineering, held at Santiago, Chile. (24)

Newmark, N. M. and Rosenblueth, E., 1971
FUNDAMENTALS OF EARTHQUAKE ENGINEERING, Prentice-Hall, Inc., Englewood Cliffs, N.J. (21B, 22)

Ngo, D. and Scordelis, A. C., 1967
FINITE ELEMENT ANALYSIS OF REINFORCED CONCRETE BEAMS, ACI Journal, American Concrete Institute, Vol. 64, No. 3. (22)

Nielsen, K. E. C., 1952
LOADS ON REINFORCED CONCRETE FLOOR SLABS AND THEIR DEFORMATION DURING CONSTRUCTION, Proceedings of the Swedish Cement and Concrete Research Institute, No. 15. (25)

Nilsen, A. H., 1968
NONLINEAR ANALYSIS OF REINFORCED CONCRETE, ACI Journal, American Concrete Institute, Vol. 65, No. 9. (22)

Nilsson, I. H. E. and Losberg, A., 1970
THE STRENGTH OF HORIZONTALLY LOADED PREFABRICATED BRICK PANEL WALLS, Proceedings of the 2nd International Brick Masonry Conference, H. W. H. West and K. H. Speed, eds., British Ceramic Research Association, Stoke-on-Trent, England, 1971. (27)

Nilsson, I. H. E. and Losberg, A., 1971
DISCUSSION OF OPPORTUNITIES IN BOND RESEARCH, ACI Journal, American Concrete Institute, Vol. 68, No. 5, pp. 393–396. (21D)

Nixon, D., Beaulieu, D. and Adams, P. F., 1975
SIMPLIFIED SECOND-ORDER FRAME ANALYSIS, *Canadian Journal of Civil Engineering*, Vol. 12, No. 4, pp. 602–605. (23)

Norman, H. D., 1973
SERVICE SYSTEMS, Proceedings of the 12th Regional Conference (Sydney, Australia, August 14–17, 1973), Lehigh University, Bethlehem, Pa., pp. 499–512. (21B)

Norris, C. H., 1959
STRUCTURAL DESIGN FOR DYNAMIC LOADS, McGraw-Hill Book Co., Inc., New York, Chapters 1 and 2. (22)

Nylander, H., 1952
NON-UNIFORM SHRINKAGE OF CONCRETE DUE TO SEGREGATION OF COARSE AGGREGATE, Publications of IABSE, Vol. 12, Zurich, Switzerland, p. 831. (25)

Nylander, H. and Ericsson, E., 1957
EFFECTS OF WALL DEFORMATION ON FLOOR SLAB LOADS AND FLOOR SLAB DEFORMATION IN MULTISTORY HOUSES, *Nordisk Betong*, Vol. 1, No. 4. (27)

ONORM B4200, 1970
REINFORCED CONCRETE STRUCTURES, DESIGN AND CONSTRUCTION (Stahlbetontragwerke, Berechnung und Ausfuhrung), 8 Teil (May 1969), 9 Teil (April 1970), Vienna, Austria. (26)

Oberti, G., 1963
EXPERIMENTAL RESEARCH WITH STRUCTURAL MODELS AT ISMES (La Ricerca Sperimentale su Modelli Strutturalli e la "I.S.M.E.S."), *L'Industria Italiana del Cemento*, Vol. 33, No. 5, pp. 349–370. (A38)

Oberti, G., 1968
SPECIAL DESIGN PROBLEMS, Design Philosophy and its Application to Precast Concrete Structures, Cement and Concrete Association, London, England. (21E)

Oberti, G., 1972
MODEL ANALYSIS AS AN EXTENSION OF THEORETICAL STRUCTURAL STUDIES, Conference on Structural Models (Sydney, 1972), Cement and Concrete Assoc. of Australia in conjunction with Dept. of Architectural Science, University of Sydney, and Institution of Engineers, Australia, N.S.W. Division. (A38)

Oberti, G. and Castoldi, A., 1973
NEW TRENDS IN MODEL RESEARCH ON LARGE STRUCTURES, ISMES Bulletin No. 53, Istituto Sperimentale Modelli e Strutture, Bergamo, Italy. (A38)

Oden, J. T., 1967
NUMERICAL FORMULATION OF PROBLEMS IN NONLINEAR ELASTICITY, *Journal of the Structural Division*, ASCE, Vol. 93, No. ST3, Proc. Paper 5290, p. 235. (22)

Oden, J. T., 1971a
FINITE ELEMENTS OF NONLINEAR CONTINUA, McGraw-Hill Book Co., Inc., New York. (22)

Oden, J. T., 1971b
FINITE ELEMENT APPROXIMATIONS IN NONLINEAR ELASTICITY, NATO Advanced Study Institute on Finite Element Methods in Continuum Mechanics, Lisbon, Portugal. (22)

Office of the Ministry, 1971
PRELIMINARY RULES FOR THE "GENERAL STANDARDS FOR DESIGN OF STRUCTURES" (Instructions provisoires sur les "Directives communes relatives au calcul des constructions"), Bulletin, Office de Min. de l'Equipement et du Logement, Fasc. Spec. No. 71-100 bis, Paris, France. (26)

Ogura, K., Kokusho, S. and Matsuura, M., 1952
TESTS TO FAILURE OF TWO-STORY RIGID FRAMES WITH WALLS, PART 24, EXPERIMENTAL STUDY NO. 6 (in Japanese), Report No. 18, Architectural Institute of Japan, Tokyo, February 1952. (21D)

Ohmori, S., Takahashi, T., Tanaka, H. and Watanabe, S., 1976
STUDIES ON REINFORCED CONCRETE SLITTED SHEAR WALLS, Report No. 21, Kajima Institute of Construction Technology, February 1976. (21D)

Ohsaki, Y., Watabe, M. and Matsushima, Y., 1970
EXPERIMENTAL STUDY OF FIVE-STORY FULL-SIZE APARTMENT HOUSE OF REINFORCED CONCRETE WALL FRAMES, Proceedings of the U.S.-Japan Seminar on Earthquake Engineering with Emphasis on the Safety of School Buildings, Sendai, Japan, September 1970, pp. 240–266. (22)

Ojha, S. K., 1974
DEFORMATIONS OF REINFORCED CONCRETE RECTANGULAR BEAMS UNDER COMBINED TORSION, BENDING, AND SHEAR, *ACI Journal*, American Concrete Institute, Vol. 71, No. 8. (24)

Okamura, H., Pagay, S. N., Breen, J. E. and Ferguson, P. M., 1970
ELASTIC FRAME ANALYSIS—CORRECTIONS NECESSARY FOR DESIGN OF SHORT CONCRETE COLUMNS IN BRACED FRAMES, *ACI Journal*, American Concrete Institute, Vol. 67, No. 11, p. 894. (21D, 23)

Onn, L. Y., Paramasivam, P. and Koh, M. S., 1974
COMPUTER ANALYSIS OF FRAME-SHEAR WALL INTERACTION BY GENERALIZED HARDY CROSS METHOD, Proceedings of the 25th National/Regional Conference on Tall Buildings (Kuala Lumpur, Malaysia, December 2–5, 1974), Institution of Engineers, Kuala Lumpur, pp. 4.32–4.37. (21C)

Osaka, Y., Tanaka, T., Murakami, M. and Kitagawa, Y., 1969
EARTHQUAKE MEASUREMENTS IN AND AROUND A REINFORCED CONCRETE BUILDING, Proceedings of the 4th World Conference on Earthquake Engineering (Santiago, Chile), Vol. 1, pp. B–1, 1–16. (22)

PCA, 1953
EXPANSION JOINTS IN CONCRETE BUILDINGS, Portland Cement Association, Structural Bureau, Concrete Information Sheet AC-12-2, pp. 1–4. (25)

PCA, 1965a
DEFLECTIONS OF FLAT PLATE FLOORS OF APARTMENT BUILDINGS, Concrete Report CR008-010 (XS6504), Portland Cement Association, Skokie, Ill. (25)

PCA, 1965b
DESIGN OF COMBINED FRAMES AND SHEAR WALLS, Advanced Engineering Bulletin No. 14, Portland Cement Association, Skokie, Ill. (22)

PCA, 1976
CONCRETE MASONRY HANDBOOK, Portland Cement Association, Skokie, Ill. (27)

PCI, 1969
SUMMARY OF BASIC INFORMATION ON PRECAST CONCRETE CONNECTIONS, *Journal of the Prestressed Concrete Institute*, Vol. 14, No. 6, pp. 14–58. (21E)

PCI, 1970
MANUAL FOR QUALITY CONTROL, MN 116-70, Prestressed Concrete Institute, Chicago, Ill. (21E)

PCI, 1971
PCI DESIGN HANDBOOK—PRECAST AND PRESTRESSED CONCRETE, Prestressed Concrete Institute, Chicago, Ill. (21A, 21E, 23, 25)

PCI, 1973a
MANUAL ON DESIGN OF CONNECTIONS FOR PRECAST, PRESTRESSED CONCRETE, Prestressed Concrete Institute, Chicago, Ill. (21A, 21D, 21E)

PCI, 1973b
NEW PRECAST PRESTRESSED SYSTEM SAVES MONEY IN HAWAII HOTEL, *Journal of the Prestressed Concrete Institute*, Vol. 18, No. 3, pp. 10–13. (21E)

PCI, 1975
DESIGN CONSIDERATIONS FOR A PRECAST, PRESTRESSED APARTMENT BUILDING, Prestressed Concrete Institute, Chicago, Ill. (21A)

PCI Commission on Columns, 1968
TENTATIVE RECOMMENDATIONS FOR THE DESIGN OF PRESTRESSED CONCRETE COLUMNS, *Journal of the Prestressed Concrete Institute*, Vol. 13, No. 5, pp. 12–21. (23)

PCI Committee on Prestress Losses, 1975
RECOMMENDATIONS FOR ESTIMATING PRESTRESS LOSSES, *Journal of the Prestressed Concrete Institute*, Vol. 20, No. 4, pp. 43–75. (25)

Paduart, A. A., 1971
  LIMIT STATES DESIGN, 5th Regional Conference Proceedings, 5th National/Regional Conference (Chicago, Ill., November 29–December 1, 1971), Joint Committee on Tall Buildings, Lehigh University, Bethlehem, Pa., pp. 90–91. (26)
Paduart, A. A., 1973
  CURRENT APPLICATIONS OF LIMIT STATE PHILOSOPHY, Planning and Design of Tall Buildings, Proceedings of 1972 ASCE-IABSE International Conference, ASCE, New York. (20)
Pagano, M., 1968
  THEORY OF BUILDINGS (Teoria degli Edifice), Lignori Editore, Naples, Italy. (21E)
Pagano, M., Saracino, D. and Ramasco, R., 1970
  ON THE CALCULATION OF BEARING MASONRY BUILDINGS WITH THE HELP OF THE ELECTRONIC COMPUTER, Proceedings of the 3rd International Brick Masonry Conference, Bundesverband der Deutschen Ziegelindustrie e.V., Essen, Germany. (27)
Pagay, S. N., Ferguson, P. M. and Breen, J. E., 1970
  IMPORTANCE OF BEAM PROPERTIES ON CONCRETE COLUMN BEHAVIOR, ACI Journal, American Concrete Institute, Vol. 67, No. 10, p. 808. (21D)
Paloheimo, E., 1970
  A METHOD TO DETERMINE THE DIMENSIONS OF A STRUCTURAL ELEMENT CORRESPONDING TO A GIVEN PROBABILITY OF FAILURE, S.B.I. Rapport 66, Copenhagen, Denmark. (26)
Paloheimo, E. and Hannus, M., 1974
  STRUCTURAL DESIGN BASED ON WEIGHTED FRACTILES, Journal of the Structural Division, ASCE, Vol. 100, No. ST7, Proc. Paper 10663, pp. 1367–1378. (26)
Palumbo, P., 1968
  THE EFFECTS OF HORIZONTAL FORCES ON PREFABRICATED PANEL STRUCTURES, Design Philosophy and its Application to Precast Concrete Structures, Cement and Concrete Association, London, England. (21E)
Pankow, C., 1976
  INTEGRATED PRECAST AND CAST-IN-PLACE BUILDING CONSTRUCTION, unpublished communication to the Joint Committee, June 1976. (21E)
Paparoni, M., 1973
  MODEL STUDIES OF COUPLING BEAMS, Planning and Design of Tall Buildings, Proceedings of 1972 ASCE-IABSE International Conference, Vol. III, No. 24-3, ASCE, New York. (24)
Paparoni, M. and Holoma, S., 1971
  A MODEL STUDY OF COUPLING BEAMS FOR THE PARQUE CENTRAL BUILDINGS, Caracas, Venezuela, April 1971. (24)
Parameswar, H. C., 1968
  COMPATIBILITY PROBLEMS IN LIMIT DESIGN, thesis presented to the University of Waterloo, Ontario, Canada, in 1968, in partial fulfillment of the requirements for the degree of Doctor of Philosophy. (22)
Parcel, J. I. and Moorman, R. B., 1962
  ANALYSIS OF STATICALLY INDETERMINATE STRUCTURES, John Wiley & Sons, Inc., New York, p. 391. (24)
Park, R., 1972
  THEORIZATION OF STRUCTURAL BEHAVIOR WITH A VIEW TO DEFINING RESISTANT AND ULTIMATE DEFORMABILITY, Introductory report for Theme I of the IABSE Symposium on Resistance and Ultimate Deformability of Structures Acted upon by Repeated Forces, Lisbon, Portugal. (22)
Park, R. and Paulay, T., 1973
  BEHAVIOR OF REINFORCED CONCRETE EXTERNAL BEAM-COLUMN JOINTS UNDER CYCLIC LOADING, Proceedings of the 5th World Conference on Earthquake Engineering, Rome, Italy. (21D)
Park, R. and Paulay, T., 1975
  REINFORCED CONCRETE STRUCTURES, John Wiley & Sons, Inc., New York. (21D)
Park, R., Kent, D. and Sampson, R., 1972
  REINFORCED CONCRETE MEMBERS WITH CYCLIC LOADING, Journal of the Structural Division, ASCE, Vol. 98, No. ST7, Proc. Paper 9011, pp. 1341–1360. (22)

Parme, A. L., 1966
CAPACITY OF RESTRAINED ECCENTRICALLY LOADED LONG COLUMNS, Symposium on Reinforced Concrete Columns, Publication No. SP-13, American Concrete Institute, pp. 325, 355–360. (21D, 23)

Patton, R. N., 1972
BEHAVIOR UNDER SEISMIC LOADING OF REINFORCED CONCRETE BEAM-COLUMN JOINTS WITH ANCHOR BLOCKS, thesis presented to the University of Canterbury, at Christchurch, New Zealand, in 1972, in partial fulfillment of the requirements for the degree of Master of Engineering. (22)

Paulay, T., 1969a
THE COUPLING OF REINFORCED CONCRETE SHEAR WALLS, Proceedings of the 4th World Conference on Earthquake Engineering (Santiago, Chile, January 1969), B-2, pp. 75–90. (22)

Paulay, T., 1969b
THE COUPLING OF SHEAR WALLS, University of Canterbury, Christchurch, New Zealand. (21D)

Paulay, T., 1970a
AN ELASTO-PLASTIC ANALYSIS OF COUPLED SHEAR WALLS, ACI Journal, American Concrete Institute, Vol. 67, No. 11. (22)

Paulay, T., 1970b
THE SHEAR STRENGTH OF SHEAR WALLS, Bulletin, New Zealand Society of Earthquake Engineering, Vol. 3, No. 4, pp. 148–162. (22)

Paulay, T., 1971a
SIMULATED SEISMIC LOADING OF SPANDREL BEAMS, Journal of the Structural Division, ASCE, Vol. 97, No. ST9, Proc. Paper 8365, pp. 2407–2419. (22)

Paulay, T., 1971b
AN APPROACH TO THE DESIGN OF COUPLED SHEAR WALLS, Proceedings, 3rd Australian Conference on the Mechanics of Structures and Materials (Auckland, New Zealand, August 1971). (22)

Paulay, T., 1971c
COUPLING BEAMS OF REINFORCED CONCRETE SHEAR WALLS, Journal of the Structural Division, ASCE, Vol. 97, No. ST3, Proc. Paper 7984, pp. 843–862. (22, 24)

Paulay, T., 1972
SOME ASPECTS OF SHEAR WALL DESIGN, Bulletin, New Zealand Society for Earthquake Engineering, Vol. 5, No. 3, pp. 89–105. (22)

Paulay, T., 1973
SOME SEISMIC ASPECTS OF COUPLED SHEAR WALLS, Proceedings, 5th World Conference on Earthquake Engineering. (21D)

Paulay, T., 1974
DESIGN ASPECTS OF SHEAR WALLS FOR SEISMIC AREAS, Research Report, University of Canterbury, Christchurch, New Zealand. (21D)

Paulay, T. and Binney, J. R., 1974
DIAGONALLY REINFORCED COUPLING BEAMS OF SHEAR WALLS, Publication No. SP-42, American Concrete Institute. (22)

Paulay, T., Park, R. and Phillips, M. H., 1974
HORIZONTAL CONSTRUCTION JOINTS IN CAST-IN-PLACE REINFORCED CONCRETE, Shear in Reinforced Concrete, Publication No. SP-42, American Concrete Institute. (22)

Pauw, A., 1972
TENSILE TIES IN PRECAST CONCRETE SYSTEMS, Discussion 6, Committee 23, ASCE-IABSE International Conference on Tall Buildings (August 1972), pp. 623–624. (21E)

Pauw, A., 1976
PRECAST CONCRETE BULLDINGS, Irish Engineers, Journal of the Institution of Engineers of Ireland, January 1976, pp. 24–28. (21E)

Pauw, A., Stroband, J. and Smink, L. M. G., 1976
WALL-FLOOR CONNECTIONS BETWEEN PREFABRICATED ELEMENTS (Wand-Floer Verbindingen tussen Geprefabriceerde Elementen), Cement, Vol. 28, No. 5, pp. 207–208. (21E)

Peirs, G., 1970
THE MEASUREMENT OF MODULUS IN BRICK BUILDING (Die Modularmassordnung im Ziegelbau), Proceedings of the 3rd International Brick Masonry Conference, Bundesverband der Deutschen Ziegelindustrie e. V., Essen, Germany. (27)

Penzien, J., Bouwkamp, J. G., Clough, R. W. and Dixon, R., 1967
FEASIBILITY STUDY OF LARGE SCALE EARTHQUAKE SIMULATOR FACILITY, Report No. EERC 67-1, Earthquake Engineering Research Center, University of California, Berkeley. (22)

Perchat, J., 1973
SERVICEABILITY FACTORS, Planning and Design of Tall Buildings, Proceedings of 1972 ASCE-IABSE International Conference, Vol. III, No. 26-5, ASCE, New York. (20, 26)

Pereira, J. J., 1965
DIMENSIONAL THEORY FOR DYNAMIC MODELS, Technical Note, Laboratório Nacional de Engenharia Civil, Lisbon, Portugal. (A38)

Petcu, V. and Cohn, M. Z., 1961
ON THE MOMENT REDISTRIBUTION IN REDUNDANT HIGHLY REINFORCED CONCRETE BEAMS, Bulletin de l'Académie Polonaise des Sciences, Série des Sciences Techniques, 9, No. 10, 593, 600. (22)

Peter, J., 1964
REINFORCEMENT OF SHELLS AND IN-PLANE LOADED SLABS (Zur Bewehrung von Scheiben und Schalen), dissertation presented to the Technische Hochschule, Stuttgart, Germany. (22)

Petersson, H., 1974a
ANALYSIS OF LOAD BEARING WALLS IN MULTI-STOREY BUILDINGS, Doktorsavhandlingar vid Chalmers Tekniskan Hogskola, Göteborg, Sweden. (21C, 21E)

Petersson, H., 1974b
INVESTIGATION OF VERTICAL JOINTS BETWEEN WALL PANELS, Dept. of Building Construction, Chalmers University of Technology, Göteborg, Sweden. (21E)

Pfefferkorn, W., 1973
DESIGN PRINCIPLES FOR REINFORCED CONCRETE ROOF DECKS ON LOAD-BEARING BRICKWORK (Konstruktionsgrundlagen für Stahlbeton-Dachdecken auf tragendem Mauerwerk), Proceedings of the 3rd International Brick Masonry Conference, Bundesverband der Deutschen Ziegelindustrie e.V., Essen, Germany. (27)

Pfeffermann, O., 1970
THE BEHAVIOUR OF BRICK PARTITIONS WITH DEFORMATION OF THEIR SUPPORT, Proceedings of the 2nd International Brick Masonry Conference, H. W. H. West and K. H. Speed, eds., British Ceramic Research Association, Stoke-on-Trent, England, 1971. (27)

Pfeffermann, O., 1976
RESEARCH ON THE APPLICATION OF REINFORCED CONCRETE (Recherche sur l'application de la maçonnerie armée), Proceedings of the 4th International Brick Masonry Conference, Groupement National de l'Industrie de la Terre Cuite, rue des Poissoniers 13, Brussels, Belgium. (27)

Pfeffermann, O. and Pattigny, J. J., 1975
CRACKS OF PARTITIONS OF MASONRY DUE TO AN EXCESSIVE DEFORMATION OF THE SUPPORT (Scheurvorming in Metselwerkwanden door een overmatige Vervorming van het Draagvlak), Tijdschrift WTCB, Brussels, Belgium. (27)

Pfeifer, D. W., 1969
REINFORCED LIGHTWEIGHT CONCRETE COLUMNS, Journal of the Structural Division, ASCE, Vol. 95, No. ST1, Proc. Paper 6362, p. 57. (21D, 25)

Pfeifer, D. W., 1971
FULL-SIZE LIGHTWEIGHT CONCRETE COLUMNS, Journal of the Structural Division, ASCE, Vol. 97, No. ST2, Proc. Paper 7903, p. 495. (21D, 25)

Pfeifer, D. W. and Hognestad, E., 1968
INCREMENTAL LOADING OF REINFORCED LIGHT-WEIGHT CONCRETE COLUMNS, Proceedings of 8th Congress of IABSE (September 1968), pp. 1055–1063. (25)

Pfister, J. F., 1964
INFLUENCE OF TIES ON THE BEHAVIOR OF REINFORCED CONCRETE COLUMNS, ACI Journal, Vol. 61, No. 5, p. 521. (21D)

Pfister, J. F. and Mattock, A. H., 1963
HIGH STRENGTH BARS AS CONCRETE REINFORCEMENT (PART 5) LAPPED SPLICES IN CONCENTRICALLY LOADED COLUMNS, *Journal of the Portland Cement Association*, Research and Development Laboratories, Vol. 5, No. 2, Bulletin D63. (21D)

Pfrang, E. O., 1964
A STUDY OF THE INFLUENCE OF CREEP ON THE BEHAVIOR AND CAPACITY OF REINFORCED CONCRETE COLUMNS, Technical Report No. 4, Dept. of Civil Engineering, University of Delaware, October 1964. (21D)

Pfrang, E. O., 1966
BEHAVIOR OF REINFORCED CONCRETE COLUMNS WITH SIDESWAY, *Journal of the Structural Division*, ASCE, Vol. 92, No. ST3, Proc. Paper 4853, p. 225. (21D, 22)

Pfrang, E. O. and Siess, C. P., 1964a
PREDICTING STRUCTURAL BEHAVIOR ANALYTICALLY, *Journal of the Structural Division*, ASCE, Vol. 90, No. ST5, Proc. Paper 4110, p. 99. (22)

Pfrang, E. O. and Siess, C. P., 1964b
BEHAVIOR OF RESTRAINED REINFORCED CONCRETE COLUMNS, *Journal of the Structural Division*, ASCE, Vol. 90, No. ST5, Proc. Paper 4111, p. 113. (21D, 23)

Pfrang, E. O., Siess, C. P. and Sozen, M. A., 1964
LOAD-MOMENT-CURVATURE CHARACTERISTICS OF REINFORCED CONCRETE CROSS SECTIONS, *ACI Journal*, American Concrete Institute, Vol. 61, No. 7, p. 763. (21D, 22, 23)

Philleo, R. E., 1966
ELASTIC PROPERTIES AND CREEP, Special Technical Publication 169A, American Society for Testing and Materials, pp. 160–175. (25)

Philleo, R. E., 1971
SUMMARY OF SYMPOSIUM OF DESIGNING FOR EFFECTS OF CREEP, SHRINKAGE AND TEMPERATURE, Publication SP-27, Paper 12, American Concrete Institute, p. 247. (21E)

Pieper, K. and Hage, D., 1970
DEFORMATION PROPERTIES OF BRICKWORK, Proceedings of the 2nd International Brick Masonry Conference, H. W. H. West and K. H. Speed, eds., British Ceramic Research Association, Stoke-on-Trent, England, 1971. (27)

Pieper, K. and Trautsch, W., 1970
SHEAR TESTS ON WALLS, Proceedings of the 2nd International Brick Masonry Conference, H. W. H. West and K. H. Speed, eds., British Ceramic Research Association, Stoke-on-Trent, England, 1971. (27)

Pieper, K. and Gremmell, M., 1976
THE LOAD CAPACITY OF THIN MASONRY WALLS (Die Tragfähigkeit von schlanden Mauerwerkswanden), Proceedings of the 4th International Brick Masonry Conference, Groupement National de l'Industrie de la Terre Cuite, rue des Poissoniers 13, Brussels, Belgium. (27)

Plowman, J. M., 1965
THE MODULUS OF ELASTICITY OF BRICKWORK, *Proceedings*, British Ceramic Society, No. 4, pp. 37–44. (27)

Plowman, J. M., 1968
DAMP-PROOF COURSING IN LOAD-BEARING BRICKWORK, *Proceedings*, British Ceramic Society, No. 11. (27)

Plowman, J. M. and Smith, W. F., 1970
THE SELECTION OF DAMP-PROOF-COURSE MATERIAL FOR LOAD-BEARING STRUCTURES, Proceedings of the 2nd International Brick Masonry Conference, H. W. H. West and K. H. Speed, eds., British Ceramic Research Association, Stoke-on-Trent, England, 1971. (27)

Plummer, H. C., 1965
BRICK AND TILE ENGINEERING, Structural Clay Products Institute, Washington, D.C. (25, 27)

Plummer, H. C. and Blume, J. A., 1965
REINFORCED BRICK MASONRY, Structural Clay Products Institute, Washington, D.C. (27)

Pogorzelski, A. and Zieleniewski, S., 1969
METHOD OF COMPUTING THE LOAD BEARING CAPACITY OF HORIZONTAL JOINTS, CIB International Symposium on Bearing Walls, Warsaw, Poland. (21E)
Pogorzelski, A. and Zieleniewski, S., 1975
ECCENTRICITIES OF LONGITUDINAL FORCE IN WALLS DEEMED TO BE CONTINUOUSLY CONNECTED WITH FLOORS, CIB 2nd International Symposium on Bearing Walls (Warsaw, Poland, September 1975), Theme I, Paper 9, pp. 77–95. (21E, 27)
Polish Standard, 1969
THE STRUCTURES OF LARGE PANEL BUILDINGS, Polish Standard PN-68-B03253. (21E)
Polyakov, S., 1974
DESIGN OF EARTHQUAKE RESISTANT STRUCTURES, MIR Publishers, Moscow, USSR. (21E)
Polyakov, S. and Szorochov, G. G., 1967
SHEAR TESTS OF REINFORCED CONCRETE JOINTS IN LARGE PANEL WALLS (Ispytanie na sdwig zelezobetonnych/zamonolicennych stykov krypnopanelych zdanie), CNIISK, Moscow, USSR. (21E)
Pommeret, M., 1971
SHEAR RESISTANCE OF VERTICAL JOINTS IN COPLANAR LARGE PREFAB-RICATED PANELS (La résistance aux efforts tangents des joints verticaux grands panneaux préfabriqués coplanaires), Bulletin, Service d'Etude des Structures, June 1971. (21E)
Pommeret, M. and Lacombe, G., 1974
STRUCTURAL JOINTS IN CONSTRUCTION WITH LARGE PREFABRICATED PANELS (Les joints structuraux dans les constructions en grands panneaux pré-fabriqués), Annales de l'institut technique du bâtiment et des travaux publiques, No. 314, Paris, France. (21E)
Popoff, A., Jr., 1972
STABILITY OF PRECAST CONCRETE SYSTEMS BUILDINGS, SOA Report 5 Committee 23, Proceedings of ASCE-IABSE International Conference on Tall Buildings, Vol. III-23, ASCE, New York, pp. 73–85. (21E)
Popoff, A., Jr., 1973
WHAT DO WE NEED TO KNOW ABOUT BEHAVIOR OF STRUCTURAL CON-CRETE SHEAR WALL STRUCTURES? Publication SP-36-1, American Concrete Institute. (21B)
Popoff, A., Jr., 1975
DESIGN AGAINST PROGRESSIVE COLLAPSE, *PCI Journal*, Vol. 20, No. 2, pp. 44–57. (21E)
Powell, G., 1972
NOTES ON INELASTIC DYNAMIC ANALYSIS OF TALL BUILDINGS, Course on Earthquake Resistant Design of Engineering Structures, University of California Exten-sion, Berkeley, Calif. (22)
Powers, T. C., 1968
THE PROPERTIES OF FRESH CONCRETE, John Wiley & Sons, Inc., New York. (25)
Preece, W. P. and Davis, J. P., 1964
MODELS FOR STRUCTURAL CONCRETE, C. R. Books, London, England. (A38)
Pretzer, C., 1972
UNUSUAL APPLICATION OF PRESTRESSED WAFFLE SLABS AND COMPOSITE BEAMS, *ACI Journal*, American Concrete Institute, Vol. 69, No. 12, pp. 765–769. (21A)
Priestley, M. J., 1969
DYNAMIC STUDY OF A 22-STORY REINFORCED CONCRETE BUILDING, Report, Laboratório Nacional de Engenharia Civil, Lisbon, Portugal. (A38)
Pume, D., 1962a
RESEARCH ON THE BEARING CAPACITY OF MASONRY WALLS, Proceedings of RILEM Symposium held at Milan, Italy. (27)
Pume, D., 1962b
BUCKLING OF MASONRY PIERS AND WALLS, Publication of Building Research Institute, Prague, Czechoslovakia. (27)

Pume, D., 1963
BEARING CAPACITY OF VIBRATED MASONRY OF CLAY TILE WALLS, *Stavebni Vyzkum*, No. 6. (27)
Pume, D., 1967a
SHEAR STRENGTH OF VERTICAL JOINTS IN PANEL WALLS (Pevnost ve smyku svislych styku betonnovich dilcu), Stavebnicky Casopis 3. (21E)
Pume, D., 1967b
SHEAR STRENGTH OF VERTICAL SPLICES (Scherfestigkeit senkrechter Stösse), *Bauplanung-Bautechnik*, Vol. 21, No. 5. (22)
Pume, D., 1967c
BEARING CAPACITY OF CLAY TILE WALL ELEMENTS, *Baustoffindustrie*, No. 2. (27)
Pume, D., 1969
BEARING CAPACITY OF JOINTS BETWEEN WALL PANELS AND FLOOR SLABS, CIB Symposium on Bearing Walls, Warsaw, Poland. (21E)
Pume, D., 1970a
STRUCTURAL PERFORMANCE OF CLAY TILE WALL PANELS, Design engineering and Constructing with Masonry Products, F. Johnson, ed., Gulf Publishing Co., Houston, Tex. (27)
Pume, D., 1970b
DESIGN METHODS OF BRICK MASONRY STRUCTURES IN CZECHOSLOVAKIA, Proceedings of the 2nd International Brick Masonry Conference, H. W. H. West and K. H. Speed, eds., British Ceramic Research Association, Stoke-on-Trent, England, 1971. (27)
Pume, D., 1970c
STRESS DISTRIBUTION AND ULTIMATE STRENGTH OF JOINTS (Der Spannungs Zustand und die Tragfahigkeit der Verbindungen), *Die Bautechnik*, No. 12. (22)
Pume, D., 1973
LOAD-BEARING CAPACITY OF VERTICAL JOINTS BETWEEN WALL ELEMENTS, 10th Regional Conference Proceedings, 10th National/Regional Conference (Bratislava, Czechoslovakia, April 1973), pp. 464–474. (21E)
Putkonen, A. I., 1961
ANALYSIS OF FRAMES WITH UNREINFORCED COMPONENTS (Berechnung von Rahmentragwerken mit unbewehrten Stielen), Helsinki, Finland. (21E)

Qadeer, A. and Stafford-Smith, B., 1969
THE BENDING STIFFNESS OF SLABS CONNECTING SHEAR WALLS, *ACI Journal*, American Concrete Institute, Vol. 66, No. 6, p. 464. (21C, 21D)
Qadeer, A. and Stafford-Smith, B., 1974
ACTIONS IN SLABS CONNECTING SHEAR WALLS, Proceedings of Symposium on Tall Buildings, Vanderbilt University, November 1974, p. 315. (21C)

RILEM, 1958
SYMPOSIUM ON BOND AND CRACK FORMATION IN REINFORCED CONCRETE, Proceedings of Symposium held in Stockholm, Sweden, Réunion Internationale des Laboratoires d'Essais et de Recherches sur les Matériaux et les Constructions. (22)
RILEM, 1971
OBSERVATIONS ON THE INTERNATIONAL SYMPOSIUM ON CONCRETE AND REINFORCED CONCRETE IN HOT COUNTRIES, held at Haifa, Israel (August 1971), Réunion Internationale des Laboratoires d'Essais et de Recherches sur les Matériaux et les Constructions. (25)
Rackwitz, R., 1975
PRINCIPLES AND METHODS FOR A PRACTICE PROBABILISTIC APPROACH TO STRUCTURAL DESIGN, Technical University of Munich, Germany. (26)
Rafla, K. F., 1969
APPROXIMATE CALCULATION OF THE CRITICAL BUCKLING LOADING OF REINFORCED CONCRETE BEAMS (Naherungsweise Berechnung der Kritischen Kipplasten von Stahlbetonbalken), *Beton- und Stahlbetonbau*, Vol. 64, p. 183. (23)

Rahles, K., 1970
ABOUT THE TORSIONAL STIFFNESS OF RECTANGULAR REINFORCED CON-
CRETE MEMBERS (Zur Torsionssteifigkeit von Stahlbeton Rechtecksquerschnitten),
Beton- und Stahlbetonbau, September 1970, pp. 226–227. (24)

Ramadrishnan, V., 1976
COMPARISON OF THREE-DIMENSIONAL ANALYSIS OF CONCRETE SHEAR
WALL BUILDINGS AND THEIR ACTUAL BEHAVIOR, Proceedings of ASCE
National Structural Engineering Conference, Methods of Structural Analysis (Madison,
Wis., August 22–25, 1976), Vol. 1, pp. 95–114. (21C)

Ramaswamy, G. S., 1961
ANALYSIS, DESIGN AND CONSTRUCTION OF A SHELL OF DOUBLE CUR-
VATURE, Proceedings of Symposium on Shell Research, North Holland Publishing Co.,
Amsterdam, The Netherlands. (21D)

Ramaswamy, G. S., 1970
FUNICULAR BRICK SHELL ROOFS FOR INDUSTRIAL BUILDINGS, Design
Engineering and Constructing with Masonry Products, ed. F. Johnson, Gulf Publishing
Co., Houston, Tex. (27)

Ramesh, C. K., Mori, V. V. and Swaminathan, T. R., 1973
TALL BUILDINGS WITH SHEAR-WALL SYSTEMS—A STATUS REPORT, 8th
National/Regional Conference on Tall Buildings (New Delhi, India, January 22–24,
1973), Indian National Group of IABSE, New Delhi, pp. III 103–131. (21C, 21E)

Rangan, B. V., 1973
LIMIT DESIGN OF SLABS UNDER UNIFORMLY DISTRIBUTED LOADS USING
LOWER BOUND APPROACH, UNICIV Report R-111, University of New South
Wales, Australia. (22)

Rankine, J., 1973
SUMMARY REPORT: CREEP, SHRINKAGE AND TEMPERATURE EFFECTS,
Planning and Design of Tall Buildings, Proceedings of 1972 ASCE-IABSE International
Conference, Vol. III, No. 25-Summary, ASCE, New York. (25)

Rao, K. L., 1951
A RATIONAL CONCEPTION OF CREEP IN CONCRETE, Proceedings of 4th Congress
on Large Dams (New Delhi, India). (25)

Raths, C. H., 1974
DESIGN OF LOAD BEARING WALL PANELS, Design Considerations for a Precast
Prestressed Apartment Building, *Journal of the Prestressed Concrete Institute*, Vol. 19, No.
1, pp. 54–61, and No. 2, pp. 66–92. (21E)

Ravara, A., Carvalho, E. C., Pereira, J. J. and Azevedo, M. C., 1976
SEISMIC STUDY OF PARQUE CENTRAL OFFICE TOWERS (Estudo Sísmico das
Torres de Parque Central Sul. Ensaios Sobre Modelo), Report, Laboratório Nacional de
Engenharia Civil, Lisbon, Portugal. (A38)

Reaton, G., 1972
THE BEHAVIOR OF REINFORCED CONCRETE BEAM-COLUMN JOINTS
UNDER CYCLIC LOADING, thesis presented to the University of Canterbury,
Christchurch, New Zealand, in 1972, in partial fulfillment of the requirements for the
degree of Master of Engineering. (22)

Redmond, T. B., and Patterson, D. C., 1975
COMPRESSIVE STRENGTH OF COMPOSITE MASONRY WALLS, presented at
ASCE National Structural Engineering Convention. (27)

Reese, R. T. and Kostem, C. N., 1973
A METHOD TO DETERMINE THE SENSITIVITY OF MATHEMATICAL MODELS
IN DETERMINISTIC STRUCTURAL DYNAMICS, Fritz Engineering Laboratory
Report No. 400.9, Lehigh University, Bethlehem, Pa. (21A)

Rehm, G., 1961
CONCERNING THE FUNDAMENTALS OF BOND BETWEEN STEEL AND CON-
CRETE (Uber die Grundlagen des Verbundes zwischen Stahl und Beton), Bulletin 138,
Deutscher Ausschuss fur Stahlbeton, Berlin, Germany. (22)

Rehm, G. and Martin, H., 1968
ON THE QUESTION OF CRACK LIMITATIONS IN REINFORCED CONCRETE
STRUCTURES (Zur Frage der Rissebegrenzung in Stahlbetonbau), *Beton- und Stahl-
betonbau*, Vol. 63, p. 175. (25)

Reimitz, P., 1973
EFFECTIVENESS OF ACOUSTIC BRICKS (Wirksamkeit von Akustik-Ziegeln), Proceedings of the 3rd International Brick Masonry Conference, Bundesverband der Deutschen Ziegelindustrie e.V., Essen, Germany. (27)

Reinders, R., 1973
THE INFLUENCE OF POROSITY AND PERFORATION ON HEAT CONDUCTIVITY OF BUILDING MATERIALS FOR WALLS (Der Einfluss von Porosität und Lochung auf die Warmeleitfahigkeit von Wandbaustoffen), Proceedings of the 3rd International Brick Masonry Conference, Bundesverband der Deutschen Ziegelindustrie e.V., Essen, Germany. (27)

Reinschmidt, K., Hansen, R. J. and Yang, C. Y., 1964
DYNAMIC TESTS OF REINFORCED CONCRETE COLUMNS, *ACI Journal*, American Concrete Institute, Vol. 61, No. 3, p. 317. (21D)

Reiss, M. and Sokal, J., 1972
CALCULATION OF CONTINUOUS ORTHOTROPIC RIBBED FLOORS WITHOUT TORSIONAL RIGIDITY, *Beton- und Stahlbetonbau*, Vol. 67, No. 2, pp. 45–46. (21A)

Reznik, S., 1972
QUALITY CONTROL OF PREFABRICATED COMPONENTS FOR TALL BUILDINGS, SOA Report 8, Committee 9, Proceedings of ASCE-IABSE International Conference on Tall Buildings, Vol. Ib-9, ASCE, New York, pp. 93–96. (21E)

Ricaldoni, J., 1958
NOTE ON THE EFFECT OF TORSION ON TALL BUILDINGS (Nota Sobre el Efecto de Torsion en Edificios Elevados), Publication No. 16, Instituto de Estatica, Facultad de Ingenieria y Agrimensura, Montevideo, Uruguay, pp. 1–13. (24)

Richardson, J. G., 1973
PRECAST CONCRETE PRODUCTION, Cement and Concrete Association, London, England. (21E)

Richter, P. J., Reddy, D. P. and Agbabian, M. S., 1971
THREE-DIMENSIONAL FINITE ELEMENT DYNAMIC ANALYSIS OF A MULTI-STORY OFFICE BUILDING, Agbabian Jacobson Associates. (21A)

Risager, S., 1969a
STRUCTURAL BEHAVIOUR OF LINEAR ELASTIC WALLS HAVING NO TENSILE STRENGTH, Design Engineering and Constructing with Masonry Products, F. Johnson, ed., Gulf Publishing Co., Houston, Tex. (27)

Risager, S., 1969b
THE FAILURE LOAD OF LINEAR ELASTIC WALLS WITHOUT TENSILE STRENGTH, CIB International Symposium on Bearing Walls, Warsaw, Poland. (21E)

Risager, S., 1970
THE BUCKLING LOAD OF LINEAR ELASTIC WALLS WITHOUT TENSILE STRENGTH, Proceedings of the 2nd International Brick Masonry Conference, H. W. H. West and K. H. Speed, eds., British Ceramic Research Association, Stoke-on-Trent, England, 1971. (27)

Risager, S., 1976
BRICKWORK: STRENGTH, STATISTICS AND STANDARDS, extracts from the 2nd Nordic Symposium on Masonry Construction, Copenhagen, Denmark, 1975; Proceedings of the 4th International Brick Masonry Conference, Groupement National de l'Industrie de la Terre Cuite, rue des Poissoniers 13, Brussels, Belgium. (27)

Ritchie, T., 1973
WATER PENETRATION TESTS OF TTW BRICK WALLS, Proceedings of the 3rd International Brick Masonry Conference, Bundesverband der Deutschen Ziegelindustrie e.V., Essen, Germany. (27)

Ritchie, T., 1976
MOISTURE DEGRADATION IN MASONRY WALLS, Proceedings of the 1st Canadian Masonry Symposium, E. L. Jessop and M. A. Ward, eds., University of Calgary, Canada. (27)

Rjanitzin, A. R., 1959
DESIGN OF STRUCTURES FOR STRENGTH AND SAFETY (Calcul à la rupture et sécurité des constructions), Eyrolles, Paris, France. (26)

Roberts, J. J., 1976a
THE EFFECT UPON THE INDICATED STRENGTH OF CONCRETE BLOCKS IN COMPRESSION OF REPLACING MORTAR WITH BOARD CAPPING, Proceed-

ings of the 1st Canadian Masonry Symposium, E. L. Jessop and M. A. Ward, eds., University of Calgary, Canada. (27)

Roberts, J. J., 1976b
THE BEHAVIOUR OF VERTICALLY REINFORCED CONCRETE BLOCKWORK SUBJECT TO LATERAL LOADING, Proceedings of the 1st Canadian Masonry Symposium, E. L. Jessop and M. A. Ward, eds., University of Calgary, Canada. (27)

Robles, F., 1973
STRENGTH FACTORS: MATERIAL AND GEOMETRICAL ASPECTS, Planning and Design of Tall Buildings, Proceedings of 1972 ASCE-IABSE International Conference, Vol. III, No. 26-4, ASCE, New York. (20, 26)

Rohm, G. and von Wachter, K. D., 1974
PREFABRICATED REINFORCED CONCRETE CONSTRUCTION WITH LARGE ELEMENTS (Stahlbeton Fertigteil Konstruktionen mit weitgespannten Elementen), *Betonwerk + Fertigteil Technik*, Heft 9. (21E)

Rose, G. M., 1976
LIMIT STATE CODES AND STANDARDS IN THE U.K. 1976—THE TURNING POINT, Proceedings of the 1st Canadian Masonry Symposium, E. L. Jessop and M. A. Ward, eds., University of Calgary, Canada. (27)

Rosenblueth, E., 1965
SLENDERNESS EFFECTS IN BUILDINGS, *Journal of the Structural Division*, ASCE, Vol. 91, No. ST1, Proc. Paper 4235, pp. 229–252. (23)

Rosenblueth, E. and Esteva, L., 1972
RELIABILITY BASIS FOR SOME MEXICAN CODES, Probabilistic Design of Reinforced Concrete Buildings, Publication SP-31, American Concrete Institute, pp. 1–41. (26)

Rosenhaupt, S., 1961a
A STUDY OF THERMAL CRACKS IN MASONRY WALLS, Bulletin No. 3, Concrete Industrial Board. (25)

Rosenhaupt, S., 1961b
ELASTIC ANALYSIS OF COMPOSITE WALLS, Bulletin of Research Council of Israel, Section C, Technology, Vol. 10C, No. 1-2. (21D)

Rosenhaupt, S., 1964
STRESSES IN POINT SUPPORTED COMPOSITE WALLS, *ACI Journal*, American Concrete Institute, Vol. 61, No. 7, p. 795. (21D)

Rosman, R., 1960
CONTRIBUTION TO THE STATICAL CALCULATION OF HORIZONTALLY LOADED SHEAR WALLS (Beitrag zur statischen Berechnung waagrecht belasteter Querwaende bei Hochbauten), *Der Bauingenieur*, H4, 1960; H1, 1962; H8, 1962. (21C)

Rosman, R., 1962
PHOTOELASTIC INVESTIGATION OF A SHEAR WALL (Spannungsoptische Untersuchung einer Querwand eines Hochhauses), *Der Bauingenieur*, H2, pp. 466–469. (24)

Rosman, R., 1964
APPROXIMATE ANALYSIS OF SHEAR WALLS SUBJECT TO LATERAL LOADS, *ACI Journal*, American Concrete Institute, Vol. 61, No. 6, p. 717. (21C, 22)

Rosman, R., 1966
TABLES FOR THE INTERNAL FORCES OF PIERCED SHEAR WALLS SUBJECT TO LATERAL LOADS, *Bauingenieur-Praxis*, H66, W. Ernst und Sohn, Berlin, Germany. (21C)

Rosman, R., 1967
PIERCED SHEAR WALLS WITH STEPPED VARIATIONS IN CROSS SECTIONS (in German), *Bauingenieur-Praxis*, H67, W. Ernst und Sohn, Berlin, Germany. (21C)

Rosman, R., 1968
STATICS AND DYNAMICS OF SHEAR WALL SYSTEMS IN TALL BUILDINGS (in German), Springer Verlag, Berlin, Germany. (22)

Rosman, R., 1969a
TORSION OF PERFORATED CONCRETE SHAFTS, *Journal of the Structural Division*, ASCE, Vol. 95, No. ST5, Proc. Paper 6578, pp. 991–1010. (21C, 24)

Rosman, R., 1969b
INVESTIGATION OF HIGH BUILDINGS WITH A STRUCTURE OF A CENTRAL CORE AND MULTISTORY FRAMES (in German), *Beton- und Stahlbetonbau*, Vol. 64, December, p. 284. (21C)

Rosman, R., 1971
STATICS OF NON-SYMMETRIC SHEAR WALL STRUCTURES, *Proceedings*, Institution of Civil Engineers, London, Vol. 48, Paper 7393S, p. 211. (21C)

Rosman, R., 1974a
ANALYSIS OF SPATIAL CONCRETE SHEAR-WALL SYSTEMS, Jugoslavenska Akademija Znanosti i Umjetnosti, Zagreb, Yugoslavia. (21E)

Rosman, R., 1974b
STABILITY AND DYNAMICS OF SHEAR-WALL FRAME STRUCTURES, *Building Science*, Vol. 9, Pergamon Press, England, pp. 55–63. (23)

Rosman, R., 1975
RESPONSE OF RANDOM COUPLED SHEAR WALLS, CIB 2nd International Symposium on Bearing Walls (Warsaw, Poland, September 1975), Theme 2, Paper 13, pp. 241–253. (21E)

Ross, A. D., 1958
CREEP OF CONCRETE UNDER VARIABLE STRESS, *ACI Journal*, American Concrete Institute, Vol. 29, pp. 739–758. (25)

Rostampour, M., 1973
ASPECTS OF THE DESIGN OF MULTISTOREY BUILDINGS IN LIGHT-WEIGHT CONCRETE BLOCKWORK, thesis presented to the University of Edinburgh, Scotland, in partial fulfillment of the requirements for the degree of Doctor of Philosophy. (27)

Roy, H. E. H. and Sozen, M., 1964
DUCTILITY OF CONCRETE, Proceedings of the ASCE-ACI International Symposium on the Flexural Mechanics of Reinforced Concrete (Miami, Fla.), with discussion by V. V. Bertero, C. Felippo; Publication No. SP-12, American Concrete Institute, 1965. (22)

Rozvan, M. I., 1975
CONCLUSIONS ON THE DESIGN AND ERECTION OF AN 11-STORY TALL BUILDING OF CAST-IN-SITU CONCRETE CORE AND PRECAST STRUCTURAL UNITS (Concluzii pe marginea proiectarii si executarii unui bloc cu 11 niveluri din elemente prefabricate si un nucleu central de beton armat mondlit), Reinforced Concrete Tall Buildings, Vol. II, 34th National/Regional Conference (Iasi, Romania, October 1975), pp. 179–198. (21E)

Rozvany, G. I. N. and Cohn, M. Z., 1970
A LOWER BOUND APPROACH TO THE OPTIMAL DESIGN OF CONCRETE FRAMES AND SLABS, *Journal of the Engineering Mechanics Division*, ASCE, Vol. 96, No. EM6, Proc. Paper 7778, pp. 1013–1030. (22)

Rubenstein, M. F., 1966
MATRIX COMPUTER ANALYSIS OF STRUCTURES, Prentice-Hall, Inc., Englewood Cliffs, N.J. (21C)

Ruiz, W. M. and Winter, G., 1969
REINFORCED CONCRETE BEAMS UNDER REPEATED LOADS, *Journal of the Structural Division*, ASCE, Vol. 95, No. ST6, Proc. Paper 6601, pp. 1189–1211. (22)

Rüsch, H., 1960
RESEARCHES TOWARD A GENERAL FLEXURAL THEORY FOR STRUCTURAL CONCRETE, *ACI Journal*, Vol. 57, No. 7. (22)

Rüsch, H. and Stöckl, S., 1963
THE EFFECT OF STIRRUPS AND COMPRESSION REINFORCEMENT, Bulletin 148, Deutscher Ausschuss fur Stahlbeton, Berlin, Germany. (22)

Rüsch, H. and Stöckl, S., 1967
PARAMETERS FOR THE BEHAVIOR OF THE COMPRESSIVE ZONE OF REINFORCED CONCRETE BEAMS UNDER SHORT-TIME LOADING—SUMMARY OF NEWER INVESTIGATIONS (Kennzahlen für das Verhalten der Biegedruckzone von Stahlbetonbalken unter kurzzeitiger Belastung—Zusammenfassung neuerer Forschungsarbeiten), Deutscher Ausschuss für Stahlbeton, Bulletin 196, Berlin, Germany. (23)

Rüsch, H., Jungwirth, D. and Hilsdorf, H., 1973
CRITICAL REVIEW OF THE METHOD OF CONSIDERATION OF THE INFLUENCES OF CREEP AND SHRINKAGE OF CONCRETE ON THE BEHAVIOUR OF THE STRUCTURE (Kritische Sichtung der Verfahren zur Berücksichtigung der Einflüsse von Kriechen und Schwinden des Betons auf das Verhalten der Tragwerke), *Beton- und Stahlbetonbau*, Vol. 68, pp. 46–60, 76–86, and 152–158. (25)

Rüsch, H., Sell, R., Rasch, C., Grasser, E., Hummel, A., Wesche, K. and Flatten, H., 1968
STRENGTH AND DEFORMATION OF PLAIN UNREINFORCED CONCRETE UNDER SUSTAINED LOAD (Festigkeit und Verformung von unbewehrten Beton unter konstanter Dauerlast), Bulletin 198, Deutscher Ausschuss fur Stahlbeton, Berlin, Germany. (22)

Russell, A. and Reinschmidt, K. F., 1973
A COORDINATED BUILDING DESIGN SYSTEM, Proceedings of the 12th Regional Conference (Sydney, Australia, August 14–17, 1973), Lehigh University, Bethlehem, Pa., pp. 571–589. (21B)

Rutenberg, A., 1972
Discussion of FRAMED-TUBE STRUCTURES FOR HIGH-RISE BUILDINGS, by A. Coull and N. K. Subedi, Journal of the Structural Division, ASCE, Vol. 98, No. ST4, Proc. Paper 8802, p. 942. (21C)

Rutenberg, A., 1974
ANALYSIS OF TUBE STRUCTURES USING PLANE FRAME PROGRAMS, Proceedings of the 22nd National/Regional Conference on Tall Buildings (Bangkok, Thailand, January 23–25, 1974), Asian Institute of Technology, Bangkok, p. 397. (21C)

Rutenberg, A. and Heidebrecht, A. C., 1975
APPROXIMATE ANALYSIS OF ASYMMETRIC WALL-FRAME STRUCTURES, Building Science, London, Vol. 10, p. 27. (21C)

SCPI, 1965
PROCEEDINGS OF THE FIRST NATIONAL BRICK AND TILE BEARING WALL CONFERENCE, Structural Clay Products Institute, Washington, D.C. (27)

SEAOC, 1973
RECOMMENDED LATERAL FORCE REQUIREMENTS AND COMMENTARY, Structural Engineers Association of California. (21D)

SIA 113, 1965
STANDARD FOR THE CALCULATION AND EXECUTION OF MANUFACTURED BLOCKS AND BRICKS, Société Suisse des Ingénieurs et Architectes, Zurich, Switzerland. (27)

SIA 177, 1977
MASONRY STANDARD 177 (Norm 177 Mauerwerk), Schweizerischer Ingenieur- und Architekten-Verein, Zurich, Switzerland. (27)

SNiPII-V.1-62, 1962
CODES AND TECHNICAL RECOMMENDATIONS FOR DESIGN OF CONCRETE AND REINFORCED CONCRETE STRUCTURES (Betonnie i jelezobetonnie konstruktii, Normi proektirovania), Gostroizdat, Moscow, USSR. (26)

STRUDL II, 1971
USER'S MANUAL, M.I.T. Press, Cambridge, Mass. (21C)

Sabnis, G. and White, R., 1969
BEHAVIOR OF REINFORCED CONCRETE FRAMES UNDER CYCLIC LOADS USING SMALL SCALE MODELS, ACI Journal, Vol. 66, No. 9, pp. 703–715. (22)

Saenz, L. P. and Martin, I., 1961
SLABLESS TREAD-RISER STAIRS, ACI Journal, American Concrete Institute, Vol. 58, Title No. 58-17, p. 353. (21D)

Sahlin, S., 1959
STRUCTURAL INTERACTION OF WALLS AND FLOOR SLABS, Stockholm, Sweden. (21E)

Sahlin, S., 1969
INTERACTION OF BRICK MASONRY WALLS AND CONCRETE SLABS, Design Engineering and Constructing with Masonry Products, F. Johnson, ed., Gulf Publishing Co., Houston, Tex. (27)

Sahlin, S., 1971a
IMPERFECTIONS IN STRUCTURES CONSTRUCTED WITH PREFABRICATED CONCRETE ELEMENTS, Tekniska Meddelanden No. 25, Halmstads Jarnverks AB, Halmstad, Sweden. (22)

Sahlin, S., 1971b
STRUCTURAL MASONRY, Prentice-Hall, Inc., Englewood Cliffs, N.J. (22, 27)

Sahlin, S., 1973
    METHODS OF STEP-BY-STEP NONLINEAR ANALYSIS, Planning and Design of Tall
    Buildings, Proceedings of 1972 ASCE-IABSE International Conference, Vol. III, No.
    22-Summary, ASCE, New York. (22)
Sallada, J. W. and Wakefield, D. A., 1970
    PARK LANE TOWERS COMPLEX, DENVER, COLORADO, Proceedings of the 2nd
    International Brick Masonry Conference, H. W. H. West and K. H. Speed, eds., British
    Ceramic Research Association, Stoke-on-Trent, England, 1971. (27)
Sandi, H., 1973
    LIMIT STATES FOR DYNAMIC LOADS, Planning and Design of Tall Buildings,
    Proceedings of 1972 ASCE-IABSE International Conference, Vol. III, No. 26-D3, ASCE,
    New York. (20, 26)
Santhakumar, A. R., 1976
    ANALYSIS OF NON-UNIFORM COUPLED SHEAR WALLS WITH TWO ROWS OF
    OPENINGS, Proceedings of International Symposium on Earthquake Engineering (St.
    Louis, Mo., August 1976), pp. 1249–1262. (21E)
Sargin, M., 1971
    STRESS-STRAIN RELATIONSHIPS FOR CONCRETE AND THE ANALYSIS OF
    STRUCTURAL CONCRETE SECTIONS, Study No. 4, Solid Mechanics Section,
    University of Waterloo, Canada. (22, 23)
Savassi, W., 1975
    FINITE ELEMENT METHOD ANALYSIS OF TALL BUILDINGS, unpublished
    communication to the Council, October 1975. (21C)
Sawczuk, A. and Jaeger, T., 1963
    THEORY OF ULTIMATE LOAD CARRYING CAPACITY FOR SLABS (Grenz-
    tragfähig Keitstheorie der Platten), Springer Verlag, Berlin, Germany. (21D)
Sawyer, H. A., Jr., 1955
    ELASTIC-PLASTIC DESIGN OF SINGLE-SPAN BEAMS AND FRAMES, Proceedings,
    ASCE, Vol. 81, Proc. Sep. No. 851. (22)
Sawyer, H. A., Jr., 1964a
    STATUS AND POTENTIALITIES OF NONLINEAR DESIGN OF CONCRETE
    FRAMES, Proceedings of ASCE-ACI Symposium on the Flexural Mechanics of
    Reinforced Concrete (Miami, Fla.); Publication No. SP-12, American Concrete Institute,
    pp. 7–28. (22)
Sawyer, H. A., Jr., 1964b
    DESIGN OF CONCRETE FRAMES FOR TWO FAILURE STAGES, Proceedings of
    ASCE-ACI Symposium on the Flexural Mechanics of Reinforced Concrete (Miami, Fla.);
    Publication No. SP-12, American Concrete Institute, 1965, pp. 405–438. (22)
Sawyer, H. A., Jr., 1973
    SUMMARY REPORT: NONLINEAR ANALYSIS AND LIMIT DESIGN, Planning and
    Design of Tall Buildings, Proceedings of 1972 ASCE-IABSE International Conference,
    Vol. III, No. 22-Summary, ASCE, New York. (22)
Scanlon, A. and Murray, D. W., 1972
    AN ANALYSIS TO DETERMINE THE EFFECTS OF CRACKING IN REINFORCED
    CONCRETE SLABS, Proceedings of the Specialty Conference on Finite Element
    Method in Civil Engineering, June 1972, McGill University, Montréal, Canada, pp.
    841–867. (22)
Schafer, B. L., Stevens, T. J. and Beresford, F. D., 1973
    A STUDY OF CONCRETE PANEL CONSTRUCTION, Part 2, Model investigation of
    bearing wall substructure interaction, C.S.I.R.O. Division of Building Research, Mel-
    bourne, Australia. (A38)
Schaub, H., 1973
    CALCULATION OF TWO-SHELL MASONRY WITH INSULATION BETWEEN
    (Berechnung von Zweischalenmauerwerk mit Zwischenisolation), Proceedings of the 3rd
    International Brick Masonry Conference, Bundesverband der Deutschen Ziegelindustrie
    e.V., Essen, Germany. (27)
Schellbach, G., 1970
    THE INFLUENCE OF PERFORATION ON THE LOAD-BEARING CAPACITY OF
    HOLLOW BRICK MASONRY STRUCTURES, Proceedings of the 2nd International
    Brick Masonry Conference, H. W. H. West and K. H. Speed, eds., British Ceramic
    Research Association, Stoke-on-Trent, England, 1971. (27)

Schellbach, G., 1973
CONSTRUCTION AND DIMENSIONING OF BRICK MASONRY (EVALUATION OF STANDARDS AND INSTRUCTIONS) [Ausfuhrung und Bemessung von Ziegelmauerwerk (Auswertung von Normen und Richtlinien)], Proceedings of the 3rd International Brick Masonry Conference, Bundesverband der Deutschen Ziegelindustrie e.V., Essen, Germany. (27)

Schellbach, G., 1976
RECOMMENDATIONS FOR THE DIMENSIONING AND CONSTRUCTION OF MASONRY (Empfehlungen für die Bemessung und Ausfuhrung von Mauerwerk), Proceedings of the 4th International Brick Masonry Conference, Groupement National de l'Industrie de la Terre Cuite, rue des Poissoniers 13, Brussels, Belgium. (27)

Schleeh, W., 1961
RECTANGULAR DIAPHRAGM WITH ARBITRARY LOAD ON THE SHORT EDGE (Die Rechteckscheibe mit beliebiger Belastung der kurzen Rander), *Beton- und Stahlbetonbau*, Vol. 56, H3. (21D)

Schleeh, W., 1964
A SIMPLE PROCEDURE FOR SOLVING DIAPHRAGM PROBLEMS (Ein einfaches Verfahren zur Lösung von Scheibenaufgaben), *Beton- und Stahlbetonbau*, Vol. 59, H3–5. (21D)

Schmidt, L. C. (undated)
CONSTRUCTION AND TESTING OF AN ELASTIC MODEL OF NAURU HOUSE, unpublished report, Melbourne, Australia. (A38)

Schneider, K. H., 1973
RIGIDITY AGAINST WIND BY MASONRY TALL BUILDINGS (Windaussteifung gemauerter Hochhauser), Proceedings of the 3rd International Brick Masonry Conference, Bundesverband der Deutschen Ziegelindustrie e.V., Essen, Germany. (27)

Schneider, R. R., 1959
LATERAL LOAD TESTS ON REINFORCED GROUTED MASONRY SHEAR WALLS, Report No. 70-101, University of Southern California Engineering Center. (27)

Schneider, R. R., 1969
SHEAR IN CONCRETE MASONRY PIERS, Reports on Tests at California State Polytechnic College, Pomona, Calif. (27)

Schrefler, B., 1971
CALCULATION OF GENERAL TYPE REINFORCING SYSTEMS FOR TALL BUILDINGS, *Beton- und Stahlbetonbau*, Vol. 66, No. 9, pp. 213–219. (21A)

Schubert, P. and Wesche, K., 1977
DEFORMATIONS AND CRACKING CHARACTERISTICS OF MASONRY (Verformung und Risssicherheit von Mauerwerk), Mauerwerk-Kalender, Wilhelm Ernst & Sohn, Berlin, Germany. (27)

Schultz, D. M. and Fintel, M., 1975
DESIGN AND CONSTRUCTION OF LARGE-PANEL CONCRETE STRUCTURES —LOADING CONDITIONS, Report 1, HUD Contract No. H-2131R, Portland Cement Association. (21E)

Schupack, M. and McDonald, A., 1969
HIGH TENSION ADHESIVE MORTAR IN CONCRETE MASONRY STRUCTURAL SYSTEMS, Design Engineering and Constructing with Masonry Products, F. Johnson, ed., Gulf Publishing Co., Houston, Tex. (27)

Schuring, D. J., 1977
SCALE MODELS IN ENGINEERING—FUNDAMENTALS AND APPLICATIONS, Pergamon Press, New York. (A38)

Schuster, J., 1964
HELICAL STAIRS (Wendeltreppen), Julius Hoffman, Stuttgart, Germany. (21D)

Schwaighofer, J., 1969
A CONTRIBUTION TO THE SHEAR WALL PROBLEM (Ein Beitrag zum Windscheiben Problem), *Der Bauingenieur*, Vol. 10, pp. 370–373. (24)

Schwaighofer, J., 1972
MODELS OF SHEAR WALL STRUCTURES, Conference on Structural Models (Sydney, 1972), Cement and Concrete Assoc. of Australia in conjunction with Dept. of Architectural Science, University of Sydney, and Institution of Engineers, Australia, N.S.W. Division. (21C, A38)

Schwaighofer, J. and Collins, M. P., 1976
COUPLING SLABS IN SHEAR WALL BUILDINGS, Research Report, Department of Civil Engineering, University of Toronto, Canada. (24)

Schwaighofer, J. and Microys, H. F., 1969
ANALYSIS OF SHEAR WALL STRUCTURES USING STANDARD COMPUTER PROGRAMS, *ACI Journal*, American Concrete Institute, Vol. 66, No. 12, pp. 1005–1008. (21C, 24)

Schwaighofer, J. and Microys, H. F., 1974
EFFECTS OF SHEAR WALLS ON STIFFNESS, presented at the ASCE Structural Engineering Conference held at Cincinnati, Ohio, April 1974. (24)

Schwarz, H. and Kasparek, K., 1967
A CONTRIBUTION TO THE BEARING OF ECCENTRICALLY LOADED CONCRETE COLUMNS (Ein Beitrag zur Klarung der Tragverhaltens exzentrisch beanspruchter Stahlbetonstutzen), *Der Bauingenieur*. (23)

Schwing, H. and Mehlhorn, G., 1974
OVERALL BEHAVIOR OF LARGE PANEL SHEAR WALLS (Zum Tragverhalten von Wanden aus Fertigteiltafeln), *Betonwerk + Fertigteil Technik*, Heft 5. (21E)

Scordelis, A. C., 1972
FINITE ELEMENT ANALYSIS OF REINFORCED CONCRETE STRUCTURES, Proceedings of the Specialty Conference on Finite Element Method in Civil Engineering (sponsored by McGill University, Canadian Society of Civil Engineers, Engineering Institute of Canada) June 1972, Montréal, Canada, pp. 71–113. (21C, 22)

Scrivener, J. C., 1966
CONCRETE MASONRY WALL PANEL TESTS—STATIC RACKING TESTS WITH PREDOMINANT FLEXURAL EFFECT, *N.Z. Concrete Construction*, Vol. 10, No. 7. (27)

Scrivener, J. C., 1969a
FACE LOAD TESTS ON REINFORCED HOLLOW BRICK NON-LOADBEARING WALLS, *N.Z. Engineering*, July 1969. (27)

Scrivener, J. C., 1969b
STATIC RACKING TESTS ON CONCRETE MASONRY WALLS, Design Engineering and Constructing with Masonry Products, F. Johnson, ed., Gulf Publishing Co., Houston, Tex. (27)

Scrivener, J. C., 1972
REINFORCED MASONRY—SEISMIC BEHAVIOUR AND DESIGN, *Bulletin*, N.Z. Society for Earthquake Engineering, Vol. 5, No. 4. (27)

Scrivener, J. C., 1976a
COMMENTS ON THE NEW CODE FOR NEW ZEALAND MASONRY BUILDINGS, Proceedings of the 4th International Brick Masonry Conference, Groupement National de l'Industrie de la Terre Cuite, rue des Poissoniers 13, Brussels, Belgium. (27)

Scrivener, J. C., 1976b
REINFORCED MASONRY IN A SEISMIC AREA—RESEARCH AND CONSTRUCTION DEVELOPMENT IN NEW ZEALAND, Proceedings of the 1st Canadian Masonry Symposium, E. L. Jessop and M. A. Ward, eds., University of Calgary, Canada. (27)

Scrivener, J. C. and Williams, D., 1971a
COMPRESSIVE BEHAVIOUR OF MASONRY PRISMS, Proceedings of the 3rd Australasian Conference on the Mechanics of Structures and Materials (Auckland, New Zealand, August 1971). (27)

Scrivener, J. C. and Williams, D., 1971b
BEHAVIOUR OF REINFORCED MASONRY SHEAR WALLS UNDER CYCLIC LOADING, *Bulletin*, N.Z. Society for Earthquake Engineering, Vol. 4, No. 2. (27)

Sebestyen, G., 1965
LARGE-PANEL BUILDINGS, Publishing House of the Hungarian Academy of Sciences, Budapest, Hungary. (21E)

Seddon, A. E., 1956
THE STRENGTH OF CONCRETE WALLS UNDER AXIAL AND ECCENTRIC LOADS, Symposium on the Strength of Concrete Structures, London, England, May 1956. (21E)

Sedo, V., 1973
PRACTICAL APPLICATION OF NEW METHODS OF CALCULATION OF BUILD-INGS OF LARGE PRECAST CONCRETE PANELS IN EXISTING DESIGN PRACTICE, 10th Regional Conference Proceedings, 10th National/Regional Conference (Bratislava, Czechoslovakia, April 1973), pp. 379–383. (21E)

Seetharamulu, K. and Kumar, A., 1974
THE ANALYSIS OF TALL BUILDING STRUCTURES BY THE TRANSFER MA-TRIX METHOD, Proceedings of the Regional Conference on Tall Buildings, National/Regional Conference (Bangkok, Thailand, January 23–25, 1974), Asian Institute of Technology, Bangkok, pp. 367–379. (21C)

Sefton Jenkins, R. A., Plowman, J. M. and Haseltine, B. N., 1965
INVESTIGATIONS INTO THE CAUSES OF THE DEFLECTION OF HEATED CONCRETE FLOORS, INCLUDING SHRINKAGE, Structural Engineering, Vol. 43, pp. 105–118. (25)

Sejnoha, J., 1973
ANALYSIS OF MIXED WALL SYSTEMS COMPOSED OF CONCRETE ELEMENTS OF DIFFERENT AGE, 10th Regional Conference Proceedings, 10th National/Regional Conference (Bratislava, Czechoslovakia, April 1973), Lehigh University, Bethlehem, Pa., pp. 447–455. (21E, 25)

Sejnoha, J. and Pelikan, P., 1973
NONLINEAR ULTIMATE STRENGTH OF THREE-DIMENSIONAL WALL SYS-TEMS, 10th Regional Conference Proceedings, 10th National/Regional Conference (Bratislava, Czechoslovakia, April 1973), pp. 384–394. (21E)

Semencov, S. A., 1968
STRENGTH OF JOINTS BETWEEN WALL AND FLOORS IN LARGE PANEL BUILDINGS (Procnost uslov sopriazenie sten i perekrytii v krupnopanelnych zdaniach), Beton i Zhelezobeton. (21E)

Sethurathnam, A. and Dayaratnam, P., 1974
INTERACTION OF FRAME AND SHEAR WALL WITH OPENINGS, Proceedings of the Regional Conference on Tall Buildings, 22nd National/Regional Conference (Bangkok, Thailand, January 23–25, 1974), Asian Institute of Technology, Bangkok, pp. 301–313. (21C)

Shah, M. J. and Gesund, H., 1972
THE ANALYSIS OF NONLINEAR THREE-DIMENSIONAL FRAMES, Computers and Structures, Vol. 2, pp. 943–954. (22)

Shah, S. P., Sturman, G. M. and Winter, G., 1965
MICROCRACKING AND INELASTIC BEHAVIOR OF CONCRETE, Proceedings of ASCE-ACI Symposium on the Flexural Mechanics of Reinforced Concrete, Publication No. SP-12, American Concrete Institute. (22)

Shapiro, G. A. and Sokolov, M. E., 1963
ON THE STRENGTH AND DEFORMABILITY OF HORIZONTAL JOINTS IN LARGE PANEL WALLS (O procnosti i deformativnosti gorizontalnych stykov krypno-panelnych zdanie), Beton i Zhelezobeton, 6. (21E)

Shemie, M., 1973
BOLTED CONNECTIONS IN LARGE PANEL SYSTEM BUILDINGS, Journal of the Prestressed Concrete Institute, Vol. 18, No. 1, pp. 27–33. (21E)

Shiedeler, J. J., 1957
LIGHTWEIGHT AGGREGATE FOR STRUCTURAL USE, ACI Journal, American Concrete Institute, Vol. 54, No. 10. (22)

Shiedeler, J. J., 1963
CARBONATION SHRINKAGE OF CONCRETE MASONRY UNITS, Bulletin D.69, Development Department, Portland Cement Association. (27)

Shiga, T., Shibata, A. and Shibuya, J., 1971
A STUDY ON DYNAMIC CHARACTERISTICS OF REINFORCED CONCRETE SHEAR WALLS (in Japanese), Summaries of Technical Papers of Annual Meeting of Architectural Institute of Japan (November 1971), University of Tohoku, Sendai, Japan. (21D)

Shiga, T., Ogawa, J., Shibata, A. and Shibuya, J., 1970
THE DYNAMIC PROPERTIES OF REINFORCED CONCRETE FRAMES, Proceedings of the U.S.-Japan Seminar on Earthquake Engineering with Emphasis on Safety of School Buildings (Sendai, Japan, September 1970), pp. 346–365. (22)

Shiga, T., Shibata, A., Shibuya, J. and Takahashi, J., 1972
A STUDY ON DYNAMIC CHARACTERISTICS OF REINFORCED CONCRETE SHEAR WALLS (in Japanese), Summaries of Technical Papers of Annual Meeting of Architectural Institute of Japan (October 1972), University of Tohoku, Sendai, Japan. (21D)

Shiga, T., Shibuya, J., Takahashi, J. and Kanai, M., 1974
A STUDY ON DYNAMIC CHARACTERISTICS OF REINFORCED CONCRETE SHEAR WALLS (in Japanese), Summaries of Technical Papers of Annual Meeting of Architectural Institute of Japan (October 1974), University of Tohoku, Sendai, Japan. (21D)

Shinagawa, T. and Hirosawa, M., 1971
LATERAL LOAD TEST ON FIVE-STORIED FULL-SIZE BUILDING OF PRECAST REINFORCED CONCRETE WALL CONSTRUCTION, Seminar under the Japan-U.S. Cooperative Science Program, Construction and Behavior of Precast Concrete Structures, Report by Japanese Participants, Part I (Seattle, Wash., August 1970), pp. 81–90. (22)

Siev, A., 1962
ANALYSIS OF FREE STRAIGHT MULTIFLIGHT STAIRCASES, *Journal of the Structural Division*, ASCE, Vol. 88, No. ST3, Proc. Paper 3168, pp. 207–232. (21D)

Singh, A., Gerstle, K. H. and Tulin, L. G., 1965
THE BEHAVIOR OF REINFORCING STEEL UNDER REVERSED LOADING, *Materials Research and Standards*, Vol. 5, No. 1. (22)

Singh, H. N., Gerstle, K. H. and Tulin, L. G., 1969
SHEAR STRENGTH OF CONCRETE BEAMS UNDER CYCLIC LOADING, presented at International Symposium on Shear, Bond and Torsion, P.S.G. College of Technology, Coimbatore, India. (22)

Sinha, B. P., 1976
TEST ON A THREE-STOREY CAVITY WALL STRUCTURE, Proceedings of the 4th International Brick Masonry Conference, Groupement National de l'Industrie de la Terre Cuite, rue des Poissoniers 13, Brussels, Belgium. (27)

Sinha, B. P. and Hendry, A. W., 1965
THE EFFECT OF BRICKWORK BOND ON THE LOADBEARING CAPACITY OF BRICK WALLS, *Proceedings*, British Ceramic Society, No. 11. (27)

Sinha, B. P. and Hendry, A. W., 1973
THE LATERAL LOAD ANALYSIS OF BRICK MULTI-STOREY SHEAR-WALL STRUCTURES, Proceedings of the 3rd International Brick Masonry Conference, Bundesverband der Deutschen Ziegelindustrie e.V., Essen, Germany. (27)

Sinha, B. P., Gerstle, K. H. and Tulin, L. G., 1964a
RESPONSE OF SINGLY REINFORCED BEAMS TO CYCLIC LOADING, *ACI Journal*, American Concrete Institute, Vol. 61, No. 8. (22)

Sinha, B. P., Gerstle, K. H. and Tulin, L. G., 1964b
STRESS-STRAIN RELATIONS FOR CONCRETE UNDER CYCLIC LOADING, *ACI Journal*, American Concrete Institute, Vol. 61, No. 2. (22)

Sinha, B. P., Maurenbrecher, A. H. P. and Hendry, A. W., 1970
MODEL AND FULL-SCALE TESTS ON A FIVE-STOREY CROSS-WALL STRUCTURE UNDER LATERAL LOADING, Proceedings of the 2nd International Brick Masonry Conference, H. W. H. West and K. H. Speed, eds., British Ceramic Research Association, Stoke-on-Trent, England, 1971. (27)

Sinha, N. C. and Ferguson, P. M., 1964
ULTIMATE STRENGTH WITH HIGH STRENGTH REINFORCING STEEL WITH AN INDEFINITE YIELD POINT, *ACI Journal*, American Concrete Institute, Vol. 61, No. 4, p. 399. (21D)

Smith, B. J., 1972
EXTERIOR REINFORCED CONCRETE JOINTS WITH LOW AXIAL LOAD UNDER SEISMIC LOADING, thesis presented to the University of Canterbury, at Christchurch, New Zealand, in partial fulfillment of the requirements for the degree of Master of Engineering. (22)

Smith, J. O. and Sidebottom, O. M., 1965
INELASTIC BEHAVIOR OF LOAD-CARRYING MEMBERS, John Wiley & Sons, New York. (22)

Smith, W. F., 1968
A 15-STOREY TOWER BLOCK IN LOAD-BEARING BRICKWORK AND ITS PROBLEMS, *Proceedings*, British Ceramic Society, No. 11. (27)

Smolira, M., 1975
ANALYSIS OF TALL BUILDINGS BY THE FORCE DISPLACEMENT METHOD, McGraw-Hill Book Co., Inc., New York, N.Y. (21C)

Snech, T., 1976
WINTER MASONRY CONSTRUCTION, Proceedings of the 1st Canadian Masonry Symposium, E. L. Jessop and M. A. Ward, eds., University of Calgary, Canada. (27)

Soane, A. J. M., 1967
MODEL ANALYSIS OF ESSEX UNIVERSITY TOWER BLOCK, Research Note, Clay Products Technical Bureau, Vol. 1, No. 1. (27)

Soane, A. J. M., 1969
INTERACTION OF BRICKWORK WALLS AND CONCRETE FLOORS UNDER LATERAL LOAD, Design Engineering and Constructing with Masonry Products, F. Johnson, ed., Gulf Publishing Co., Houston, Tex. (27)

Soane, A. J. M. and Hendry, A. W., 1968
THE BEHAVIOUR OF ESSEX UNIVERSITY TOWER BLOCK UNDER WIND LOADING, *Proceedings*, British Ceramic Society, No. 11, pp. 131-133. (27, A38)

Somerville, G. and Taylor, H. P. J., 1972
THE INFLUENCE OF REINFORCEMENT DETAILING ON THE STRENGTH OF CONCRETE STRUCTURES, *The Structural Engineer*, Vol. 50, No. 1, pp. 309-321. (21D)

Sontag, H., 1973
PRECAST COMPOSITE FLOORING, SOA Report 10, Committee 3, Proceedings of 1972 ASCE-IABSE International Conference on Tall Buildings, Vol. Ia-3, ASCE, New York, pp. 191-202. (21E)

Sorete, S., 1971
DEFORMATION: STATE OF THE ART IN 1970 (Déformations: Etat des connaissances en 1970), Bulletin d'information no. 77, Comité Européen du Béton, Paris, France. (25)

Sparkes, S. R. and Chapman, J. C., 1961
MODEL METHODS, WITH PARTICULAR REFERENCE TO THREE RECENT APPLICATIONS IN THE FIELDS OF STEEL, COMPOSITE AND CONCRETE CONSTRUCTION, *The Structural Engineer*, Vol. 39, No. 3, pp. 85-99. (A38)

Speyer, I. J., 1976
CONSIDERATIONS FOR THE DESIGN OF PRECAST CONCRETE BEARING WALL BUILDINGS TO WITHSTAND ABNORMAL LOADS, *Journal of the Prestressed Concrete Institute*, Vol. 21, No. 2, pp. 2-35. (21E)

Spillers, W. R., 1963
APPLICATIONS OF TOPOLOGY IN STRUCTURAL ANALYSIS, *Journal of the Structural Division*, ASCE, Vol. 89, No. ST4, Proc. Paper 3600, pp. 301-313. (22)

Spiridonov, V. V., 1957
BEARING CAPACITY OF HORIZONTAL JOINTS IN LARGE PANEL BUILDINGS (Niesuscaja sposobnost gorizontalnych stykov krupnopanelnych zdanie), *Beton i Zhelezobeton*, 5. (21E)

Springfield, J. and Adams, P. F., 1972
ASPECTS OF COLUMN DESIGN IN TALL STEEL BUILDINGS, *Journal of the Structural Division*, ASCE, Vol. 98, No. ST5, Proc. Paper 8911, pp. 1069-1083. (23)

Stafford-Smith, B., 1970
MODIFIED BEAM METHOD FOR ANALYSIS OF SYMMETRICAL INTERCONNECTED SHEAR WALLS, *ACI Journal*, American Concrete Institute, Vol. 67, No. 12, p. 977. (21C)

Stafford-Smith, B. and Carter, C., 1969
A METHOD OF ANALYSIS FOR INFILLED FRAMES, *Proceedings*, Institution of Civil Engineers, London, September 1969, pp. 31-48. (27)

Stafford-Smith, B. and Coull, A., 1973
ELASTIC ANALYSIS OF TALL CONCRETE BUILDINGS, Planning and Design of Tall Buildings, Proceedings of 1972 ASCE-IABSE International Conference, Vol. III, No. 21-1, ASCE, New York. (21C)

Stafford-Smith, B. and Rahman, K. M. K., 1973
THE VARIATION OF STRESSES IN BRICKWORK WALLS SUBJECT TO SHEAR FORCES, Proceedings of the 3rd International Brick Masonry Conference, Bundesverband der Deutschen Ziegelindustrie e.V., Essen, Germany. (27)

Stafford-Smith, B. and Taranath, B. S., 1972
ANALYSIS OF TALL CORE-SUPPORTED STRUCTURES SUBJECT TO TORSION, Proceedings, Institution of Civil Engineers, London, Vol. 53, p. 173. (21C)

Stamato, M. C., 1966
DISTRIBUTION OF THE WIND LOADS AMONG THE WIND-RESISTANT PANELS (Distribuciao das Cargas do Vento entre os Paineis de Contraventamento), XIas Jornadas Sulamericanas de Engenharia Estrutural, São Paulo, Brazil, pp. 203–225. (24)

Stamato, M. C., 1972
THREE-DIMENSIONAL ANALYSIS OF TALL BUILDINGS, Report No. 24-4, Proceedings of ASCE-IABSE International Conference on Planning and Design of Tall Buildings, Lehigh University, Bethlehem, Pa., Vol. 3, p. 683. (21C)

Stamato, M. C. and Mancini, E., 1973
THREE-DIMENSIONAL INTERACTION OF WALLS AND FRAMES, Journal of the Structural Division, ASCE, Vol. 99, No. ST12, Proc. Paper 10193, p. 2375. (21C)

Stamato, M. C. and Stafford-Smith, B., 1969
APPROXIMATE METHOD FOR THE THREE-DIMENSIONAL ANALYSIS OF TALL BUILDINGS, Proceedings, Institution of Civil Engineers, London, Vol. 43, p. 361. (21C, 22)

Standards Association of Australia, 1963
CODE FOR CONCRETE IN BUILDINGS, CA-2. (25)

Statens Betongkommitte, 1968
REGULATIONS FOR CONCRETE STRUCTURES, GENERAL DESIGN REGULATIONS (Bestammelser for Betongkonstruktioner, Allmanna Konstruktionsbestimmelser), B7, Stockholm, Sweden. (23)

Stedham, M. E. C., 1968
QUALITY CONTROL FOR LOAD-BEARING BRICKWORK: 111 WALL TESTS, Proceedings, British Ceramic Society, No. 11. (27)

Stevens, L. K., 1967
ELASTIC STABILITY OF PRACTICAL MULTI-STOREY FRAMES, Proceedings, Institution of Civil Engineers, London, Vol. 36, pp. 99-117. (23)

Stevenson, J. and Moses, F., 1970
RELIABILITY ANALYSIS OF FRAME STRUCTURES, Journal of the Structural Division, ASCE, Vol. 96, No. ST11, Proc. Paper 7692, pp. 2409–2427. (21A)

Stigter, J., 1966
AUSTRALIA SQUARE, SYDNEY, Constructional Review, September 1966. (21E)

Stiller, M., 1965
DISTRIBUTION OF HORIZONTAL FORCES ON THE DIAPHRAGM SYSTEM OF TALL BUILDINGS (Verteilung der Horizontalkrafte auf die aussteifenden Scheibensysteme von Hochhausern), Beton- und Stahlbetonbau, Vol. 60, pp. 42–45. (24)

Stiller, M., 1973a
REVIEW OF CODES OF PRACTICE IN WEST EUROPEAN COUNTRIES —CONCRETE TALL BUILDINGS, Planning and Design of Tall Buildings, Proceedings of the 1972 ASCE-IABSE International Conference, Vol. III, No. 20-2, ASCE, New York. (20, 26)

Stiller, M., 1973b
STANDARDIZED EUROPEAN REGULATIONS FOR CONSTRUCTION (Einheitliche Europaische Bauvorschriften—Wunsch und Wirklichkeit), Beton- und Stahlbetonbau, Heft 5. (20)

Stiller, M., 1975
GERMAN BUILDINGS WITH PRECAST CONCRETE ELEMENTS, unpublished communication to the Joint Committee, December 1975. (21E)

Stockbridge, J. G., 1967
A STUDY OF HIGH-RISE LOAD-BEARING BRICKWORK IN BRITAIN, thesis presented to the University of Edinburgh, Scotland, in partial fulfillment of the requirements for the degree of Master of Architecture. (27)

Stockbridge, J. G., 1969
REMARKS ON PAPER 44, Design Engineering and Constructing with Masonry Products, F. Johnson, ed., Gulf Publishing Co., Houston, Tex., p. 385. (27)

Stockley, W. G., Jumikis, T., Hunt, R. W. and Kimpton, F., 1973
CASE HISTORY—RECENT "HIGH-RISE" LOAD-BEARING BRICK CONSTRUCTION IN SYDNEY, Proceedings of Structural Brickwork Seminar, Macquarie University, Sydney, Australia, pp. 42-63. (27)

Strating, J., 1972
LOAD FACTOR DESIGN, 6th Regional Conference Proceedings, 6th National/Regional Conference (Delft, The Netherlands, May 1972), Joint Committee on Tall Buildings, Lehigh University, Bethlehem, Pa., pp. 56–58. (26)

Suenaga, Y., 1974
ON BOX-FRAME-TYPE PRECAST REINFORCED CONCRETE CONSTRUCTION OF FIVE-STORIED MULTIPLE HOUSES—PROBLEMS IN THE PRESENT JOINTING METHODS AND STRESS CONVEYANCE METHODS IN EARTHQUAKES, *Concrete Journal*, Japan, Vol. 12, No. 7. (21E)

Sugano, S., 1970
STATIC TEST OF CONCRETE SHEAR WALLS REINFORCED WITH WIRE FABRIC, Experimental Studies on Reinforced Concrete Members and Composite Steel and Reinforced Concrete Members, Umemura Laboratory, Tokyo University, Japan, pp. 151–159. (22)

Suter, G. T. and Hendry, A. W., 1975a
LIMIT STATE SHEAR DESIGN OF REINFORCED BRICKWORK BEAMS, *Proceedings*, British Ceramic Society, No. 24, pp. 191–196. (27)

Suter, G. T. and Hendry, A. W., 1975b
SHEAR STRENGTH OF REINFORCED BRICKWORK BEAMS, *The Structural Engineer*, Vol. 53, No. 6, pp. 249–253. (27)

Suter, G. T. and Keller, H., 1976a
SHEAR STRENGTH OF GROUTED REINFORCED MASONRY BEAMS, Proceedings of the 4th International Brick Masonry Conference, Groupement National de l'Industrie de la Terre Cuite, rue des Poissoniers 13, Brussels, Belgium. (27)

Suter, G. T. and Keller, H., 1976b
SHEAR STRENGTH OF REINFORCED MASONRY BEAMS AND CANADIAN CODE IMPLICATIONS, Proceedings of the 1st Canadian Masonry Symposium, E. L. Jessop and M. A. Ward, eds., University of Calgary, Canada. (27)

Sutherland, R. J. M., 1968
THE DEVELOPMENT OF THE DESIGN OF THE BRICK APARTMENT TOWERS AT ESSEX UNIVERSITY, *Proceedings*, British Ceramic Society, No. 11. (27)

Sutherland, R. J. M., 1969
DESIGN ENGINEER'S APPROACH TO MASONRY CONSTRUCTION, Design Engineering and Constructing with Masonry Products, F. Johnson, ed., Gulf Publishing Co., Houston, Tex. (27)

Suzuki, E., 1971
THE HIGH-RISE APARTMENTS AND SILOS USING LARGE PRECAST PANELS, 3rd Regional Conference Proceedings, 3rd National/Regional Conference (Tokyo, Japan, September 1971), pp. 17–20. (21E)

Swanson, V. E., 1975
THE ECONOMICS OF HIGH RISE OFFICE BUILDINGS, Pan-Pacific Tall Buildings Conference (Honolulu, Hawaii, January 26–29, 1975), University of Hawaii, Honolulu, pp. 97–110. (21B)

Swedish Standard, 1967
SWEDISH REGULATIONS ON LARGE PANELS, Svensk Byggnorm 67. (21E)

Szabo, P., 1973
INFLUENCE OF STONE SIZE OVER LOAD CAPACITY AND SHEAR STRENGTH OF MASONRY (Einfluss der Steinformate auf die Tragfähigkeit und Schubfestigkeit des Mauerwerks), Proceedings of the 3rd International Brick Masonry Conference, Bundesverband der Deutschen Ziegelindustrie e.V., Essen, Germany. (27)

Szoke, D., 1973
QUALITY CONTROL OF BUILDINGS OF LARGE PRECAST CONCRETE PANELS, 10th Regional Conference Proceedings, 10th National/Regional Conference (Bratislava, Czechoslovakia, April 1973), pp. 333–342. (21E)

Szoke, D., 1975
BEARING CAPACITY OF WELDED STEEL JOINTS BETWEEN WALL PANELS, CIB 2nd International Symposium on Bearing Walls (Warsaw, Poland, September 1975), Theme 1, Paper 10, pp. 97–106. (21E)

Tadros, M. K., Ghali, A. and Dilger, W. H., 1975
TIME-DEPENDENT PRESTRESS LOSS AND DEFLECTION IN PRESTRESSED CONCRETE MEMBERS, Journal of the Prestressed Concrete Institute, Vol. 20, No. 3, pp. 86–98. (25)

Tadros, M. K., Ghali, A. and Dilger, W. H., 1977
EFFECT OF NONPRESTRESSED STEEL ON PRESTRESS LOSS AND DEFLECTION, Journal of the Prestressed Concrete Institute, Vol. 22, No. 2, pp. 50–63. (25)

Takeda, T. and Eto, H., 1976
See Eto, H. and Takeda, T.

Takeda, T., Sozen, M. A. and Nielsen, N. N., 1970
REINFORCED CONCRETE RESPONSE TO SIMULATED EARTHQUAKES, Journal of the Structural Division, ASCE, Vol. 96, No. ST12, Proc. Paper 7759, pp. 2557–2573. (22, 24)

Tal', K. E. and Chistiakov, E. A., 1952
EXPERIMENTAL INVESTIGATIONS OF SLENDER REINFORCED CONCRETE COLUMNS UNDER LONG-TIME LOADING, Sbornik Niizhb, Special problems of deformation of concrete and reinforced concrete and the use of computers for evaluation of their effect on behavior of structures, Gosstroizdat, Moscow, USSR, pp. 30–58. (23)

Tal', K. E., Chistiakov, E. A. and Shubik, A. V., 1969
SLENDER AXIALLY COMPRESSED CONCRETE ELEMENTS UNDER THE ACTION OF A LONG-TIME LOADING, Sbornik Niizhb, Special problems of deformation of concrete and reinforced concrete and the use of computers for evaluation of their effect on behavior of structures, Stroiizdat, Moscow, USSR, pp. 98–105. (23)

Tani, S., 1974
STEEL-REINFORCED CONCRETE STRUCTURE—PREFABRICATED (HPC), Proceedings of National Conference on Tall Buildings, 14th National/Regional Conference (Tokyo, Japan, August 1973), pp. 39–51. (21E)

Taoka, G. T., Furumoto, A. S. and Chiu, A. M., 1973
NATURAL PERIODS OF A TALL SHEAR WALL BUILDING, Proceedings, 5th World Conference on Earthquake Engineering (Rome, Italy, June 1973). (24)

Tasker, H. E., 1975
RECOMMENDATIONS FOR THE USE OF PRESTRESSED BRICK OR BLOCK WALLS ON REACTIVE SOILS, Technical Record, 52:75:349, Department of Works, Commonwealth Experimental Building Station. (27)

Taylor, H. P. J., 1974
THE BEHAVIOR OF IN-SITU CONCRETE BEAM-COLUMN JOINTS, Technical Report 42.492, Cement and Concrete Association, London, England. (21D)

Taylor, H. P. J. and Clarke, J. L., 1976
SOME DETAILING PROBLEMS IN CONCRETE FRAME STRUCTURES, The Structural Engineer, Vol. 54, No. 1, pp. 19–32. (21D)

Taylor, P. J., 1970
INITIAL AND LONG-TERM DEFLECTIONS OF A REINFORCED CONCRETE FLAT PLATE STRUCTURE, Civil Engineering Transactions, Institution of Engineers, Australia, Vol. CE12. (25)

Taylor, P. J. and Heiman, J. L., 1970
A LONG-TERM INVESTIGATION OF DEFLEXIONS OF A FLAT SLAB STRUCTURE, Proceedings of the 4th Australian Building Research Congress (Sydney, Australia, 1970). (25)

Templeman, A. B., 1971
A STEEPEST GRADIENT METHOD FOR OPTIMUM STRUCTURAL DESIGN, International Journal for Numerical Methods in Engineering, Vol. 3, No. 2, pp. 249–259. (22)

Terzaghi, K., 1955
COEFFICIENTS OF SUBGRADE REACTIONS, Geotechnique, London, England, December 1955. (21D)

Tezcon, S. S., 1967
ANALYSIS AND DESIGN OF SHEAR WALL STRUCTURES, *Tall Buildings*, Pergamon Press, London, England, pp. 401–410. (22)
Thakkar, M. C. and Sridhar Rao, J. K., 1973
POSSIBLE OPTIMIZATION OF STRUCTURAL LAYOUT IN DESIGN OF TALL BUILDINGS, Proceedings, National Conference on Tall Buildings (New Delhi, India, January 22–24, 1973), Indian National Group of IABSE, New Delhi, India, pp. III 133–III 137. (21B)
The Concrete Society, 1968
PROCEEDINGS OF THE 1ST INTERNATIONAL CONGRESS ON LIGHTWEIGHT CONCRETE, Vol. 1 and Vol. 2, London, England. (21E)
Theocaris, P. S., 1969
MOIRÉ FRINGES IN STRAIN ANALYSIS, Pergamon Press, Oxford, England. (A38)
Thomas, F. G., 1953
THE STRENGTH OF BRICKWORK, *The Structural Engineer*, Vol. 31, No. 2. (27)
Thomas, K., 1966
MOVEMENT JOINTS IN BRICKWORK, C.P.T.B. Technical Note, Vol. 1, No. 10. (27)
Thomas, K., 1968
REINFORCED BRICKWORK, *Proceedings*, British Ceramic Society, No. 11. (27)
Thomas, K., 1970
THE STRENGTH FUNCTION AND OTHER PROPERTIES OF WALL-TIES, *Proceedings*, British Ceramic Society, No. 17. (27)
Thomas, K., 1972
STRUCTURAL BRICKWORK—MATERIALS AND PERFORMANCE, *The Structural Engineer*, Vol. 49, No. 10, 1971; with discussion, Vol. 50, No. 3, 1972. (27)
Thomas, K. and O'Leary, D. C., 1970
TENSILE STRENGTH TESTS ON TWO TYPES OF BRICK, Proceedings of the 2nd International Brick Masonry Conference, H. W. H. West and K. H. Speed, eds., British Ceramic Research Association, Stoke-on-Trent, England, 1971. (27)
Thomas, K. and Ploughman, J., 1969
CURRENT POST-TENSIONED AND PRESTRESSED BRICKWORK AND CERAMICS IN GREAT BRITAIN, Design Engineering and Constructing with Masonry Products, F. Johnson, ed., Gulf Publishing Co., Houston, Tex. (27)
Thomas, K. and Sozen, M. A., 1965
A STUDY OF THE INELASTIC ROTATION MECHANISM OF REINFORCED CONCRETE CONNECTIONS, C.E. Studies, Structural Engineering Series No. 301, University of Illinois. (22)
Thomas, K., Coutie, M. G. and Pateman, J., 1970
THE EFFECT OF PIGMENT ON SOME PROPERTIES OF MORTAR FOR BRICKWORK, Proceedings of the 2nd International Brick Masonry Conference, H. W. H. West and K. H. Speed, eds., British Ceramic Research Association, Stoke-on-Trent, England, 1971. (27)
Thongcharoen, V. and Davies, S. R., 1973
THE COMPOSITE ACTION OF SIMPLY SUPPORTED REINFORCED BRICKWORK WALLS AND REINFORCED CONCRETE BEAMS, Proceedings of the 3rd International Brick Masonry Conference, Bundesverband der Deutschen Ziegelindustrie e.V., Essen, Germany. (27)
Thürlimann, B., 1972
ELASTIC ANALYSIS, STRENGTH OF SECTIONS, Proceedings, 6th National/Regional Conference (Delft, The Netherlands, May 1972), Joint Committee on Tall Buildings, Lehigh University, Bethlehem, Pa., pp. 59–61. (21C)
Thürlimann, B., 1973
ELASTIC ANALYSIS—STRENGTH OF MEMBERS AND CONNECTIONS, SUMMARY REPORT, Planning and Design of Tall Buildings, Proceedings of 1972 ASCE-IABSE International Conference, Vol. III, No. 21-Summary, ASCE, New York. (21C, 21E)
Thürlimann, B., Fling, R. S., Macchi, G. and Stafford-Smith, B., 1971
TALL BUILDINGS, YES OR NO—TECHNOLOGY, CURSE OR BLESSING? (Hochhaüser, ja oder nein—Technik, Fluch oder Segen?), Berichte 1 Hochhaüser, 17th National/Regional Conference on Tall Buildings (Zürich, Switzerland, October 1971),

SIA-Fachgruppen für Bruckenbau and Hochbau (FBH) and für Architektur (FGA), Zürich, Switzerland, pp. 23-27. (21A)

Tichy, M., 1973
INSTABILIY OF REINFORCED CONCRETE IN PLASTIC DOMAIN, Acta Technica CSAV, No. 2. (23)

Tichy, M., 1975
PLASTIC ANALYSIS OF CONCRETE FRAMES (Calcul plastique des ossatures en béton), Editions Eyrolles, Paris, France. (22)

Tichy, M. and Vorlicek, M., 1972
STATISTICAL THEORY OF CONCRETE STRUCTURES WITH SPECIAL REFERENCES TO ULTIMATE DESIGN, Czechoslovak Academy of Science, Prague, Czechoslovakia. (26)

Timoshenko, S., 1965
STRENGTH OF MATERIALS, Van Nostrand Co., New York, N.Y. (21D)

Timoshenko, S. and Gere, J. M., 1961
THEORY OF ELASTIC STABILITY, 2nd ed., McGraw-Hill Book Co., Inc., New York. (23)

Todeschini, C., Bianchini, A. C. and Kesler, C. E., 1964
BEHAVIOR OF CONCRETE COLUMNS REINFORCED WITH HIGH STRENGTH STEELS, ACI Journal, American Concrete Institute, Vol. 61, No. 6, p. 701. (21D)

Toennies, H. T. and Redmond, T. B., 1967
SILICEOUS FINES IN THE CEMENTING MEDIUM OF STEAM-CURED CONCRETE MASONRY UNITS, National Concrete Masonry Association. (27)

Tomii, M., 1957
STUDIES ON SHEARING RESISTANCE OF REINFORCED CONCRETE PLATE (in Japanese), Report of the Institute of Industrial Science, University of Tokyo, Japan, Vol. 6, No. 3. (21D)

Tomii, M., 1963
SHEAR WALL (in Japanese), Limit Analysis of Building Structures, Reinforced Concrete Structure, Architectural Institute of Japan, Section 2, Chapter 7. (21D)

Tomii, M., 1971
PART 2.1 SHEAR WALLS, 3rd Regional Conference Proceedings (Tokyo, Japan, September 1971), Muto Institution of Structural Mechanics, Room 2928 Kasumigaseki Building, Kasumigaseki 3-Chome, Chiyodaku, Tokyo, pp. 212-215. (21C, 22)

Tomii, M., 1973a
JAPANESE STRUCTURAL STANDARDS FOR REINFORCED CONCRETE BUILDINGS, Planning and Design of Tall Buildings, Proceedings of 1972 ASCE-IABSE International Conference, Vol. III, No. 20-D1, ASCE, New York. (20, 26)

Tomii, M., 1973b
SHEAR WALLS, SOA Report 4, Committee 21, Proceedings of 1972 ASCE-IABSE International Conference on Tall Buildings, Vol. III-21, ASCE, New York, pp. 57-75. (21E, 22)

Tomii, M. and Hiraishi, H., 1976a
ELASTIC ANALYSIS OF FRAMED SHEAR WALLS BY CONSIDERING SHEARING DEFORMATION OF THE BEAMS AND COLUMNS OF THEIR BOUNDARY FRAMES, Memoirs of the Faculty of Engineering, Kyushu University, Fukuoka, Japan, Vol. 35, No. 1. (21D)

Tomii, M. and Hiraishi, H., 1976b
ELASTIC ANALYSIS OF FRAMED SHEAR WALLS BY ASSUMING THEIR IN-FILLED PANEL WALLS TO BE 45-DEGREE ORTHOTROPIC PLATES, Memoirs of the Faculty of Engineering, Kyushu University, Fukuoka, Japan, Vol. 36, No. 1. (21D)

Tomii, M. and Miyata, S., 1960
STUDY ON SHEARING RESISTANCE OF EARTHQUAKE RESISTING WALLS HAVING VARIOUS OPENINGS, PART 1 AND 2, PART 3, PART 4 (in Japanese), Transactions, Architectural Institute of Japan, No. 66, October 1960; No. 67, February 1961; No. 68, June 1961. (21D)

Tomii, M. and Takeushi, M., 1968
THE RELATIONS BETWEEN THE DEFORMED ANGLE AND THE SHEARING FORCE RATIO (0.80—1.00) WITH REGARD TO 200 SHEAR WALLS, Transactions, Architectural Institute of Japan, No. 153, November 1968. (21D)

Tomii, M. and Tokuhiro, I., 1970
THE RELATION BETWEEN THE SHAPE AND THE LOCATION OF THE FIRST SHEAR CRACK ON THE SHEAR WALL LOADED ANTISYMMETRICALLY WITH REGARD TO THEIR LONGITUDINAL AND TRANSVERSE CENTER LINES (in Japanese), Summaries of Technical Papers of Annual Meeting of Architectural Institute of Japan, September 1970. (21D)

Tomii, M. and Yamakawa, T., 1974
RELATIONS BETWEEN THE NODAL EXTERNAL FORCES AND THE NODAL DISPLACEMENTS ON THE BOUNDARY FRAMES OF RECTANGULAR ELASTIC FRAMED SHEAR WALLS, Memoirs of the Faculty of Engineering, Kyushu University, Fukuoka, Japan, Vol. 34, No. 1. (21D)

Torroja, E., 1958
THE STRUCTURES OF EDUARDO TORROJA, F. W. Dodge, New York. (A38)

Townsend, W. H., 1972
THE INELASTIC BEHAVIOR OF REINFORCED CONCRETE BEAM-COLUMN CONNECTIONS, thesis presented to the University of Michigan, at Ann Arbor, Mich., in partial fulfillment of the requirements for the degree of Doctor of Philosophy. (22)

Troxell, G. E., Davis, H. E. and Kelley, J. W., 1968
COMPOSITION AND PROPERTIES OF CONCRETE, McGraw-Hill Book Co., Inc., New York. (25)

Troxell, G. E., Raphael, J. M. and Davis, R. E., 1958
LONGTIME CREEP AND SHRINKAGE TESTS OF PLAIN AND REINFORCED CONCRETE, Proceedings, American Society for Testing and Materials, Vol. 58, pp. 1101–1120. (25)

Tso, W. K. and Biswas, J. K., 1973
GENERAL ANALYSIS OF NONPLANAR COUPLED SHEAR WALLS, Journal of the Structural Division, ASCE, Vol. 99, No. ST3, Proc. Paper 9604, pp. 365–380. (24)

Tso, W. K. and Chan, P. C. K., 1973
STATIC ANALYSIS OF STEPPED COUPLED WALLS BY TRANSFER MATRIX METHOD, Building Science, London, England, Vol. 8, p. 167. (21C)

Tsoukantas, S. and Tassios, T. P., 1975
MECHANICAL BEHAVIOR OF LARGE REINFORCED CONCRETE PANEL JOINTS UNDER DYNAMIC LOADING, Hellenic Conference on Tall Buildings, 33rd National/Regional Conference (Athens, Greece, October 1975). (21E)

Tsuboi, Y. and Suenaga, Y., 1968
A STUDY OF THE STRENGTH PROPERTIES OF PRECAST REINFORCED CONCRETE BOX-FRAME UNITS, Design Philosophy and its Application to Precast Concrete Structures, Cement and Concrete Association, London, England. (21E)

Tsuboi, Y. and Tomii, M., 1954
ANALYSIS OF SHEARING RESISTANCE OF CRACKED SHEAR WALLS BASED UPON 45 DEGREE ORTHOTROPIC ELASTIC PLATE THEORY (in Japanese), Transactions, Architectural Institute of Japan, No. 48, March 1954. (21D)

Turkstra, C. and Ojinaga, J., 1976
THE MOMENT-MAGNIFIER METHOD APPLIED TO BRICK WALLS, Proceedings of the 4th International Brick Masonry Conference, Groupement National de l'Industrie de la Terre Cuite, rue des Poissoniers 13, Brussels, Belgium. (27)

Turnsek, V. and Cacovic, F., 1970
SOME EXPERIMENTAL RESULTS ON THE STRENGTH OF BRICK MASONRY WALLS, Proceedings of the 2nd International Brick Masonry Conference, H. W. H. West and K. H. Speed, eds., British Ceramic Research Association, Stoke-on-Trent, England, 1971. (27)

UL, 1971
BUILDING MATERIALS LIST, Underwriters Laboratories, Inc., Chicago, Ill. (21D)

USBR, 1956
CONCRETE MANUAL, Revised 6th ed., U.S. Bureau of Reclamation, Denver, Colo. (25)

USSR Standard, 1965
REGULATIONS FOR DESIGN OF LARGE PANEL STRUCTURES FOR RESIDENTIAL BUILDINGS (Ukasanie po proiecterivaniyu konstrukji krupnopanielnych jilycht domov), SN 321-65, Moscow, USSR. (21E)

Ulitskii, I. I., 1962
A PRACTICAL METHOD FOR COMPUTING CREEP AND SHRINKAGE OF CONCRETE (Prakticheskii Metod Raschetnogo Opredeleniya Deformatsii Polzuchesti i Usadki Betonov), *Beton i Zhelezobeton*, No. 4, p. 174. (25)

Ulmeanu, D., 1973
CONTRIBUTION TO THE OPTIMIZATION OF PERFORATED BRICKS (Beitrag zur Optimierung der Querschnitte von Hochlochsteinen), Proceedings of the 3rd International Brick Masonry Conference, Bundesverband der Deutschen Ziegelindustrie e.V., Essen, Germany. (27)

Umemura, H., 1970
EARTHQUAKE RESISTANT DESIGN OF STRUCTURES, University of Tokyo, Japan. (22)

Umemura, H. and Aoyama, H., 1969
EVALUATION OF INELASTIC SEISMIC DEFLECTION OF REINFORCED CONCRETE FRAMES BASED ON THE TESTS OF MEMBERS, Proceedings of the 4th World Conference on Earthquake Engineering (Santiago, Chile), Vol. 1, pp. B-2, 91–107. (22)

Umemura, H. and Ikeda, A., 1963
STUDY ON IMPROVEMENT OF STRUCTURAL ABILITY OF REINFORCED CONCRETE CONSTRUCTION, 1—Tests of the Beam-Column Connections Under Repeated Loading, *Transactions*, Architectural Institute of Japan, No. 89. (22)

Umemura, H. and Ikeda, A., 1964
STUDY ON IMPROVEMENT OF STRUCTURAL ABILITY OF REINFORCED CONCRETE CONSTRUCTION, 2—Tests of the Beam-Column Connections with Special Reinforcement, *Transactions*, Architectural Institute of Japan, No. 103. (22)

Umemura, H., Aoyama, H. and Itao, M., 1970
EXPERIMENTAL STUDIES ON REINFORCED CONCRETE MEMBERS AND COMPOSITE STEEL AND REINFORCED CONCRETE MEMBERS, Umemura Laboratory Report, University of Tokyo, Japan. (22)

University of Sydney, 1972
STRUCTURAL MODELS, Proceedings of Conference on Structural Models (Sydney, 1972), Cement and Concrete Association of Australia in conjunction with Dept. of Architectural Science, University of Sydney, and Institution of Engineers, Australia, N.S.W. Division. (A38)

Uzumeri, S. M. and Seckin, M., 1974
BEHAVIOR OF REINFORCED CONCRETE BEAM-COLUMN JOINTS SUBJECTED TO SLOW LOAD REVERSALS, Publication 74-05, Dept. of Civil Engineering, University of Toronto, Canada. (21D)

Vahakallio, P. and Makela, K., 1973
CONCERNING THE COMPUTATIONS OF MASONRY ECCENTRICITY (Uber die Exzentrizitätsberechnungen von Mauerwerk), Proceedings of the 3rd International Brick Masonry Conference, Bundesverband der Deutschen Ziegelindustrie e.V., Essen, Germany. (27)

Vahakallio, P. and Makela, K., 1976
METHOD FOR CALCULATING RESTRAINING ON JOINT MOMENTS IN UNREINFORCED MASONRY STRUCTURES, Proceedings of the 4th International Brick Masonry Conference, E. L. Jessop and M. A. Ward, eds., University of Calgary, Canada. (27)

Van Koten, H., undated
LIMITS FOR DYNAMIC MOVEMENTS, Report IBBC-TNO BI 67-107, Delft, The Netherlands. (26)

Van Langendonck, T., 1975
CRITICAL LOADS OF BUILDING FRAMES, Publications of IABSE, Vol. 35-II, Zurich, Switzerland, pp. 149–158. (23)

Vasiliev, A. P., Bychenkov, Y. D. and Matkov, N. G., 1973
PREFABRICATED REINFORCED CONCRETE MULTI-STORY FRAME BUILDINGS IN THE USSR, Proceedings of the 1972 ASCE-IABSE International Conference on Tall Buildings, Vol. Ia-3, ASCE, New York, pp. 87–97. (21E)

Veneziano, D., 1974
CONTRIBUTION TO SECOND MOMENT RELIABILITY THEORY, Structures Publication No. 389, Massachusetts Institute of Technology, Cambridge, Mass. (26)

Verbeck, G. and Helmuth, R., 1969
STRUCTURES AND PHYSICAL PROPERTIES OF CEMENT PASTES, Proceedings of the 5th International Symposium on the Chemistry of Cement (Tokyo, Japan, 1968), Part 3, Vol. 3, The Cement Association of Japan, Tokyo, pp. 1–32. (25)

Vickery, B. J., 1972
ON THE AEROELASTIC MODELLING OF STRUCTURES IN WIND, Conference on Structural Models (Sydney, 1972), Cement and Concrete Assoc. of Australia in conjunction with Dept. of Architectural Science, University of Sydney, and Institution of Engineers, Australia, N.S.W. Division. (A38)

Visontai, J., undated
PHOTOELASTIC INVESTIGATION OF A SHEAR WALL FOR A 24-STOREY BUILDING (Spannungsoptische Untersuchung der Windversteifungswand eines 24 Stöckigen Hochhauses), reprint from Spannungsanalyse VI, Akademie-Verlag, Berlin, Germany, pp. 113–126. (A38)

Vlasov, V. Z., 1961
THIN-WALLED ELASTIC BEAMS (in Russian), translated by Program for Scientific Translations, Jerusalem, Israel. (24)

Volkamer, J. P., 1973
OLD-FASHIONED THOUGHTS OF AN ARCHITECT (Unmoderne Gedanken eines Architekten), Proceedings of the 3rd International Brick Masonry Conference, Bundesverband der Deutschen Ziegelindustrie e.V., Essen, Germany. (27)

Waddell, J. J., 1974
PRECAST CONCRETE: HANDLING AND ERECTION, Monograph No. 8, American Concrete Institute. (21E)

Wakabayashi, M., 1965
THE RESTORING FORCE CHARACTERISTICS OF MULTI-STOREY FRAMES, Bulletin of the Disaster Prevention Research Institute, Kyoto University, Japan, Vol. 14, Part 2. (23)

Wakabayashi, M., Minami, K. and Yamaguchi, T., 1971
AN EXPERIMENTAL STUDY ON SHEAR FAILURE OF REINFORCED CONCRETE COLUMNS UNDER CYCLIC LOADING, Kyoto University, Japan, April 1971. (22)

Wallo, E. M. and Kesler, C. E., 1968
PREDICTION OF CREEP IN STRUCTURAL CONCRETE, Bulletin 498, Engineering Experiment Station, University of Illinois. (25)

Wang, C. K. and Salmon, C. G., 1973
REINFORCED CONCRETE DESIGN, Intext Press, New York. (21D)

Warner, R. F., 1969
LONG REINFORCED CONCRETE COLUMNS IN BIAXIAL BENDING, Publications of IABSE, Vol. 29-I, p. 133. (21D)

Warner, R. F., 1974
BEARING CAPACITY OF SLENDER CONCRETE COLUMNS MONOAXIALLY AND BIAXIALLY LOADED UNDER SHORT-TIME AND SUSTAINED LOADS, Deutscher Ausschuss für Stahlbeton, Bulletin 236, Berlin, Germany. (23)

Warner, R. F., 1975
AXIAL SHORTENING OF REINFORCED CONCRETE COLUMNS, UNICIV Report R-143, University of New South Wales, Australia. (25)

Warner, R. F. and Thürlimann, B., 1963
CREEP FAILURE OF REINFORCED CONCRETE COLUMNS, Publications of IABSE, Vol. 23, Zurich, Switzerland. (23)

Washa, G. W., 1966
VOLUME CHANGES, Special Technical Publication 169A, American Society for Testing and Materials, pp. 189–201. (25)

Washa, G. W. and Fluck, P. C., 1952
THE EFFECT OF COMPRESSIVE REINFORCEMENT ON THE PLASTIC FLOW OF REINFORCED CONCRETE BEAMS, ACI Journal, American Concrete Institute, Vol. 49, No. 10, pp. 89–108. (25)

Washa, G. W. and Fluck, P. G., 1956
PLASTIC FLOW (CREEP) OF REINFORCED CONCRETE CONTINUOUS BEAMS, *ACI Journal*, American Concrete Institute, Vol. 53, No. 5, pp. 549–561. (25)

Wastlund, G., 1972
STABILITY OF CONCRETE STRUCTURES, 6th Regional Conference Proceedings, 6th National/Regional Conference (Delft, The Netherlands, May 1972), Joint Committee on Tall Buildings, Lehigh University, Bethlehem, Pa., pp. 64–70. (23)

Watson, V. and Hirst, M. J. S., 1972
EXPERIMENTS FOR THE DESIGN OF A SYSTEM USING LARGE PRECAST CONCRETE PANEL COMPONENTS, *The Structural Engineer*, Vol. 50, No. 9. (21E)

Watstein, D., 1971
RELATION OF UNRESTRAINED COMPRESSIVE STRENGTH OF BRICK TO STRENGTH OF MASONRY, *Journal of Materials*, ASTM, Vol. 6, No. 2. (27)

Watstein, D. and Allen, M. H., 1970
STRUCTURAL PERFORMANCE OF CLAY MASONRY ASSEMBLAGES BUILT WITH HIGH-BOND ORGANIC MODIFIED MORTARS, Proceedings of the 2nd International Brick Masonry Conference, H. W. H. West and K. H. Speed, eds., British Ceramic Research Association, Stoke-on-Trent, England, 1971. (27)

Watstein, D. and Johnson, P. V., 1969
EXPERIMENTAL DETERMINATION OF ECCENTRICITY OF FLOOR LOADS APPLIED TO A BEARING WALL, Design Engineering and Constructing with Masonry Products, F. Johnson, ed., Gulf Publishing Co., Houston, Tex. (27)

Weaver, W. and Nelson, M. F., 1966
THREE-DIMENSIONAL ANALYSIS OF TIER BUILDINGS, *Journal of the Structural Division*, ASCE, Vol. 92, No. ST6, Proc. Paper 5019, p. 385. (21C)

Weaver, W., Brandow, G. E. and Manning, T. A., 1971
TIER BUILDINGS WITH SHEAR CORES, BRACING, AND SETBACKS, *Computers and Structures*, Vol. 1, p. 57. (21C)

Wegmuller, A. W. and Kostem, C. N., 1972
ELASTIC-PLASTIC ANALYSIS OF PLATES, Proceedings of Symposium, International Association for Shell and Spatial Structures, Calgary, Canada. (21A)

Weidlinger, P., 1964
TEMPERATURE STRESSES IN TALL REINFORCED CONCRETE BUILDINGS, *Civil Engineering*, ASCE, Vol. 34, August 1964, p. 58. (25)

Weil, G., 1959
INFLUENCE OF DIMENSIONS AND CONSTRAINTS ON SHRINKAGE AND CREEP OF CONCRETE (Influence des dimensions et des contraintes sur le retrait et le fluage du béton), RILEM Bulletin no. 3, Réunion Internationale des Laboratoires d'Essais et de Recherches sur les Matériaux et les Constructions, pp. 4–14. (25)

Wells, F. R., 1974
STRUCTURAL SYSTEMS OF THREE SYDNEY HIGH-RISE BUILDINGS, Proceedings, Conference on Tall Buildings, Kuala Lumpur, Malaysia, pp. 9-1–9-14. (21A)

Wesche, K. and Schubert, P., 1976
COMPARISON OF LOADBEARING MASONRY IN SOME EUROPEAN COUNTRIES, Proceedings of the 1st Canadian Masonry Symposium, E. L. Jessop and M. A. Ward, eds., University of Calgary, Canada. (27)

West, H. W. H., Everill, J. B. and Beech, D. G., 1968
EXPERIMENTS IN THE USE OF THE 9 INCH BRICKWORK CUBE FOR SITE CONTROL TESTING, *Proceedings*, British Ceramic Society, No. 11. (27)

West, H. W. H., Ford, R. W. and Goodwin, J. F., 1973
MORTAR MODIFIED WITH SARABOND, Proceedings of the 3rd International Brick Masonry Conference, Bundesverband der Deutschen Ziegelindustrie e.V., Essen, Germany. (27)

West, H. W. H., Ford, R. W. and Peake, F., 1973
SINGLE LEAF MASONRY: THE RESISTANCE TO RAIN PENETRATION OF SOME COMPOSITE SYSTEMS, Proceedings of the 3rd International Brick Masonry Conference, Bundesverband der Deutschen Ziegelindustrie e.V., Essen, Germany. (27)

West, H. W. H., Hodgkinson, H. R. and Haseltine, B. A., 1976
THE EFFECT OF FLOOR AND WIND LOADS APPLIED SEPARATELY OR SIMULTANEOUSLY TO A TWO-STOREY HEIGHT WALL, Proceedings of the 4th

International Brick Masonry Conference, Groupement National de l'Industrie de la Terre Cuite, rue des Poissoniers 13, Brussels, Belgium. (27)

West, H. W. H., Hodgkinson, H. R. and Webb, W. F., 1973a
LATERAL LOADING TESTS ON WALLS WITH DIFFERENT BOUNDARY CONDITIONS, Proceedings of the 3rd International Brick Masonry Conference, Bundesverband der Deutschen Ziegelindustrie e.V., Essen, Germany. (27)

West, H. W. H., Hodgkinson, H. R. and Webb, W. F., 1973b
THE RESISTANCE OF CLAY BRICK WALLS TO LATERAL LOADING, Proceedings, British Ceramic Society, No. 21. (27)

West, H. W. H., Hodgkinson, H. R., Beech, D. G. and Davenport, S. T. E., 1970
THE COMPARATIVE STRENGTH OF WALLS BUILT OF STANDARD AND MODULAR BRICKS, Proceedings of the 2nd International Brick Masonry Conference, H. W. H. West and K. H. Speed, eds., British Ceramic Research Association, Stoke-on-Trent, England, 1971. (27)

West, H. W. H., Hodgkinson, H. R., Beech, D. G., Davenport, S. T. E. and Picken, R. N., 1968
THE PERFORMANCE OF WALLS BUILT OF WIRECUT BRICKS WITH AND WITHOUT PERFORATIONS, Transactions, British Ceramic Society, Vol. 67, No. 10. (27)

Western Construction, 1969
BELLEVUE BUILDING GOES UP FAST, Western Construction, May 1969. (21E)

Wiberg, N. E., 1971a
APPROXIMATE METHODS OF ANALYSIS FOR TALL BUILDINGS (in Swedish), IS 115, Dept. of Structural Mechanics, Chalmers University of Technology, Göteborg, Sweden. (22)

Wiberg, N. E., 1971b
Discussion of EFFICIENT REANALYSIS OF MODIFIED STRUCTURES, by D. Kavlie and G. H. Powell, Journal of the Structural Division, ASCE, Vol. 97, No. ST10, Proc. Paper 8411, pp. 2612–2619. (22)

Wiberg, N. E., 1971c
SYSTEM ANALYSIS IN STRUCTURAL MECHANICS, Thesis No. 105, Chalmers University of Technology, Göteborg, Sweden. (22)

Wiegand, E., 1971
A CONTRIBUTION TO THE BUCKLING STABILITY OF REINFORCED CONCRETE WALLS WITH NONLINEAR ELASTIC MATERIAL BEHAVIOR (Ein Beitrag zur Beulstabilität von Stahlbetonwanden mit nichtlinear-elastischern Werkstoffgesetz), thesis presented to the Technical University of Darmstadt, Germany, in partial fulfillment of the requirements for the degree of Doctor of Engineering. (23)

Wierzbicki, S. and Greszta, J., 1975
BEARING CAPACITY AND DEFORMABILITY OF LINTELS IN STRUCTURAL WALLS, CIB 2nd International Symposium on Bearing Walls (Warsaw, Poland, September 1975), Theme 2, Paper 14, pp. 255–276. (21E)

Wight, J. K. and Sozen, M. A., 1973
SHEAR STRENGTH IN REINFORCED CONCRETE COLUMNS SUBJECTED TO LARGE DEFLECTION REVERSALS, Dept. of Civil Engineering, University of Illinois, SRS 403, August 1973. (21D)

Will, G. T., Uzumeri, S. M. and Sinha, S. K., 1972
APPLICATION OF FINITE ELEMENT METHOD TO THE ANALYSIS OF REINFORCED CONCRETE BEAM-COLUMN, Proceedings of the Specialty Conference on Finite Element Method in Civil Engineering, June 1972, McGill University, Montréal, Canada, pp. 745–766. (22)

Williams, D., 1971
SEISMIC BEHAVIOUR OF REINFORCED MASONRY SHEAR WALLS, thesis presented to the University of Canterbury, at Christchurch, New Zealand, in partial fulfillment of the requirements for the degree of Doctor of Philosophy. (27)

Williams, D. and Scrivener, J. C., 1973
RESPONSE OF REINFORCED MASONRY SHEAR WALLS TO STATIC AND DYNAMIC CYCLIC LOADING, Proceedings of the 5th World Conference on Earthquake Engineering (Rome, Italy), Vol. 2, Paper 185. (27)

Williams, G. M. J. and Rutter, P. A., 1967
THE DESIGN OF TWO BUILDINGS WITH SUSPENDED STRUCTURES IN HIGH YIELD STEEL, The Structural Engineer, Vol. 45, No. 4, pp. 143–152. (A38)

Williams, H. A. and Benjamin, J. R., 1952–1956
INVESTIGATION OF SHEAR WALLS, PART 1–PART 11, Stanford University, Stanford, Calif., April 1952–December 1956. (21D)

Wilson, E., 1960
MATRIX ANALYSIS OF NONLINEAR STRUCTURES, Proceedings of 2nd ASCE Conference on Electronic Computation (Pittsburgh, Pa., September 1960), pp. 415–428. (22)

Winkler, U., 1973
ACOUSTIC INSULATION AS PART OF CONSTRUCTION PHYSICS (Schallschutz als Teil der integrierten Bauphysik), Proceedings of the 3rd International Brick Masonry Conference, Bundesverband der Deutschen Ziegelindustrie e.V., Essen, Germany. (27)

Winokur, A. and Glück, J., 1968a
LATERAL LOADS IN ASYMMETRIC MULTISTORY STRUCTURES, *Journal of the Structural Division*, ASCE, Vol. 94, No. ST3, Proc. Paper 5842, pp. 645–656. (21C, 24)

Winokur, A. and Glück, J., 1968b
ULTIMATE STRENGTH ANALYSIS OF COUPLED SHEAR WALLS, *ACI Journal*, American Concrete Institute, Vol. 65, No. 12, pp. 1029–1035. (22)

Winter, G. and Nilson, A. H., 1972
DESIGN OF CONCRETE STRUCTURES, McGraw-Hill Book Co., Inc., New York. (21D)

Wiss, J. R. and Curth, D., 1970
WIND DEFLECTIONS OF TALL CONCRETE FRAME BUILDINGS, *Journal of the Structural Division*, ASCE, Vol. 96, No. ST7, Proc. Paper 7413, pp. 1461–1480. (24)

Wolfensberger, R., 1964
OPTIMUM DIMENSIONING OF SLABS FOR GIVEN LOADS (Traglast und Optimale Bemessung von Platten), dissertation presented to Swiss Federal Institute of Technology, Zürich, Switzerland. (21D)

Wolff, H., 1973
PAVEMENT OF BAKED MATERIAL IN OLD AND MODERN TIMES (Pflasterungen aus gebranntem Material in alter und neuer Zeit), Proceedings of the 3rd International Brick Masonry Conference, Bundesverband der Deutschen Ziegelindustrie e.V., Essen, Germany. (27)

Wood, B. R., Beaulieu, D. and Adams, P. F., 1976a
COLUMN DESIGN BY P-DELTA METHOD, *Journal of the Structural Division*, ASCE, Vol. 102, No. ST2, Proc. Paper 11936, pp. 411–427. (23)

Wood, B. R., Beaulieu, D. and Adams, P. F., 1976b
FURTHER ASPECTS OF DESIGN BY P-DELTA METHOD, *Journal of the Structural Division*, ASCE, Vol. 102, No. ST3, Proc. Paper 11973, pp. 487–500. (23)

Wood, R. H., 1952
STUDIES IN COMPOSITE CONSTRUCTION, Part I. The Composite Action of Brick Panel Walls Supported on Reinforced Concrete Beams, Paper 13, National Building Studies and Research, HMSO, London, England. (25)

Wood, R. H., 1958
THE STABILITY OF TALL BUILDINGS, *Proceedings*, Institution of Civil Engineers, London, Vol. 11, pp. 69–102. (23)

Woodland, D. J., 1973
PRELIMINARY DESIGN CONSIDERATIONS FOR HIGH-RISE ENGINEERED BRICK MASONRY BUILDINGS, Proceedings of the 3rd International Brick Masonry Conference, Bundesverband der Deutschen Ziegelindustrie e.V., Essen, Germany. (27)

Wright, D. T., 1965
Discussion of SLENDERNESS EFFECTS IN BUILDINGS, by E. Rosenblueth, *Journal of the Structural Division*, ASCE, Vol. 91, No. ST5, Proc. Paper 4498, p. 396. (23)

Wynhoven, J. H. and Adams, P. F., 1970
Discussion of LATERAL-LOAD ANALYSIS OF ASYMMETRIC MULTISTORY STRUCTURES, by J. Glück, *Journal of the Structural Division*, ASCE, Vol. 96, No. ST11, Proc. Paper 7644, p. 2538. (22)

Wynhoven, J. and Adams, P. F., 1972a
ANALYSIS OF THREE-DIMENSIONAL STRUCTURES, *Journal of the Structural Division*, ASCE, Vol. 98, No. ST1, Proc. Paper 8643, pp. 233–248. (23)

Wynhoven, J. and Adams, P. F., 1972b
BEHAVIOR OF STRUCTURES UNDER LOADS CAUSING TORSION, *Journal of the Structural Division*, ASCE, Vol. 98, No. ST7, Proc. Paper 9010, pp. 1361–1376. (23)

Yamada, M., 1973
ULTIMATE DEFORMATION OF REINFORCED CONCRETE, Planning and Design of Tall Buildings, Proceedings of 1972 ASCE-IABSE International Conference, Vol. III, No. 22-D6, ASCE, New York. (22)

Yamada, M., 1974a
SHEAR STRENGTH, DEFORMATION AND EXPLOSION OF REINFORCED CON-CRETE SHORT COLUMNS, Shear Symposium, Special Publication, American Concrete Institute. (22)

Yamada, M., 1974b
BEHAVIOR OF REINFORCED CONCRETE BEAM-COLUMNS UNDER CYCLIC LOADING, unpublished communication to the Council, July 1974. (22)

Yamada, M. and Furui, S., 1968
SHEAR RESISTANCE AND EXPLOSIVE CLEAVAGE FAILURE OF REINFORCED CONCRETE MEMBERS SUBJECTED TO AXIAL LOAD, Proceedings of 8th Congress , IABSE (New York, September 1968), p. 1091. (21D, 22)

Yamada, M. and Kawamura, H., 1967
STUDY ON THE ELASTO-PLASTIC FLEXURAL BEHAVIOR OF REINFORCED CONCRETE MEMBERS SUBJECTED TO FLEXURAL LOAD, Part III, Moment-Curvature Relation Under Cyclic Bending Moment (in Japanese), *Transactions*, Architectural Institute of Japan, No. 136, pp. 15–21. (22)

Yamada, M. and Kawamura, H., 1968
ELASTO-PLASTIC BENDING DEFLECTIONS OF REINFORCED CONCRETE COL-UMNS AND BEAMS (Elasto-Plastische Biegeformänderungen der Stahlbetonsäulen und Balken), Publications of IABSE, Vol. 28-1, Zurich, Switzerland, pp. 193–220. (22)

Yamada, M. and Kawamura, H., 1973
FUNDAMENTAL NEW ASEISMIC DESIGN OF REINFORCED CONCRETE BUILDINGS, Proceedings of 5th World Conference on Earthquake Engineering (Rome, Italy), Vol. 3A, No. 102. (22)

Yamada, M. and Kawamura, H., 1974
SIMPLIFIED CALCULATION METHOD FOR FLEXURAL AND SHEAR STRENGTH AND DEFORMATION OF REINFORCED CONCRETE COLUMNS UNDER CONSTANT AXIAL LOAD, Preliminary Report, Symposium of IABSE (Québec, Canada). (22)

Yamada, M. and Yagi, S., 1973
SHEAR EXPLOSION OF REINFORCED CONCRETE SHORT COLUMNS FOR THE BASIS TO ESTABLISH A NEW ASEISMIC DESIGN OF REINFORCED CON-CRETE STRUCTURES, Proceedings of 5th World Conference on Earthquake Engineering (Rome, Italy), Vol. 2D, No. 90. (22)

Yamada, M., Kawamura, H. and Kataihara, K., 1974a
REINFORCED CONCRETE SHEAR WALLS WITHOUT OPENINGS, TEST AND ANALYSIS, Shear in Reinforced Concrete, Publication SP-42, American Concrete Institute. (21D)

Yamada, M., Kawamura, H. and Kataihara, K., 1974b
REINFORCED CONCRETE SHEAR WALLS WITH OPENINGS, TEST AND ANAL-YSIS, Shear in Reinforced Concrete, Publication SP-42, American Concrete Institute. (21D)

Yamashiro, R. and Siess, C. P., 1962
MOMENT-ROTATION CHARACTERISTICS OF REINFORCED CONCRETE MEM-BERS SUBJECT TO BENDING, SHEAR, AXIAL LOAD, Civil Engineering Studies, Structural Research Series No. 260, University of Illinois. (22)

Yashin, A. V., 1970
DEFORMATION OF CONCRETE UNDER LONG-TERM LOADING AT HIGH STRESSES AND ITS LONG-TIME STRENGTH UNDER COMPRESSION, Sbornik Niizhb; see "Creep in Plain, Reinforced and Prestressed Concrete," by A. M. Neville, pp. 38–76. (23)

Yee, A. A. and Masuda, F. R., 1974
  DESIGN FOR ERECTION CONSIDERATIONS, Design Considerations for a Precast
  Prestressed Apartment Building, *Journal of the Prestressed Concrete Institute*, Vol. 19, No.
  6, pp. 16–27. (21E)
Yokel, F. Y. and Dikkers, R. D., 1971
  STRENGTH OF LOAD-BEARING MASONRY WALLS, *Journal of the Structural
  Division*, ASCE, Vol. 97, No. ST5, Proc. Paper 8143, p. 1593. (27)
Yokel, F. Y. and Wright, R. N., 1973
  SUMMARY REPORT: LIMIT STATES DESIGN, Planning and Design of Tall Buildings,
  Proceedings of 1972 ASCE-IABSE International Conference, Vol. III, No. 26-Summary,
  ASCE, New York. (20, 26)
Yokel, F. Y., Mathey, R. G. and Dikkers, R. D., 1971
  STRENGTH OF MASONRY WALLS UNDER COMPRESSION AND TRANSVERSE
  LOADS, Building Science Series No. 34, U.S. Dept. of Commerce, Washington, D.C. (27)
Yokel, F. Y., Pielert, J. H. and Schwab, A. R., 1975
  THE IMPLEMENTATION OF A PROVISION AGAINST PROGRESSIVE COLLAPSE,
  Publication NBSIR 75-715, National Bureau of Standards, U.S. Govt. Printing Office,
  Washington, D.C. (21E)
Yorkdale, A. H., 1976
  STRUCTURAL RESEARCH AND INVESTIGATION FOR THE DEVELOPMENT OF
  A RATIONAL ENGINEERING DESIGN STANDARD FOR HOLLOW BRICK
  MASONRY, Proceedings of the 4th International Brick Masonry Conference, Groupe-
  ment National de l'Industrie de la Terre Cuite, rue des Poissoniers 13, Brussels, Belgium.
  (27)
Yorkdale, A. H. and Grogan, J. C., 1973a
  DESIGN AND CONSTRUCTION PRACTICES FOR CONTEMPORARY BRICK
  BEARING WALL BUILDINGS IN THE UNITED STATES, Proceedings of the 3rd
  International Brick Masonry Conference, Bundesverband der Deutschen Ziegelindustrie
  e.V., Essen, Germany. (27)
Yorkdale, A. H. and Grogan, J. C., 1973b
  CONTEMPORARY BRICK BEARING WALL BUILDINGS IN THE U.S.—A
  PROGRESS REPORT, Proceedings of the 3rd International Brick Masonry Conference,
  Bundesverband der Deutschen Ziegelindustrie e.V., Essen, Germany. (27)
Yu, W. W. and Winter, G., 1960
  INSTANTANEOUS AND LONG-TIME DEFLECTIONS OF REINFORCED CON-
  CRETE BEAMS UNDER WORKING LOADS, *ACI Journal*, American Concrete
  Institute, Vol. 57, No. 1, pp. 29–50. (25)

Zarzycki, A., 1975
  THE INFLUENCE OF SUPPORTING LENGTH AND BEARING STIFFENERS ON
  THE EFFECTIVE DEPTH OF BEAM WALLS, CIB 2nd International Symposium on
  Bearing Walls (Warsaw, Poland, September 1975), Theme 1, Paper 11, pp. 107–122. (21E)
Zavelani, R. A., 1971
  OPTIMAL SHAKE-DOWN DESIGN OF REINFORCED CONCRETE BEAMS, Istituto
  Lombardo di Scienze e Lettere (A), Vol. 105. (22)
Zeck, U. I., 1976
  JOINTS IN LARGE PANEL PRECAST CONCRETE STRUCTURES, Seismic Resis-
  tance of Precast Concrete Panel Buildings, Report 1, Publication No. R76-16, Dept. of
  Civil Engineering, MIT, Cambridge, Mass. (21E)
Zelger, C., 1970
  SHEAR DESIGN OF BRICK LINTELS, Proceedings of the 2nd International Brick
  Masonry Conference, H. W. H. West and K. H. Speed, eds., British Ceramic Research
  Association, Stoke-on-Trent, England, 1971. (27)
Zelger, C., 1973
  BASICS FOR THE DIMENSIONING OF SEDERITE CEILINGS (Grundlagen für die
  Bemessung von Stahlsteindecken), Proceedings of the 3rd International Brick Masonry
  Conference, Bundesverband der Deutschen Ziegelindustrie e.V., Essen, Germany. (27)
Zelman, M. I., Heidebrecht, A. C., Tso, W. K. and Johnston, W. A., 1970
  PRACTICAL PROBLEMS AND COSTS OF FABRICATING MULTI-STOREY MOD-
  ELS, Publication No. 24, American Concrete Institute, pp. 159–186. (A38)

Zia, P. and Guillermo, E. G., 1967
  COMBINED BENDING AND AXIAL LOAD IN PRESTRESSED CONCRETE COL-
  UMNS, *Journal of the Prestressed Concrete Institute*, Vol. 12, No. 3, pp. 52–59. (23)
Zienkiewicz, O., 1971
  THE FINITE ELEMENT METHOD IN ENGINEERING SCIENCE, McGraw-Hill
  Book Co., Inc., New York, NY. (21C, 22)
Zienkiewicz, O. C. and Irons, B. M., 1970
  MATRIX ITERATION AND ACCELERATION PROCESS IN FINITE ELEMENT
  PROBLEMS OF STRUCTURAL MECHANICS, *Numerical Methods for Nonlinear
  Algebraic Equations*, ed. Rabinowitz, Gordon and Breach Science Publishers, London,
  England. (22)
Zienkiewicz, O., Parekh, C. J. and Teply, B., 1971
  THREE-DIMENSIONAL ANALYSIS OF BUILDINGS COMPOSED OF FLOOR AND
  WALL PANELS, *Proceedings*, Institution of Civil Engineers, London, Vol. 49, pp.
  319–332. (21C, 22)
Zingone, G., 1968
  LIMIT ANALYSIS OF A BEAM IN BENDING IMMERSED IN AN ELASTOPLASTIC
  MEDIUM, *Journal of the Italian Association of Theoretical and Applied Mechanics*,
  Tamburini, Milan, Italy, Vol. 3, No. 1. (22)
Zingone, G., 1972a
  THE LIMIT STATE OF INDEFINITE PLATES ON ELASTOPLASTIC CONTINUUM,
  Journal of the Italian Association of Theoretical and Applied Mechanics, Tamburini, Milan,
  Italy, Vol. 7, No. 2. (22)
Zingone, G., 1972b
  PROBABLE COLLAPSE MECHANISM IN INDEFINITE PLATES ON AN ELASTO-
  PLASTIC CONTINUUM, *Journal of the Italian Association of Theoretical and Applied
  Mechanics*, Tamburini, Milan, Italy, Vol. 7, No. 3. (22)
Zirpke, P., 1976
  A CONTRACTOR LOOKS AT LOAD-BEARING MASONRY DESIGN, Proceedings of
  the 1st Canadian Masonry Symposium, E. L. Jessop and M. A. Ward, eds., University of
  Calgary, Canada. (27)

Contributors

The following list identifies those who have contributed material specifically for possible use in Volume CB. The names, affiliations, and countries are given, together with the chapter(s) to which a contribution was made. The committee chairmen and editors were given quite complete latitude in the use of material, and frequently length limitations prevented the inclusion of much valuable material. Thus, every contributor is listed, whether or not the material was used in the final version. The effort here is to recognize and acknowledge the contributions.

Some of the material came to headquarters directly, some came from the Proceedings of the first international conference, some were stimulated at the special sessions held at the regional conferences, and some came directly to the committee leaders. The bibliography contains all contributions, and most of the unpublished documents are in the Council data base.

Aas-Jakobsen, A., Consulting Engineer, Oslo, N (8)
Aas-Jakobsen, K., Consulting Engineer, Oslo, N (8)
Abeles, P. W. (Deceased), Jan Bobrowski & Partners, Twickenham, GB (12)
Allen, D. E., National Research Council, Ottawa, CDN (2)
Amaral, N. A., São Paulo Institute of Technology, São Paulo, BR (1, 2)

Ambos, G., Institut fur Massivbau, Darmstadt, BRD (8)
Anastasescu, D. M., Design Institute of Timisoara, R (1, 2, 5)
Aoyama, H., University of Illinois, Urbana, IL, USA (6)
Au, L., Consulting Engineer, Los Angeles, CA, USA (R)*
Avram, C. N., Institutul Politechnic Timisoara, R (1, 2, 5)

Aycardi, L. G., Aycardi Ingenieria, Bogota, CO (11)
Baker, A. L. L., Imperial College of Science and Technology, London, GB (6)
Bardhan-Roy, B. K., Jan Bobrowski & Partners, Twickenham, GB (12)
Batanero, J. G., Ciudad Universitaria, Madrid, E (2) (R)
Beck, H., Technische Hochschule, Darmstadt, BRD (8)

Bennett, W. B., Prestressed Concrete Institute, Chicago, IL, USA (3)
Beresford, D., CSIRO, Highett, AUS (7)
Bertero, V. V., University of California, Berkeley, CA, USA (6, 9)
Blakey, F. A., Dept. of Housing & Construction, Melbourne, AUS (10)
Blessmann, J., Porto Alegre, BR (R)

*Designates organizer of National/Regional Conference.

Bobrowski, J., Jan Bobrowski & Partners, Twickenham, GB (12)
Brakel, J., T. H. Delft, Delft, NL (1, 2)
Bresler, B., University of California, Berkeley, CA, USA (8)
Bretnall, W. G., R. M. Gensert Associates, Cleveland, OH, USA (13)
Brondum-Nielsen, T., Technical University of Denmark, Lyngby, DK (2)

Bruggeling, A. S. G., Technical University, Delft, NL (12)
Bruinette, K. E., Bruinette, Kruger, Stoffberg & Hugo, Pretoria, ZA (1, 2, 4, 6)
Bubenheim, H., Ingenieursozietat BGS, Frankfurt, BRD (8)
Bubnov, S., Yugoslav Association of Earthquake Engineering, Jubljana, YU (R)
Buen, O. de, University of Mexico, Mexico City, MEX (R)*

Bychenkov, Y. D., Gosstroi U.S.S.R., Moscow, SU (12)
Calcagni, E. A., University of Chile, Santiago, RCH (11)
Cardenas, A. E., Cardenas and Bautista, Lima, PE (11)
Cerny, L., University of Minnesota, Minneapolis, MN, USA (11)
Chastain, T. Z., Chastain and Tindel, Inc., Tucker, GA, USA (11)

Chen, W. F., Purdue University, West Lafayette, IL, USA (8, 11)
Cheng, H. K., H. K. Cheng & Associates, HK (2)
Chistiakov, E. A., Research Institute for Concrete, Moscow, SU (8)
Chiu, A., University of Hawaii, Honolulu, HI, USA (R)
Cholewicki, A., Center for Building Systems, Warsaw, PL (12)

Cohen, E., Ammann and Whitney, New York, NY, USA (1, 2)
Cohn, M. Z., University of Waterloo, CDN (1, 4, 6)
Colaco, J. P., Colaco Engineers, Inc., Houston, TX, USA (3, 5, 9, 11)
Conway, D., American Institute of Architects, Washington, D.C., USA (R)
Coroneos, D., Hellenic Group of IABSE, Athens, GR (R)

Coull, A., University of Glasgow, Glasgow, GB (5, 7) (R)
Cowan, H. J., The University of Sydney, Sydney, AUS (7)
Cusens, A. R., The University of Dundee, Dundee, GB (11, 12)
Danay, A., Consulting Engineer, London, GB (5)
Daschner, F., affiliation not available, Munich, BRD (12)

Deschapelles, B., Hernandez & Hernandez, San Juan, PR (5, 9)
DeSimone, V. J., DeSimone and Chaplin, New York, NY, USA (4)
Despeyroux, J., Tech. Socotech., Paris, F (1, 2)
Dicke, D., Delft University of Technology, Delft, NL (8)
Dickey, W. L., Masonry Institute of America, Los Angeles, CA, USA (13)

Dikkers, R. D., National Bureau of Standards, Washington, D.C., USA (13)
Efsen, A., Technical University of Denmark, Gentofte, DK (11)
El-Demirdash, I. A., Cairo University, Giza, ET (R)
Faltus, F., Tech. University Fis Ocel Konstr., Prague, CS (R)
Ferry Borges, J., Laboratorio Nacional de Engenharia Civil, Lisbon, P (2, 9)

Fintel, M., Portland Cement Association, Skokie, IL, USA (9, 10)
Finzi, L., University of Milano, Milan, I (R)*
Fling, R. S., R. S. Fling & Partners, Inc., Columbus, OH, USA (5, 12)
Flint, A. R., Flint and Neill, London, GB (7)
Frunza, R., Institute Politech., Timisoara, R (10)

Fumagalli, E., ISMES, Bergamo, I (7)
Funk, P., Institut für Bautechnik, Berlin, BRD (9)
Furlong, R. W., University of Texas at Austin, Austin, TX, USA (6, 8)
Gellert, M., Israel Institute of Technology, Haifa, IL (5, 8)
Gensert, R. M., Gensert Peller Associates, Cleveland, OH, USA (13)

Gergely, P., Cornell University, Ithaca, NY, USA (9)
Gerstle, K. H., University of Colorado, Boulder, CO, USA (6)
Gesund, H., University of Kentucky, Lexington, KY, USA (6)
Ghali, A., University of Calgary, Calgary, CDN (10)
Gibson, J. E., The City University, London, GB (7)

Gluck, J., Israel Institute of Technology, Haifa, IL (5, 6, 8)
Goschy, B., Technical Advisor, Budapest, H (5)
Gramolin, I., Gosstroi U.S.S.R., Moscow, SU (R)
Grases, J., University Central de Venezuela, Caracas, YV (11)
Grasser, E., Technische Universität München, Munich, BRD (6, 12)

Grestza, J., Center for Building Systems Research & Development, Warsaw, PL (12)
Gruner, I., Instit. Politeh. Traian Vuia, Timisoara, R. (10)
Guedelhoefer, O. C., Wiss, Janney, Elstner, & Associates, Northbrook, IL, USA (7)
Gvozdev, A. A., Research Institute for Concrete, Moscow, SU (8)
Halasz, O., Technical University, Budapest, H. (7)

Hansen, L. P., Danmarks Ingeniorakademi, Aalborg, DK (11)
Harris, R. W. F., Purley, Surrey, GB (9)
Heiman, J. L., Experimental Building Station, Chatswood, AUS (10)
Henclewski, T., Center for Building Systems Research & Development, Warsaw, PL (12)
Henderson, R. D., University of Edinburgh, Edinburgh, GB (R)

Hendry, A. W., University of Edinburgh, Edinburgh, GB (7, 13)
Heunisch, M., König und Heunisch, Frankfurt, BRD (8)
Higashi, Y., Tokyo Met. University, Tokyo, J (9, 11)
Hilsdorf, H. K., Institut für Baustofftechnologie, Karlsruhe, BRD (10, 13)
Hirosawa, M., Ministry of Construction, Tokyo, J (9)

Holland, E. P., Wiesinger-Holland Ltd., Chicago, IL, USA (10)
Hongladaromp, T., Asian Institute of Technology, Bangkok, T (R)
Holmes, M., University of Aston, Birmingham, GB (7)
Holzenbein, H., Schmidtstahwerke, Vienna, A (9)
Hopkins, W., Wiss. Janney & Elstner, Chicago, IL, USA (7)

Huang, T., Lehigh University, Bethlehem, PA, USA
Jackson, N., University of Dundee, Dundee, GB (6, 8, 9)
Jirsa, J. O., University of Texas at Austin, Austin, TX, USA (11)
Jumikis, T., Woolacott, Hale, Corlett and Jumikis, Sydney, AUS (4)
Jungwirth, D., Dyckerhoff and Widmann, Munich, BRD (10)

Kaddah, H., Hamed Kaddah & Partners, Cairo, ET (R)
Kalev, I., Israel Aircraft Industries, Lod, IL (5)
Karman, T., Institute for Building Science, Budapest, H (1, 2)
Karp, J. J., Farkas, Barron & Partners, Englewood Cliffs, NJ, USA (10)
Karrholm, G., Chalmers University of Technology, Goteborg, S (5)

Karthahardja, A., Directorate of Building Research, Bandung, RI (R)
Kavyrchine, M., CEBTP, Paris, F (11, 12)
Kemp, E. L., West Virginia University, Morgantown, WV, USA (1)
Kesler, C. E., University of Illinois, Urbana, IL, USA (10)
Khan, F. R., Skidmore, Owings & Merrill, Chicago, IL, USA (7)

Khan, R., Ministry of Labour & Works, Islamabad, PAK (12)
Kokubu, M., University of Tokyo, J (12)
König, G. F., König and Heunisch, Frankfurt, BRD (8, 11)
Kordina, K., Tech. Universität Braunschweig, BRD (8, 9, 11)
Kostem, C. N., Lehigh University, Bethlehem, PA, USA (4, 6)

Kostro, G., Electronic Calculus, Inc., New York, NY (4)
Kowalczyk, R. M., Polish Academy of Sciences, Warsaw, PL
Kozak, J., Vitkovice Design Office, Floglova, CS (R)
Krauss, M., Electrical Corporation of Israel, Haifa, IL (5)
Krell, W. C., Ellis/Naeyaert Association, Inc., Detroit, MI, USA (3)

Ku, J., Institution of Structural Engineers, HK (R)
Kulicki, J. M., Modjeski and Masters, Mechanicsburg, PA, USA (6)
Leabu, V. F., Giffels Associates, Detroit, MI, USA (3)
Lee, S., University of Singapore, SGP (R)
Leonhardt, F., Leonhardt Andra, Stuttgart, BRD (9)

Levi, F., Politecnico di Torino, I (1, 2, 3)
Lewicki, B., COBPBO, Warsaw, PL (12)
Libbey, R. M., Richard M. Libbey, Inc., Honolulu, HI, USA (9)
Lichardus, S., Ustarch-SAV, Bratislava, CS (7)
Lim, B., University of Singapore, SGP (R)

Lin, T. Y., University of California, Berkeley, CA, USA (3, 5, 9)
Lorentsen, M., A. B. Jacobson & Widmark, Goteborg, S (8)
Lu, L. W., Lehigh University, Bethlehem, PA, USA (R)
Lubinski, M., Politechnika Warszawska, Warsaw, PL (R)
Lyse, I. M., The Norwegian Institute of Technology, Trondheim, N

Macchi, G., Istituto de Scienza e Tecnica, Pavia, I (6, 10)
MacGregor, J. G., University of Alberta, Edmonton, CDN (1, 2, 4, 8, 9)
Mackey, S., University of Hong Kong, HK (R)
MacLeod, I. A., Paisley College of Science and Technology, Paisley, Scotland (5, 7)
Mainstone, R. J., British Research Station, Garston, GB (13)

Maldague, J. G., CEBTP, Paris, F (6)
Mallett, R. J., The Brick Research Institute, Crows Nest, AUS (13)
Mancini, E., Escola de Engenharia São Carlos, BR (5)
Marincek, M., University of Ljubljana, YU (R)
Martin, I., Capacete-Martin & Associates, San Juan, PR (5, 7, 11)

Matkov, N. G., Gosstroi U.S.S.R., Moscow, SU (12)
Mazilu, P., Institute of Civil Engineering, Bucarest, R (R)
Microys, H. F., Consulting Engineer, Toronto, CDN (11)
Mikluchin, P. T., P. T. Mikluchin and Associates, Toronto, CDN (13)
Mirsu, A. O., Institutul Politechnic Timisoara, R (5)

Moharram, A., Arab Consulting Engineers, Cairo, ET (R)
Monge, J. E. (11)
Moran, F., Instituto Eduardo Torroja, Madrid, E (11)
Moretto, O., A. J. L. Bologonesi, D. Moretto, Luis S. Perea, Buenos Aires, RA (11)
Muller, T., Voest-Alpine, Linz, A (7)

Muto, K., Muto Institute of Structural Mechanics, Inc., Tokyo, J (R)
Naka, T., University of Tokyo, J (R)*
Nassar, G., Arab Consulting Engineers, Cairo, ET (R)
Nasser, J., Consulting Engineer, Beirut, RL (1, 2)
Negoita, A., Instytut Polytecnic, Iasi, R (6)

Neville, A. M., University of Dundee, Dundee, GB (10)
Nori, V. V., Consulting Engineer, Shrish Patel & Assoc., Bombay, IND (12)
Oberti, G., ISMES, Bergamo, I (7)
Owada, Y., Shibaura Institute of Technology, Tokyo, J (11)
Paduart, A., Université Libre de Bruxelles, B (2)

Paparoni, M., Equisticaca Consultores Assoc., Caracas, YV (7, 9)
Paulay, T., University of Canterbury, Christchurch, NZ (6, 11)
Pauw, A. (Deceased), University of Missouri, Columbia, MO, USA (8, 12)
Paxton, W., William Paxton Associates, Southfield, MI, USA (3)
Perchat, J., U T I, Paris, F (1, 2)

Peterson, J. F., Dansk Ingeniorforening Ingeniorh, Copenhagen, DK (5)
Pfeffermann, O., Centre Sci. et Tech. de la Construction, Bruxelles, B (13)
Plewes, W. G. (Retired), National Research Council, Ottawa, CDN (13)
Pogorzelski, A., Center for Building Systems Research & Development, Warsaw, PL (12)
Pommeret, M., Service d'Etude des Structures, CEBTP, Paris, F (11)

Pop, I. G., Polytechnic Institute Iasi, R (6)
Popoff, Jr., A., ABAM Engineers Incorporated, Tacoma, WA, USA (8, 12)
Priestley, M. J., Laboratorio Nacional de Engenharia Civil, Lisbon, P (7)
Rahulan, G., Sepakat Setia Perunding, Kuala Lumpur, PTM (R)
Ramaswamy, G. S., Caribbean Industrial Research Institute, Port-of-Spain, TT (11)

Ramesh, C. K., Indian Institute of Technology, Bombay, IND (12)
Rankine, J., Rankine & Hill Engineering Consultants, Sydney, AUS (10)
Ravara, A., Laboratorio Nacional de Engenharia Civil, Lisbon, P (7)
Reese, A. M., information not available (2)
Reese, R. C., Raymond Reese Associates, Toledo, OH, USA (3, 7)

Reinitzhuber, F., affiliation not available, BRD (R)
Robles, F., Instituto de Ingenieria, Mexico City, MEX (1, 2)
Rohn, G., affiliation not available, BRD (12)
Roosseno, R., Jakarta Pusat, RI (R)
Rosman, R., Arhitektonski Fakulet, Zagreb, YU (11)

Rotaru, G., Instit. Politeh., Taian Vuia, Timisoara, R (10)
Rowe, R. E., Cement and Concrete Association, GB (7)
Rubanenko, B., Research and Design Institute for Dwelling, Moscow, SU (R)
Rüsch, H., Technische Universität München, Munich, BRD (10)
Sahlin, S., Chalmers University of Technology, Goteborg, S (6, 13)

Sandberg, H. R., Alfred Bensch & Company, Chicago, IL, USA (R)
Sandi, H., Building Research Institute, Bucarest, R (2)
Savassi, W., Faculdade de Engenharia, Limeira, BR (5)
Sawyer, H. A., Consulting Engineer, Gainesville, FL, USA (6)
Schmidt, L. A., University of California, Los Angeles, CA, USA (7)

Schousboe, I., University of Illinois, Urbana, IL, USA (11)
Schulz, G., Inst. für Baustatik Uni Innsbruck, A (R)
Schwaighofer, J., University of Toronto, CDN (7, 9)
Scrivener, J. C., University of Melbourne, AUS (13)
Sfintesco, D., C T I C M, Puteaux, F (R)

Shepherd, R., University of Auckland, NZ (R)
Somerville, G., Cement and Concrete Association, Slough, GB (7)
Sontag, H., Krupp Industrie- und Stahlbau, Berlin, BRD (12)
Soretz, S., Tor-Isteg Steel Corporation, Wien, A (9)
Sparkes, S. R. (Deceased), Imperial College of Science and Technology, London, GB (7)

Stafford-Smith, B., McGill University, Montreal, CDN (5, 7)
Stamato, M. C. (Deceased), Escola de Engenharia de São Carlos, BR (9, 11)
Stigter, J., Consulting Engineer, Melbourne, AUS (12)
Stiller, M., Deutscher Beton-Verein, Wiesbaden, BRD (1, 2, 11)
Stroband, J., Dikker en Stroband, Amsterdam, NL (12)

Sundara Rao, B., Life Insurance Corporation of India, Bangalore, IND (3)
Sutherland, R. J., Harris & Sutherland, London, GB (13)
Swami-Nathan, T. R., Monenco Asia PTE, Ltd., SGP (12)
Takeda, S., Kobe Steel Company, Hyogo, J (9)
Thomas, P. K., Ministry of Shipping & Transport, New Delhi, IND (13)

Thürlimann, B., Swiss Federal Institute of Technology, Zurich, CH (3, 5, 12)
Tichy, M., Building Research Institute, Prague, CS (2)
Tomii, M., Kyushu University, Fukuoka-Shi, J (1, 11)
Turner, R. W., R. J. Crocker & Partners, Kent, GB (9)
Van Douwen, A., Technical University of Delft, Delft, NL (R)

Vandevelde, C. E., U.S. Army Engineer Division POD, Fort Shafter, HI, USA (6)
Vasiliev, A. P., Gosstroi U.S.S.R., Moscow, SU (12)
Vavaroutas, B., Technical Chamber of Greece, Athens, GR (R)
von Wachter, affiliation not available, BRD (12)
Waddell, J. J., Construction Materials Consultant, Riverside, CA, USA (12)

Walther, R., Ecole Polytechnique Fédérale, Lausanne, CH (11)
Wastlund, G. (Retired), The Royal Institute of Technology, Stockholm, S
Weidlinger, P., Paul Weidlinger Associates, New York, NY, USA (9)
Wierzbicki, S., Center for Building Systems Research & Development, Warsaw, PL (12)
Wright, R. N., National Bureau of Standards, Washington, D.C., USA (2)

Yamada, M., Kobe University, Hyogo, J (6)
Yokel, F. Y., National Bureau of Standards, Washington, D.C., USA (2)
Yorkdale, A. H., Brick Institute of America, McLean, VA, USA (13)
Young, R. J., Georgia Institute of Technology, Atlanta, GA, USA (13)
Zeck, U., Massachusetts Institute of Technology, Cambridge, MA, USA (12)

Zia, P., North Carolina State University, Raleigh, NC, USA (7)
Zieleniewski, S., Center for Building Systems Research & Development, Warsaw, PL (12)
Zilch, K., Alfred-Messel-Weg, Darmstadt, BRD (8)
Zimmerli, B., Swiss Federal Institute of Technology, Zurich, CH (11)

Building Index

The following index enables the reader to identify the page number on which a particular building is mentioned. Numbers in italics designate page numbers for figures. Numbers in italics that follow cities refer to panoramic photographic views.

841

Name Index

The following list cites the page numbers on which the indicated names are mentioned. The list includes the authors as well as other individuals or organizations named in the text.

Names followed by years refer to bibliographic citations that are included in the appendix entitled "References/Bibliography." When the name is followed by initials, the designated page shows membership in one of the committees of the Council.

Subject Index